Textbook of

MEDICAL PHYSIOLOGY

SECOND EDITION, Illustrated

ARTHUR C. GUYTON, M.D.

Professor and Chairman of the
Department of Physiology and Biophysics,
University of Mississippi School of Medicine

W. B. SAUNDERS COMPANY

Philadelphia and London

Reprinted March, 1961, October, 1961 and June, 1962

© 1961, by W. B. Saunders Company

Copyright, 1956, by W. B. Saunders Company

COPYRIGHT UNDER THE INTERNATIONAL COPYRIGHT UNION

All Rights Reserved. This book is protected by copyright.
No part of it may be duplicated or reproduced in any manner
without written permission from the publisher.

Made in the United States of America

PRESS OF W. B. SAUNDERS COMPANY

Library of Congress Catalog Number: 61–5107

DEDICATED TO

MY FATHER

for the uncompromising principles that have guided his life

MY MOTHER

for leading her children into intellectual pursuits

MY WIFE

for her magnificent devotion to her family

MY CHILDREN

for making everything worth while

PREFACE

Writing the first edition of this textbook was a formidable task that required both a broad study into all fields of physiology and prolonged collating, organizing, and casting of the material into a final form. But, however formidable this was, the task of the second edition has been even greater, principally because the widespread acceptance of the text demanded that I do all I could, first, to insure accuracy of the factual material and, second, to preserve or improve the clarity of presentation as much as possible.

To achieve the first objective, I submitted almost every chapter of the first edition to several authorities and teachers in each special field, asking for critical appraisal and, particularly, suggested improvements both in factual material and manner of presentation. More than 120 different physiologists were thus approached, and, in the light of their appraisals, as well as in the light of a tremendous amount of additional study on my own part, essentially all parts of the book have been entirely recast and rewritten *de novo*. The result is a book that gives me infinitely more satisfaction than did the first edition and, I hope, a book whose teaching value is greatly enhanced.

To achieve the second objective of the new edition, that is, to improve the clarity of the text, I have kept records of our own students' comments on the parts of the text that caused difficulty, and have made special attempts to reinforce, to simplify, and to clarify the presentations of those physiological mechanisms that are habitually poorly understood by students. Also, I have made a real effort to avoid ambiguities of thought and have even endeavored to learn, as any author must always learn, new methods for presenting in concise and clear form the scientific perplexities of the human body.

Even the figures of the previous text have not gone unmolested; most of these have been changed to fit the new presentation. Over half are entirely new, and two hundred additional figures have been included. In general, the figures have been designed to illustrate bodily mechanisms, particularly mechanisms that can be depicted pictorially much more concisely, scientifically, and accurately than they can be described verbally.

Another feature of the book, which I believe sets it apart from other physiology texts, is the presentation of the human body as a single functioning organism controlled by a myriad of regulatory systems, with emphasis on the automaticity of the life processes. Throughout the text, the principles of control theory are discussed as they apply to specific bodily mechanisms, and much attention has been given to the interrelationships of functions of the different organ systems of the body. The formulation of such interrelationships and the presentation of physiology as a functional subject rather than as a descriptive subject can be far more fully realized, I am convinced, in a single author textbook than in a multiple contributor book. It is my belief that a course in physiology, after all, is meant to teach these interrelationships equally as much as to describe the individual units. And were it not for my faith in the all importance of this principle, I could not justify the time and effort that have gone into the development of this textbook of physiology.

A word of explanation is needed about the bibliographies, for I have used a different system from that in most other textbooks of physiology. The references are chosen for their coverage of the specific subjects, their up-to-dateness, and also for their own bibliographies. By using both these references and cross-references from them, I believe that a student can cover almost any phase of physiology. I have chosen this system of references because I recall that, when I was a medical student, I used the references from my physiology textbooks only twice, even though I referred to the physiological literature perhaps more than most of my fellow students. I soon gave up consulting the textbook references in favor of better sources because the references had been chosen to prove minor points rather than for their reading value. Remembering this, I have tried to provide the student with the type of reading list that I had wanted.

Once again, I owe much to many others who have helped in the preparation of this book. Particularly am I grateful to Miss Sue Cathey and Mrs. Grace Gulledge for all their excellent secretarial aid, to Mrs. Carolyn Hull and Mr. Brantley Pace for the new illustrations, to the staff of the W. B. Saunders Company for its continued help, and, most of all, to the many physiologists who have helped me clarify my own understanding of many physiological mechanisms, thereby contributing immeasurably to whatever success may be achieved in the revision of this book.

ARTHUR C. GUYTON

Jackson, Mississippi

CONTENTS

PART I. INTRODUCTION TO PHYSIOLOGY: THE CELL

PART II. BODY FLUIDS

PART IV. PERIPHERAL NERVOUS AND MUSCULAR SYSTEMS

Chapter 17

ELECTRICAL CHARACTERISTICS OF EX-
CITABLE CELLS—MEMBRANE POTEN-
TIALS, ACTION POTENTIALS, EXCITA-
TION, AND RHYTHMICITY

Chapter 18

TRANSMISSION OF SIGNALS BY NERVES;
THE NEUROMUSCULAR JUNCTION 233

Chapter 19

CONTRACTION OF SKELETAL AND SMOOTH
MUSCLE 244

Chapter 20

THE AUTONOMIC NERVOUS SYSTEM 259

PART V.   HEART

✓Chapter 21

✓Chapter 22

Chapter 23

PART VII. RESPIRATION

PART VIII. AVIATION AND DEEP SEA DIVING

PART IX. CENTRAL NERVOUS SYSTEM AND SPECIAL SENSES

PART X. ALIMENTARY TRACT

PART XI. METABOLISM AND TEMPERATURE REGULATION

PART XII.   ENDOCRINOLOGY AND REPRODUCTION

PART XIII.   RADIATION

Chapter 82

NUCLEAR PHYSICS, X-RAYS, AND THEIR RELATIONSHIPS TO THE HUMAN BODY 1131

Part One

INTRODUCTION TO PHYSIOLOGY:

THE CELL

Chapter 1

Functional Organization of the Human Body and Control of the "Internal Environment"

Physiology, the study of function in living matter, encompasses the physical and chemical factors that are responsible for the origin, development, and progression of life. Each type of life, from the monomolecular virus up to the largest tree or the complicated human being, has its own functional characteristics. Therefore, the vast field of physiology can be divided into *viral physiology, bacterial physiology, cellular physiology, plant physiology, human physiology,* and many more subdivisions. In the present text, entitled *Medical Physiology,* an attempt has been made to present the organization of the human body in such a way that the student of medicine can understand the intricate mechanisms and control systems that normally allow all the unit parts of the body to operate in harmony, though unfortunately sometimes in disharmony, which we call sickness.

Human Physiology

In human physiology we attempt to explain all aspects of function in the human being, including the chemical reactions that occur in the cells throughout the body, the transmission of nerve impulses from one part of the body to another, movement by means of the muscles, reproduction, and even the minute details of transformation of light energy into chemical energy to excite the eyes, thus allowing us to see the world. The fact that we remain alive is almost beyond our own control, for hunger makes us seek food and fear makes us seek refuge. Sensations of cold make us provide warmth, and other forces cause us to seek fellowship and reproduce. Thus, the human being is actually an automaton, and the fact that we are sensing, feeling, and knowledgeable beings is part of this automatic sequence of life; these special attributes allow us to exist under widely varying conditions, which otherwise would make life impossible.

In an elementary discussion of physiology one attempts to answer such questions as: What is life? How do we live? How does the muscular system cause us to move? How does the auditory system make us perceive sound? However, the medical student has already learned at least partial answers to most of these questions in his study of anatomy. Therefore, this treatise on human physiology is directed more toward the basic physical and chemical mechanisms underlying the major functions of the body.

OVERALL ORGANIZATION OF THE BODY

Among the different organs and structures that perform widely varying functions in the body are the *skin,* which covers the body and protects the internal structures from the outside elements, the *musculoskeletal system,* which provides locomotion, the *nervous system,* which provides a sensing mechanism and a system for control of motor functions,

3

the *cardiovascular system,* which transports fluid and nutrients from one part of the body to another, the *respiratory system,* which provides interchange of oxygen and carbon dioxide with the air, the *urinary system,* which continually cleanses the body fluids and adjusts their concentrations of dissolved substances, the *liver,* which provides many intermediary chemical reactions necessary for the functioning of other portions of the body, the *endocrine glands,* which help to regulate metabolism and other functions throughout the body, and, finally, the *reproductive system,* which provides for regeneration of new human beings similar to their parents. Since each of these different functional systems has characteristics peculiar to itself, the manner in which each operates will be considered in detail in this text.

CELLS AS LIVING UNITS

The basic living unit of the body is the cell, and each organ is actually an aggregate of many different cells held together by intercellular supporting structures. Each type of cell is specially adapted to perform one particular function. For instance, the red blood cells, twenty-five trillion of which are present in the body, transport oxygen from the lungs to the tissues. Though this type of cell is perhaps the most abundant of any in the whole body, there are approximately another seventy-five trillion cells in all, making the entire body contain some one hundred trillion cells. Five different types of tissues are shown in Figure 1, illustrating some of the different types of cells and their incorporation in the tissues.

However much the many cells of the body differ from each other, all of them have certain basic characteristics that are alike. For instance, each cell requires nutrition for maintenance of life, and all of them utilize almost identically the same types of nutrients. All cells use oxygen as one of the major substances from which energy is derived. The oxygen combines with either a carbohydrate, a fat, or a protein, and the general mechanisms for changing nutrients into energy are basically the same in all cells. All cells also deliver end-products of their chemical reactions into the surrounding fluids.

Almost all cells also have the ability to reproduce, and whenever cells of a particular type are destroyed for one cause or another, the remaining cells of this type will usually

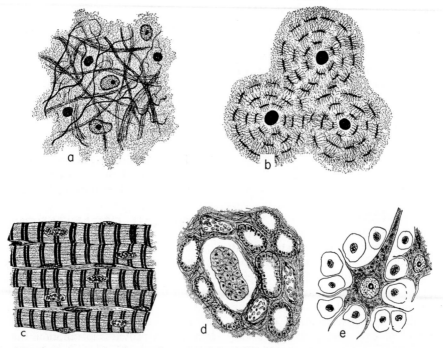

Figure 1. Histological sections of several tissues of the body, showing structural characteristics of different types of cells: (a) connective tissue, (b) bone, (c) muscle, (d) kidney, and (e) nerve.

divide again and again until the appropriate number is replenished.

THE EXTRACELLULAR FLUID—THE INTERNAL ENVIRONMENT

About 60 per cent of the human body is composed of fluid. Some of this fluid is inside the cells, and is called the *intracellular fluid*. The fluid which is in the spaces outside the cells is called the *extracellular fluid*. Among the dissolved constituents of the extracellular fluid are the nutrients needed by the cells for maintenance of life; because the extracellular fluid is in constant motion throughout the body and is constantly mixing, all cells live in essentially the same environment. Therefore, the extracellular fluid is often called the *internal environment* or the *internal milieu* of the body.

Cells are automatons that are capable of living, growing, and providing their special functions so long as the proper concentrations of oxygen, glucose, the different electrolytes, amino acids, and fatty substances are available in the internal environment.

Differences between Extracellular and Intracellular Fluids. About one third of the body fluids is extracellular, while the two thirds that is inside the many trillions of cells comprises the intracellular fluid. The extracellular fluid contains large amounts of sodium, chloride, and bicarbonate ions and nutrients for the cells as well as the excretory products of the cells. The principal function of the extracellular fluid is transport of substances from one part of the body to another—for instance, oxygen from the lungs to the cells, carbon dioxide from the cells back to the lungs, urea from the liver to the kidneys, and glucose from the gastrointestinal tract to the cells.

The intracellular fluid is much the same from one cell to another; it almost always contains large amounts of potassium, magnesium, and phosphate instead of the sodium and chloride found in the extracellular fluid. It also contains the nutrients required for chemical reactions in the cell and excretory products awaiting removal through the cellular membranes. The essential difference between intracellular and extracellular fluid lies not in the nutrients or excretory products but, instead, in the types of electrolytes. Special mechanisms for transporting ions through the cellular membranes maintain this difference. These mechanisms will be discussed in detail in Chapter 3.

The different compositions of electrolytes in the extracellular and intracellular fluids cause an electrical charge to develop across the membrane of each cell, which is negative on the inside and positive on the outside. It is this charge that allows nerves to transmit impulses, muscles to contract, glandular cells to secrete, and probably even macrophages to move toward certain areas. Therefore, simply because the intra- and extracellular fluids have different electrolytes, electrical reactions occurring at the cellular membrane help to regulate the functions of the cells themselves.

"HOMEOSTATIC" MECHANISMS OF THE MAJOR FUNCTIONAL SYSTEMS OF THE BODY

Homeostasis

The term *homeostasis* is used by physiologists to mean *maintenance of static, or constant, conditions in the internal environment.* Essentially all the organs and tissues of the body perform functions that help to maintain these constant conditions. For instance, the lungs provide new oxygen as it is required by the cells, the kidneys maintain constant electrolyte concentrations, and the gut provides nutrients. A very large segment of this text will be concerned with the manner in which each organ or tissue contributes to homeostasis. To begin this discussion, the different functional systems of the body and their homeostatic mechanisms will be outlined briefly; then the basic theory of the control systems that cause the functional systems to operate in harmony with each other will be discussed.

The Fluid Transport System

Extracellular fluid is transported to all parts of the body in two different stages. The first step entails movement of the blood around and around the circulatory system, and the second, movement of fluid between the blood capillaries and the cells. Figure 2 illustrates the overall circulation of blood, showing that the heart is actually two separate pumps, one of which propels blood

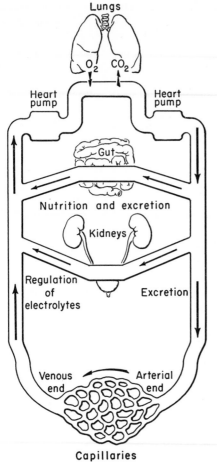

Capillaries

Figure 2. General organization of the circulatory system.

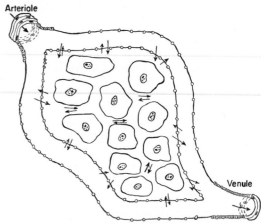

Figure 3. Diffusion of fluid through the capillary wall and through the interstitial spaces.

ward through the pores and some inward. This allows continual transfer of individual molecules of water, electrolytes, nutrients, and excretory substances through the capillary membranes. Furthermore, these same substances are continually diffusing in all directions in the interstitial spaces. Almost no cell is located more than 25 to 50 microns from a capillary, which allows movement of any substance from the capillary to the cell or in the opposite direction within a few seconds. Thus, the extracellular fluid throughout the body is continually mixed and thereby maintains almost complete homogeneity.

Origin of Nutrients in the Extracellular Fluid

The Respiratory System. Figure 2 shows that each time the blood passes through the body it also flows through the lungs. The blood picks up oxygen in the alveoli, thus acquiring the oxygen needed by the cells. The membrane between the alveoli and the lumen of the pulmonary capillaries is only 1 to 4 microns in thickness, and oxygen diffuses through this membrane into the blood in exactly the same manner that water, nutrients, and excreta diffuse through the tissue capillaries.

The Gastrointestinal Tract. Figure 2 also shows that a large portion of the blood pumped by the heart passes through the walls of the gastrointestinal organs. Here, different dissolved nutrients, including carbohydrates, fatty acids, amino acids, and

through the lungs and the other through the systemic circulation. All the blood in the circulation traverses the entire circuit of the circulation an average of once each minute when a person is at rest and as many as five times each minute when he becomes extremely active.

As blood passes through the capillaries, continual exchange occurs between the plasma portion of the blood and the interstitial fluid in the spaces surrounding the capillaries. This process is illustrated in Figure 3. Note that the capillaries are porous so that large amounts of fluid can *diffuse* back and forth between the blood and the tissue spaces, as illustrated by the arrows. This process of diffusion is caused by kinetic motion of the molecules in both the plasma and the extracellular fluid. That is, all fluid molecules are continually moving and bouncing in all directions, some out-

others, are absorbed into the extracellular fluid.

The Liver and Other Organs That Perform Primarily Metabolic Functions. Not all substances absorbed from the gastrointestinal tract can be used in their absorbed form by the cells. The liver alters the chemical compositions of many of these to more usable forms, and other tissues of the body, such as the fat cells, the gastrointestinal mucosa, the kidneys, and the endocrine glands, help to modify the absorbed substances or store them until they are needed at a later time. This storage and modification of the chemical substances before use for energy or for other purposes by the cells is the first stage of *intermediary metabolism,* which is defined as the sum of all the metabolic processes that occur between the intake of food and oxygen and the excretion of the end-products of metabolism.

Musculoskeletal System. Sometimes the question is asked: How does the musculoskeletal system fit into the homeostatic functions of the body? Were it not for this system, the body could not move to the appropriate place at the appropriate time to obtain the foods required for nutrition. The musculoskeletal system also provides motility for protection against adverse surroundings, without which the entire body, and along with it all the homeostatic mechanisms, could be destroyed instantaneously.

Removal of Metabolic End-Products

Removal of Carbon Dioxide by the Lungs. At the same time that blood passes through the lungs to pick up oxygen, carbon dioxide is released from the capillaries into the alveoli, and the respiratory movement of air into and out of the alveoli carries the carbon dioxide on into the atmosphere. Carbon dioxide is the most abundant of all the end-products of metabolism.

The Kidneys. Passage of the blood through the kidneys removes those substances from the plasma that are not needed by the cells. This includes especially different end-products of metabolism and excesses of electrolytes or water that might have accumulated in the extracellular fluids. The kidneys perform their function by, first, filtering very large quantities of plasma through the glomeruli into the tubules and then reabsorbing glucose, amino acids, large amounts of water, and many of the electrolytes, all of which are substances needed by the cells. However, substances not needed by the cells are not reabsorbed but, instead, pass on through the renal tubules into the urine. Thus, in a roundabout way, the extracellular fluid loses unwanted substances while retaining those that are still needed for cellular function.

Regulation of Body Functions

The Nervous System. The nerves interconnect the different parts of the body and help to keep them all operating in unison. The nervous system is composed of three major parts: the *sensory portion,* the *central nervous system,* or *integrative portion,* and the *motor portion.* Sensory nerves detect the state of the body or the state of the surroundings. For instance, nerves present everywhere in the skin apprise one every time an object touches him at any point. The eyes are sensory organs which give one a visual image of the surrounding area. The ears also are sensory organs. The central nervous system is comprised of the brain and spinal cord. The brain can store information, generate thoughts, create ambition, and determine reactions that the body should perform in response to various sensations. Appropriate signals are then transmitted through the motor portion of the nervous system to carry out the person's desires.

A large segment of the nervous system, called the *autonomic system,* operates at a subconscious level and controls many of the functions of the internal organs, including the action of the heart, the movements of the gastrointestinal tract, and the secretion by different glands.

The Hormonal System of Regulation. Located in the body are eight major endocrine glands that secrete chemical substances called *hormones.* Hormones are transported in the extracellular fluids to all parts of the body to help regulate function. For instance, thyroid hormone increases the rates of almost all the chemical reactions in all cells. In this way thyroid hormone helps to set the tempo of bodily activity, increasing the overall rate of activity when it is secreted in abundance or decreasing the activity when the amount of hormone is decreased. Likewise, insulin controls glucose metabolism, adrenocortical hormones control electrolyte and protein metabolism, parathormone controls bone metabolism, etc. Thus, the hormones represent a system of regulation independent of the nervous system. The nervous system, in general, regulates rapid muscular and secretory actions of the body, whereas the hormonal system regulates mainly the metabolic functions.

Reproduction

Reproduction is another function of the body that sometimes is not considered to be a homeostatic function. But it does help to maintain a static situation by generating new beings to take the place of ones that are dying. This perhaps sounds like a farfetched usage of the term homeostasis, but it does illustrate that, in the final analysis, essentially all structures of the body are so organized that they help to maintain continuity of life.

THE CONTROL SYSTEMS OF THE BODY

Examples of Control Mechanisms

Regulation of Oxygen and Carbon Dioxide Concentrations in the Extracellular Fluid. Since oxygen is one of the major substances required for chemical reactions in the cells, the rates of the chemical reactions are, to a great extent, dependent on the concentration of oxygen in the extracellular fluid. If the oxygen becomes increased, the rates of the reactions also increase; or, if the oxygen is decreased, the rates of the reactions can decrease almost to a standstill. For this reason a special control mechanism is available for maintenance of an almost exact and constant oxygen concentration in the extracellular fluids. This mechanism depends principally on the chemical characteristics of *hemoglobin*, which is present in all the red blood cells. Hemoglobin combines with oxygen as the blood passes through the lungs. In the tissue capillaries it will not release oxygen into the interstitial fluid if too much oxygen is already there but, if the oxygen concentration is too little,

sufficient oxygen will be released to reestablish an adequate interstitial fluid concentration. Thus, the regulation of oxygen concentration in the tissues is vested principally in the chemical characteristics of hemoglobin itself. This regulation is called the *oxygen-buffering function of hemoglobin.*

Carbon dioxide is one of the major endproducts of the oxidative reactions in cells. If all the carbon dioxide formed in the cells should continue to accumulate in the tissue fluids, the *mass action* of the carbon dioxide itself would soon halt all the energy-giving reactions of the cells. On the other hand, if the concentration of carbon dioxide should fall extremely low, the opposite effect would occur—increased rapidity of chemical activity in the cells. It is more important to have a constant rate of activity than an extremely rapid activity at times with inactivity at other times. The following mechanism maintains a constant and reasonable concentration of carbon dioxide in the extracellular fluids: A very high carbon dioxide concentration *excites the respiratory center*, causing the person to breathe rapidly and deeply. This increases the rate of removal of carbon dioxide from the alveoli, which in turn allows rapid diffusion of carbon dioxide out of the blood, thus lowering the carbon dioxide concentration in the extracellular fluids. Conversely, a low concentration of carbon dioxide causes less rapid breathing with subsequent accumulation of greater and greater quantities of carbon dioxide in the extracellular fluid until the concentration returns to normal.

Regulation of Glucose Concentration. Figure 4 illustrates the control of extracellular glucose concentration under several different conditions. At first the glucose concentration of the animal was approximately 90

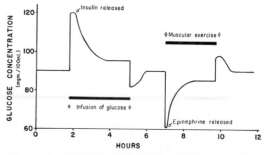

Figure 4. Regulation of blood glucose concentration.

milligrams in each 100 ml. of extracellular fluid. Then an infusion of glucose was started; almost immediately the glucose level rose to 120 mg./100 ml. Within a few moments this high level caused the *pancreas* to secrete large quantities of *insulin,* and the insulin in turn *promoted rapid movement of the glucose out of the extracellular fluid into the cells.* As a result, the glucose concentration in the extracellular fluid fell back to a value of about 95 mg./100 ml. and remained at this level as long as the glucose infusion continued. Thus, secretion of insulin by the pancreas constitutes a regulatory mechanism for maintenance of relatively constant glucose concentration in the extracellular fluid despite the rapid influx of additional glucose.

Later the animal began to exercise very severely and used up large portions of the glucose. Almost immediately, however, sympathetic stimulation caused glycogen stored in the liver to split into glucose, which was then released into the extracellular fluid. Therefore, in a matter of only a few minutes the glucose concentration reapproached normal and remained there until the end of the exercise. This time a different control system helped to maintain relatively constant glucose concentration in the extracellular fluid.

Regulation of Arterial Pressure. Several different systems contribute to the regulation of arterial pressure. One of these, the *pressoreceptor system,* is very simple and provides an excellent example of a control mechanism. In the walls of most of the great arteries of the upper body, including especially the bifurcation region of the carotids and the walls of the aorta, are many nerve receptors, called *pressoreceptors,* which are stimulated by stretch of the arterial wall. When the arterial pressure becomes great, these pressoreceptors are stimulated excessively, and impulses are transmitted to the medulla of the brain. Here the impulses inhibit the *vasomotor center,* which in turn decreases the number of impulses transmitted through the sympathetic nervous system to the heart and blood vessels. Lack of these impulses causes diminished pumping activity by the heart and increased ease of blood flow through the peripheral vessels, both of which lower the arterial pressure back toward normal. Conversely, a fall in arterial pressure relaxes the stretch receptors,

allowing the vasomotor center to become more active than usual and thereby causing the arterial pressure to rise back toward a normal value.

Characteristics of Control Systems

The above examples of homeostatic control mechanisms are only a few of the many hundreds in the body. Some of these mechanisms control very important conditions, such as arterial pressure, oxygen concentration in the tissue fluids, carbon dioxide concentration, while many others regulate such minor factors as the rates of individual chemical reactions in individual cells. Nevertheless, essentially all the control systems of the body have in common certain characteristics. These are explained in the following pages.

Reflex Nature of Control Systems. Most of the major control systems of the body operate by means of reflexes. That is, one element in the system acts as a *receptor,* a second element as a *transmitter,* and a third as an *effector.* In the case of nervous reflexes, the sensory organs are the receptors; the nerves, including the pathways through the central nervous system, are the transmitters; and the organs at the ends of the motor nerves—the muscles of the skeletal muscle system, the muscles of the blood vessels, the cardiac muscle, the glands of the body, and other structures—are the effectors. In the case of the pressoreceptor system above, the stretch receptors of the arteries are the receptors, the nerves to and from the brain and the vasomotor center itself constitute the transmitters, and, finally, the heart and the blood vessels constitute the effectors.

Hormonal reflexes also provide many control systems for the body. In the case of the glucose regulatory mechanism described above, the receptor of the hormonal reflex was the *islets of Langerhans* of the pancreas, which secrete insulin in response to an increase in glucose concentration. The transmitter is *insulin,* and the effectors are the *membranes of all the cells of the body,* which are stimulated by insulin to increase their rates of glucose transport from the extracellular fluids into the intracellular fluids.

Occasionally, control systems do not have

receptors, transmitters, and effectors, but instead depend on other physical properties of the system. For instance, in regulating oxygen concentration in the tissue fluid, hemoglobin releases oxygen to the tissues at a reasonably constant concentration. In strict terminology this is a "buffering action" rather than a control action, but in a very broad sense it is also a control function. Later we will discuss also the buffering action of various acid-base buffers for regulation of hydrogen ion concentration. Yet, for the most part, the control mechanisms of the body do involve either nervous or hormonal reflexes.

Negative Feedback Nature of Control Systems.

The reflex control systems of the body act by a process of *negative feedback,* which can be explained best by reviewing some of the homeostatic control systems mentioned above. In the regulation of carbon dioxide concentration, a high level of carbon dioxide in the extracellular fluid causes increased pulmonary ventilation, and this in turn causes decreased carbon dioxide concentration. In other words, the response is *negative* to the initiating stimulus. Conversely, if the carbon dioxide concentration falls too low, this causes feedback through the control system to raise the carbon dioxide concentration. This response also is negative to the initiating stimulus.

In the glucose regulatory mechanism a high level of glucose causes insulin release, and this in turn promotes diminished glucose concentration. Thus, the response is negative to the elevated glucose level that initiated the response. Conversely, a low glucose level promotes sympathetic stimulation and release of glucose from the liver, thereby bringing the glucose concentration of the fluids back toward normal. Here again, a low level causes a high level, or, in other words, a response that is negative to the initiating stimulus.

Finally, in the arterial pressure–regulating mechanism, a high pressure causes a series of reactions that promote a lowered pressure, or a low pressure causes a series of reactions that promote an elevated pressure. In both instances these effects are negative with respect to the initiating stimulus.

Therefore, in general, if some constituent of the extracellular fluid becomes excessive or too little, a control system initiates a series of changes that cause an opposite reaction, in this way always keeping the constituent near a certain mean concentration and thus maintaining homeostasis.

Amplification, or gain, of a control system. The degree of effectiveness with which a control system maintains constant conditions is called the *amplification,* or *gain,* of the system. For instance, in Figure 4 the infusion of glucose caused immediately a 30 mg./100 ml. change in glucose concentration; but after the control system had become maximally effective, this change was only 5 mg. The gain of a system is equal to the initial degree of abnormality divided by the final degree of abnormality minus 1. Therefore, the gain of this system was 5. To state this in other words, *the displacement of the glucose concentration from the mean was 6 times less than it would have been had the control system not been operative.*

The gain of the pressoreceptor system as measured in dogs is approximately 2. That is, any extraneous factor that tends to increase or decrease the arterial pressure does so only one third as much as would occur if this control system were not present.

Oscillation of negative feedback control systems. Unfortunately, negative feedback control systems can sometimes become unstable and oscillate. Figure 5 illustrates blood pressure waves caused by oscillation of the pressoreceptor system described above. This oscillation occurs as follows: Some extraneous factor causes the arterial pressure to become too high, and this initiates impulses that go through the central nervous system back to the vascular system

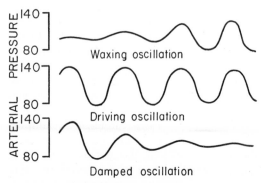

Figure 5.   Arterial pressure waves caused by oscillation of the pressoreceptor system.

to lower the pressure. However, 5 to 15 seconds are required for maximal transmission of the pressoreceptor signals. Consequently, the blood pressure keeps on falling long beyond the point at which it would have become normal and, as a result, becomes too low. This in turn initiates a second set of reactions which cause the blood pressure to rise too high. Here again, delay in transmission of the signal allows the pressure to keep on rising long after the pressure has passed the normal mean value. Thus, the cycle is reinitiated, causing the pressure to rise and fall continuously in a state of oscillation.

Damping of control systems. Fortunately, oscillation of the blood pressure, as shown in Figure 5, does not occur very often but only under certain peculiar conditions, such as decreased blood volume and ischemia of the brain. The reason for lack of oscillation is that most of the control mechanisms of the body are highly damped, which results from very rapid transmission of the control signals by the transmitter in comparison with the rapidity of response by the effector. Though the pressoreceptor system can occasionally oscillate, it is normally damped in the following way. When the pressure has been too high and has elicited a reflex, the blood pressure will begin to fall. But, as the pressure approaches the normal mean value, the number of stretch impulses transmitted by the pressoreceptors also falls, thereby slowing the further fall in pressure. This cessation of the reflex signal before the pressure actually gets to its normal mean value prevents an overshoot in the negative direction, and this constitutes damping.

A few control systems are not damped, but continue to oscillate indefinitely. One of these is the control system that causes respiration, which results from oscillation, or "reverberation," of impulses between inspiratory and expiratory centers in the brain stem. Another continuous oscillation is responsible for the monthly sexual cycle of the female. Hormones secreted by the pituitary gland stimulate the ovaries to produce ovarian hormones, and these in turn act on the pituitary gland to inhibit its secretion. Lack of the pituitary hormones then causes the ovaries to stop secreting their hormones, and this in turn allows the pituitary to begin secreting once more. In this way the hormones of the glands oscillate back and forth, providing the rhythm of the sexual cycle.

Positive Feedback as a Cause of Death —Vicious Cycles. One might ask the question: Why do essentially all control systems of the body operate by negative feedback rather than positive feedback? However, if he should consider the nature of positive feedback, it would immediately be evident that positive feedback does not lead to control but to instability. Unfortunately, extraneous types of positive feedback occasionally inadvertently occur in the body, and these often lead to such unstable states that they cause death.

Figure 6 illustrates an instance in which death can ensue from positive feedback. This figure depicts the pumping effectiveness of the heart, showing that the heart of the normal human being pumps about 5 liters per minute. However, if the person is suddenly bled 2 liters, the amount of blood in his body is decreased to such a low level that not enough is available for his heart to pump effectively. As a result, the arterial pressure falls, and the flow of blood to the heart muscle through the coronary vessels diminishes. This results in weakening of the heart, further diminished pumping, further decrease in coronary blood flow, and more weakness of the heart; the cycle repeats itself again and again until death. Note that each cycle in the feedback results in further weakness of the heart. In other words, the initiating stimulus causes more of the same, which is *positive feedback*.

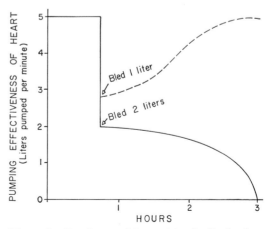

Figure 6. Death caused by positive feedback when 2 liters of blood are removed from the circulation.

Positive feedback is better known as a "vicious cycle," but actually a mild degree of positive feedback can be overcome by the negative feedback control mechanisms of the body, and a vicious cycle will fail to develop. For instance, if the person in the above example were bled only 1 liter instead of 2 liters, the normal negative feedback mechanisms for controlling cardiac output and arterial pressure would overbalance the positive feedback and the person would recover, as shown by the dashed line of Figure 6.

Automaticity of the Body

The purpose of the discussion in this chapter has been to point out, first, the overall structural organization of the body and, second, the means by which the different parts of the body operate in harmony. To summarize, the body is actually an *aggregate of about one hundred trillion cells* held together by appropriate supporting tissues. These cells in turn are organized into different functional structures, some of which are called *organs*. Each functional structure provides its share in the maintenance of homeostatic conditions in the extracellular fluid, called also the *internal environment*. As long as normal conditions are maintained in the internal environment, the cells of the body will continue to live and function properly. Thus, each cell benefits from homeostasis, and in turn each cell contributes its share toward the maintenance of this state. This reciprocal interplay provides continuous automaticity of the body until one or more

of the functional systems loses its ability to contribute its share of function. When this happens, all the cells of the body suffer. Extreme dysfunction of any one of the integrated systems leads to death, while moderate dysfunction leads to sickness.

REFERENCES

Adolph, E. F.: General and specific characteristics of physiological adaptations. *Am. J. Physiol.*, 184:18, 1956.

Adolph, E. F.: Physiological Regulations. Lancaster, Pennsylvania, The Jaques Cattell Press, 1943.

Adolph, E. F.: Physiology of Man in the Desert. New York, Interscience Publishers, 1947.

Ashby, R. W.: An Introduction to Cybernetics. New York, John Wiley and Sons, 1956.

Bayliss, L. E.: Principles of General Physiology. Volume I. New York, Longmans, 1959.

Cannon, W. B.: Organization for physiological homeostasis. *Physiol. Rev.*, 9:399, 1930.

Cannon, W. B.: The Wisdom of the Body. New York, W. W. Norton Co., 1932.

Guyton, A. C., and Lindsey, A. W.: Positive reflexes as a cause of vicious cycles in circulatory control systems. *Fed. Proc.*, 15:85, 1956.

Kleitman, N.: Biological rhythms and cycles. *Physiol. Rev.*, 29:1, 1949.

Schmidt-Nielsen, K.: Animal Physiology. Englewood Cliffs, Prentice-Hall, 1960.

Sherrington, C. S.: Man on His Nature. New York, The Macmillan Co., 1941.

Symposium on Biological Rhythms. *Fed. Proc.*, 18: 1232, 1959.

Trimmer, J. D.: Response of Physical Systems. New York, John Wiley and Sons, 1950.

von Foerster, H., Mead, M., and Teuber, H. L.: Cybernetics: Circular Causal and Feedback Mechanisms in Biological and Social Systems. New York, Josiah Macy, Jr., Foundation, 1951.

Webb, H. M., and Brown, F. A., Jr.: Timing long-cycle physiological rhythms. *Physiol. Rev.*, 39:127, 1959.

Chapter 2

The Cell and Its Function

The human being is composed of one hundred trillion cells, and because the overall function of the body is the sum of the minute functions of all these cells, any understanding of human physiology requires first a knowledge of cellular function. The present chapter, therefore, will discuss the basic organization of the cell and the functions of its component parts.

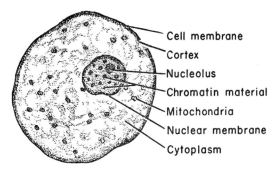

Figure 7. Structure of the cell as seen with the light microscope.

ORGANIZATION OF THE CELL

A typical cell as seen by the light microscope is illustrated in Figure 7. Its two major parts are the *nucleus* and the *cytoplasm*. The nucleus is separated from the cytoplasm by the *nuclear membrane,* and the cytoplasm is separated from the surrounding fluids by the *cell membrane.*

Cytoplasm

Cytoplasmic Matrix. Figure 8 illustrates the cytoplasmic cavity of a cell showing many solid or semi-solid structures in the cytoplasm. In between these structures is the *cytoplasmic matrix,* which is a viscid fluid containing large amounts of dissolved substances and suspended particles. Among the dissolved substances are *proteins, polysaccharides, amino acids,* and the electrolytes *potassium, magnesium, phosphate, sulfate,* and *bicarbonate.* The suspended par-

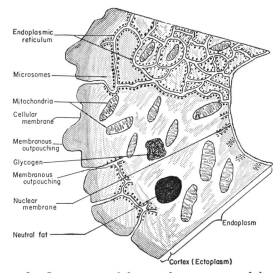

Figure 8. Organization of the cytoplasmic portion of the cell.

ticles are comprised mainly of *lipoproteins* that are composed of a mixture of *protein* with *phospholipids, cholesterol,* and *neutral fat.* Other suspended particles in the cytoplasmic matrix are insoluble proteins or conjugated proteins. All these suspended particles are collectively called *micelles,* which means simply suspended colloid particles, and the matrix itself is frequently called a *colloidal solution.* Actually, the matrix is both a true solution of many dissolved substances as well as a colloidal solution of substances which will not dissolve but will remain in suspension. Many of the different micelles seem to be aggregates of protein enzyme systems that catalyze much of the chemical activity responsible for cellular life.

Endoplasmic Reticulum. Threading its way through the entire cytoplasmic cavity is a meshwork of tubular structures called the *endoplasmic reticulum.* Figure 8 illustrates that the entire reticulum is interconnected and that it also connects with a small space between the two layers of the nuclear membrane, which will be discussed below. In addition, the cell membrane folds inward at many points, and these infoldings often connect with the lumen of the reticular tubules, possibly providing a direct means of communication between the extracellular fluids and the interior of the cell.

In almost all types of cells, the entire outer surface of the endoplasmic reticulum is studded with many small, granular structures called *microsomes.* These are composed of a special type of conjugated protein called *ribose nucleoprotein,* which is involved in the synthesis of other proteins within the cell. This will be discussed in greater detail later in the chapter.

Very little is known about the function of the endoplasmic reticulum except, first, that it provides a structural network in the cytoplasmic cavity and, second, that it is involved in protein synthesis because of the microsomes attached to its outer surfaces. Other suggested functions include (1) that it perhaps acts as a canalicular system for transport of materials from one part of the cytoplasm to another, or to or from the exterior of the cell or nucleus, and (2) that it might provide a membranous surface within the cell for transport of electrochemical impulses that control many intracellular activities.

Mitochondria. Located throughout the cytoplasmic chamber are many small, oblong structures called *mitochondria.* These are normally approximately one-half micron in diameter and one or more microns in length, though they can be much more slender and longer. Mitochondria have a lipoprotein membrane similar to the cell and nuclear membranes but characterized by many deep folds projecting to the inside of the mitochondrion. These folds form *shelves* on the inside of the mitochondrion, giving it a cross-striated appearance and providing a very large surface area on which enzymatic functions supposedly occur.

The mitochondrion has been considered to be the "powerhouse" of the cell, because it is here that the nutrients, including oxygen and the various foodstuffs, are metabolized to supply energy for the remainder of the cell. This process also will be discussed in detail later in the chapter.

Other Structures in the Cytoplasm. Figure 8 also illustrates a glycogen granule and a fat globule in the cytoplasm. Glycogen is an insoluble polymer of glucose, polymerized under the influence of enzymes in some of the micelles in the cytoplasm and stored in the cell in the granular form until it is needed as a food. Then additional enzymes among the micelles cause *glycogenolysis,* resulting in the reformation of dissolved glucose.

The fat globule is an accumulation of neutral fat in the cytoplasm. The fat can be split into fatty acids and glycerol by cytoplasmic enzyme systems when the fat is needed for other purposes. In the *cells* of the fat tissues as much as 95 per cent of all the cytoplasm can be one or more very large fat globules, though in the average cell the fat content is only a few per cent.

Cells that perform special functions usually have special structures in addition to the usual ones. These include the Golgi apparatus in many secretory cells and in neuronal cells, fibrils in muscle cells and ciliated cells, and special canaliculi and secretory globules in many secretory cells. Most of the specialized structures will be discussed at other points in this text in connection with the functions performed by the individual cells. However, the Golgi apparatus deserves special comment because of the long-time interest that histologists have had in this structure.

Anatomically, the Golgi apparatus seems to be continuous with the endoplasmic reticulum, and perhaps represents a special elaboration of this system. Its function is yet unknown, but, because of its appearance and its connection with the reticulum, cytologists have often supposed that the Golgi apparatus represents a special area of the cell where substances synthesized elsewhere in the cell come together and react chemically to produce a final product. Unfortunately, this is still speculation, but it shows how difficult it has been to deduce accurate functional information about intracellular structures even as large and prominent as the Golgi apparatus.

The Cell Membrane

Figure 8 illustrates the cell membrane, which is a thin covering over the outer surface of the cytoplasmic cavity. This membrane has many outpouchings which, in certain areas of the body at least, interdigitate with outpouchings from adjacent cells. The figure also illustrates many infoldings, some of which are continuous with the endoplasmic reticulum. As pointed out above, these perhaps provide a means by which materials can be transported from the exterior to the interior of the cell, though this has not yet been proved; the connections have been demonstrated only in electron micrographs rather than by functional experiments.

Studies on the transfer of substances through the cell membrane have shown it to have the following characteristics: First, lipid substances are miscible with it and therefore can be transported through the membrane with ease. Also, lipid solvents can dissolve the membrane and cause rupture of the cell. Second, small molecular substances, even though they are not lipid soluble, can diffuse directly through the cell membrane. Consequently, it can be assumed that the membrane has many minute *pores,* though actually these have not been demonstrated even by electron micrographs. Third, in addition to its lipid and porous nature, the cell membrane has elastic resilience which is mainly characteristic of proteins. Furthermore, chemical analyses of red blood cell membranes have shown them to be a mixture of a protein called *stromatin,* of a large amount of *phospholipids,* and of smaller amounts of *neutral fat* and *cholesterol.* It is assumed, therefore, that the membrane is composed of a meshwork of protein fibrils, most of the spaces of which are filled with a *lipid matrix.* However, it is supposed that some of these spaces are not filled with the matrix, and these constitute the pores. The thickness of dried red blood cell membranes has been measured to be approximately 7 millimicrons, and it is believed that the membranes of other cells have this same order of thickness.

Formation of a New Cell Membrane —the Surface Precipitation Reaction. Whenever the membrane of a cell becomes ruptured, some of the cytoplasm streams out of the opening. However, before it can flow far into the surrounding fluids, a *surface precipitation reaction* occurs. That is, proteins precipitate on the surface, and fatty materials immediately become entrapped, thereby forming a new structure that is essentially identical with the original membrane. This reaction will not occur when the concentration of calcium ions in the extracellular fluids is very low. Therefore, one of the very important functions of this ion is probably to maintain the integrity of the cell membrane itself.

The Cellular Cortex. Immediately inside the cell membrane is usually a layer of coagulated cytoplasm of variable thickness, called the cell *cortex* or the *ectoplasm,* which is illustrated in Figure 8. Whenever the surface precipitation reaction occurs, a new cortex develops beneath the new membrane. The thickness of the cortex varies from cell to cell and also varies from time to time during different functional states of the same cell. How extensive the cortex is in the different cells of the human body is unknown, for appropriate studies have not yet been made on living human cells. Yet, on the basis of studies in unicellular animals, it is reasonable to assume that thick cortices do often exist and perhaps are very important to the function of the cell membrane.

The cortex, like the membrane itself, is highly responsive to calcium ion concentration in the surrounding fluids—the greater this concentration the thicker becomes the cortex. On the other hand, large quantities of sodium and potassium decrease its thickness.

Since the cortex seems to be nothing more than gelled cytoplasmic matrix, it, like the matrix itself, contains many special protein enzymes, and functions have been ascribed to these for transport of non-miscible substances through the cell membrane. This process, called *active transport,* is so important to cell function that it will be described in detail in Chapter 3.

The Cellular Nucleus

While the cytoplasm is concerned principally with the energy-giving chemical reactions of the cells and also with the performance of specialized functions, such as secretion, contraction, and other functions important to the whole body, the nucleus is concerned with controlling intracellular activities and with the processes of cellular reproduction. The structures of the nucleus responsible for these functions are the following.

The Nuclear Membrane. The nuclear membrane is a two-layered structure with a thin space between the two layers connecting with the lumen of the tubular endoplasmic reticulum. This fact suggests that the nuclear membrane and reticulum might be responsible for collecting and transporting substances back and forth between the cytoplasm and the nucleus. Also, large pores can be seen in the nuclear membrane in electron micrographs, and, indeed, very large protein molecules have been observed passing through the membrane. Therefore, it is believed that the nuclear membrane causes very little resistance to the transfer of dissolved materials into or out of the nucleus. Furthermore, during cellular reproduction the nuclear membrane actually disappears during much of the division process. Thus, for practical purposes, the nuclear membrane can probably be considered to be an envelope holding the nuclear parts together but not separating the dissolved substances of the nucleus from those of the cytoplasm.

The Nucleoplasm. All the substance inside the nuclear membrane is collectively called the *nucleoplasm*. This contains, in addition to the dissolved substances, two major types of semi-solid structures, the *chromosomes* and the *nucleolus*, which are shown in Figure 9. In the spaces between these structures is the *nucleoplasmic matrix*, which is sometimes also called *nuclear sap*. The constituents of this matrix are the same as those of the cytoplasmic matrix. Therefore, it, too, is both a true solution of many dissolved substances and a colloidal suspension of mainly lipoprotein particles. These particles, as those in the cytoplasm, contain protein enzymes that are responsible for many of the chemical functions of the nucleus.

The Chromosomes and Genes. Figure 9 illustrates six different pairs of chromosomes in the nucleus. Until recently it has been taught that the human nucleus contains 24 such pairs, but now it is believed that only 23 pairs exist. Each chromosome in turn contains many *genes*, estimated from a few hundred to a few thousand. Each member of a pair of chromosomes contains essentially the same number of genes as the other member, and, except in rare instances, each type of gene in one of the chromosomes is paired with a like type of gene in the companion chromosome. Thus, the genes, like the chromosomes, exist in pairs, most estimates suggesting a total of about 25,000 pairs of genes in each cell nucleus. The genes in turn are responsible for transmission of hereditary characteristics from one generation of cells to the next and also from one generation of human beings to the next. This will be discussed in detail in Chapter 80.

Electron micrographs of chromosomes have indicated that the genes are long fibrillar structures bound together in bundles to form the chromosomes. An older theory suggested that the genes were located like small granules along the chromosomal threads. However, when the chromosomes are stretched, the "granules" disappear, which indicates that they are probably nothing more than folds in the long fibrils.

Each fibril, or gene, is believed to be a large *deoxyribose nucleoprotein* molecule composed of a chemical substance called *deoxyribonucleic acid* conjugated with a protein. It is the deoxyribonucleic acid rather than the protein that is responsible for transmission of genetic characteristics.

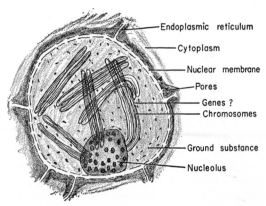

Figure 9. Structure and organization of the nucleus.

Therefore, the gene itself can be considered to be this substance, commonly abbreviated *DNA*.

The genes of the nucleus are transmitted from one generation of cells to the next, each new cell developing precisely the same complement of chromosomes and genes as in the preceding parent cell. This fact is extremely important, for, in addition to controlling heredity from one generation of man to the next, the genes also control the internal functions of each one of the cells itself, which will be discussed later in the chapter.

Chemical Nature of DNA. Deoxyribonucleic acid (DNA) is a combination of three different types of substances: phosphoric acid, deoxyribose (a sugar), and several different purine and pyrimidine bases. Two purine bases, adenine and guanine, and three pyrimidine bases, cytosine, thymine, and sometimes methylcytosine, are found in DNA. The phosphoric acid and deoxyribose portions of the nucleic acid are believed to be arranged in a helical manner around the purine and pyrimidine bases, as shown in Figure 10. The five different bases in each type of gene supposedly occur in a definite pattern along the strand of the fibril. The "pattern" in turn constitutes a "key" to the function of the gene. That is, the pattern adenine - cytosine - guanine - thymine would give a nucleic acid different from that given by the pattern guanine-cytosine-adenine-thymine. The molecular weight of the DNA molecule is about one million, which means that many thousands of these purine and pyrimidine bases can be arranged in different patterns. This explains how it is possible for each type of gene to be completely different from all other types.

The Nucleolus. A granular structure called the nucleolus is often present in the nucleus and is always adherent to at least a few of the chromosomes. Chemical analysis of the nucleolus shows it to contain a large amount of *ribose nucleoprotein,* which is chemically similar to the deoxyribose nucleoprotein of the genes but contains ribose instead of deoxyribose. It is believed that the genes of the chromosomes synthesize the ribose nucleoprotein and that this collects in the nucleolus. During certain stages of cellular function, the material of the nucleolus diffuses outward through the pores of the nuclear membrane into the cytoplasm and is dispersed in this way among the cytoplasmic matrix. After these episodes, the nucleolus is not seen in the nucleus until new ribose nucleoprotein is synthesized.

SOME BASIC FUNCTIONS OF THE CELL

Extraction of Energy from Nutrients

The principal nutrient substances from which cells extract energy are *oxygen* and one or more of the foodstuffs—*carbohydrates, fats,* and *proteins.* Carbohydrates are digested into glucose in the digestive tract or transformed into glucose in the liver, and it is in this form that almost all carbohydrates are transported into the cell. In a similar manner most fats are split into fatty

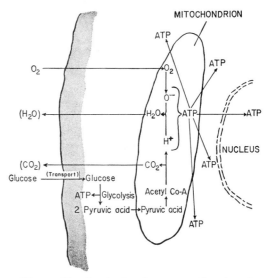

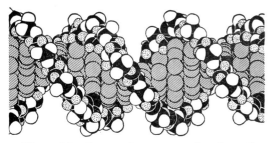

Figure 10. Suggested structure of a deoxyribonucleic acid molecule. The central shaded nuclei are the purine and pyrimidine bases.

Figure 11. Synthesis of energy-rich adenosine triphosphate molecules as a result of anaerobic and oxidative metabolism of glucose.

acids, while proteins are split into amino acids before they are transported into the cells. Inside the cells each one of these materials is further split into still smaller compounds that can react chemically with oxygen to liberate large amounts of energy.

Glycolysis. Figure 11 illustrates in detail the manner by which energy is derived from glucose. Glucose cannot diffuse through the cell membrane but instead is transported to the interior of the cell by means of an enzymatic carrier mechanism. Once inside the cell, enzymes of the cytoplasmic micelles convert glucose into *pyruvic acid* by the process of *glycolysis,* which is actually 14 different stages of molecular transformation, splitting, or other changes. To promote these changes, at least 12 different enzyme systems are required. At the completion of glycolysis, two molecules of pyruvic acid will have been formed, and the released energy has been

with the hydrogen ions to form water. This, too, diffuses into the extracellular fluid. Thus, the final products are carbon dioxide and water.

During the oxidation of pyruvic acid a tremendous amount of energy is released, and, by means of *coupled reactions,* this energy is used to synthesize still more adenosine triphosphate. More than 10 times as many adenosine triphosphate molecules are formed by this oxidative process as by the process of glycolysis. Again, these many adenosine triphosphate molecules diffuse throughout the cell to provide energy for any cellular function that requires it.

Adenosine Triphosphate. The adenosine triphosphate molecule, commonly abbreviated *ATP,* is a nucleotide composed of the nitrogenous base *adenine,* the pentose sugar *ribose,* and three molecules of *phosphoric acid,* the formula for which is:

used to form three molecules of a chemical substance called *adenosine triphosphate.* This substance, a highly reactive chemical that contains large amounts of energy, then diffuses throughout the cytoplasmic matrix to promote many different types of chemical reactions.

Oxidation of Pyruvic Acid in the Mitochondria. Once pyruvic acid is formed, it diffuses into the mitochondria and is converted under the influence of still another enzyme into *acetyl co-enzyme A.* This rapidly undergoes another series of transformations, collectively called the *Krebs cycle* or the *tricarboxylic cycle,* during which the pyruvic acid is converted into carbon dioxide and hydrogen atoms combined with hydrogen "carriers." The carbon dioxide diffuses out of the cell into the extracellular fluid while the hydrogen atoms are converted by still other enzymes into hydrogen ions. Simultaneously, another enzyme converts dissolved oxygen in the mitochondria into hydroxyl ions, and these immediately react

The last two phosphoric acid radicals are connected with the remainder of the molecule by means of so-called *high energy phosphate bonds,* which are represented by the symbol $\sim$. These high energy bonds contain about 7,000 calories of energy per mol of adenosine triphosphate, which is many times the energy stored in the average chemical bond, thus giving rise to the term "high energy" bond. Furthermore, the high energy phosphate bonds are highly labile and can split very rapidly on demand wherever in the cell energy is required to promote other chemical reactions. Thus, adenosine triphosphate is an explosive-like compound carrying large amounts of energy, a compound that diffuses from its glycolytic and oxidative points of formation throughout the cell to be used rapidly and easily on demand any place in the cell where energy is required.

When adenosine triphosphate releases its energy, a *phosphoric acid radical* is split away and *adenosine diphosphate* is formed.

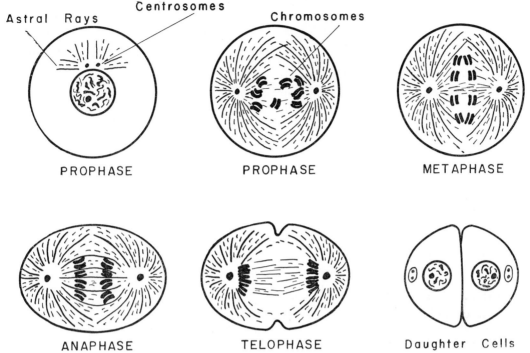

Figure 14. Mitotic division of the cell. (Modified from Wilson: The Cell in Development and Heredity. The Macmillan Co.)

anaphase also lasts only a short time in comparison with the prophase.

Then begins the *telophase*, which is the period of cell division. It is in this phase that solation of the gelled protoplasm occurs, beginning first around the two centrosomes at each end of the cell. This is believed to cause the elastic tension of the cell in the regions of the centrosomes to become greatly reduced while the elastic tension in the middle of the cell remains great because of the thick cortex which is still present. Therefore, very much like a tire with weak spots in two areas, the cell balloons out at both ends near the centrosomes and contracts in the center because of excessive elastic tension in that area, until the cell finally breaks in two. At this same time, for reasons totally unexplained, a new nuclear membrane is formed in each cell.

Development of the Human Body from the Fertilized Ovum—Cellular Differentiation

After an ovum is fertilized it divides to form successively new generations of daughter cells, many of which gradually become different from each other. This is called *cellular differentiation.* For many years embryologists have believed that differentiation results from unequal division of the cytoplasm during successive stages of mitosis. Supposedly, the cell that gets a greater proportion of a certain cytoplasmic constituent would be different from the other cell that receives the lesser share. However, on the basis of this theory it has been impossible to explain how cellular differentiation can be exact enough to produce over and over again human beings that are not far different from each other. That is, this theory fails because cytoplasmic substances undergo a continuous mixing, and one could never be certain that one ovum would divide in the same way that another ovum would divide.

Recent experiments, however, have shown that the genetic complements of the cellular nuclei change, sometimes to a considerable extent, during successive stages of differentiation. For this reason the following theory seems now to be far more pertinent than the long held cytoplasmic division theory.

Differentiation as a Result of Loss or Alteration of Genes. Most of the 25,000 or more genes in the chromosomes probably reproduce themselves completely before each cell division takes place, but, because of the rapid rate of division in the embryo, it is probable that one or more of the genes may not have reproduced or may have reproduced incompletely by the time a particular cell divides. Therefore, the two daughter cells would be slightly different from each other as a result of their different genetic make-up, and because of these differences the cytoplasmic nucleoproteins and the cytoplasmic enzymes would also be different in the two daughter cells, thus giving rise to different functional capabilities and different physical appearances of the offspring cells. Through a succession of other rapid divisions still more genes might be lost or modified, forming new cells containing different genetic make-ups.

In essence, then, if this theory is correct, the different types of cells of the body would result from different rates of autoreproduction of the genes in the rapidly multiplying primordial cells of the embryo. Those genes that can autocatalytically reproduce themselves very rapidly would be transmitted from the primordial cells into all the differentiated cells, whereas those genes that are not capable of autocatalytically reproducing themselves rapidly would be the ones successively lost or altered in the different cells, thereby causing the cells to become progressively different from each other. It should be noted specifically that only a few genes need be lost from any one particular type of cell in order to cause its functions and structure to become completely different from those of the other types of cells.

Once the different types of cells have become differentiated from each other, they continue to reproduce new cells similar to themselves and, therefore, grow into organs or specific structures of the body. Here again it is the basic characteristics of these different cells that determine how rapidly each respective type will grow and, therefore, determine the relative rates of growth of the different types of cells. The liver becomes a large organ because of the rapid growth that is characteristic of liver cells, while the pituitary gland becomes a very small organ because of the relatively slow growth of pituitary cells.

Stimulation of Cell Growth by Local Factors in the Body. While the body is developing, the local environmental factors in each part of the body play a role in determining the size of the different structures. For instance, elongation of the bones stretches the muscle fibers and causes them to grow. Growth of all parts of the body stretches the skin, and the skin grows.

Also, local environmental factors can determine the cell type. In the embryo, growth of the neural elements of the eye causes the overlying epithelial cells to invaginate and form the lens, and growth of nerve fibers for mediating taste into the mouth causes the epithelial cells to form taste buds. This same mechanism is responsible for formation of many other discrete structures of the body.

Even after the adult is formed, local factors can still play a role in growth or regrowth of tissues. Destruction of the skin by abrasion, by cutting, or by irradiation causes enhanced growth of the remaining skin cells until new skin replaces that which has been lost. Also, damage deep in the tissues causes rapid proliferation of fibroblasts and growth of connective tissue. The factors which cause rapid growth of skin and connective tissue are probably local effects such as exposure of the basal layers of the skin to the atmosphere and exposure of the fibroblasts to irritation.

Growth Limits of the Different Organs of the Body. While the embryo is forming, and even in the adult body, the cells maintain specific quantitative ratios to each other because of other factors besides the genes. If seven eighths of the liver is removed from an adult, the remaining one eighth begins to grow immediately until the size of the liver becomes almost as large as it had been previously. Why should the liver return to its previous size and then stop growing? The correct answer to this question is not known, but one approach is on the basis of nutritional factors. Because of the differences between the liver and other structures of the body, the liver undoubtedly requires some nutrients that other tissues do not require, while the other tissues require still different nutrients. When liver cells are present in a ratio far below normal, it is to be expected that an excess quantity of those specific nutrients needed by the liver will be available so that the liver cells can grow rapidly. Also, it is probable that the liver uses for growth some nutrients that are actually manufactured in other cells of the body—the hormones, for instance—and, when the quantity of liver cells in the body is very slight, an excess of these manufactured nutrients is available for rapid growth of liver cells until the number of liver cells has reached its normal ratio to the rest of the body.

Still other theories have been offered for explaining growth limits. It has been postulated that each type of cell might secrete into the body fluids some specific substance that, after it accumulates in large enough quantities, is capable of inhibiting further multiplication of that specific type of cell. Another variation of this theory is that each type of cell might secrete some substance to which the reticuloendothelial system of the body forms immune bodies. These immune bodies in turn react with the growing cells of each specific type to prevent excessive growth and multiplication. Because such immune bodies, or "cellular antihormones," have not been shown to exist, it is doubtful that cellular growth is limited by these means. Yet, it is extremely important to keep these theories in mind because cancer, one of the most important problems of clinical medicine, is caused by failure of the body to limit growth of specific cell types, whatever the body's mechanism for accomplishing these limits may be.

Cancer—Cellular Disrespect for Growth Limits

When the genes of a cell mutate, the ability of the cell to grow usually changes for the worse but occasionally for the better, depending upon which one of the genes or group of genes in the cell mutates. Probably not over one out of a million mutated cells exhibits more rapid growth characteristics than previously. Yet, because the human body contains about 100 trillion cells and probably a billion new cells are formed in the body each minute, it is quite easy to understand how, sooner or later, at least one mutated cell that ignores growth limits can be formed. This cell, by progressive multiplication and continued inheritance of the same disrespect for growth limits, eventually grows into a tumor.

If the tumor cells also have the ability to spread into surrounding tissues, they are said to exhibit the property of "invasiveness," and eventually some of the daughter cells will break away from the original tumor mass and begin to grow elsewhere in the body, thus exhibiting the characteristics of "malignant" cancer cells.

Most cancers in human beings result from naturally occurring mutations, but some are caused by physical or chemical carcinogenic agents. In general, these agents are believed to induce cancer by causing very rapid mutation until at least one malignant cell is generated. Many cyclic organic compounds are carcinogenic; one of the most potent of these is methylcholanthrene. Also, x-ray and gamma ray radiation very frequently causes cancer, for such radiation temporarily ionizes some of the genes and thereby causes some of these to mutate. Even prolonged irritation of cells caused by mechanical trauma, heat, ultraviolet radiation, and many other causes can initiate cancer, for such irritation increases the rate of cellular mitosis, which in turn leads to an increased rate of mutation. This effect explains the high rate of cancer in the skin of workers exposed to the sun and the high rate of cancer in the constantly irritated cervix of women or the stomach of men.

Even though cancer cells do not respect normal growth limits, their rate of growth can in some instances still be partially regulated by the control systems of the body. For instance, growth of normal glandular cells in the breast of a normal female is dependent upon the sex hormones from the ovaries. When a glandular cell cancer of the breast occurs, removal of the ovaries usually greatly inhibits the rate of growth of the breast cancer, illustrating that even cancer cells sometimes require certain stimulants—the ovarian hormones in this instance—for growth. Prostatic cancer, other types of cancer of the sexual organs, and thyroid cancer are also examples of cancer tissue whose growth can be limited to a certain extent by removal of different hormones from the body. Yet, most cancers are not subject to even the slightest degree of control; instead, they grow at their own intrinsically determined growth rate until the individual dies.

The inherent ability of normal cells to respect growth limits is one of the most important and one of the least understood of all the genetic attributes of cells. The complete answer to cancer will never be attained until all the minute details of cellular control by the genes are worked out, and, unfortunately, the tremendous complexity of this problem will probably be too great for comprehension by a single mortal man. Nevertheless, it is hoped that enough will be learned to make it possible at least to prevent or control most cancers by clinical methods.

PHYSIOLOGY OF PRE-CELLULAR DEVELOPMENT

In the same manner that the human being has evolved through many stages of evolution from a single cell, the cell itself evolved through many stages from still smaller living organisms. An understanding of pre-cellular development aids greatly in explaining the so-called thread-of-life from the beginning of life on earth to the present heights of animalhood and planthood. Furthermore, it helps one to understand the value and functions of many of the intracellular structures.

The Origin of Life—Spontaneous Chemical Evolution

The most plausible theory for the origin of life is that of *spontaneous chemical evolution.* The early, highly reactive atmosphere of the earth contained large quantities of hydrogen, carbon, nitrogen, and oxygen—the essential building stones of all living matter on earth. These substances, in the presence of heat and metallic catalysts and under the influence of sunlight, can be converted very easily into many different organic compounds. Indeed, by spectrographic analysis of light rays from the incandescent stars, organic substances such as methane have been discovered on their surfaces even though no life exists there, and the atmosphere of our near neighbor, Venus, has a high percentage of carbon dioxide, which is a compound very closely associated with organic matter. Also, ammonia is often catalyzed into existence by the reaction of steam and metallic nitrides, which undoubtedly existed on the earth's early surface. It is not a long step from carbon dioxide, the simple sugars, methane, and ammonia to the various simple amino acids such as glycine and alanine, and it is quite easy to understand how amino acids, by the process of peptide linkage, could have combined to form simple or even complicated proteins while the earth was still young. Thus, because proteins are the basic substances of life, the origin of life could have come about very easily as a result of spontaneous chemical evolution.

Reproduction as the Secret of Life

Though it is quite easy to understand how even complex molecules such as proteins undoubtedly were spontaneously generated on the highly reactive surface of the early earth, nevertheless, remaining to be developed was the key to the progression of life—that is, *reproduction.*

One of the most familiar studies in chemistry is that of catalysts, and many proteins are enzymes, which are actually a type of catalyst. A few catalysts are *autocatalytic,* for they catalyze the formation of more molecules of their own type. Among the simplest of the autocatalytic agents is iron oxide, or what is commonly known as rust. When rust once appears on new iron, it autocatalyzes the development of more iron oxide. Of special interest to students of life are the

nucleoproteins, discussed earlier in the chapter, which are proteins conjugated with nucleic acid. These often are autocatalysts. Once autocatalytic nucleoproteins have been formed and are mixed with appropriate organic chemical compounds for building stones, they can catalyze the formation of other nucleoproteins having molecular structures that duplicate their own. Thus, in the early development of the world, only one such reproducible nucleoprotein was all that would have been needed to start the unbroken chain of life, for thereafter continuous formation of new living structures could have proceeded indefinitely.

If this theory of the origin of life is correct, the original living nucleoprotein was very similar to some of the present well known viruses, for the small viruses are probably single nucleoprotein molecules. For instance, chemical tests show the tobacco mosaic virus to be a nucleoprotein molecule with a molecular weight of approximately 40,000,000.

Communal Organization of Nucleoproteins to Form Complex Structures

Mutation and the Formation of Multimolecular Organisms. In order for the original living nucleoprotein to develop into the animal and plant kingdoms, another essential milestone had to be passed: that is, the reproducing nucleoprotein molecules had to change their molecular structures progressively and then continue to reproduce the new molecules indefinitely. Such changes are known as "mutations."

Though some molecules of nucleoprotein are theoretically capable of living separately from each other in the appropriate surroundings, these molecules tend to aggregate and, as new offspring molecules are formed, the offspring become part of the aggregate. Some of the offspring of the original living nucleoprotein undoubtedly mutated to become new nucleoproteins which remained in the aggregate. Also, some of the new nucleoproteins were undoubtedly able to perform certain chemical functions more efficiently than could the original nucleoprotein, whereas the original nucleoprotein was still able to perform other chemical functions more efficiently than could the new ones. For instance, it is possible that one nucleoprotein would have been able to catalyze the formation of sugar from formaldehyde very easily, while another might have been able to catalyze the formation of ammonia from water and nitrides. Therefore, the aggregate structure probably had an even better chance of surviving and reproducing than had the separate nucleoprotein molecules, thus originating a multimolecular organism. By further mutation and further aggregation of molecules, still many more different and progressively more complex types of multimolecular organisms could have developed on the early earth, and such are still developing almost infinitely in the form of the viruses.

Development of Specialized Functions in Viruses and the Development of Rickettsiae and Bacteria.

As the structure of viruses became more complex, and their sizes became larger, as shown in Figure 15, some of the molecules presumably became specialized as *enzymes*, some became specialized for the formation of a surface barrier, or what might be called a *primitive membrane*, and others perhaps specialized for the purpose of controlling reproduction. Finally, the aggregating mixture of nucleoproteins attracted around it quantities of electrolytes, sugars, fats, and many other substances. At this stage of development, the viruses became *rickettsiae*, and, with still further growth and organization, these became *bacteria*.

It was in the stage of bacteria that tremendous advances in the specialized functions of living matter occurred. For instance, these organisms invented *motility*, they developed specialized *organs* segregated to special parts of the cell body, and they originated special mechanisms for *imbibing food* and *discharging excreta*. *Respiratory systems* were organized in bacteria, and a few bacteria evolved the process of *photosynthesis* by developing the well-known chemical chlorophyll. In general, it was the bacteria with the ability of photosynthesis that progressed into planthood, and it was the motile bacteria that progressed into animalhood. The plants capture energy from the sunlight, turning this energy into organic foods, and the animals in turn live parasitically on the organic foods of the plants.

Development of the Cellular Animal.

The step from the bacterium to the cellular animal was hardly a step at all. Indeed, still present among the living organisms of the world are representatives of all stages between bacteria and cellular animals.

The major difference between a bacterium and a cellular animal is that the cellular animal has a nucleus with cytoplasm surrounding it while the bacterium does not have this internal differentiation. The bacterium contains throughout its entire structure nucleoproteins similar to those in the nucleus of the cell. It is these nucleoproteins which control the metabolic processes and reproduction in both the bacterium and the cell. In short, the bacterium is almost analogous to the nucleus of the cell, and the cytoplasm of the cell is merely an additional storehouse of metabolic substrates and enzymes which the cell has developed to function at the will of the cellular nucleus.

Development of Multicellular Animals.

Evolution from the stage of the unicellular animal up to the human being is a well-known story taught universally in all biology courses. Therefore, it need not be repeated in the present text other than to point out the similarity between pre-cellular and post-cellular evolution. When cells divide to form new cells, a daughter cell occasionally mutates to become slightly different from the parent cell. Also, cells tend to aggregate in clumps. Therefore, after aggregates of cellular animals developed on earth, some of the cells undoubtedly mutated to become especially adapted for performance of particular functions while the other cells of the aggregate continued to operate differently. Thus, the phenomenon of cellular specialization appeared in the aggregates, and the different cells thereafter mutually aided each other, originating the multicellular organism. As specialized cells multiplied, specialized organs soon appeared, and other structures developed to support the organs. Little by little, new and more complex animals developed in minute incremental steps until a very complex mass of cells, regulated by a myriad of control systems and known as the human being, evolved on the face of the earth.

CELLS OF THE HUMAN BEING

It seems foolish to state that cells in the human being are the same as unicellular animals such as the ameba, but such a statement is not far wrong. The ameba has all the functions of an animal, including the ability to move about, the ability to ingest food, the ability to metabolize food, the ability to respire, and the ability to excrete. Furthermore, the ameba is capable of growing and reproducing indefinitely in an appropriate fluid medium containing adequate foods. A few cells in the human body exhibit almost identically the same functions as amebae. These cells—called the wandering cells, macrophages, wandering histiocytes, or a number of other names

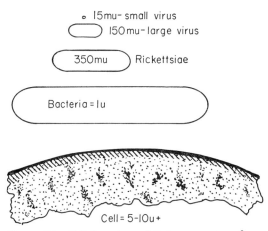

Figure 15. Relative sizes of living organisms from the virus to the cell.

—can move through the tissues of the body by *ameboid motion*, can ingest food from the tissue fluids, can inspire oxygen from the fluids, and can excrete carbon dioxide and other end-products of metabolism back into the fluid. Indeed, these cells are so nearly like amebae that they are frequently described as "ameba-like."

Most of the remaining cells are sessile, but, although they have lost the ability to move, they have gained other qualities more important to the human body.

REFERENCES

Anfinsen, C. B.: The Molecular Basis of Evolution. New York, John Wiley and Sons, 1959.

Bass, A. D.: Chemical influences on cell division and development. *Ann. Rev. Physiol.*, 21:49, 1959.

Beadle, G. W.: Physiological aspects of genetics. *Ann. Rev. Physiol.*, 22:45, 1960.

Brachet, J.: Biochemical Cytology. New York, Academic Press, 1957.

Brachet, J.: The Cell. Volume I. New York, Academic Press, 1958.

Brachet, J. (editor): The Cell. 5 Volumes. New York, Academic Press, 1960.

Brown, D. M., and Todd, A. R.: Nucleic acids. *Ann. Rev. Biochem.*, 24:311, 1955.

Ciba Foundation, Symposia Volumes: Biochemistry of Human Genetics. Boston, Little, Brown and Company, 1959.

Ciba Foundation, Symposia Volumes: Regulation of Cell Metabolism. Boston, Little, Brown and Company, 1959.

Clifton, C. E.: Introduction to Bacterial Physiology. New York, McGraw-Hill Book Co., Inc., 1957.

Dalton, H. C.: Molecular events in differentiation related to specificity of cell. New York, N. Y. Academy of Science, 1955.

Dilbruck, M.: Cellular Mechanisms in Differentiation and Growth. Princeton, New Jersey, Princeton University Press, 1956.

Dodson, E. O.: Evolution. New York, Reinhold Publishers, 1960.

Engstrom, A. and Finean, J. B.: Biological Ultrastructure. New York, Academic Press, 1958.

Ernster, L., and Lindberg, O.: Animal mitochondria. *Ann. Rev. Physiol.*, 20:13, 1958.

Gale, E. F.: Nucleic acids and protein synthesis. *Harvey Lect.*, 51:25, 1955.

Giese, A. C.: Cell Physiology. Philadelphia, W. B. Saunders Co., 1957.

Gottschalk, A.: Virus enzymes and virus templates. *Physiol. Rev.*, 37:66, 1957.

Harris, R. J. C. (editor): The Relationship Between Nucleus and Cytoplasm. Supplement 6. New York, Academic Press, 1959.

Heilbrunn, L. V.: Outline of General Physiology. Philadelphia, W. B. Saunders Co., 1953.

Homburger, F.: Physiopathology of Cancer. 2nd ed., New York, Paul B. Hoeber, 1958.

Horowitz, N. H., and Owen, R. D.: Physiological aspects of genetics. *Ann. Rev. Physiol.*, 16:81, 1954.

Hyden, H.: Physical properties of protoplasm. *Ann. Rev. Physiol.*, 16:11, 1954.

Johnson, F. H., Eyring, H., and Polissar, M. J.: Kinetic Basis of Molecular Biology. New York, John Wiley and Sons, 1954.

McElroy, W. D.: Cellular Physiology and Biochemistry. Englewood Cliffs, Prentice-Hall, 1960.

Oparin, A. I.: The Origin of Life on the Earth. New York, Academic Press, 1957.

Porter, K. R.: The submicroscopic morphology of protoplasm. *Harvey Lect.*, 51:175, 1955.

Prescott, D. M.: Nuclear function and nuclear-cytoplasmic interactions. *Ann. Rev. Physiol.*, 22:17, 1960.

Swanson, C. P.: The Cell. Englewood Cliffs, Prentice-Hall, 1960.

Symposium on Biochemical Aspects of Cell Structure and Function. *Fed. Proc.* 18:957, 1959.

Thomas, M.: Plant Physiology. New York, Philosophical Library, 1956.

Wagner, R. P.: Genetics and Metabolism. New York, John Wiley and Sons, 1955.

Walker, P. M. B. (editor): New Approaches in Cell Biology. New York, Academic Press, 1960.

Willmer, E. N.: Cytology and Evolution. New York, Academic Press, 1960.

Zamenhof, S.: The Chemistry of Heredity. Springfield Illinois, Charles C Thomas, 1959.

Part Two

BODY FLUIDS

Chapter 3

Extracellular and Intracellular Fluid; Transport Through the Cell Membrane

Total Body Water

The total amount of water in a man of average weight (70 kgm.) is approximately 40 liters (see Fig. 16) or 57 per cent of his total body weight. In a newborn infant this amount may be as much as 75 per cent of the body weight, but it progressively decreases from birth to old age, most of the decrease occurring in the first 10 years of life. The function of all this water is, first, to provide a medium of transport from one part of the body to another and, second, to provide an intracellular medium in which the chemical reactions of the cells can occur.

BODY FLUID COMPARTMENTS

The Intracellular Compartment

About 25 of the 40 liters of fluid in the body are inside the 100 trillion cells of the

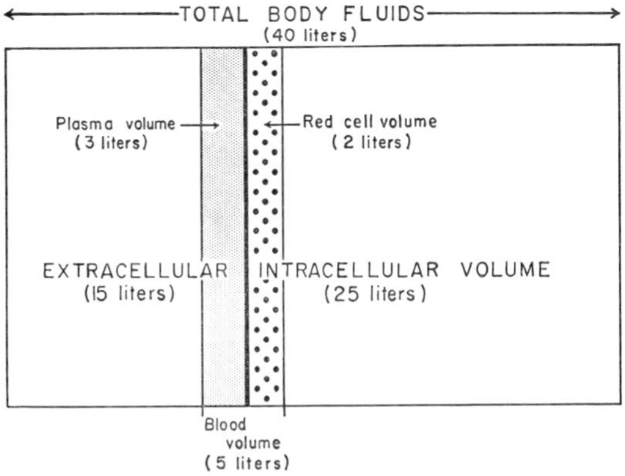

Figure 16. Diagrammatic representation of the body fluids, showing the extracellular fluid volume, intracellular fluid volume, blood volume, and total body fluids.

body and are called the *intracellular fluid.* The fluid of each cell contains its own individual complement of different constituents, but the concentrations of these constituents are reasonably similar from one cell to another. For this reason the intracellular fluid of all the different cells is considered to be one large fluid compartment, even though in reality it is an aggregate of trillions of minute compartments.

The intracellular fluid of the red blood cells is somewhat different from that of most of the other cells, for it contains moderate quantities of both sodium and chloride ions while other cells contain only small quantities of these. And, except for hemoglobin, the red cells contain smaller quantities of organic substances than the other cells. However, even these differences are usually of little significance so that the fluid of the red blood cells can justly be considered along with the remainder of the intracellular fluid.

The Extracellular Fluid Compartment

All the fluids outside the cells are called *extracellular fluid,* and these fluids are constantly mixing, as was explained in Chapter 1. Therefore, the extracellular compartment is in fact one single communicating fluid chamber and not merely a term used for physiological convenience. The total amount of fluid in the extracellular compartment averages 15 liters in a 70 kgm. adult.

The extracellular fluid can be further divided into *interstitial fluid, plasma, cerebrospinal fluid, fluids of the gastrointestinal tract,* and *fluids of the potential spaces.*

Interstitial Fluid. The interstitial fluid lies in the spaces between the cells. A small

31

portion of it is free in the form of actual flowing fluid, while the major portion is held tightly by hydrated substances in the interstitial spaces. For instance, large quantities of water are absorbed by collagen fibers, and still larger quantities are bound with polymerized hyaluronic acid, which forms a gel-like substance between the cells in most areas of the body. Yet, despite this binding of water, dissolved substances can still move through all this water by the process of diffusion, which will be explained later in the chapter.

Plasma. The plasma is the non-cellular portion of the blood. It is part of the extracellular fluid and communicates continually with the interstitial fluid through the capillary pores. The total blood volume is about 5 liters, 3 of which are plasma and 2 of which are red blood cells. Loss of plasma from the circulatory system through the capillary pores is prevented by the colloid osmotic pressure exerted by the plasma proteins, which will be explained in Chapter 4. Yet, the capillaries are porous enough that dissolved substances and water molecules *diffuse* freely, allowing constant mixing between the plasma and interstitial fluid.

Fluid in Other Extracellular Spaces. The *cerebrospinal fluid* comprises all the fluid in the ventricles of the brain and in the subarachnoid spaces surrounding both the brain and spinal cord. This fluid has slightly different constituents from the interstitial fluid and plasma because of somewhat restricted diffusion back and forth between plasma and the cerebrospinal fluid and because of active secretion of a few substances by the choroid plexus. Nevertheless, from the point of view of the present discussion, cerebrospinal fluid is so nearly like interstitial fluid that it will be considered to be actually a part of it. In Chapter 7 the special dynamics of the cerebrospinal fluid will be presented in detail.

The *intraocular fluid,* the fluid in the eyes, has properties similar to those of the cerebrospinal fluid, and here again the fluid is a product of both diffusion and secretion. These fluids, too, will be discussed in detail in Chapter 7, and, for the purpose of the present discussion, will be considered to be part of the interstitial fluid.

Many spaces exist in the body that normally contain very little fluid but under special conditions can become filled with very large amounts. These are called *potential spaces.* An example of a potential space is the space between the visceral and parietal pleuras of the lungs. Normally only 10 to 15 ml. of very viscid fluid are present in this space, but under abnormal circumstances the amount can become as great as several liters. Other potential spaces are the *peritoneal cavity*, the *pericardial cavity,* all the *joint spaces,* and the *bursae.*

Finally, moderate amounts of extracellular fluid are normally inside the *gastrointestinal tract.* The quantity of these fluids varies greatly at different times of the day in relation to the intake and digestion of food. As much as a liter of digestive juices is sometimes in the gastrointestinal tract at once, and under certain pathological conditions, such as gastrointestinal obstruction, this can become as much as 10 liters. The gastrointestinal fluids, in general, have electrolyte compositions similar to that of the interstitial fluid, and these fluids are usually considered to be part of the extracellular fluid.

Measurement of Fluid Volumes

The Dilution Principle for Measuring Fluid Volumes. Figure 17 illustrates the dilution principle for measuring the volume of any fluid compartment of the body. A small quantity of dye or other foreign substance is placed in fluid chamber A, and the substance is dispersed throughout the chamber until it becomes mixed in equal concentrations in all areas. Then a sample of the dispersed fluid is removed and the concentration of the substance is analyzed either

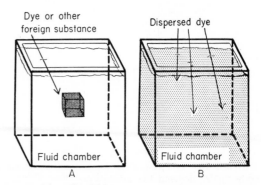

Figure 17. The dilution principle for measuring the volume of a fluid compartment.

chemically, photoelectrically, or by any other means. The volume of the chamber can then be determined from the following formula:

up to as high as 22 liters; but the average measurement has been about 15 liters.

A major difficulty often encountered in measuring the volume of any fluid compart-

$$\text{Volume in ml.} = \frac{\text{Quantity of test substance instilled}}{\text{Concentration per ml. of dispersed fluid}}$$

It should be noted that all that one needs to know is (1) the *total quantity of the test substance* put into the chamber and (2) the *concentration in the fluid after dispersement*.

Measurement of the Extracellular Fluid Volume. To use the dilution principle for measuring the volume of the extracellular fluid one injects into the blood stream a substance that can diffuse readily throughout the entire extracellular fluid chamber but not through the cell membranes into the cells. After half an hour or more of mixing, a sample of extracellular fluid is obtained by removing some blood and separating the plasma from the cells by centrifugation. The plasma is then analyzed for the injected substance.

Substances that have been used for measuring extracellular fluid volume are *radioactive sodium, radioactive chloride, radioactive bromide, thiosulfate ion, thiocyanate ion, inulin,* and *sucrose*. Some of these, sucrose and inulin especially, do not diffuse readily into all the out-of-the-way places of the extracellular fluid compartment, such as into the bound fluid of the collagen fibers. Therefore, the volume of extracellular fluid measured with these is likely to be lower than the actual volume of the compartment. On the other hand, others of these substances—radioactive chloride, radioactive bromide, radioactive sodium, and thiocyanate ion, for instance—are likely to penetrate into the cells to a slight extent and, therefore, to measure a space somewhat in excess of the extracellular fluid volume. Because there is no single substance that measures the exact extracellular fluid volume, one usually speaks of the *sodium space,* the *thiocyanate space,* the *inulin space,* etc., rather than the extracellular space. At present it is impossible to say exactly which one of the "spaces" most nearly approximates the precise extracellular volume. Measurements for the normal 70 kgm. adult, when different ones of the above substances have been used, have ranged from as little as 8 liters

ment is loss of much of the test substance from the compartment before complete dispersion has taken place. In measuring the extracellular fluid volume of a normal person, at least 30 minutes is required for complete dispersion, and, if major amounts of the substance are lost from the extracellular fluid compartment during this time, an error will be made in the measurement. For this reason measurements employing each one of the different test substances require different systems of correction. Figure 18 illustrates a method for using inulin, which, unfortunately, is rapidly excreted into the urine, for measuring the volume of the extracellular fluid compartment. The inulin is infused at a slow continuous rate for half an hour or more until the inulin concentration in the plasma reaches a constant value. Then the infusion is suddenly stopped, and all the inulin present in the body at that time is excreted into the urine during the next hour or so. A quantitative determination of the inulin that enters the urine is considered to be the amount of inulin in the body immediately before stopping the infusion. This

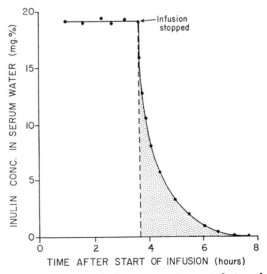

Figure 18. A method, using continuous infusion of inulin, for measuring extracellular fluid volume.

value is then divided by the concentration of the inulin in the plasma immediately before stopping the infusion to determine the total extracellular fluid volume.

Measurement of Total Body Water. The total body water can be measured in exactly the same way as the extracellular fluid volume except that a substance must be used that will diffuse into the cells as well as throughout the extracellular compartment. The substance which has given the best results is *heavy water*, which can be quantitatively analyzed either by very accurate specific gravity measurements of water samples or by infrared spectrophotometry. After administration of the heavy water, several hours are required for complete mixing with all the water of the body, and appropriate corrections must be made for any fluid that is lost either into the urine or otherwise during this period of mixing. The concentration of the heavy water in the dispersed sample can be obtained by simply measuring the heavy water concentration in the plasma.

Another substance that has proved very satisfactory for measuring total body water is *antipyrine*, which diffuses almost completely into all the cells of the body and which can be analyzed readily by chemical means.

Measurements of total body water in the 70 kgm. adult have ranged from as low as 30 liters up to as high as 50 liters, with a reasonable average of approximately 40 liters.

Measurement of Blood Volume. Substances that combine with red blood cells or with the plasma proteins will not diffuse out of the capillaries through the pores and therefore can be used to measure the total blood volume. Those that bind with the red cells are *radioactive chromium*, *radioactive phosphate*, and *radioactive iron*, while those that bind with the plasma proteins are *radioactive iodine* and the blue dye called *T-1824*. The techniques for measuring blood volume will be presented at greater length in Chapter 34 in connection with the discussion of blood volume and its regulation.

Measurement of Interstitial Fluid Volume. Since any substance that will pass into the interstitial fluid will also pass into almost all other portions of the extracellular fluid, there is no direct method for measuring interstitial fluid volume separately from the entire extracellular fluid volume. However, if the extracellular fluid volume

and plasma volume have both been measured, the interstitial fluid volume can be approximated by *subtracting the plasma volume from the total extracellular fluid volume*. This, obviously, is not a completely accurate procedure because the calculated volume then comprises also the fluid of other extracellular spaces such as cerebrospinal fluid, the gastrointestinal fluids, and so forth.

CONSTITUENTS OF EXTRACELLULAR AND INTRACELLULAR FLUIDS

Figure 19 illustrates diagrammatically the major constituents of the extracellular and intracellular fluids. The quantities of the different substances are represented in this diagram in *milliequivalents* or *millimols per liter*. However, the protein molecules and some of the nonelectrolyte molecules are extremely large in comparison with the more numerous small ions. Therefore, *in terms of mass*, the proteins and nonelectrolytes actually comprise about 90 per cent of the dissolved constituents in the plasma, about 60 per cent in the interstitial fluid, and about 97 per cent in the intracellular fluid. Figure

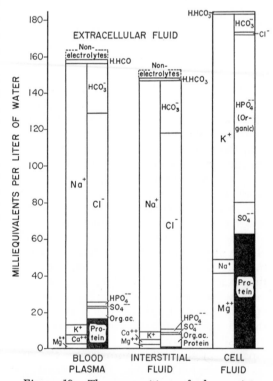

Figure 19. The compositions of plasma, interstitial fluid, and intracellular fluid (Modified from Gamble: Extracellular Fluid. Harvard University Press.)

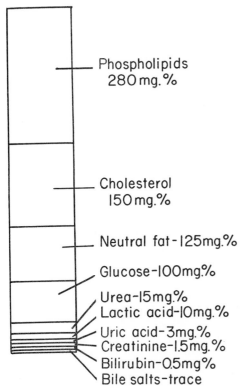

Phospholipids
280 mg.%

Cholesterol
150 mg.%

Neutral fat-125mg.%

Glucose-100mg.%

Urea-15mg.%
Lactic acid-10mg.%

Uric acid-3mg.%
Creatinine-1.5mg.%
Bilirubin-0.5mg%
Bile salts-trace

Figure 20.   The nonelectrolytes of the extracellular fluid.

20 illustrates the distribution of the non-electrolytes in the plasma, and most of these same substances are also present in almost equal concentrations in the interstitial fluid except that some of the fatty compounds exist in the blood in large suspended particles, the *lipoproteins*, and, therefore, do not pass to any significant extent into the interstitial spaces.

From the point of view of most chemical and physical reactions of the fluids, it is usually the *concentration of molecules or ions* of a particular substance that is important. Therefore, in this text we will generally express all concentrations as presented in Figure 19—that is, either in millimols of nonelectrolytes or milliequivalents of electrolytes.

A concentration of 1 mol per liter is 1 gram molecular weight of the dissolved substance in each liter of water, and a concentration of 1 millimol is one thousandth of this.

Use of the term *equivalents* applies only to ionized substances. If a molecule divides into two univalent ions, one positive and one negative, then 1 mol of this substance is equal to 2 equivalents. If a molecule divides into more than two ionized particles or if the ionized particles carry more than 1 electrical charge each, the number of equivalents is equal to the sum of all the positive and negative electrical charges. That is, 1 mol of calcium chloride ($CaCl_2$) on ionizing would form 4 equivalents. In general, the concentrations of the different substances in the body are far less than 1 equivalent per liter and, therefore, are expressed in terms of *milliequivalents,* which are equal to one thousandth of an equivalent.

Also, in the following discussions the student should remember that a *positive ion is called a cation* because it will be attracted to the cathode when electricity passes through a solution, and a *negative ion is called an anion* because it is attracted to the anode.

Constituents of the Extracellular Fluid. Referring to Figure 19, it is evident that extracellular fluid, both that of the blood plasma and of the interstitial fluid, contains very large quantities of *sodium* and *chloride* ions, reasonably large quantities of *bicarbonate ion,* but only small quantities of potassium, calcium, magnesium, phosphate sulphate, and organic acid ions. In addition, plasma contains a large amount of protein while interstitial fluid contains very little. In Chapter 1 it was pointed out that the extracellular fluid is called the *internal environment* of the body, and its constituents are very accurately regulated so that the cells remain bathed continually in a fluid containing the proper electrolytes and nutrients for continued cellular function. The regulation of most of these constituents will be presented in detail in Chapter 9.

Constituents of the Intracellular Fluid. From Figure 19 it is also readily apparent that the intracellular fluid contains only small quantities of sodium and chloride ions and almost no calcium ions; but it does contain very large quantities of *potassium* and *phosphate* and moderate quantities of *magnesium* and *sulfate ions,* all of which are present in only small concentrations in the extracellular fluid. In addition, cells contain very large amounts of proteins, approximately four times as much as the plasma.

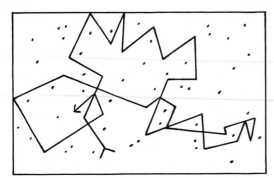

Figure 21. Diffusion of a fluid molecule during a fraction of a second.

Diffusion of Constituents in the Fluids

All molecules and ions in the body fluids, including both the water and dissolved substances, are in constant motion, and each particle in a fluid medium moves its own separate way. Actually, motion of the molecules is what physicists know as "heat"—the greater the motion the higher is the temperature—and motion never ceases under any conditions except absolute zero temperature. When one molecule bounces against another, its electrostatic forces repel the second, momentarily adding to the energy of motion of the new molecule while losing this energy itself. Consequently, the new molecule moves more rapidly than before while the older one slows down or perhaps even momentarily stops. Furthermore, molecules can be repelled first in one direction, then in another, and so forth. Figure 21 illustrates the movement of a single molecule within a small chamber during a fraction of a second, showing that the molecule bounced among the other molecules first in one direction, then another, then another, and so forth. At times it traveled a far distance before striking the next molecule and at other times only a short distance. This continual movement of molecules among each other in liquids, or also in gases, is called *diffusion.* Ions diffuse in exactly the same manner as whole molecules, and even suspended colloid particles diffuse in a like way except that their very large size causes their velocity of diffusion to be far less than that of molecular substances.

Kinetics of Diffusion—the Diffusion Gradient. When a large amount of dissolved substance is placed in a solvent at one end of a chamber, it will immediately begin to diffuse toward the opposite end of the chamber. If the same amount is placed in the opposite end of the chamber, it will begin to diffuse toward the first end, the same amount diffusing in each direction. As a result, the *net rate of diffusion* from one end to the other is zero. If, however, the concentration of the substance is greater at one end of the chamber than at the other end, the net rate of diffusion from the area of high concentration to low concentration will be directly proportional to the larger concentration minus the lower concentration. This concentration difference is called a *concentration gradient* or a *diffusion gradient.*

The rapidity with which a molecule will diffuse from one point to another is less the greater the molecular size, because large particles are not so easily impelled by collisions with other molecules. In gases, the rate of diffusion is approximately inversely proportional to the square root of the molecular weight, but in fluids it is more nearly inversely proportional to the molecular weight itself.

If we consider all the different factors that affect the rate of diffusion of a substance from one area to another, they are the following: (1) The greater the diffusion gradient, the greater is the rate of diffusion. (2) The less the molecular weight, the greater is the rate of diffusion. (3) The shorter the distance, the greater is the rate. (4) The greater the cross-section of the chamber in which diffusion is taking place, the greater is the rate of diffusion. (5) The greater the temperature, the greater is the molecular motion and also the greater is the rate of diffusion. All of these can be placed in the following approximate formula for diffusion in solutions.

$$\text{Diffusion rate} \propto \frac{\text{Diffusion gradient} \times \text{cross-sectional area} \times \text{temperature}}{\text{Molecular weight} \times \text{distance}}$$

Relationship of Plasma to Interstitial Fluid

The essential difference between plasma and interstitial fluid is the large amount of proteins in the plasma and the small amount in the interstitial fluids. This difference is caused by the relatively large size of protein molecules in relation to capillary pore size. Only a small fraction of the pores is large enough for protein molecules to pass through, while essentially all other substances can pass freely between the two fluids.

In addition, plasma has a slightly higher concentration of electrolytes than the interstitial fluids for the following reason: The proteins of the plasma are negatively charged electrolytes and are responsible for a total concentration of approximately 17 milliequivalents per liter of anions. Except under special conditions, *the number of anions and cations in a solution must always remain equal*, which is a general chemical law relating to the balance of electrical charges. Therefore, for every milliequivalent of protein in the plasma a milliequivalent of cations, usually sodium, must also be present. And, since protein fails to diffuse into the interstitial spaces, it also holds a certain number of extra cations in the plasma as well, thus making the total concentration of electrolytes approximately 5 per cent greater in the plasma than in the interstitial fluids.

Donnan Equilibrium. Another chemical principle is that *the number of diffusible anions* **times** *the number of diffusible cations on one side of a semipermeable membrane* **is equal to** *the number of diffusible cations* **times** *the number of diffusible anions on the other side.* If we exclude the protein, which is non-diffusible, and multiply the remaining anions times the cations, the product for the plasma will equal that for the interstitial fluid. The presence of large quantities of protein in the plasma, which constitutes a large number of non-diffusible anions, causes the total number of *diffusible* anions to be about 5 per cent less in the plasma than in the interstitial fluid and the total number of diffusible cations to be about 5 per cent greater in the plasma.

TRANSPORT OF SUBSTANCES THROUGH THE CELL MEMBRANE

As discussed in the previous chapter, the cell membrane is believed to be composed of a meshwork of protein fibers filled with a matrix of lipid material, the postulated structure of which is shown in Figure 22.

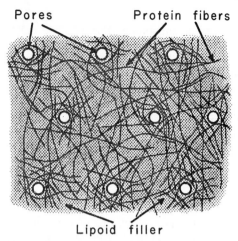

Figure 22. Structure of the cell membrane.

At various intervals in the membrane are small pores, which represent spaces among the meshwork of fibers not filled with the lipid material. On studying this membrane structure it becomes obvious that there are two general ways in which substances could go through the cell membrane: first, by diffusing directly through the pores still dissolved in the water itself, or, second, by passing through the lipid matrix between the pores.

Diffusion through the Pores

The pores of the cell membrane are only slightly larger than the smallest dissolved molecules. In general, most organic molecules are too large to pass through the pores, whereas many of the very small molecules do pass through. Table 1 lists the

Table 1. Estimated Resistance of the Cell Membrane to Diffusion of Different Substances

H_2O	1
CO_2	0 004
O_2	0 004
Cl^-	70.
HCO_3^-	400.
Urea molecule	400.
H^+	500.
K^+	1,000.
Na^+	36,000.
Glucose molecule	40,000.

Note: The CO_2 and O_2 values are estimated from studies in lungs, the Cl^- and HCO_3^- from studies in red cells, the urea and glucose from studies in unicellular animals, and the K^+ and Na^+ from studies in resting nerve.

relative values for the resistance to passage of different substances through the cellular membrane, assuming that the resistance to the passage of the water molecule is 1. This table shows that carbon dioxide and oxygen probably pass through the membrane much more easily than water itself, because these two substances are moderately soluble in the lipid portion of the membrane, while the water molecules can pass only through the pores. On the other hand, dissolved ions in general usually experience many hundreds times as much difficulty in passing through the pores as does water. Urea, the smallest organic ion of any significance in the body fluids, passes through the membrane with approximately four hundred times the resistance of water, bicarbonate ions with about this same resistance, potassium ions with still more resistance, and glucose molecules with so much resistance that they usually are considered to be totally non-diffusible. *These ratios of resistance are highly speculative,* because all the necessary measurements have not yet been made and because the values are different from one cell to another.

Especially should it be noted that the resistance to the passage of sodium, at least in the resting nerve and muscle cells, is about 36 times as great as for potassium despite the lower atomic weight of sodium. The reason for this is that both of these ions are present in the body fluids in hydrated forms, and the hydrated form of the sodium ion has a molecular diameter 1.4 times that of the potassium ion.

Even though Table 1 shows the cell membrane to be many times less permeable to hydrogen ions, chloride ions, potassium ions, and bicarbonate ions than to water, nevertheless, the rates of diffusion of these substances are still rapid enough that very large amounts of them can diffuse through the membrane in a few minutes to hours. On the other hand, *extreme* amounts of water can diffuse through the cellular membrane in only a few seconds.

Diffusion through the Cellular Lipid Matrix

Any substance that is lipid soluble can dissolve in the lipid phase of the membrane and then diffuse directly through the cell membrane. Thus, the fat soluble substances, such as phospholipids, cholesterol, neutral fats, alcohol, and so forth, on coming in contact with the cell membrane, pass almost immediately into the cell.

In addition to the above substances, even carbon dioxide and oxygen are slightly soluble in the lipid matrix, which probably accounts for the very rapid rates of transfer of these two gases between the extracellular and intracellular fluids.

Active Transport through the Cell Membrane

Enzymatic Carrier Systems for Active Transport. Active transport means transport through the membrane caused by chemical processes rather than by simple diffusion through either the pores or the lipid matrix. Figure 23 illustrates the basic ingredients of a *carrier system* for active transport of a substance through the lipid matrix. *Substance S* in the extracellular fluid is shown to combine at the outer surface of the membrane with *carrier C*. The combination is soluble in the membrane and can diffuse to the inside where S is removed from C. C then returns to the outer surface to carry still more of substance S to the interior.

In general, each chemical change which occurs during active transport requires a protein enzyme to catalyze the reaction. For instance, in the schema of Figure 23 the combination of C with S would require one enzyme, and the splitting of S from C would require still another. Since the en-

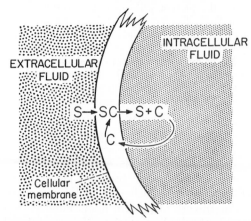

Figure 23. Active transport of substance S by carrier C through the cell membrane.

zymes are proteins formed under the control of genes in the nucleus, active transport processes are another one of the cellular functions dictated by specific nuclear genes. Furthermore, every type of substance actively transported requires its own specific carrier system and a separate set of specific enzymes.

Though Figure 23 shows the general principles of active transport, the actual carrier systems are probably never simple. Instead, many substances are probably transported through several stages, being passed from one carrier to another and involving multiple enzymes. Also, some carrier systems are so organized that transport of one substance to the inside of the cell is linked with transport of another to the outside. Such a linkage occurs between sodium and potassium in at least some cells, sodium going out while potassium goes in.

Active transport is of particular value to the cell under two specific conditions: (1) to transport through the membrane substances that are neither lipid soluble nor small enough to diffuse through the cellular pores—these include especially the nutrients such as glucose and amino acids, and (2) to transport substances through the membrane against a concentration gradient, that is, from a fluid of low concentration to one of high concentration—these include especially the electrolytes.

Energy Requirements for Active Transport. Active transport requires energy for two different reasons: first, energy is needed to cause the chemical reactions of the carrier mechanism to take place; but, more important, energy is also required for moving a substance from a medium of low concentration to a medium of high concentration. For instance, transport of potassium from the extracellular fluid to the intracellular fluid involves an increase in concentration of the potassium from 5 milliequivalents per liter up to 141 milliequivalents per liter, or approximately 28-fold. From an energy point of view, this is the same as compressing a volume of air 28 times, which would require a very considerable amount of energy. In some instances, therefore, the energy required for active transport is a sizable portion of the total energy expenditure of a cell, calculated to be as much as 10 per cent for some cells.

Active Transport of Specific Substances

Active Transport of Glucose. From Table 1 it was evident that almost no glucose can enter the cell by simple diffusion, despite the fact that glucose is one of the major nutrients of the cell. Glucose has been shown to be actively transported through the membrane by an enzymatic carrier system, but the precise chemical processes involved have not yet been discovered. An extremely important fact is that large quantities of *insulin,* a hormone secreted by the pancreas, can increase the rate of active glucose transport by as much as 25-fold in comparison with total lack of insulin. In this way the pancreas controls glucose transport and also controls the rate of glucose metabolism by the tissues, as will be discussed in Chapter 76.

Along with glucose, a small amount of potassium and phosphate is normally actively transported to the interior of the cells. For this reason attempts have been made to explain glucose transport by assuming that glucose combines in the cell membrane with one or both of these ions. However, at present it seems that both of them are transported independently of the glucose and for allied reasons but not in actual combination with the glucose.

Active Transport of Amino Acids. Amino acids, like glucose, do not diffuse to any significant extent through the cellular pores. They, too, are transported by active processes, though here again the precise carrier mechanisms are not understood. An especially interesting feature of amino acid transport is that some of the different amino acids interfere with transport of each other, indicating that they utilize either partially or totally the same carrier system. It is by studying such interactions between different substances, study of the effects of toxic substances, determination of the energy required for transport, and so forth, that physiologists hope in the future to discover the precise chemistry of the carrier processes.

Active Transport of Sodium and Potassium. The concentration of sodium outside the cell averages 144 milliequivalents and inside only 10 milliequivalents, while the concentration gradient of potassium lies in the opposite direction, with 141 milliequivalents inside and 5 milliequivalents outside.

These differences are maintained by continuous transport of sodium to the exterior and potassium to the interior. Red blood cells, for instance, transport three sodium ions outwards for every two potassium ions inward. This transport continues indefinitely as long as the cells live, and whenever sodium leaks inward through the pores or potassium outward, the active transport systems immediately move these ions back across the membrane, maintaining appropriate concentration gradients despite the leaks.

In some cells potassium transport has not been proved to occur, though sodium transport has been shown for all cells studied. This does not mean that the two are not always linked but only that research workers have thus far failed to find the linkage in some cells. The transport of sodium to the exterior is so important in cellular function that it is commonly called the *sodium pump*. In Chapter 17 it will be especially evident that the sodium pump plays an extremely important role in the transmission of the nerve impulse.

Because of the importance of sodium transport, more research has been directed toward elucidating the mechanism of this than of almost any other active transport system. Even so, very little is yet known. Figure 24 illustrates one of the simpler explanations that have been offered. This is a double carrier system in which a negatively charged intracellular carrier, C_i, combines with sodium under the influence of an enzyme. The sodium is then carried into the lipid matrix of the membrane, where it is transferred along with an electron to a second non-ionized carrier, C_m; this transfer is catalyzed by a second enzyme. Then a third enzyme removes the sodium ion from the membrane carrier C_m and allows it to diffuse into the extracellular fluid. The membrane carrier C_m retains the electron and carries it back to the inner surface of the membrane. There the electron in turn is retransferred to the intracellular carrier C_i, which then becomes available to carry sodium into the membrane once again. Obviously, this mechanism does not explain the linkage with potassium and should be recognized as only a tentative theory.

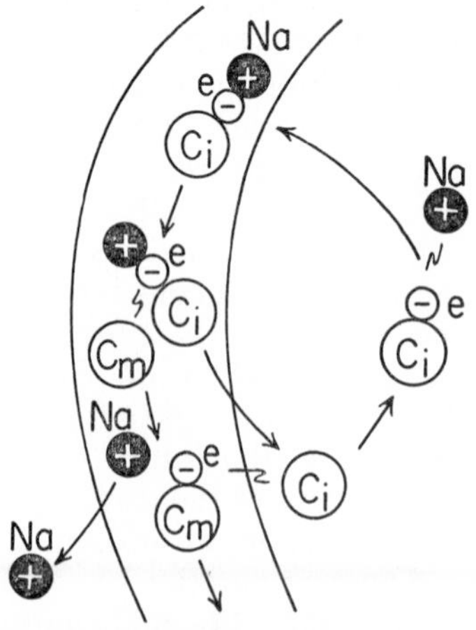

Active Transport of Other Substances. Other substances that are known to be actively transported through the membranes of at least certain cells are *phosphate ion, chloride ion, sulfate ion, magnesium ion, hydrogen ion, creatinine,* and *uric acid*. Also, it is possible that whole or partial protein molecules can be actively transported under some conditions. In other words, active transport mechanisms exist for essentially all important electrolytes and non-fat soluble nutrients. And in special areas of the body, such as the kidneys and glands, many special substances are selectively transported.

Extracellular Membrane Cell

Figure 24. Active transport of sodium out of the cell (From Elkinton and Danowski: The Body Fluids. Williams and Wilkins Co.)

REFERENCES

Adolph, E. F.: Physiology of Man in the Desert. New York, Interscience Publishers, 1947.

Bolingbroke, V., and Maizels, M.: Calcium ions and the permeability of human erythrocytes. *J. Physiol., 149*:563, 1959.

Carey, M. J., Conway, E. J., and Kernan, R. P.: Secretion of sodium ions by the frog's sartorius. *J. Physiol., 148*:51, 1959.

Clarke, H. T., and Nachmansohn, D.: Ion Transport Across Membranes. New York, Academic Press, 1954.

Fuhrman, F. A.: Transport through biological membranes. *Ann. Rev. Physiol., 21*:19, 1959.

Gamble, J. L.: Chemical Anatomy, Physiology and Pathology of Extracellular Fluid: A Lecture Syllabus. 6th ed., Cambridge, Harvard University Press, 1954.

Hardy, J. D.: Fluid Therapy. Philadelphia, Lea & Febiger, 1954.

Harris, E. J.: Transport and Accumulation in Biological Systems. New York, Academic Press, 1956.

Harris, E. J.: Transport through biological membranes. *Ann. Rev. Physiol., 19*:13, 1957.

Keynes, R. D., and Swan, R. C.: The effect of external sodium concentration on the sodium fluxes in frog skeletal muscle. *J. Physiol., 147:*591, 1959.

Levy, M. N., Ankeney, J. L., and Berne, R. M.: Kinetics of inulin distribution and excretion following constant infusion. *Am. J. Physiol., 169:*363, 1952.

Maizels, M., and Remington, M.: Cation exchanges of human erythrocytes. *J. Physiol., 145:*641, 1959.

Manery, J. F.: Water and electrolyte metabolism. *Physiol. Rev., 34:*334, 1954.

Neely, W. A.: Apparent sodium space of the dog. *Am. J. Physiol., 196:*1333, 1959.

Post, R. L., and Jolly, P. C.: The linkage of sodium, potassium, and ammonium active transport across the human erythrocyte membrane. *Biochem. Biophys. Acta, 25:*118, 1957.

Renkin, E. M.: Exchangeability of tissue potassium in skeletal muscle. *Am. J. Physiol., 197:*1211, 1959.

Robertson, J. S.: Theory and use of tracers in determining transfer rates in biological systems. *Physiol. Rev., 37:*133, 1957.

Robinson, J. R.: Metabolism of intracellular water. *Physiol. Rev., 40:*112, 1960.

Shanes, A.: Electrolytes in Biological Systems. Washington, D.C., Am. Physiol. Soc., 1955.

Society for Experimental Biology. Active Transport and Secretion. New York, Academic Press, 1955.

Teorell, T.: Permeability properties of erythrocyte ghosts. *J. Gen. Physiol., 35:*669, 1952.

Ulrich, F.: Active transport of potassium by heart mitochondria. *Am. J. Physiol., 198:*847, 1960.

Ussing, H. H.: Transport through biological membranes. *Ann. Rev. Physiol., 15:*1, 1953.

White, H. L., and Rolf, D.: Inulin space as a function of equilibration time. *Am. J. Physiol., 185:*152, 1956.

Wilde, W. S.: Transport through biological membranes. *Ann. Rev. Physiol., 17:*17, 1955.

See also Chapter 4, Transport through cellular membranes.

Osmotic Equilibria and Fluid Shifts Between the Extracellular and Intracellular Fluids

One of the most troublesome of all problems in clinical medicine is the maintenance in seriously ill patients of adequate body fluids and proper chemical equilibria between the extracellular and intracellular fluids. Since fluid is constantly shifting as a result of osmosis back and forth between the two compartments, the present chapter will be devoted, first, to a discussion of the principles of osmotic equilibria and then to some problems of fluid balance.

BASIC PRINCIPLES OF OSMOSIS AND OSMOTIC EQUILIBRIA

Whenever a membrane between two fluid compartments is permeable to water but not to some of the dissolved solutes (this is called a *semipermeable membrane*), and the concentration of non-diffusible substances is greater on one side of the membrane than on the other, water will pass through the membrane toward the side with the greater concentration. This phenomenon is called *osmosis*.

Osmosis results from the kinetic motion of the molecules in the solutions on the two sides of the membrane and can be explained in the following manner: The individual molecules on both sides of the membrane in Figure 25 are equally active because the temperature, which is a measure of the activity of the molecules, is the same on both sides. However, the non-diffusible solute on side A, represented by the large particles in

the figure, displaces some of the water molecules, thereby reducing the number of water molecules in each ml. As a result, the *total activity* of water molecules against the membrane on side A is less than on side B; and a greater number of water molecules will strike the pores of the semipermeable membrane from side B than from side A, resulting in more water molecules flowing toward A than toward B. The net rate of flow toward A is the *rate of osmosis*.

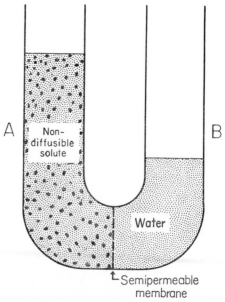

Figure 25. Demonstration of osmotic pressure on the two sides of a semipermeable membrane.

Osmotic Pressure

If osmosis continues for a while, the height of the solution in column A becomes greater than in column B. The difference in these two heights is a measure of the pressure across the semipermeable membrane. Eventually, the pressure rises high enough to prevent further osmosis into chamber A. This pressure difference, when equilibrium is established, is called the *osmotic pressure* of the solution containing the non-diffusible solute.

Relationship of Molecular Concentration to Osmotic Pressure. It is obvious that the "total activity" of the water molecules in chamber A of Figure 25 is reduced almost directly in proportion to the concentration of non-diffusible molecules in the chamber. That is, each molecule of solute dilutes the water molecules by a given amount. Consequently, the rate of osmosis and also the osmotic pressure are directly proportional to the concentration of non-diffusible molecules. Furthermore, this relationship holds true for all non-diffusible molecules almost regardless of their molecular weight. For instance, one molecule of albumin with a molecular weight of 70,000 has the same osmotic effect as a molecule of glucose with a molecular weight of 180.

The osmotic pressure of a solution at body temperature can be determined approximately from the following formula:

ionizable substance is equal to 1 osmol. On the other hand, if a substance ionizes into 2 ions (sodium chloride into sodium and chloride ions for instance) then one-half gram mol of the substance would equal 1 osmol.

In general, the osmol is too large a unit for satisfactory use in expressing osmotic activity of solutions in the body. Therefore, the term *milliosmol, which equals* one-thousandth osmol, is commonly used.

Osmolarity of the Body Fluids

Table 2 lists the osmotically active substances in plasma, interstitial fluid, and intracellular fluid. The milliosmols of each of these per liter of fluid is given. Note especially that approximately four fifths of the total osmolarity of the interstitial fluid and plasma is caused by sodium and chloride ions, while approximately one half of the intracellular osmolarity is caused by potassium ions, the remainder being divided among the many other intracellular substances.

As noted at the bottom of Table 2, the total osmolarity of each of the three compartments is almost exactly 300 milliosmols, with that of the plasma 1.5 milliosmols greater than that of the interstitial and intracellular fluids. This slight difference between plasma and interstitial fluid is caused by the osmotic effect of the plasma proteins, which

$$\text{Osmotic pressure (in mm. Hg)} = 19,300 \times \text{concentration in osmols}$$

Osmotic Activity of Ions. Non-diffusible ions cause osmosis and osmotic pressure in exactly the same manner as do non-diffusible molecules. Furthermore, when a molecule dissociates into two or more ions, each one of the ions then exerts osmotic pressure individually. Therefore, to determine the osmotic effect, all the non-diffusible ions must be added to all the non-diffusible molecules; but it should be noted that a bivalent ion such as calcium exerts no more osmotic pressure than does a univalent ion such as sodium.

Osmols. The ability of solutes to cause osmosis and osmotic pressure is measured in terms of "osmols." *One gram molecular weight of dissolved non-diffusible and non-*

maintains about 25 mm. Hg greater pressure in the capillaries than in the surrounding interstitial fluid spaces.

Corrected Osmolar Activity of the Body Fluids. Also at the bottom of Table 2 is shown a corrected osmolar activity of the three different fluids. The reason for this correction is the following: All molecules and ions in solution exert either *intermolecular attraction* or *intermolecular repulsion*, and these two effects can cause, respectively, a decrease or an increase in the osmotic "activity" of the dissolved substance. In general, there is more intermolecular attraction than repulsion so that the overall osmotic activity of the substances is only about 93 per cent of that which one would calculate from the number of milliosmols present. For this reason, the actual osmotic pressure of the body fluids is proportional to the

Table 2. Osmolar Substances in Extracellular and Intracellular Fluids

	Plasma	Interstitial	Intracellular
	(mOsmols./L. of H_2O)	(mOsmols./L. of H_2O)	(mOsmols./L. of H_2O)
Na^+	144	137	10
K^+	5	4.7	141
Ca^{++}	2.5	2.4	0
Mg^{++}	1.5	1.4	31
Cl^-	107	112.7	4
HCO_3^-	27	28.3	10
HPO_4^{--} $H_2PO_4^-$	2	2	11
SO_4	0.5	0.5	1
Phosphocreatine			45
Carnosine			14
Amino acids	2	2	8
Creatine	0.2	0.2	9
Lactate	1.2	1.2	1.5
Adenosine triphosphate			5
Hexose monophosphate			3.5
Glucose	5.6	5.6	
Protein	1.2	0.2	4
Urea	4	4	4
Total	303.7	302.2	302.2
Corrected osmolar activity (mOsmols.)	282.2	280.9	280.9
Total osmotic pressure at 30° C. (mm. Hg)	5455	5430	5430

corrected osmolar activity, which amounts to approximately 280 milliosmols per liter.

Total Osmotic Pressure Exerted by the Body Fluids. At the very bottom of Table 2 is shown the total osmotic pressure in terms of mm. Hg that would be exerted by each one of the different fluids if it were placed on one side of a cellular membrane with pure water on the other side. Note that this total pressure averages about 5450 mm. Hg and also that the osmotic pressure of plasma is 25 mm. Hg greater than that of the interstitial fluids, this representing the approximate pressure difference between the pressure of the blood inside the capillaries and the pressure in the interstitial fluid outside the capillaries.

Maintenance of Osmotic Equilibrium between Extracellular and Intracellular Fluids

The tremendous osmotic pressure that can develop across the cell membrane when one side is exposed to pure water—about 5500 mm. Hg—illustrates how much force could become available to push water molecules through the membrane should the solutions on the two sides of the membrane not be in osmotic equilibrium. For instance, in Figure 26A a cell is placed in a solution that has

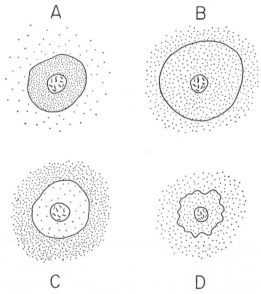

Figure 26. Establishment of osmotic equilibrium when cells are placed in a hypo- or hypertonic solution.

Table 5. Effect of Administering 8 Liters of ¼ Isotonic Potassium Phosphate

	Extracellular			Intracellular			Total Body Water		
	Volume (Liters)	Concentration (mOsmols./L.)	Total mOsmols.	Volume (Liters)	Concentration (mOsmols./L.)	Total mOsmols.	Volume (Liters)	Concentration (mOsmols./L.)	Total mOsmols.
Initial	15	300	4500	20	300	6000	35	300	10500
Solution added	8	75	600	0	0	0	8	75	600
Instantaneous effect	23	222	5100	20	300	6000	43	No equilibrium	11100
After osmotic equilibrium	19.8	258	5100	23.2	258	6000	43	258	11100
After metabolic transfer of potassium phosphate	17.8	258	4600	25.2	258	6500	43	258	11100
After loss of 6 liters of water	15.3	300	4600	21.7	300	6500	37	300	11100

stantaneous effect is an increase in extracellular fluid volume. After osmotic equilibrium has occurred a moderate amount of water will have moved into the cells. Then, it is assumed that five sixths of both the potassium and phosphate ions are transferred by active transport into the cells. This decreases the total milliosmols in the extracellular fluid and increases the total in the intracellular fluid, with a concurrent shift of proportional amounts of water. Finally, because the original injection of the solution had diluted the body fluids to a low osmolarity, large amounts of very dilute urine, consisting of almost pure water are excreted, which effect will be discussed in Chapter 9. This loss of water reconcentrates all of the body fluids back to their normal milliosmolar concentration of 300.

The changes calculated in Table 5 are illustrated also in Figure 29, which shows the time relationships of the changes. Here again a precise study of Table 5 and Figure 29 by the student will add greatly to his understanding of fundamental fluid transfer problems between extra- and intracellular fluids.

Infused potassium does not always go into the cell, however, for normal cells have a tendency to saturate themselves with potassium whenever the extracellular potassium concentration is above approximately 2 milliequivalents per liter, a value less than one half the normal concentration. Therefore, even moderate potassium infusions into a person whose cells already have adequate potassium can lead to potassium toxicity with accompanying cardiac debility.

Effect of Infusing Hypertonic Glucose, Sucrose, or Urea Solutions

Very concentrated glucose, sucrose, or urea solutions are often injected into patients to cause immediate decrease in intracellular fluid volume. For instance, in severe cerebral edema the patient will often die because of too much pressure in the cranial vault, this pressure obstructing the flow of blood to the brain. The condition can be relieved, however, in a matter of a few minutes by injecting a hypertonic solution of a substance that will not enter the intracellular compartment. The dynamics of the resulting changes are shown in Figure 30, illustrating that the intracellular fluid volume

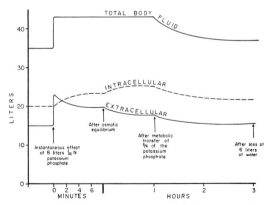

Figure 29. The time course of changes in the body fluids following intravenous infusion of 8 liters potassium phosphate solution of one-fourth isotonic milliosmolarity.

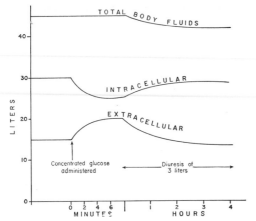

Figure 30. Time course of the body fluid changes following infusion of very concentrated glucose into the extracellular fluids.

can be decreased by several liters in a matter of a few minutes.

But glucose, sucrose, and urea are all excreted rapidly by the kidneys, and glucose is also metabolized by the cells for energy. Therefore, within two to four hours the osmotic effects of these substances are lost so that large quantities of water can then rediffuse into the intracellular compartment. Thus, this procedure causes only a temporary benefit, lasting a few hours, rather than

a permanent effect. Nevertheless, from the standpoint of saving the life of a patient it is often very valuable, for other therapeutic measures can then be instituted during the period of grace.

Glucose and Other Solutions Administered for Nutritive Purposes

Many different types of solutions are often administered intravenously to provide nutrition to patients who cannot otherwise take adequate amounts of food. Especially used are glucose solutions, to a lesser extent amino acid solutions, and, rarely, homogenized fat solutions. In administering all these, their concentrations are adjusted nearly to isotonicity, or they are given slowly enough that they do not upset the osmotic equilibria of the body fluids. However, after the glucose or other nutrient is metabolized, an excess of water often remains. Ordinarily, the kidneys secrete this in the form of a very dilute urine. Thus, the net result is only addition of the nutrient to the body.

But occasionally the kidneys are functioning very poorly, such as often occurs after a surgical operation, and the body becomes greatly overhydrated, resulting sometimes in "water intoxication," which is characterized by mental irritability and even convulsions.

SOLUTIONS USED FOR PHYSIOLOGIC AND CLINICAL REPLACEMENT PURPOSES

Below are listed the compositions of several solutions commonly used for replacing fluids lost from the body or for nutrition:

Isotonic saline (normal saline) solution for extracellular fluid replacement:
    Na^+ — 155 mEq./l. Cl^- — 155 mEq./l.
Glucose solutions for nutrition:
    I. Glucose — 2.5%, 5%, or 10%
    II. Glucose — 2.5%, 5%, or 10%
        Na^+ — 155 mEq./l. Cl^- — 155 mEq./l.
Tyrode's solution for extracellular fluid replacement:
    Na^+ — 149.4 mEq./l. Cl^- —   145.1 mEq./l.
    K^+ —   2.7 HCO_3^- — 12.0
    Ca^{++} — 3.6 HPO_4^{--} — 0.7
    Mg^{++} — 2.1
        Glucose 0.1%
Ringer's solution for frog and turtle experiments:
    Na^+ — 115 mEq./l. Cl^- —   106 mEq./l.
    K^+ —   1 HCO_3^- — 12
    Ca^{++} — 2
Ringer's solution for extracellular fluid replacement:
    Na^+ — 146 mEq./l. Cl^- — 155.4 mEq./l.
    K^+ —   4
    Ca^{++} — 5.4
Modified Hartmann's solution for extracellular fluid replacement:
    Na^+ — 128 mEq./l. Cl^- —   110.6 mEq./l.
    K^+ —   4   Lactate$^-$ — 25
    Ca^{++} — 3.6

Darrow's solution for potassium and extracellular fluid replacement:

Na$^+$ — 122 mEq./l.   Cl$^-$ — 104 mEq./l.

K$^+$ — 35   Lactate$^-$ — 52

Sodium lactate solution (⅙ molar) for correcting acidosis:

Na$^+$ — 167 mEq./l.   Lactate$^-$ — 167 mEq./l.

Ammonium chloride solution (⅙ molar) for correcting alkalosis:

NH$_4$$^+$ — 167 mEq./l.   Cl$^-$ — 167 mEq./l.

Amigen solution for nutrition:

Amigen — 5% or 10%

Glucose — 5%

Plasma for nutrition or replacement:

Protein — 7%

(for other constituents see Table 2)

Fat emulsion for nutrition:

Fat — 15%

REFERENCES

Barger, A. C.: The pathogenesis of hyponatremia: physiologic and therapeutic implications. *Metabolism, 5:*480, 1956.

Black, D. A. K.: The Essentials of Fluid Balance. 2nd ed., Springfield, Illinois, Charles C Thomas, 1960.

Brodsky, W. A., Appelboom, J. W., Dennis, W. H., Rehm, W. S., Miley, J. F., and Diamond, I.: The freezing point depression of mammalian tissues in relation to the question of osmotic activity of cell fluid. *J. Gen. Physiol., 40:*183, 1956.

Brodsky, W. A., Rehm, W. S., and Dennis, W. H.: Osmotic gradients across cellular membranes. *Science, 124:*221, 1956.

Brodsky, W. A., Rehm, W. S., Dennis, W. H., and Miller, D. G.: Thermodynamic analysis of the intracellular osmotic gradient hypothesis of active water transport. *Science, 121:*302, 1955.

Darrow, D. C., and Hellerstein, S.: Interpretation of certain changes in body water and electrolytes. *Physiol. Rev., 38:*114, 1958.

Elkinton, J. R., and Danowski, T. S.: The Body Fluids. Baltimore, Williams & Wilkins Co., 1955.

Fitzgerald, L. R.: Cutaneous respiration in man. *Physiol. Rev.,* 37:325, 1957.

Geyer, R. P.: Parenteral nutrition. *Physiol. Rev., 40:* 150, 1960.

Hardy, J. D.: Pathophysiology in Surgery. Baltimore, Williams and Wilkins Co., 1958.

Hober, R.: Physical Chemistry of Cells and Tissues. Philadelphia, Blakiston, 1945

Holley, H. L., and Carlson, W. W.: Potassium Metabolism in Health and Disease. New York, Grune & Stratton, Inc., 1955.

Keith, N. M.: Water metabolism. *Ann. Rev. Physiol., 15:*63, 1953.

Martin, G. J.: Ion Exchange and Adsorption Agents in Medicine. Boston, Little, Brown and Co., 1955.

Strajman, E., Warner, G. F., Pace, N., and Johnston, M.: Sodium kinetics in various regions of the human body following a single intravenous injection. *Acta Med. Scand., 156:*57, 1956.

Statland, R.: Fluid and Electrolytes in Practice. 2nd ed., Philadelphia, Lippincott Co., 1957.

Strauss, M. B.: Body Water in Man. Boston, Little, Brown and Co., 1957.

Walker, W. G., and Wilde, W. S.: Kinetics of radiopotassium in circulation. *Am. J. Physiol., 170:*401, 1952.

Walt, L. G.: Clinical Disorders of Hydration and Acid-Base Equilibrium. Boston, Little, Brown and Co., 1955.

Water and Electrolyte Metabolism in Relation to Age and Sex. Volume IV. Boston, Little, Brown and Co., 1958.

Weisberg, H. F.: Water, Electrolyte, and Acid-Base Balance: Normal and Pathologic Physiology as a Basis for Therapy. Baltimore, Williams & Wilkins Co., 1953.

See also Chapter 3, Osmotic equilibria.

Chapter 5

Interchange of Fluid

Through the Capillary Membrane

Fluid continually exchanges through the capillary membrane, both from the blood into the interstitial spaces and from the interstitial spaces back into the blood. Most of this exchange occurs by the process of *diffusion,* but in addition a small amount of *bulk filtration* of fluid occurs from the plasma into the interstitial fluid, and a small amount of *bulk absorption* recurs back into the plasma. In general, the processes of exchange are so well balanced that both the plasma volume and the interstitial fluid volume hardly change from moment to moment or even from day to day, despite the rapid exchange of fluid and dissolved constituents. This chapter presents the physiologic basis of this fluid exchange and some of its abnormalities.

PHYSIOLOGIC ORGANIZATION OF THE CAPILLARIES

Basic Structure of the Capillary

Figure 31 illustrates a typical capillary bed showing the flow of blood from an *arte-*

riole into the *capillaries* and then into a *venule.* The arterioles and venules both have a muscular coat that constricts when excited by nerve impulses or humoral agents, though the muscle of the arteriole is much stronger than that of the venule. The arteriole divides into a number of *metarterioles,* which also have sparse muscle fibers in their walls, as illustrated by the darkened areas in Figure 31. The metarteriole gives rise to *true capillaries.* Some of the blood flows through *preferential channels,* which are large, direct connecting capillaries between the *metarterioles* and the venule. However, in addition are many collateral channels through shorter and smaller capillaries that spread everywhere in the tissues. At the origin of each capillary from a metarteriole is usually a *precapillary sphincter,* which is a muscular band that can constrict or relax to control blood flow through the capillary.

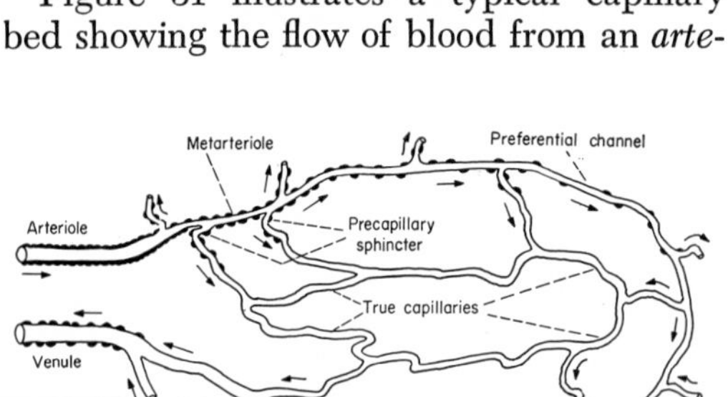

Structure of the Capillary Wall. Figure 32 illustrates the structure of a small segment of the capillary wall. The usual diameter of the capillary is about 8 microns, though this varies from as small as 4 microns to as large as 16 microns. The capillary wall consists of a very thin endothelial layer supported on the outside by a thin

Figure 31. Overall structure of a capillary bed. (From Zweifach: Factors Regulating Blood Pressure, Josiah Macy, Jr., Foundation, 1950.)

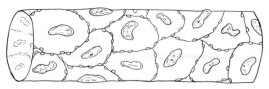

Figure 32. Detailed organization of the capillary membrane.

mately 24 mm. Hg. This pressure gradient constantly tends to force molecules outward through the capillary membrane, but, fortunately, it is normally opposed by the colloid osmotic pressure of the plasma proteins, which will be explained in the following section.

COLLOID OSMOTIC PRESSURE AT THE CAPILLARY MEMBRANE

Colloid Osmotic Pressure Caused by Proteins

The proteins are the only dissolved substances of the plasma that do not diffuse readily from the plasma into the interstitial fluids, and, as a result, the protein concentration of the plasma averages approximately five times that of the interstitial fluid—7.3 gm. per 100 ml. in the plasma versus 1.5 gm. per 100 ml. in the interstitial fluid.

In the discussion of osmotic pressure in Chapter 4 it was pointed out that *only those substances that fail to pass through the pores of a semipermeable membrane exert osmotic pressure.* Therefore, the dissolved proteins are the only substances responsible for osmotic pressure at the capillary membrane. To distinguish this osmotic pressure from that which occurs at the cellular membrane, it is sometimes called *oncotic pressure* or, more often, *colloid osmotic pressure,* so-named because proteins in solutions resemble colloids despite the fact that they are actually in true solution. On the other hand, the osmotic pressure that results at the cellular membrane is often called *crystalloidal osmotic pressure,* because essentially all dissolved substances of the body fluids, mainly crystalloidal substances, exert osmotic pressure at the cell membrane.

Effect of Donnan Equilibrium on the Colloid Osmotic Pressure. A principle of physical chemistry, called the Donnan equilibrium, states that the number of diffusible anions times the number of diffusible cations on the two sides of a semipermeable membrane will be equal. Plasma contains large amounts of proteins which are non-diffusible. However, these proteins carry electronegative charges so that they are actually *anions,* and to maintain electrostatic equilibrium in the plasma large amounts of cations, mainly sodium, are held in the plasma by the negative proteins. Normally the *number of extra*

cations held in this manner in the plasma as a result of the Donnan equilibrium is equal approximately to half the number of protein molecules. Therefore, roughly two thirds of the colloid osmotic pressure developed by the plasma is caused by proteins and approximately one third by the extra cations held in the plasma to maintain electrical neutrality.

The Normal Colloid Osmotic Pressure of the Plasma. The total colloid osmotic pressure of normal human plasma averages approximately 28 mm. Hg; 19 mm. of this is caused by the dissolved protein and 9 mm. by cations held in the plasma by proteins, as discussed above. Figure 35 illustrates the significance of this colloid osmotic pressure. Plasma is placed in an enclosed chamber A and interstitial fluid without any proteins is placed in chamber B, which is open to the atmosphere. Between the two chambers is a semipermeable membrane with the same degree of permeability as that of the capillaries. Because of osmotic forces developing at the membrane, a small amount of fluid flows from chamber B to chamber A until the pressure in chamber A reaches 28 mm. Hg. At this point the hydrostatic pressure exactly equals and opposes the colloid osmotic force so that no further rise in pressure occurs. This is precisely the same effect that occurs at the capillary membrane. That is, a hydrostatic pressure gradient is always tending to push molecules outward through the capillary membrane, while osmotic forces are always tending to move molecules into the capillaries, the two forces normally exactly equaling and opposing each other.

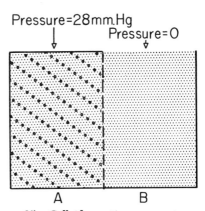

Figure 35. Colloid osmotic pressure at a semipermeable membrane that is permeable to all constituents of the fluids besides plasma proteins.

Effect of the Different Plasma Proteins on Colloid Osmotic Pressure. It should be recalled that the osmotic pressure developed by dissolved substances at a membrane *is proportional to the number of non-diffusible molecules and not to the mass of substance dissolved*. That is, one sodium ion, having a mass approximately $\frac{1}{3000}$ that of a protein molecule nevertheless exerts the same osmotic pressure at a semipermeable membrane through which both of these molecules fail to pass.

The plasma proteins are actually a mixture of proteins having molecular weights varying from as little as 69,000 up to as high as a million or more. However, there are three major protein fractions called albumin, globulins, and fibrinogen. The average molecular weight of the albumin is approximately 69,000, while that of the globulins is approximately 140,000 and of the fibrinogen 400,000. Thus, one gram of globulin contains only approximately one half as many molecules as one gram of albumin, and one gram of fibrinogen contains only one sixth as many molecules as one gram of albumin. Furthermore, the relative concentrations of these different types of proteins in the plasma average the following:

Albumin .... 4.5 gm.%
Globulins .... 2.5 gm.%
Fibrinogen .... 0.3 gm.%
　　TOTAL .... 7.3 gm.%

Therefore, because each gram of albumin exerts twice the osmotic pressure of a gram of globulins and because there is almost twice as much albumin in the plasma as globulins, one finds that about three fourths of the total colloid osmotic pressure of the plasma results from the albumin fraction and only about one fourth from the globulins and fibrinogen. Therefore, from the point of view of capillary dynamics, it is mainly albumin that is important; but, on the other hand, from the point of view of many other functions of the plasma proteins, such as providing circulating antibodies for defense of the body against invading bacteria, it is the globulins that are important; and fibrinogen is important to provide blood clotting so that a person will not lose excessive amounts of blood when vessels are ruptured. The antibody functions of the globulins will be discussed in Chapter 14, the clotting function of fibrinogen in Chapter 16, and the overall relationship of plasma proteins to other body proteins in Chapter 67.

Figure 36 illustrates graphically the colloid osmotic pressure exerted by different concentrations of albumin and of four different fractions of globulins. Though alpha$_1$ globulin exerts very large amounts of colloid osmotic pressure, this is present in the plasma in only very small concentration, while the bulk of the globulins exert a colloid osmotic pressure equal to only about one

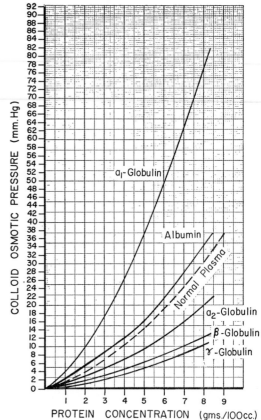

Figure 36. The osmotic pressure of five fractions of the plasma proteins at different concentrations. Also, the dashed line shows the osmotic pressure of normal plasma proteins, which are a mixture of the others. (Modified from Ott: *Klin. Wochenschrift* 34: 1079, 1956.)

half that of the albumin. Note especially that each gram of dissolved protein exerts considerably less colloid osmotic pressure at low concentrations than at higher concentrations. This means that small amounts of protein in a solution, such as occurs in the interstitial fluid, will exert even less colloid osmotic pressure than might otherwise be expected, whereas only slight changes in protein concentration up in the higher range will cause a relatively large change in colloid osmotic pressure. The cause of this increasing effect of concentration on colloid osmotic pressure is the Donnan equilibrium factor discussed above, which becomes progressively more significant at higher and higher protein concentrations.

The Interstitial Fluid Proteins and Their Colloid Osmotic Pressure

Despite the fact that the usual capillary pore is smaller than the molecular size of the plasma proteins, a small amount of plasma proteins do leak into the interstitial fluid spaces through aberrantly large pores or perhaps sometimes through broken places in the capillary. Albumin molecules, because they are smaller than most globulin molecules, normally leak about 1.6 times as easily as the globulins, causing the proteins in the interstitial fluids to have a disproportionately high ratio of albumin. The total amount of protein in the entire 12 liters of interstitial fluid in the body is almost exactly equal to the total amount of protein in the plasma itself, and the average protein concentration of the interstitial fluid is approximately 1.5 gms. per cent. Referring to the diagram in Figure 36, one finds that the average colloid osmotic pressure of the interstitial fluid proteins is approximately 4 mm. Hg.

"Effective" Colloid Osmotic Pressure Gradient at the Capillary Membrane

From the above discussion it is evident that the osmotic pressure caused by the plasma proteins is normally about 28 mm. Hg, while that caused by the interstitial fluid proteins is normally about 4 mm. Hg. Therefore, the normal *colloid osmotic pressure gradient* across the capillary membrane is 28 minus 4, or 24 mm. Hg. This is exactly equal to the normal mean hydrostatic pressure gradient across the membrane but in the opposite direction, the two opposing each other and normally exactly balancing each other so that there will be no loss or gain of blood volume nor interstitial fluid volume.

Comparison of Colloid Osmotic Pressure with Crystalloidal Osmotic Pressure. In Chapter 4 it was pointed out that the crystalloidal osmotic pressure which would develop at the cell membrane if pure interstitial fluid were placed on one side of the membrane and pure water on the other side would be approximately 5,450 mm. Hg. If plasma were placed on one side of the capillary membrane and water on the other side, the osmotic pressure that would develop would be only 28 mm. Hg. Therefore, it is obvious that the osmotic forces acting at the cellular membrane are tremendous in comparison with those that act at the capillary membrane. Yet, the concentrations of the osmotically active substances on the two sides of the cell membrane are almost always

exactly equal, so that only rarely does any actual pressure difference develop between the two sides of the membrane. In the case of the capillary membrane the concentration of the plasma proteins is always far greater than that of the surrounding interstitial fluids, so that an actual pressure difference, the hydrostatic pressure gradient discussed above, does exist between the two sides of the capillary membrane despite the fact that the total quantity of osmotically active substances at the capillary membrane is only 1/200 the quantity acting at the cell membrane.

BULK FLOW OF WATER AND DISSOLVED SUBSTANCES THROUGH THE CAPILLARY MEMBRANE

In addition to the diffusion of molecules through the capillary membrane, both hydrostatic and colloid osmotic pressures can cause *bulk flow* of fluid through the capillary pores. That is, instead of single molecules passing through one at a time, as occurs in diffusion, large masses of molecules can *stream* through in unison in the same way that water flows in bulk along a pipe when pressure forces it to move.

Ordinarily, the pressure gradients that exist across the capillary membrane are slight enough that the rate of bulk flow is several hundred to several thousand times less than the rate of diffusion of these same substances through the membrane. Yet, *bulk flow is extremely important to the normal regulation of plasma volume and interstitial fluid volume for the following reason: Bulk flow at any given point in a capillary is unidirectional, whereas diffusion occurs almost exactly equally in both directions at the same time, thus resulting in almost no changes in fluid volumes.*

Outflow of Fluid (Filtration) at the Arterial Ends of the Capillaries. Referring to Figure 37, it will be noted that the average capillary pressure at the arterial end of the capillary is 35 mm. Hg, while the tissue pressure is 1 mm. Hg. In other words, the total hydrostatic pressure gradient tending to cause flow of fluid outward through the pores is 34 mm. Hg. On the other hand, the plasma colloid osmotic pressure is 28 mm. Hg, while the tissue colloid osmotic pressure is 4 mm. Hg, or a net effective

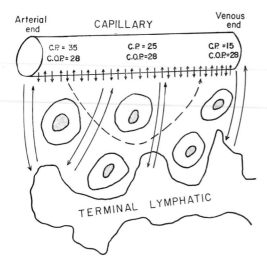

Tissue pressure = 1 mm. Hg.
Tissue colloid osmotic pressure = 4mm.Hg.

Figure 37. Exchange of fluid between the capillary and interstitial fluid spaces.

colloid osmotic pressure of 24. Thus, the hydrostatic gradient is 10 mm. Hg greater than the colloid osmotic pressure gradient. This causes flow of fluid outward through the arterial ends of the capillary membrane, the total amount averaging approximately 1 liter per hour in the entire body. The 10 mm. Hg difference between the hydrostatic and colloid osmotic gradients, which is responsible for this outward flow of fluid, is called the *filtration pressure.*

Absorption of Fluid at the Venous Ends of the Capillaries. Referring again to Figure 37, it will be noted that the effective colloid osmotic pressure at the venous ends of the capillaries is 10 mm. Hg greater than the hydrostatic pressure gradient. This causes absorption of fluid into the venous ends of the capillaries. The normal rate of absorption at all the venous ends of the capillaries of the body is approximately 900 ml. per hour. An additional 100 ml. of fluid normally flows each hour into the lymphatics and through these back into the blood. Thus, an equal amount of fluid, approximately 1 liter per hour, filters into the interstitial fluid, but at the same time is returned to the blood, mainly by absorption into the venous ends of the capillaries but to a much less extent by flow through the lymphatics. If ever these get out of balance with each other, large volumes of plasma or interstitial

fluid will begin transferring to the opposite chamber, which will be discussed below.

THE "LAW OF THE CAPILLARIES"— EQUILIBRIUM BETWEEN PLASMA VOLUME AND INTERSTITIAL FLUID VOLUME

The so-called *law of the capillaries,* which was first formulated by Starling, states that the following relationship normally exists at capillary membranes.

Mean capillary pressure + Tissue colloid osmotic pressure = Tissue pressure + Plasma colloid osmotic pressure.

In other words, the sum of all the forces tending to move fluids out of the capillaries equals the sum of the forces tending to move fluids inward. When the sum of the forces tending to move fluid outwards is greater than that tending to move fluids inward, there will be greater outflow of fluid from the arterial ends of the capillaries than return into the venous capillaries, thus causing a net loss of plasma volume. Furthermore, this loss of plasma will not stop until the tissue pressure rises high enough or the mean hydrostatic pressure in the capillaries falls low enough to make the outward forces once again equal to the inward forces.

On the other hand, when the sum of the outward forces is less than that of the inward forces, fluid will flow into the capillaries from the interstitial spaces and will continue until the capillary pressure rises sufficiently or the tissue pressure falls sufficiently to bring the forces back into equilibrium.

Factors That Cause Lack of Equilibrium between Inflow and Outflow

Effect of High Capillary Pressure. If the mean capillary pressure is raised from 25 mm. Hg up to 35 mm. Hg—that is, the pressure at the arterial end up to 45 mm. Hg and that at the venous end to 25 mm. Hg—then the rate of filtration at the arterial ends of the capillaries will be greatly increased, while the rate of absorption at the venous ends will be 0. Indeed, all along the extent of the capillaries, fluid will be filtering into the interstitial spaces and none will be reabsorbed. As a result, the plasma volume will be decreasing while the interstitial fluid volume will be increasing. As this continues, the pressures in the entire circulatory system, including the capillary pressure, fall while the tissue pressure rises. As a result, the forces across the capillary membrane will soon return to an equilibrium state, and the plasma and interstitial fluid volumes will again assume a steady state.

Very high capillary pressures can sometimes cause as much as a liter of fluid to filter out of the plasma into the interstitial spaces in approximately 10 minutes. This illustrates how rapidly these readjustments can be made.

Effect of Low Capillary Pressure. If the mean capillary pressure falls from 25 mm. Hg down to 15 mm. Hg, this obviously results in rapid inward flow of fluid from the interstitial spaces into the plasma. The plasma volume and capillary pressure progressively increase, while the interstitial fluid volume and tissue pressure decrease. After a while these changes in pressure will cause a new state of equilibrium to be reached, and the fluid volumes will then stop changing.

Effect of Elevated Tissue Pressure. If the tissue pressure becomes greatly elevated while other forces at the capillary membrane remain normal, this obviously will cause increased fluid flow into the blood both by absorption through the capillaries and through the lymphatic system. Consequently, the plasma volume increases while the interstitial fluid volume decreases, thereby elevating the capillary pressure and decreasing the interstitial fluid pressure until the forces at the membrane reach a new state of equilibrium.

Rapidity with Which New Equilibria Are Reached. When the forces that cause inflow and outflow through the capillary membranes are thrown out of equilibrium by a transfusion, by hemorrhage, or by any other cause, equilibrium is gradually reestablished by fluid transfer through the capillary membrane. The rapidity of this reapproach to equilibrium has never been actually measured, but on the basis of filtration and absorption studies in capillaries, as well as measurements of the fluid volumes required to increase either capillary or tissue pressure, one can calculate that equilibrium should be half way reestablished in one to three hours. Though this seems to be a relatively slow reestablishment of equilibrium between plasma and interstitial fluid volumes, it must be recognized that severe degrees of non-equilibrium rarely develop in a short period of time. Consequently, for all practical purposes the inward forces versus the outward forces, as stated in the law of the capillaries, are rarely out of equilibrium by more than a millimeter or more of mercury at any one time.

APPENDIX

Possibility of Negative Pressure in the Interstitial Spaces

The principles of capillary dynamics presented in this chapter are those taught in almost all physiology courses and that have now become almost classical. However, since this chapter was written, a finding has been made in our laboratory that will perhaps change many of our classical concepts of fluid exchange at the capillary membrane. This finding has been that *negative pressures* develop in small plastic capsules implanted in the tissues and fenestrated with many small holes so that fluid can exchange freely between the interstitial spaces and the capsules. This pressure averages about −5 mm. Hg inside the capsule, and it is present in all tissue areas where capsules have been implanted, though sometimes the pressure is −2 to −3 mm. Hg and other times as low as −10 mm. Hg (particularly in the axillary spaces). Since the usual method of measuring tissue pressure (by inserting a needle into the tissue) is unsatisfactory, we believe these capsular pressures to be much more nearly the true tissue pressure than any pressures previously reported.

The significance of negative pressure in the tissue spaces is the following: Contrary to previous beliefs, it might not be the elastic tension of the tissue fibers that keeps the interstitial spaces in their normal, non-edematous state. Instead, it might well be the negative pressures in these spaces that keep the spaces continually collapsed. There are many evidences that this is true. First, everyone is familiar with the collapse of a blister several days after it forms. Indeed, the blister is sucked so dry by the tissues that the surface of the blister actually crinkles; this could occur only if a negative pressure should develop in the blister. Second, many newborn male children have hydroceles in the scrotum. Within a few months almost all of these completely resorb even though the walls of the hydrocele during the latter stages of resorption are actually folded upon themselves so that the pressure therein could not possibly be positive. Third, measurements of pressure in naturally occurring non-collapsible spaces such as the intrapleural space and the joint cavities have all been negative.

Negative pressure in the tissue spaces would almost certainly allow a far more stable control system for interstitial fluid volume than would a positive pressure system. The reason for this is that only a one mm. Hg pressure change in a positive pressure system would cause a tremendous change in interstitial fluid volume, whereas in a negative pressure system the interstitial fluid spaces would be kept almost as small as possible essentially all the time regardless of changes in the degree of negativity. The fluid present in the tissue spaces in this latter instance would be only that amount held in the spaces by capillarity. Calculations of the capillary forces involved show that changes in negative pressures between the limits of minus one and minus several thousand mm. Hg would not greatly affect the volume of interstitial fluid. Therefore, with a negative pressure system, capillary interchange dynamics would have to be altered far from normal before the interstitial fluid volume would be greatly affected. Indeed, this seems to be the case, for in experimental animals severe hemorrhage, which undoubtedly reduces the capillary pressure very greatly, does not transfer significant quantities of fluid from the interstitial spaces into the blood *unless the animal has been given large quantities of water to drink immediately prior to the hemorrhage.* Secondly, some human beings have been discovered to have so little protein in their blood stream that their plasma colloid osmotic pressures are as low as 10 mm. Hg. Yet, at least some of these people show essentially no edema. In a negative pressure system one can readily see that the colloid osmotic pressure could be reduced a reasonable amount before the interstitial fluid pressure would become positive and cause edema. Thus, the negative pressure system provides a *safety factor* against the development of edema.

When one considers that the body is made up of literally billions of capillaries and that it would be almost impossible to have precisely the same capillary pressures in all parts of the body at the same time, one can see once more that a negative pressure system would allow very wide variations in capillary pressure without this affecting interstitial fluid function. Therefore, the concept of negative pressures in the interstitial fluid spaces offers many explanations for already observed facts, though it will alter somewhat the classical principles of capillary dynamics as presented in this chapter.

Mechanism Causing the Negative Pressure in the Tissue Spaces. Thus far, only a few observations are available that shed light on the mechanism that causes the negative pressure in the tissue spaces. The most important of these is that mechanical movement of the tissues causes the pressure to become more negative. This indicates that the lymphatic pump, which will be explained in the following chapter, pumps fluid and protein out of the interstitial fluid spaces each time the tissues are compressed or moved in any other way. Loss of the protein would maintain a low tissue colloid osmotic pressure so that the plasma colloid osmotic pressure could cause osmosis of fluid out of the tissue spaces until the pressure would become negative. To do this, however, the mean capillary pressure would have to be somewhat lower than the 25 mm. Hg normally decreed in the classical mechanism. Since the capillary pressure measurements made with micropipettes have been made from the arterial and venous ends of the capillaries and since we now know that vasomotion might well cause very different pressures in the true capillaries from the pressures in the inflow and outflow tracks of the capillary beds, one could possibly explain the low capillary pressures on this basis.

Electron Microscopic Studies of Capillary Pores

Another recently discovered fact disconcerting to the classical picture of capillary dynamics has been the failure of the electron microscope to show pores in all capillary walls. Such studies have demonstrated pores only in the liver sinusoids and in the renal glomeruli. On the other hand, physiological studies are all so consistent with the idea that pores actually do exist in the capillary walls that we are presently forced to believe that the processes of tissue fixation prior to making the electron microscopic pictures have in some way obscured the presence of the pores. On the other hand, the pore size in the liver sinusoids is quite variable and can be as large as one micron. Therefore, when the truth is known, it is highly probable that the pores of the capillary wall will also be very variable in size though extremely small.

REFERENCES

Barlow, G., Agersborg, H. P., Jr., and Overman, R. R.: Comparison of the intravascular mixing and disappearance of radiosodium, radiopotassium and T-1824. *Circ. Res.*, 5:419, 1957.

Bennett, H. S., Luft, J. H., and Hampton, J. C.: Morphological classifications of vertebrate blood capillaries. *Am. J. Phiysiol.*, 196:381, 1959.

Blum, J. J.: Concentration profiles in and around capillaries. *Am. J. Physiol.*, 198:991, 1960.

Chambers, R., and Zweifach, B. W.: Intercellular cement and capillary permeability. *Physiol. Rev.*, 27:436, 1947.

Gilbert, R. P.: Mechanisms of the hemodynamic effects of endotoxin. *Physiol. Rev.*, 40:245, 1960.

Haddy, F. J., Richards, A. G., Alden, J. L., and Visscher, M. B.: Small vein and artery pressures in normal and edematous extremities of dogs under local and general anesthesia. *Am. J. Physiol.*, *176:* 355, 1954.

Landis, E. M.: Capillary permeability and factors affecting composition of capillary filtrate. *Ann. N. Y. Acad. Sc.*, *46:*713, 1946.

Landis, E. M.: Capillary pressure and capillary permeability. *Physiol. Rev.*, *14:*404, 1934.

Landis, E. M.: Microinjection studies of capillary blood pressure in human skin. *Heart*, *15:*209, 1930.

Mayerson, H. S., Wolfram, C. G., Shirley, H. H., Jr., and Wasserman, K.: Regional differences in capillary permeability. *Am. J. Physiol.*, *198:*155, 1960.

Nelson, T. E., Jr., Castronova, E., and Hyman, C.: The effect of dicumarol on the transvascular exchange of T-1824-labeled protein in rabbits. *Cir. Res.*, *4:*308, 1956.

Nicoll, P. A., and Webb, R. L.: Vascular patterns and active vasomotion as determiners of flow through minute vessels. *Angiology*, *6:*291, 1955.

Opdyke, D. F., and Clark, T.: Plasma half life of Na^{22} in dogs. *Proc. Soc. Exp. Biol. & Med.*, *88:*207, 1955.

Ott, H.: Die errechnung des kolloidosmotischen serundruckes aus dem eiweisspektrum und das mittlere molekulargewicht der serumeiweissfraktionen. *Klin. Wschr.*, *34:*1079, 1956.

Pappenheimer, J. R.: Capillary permeability; deductions concerning the number and dimensions of ultramicroscopic openings in the capillary walls. *Ann. N. Y. Acad. Sc.*, *55:*465, 1952.

Pappenheimer, J. R.: Passage of molecules through capillary walls. *Physiol. Rev.*, *33:*387, 1953.

Pappenheimer, J. R., and Soto-Rivera, A.: Effective osmotic pressure of plasma proteins and other quantities associated with capillary circulation in hindlimbs of cats and dogs. *Am. J. Physiol.*, *152:* 471, 1948.

Renkin, E. M.: Capillary and cellular permeability to some compounds related to antipyrine. *Am. J. Physiol.*, *173:*125–130, 1953.

Renkin, E. M.: Effects of blood flow on diffusion kinetics in isolated, perfused hindlegs of cats; a double circulation hypothesis. *Am. J. Physiol.*, *183:*125, 1955.

Renkin, E. M.: Filtration, diffusion, and molecular sieving through porous cellulose membranes. *J. Gen. Physiol.*, *38:*225, 1954.

Renkin, E. M.: Transport of potassium-42 from blood to tissue in isolated mammalian skeletal muscles. *Am. J. Physiol.*, *197:*1205, 1959.

Renkin, E. M., and Zaun, B. D.: Effects of adrenal hormones on capillary permeability in perfused rat tissues. *Am. J. Physiol.*, *180:*498, 1955.

Spector, W. G.: Substances which affect capillary permeability. *Pharmacol. Rev.*, *10:*475, 1958.

Ussing, H. H.: Transport through biological membranes. *Ann. Rev. Physiol.*, *15:*1, 1953.

Wasserman, K., and Mayerson, H. S.: Exchange of albumin between plasma and lymph. *Am. J. Physiol.*, *165:*15, 1951.

Wasserman, K., and Mayerson, H. S.: Relative importance of dextran molecular size in plasma volume expansion. *Am. J. Physiol.*, *176:*104, 1954.

Wasserman, K., Joseph, J. D., and Mayerson, H. S.: Kinetics of vascular and extravascular protein exchange in unbled and bled dogs. *Am. J. Physiol.*, *184:*175, 1956.

Wasserman, K., Loeb, L., and Mayerson, H. S.: Capillary permeability to macro-molecules. *Circ. Res.*, *3:*594, 1955.

Webb, R. L., and Nicoll, P. A.: The bat wing as a subject for studies in homeostasis of capillary beds. *Anat. Rec.*, *120:*253, 1954.

See also Chapter 6, Lymphatics; Chapter 7, The special fluid systems.

The Lymphatic System; Edema

THE LYMPHATIC SYSTEM

The lymphatic system represents an accessory route by which fluids can flow from the interstitial spaces into the blood. And, most important of all, the lymphatics can carry proteins and even large particulate matter away from the tissue spaces, neither of which can be removed by absorption directly into the blood capillary. We shall see that this removal of proteins from the tissue spaces is an absolutely essential function, without which we would die probably within 24 hours.

The Lymph Channels of the Body. Only a few of the tissues of the body do not have lymphatic channels. These include the superficial

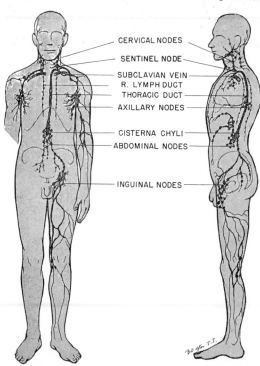

CERVICAL NODES

SENTINEL NODE

SUBCLAVIAN VEIN
R. LYMPH DUCT
THORACIC DUCT
AXILLARY NODES

CISTERNA CHYLI
ABDOMINAL NODES

INGUINAL NODES

Figure 38. The lymphatic system of the body.

portions of the skin, the central nervous system, deeper portions of peripheral nerves, the endomysium of the muscles, and the bones. However, even in these structures are minute passages through which extracellular fluid can flow, and eventually this fluid flows to other areas that do have lymphatic channels or that can empty directly back into the blood.

Essentially all the lymph from the lower part of the body—even that from the legs—flows up the *thoracic duct* and empties into the venous system at the juncture of the left internal jugular vein and subclavian vein, as illustrated in Figure 38. However, some of the lymph from the lower part of the body can enter the veins in the inguinal region and perhaps also at various points in the abdomen.

Lymph from the left side of the head, from the left arm, and left chest region also enters the thoracic duct before it joins the venous system. Lymph from the right side of the neck and head, from the right arm, and from parts of the right thorax enters the *right lymph duct*, which then empties into the venous system at the juncture of the right subclavian vein and right internal jugular vein.

The lymphatics of the gastrointestinal tract pass through the mesentery to a common reservoir known as the *cisterna chyli*. The cisterna chyli is not a single large cistern, as its name implies, but instead is a multilocular plexus of connecting tubes that form the beginning of the thoracic duct.

The Terminal Lymphatics and Their Permeability. Most of the fluid leaving the arterial capillaries flows among the cells and finally back into the venous capillaries, but normally about one tenth of the fluid enters the terminal lymphatics. This quantity is extremely important, for substances of large molecular weight such as the proteins cannot enter the venous capillaries but can enter the lymphatics. The reason for this is that the lymphatic capillaries are far more permeable than are the blood capillaries.

Though the walls of the lymphatic capillaries are lined with a thin endothelium, *they offer almost no resistance to the flow of fluids, proteins, or even particulate matter from the interstitial spaces.* In other words, from a physiologic point of view there does not seem to be any limit to the porosity of the lymphatic capillaries. About the only factor that limits the size of foreign matter that can pass up the lymphatic capillaries is the size of the lymphatic capillaries themselves.

Formation of Lymph

As best can be determined, lymph is nothing more than interstitial fluid that filters into the lymphatics. Therefore, except for its low protein concentration, the constituents of lymph are almost identical with those of the plasma. The concentration of proteins in the lymph from most areas of the body is about 1.5 gm. per cent, which is also the protein concentration of the interstitial fluid, though lymph formed in the liver and to a lesser extent that formed in the gastrointestinal tract contains protein concentrations as high as 3 to 5 gm. per cent. Yet, approximately half of all the lymph formed in the normal resting human being is derived from the liver and intestines. Therefore, thoracic lymph, which is a mixture of all lymph, usually has a protein concentration of 3 to 4 gm. per cent.

The lymphatic system is one of the major channels of absorption from the gastrointestinal tract, being responsible principally for the absorption of fats. Essentially all the fats are absorbed through the intestinal villi into central lymphatic capillaries called *central lacteals*. The absorbed material then passes upward through the thoracic duct to enter the blood stream. After a fatty meal, thoracic duct lymph sometimes contains as high as 1 to 2 per cent fat. This will be considered at length in Chapter 66.

Total Rate of Flow through the Lymphatic Channels. Approximately 100 ml. of lymph flow through the thoracic duct of a resting man per hour. This is less than 1/100,000 of the calculated rate of fluid diffusion back and forth through the capillary membranes, and it is also only one-tenth the rate of bulk fluid flow out of the arterial ends of the capillaries into the tissue spaces. These facts illustrate that the flow of lymph is relatively small in comparison with the total exchange of fluid between the plasma and the interstitial fluid.

Factors That Determine the Rate of Lymph Flow. *Effect of tissue pressure.* Elevation of tissue pressure above normal increases the flow of interstitial fluid into the terminal lymphatics and consequently also increases the rate of lymph flow. When the tissue pressure rises to as high as 10 to 20 mm. Hg, which is many times the normal value, the rate of lymph flow at times increases to as much as 10 times normal. Therefore, any factor, besides obstruction of the lymphatic system itself, that tends to increase tissue pressure will increase the rate of lymph flow. This includes *elevated capillary pressure, decreased plasma colloid osmotic pressure, increased total extracellular fluid volume,* and *increased permeability of the capillaries.*

The lymphatic pump. Lymphatic valves (see Fig. 39) exist in all lymph channels, even in the very minute collecting channels from the terminal lymphatics. Every time the lymph vessel is compressed by pressure from any source, lymph tends to be squeezed in both directions, but, because the valves open only in the central direction, the fluid moves unidirectionally. Each contraction of any muscle compresses lymphatic vessels in the surrounding tissues, and compression of the skin from the outside or even passive movement of the limbs or tissues also compresses lymphatic channels. Each such com-

Figure 39. A lymphatic valve.

pression acts as a local pump to push the fluid progressively toward the point of entry into the circulatory system. This is called the *lymphatic pump.*

Obviously, the lymphatic pump becomes very active during exercise but very sluggish under resting conditions. During exercise the rate of lymph flow can increase to as high as 3 to 10 times normal because of the increased activity.

In addition to the lymphatic pump, most small lymphatic vessels contract rhythmically in the same manner that vasomotion occurs in the metarterioles and precapillary sphincters of the blood capillary system. It is possible that this contraction is of some importance for squeezing fluid forward along the lymphatic channels. However, experiments have shown that most of the forward movement of lymph is caused by the lymphatic pump. *In summary, then, the rate of lymph flow is determined principally by the product of tissue pressure times the activity of the lymphatic pump.*

Filtration of Lymph by the Lymph Nodes. The lymph nodes provide a filtration system for removing particulate matter from lymph before it enters the veins. Figure 40 illustrates a typical lymph node, showing that the lymph enters through *afferent lymphatics* around the periphery of the node and leaves through *efferent lymphatics* at the hilus. Inside the node, lymph must weave its way through the *medullary sinuses,* which are lined by *reticulum cells* and other phagocytic cells that are capable of ingesting foreign particles, thereby removing them from the lymph before it is emptied into the blood.

In addition to filtering the lymph, the nodes have the ability to form immune bodies. Thus, when bacteria and protein antigens arrive at lymph nodes, they are first phagocytized, and then during the following week or more, specific immune bodies are formed against them and emptied into the circulating body fluids to destroy additional bacteria or bacterial toxins. This function of the lymph nodes will be discussed much more fully in Chapter 14 in relation to immunity.

The major function of the lymph node is to prevent the spread of infection and toxins in the body. When infection develops in a particular region of the body, the lymph

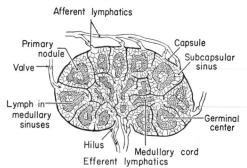

Figure 40.   Functional diagram of a lymph node.

nodes draining the region usually swell considerably because of hypertrophy of the lymphoid tissue in the node, thus allowing the node to function even more effectively than normally.

Absorption of Fluids Injected into the Tissues. Foreign fluids injected into the tissue spaces temporarily cause abnormal capillary and interstitial fluid dynamics because of greatly increased local tissue pressure. This pressure increases both the rate of lymph flow and also the rate of fluid absorption by the capillaries. Thus, injected fluids enter the circulatory system by two routes. However, if the injected fluid contains dissolved substances such as proteins that cannot be absorbed through the capillary walls, these must necessarily enter the circulation by way of the lymphatics alone. For instance, snake venom toxin is a very large protein molecule and cannot be absorbed into the capillaries. Therefore, temporary blockage of the lymphatic channels after a snake bite can greatly delay systemic toxicity from the poison.

Regulation of Interstitial Fluid Protein by the Lymphatics

Since protein is continually leaking from the capillaries into the interstitial fluid spaces, it must also be continually removed from these spaces, or otherwise the tissue colloid osmotic pressure will become so high that normal capillary dynamics can no longer continue. Unfortunately, only a small proportion of the proteins that leak into the tissue spaces can diffuse back into the capillaries because there are five times as many proteins already in the plasma as in the interstitial fluid. Therefore, probably by far the most important of all the lymphatic functions is the maintenance of low protein concentrations in the interstitial fluid. The mechanism of this is the following:

As fluid leaks from the arterial ends of the capillaries into the interstitial spaces, only very small quantities of protein accompany it, but then, as the fluid is reabsorbed at the venous ends of the capillaries, most of the protein is left behind. Therefore, *protein progressively accumulates in the interstitial fluid,* and this in turn *increases the tissue colloid osmotic pressure.* The osmotic pressure decreases reabsorption of fluid by the capillaries, thereby *promoting increased tissue fluid volume* and *increased tissue pressure.* The increased pressure then forces interstitial fluid into the lymphatic channels which carries with it the excess protein that had accumulated. As a result, normal capillary dynamics ensue once again. To summarize, an increase in tissue fluid protein increases the rate of lymph flow, and this, by washing the proteins out of the tissue spaces, automatically returns the protein concentration to its normal low level.

The importance of this function of the lymphatics cannot be stressed too strongly, for *there is no other route besides the lymphatics through which proteins can return to the circulatory system.* If it were not for this continual removal of proteins, the dynamics of the capillaries would become so abnormal within only a few hours that life could no longer continue. There is certainly no other function of the lymphatics that can even approach this in importance.

Regulation of Tissue Pressure by the Lymphatic System. Obviously, at the same time that the protein concentration is being regulated in the interstitial fluids, the tissue pressure is also regulated. That is, elevated tissue pressure causes rapid flow of lymph, which in turn reduces the tissue colloid osmotic pressure and also reduces the tissue pressure itself. In this way the tissue pressure is normally kept at the very low level of only a millimeter or so of mercury. However, if the rate of filtration of plasma into the interstitial fluid becomes more than 5 to 10 times normal, then the lymphatics can no longer remove the excess fluid as rapidly as it enters the spaces. Under these conditions the tissue pressure can often rise to as high as 10 to 25 mm. Hg.

EDEMA

Edema means swelling of the tissues with excess fluid, and this excess fluid can be in-side the cells or in the interstitial spaces. Therefore, physiologically, two separate types of edema exist, namely, *extracellular edema* and *intracellular edema.* Intracellular edema rarely occurs in all areas of the body at once but very frequently in localized areas where cells are locally injured. On the other hand, extracellular edema can occur either locally or throughout the body.

Increase in the volume of interstitial fluid distends the interstitial spaces and causes tissue pressure to rise. If the tissue pressure is elevated above approximately 3 to 6 mm. Hg, the cells of the tissue spaces are pushed progressively farther and farther apart, but when the tissue pressure is less than 3 to 6 mm. Hg, the elastic contractile properties of the tissues cause the tissue spaces to contract. In other words, the tissues can resist as much as 3 to 6 mm. Hg tissue pressure without a progressive increase in interstitial volume, but the tissues cannot resist greater pressures than these.

Extracellular Fluid Edema Resulting from Abnormal Capillary Dynamics

From the discussions of capillary and interstitial fluid dynamics in the previous few chapters, it is already evident that several different abnormalities in these dynamics can increase the tissue pressure and in turn cause extracellular fluid edema. The different causes of extracellular fluid edema are discussed below.

Increased Capillary Pressure as a Cause of Edema. Figure 41 shows the effect of increased mean hydrostatic pressure in the capillary on the dynamics of fluid exchange at the capillary membrane. When the mean hydrostatic pressure first becomes abnormally high, more fluid flows out of the capillary than returns into the capillary and, therefore, it collects in the tissue spaces until the tissue pressure rises high

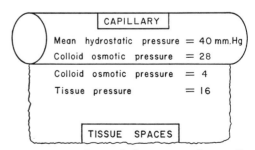

Figure 41. Abnormal dynamics at the capillary membrane resulting from elevated capillary pressure.

enough to balance the excessive level of hydro-static pressure in the capillaries. In Figure 41 the mean capillary pressure is 40 mm. Hg instead of the usual normal 25 mm. Hg. Consequently, in this instance enough fluid flows into the tissue spaces to raise the tissue pressure to 16 mm. Hg. This is far above the 3 to 6 mm. Hg that the elasticity of the tissues can withstand. Therefore, continued elevation of the tissue pressure as high as 16 mm. Hg causes progressive enlargement of the tissue spaces with tremendous expansion of the extracellular fluid volume.

Causes of increased capillary pressure. Increased capillary pressure can result from any clinical condition that causes either venous obstruction or arteriolar dilatation. Large venous blood clots frequently result in local areas of venous obstruction, which blocks the return of blood to the heart and promotes edema in the tissues normally drained by the obstructed veins.

More frequently, capillary pressure is increased by obstruction of venous return due to cardiac failure, for, when the heart no longer pumps blood out of the veins with ease, blood dams up in the venous system. The capillary pressure rises, and serious "cardiac edema" occurs. The precise dynamics of this type of edema are very complicated, however, and will be discussed in detail in Chapter 36.

When arteriolar dilatation occurs in localized areas of the body, blood flows rapidly through the locally dilated arterioles and the capillary pressure increases tremendously. Therefore, local edema results. Such local edema occurs commonly in allergic conditions and in the condition known as "angioneurotic edema." Allergic reactions (discussed in Chapter 14) cause the release of histamine into the tissues, which relaxes the smooth muscle of arterioles. The localized edematous areas that result are called "hives" or *urticaria*.

Angioneurotic edema apparently is caused by localized decrease in arteriolar tone due to abnormal vascular control by the autonomic nervous system. When a person is emotionally upset, such angioneurotic edema frequently occurs in the larynx and causes hoarseness.

Decreased Plasma Proteins as a Cause of Edema. Figure 42 illustrates the abnormal dynamics that occur at the capillary membrane when the quantity of plasma protein falls to abnormally low values. The major effect is a markedly lowered colloid osmotic pressure of the plasma. Consequently, in the capillary the mean hydrostatic pressure far overbalances the colloid osmotic pressure, increasing the tendency for fluid to leave the capillaries and enter the tissue spaces. As a result, fluid collects in the tissue spaces, and the tissue pressure rises. As long as the tissue pressure remains excessively elevated,

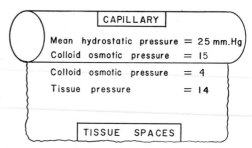

Figure 42. Abnormal dynamics at the capillary membrane resulting from decreased plasma protein.

the tissue spaces continually enlarge, with the edema becoming progressively worse.

Conditions that decrease the plasma protein concentration. Albumin is often lost from the plasma in large quantities when the skin is extensively burned. Therefore, one of the complications of severe burns is not only severe edema in the tissues surrounding the burned area but also edema throughout the body because of the lowered colloid osmotic pressure.

Often large quantities of protein, especially albumin, are lost through the kidneys into the urine in the disease known as *nephrosis*. Sometimes as much as 20 to 30 grams of albumin are lost each day, and the colloid osmotic pressure of the plasma may fall to one-half normal or even less. This results in severe edema, and the edema itself is likely to contribute to death by means that will be discussed later in the chapter.

Finally, persons who do not have sufficient protein in their diets are unable to form adequate quantities of plasma protein and, therefore, are likely to develop protein deficiency edema, which is called *nutritional edema*. This occurs frequently in war-torn areas.

Increased Permeability of the Capillaries as a Cause of Edema. Figure 43 illustrates a capillary whose membrane has become so permeable that even protein molecules pass from the plasma into the interstitial spaces with ease. The protein content of the plasma decreases while that of the interstitial spaces in-

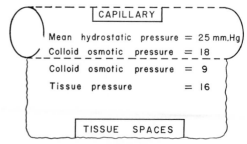

Figure 43. Abnormal dynamics at the capillary membrane resulting from increased permeability of the membrane.

creases. In the example of the figure the tissue pressure rises to 16 mm. Hg in order to balance the changes in plasma and tissue colloid osmotic pressure occasioned by the leakage of protein through the capillary membrane. The elevated tissue pressure in turn causes progressive edema.

Causes of increased capillary permeability. Capillaries become excessively permeable when any factor destroys the integrity of the capillary endothelium. Burns are a frequent cause of increased permeability of the capillaries because over-heated capillaries become friable, and their pores enlarge. Allergic reactions also frequently cause the release of histamine or various polypeptides that damage the capillary membranes and cause increased permeability.

A bacterial toxin produced by *Clostridium oedematiens* can often cause such extreme increase in capillary permeability that plasma loss into the tissues kills the patient within a few hours.

Recently it has been shown that overly increasing the pressure in the capillaries can stretch the capillary walls so greatly that the pores themselves enlarge. This is called the *stretched pore phenomenon.* Even a few minutes of overstretching can cause the condition, and at least 4 to 10 hours are required for the pores to return to normal condition.

Lymphatic Obstruction as a Cause of Edema. A small amount of protein filters continually from the capillaries into the tissue spaces, but this protein cannot be reabsorbed into the circulatory system through the capillary membrane. The only route by which the protein can be returned to the circulatory system is through the lymphatics. If the lymphatic drainage from any area of the body becomes blocked, more and more protein collects in the local tissue spaces until finally the concentration of this protein may approach the concentration of protein in the plasma. As shown in Figure 44, the colloid osmotic pressure of the tissue fluids may rise to as high as 24 mm. Hg, and, to balance this, fluid collects in

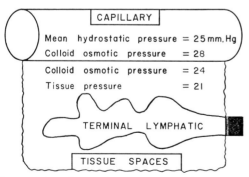

Figure 44. Abnormal dynamics at the capillary membrane resulting from lymphatic obstruction.

the tissues until the tissue pressure rises to a value of 21 mm. Hg. Such elevated tissue pressure very rapidly expands the tissue spaces, with resultant edema of the severest kind.

Causes of lymphatic obstruction. One of the most common causes of lymphatic obstruction is *filariasis*—that is, infection by nematodes of the superfamily Filarioidea. The disease is widespread in the tropics, where larvae (microfilariae) are transmitted to human hosts by mosquitoes. The larvae pass out of the capillaries into interstitial fluid and then by way of the lymph into the lymph nodes. Subsequently inflammatory reactions progressively obstruct the lymphatic channels of these nodes with scar tissue. After several years, the lymphatic drainage from one of the peripheral parts of the body may become almost totally occluded. Thus, a leg can swell to such a size that a single leg might weigh as much as all the remainder of the body. Because of this extreme degree of edema, the swollen condition is frequently called *elephantiasis*. A very interesting type of elephantiasis is that which occasionally occurs in the scrotum, which has been known to enlarge so much that the patient must carry it in a wheelbarrow in order to move about.

Lymphatic obstruction also occurs following operations for removal of cancer. Because the lymph nodes draining a cancerous area of the body must be removed in order to prevent possible spread of the cancer, the return of lymph to the circulatory system from that area will be blocked. Occasionally a radical mastectomy for removal of a cancerous breast causes the corresponding arm to swell to as much as twice its normal size, but usually the swelling regresses during the following two to three months as new lymph channels develop.

Extracellular Edema Caused by Kidney Retention of Fluid. When the kidney fails to excrete adequate quantities of urine, and the person continues to drink normal amounts of water and eat normal amounts of electrolytes, the total amount of extracellular fluid in the body will progressively increase. This fluid is absorbed from the gut into the blood and elevates the capillary pressure a slight amount. This in turn causes most of the fluid to pass into the interstitial fluid spaces, elevating the tissue pressure there as well. As more and more fluid is retained, both the capillary pressure and the tissue pressure rise concurrently, causing an increase especially in tissue fluid but also some increase in plasma volume. Therefore, simple retention of fluids by the kidneys can also result in very extensive extracellular fluid edema. Furthermore, if the retained fluids are mainly water, which contains very few electrolytes, intracellular edema will also result, as was discussed in Chapter 4.

Partition of Injected Saline Between the Plasma and the Interstitial Fluid. Injection of isotonic saline into the blood stream immediately dilutes the plasma so that the colloid osmotic pressure of the plasma falls. The greater the quantity of saline injected, the greater is the fall in plasma colloid osmotic pressure. Also, blood volume increases, and this in turn increases the hydrostatic pressure in the capillaries. Because of these two effects, fluids leave the blood rapidly, the colloid osmotic pressure of the plasma rises once again, the mean hydrostatic pressure of the capillaries falls, and the tissue pressure rises until the outward and inward forces at the capillary membrane are again in equilibrium. However, in the new state of equilibrium the plasma osmotic pressure is lower than normal because the plasma is still diluted with some of the saline. Also, because of increased volumes of fluid in the circulatory system and in the tissues, the mean hydrostatic pressure of the capillaries is higher than normal, and the tissue pressure is also above normal. For every mm. Hg fall in osmotic pressure and rise in mean hydrostatic pressure within the capillaries, the tissue pressure rises the same amount in order to oppose these factors. Also, when the new state of equilibrium is reached, the quantity of fluid leaving the arterial ends of the capillaries to enter the tissue spaces once again equals the quantity of fluid leaving the tissue spaces to re-enter the venous ends of the capillaries.

When relatively small quantities of saline are injected into the circulatory system, these are partitioned between the plasma and the interstitial fluid so that approximately four fifths of the injected fluids enter the tissue spaces within a few minutes and approximately one fifth remains in the circulatory system.

Deleterious Effects of Extracellular Fluid Edema

The purpose of the interstitial fluids is to transport nutrients from the blood to the cells and to transport excreta from the cells back to the blood. Therefore, it is normally valuable that the quantity of interstitial fluid be maintained at a minimum so that rapid transfer of these substances can occur. When extracellular fluid edema develops, the distances that nutrients and excreta must travel increase markedly, and nutrition of the cells may suffer greatly. Often a patient with severe edema of the leg, for instance, actually develops gangrene of the skin owing to the poor nutrition, and the muscles of edematous legs are usually very painful during exercise.

Edema occasionally causes severe damage because of mechanical compression of localized areas of the body. For instance, edema of the brain can compress the blood vessels against the cranium until blood flow is actually cut off. This in turn causes death of the neurons and, ultimately, of the patient. Also, severe edema in the abdomen can make it difficult for the diaphragm to descend, with the result that respiration is depressed.

Edema of the lungs can increase the thickness of the alveolar walls so greatly that oxygen cannot easily be absorbed into the blood, and this causes anoxia of the tissues with resultant death.

Yet, despite these detrimental effects of edema, patients frequently live with rather severe edema for many years.

Inflammatory Edema—Intracellular and Extracellular

When cells are damaged in a localized area of the body, several different effects occur. First, damage to the cells themselves is likely to cause autolysis of organic substances within the cell. Also, the sodium pump at the cell membrane often becomes inoperative, causing large amounts of sodium to collect inside the cell. Both of these effects increase the osmotic pressure in the cells tremendously, so that one of the most common effects of cellular damage is swelling of the cells themselves.

Damaged cells also release a number of toxic substances into the surrounding interstitial fluids. Some of these substances attack the local capillaries to make them become very permeable, and others cause the protein that diffuses into the lymphatics to coagulate. Therefore, in addition to the swelling of the cells, inflammation increases the extracellular fluids in the inflamed area as a result of both increased capillary permeability and lymphatic blockage.

"Brawny" Edema versus "Pitting" Edema. The swelling of inflammation is so hard that pressure over the swollen area does not distort the tissues. Therefore, the edema of inflammation or edema caused by other types of intracellular swelling is called "brawny" edema, which means hard edema. On the other hand, an area of edema caused by the presence of excess interstitial fluid is not resistant to pressure, but, instead, the skin can be compressed, the edema fluid flowing from the compressed area into the surrounding tissue spaces. The reason this is possible is that the tissue spaces are greatly enlarged, and fluid can flow with ease between the cells. When the pressure is removed, a pit remains where the pressure was applied, but fluid flows back into the pitted area within 15 to 20 seconds, and the pit is then no longer observed. As a result of this phenomenon, extraceullular fluid edema is usually referred to clinically as "pitting" edema.

REFERENCES

Abdou, I. A., Reinhardt, W. O., and Tower, H.: Plasma protein, equilibrium between blood and lymph protein. *J. Biol. Chem., 194:*15, 1952.

Acevedo, D.: Motor control of the thoracic duct. *Am. J. Physiol., 139:*600, 1943.

Allen, L.: Volume and pressure changes in terminal lymphatics. *Am. J. Physiol., 123:*3, 1938.

Cope, O., and Rosenfield, L.: The lymphatic system. *Ann. Rev. Physiol., 8:*297, 1946.

Crandall, L. A., Jr., Barker, S. B., and Graham, D. G.: Study of lymph flow from patient with thoracic duct fistula. *Gastroenterology, 1:*1040, 1943.

Cressman, R. D., and Blalock, A.: The effect of the pulse upon the flow of lymph. *Proc. Soc. Exp. Biol. & Med., 41:*140, 1939.

Drinker, C. K.: The lymphatic system. *Ann. Rev. Physiol., 7:*389, 1945.

Drinker, C. K.: The Lymphatic System. Stanford University, Stanford University Press, 1942.

Forder, L. L., Chaikoff, I. L., and Reinhardt, W. O.: Circulation of plasma proteins; their transport to lymph. *J. Biol. Chem., 197:*625, 1952.

Guyton, A. C.: Physiological basis of the different types of clinical edema. *Mississippi Doctor, 29:*92, 1951.

Irisawa, A., and Rushmer, R. F.: Relationship between lymphatic and venous pressure in leg of dog. *Am. J. Physiol., 196:*495, 1959.

LeBrie, S. J., and Mayerson, H. S.: Influence of elevated venous pressure on flow and composition of renal lymph. *Am. J. Physiol., 198:*1037, 1960.

McMaster, P. D.: Conditions in the skin influencing interstitial fluid movement, lymph formation and lymph flow. *Ann. N. Y. Acad. Sc., 46:*743, 1946.

McMaster, P. D.: Lymphatics. *Harvey Lect., 37:*227, 1942.

McMaster, P. D.: The lymphatic system. *Ann. Rev. Physiol., 5:*207, 1943.

Moyer, J. H., and Fucks, M.: Edema: Mechanisms and Management. Philadelphia, W. B. Saunders Co., 1960.

Rabin, E. R., and Meyer, E. C.: Cardiopulmonary effects of pulmonary venous hypertension with special reference to pulmonary lymphatic flow. *Circ. Res., 8:*324, 1960.

Ritchie, H. D., Grindlay, J. H., and Bollman, J. L.: Flow of lymph from the canine liver. *Am. J. Physiol., 196:*105, 1959.

Smith, R. O.: Lymphatic contractibility. *J. Exp. Med., 90:*497, 1949.

Starling, E. H.: The influence of mechanical factors on lymph production. *J. Physiol., 16:*224, 1894.

Wasserman, K., and Mayerson, H. S.: Exchange of albumin between plasma and lymph. *Am. J. Physiol., 165:*15, 1951.

Watkins, A. L., and Fulton, M. N.: The effect of fluids given intraperitoneally, intravenously and by mouth on the volume of thoracic duct lymph in dogs. *Am. J. Physiol., 122:*281, 1938.

Webb, R. L.: Lymphatic system. *Ann. Rev. Physiol., 14:*315, 1952.

White, A.: The lymphatic system. *Ann. Rev. Physiol., 11:*355, 1949.

Yoffey, J. M., and Courtice, F. C.: Lymphatics, Lymph and Lymphoid Tissue. Cambridge, Harvard University Press, 1956.

See also Chapter 5, Capillary exchange; Chapter 7, The special fluid systems.

The Special Fluid Systems of the Body—

Cerebrospinal, Ocular, Pleural,

Pericardial, Peritoneal, and Synovial

Several special fluid systems exist in the body, each one performing functions peculiar to itself. For instance, the cerebrospinal fluid supports the brain in the cranial vault, the intraocular fluid maintains distention of the eyeballs so that the optical dimensions of the eye will remain constant, and the potential spaces, such as the pleural and pericardial spaces, provide lubricated chambers in which the internal organs can move. All of these fluid systems have characteristics that are similar to each other and that are also similar to those of the other interstitial fluid system. However, they are also sufficiently different that they require special consideration.

THE CEREBROSPINAL FLUID SYSTEM

The entire cavity enclosing the brain and spinal cord has a volume of approximately 1650 ml., and between 100 and 200 ml. of this volume is occupied by cerebrospinal fluid. This fluid, as shown in Figure 45, is found in the ventricles of the brain, in the cisterns around the brain, and in the subarachnoid space around both the brain and the spinal cord. All these chambers are connected with each other, and the pressure of the fluid is regulated at a very constant level.

Cushioning Function of the Cerebrospinal Fluid

The major function of the cerebrospinal fluid is to cushion the brain within its solid vault. Were it not for this fluid, any blow to

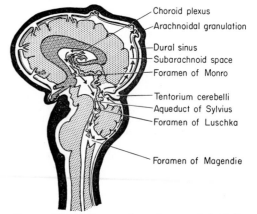

Figure 45. Pathway of cerebrospinal fluid flow. (Modified from Ranson and Clark: Anatomy of the Nervous System.)

Choroid plexus
Arachnoidal granulation
Dural sinus
Subarachnoid space
Foramen of Monro
Tentorium cerebelli
Aqueduct of Sylvius
Foramen of Luschka
Foramen of Magendie

the head would cause the brain to be juggled around and severely damaged. However, the brain and the cerebrospinal fluid have approximately the same specific gravity, so that the brain simply floats in the fluid. Therefore, blows on the head move the entire brain simultaneously, causing no one portion of the brain to be momentarily contorted by the blow.

Contrecoup. When a blow to the head is extremely severe, it usually does not damage the brain on the side of the head where the blow is struck but, instead, on the opposite side. This phenomenon is known as "contrecoup," and the reason for this effect is the following: When the blow is struck, the fluid on the struck side is so incompressible that as the skull moves the fluid pushes the brain at the same time. However, on the opposite side the sudden movement of the

pulls any excess fluid whatever into the space, this fluid automatically washes the protein immediately into the lymphatics and back into the blood stream. Loss of the protein reduces the osmotic pressure, and the space remains in a collapsed state.

Altered Capillary Dynamics as a Cause of Increased Pressure and Fluid in the Potential Spaces. Any one of the abnormal changes that can occur in capillary dynamics to cause extracellular edema, as described in the previous chapter, can also cause increased pressure and fluid in the potential spaces. Thus, *increased capillary permeability, increased capillary pressure, decreased plasma colloid osmotic pressure,* and *blockage of the lymphatics* from a potential space can all cause swelling of the space. The fluid that collects is usually called a *transudate* if it is not infected, and an *exudate* if it is infected. Excessive fluid in the peritoneal space, one of the spaces most prone to develop extra fluid, is called *ascites*.

One of the most common causes of swelling in a potential space is *infection.* White blood cells and other debris caused by the infection block the lymphatics, resulting in (1) buildup of protein in the space, (2) increased colloid osmotic pressure, and (3) consequent failure of fluid reabsorption.

The Pleural Cavity

Figure 53 shows specifically the diffusion of fluid into and out of the pleural cavity at the parietal and the visceral pleural surfaces. This occurs in precisely the same manner as in the usual tissue spaces, except that a very porous serous membrane, the *pleura,* is interspersed between the capillaries and the pleural cavity.

Large numbers of lymphatics drain from the mediastinal and lateral surfaces of the parietal pleura, and with each expiration the intrapleural pressure rises, forcing small amounts of fluid into the lymphatics; also the respiratory movements alternately compress the lymphatic vessels, promoting continuous flow along the lymphatic channels.

Maintenance of a Negative Pressure in the Pleural Cavity. The visceral pleura of the lungs continually absorbs fluid with considerable "absorptive force." This is caused by the low capillary pressure—about 5 to 10 mm. Hg—in the pulmonary system. In contrast to this low pressure, the plasma

proteins exert about 28 mm. Hg colloid osmotic pressure, causing an absorption pressure at the visceral pleura of approximately 20 mm. Hg at all times. As a result, the pressure in the intrapleural space remains negative at all times, averaging —4 mm. Hg, and it is this negative pressure that keeps the lungs from collapsing.

The Pericardial Cavity

The space around the heart operates with essentially the same dynamics as those of the pleural cavity. The pressure in the pericardial cavity, like that in the pleural cavity, is negative, averaging —4 mm. Hg. Here again, during expiration as well as during the positive thrust of the heart, the pericardial pressure often rises to a positive value, forcing excess fluid into lymphatic channels of the mediastinum.

The Peritoneal Cavity

The peritoneal cavity of the abdomen is subject to the same fluid dynamics as are the other potential spaces; fluid is filtered into the peritoneal space through the serosa and is also absorbed through the serosa. However, the peritoneal cavity is more susceptible to the development of excess fluids than most of the other cavities because the capillary pressure in the visceral peritoneum is higher than elsewhere in the body. This is caused by the resistance to portal blood flow through the liver. The extra resistance offered by the liver frequently results in the formation of *ascites* in pathological states of the liver, such as *cirrhosis, carcinoma,* or *portal vein obstruction,* which impede portal flow.

Numerous, very large lymphatic channels lead from the peritoneal cavity, especially from the lower surface of the diaphragm. With each diaphragmatic movement relatively large quantities of lymph flow out of the peritoneal cavity into the thoracic duct. This can be shown very effectively by injecting radioactive red blood cells into the abdomen. Large proportions of these cells, still in the whole form, are found in the blood within 10 to 20 minutes. Occasionally, however, carcinomatosis spreads so widely through the abdomen that it blocks the lymphatics, thereby preventing return of protein to the blood. As a result, the colloid osmotic pressure also rises and ascites ensues.

The Synovial Cavities

The joint cavities and the bursae are known as *synovial cavities*. The synovial membrane has been said not to be a true membrane at all but only a collection of fibrous tissue that lines the surface between the interstitial spaces and the cavities. For this reason these cavities might be considered to be nothing more than enlarged tissue spaces. However, the synovial cavities do contain large amounts of mucin, much more than normally present in the interstitial fluids. The origin of this is not known, though presumably it is secreted by the surrounding connective tissue cells.

In the synovial cavities, as in the other potential spaces, excess proteins are likely to collect, and these must be returned to the circulatory system through the lymphatics; otherwise the space will swell. Since the synovial membrane offers little or no barrier to the transfer of fluid into surrounding tissues, the protein likewise can flow into the lymphatics of the area.

After movements the pressure in joint cavities often falls to as low as −8 to −10 mm. Hg. This decrease probably results from the following mechanism: Compression of the cavities during movement presumably forces fluid out of the cavity into the interstitial spaces or into the lymphatics. Subsequent release of the compression then leaves a deficiency of fluid in the cavity so that negative pressure develops.

REFERENCES

Allen, L., and Weatherford, T.: Role of fenestrated basement membrane in lymphatic absorption from peritoneal cavity. *Am. J. Physiol., 197:*551, 1959.

Ascher, K. W.: The Aqueous Veins. Springfield, Illinois, Charles C Thomas, 1960.

Bakay, L.: The Blood-Brain Barrier. Springfield, Illinois, Charles C Thomas, 1956.

Baker, L., Puestow, R. C., Kruger, S., and Last, J. H.: Estimation of ascitic fluid volume. *J. Lab. & Clin. Med., 39:*30, 1952.

Bering, E. A., Jr.: Cerebrospinal fluid production and its relationship to cerebral metabolism and cerebral blood flow. *Am. J. Physiol., 197:*825, 1959.

Ciba Foundation, Symposia Volumes: Cerebrospinal Fluid: Production, Circulation and Absorption. Boston, Little, Brown and Company, 1958.

Courtice, F. C., and Simmonds, W. J.: Physiological significance of lymph drainage of serous cavities and lungs. *Physiol. Rev., 34:*419, 1954.

Davson, H.: Physiology of the Ocular and Cerebrospinal Fluids. Boston, Little, Brown and Co., 1956.

Davson, H., and Luck, C. P.: Chemistry and rate of turnover of the ocular fluids of the bush baby. *J. Physiol., 145:*433, 1959.

Davson, H., and Spaziani, E.: The blood-brain barrier and the extracellular space of brain. *J. Physiol., 149:*135, 1959.

Davson, H., and Spaziani, E.: The fate of substances injected into the anterior chamber of the eye. *J. Physiol., 151:*202, 1960.

de Vincentiis, M.: Further contributions to the study of the formation of the aqueous humour after paracentesis. *J. Physiol., 146:*252, 1959.

Edstrom, R. F., and Essex, H. E.: Swelling of damaged brain tissue. *Neurology, 5:*490, 1955.

Field, E. J., and Brierly, J. B.: The lymphatic connexions of the subarachnoid space. *Brit. M.J., 1:* 1167, 1948.

Grant, W. M.: Physiological and pharmacological influences upon intraocular pressure. *Pharmacol. Rev., 7:*143, 1955.

Josiah Macy, Jr., Foundation: Glaucoma. Transactions of the Fourth (1959) Conference. New York, Josiah Macy, Jr., Foundation, 1960.

Langham, M. E.: Aqueous humor and control of intra-ocular pressure. *Physiol. Rev., 38:*215, 1958.

McKee, F. W., Yuile, C. L., Lamson, B. G., and Whipple, G. H.: Albumin and globulin circulation in experimental ascites. Relative rates of interchange between plasma and ascitic fluid studied with C^{14} labeled proteins. *J. Exp. Med., 95:*161, 1952.

Perkins, E. S.: The effect of adenosine triphosphate on the intra-ocular pressure of rabbits. *J. Physiol., 147:*419, 1959.

Ropes, A. W., and Bauer, W.: Synovial Fluid Changes in Joint Disease. Cambridge, Harvard University Press, 1953.

Scholz, R. O., Cowie, D. B., and Wilde, W. S.: Studies on physiology of eye using tracer substances; steady-state ratio of sodium between plasma and aqueous humor in guinea pig. *Am. J. Ophth., 30:*1513, 1947.

Simer, P. H.: Drainage of pleural lymphatics. *Anat. Rec., 113:*269, 1952.

Stein, H. A., Wakim, K. G., and Rucker, C. W.: In vivo studies on the choroidal circulation of rabbits. *A.M.A. Arch. Ophth., 56:*726, 1956.

Sugar, H. S.: The Glaucomas. 2nd ed., New York, Paul B. Hoeber, 1957.

Swann, H. G.: The physiologic constrictions in the ocular veins. *Am. J. Ophth., 38:*845, 1954.

Sweet, W. H., Silverstone, B., Soloway, S., and Stetten, D., Jr.: Studies of formation, flow and absorption of cerebrospinal fluid: II. Studies with heavy water in normal man; in Surgical Forum, 1950. Philadelphia, W. B. Saunders Co., 1951, p. 376.

Waitzman, Morton B.: ATP-stimulated adenylic acid deaminase activity at site of aqueous humor production. *Am. J. Physiol., 198:*665, 1960.

See also Chapter 6, The lymphatics.

Chapter 8

Formation of Urine by the Kidney

The kidneys perform two major functions: first, they excrete the end-products of bodily metabolism and, second, they control the concentrations of most of the constituents of the body fluids. The purpose of the present chapter is to discuss the principles of urine formation and especially to discuss the mechanisms by which the kidneys excrete the end-products of metabolism.

Physiologic Anatomy of the Kidney

Each kidney is an aggregation of about 1,000,000 nephrons, each one of which is capable of forming urine by itself. Therefore, in most instances, it is not necessary to discuss the entire kidney but merely the activities in the single nephron in order to explain the function of the kidney.

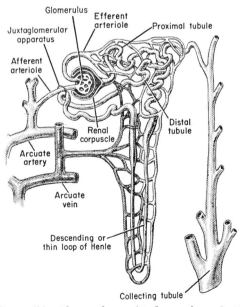

Figure 54. The nephron. (Redrawn from Smith: The Kidney. Oxford University Press.)

The nephron, which is illustrated in Figure 54, may be described as follows: Blood enters the *glomerulus* of the nephron through the *afferent arteriole* and then leaves the glomerulus through the *efferent arteriole.* The glomerulus is a network of up to 50 parallel capillaries encased in *Bowman's capsule,* in which fluid collects as it filters from the capillaries. After blood passes into the efferent arteriole from the glomerulus, most of it then flows through the *peritubular capillary network* surrounding the tubules of the nephrons and finally back into the veins, though part of it passes through capillary shunts that bypass the tubules.

The fluid that filters through the glomerulus into Bowman's capsule flows first into the *proximal tubule,* from there into a *thin segment* also called the *loop of Henle,* then into the *distal tubule,* and finally into the *collecting tubule,* which collects fluid from the distal tubules of many nephrons. As this fluid flows through the tubules, most of its water and some of its solutes are reabsorbed into the peritubular capillaries; the water and the solutes that are not reabsorbed become urine.

The Juxtaglomerular Apparatus. At the point at which the distal tubule touches the afferent arteriole, shortly before finally emptying into the collecting tubule, the tubular cells and some of the surrounding cells are excessively proliferated. It has been postulated that this structure, which is known as the *juxtaglomerular apparatus,* might have either an endocrine function or some function for controlling blood flow through the afferent arteriole, though such has never been proved.

Functional Diagram of the Nephron. Figure 55 illustrates a simplified diagram of the "physiologic nephron." This diagram contains all the nephron's functional struc-

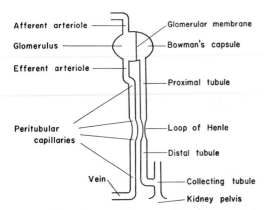

Figure 55. Schematic diagram of the "physiologic nephron."

tures, and it will be used in the present discussion to explain renal function.

Rate of Blood Flow through the Kidneys

The average blood flow through both kidneys of a 70 kg. man is approximately 1200 ml. per minute, but this varies between 500 and 1500 ml. per minute from one person to another and also in the same person from time to time.

A small proportion of the renal blood flow passes directly from the renal arteries into the veins through arteriovenous shunts ("Trueta shunts") by-passing the glomeruli and peritubular capillary plexuses. However, not more than a small percentage of the total renal blood flow is shunted in this manner. Instead, almost all the blood passes first through the glomeruli and then either through the peritubular capillary plexuses or directly into the veins.

The Renal Fraction. The portion of the total cardiac output that passes through the kidneys is called the *renal fraction*. With a basal cardiac output of 5000 ml. per minute and a blood flow through the kidneys of approximately 1200 ml. per minute, the normal renal fraction is approximately 24 per cent, but this also varies from 10 to 30 per cent, even in normal persons.

The tremendous fraction of the cardiac output that flows through the kidneys emphasizes the importance of these organs for continually removing end-products of metabolism from the body fluids and for controlling the electrolyte composition of these fluids.

Regulation of Blood Flow through the Kidneys

The afferent arterioles of the kidneys and the efferent arterioles to a less extent have well-developed smooth muscle walls which are highly innervated by sympathetic nerves. Strong stimulation of the sympathetic nerves diminishes blood flow through the kidneys almost to zero. Yet, in the normal resting person the degree of sympathetic activity is ordinarily insignificant. On the other hand, when excessive blood flow is needed elsewhere in the body, such as in the muscles during severe exercise, sympathetic stimulation can greatly diminish renal blood flow, allowing the blood to be shunted through the areas requiring increased flow. This is of great value to the momentary function of the body and does not seriously reduce the effectiveness of the kidneys; one can go as long as several hours without renal function and not suffer serious consequences.

Effect of Arterial Pressure on Renal Blood Flow—Autoregulation. The solid curve of Figure 56 illustrates the effect of increasing the arterial pressure when the kidneys have not been isolated from the body but are still intact. In this instance the blood flow increases progressively for each mm. rise in arterial pressure.

The dashed curve of Figure 56 illustrates

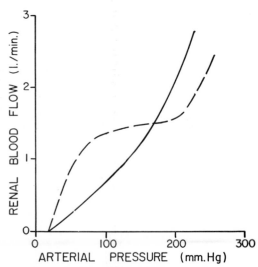

Figure 56. Effect of arterial pressure on renal blood flow. The solid curve represents normal function of the intact kidneys as extrapolated from dog experiments. The dashed curve depicts autoregulation which occurs in the isolated kidney.

the effect of arterial pressure on blood flow through the isolated kidney. This shows that, between the limits of 80 and 200 mm. Hg arterial pressure, increasing the arterial pressure increases renal blood flow very little. This phenomenon occurs even when the sympathetic nerves to the kidneys have been removed, indicating that it is an intrinsic *autoregulation* of blood flow similar to that observed in most other tissues of the body, as will be discussed in Chapter 28. Unfortunately, the mechanism of this in the case of the kidneys is not yet understood.

Thus, even though much has been written on the subject of autoregulation of blood flow in the kidneys, it is doubtful that it occurs except in perfusion experiments. In more than one hundred experiments in our laboratory we have never observed autoregulation until the tissues around the kidneys are stripped away; then it occurs every time, a strange phenomenon yet unexplained and still of doubtful importance to the normal function of the kidneys.

THE GLOMERULAR FILTRATE

The Glomerular Membrane and Nature of the Glomerular Filtrate

The fluid that filters through the glomerular membrane into Bowman's capsule is called *glomerular filtrate*, and the membrane of the glomerular capillaries is called the *glomerular membrane*. Though, in general, this membrane is similar to that of other capillaries throughout the body, it has several differences. First, it has three major layers: (1) the endothelial layer of the capillary itself, (2) a basement membrane, and (3) a layer of epithelial cells that line the surfaces of Bowman's capsule. Yet, despite the greater number of layers, the number of pores is believed to be about 25 times as great as in the usual capillary, covering as much as 5 per cent of the total surface area. The maximal size of the pores, though, is probably almost identical with that of the usual capillary. Therefore, functionally, the glomerular membrane is almost identical with other capillary membranes throughout the body, except that it is far more porous and consequently allows much more rapid filtration of water and dissolved substances.

Composition of Glomerular Filtrate. The glomerular filtrate has almost exactly the same composition as the fluid that leaks from the arterial ends of the capillaries into the interstitial fluids. It contains no red blood cells and less than 0.03 per cent protein, or less than 1/200 of the protein in the plasma.

The electrolyte and crystalloid composition of glomerular filtrate is also similar to that of the interstitial fluid. Because of the Donnan equilibrium, which was discussed in Chapter 4, the concentration of anions, including chloride and bicarbonate, is about 5 per cent higher in glomerular filtrate than in plasma; and the concentration of cations is about 5 per cent lower. However, the non-ionized crystalloidal substances, such as urea, creatinine and glucose, are not subject to Donnan equilibrium so that their concentrations are identical with those in plasma.

To summarize, for all practical purposes, glomerular filtrate is the same as plasma except that it has no significant amount of proteins.

The Glomerular Filtration Rate

The total quantity of glomerular filtrate formed each minute in all nephrons of both kidneys is called the *glomerular filtration rate*. In the normal person this averages approximately 125 ml./min., however, in different normal functional states of the kidneys, it can vary from as little as a few ml. to as high as 200 ml./min. To express this differently, the total quantity of glomerular filtrate formed each day is about 180 liters, or more than two times the total weight of the body. Over 99 per cent of the filtrate is usually reabsorbed in the tubules, the remainder passing into the urine, which will be explained below.

The Filtration Fraction. The filtration fraction is the fraction of the renal plasma flow that becomes glomerular filtrate. Since the normal plasma flow through both kidneys is 650 ml. per minute and the normal glomerular filtration rate in both kidneys is 125 ml., *the average filtration fraction is approximately 125/650, or 19 per cent.* Here again, this value can vary tremendously, both physiologically and pathologically.

Dynamics of Glomerular Filtration

Glomerular filtration occurs in almost exactly the same manner that fluid filters out of any high pressure capillary in the body. That is, *hydrostatic pressure inside the glomerular capillaries* causes bulk flow of fluid through the capillary pores into Bowman's capsule. On the other hand, *colloid osmotic pressure in the blood and hydrostatic pressure in Bowman's capsule* oppose the filtration. Ordinarily, the amount of protein in Bowman's capsule is very slight, but, if this ever becomes increased to a significant amount, its colloid osmotic pressure would obviously also be active at the glomerular membrane, promoting increased flow of fluid through the membrane.

Glomerular Pressure. The glomerular pressure is the average pressure in the glomerular capillaries. This unfortunately has never been measured either by direct or indirect means. Yet, on the basis of physiological experiments, estimates can be made. *A reasonable average value can be considered to be 70 mm. Hg,* though, as will be noted below, this can increase or decrease considerably under varying conditions.

Pressure in Bowman's Capsule. In lower animals, pressure measurements have actually been made in Bowman's capsule and at different points along the renal tubules by inserting micropipettes into the lumen. On the basis of these studies, *capsular pressure in the human being is estimated to be 20 mm. Hg.*

Colloid Osmotic Pressure in the Glomerular Capillaries. Because approximately one fifth of the plasma in the capillaries filters into the capsule, the protein concentration increases about 20 per cent as the blood passes from the arterial to the venous ends of the glomerular capillaries. If the normal colloid osmotic pressure of blood entering the capillaries is 28 mm. Hg, then it will rise to approximately 36 mm. Hg by the time the blood reaches the venous ends of the capillaries, and the average colloid osmotic pressure will be about 32 mm. Hg. (See Figure 36, in Chapter 5, which shows the relationship between protein concentration and colloid osmotic pressure.)

Filtration Pressure. The filtration pressure is the net pressure forcing fluid through the glomerular membrane, and this is *equal to the glomerular pressure minus the sum of glomerular colloid osmotic pressure and capsular pressure.* In Figure 57A *the normal filtration pressure is shown to be about 18 mm. Hg.*

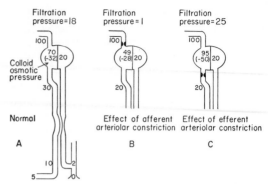

Figure 57. (A) normal pressures at different points in the nephron, and the normal filtration pressure, (B) effect of afferent arteriolar constriction on the pressures in the nephron and on the filtration pressure, (C) effect of efferent arteriolar constriction on the pressures in the nephron and on the filtration pressure.

Regulation of Glomerular Filtration Rate

The rate at which glomerular filtrate is formed is directly proportional to the filtration pressure. Therefore, any factor that changes the filtration pressure also changes the filtration rate.

Factors That Alter Glomerular Pressure. *Regulation by the afferent and efferent arterioles.* Afferent arteriolar constriction decreases the rate of blood flow into the glomerulus and thereby decreases the glomerular pressure and the filtration rate. This effect is illustrated in Figure 57B. Conversely, dilatation of the afferent arteriole increases the glomerular pressure, with a corresponding increase in glomerular filtration rate.

Constriction of the efferent arteriole increases the resistance to outflow from the glomeruli and consequently increases the glomerular pressure and usually the glomerular filtration rate as well. However, if the degree of efferent arteriolar constriction is very severe, the blood flow through the glomerulus may become very sluggish. Then, because the plasma remains for a long period of time in the glomerulus and extra large quantities of filtrate are lost into the capsule, the plasma colloid osmotic pressure rises to excessive heights, causing glomerular filtration to fall paradoxically to a very low value despite the elevated glomerular pressure.

In mild sympathetic stimulation of the kidneys, the afferent and efferent arterioles constrict approximately proportionately to each other so that the glomerular filtration rate neither rises nor falls. This allows blood flow to be shunted from the kidneys to other parts of the body during emergency states without significantly altering renal function. With strong sympathetic stimulation, however, this is not the case, because the afferent arterioles then become constricted much more than the efferent arterioles, thereby greatly reducing the filtration rate. Also, blood flow becomes so stagnant that the plasma colloid osmotic pressure in the glomerulus rises very high; this, too, markedly decreases the glomerular filtration rate. Thus, strong sympathetic stimulation reduces renal function, sometimes to the vanishing point.

Effect of arterial pressure on glomerular filtration rate. An increase in arterial pressure normally increases the glomerular pressure almost as much as the arterial pressure itself rises, and, as a result, the glomerular filtration rate greatly increases. Conversely, a fall in arterial pressure always decreases the filtration rate. When the arterial pressure falls to about 60 mm. Hg, the filtration pressure becomes zero, causing the filtration rate also to become zero and the output of urine to cease completely.

Effect of changes in plasma colloid osmotic pressure. Any effect that increases or decreases plasma protein concentration can modify glomerular filtration rate by changing the colloid osmotic pressure—the higher the colloid osmotic pressure the less the filtration rate, and the lower the colloid osmotic pressure the greater the filtration rate. For instance, after large quantities of water are drunk, the consequent dilution of the body fluids can at times change the plasma colloid osmotic pressure as much as 2 to 3 mm. Hg; this in turn can increase the glomerular filtration rate as much as 10 to 15 per cent. However, this is an insignificant amount compared to the many hundred per cent change in glomerular filtration rate that can result from afferent and efferent arteriolar constriction or from changes in arterial pressure.

TUBULAR REABSORPTION

Flow of Glomerular Filtrate through the Tubules, and Pressures in the Tubules. The glomerular filtrate formed in Bowman's capsule flows into the proximal tubule, through the loop of Henle, the distal tubule, the collecting duct, and finally into the pelvis of the kidney. In its course through the tubules almost all the water and very large proportions of the solutes are reabsorbed from the filtrate. Approximately 87 per cent of the fluid is reabsorbed in the proximal tubules and 12 per cent in the distal tubules, 1 per cent or less remaining to pass into the urine. Thus, about 8 times as much fluid flows into the proximal ends of the tubules as into the loop of Henle and more than 100 times as much as finally becomes urine. If reabsorption of water and solutes did not occur from the tubular fluid, the body would become so depleted of certain substances within a few hours that death would result.

A pressure gradient exists along the tubules, beginning with a pressure of approximately 20 mm. Hg in Bowman's capsule and ending with a pressure of approximately 2 mm. Hg in the renal pelvis. Most of this decrease occurs in the loop of Henle and distal tubules, probably for the following reason: The interstitial pressure in the spaces around the tubules, when measured by micropuncture techniques, is usually about 20 mm. Hg. This pressure probably keeps the thin segment of the loop of Henle, and perhaps also the distal tubules, in a collapsed state and causes a high resistance to flow. On the other hand the higher pressure in the proximal tubules keeps them distended and keeps their intraluminal pressure equal to that in the interstitial fluid.

Active Reabsorption of Solutes from the Tubules

Active reabsorption means transport of a substance through the tubular epithelium as the result of chemical processes in the cells. This is in contradistinction to *passive reabsorption*, which means the transport entirely by diffusion. In general, for each type of solute that is of particular value to the body, a special active, reabsorptive mechanism is present in the tubular wall.

The precise mechanism of active absorption is not known in the case of any single substance. However, many different experiments have shown the general mechanism to be basically that illustrated in Figure 58. Substance S in the tubule diffuses into the brush border of the epithelial cells and,

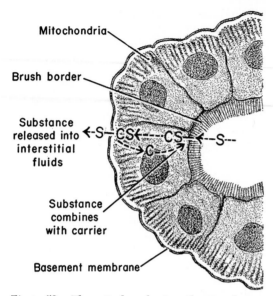

Mitochondria

Brush border

Substance
released into ←-S—CS←----CS—←--S---
interstitial   →-C--→
fluids

Substance
combines
with carrier

Basement membrane

Figure 58. Theoretical mechanism of active absorption from the tubule. S is the substance being absorbed and C is the carrier.

either at the surface of the cell or somewhere near the surface, combines with carrier C. This reaction is promoted by a specific enzyme in the epithelial cell. The combination of carrier and transported substance, CS, then diffuses to the opposite pole of the epithelial cell where additional enzymatically catalyzed reactions cause removal of substance S and its extrusion into the interstitial fluids. The carrier in turn rediffuses to the lumenal pole of the cell where it can be used again for transport, the process continuing over and over again.

Energy Required for Active Reabsorption. A very important feature of active reabsorption is that it can occur even against an unfavorable concentration gradient. That is, even when the concentration of the substance is greater in the interstitial fluids than in the tubules, the substance nevertheless can still be removed from the tubule. This is analogous to compressing air in an enclosed chamber. To effect the compression, force must be applied and must be moved through a given distance; and force times distance is energy. The changing from a dilute solution to a concentrated solution is actually a process of compression, but the energy here is provided by the tubular cells and must be provided by metabolic reactions in the cells, as described in Chapter 2.

The total amount of energy that must be expended for active reabsorption depends on the total quantity of substances that must be reabsorbed and especially on the amount that must be absorbed against a concentration gradient. Approximately 1200 grams of sodium pass into the glomerular filtrate each day, and all except a few grams of this are actively reabsorbed. This substance alone usually accounts for at least one half of the total "load" of substances that must be actively reabsorbed, and the magnitude of its reabsorption emphasizes how important active reabsorptive processes are to the function of the kidney. To provide all this energy, the rate of oxygen consumption and consumption of other nutrients by the tubular cells is almost as great as that by any other cells in the body.

Reabsorption of Specific Substances Needed for Metabolism. Among the more important substances that are actively reabsorbed by the tubules are *glucose, other related monosaccharides,* essentially all the *amino acids, aceto-acetic acid,* and *protein.* In this list will be noted essentially all the constituents of plasma that are important for metabolic functions of the cells. For instance, glucose and aceto-acetic acid are two of the major sources of energy for the cells, while the amino acids can be used either for energy or as building blocks in the synthesis of new proteins or other chemical compounds. In addition, any whole protein that filters into the tubules can also be reabsorbed. It is believed that the protein is actually "engulfed" through the brush border of the cell and when inside is digested into amino acids which are then transported on into the interstitial fluids. This process is called *athrocytosis.* Also, when hemoglobin enters the tubular fluid following hemolysis of red blood cells in the circulation, it, too, can be reabsorbed up to a limited quantity.

The active processes for reabsorbing glucose, amino acids, and all the other metabolically important substances are so effective that essentially none of them normally appears in the urine, thus illustrating how tenaciously the kidney conserves these substances.

Variable Reabsorption of Electrolytes. One of the functions of the kidney is to regulate the concentrations of most of the different electrolytes in the extracellular fluid, including especially *sodium, potassium, calcium, magnesium, chloride, bicarbonate, phosphate,* and *sulfate ions.* Each person ingests variable quantities of these electrolytes along with his food. Therefore, to regulate their concentrations in the body fluids, the kidneys must also excrete variable quantities of each. Special regulatory systems alter the ability of the tubules to reabsorb each one of them in proportion to their need in the body. As an example, if the concentration of sodium is very low in the body fluids, the adrenal gland secretes large quantities of aldosterone, which in turn causes marked reabsorption of sodium from the tubules. These regulatory mechanisms of extracellular fluid concentration are so important that they will be considered at length in the following chapter. Suffice it to say at the present time that the rates of reabsorption of most of the different electrolytes are very carefully regulated to maintain precise extracellular fluid concentrations.

Participation of the Proximal Tubules, Loop of Henle, and Distal Tubules in Active Reabsorption. Fluid has been collected through micropipettes from different segments of the tubules of lower animals. From chemical analyses we know generally the locus of reabsorption of some substances from the tubules but not of all of them.

In general, most of the metabolically important substances, including glucose, the amino acids, protein, and aceto-acetic acid, are reabsorbed in the proximal tubules (see Glucose, Figure 59). On leaving the proximal tubules, the tubular fluid contains essentially none of these substances.

Of the different electrolytes, it is known that sodium can be actively reabsorbed by

all portions of the tubules, and potassium can be actively reabsorbed by the proximal tubules but probably not by the distal tubules. The locus of active reabsorption of each of the other electrolytes is poorly, if at all, known. One of the reasons it has been difficult to determine the locus of active reabsorption of electrolytes is that active reabsorption of one ion frequently causes *diffusion* of an ion of opposite electrical charge through the same membrane to maintain electrical neutrality, and experimental methods presently available cannot always differentiate between diffusion and active absorption.

Reabsorption by Diffusion—Passive Reabsorption of Water and Electrolytes

In addition to active reabsorption of solutes from the tubules, some solutes and probably all the water are reabsorbed by the process of diffusion. This is also called *passive reabsorption* because no active chemical processes are involved.

In general, the tubules, especially the proximal tubules, are very permeable to water, hence water can diffuse with ease into the interstitial fluid. Every time a solute is actively reabsorbed, the osmolar concentration of the tubular fluid is temporarily decreased, while the osmolar concentration of the interstitial fluid is increased. As a result, water is pulled by osmosis through the membrane, "following" the solute. It is in this manner that most, if not all, of the water is reabsorbed from the tubules.

Reabsorption by diffusion can also occur as a result of electrostatic forces at the tubular membrane. For instance, active reabsorption of sodium ions, each one of which carries a positive charge, builds up a positive potential on the interstitial side of the tubular membrane. This in turn attracts anions through the membrane. Much of the chloride in the tubular fluid is probably reabsorbed by this means. The chloride then creates an osmotic force that draws still more water along with it.

In summary, passive reabsorption by the process of diffusion generally occurs secondarily to active reabsorption. That is, active reabsorption first moves some of the solutes through the membrane, and this creates either an osmotic or an electrostatic

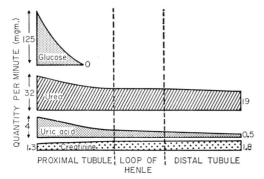

Figure 59. Quantities of nonelectrolytes still remaining in each portion of the kidney tubules, showing variable reabsorption of the different substances.

force that causes diffusion of water or other substances through the membrane. Probably all, or almost all, the reabsorbed water is absorbed by this means, and perhaps as much as one third to one half of the electrolytes.

Poor Reabsorption of Urea and Other Metabolic End-Products

Approximately 25 grams of urea and several grams of uric acid, creatinine, and other end-products of metabolism are formed in the body each day. Since these would eventually block the metabolic processes if they remained in the extracellular fluids, one of the most important functions of the kidney is to remove them as they are formed.

The tubules are only slightly permeable to *urea*, and only 40 per cent is reabsorbed during the entire passage through the tubules. This is only a small amount of reabsorption in comparison with the average of 99.4 per cent reabsorption of water. Therefore, large amounts of urea remain in the tubules to be excreted in the urine, whereas most of the water, electrolytes, and nutrients in the glomerular filtrate are returned to the blood and thus conserved for further use in the body.

Creatinine is not reabsorbed at all by the tubules, which means that all that enters the glomerular filtrate passes on into the urine. *Uric acid* also is poorly reabsorbed, and large portions of it, too, pass on into the urine. However, for reasons not completely understood, the uric acid concentration of the extracellular fluids is regulated at a fairly constant value, and, when needed, small amounts can even be actively reabsorbed. Despite this the reabsorption of uric acid is almost always 10 or more times less than the reabsorption of water, so that it becomes considerably concentrated in the urine.

In summary, then, the end-products of metabolism are either of no use or of little use to the function of the body. For this reason it is valuable that the tubules do not reabsorb these substances to a great extent but instead allow them to pass on into the urine. Indeed, this is the whole basis of renal function—reabsorption of those substances from the tubules that are needed by the body and purposeful failure to reabsorb those substances which need to be removed from the body.

TUBULAR SECRETION

In addition to active reabsorption, the tubules are also capable of active secretion, but of different substances from those actively absorbed. The only difference between the processes of active reabsorption and active secretion is the direction in which the transport mechanism operates. That is, in secretion the substance is transported from the interstitial side of the epithelial cells to the tubular side. In both instances the chemical reactions are catalyzed by specific enzymes in the cells.

In the human being active tubular secretion is not nearly so important as it is in certain lower order animals. Indeed, in some fishes the nephron has no glomerulus at all, and all urinary excretion occurs by tubular secretion. However, in the human being this process is also important especially for secretion of hydrogen ions and potassium as well as certain drugs.

Tubular Secretion of Hydrogen Ions. Large amounts of acid are formed in the body each day by the metabolic processes. Unless acids are continually removed by the kidneys, they collect in the body fluids, and acidosis results. Fortunately, the distal tubules of the kidney secrete large quantities of hydrogen ions, thus maintaining normal acid-base balance in the fluids. The details of this mechanism will be presented in Chapter 10, which considers the whole problem of acid-base balance.

Tubular Secretion of Potassium. Though very large amounts of potassium are normally reabsorbed in the proximal tubules, the distal tubules, paradoxically, are capable of secreting potassium. This special secretion by the distal tubules prevents the potassium concentration from becoming excessive in the extracellular fluids. Reabsorption of potassium in the proximal tubules is not precisely regulated, but simply follows along with the reabsorption of sodium, water, and other substances. If the extracellular fluid concentration of potassium becomes too high, the kidney automatically decreases this by simply secreting the extra amount into the distal tubules.

Tubular Secretion of Creatinine and Drugs.

Creatinine, which was mentioned above as one of the end-products of metabolism, not only is not reabsorbed by the tubules but is also actively secreted by the proximal tubules. In this way additional creatinine, besides that which enters the tubules by way of the glomerular filtrate, passes into the urine. This, however, is mainly of academic interest because the amount of creatinine secretion is relatively slight.

The proximal tubules also secrete certain drugs whenever these are present in the extracellular fluids. The most important of these are penicillin, phenolsulfonthalein, para-aminohippuric acid, and Diodrast. In the case of penicillin, active secretion makes it somewhat difficult to maintain adequate concentrations of the drug in the body fluids during therapy. Administration of a second drug, Benemid, can poison the carrier system for tubular secretion of penicillin and thereby make it easier to maintain a high concentration. Phenolsulfonthalein, para-aminohippuric acid, and Diodrast are frequently used to assess the tubular function of the kidneys, and the latter two are also used to estimate the rate of plasma flow through the kidneys, as will be described later in the chapter.

SUMMARY OF NEPHRON FUNCTION

Figure 60 illustrates a summary of the overall function of the nephron. Approximately 1200 ml. of blood flow through all the nephrons of both kidneys each minute, and, from this, 125 ml. of glomerular filtrate are formed. This has almost exactly the same composition as normal, protein-free interstitial fluid, with a pH of 7.4. As the glomerular filtrate passes through the proximal tubules, about 87 per cent of the water is reabsorbed and, usually, all the metabolically important substances, glucose, amino acids, protein, and aceto-acetic acid.

By the time the fluid leaves the proximal tubule, an average of only 16 ml. per minute remains, and in its passage through the loop of Henle and distal tubules variable reabsorption of many different substances occurs. For instance, large or small amounts of sodium may be reabsorbed, and large or small amounts of chloride ion, bicarbonate ion, phosphates, and even water may be transported back into the blood. The rates of reabsorption of these substances are individually regulated by specific control mechanisms aimed at maintaining normal electrolyte and osmotic concentrations in the extracellular fluids. In addition to the variable reabsorption of these substances, variable secretion of hydrogen and potassium ions can also occur; this, too, is regulated in accordance with the needs of the extracellular fluids.

On the average about 15/16 of the remaining 16 ml. of fluid is reabsorbed in the loop of Henle, distal tubules, and collecting ducts so that finally only 1 ml. passes into the urine each minute. A large proportion of the metabolic end-products that enter the glomerular filtrate fail to be reabsorbed and are still present in the fluid that becomes urine, though, unfortunately, small amounts of these may have been inadvertently reabsorbed.

By the time the urine has been formed, those substances needed by the body in general will have been reabsorbed from the glomerular filtrate, while those substances not needed by the body will have mostly issued forth in the urine. Water itself is one of the substances most needed by the body, and approximately 99.4 per cent of that which had entered the glomerular filtrate will have been reabsorbed, thus allowing only a small amount of water loss each day despite the very large loss of metabolic end-products.

Because of variable reabsorption of different solutes and water in the loop of Henle, distal tubules, and collecting ducts, the osmotic pressure of the urine may be as little as one-sixth that of plasma or as great as 4 times that of plasma. The mechanisms for controlling this variable reabsorption of different substances and their function in regulating extracellular fluid concentration will be presented in detail in the following chapter.

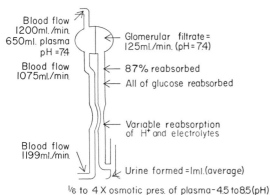

Blood flow 1200ml./min. 650ml. plasma pH =7.4

Glomerular filtrate = 125ml./min. (pH = 7.4)

Blood flow 1075ml./min.

87% reabsorbed

All of glucose reabsorbed

Variable reabsorption of H^+ and electrolytes

Blood flow 1199ml./min.

Urine formed =1ml.(average)

1/6 to 4 X osmotic pres. of plasma-4.5 to8.5(pH)

Figure 60. Summary of nephron function.

Urine Composition—Concentrating Power of the Kidney

Table 7 gives the concentrations of different substances in the glomerular filtrate and in the urine. It will be noted that many of the substances normally are of essentially the same concentration in both plasma and urine, including especially sodium, calcium, chloride, and bicarbonate ions. However, the concentrations of the metabolically important substances, such as glucose, are high in the glomerular filtrate but zero in the urine. On the other hand, the end-products of metabolism are present in very high concentrations in the urine in comparison with the plasma.

The last column of Table 7 gives the "concentrating power" of the kidney for different substances. Thus, the concentrating power for urea is about 70-fold and that for creatinine about 140-fold, while the concentrating power for the two drugs, Diodrast and PAH, may be as high as 500- to 600-fold. This column of the table illustrates the ability of the kidney to discharge selectively certain substances while retaining others. It is this concentrating power of the kidney that al-lows it to retain water while still excreting large quantities of unwanted substances into the urine.

EFFECT OF TUBULAR "LOAD" ON URINE FORMATION

Plasma Load and Tubular Load. The *plasma load* of a substance means the total amount of the substance in the plasma that passes through the kidney each minute. For instance, if the concentration of glucose in the plasma is 100 mg. per 100 ml., and 600 ml. of plasma pass through both kidneys each minute, then the plasma *load of glucose* will be 600 mg./min.

Normally a fraction of the plasma load filters into the glomeruli, and this portion is called the *tubular load*. In the above example, if 125 ml. of glomerular filtrate are formed each minute with a glucose concentration of 100 mg. per cent, then the tubular load of glucose will be 100 mg. times 1.25, or 125 mg. of glucose per minute. Similarly,

Table 7.   Relative Concentrations of Substances in the Glomerular Filtrate and in the Urine

	Glomerular Filtrate (125 ml./min.)		Urine (1 ml./min.)		Conc. Urine/ Conc. Plasma (Plasma Clearance per Minute)
	Quantity/min.	Concentration	Quantity/min.	Concentration	
Na$^+$	17.7 mEq.	142 mEq./l.	0.128 mEq.	128 mEq./l.	0.9
K$^+$	0.63	5	0.06	60	12
Ca^{++}	0.5	4	0.0048	4.8	1.2
Mg^{++}	0.38	3	0.015	15	5.0
Cl$^-$	12.9	103	0.134	134	1.3
HCO$_3^-$	3.5	28	0.014	14	0.5
H$_2$PO$_4^-$ HPO$_4^{--}$	0.25	2	0.05	50	25
SO$_4^{--}$	0.09	0.7	0.033	33	37
Glucose	125 mg.	100 mg.%	0 mg.	0 mg.%	0.0
Urea	33	26	18.2	1820	70
Uric acid	3.8	3	0.42	42	14
Creatinine	1.4	1.1	1.96	196	140
Inulin	....	....	....	....	125
Diodrast	....	....	....	....	560
PAH	....	....	....	....	585

Table 8. Loss of Water Each Day, in Milliliters

	Normal Temperature	Hot Weather	Prolonged Heavy Exercise
Insensible Loss:			
Skin	350	350	350
Lungs	350	250	650
Urine	1400	1200	500
Sweat	100	1400	5000
Feces	200	200	200
Total	2400	3400	6700

from the body under different conditions. Normally, at an atmospheric temperature of around 68 degrees, approximately 1400 ml. of the 2400 ml. of water intake is lost in the *urine*, 100 ml. is lost in the *sweat*, and 200 ml. in the *feces*. The remaining 700 ml. is lost by *evaporation through the lungs* or by *diffusion through the skin*.

Insensible water loss. Loss of water by diffusion through the skin and by evaporation from the lungs is known as *insensible water loss* because the person does not know that he is actually losing water at the time that it is leaving the body.

The average loss of water by diffusion through the skin is approximately 300 to 400 ml. per day; this amount is lost even in a person who is born with congenital lack of sweat glands. In other words, the water molecules actually diffuse through the cells of the skin themselves and are not secreted by the sweat glands. Fortunately, the cornified layer of the skin acts as a protector against still much greater loss of water by diffusion. However, when the cornified layer becomes denuded, such as after extensive burns, the rate of evaporation can increase to as much as 3 to 5 liters each day.

The water loss from the lungs varies with the vapor pressure of the air. All air that enters the lungs becomes totally saturated with moisture, to a vapor pressure of approximately 47 mm. Hg, before it is expelled. If the air entering the lungs already has a vapor pressure of 47 mm. Hg, no water whatsoever will be lost. However, this condition can occur only when the relative humidity is 100 per cent and the air temperature is at least equal to that of the body—which is a very unusual atmospheric state. The usual vapor pressure of the atmospheric air is far less than 47 mm. Hg,

so that the average water loss through the lungs is about 300 to 400 ml. per day. Also, the vapor pressure normally decreases with decreasing temperature so that the loss is greatest in very cold and least in very warm weather. This explains the dry feeling in the lungs and respiratory passages in cold weather.

Loss of water in hot weather and during exercise. In very hot weather, water loss in the sweat is occasionally increased to as much as 3½ liters an hour, which obviously can rapidly deplete the body fluids. Sweating will be discussed in detail in Chapter 71.

Exercise increases the loss of water in two ways: First, it increases the rate of respiration, which promotes increased water loss through the lungs in proportion to the increased ventilatory rate. Second, and much more important, exercise increases the body heat and consequently is likely to result in excessive sweating.

RENAL REGULATION OF EXTRACELLULAR FLUID VOLUME

Hormonal Regulation of Sodium and Water Reabsorption as a Means of Regulating Extracellular Fluid Volume

The extracellular fluid volume can be increased *by either aldosterone or antidiuretic hormone.* Any stimulus which results in the secretion of antidiuretic hormone causes an increase in extracellular fluid volume because of water retention. Any stimulus which increases aldosterone secretion results in sodium retention, which is followed secondarily by a sequence of events that causes water reabsorption: (a) the osmolarity of the extracellular fluid increases, (b) this causes increased secretion of antidiuretic hormone, (c) this results in water reabsorption with consequent increased extracellular fluid volume. This latter mechanism, involving both of these hormones, is one of the most important of all the regulators of extracellular fluid volume, because decreased extracellular fluid volume is a potent initiator of aldosterone secretion, as described earlier in the chapter. Therefore, a decrease in extracellular fluid volume initiates a sequence of hormonal events, beginning with aldosterone secretion, that automatically return the extracellular fluid volume to normal. Conversely, excess extracellular fluid volume depresses aldosterone secretion and reduces the extracellular fluid volume again toward normal.

Hemodynamic Regulation of Extracellular Fluid Volume—Effect of Arterial Pressure on Urine Output

When the *arterial pressure decreases* to a very low value as a result of hemorrhage, acute cardiac failure, or any other cause, the output of urine immediately decreases, sometimes to the point of complete anuria. The principal cause of this is the greatly decreased glomerular pressure, which results in diminished or even zero glomerular filtration. This conservation of fluid by the kidneys causes the extracellular fluid volume to increase as the person drinks more fluid and eats more salt, which in turn helps to return the arterial pressure to normal.

On the other hand, an increase in extracellular fluid volume tends very slightly to increase the arterial pressure, and this then increases the urinary output. This mechanism, too, can act as a feedback control system to help regulate the extracellular fluid volume—that is, to decrease the extracellular fluid volume toward normal. But, since the pressure changes in this instance are very small, the importance of the effect is doubtful.

Effect of the Cardiovascular and Renal Reflexes on the Regulation of Extracellular Fluid Volume

Usually, when the extracellular fluid volume increases, the blood volume also increases. This in turn can initiate cardiovascular reflexes as a result of increased arterial or venous pressures. For instance, elevated arterial pressure excites the *pressoreceptors* in the walls of the arteries, and these cause reflex inhibition of the sympathetic nervous system throughout the body. In turn, the decrease of sympathetic impulses to the kidneys allows the renal blood flow and urinary output to increase, thus reducing the extracellular fluid volume. That is, an increase in arterial pressure automatically reduces the extracellular fluid volume, and this effect then tends to return the arterial pressure also to normal. All the arterial pressure reflexes that have been studied, including the pressoreceptor reflexes and the central nervous system ischemic reflex, have been shown to have this renal effect. Indeed, the CNS ischemic reflex is so powerful that it can alter renal output as much as 100-fold between the limits of zero excitation and maximum excitation. All these reflexes will be discussed in Chapter 32.

Volume Receptors. It has also been claimed that an increase in the distention of the left atrium can promote renal loss of fluid even when the pressures elsewhere in the circulatory system are not increased. The stretch receptors in the left atrial walls, therefore, have been called *volume receptors*. It is probable that these are part of the entire circulatory reflex system, which causes homeostasis of extracellular fluid volume, blood volume, and vascular pressures.

The volume receptors are also believed to initiate hypothalamic reflexes that lead to decreased aldosterone and antidiuretic hormone secretion. This variation of the mechanism could also reduce the extracellular fluid volume.

Summary of Renal Regulation of Extracellular Fluid Volume

Though all the facets of extracellular fluid volume regulation are not known, nevertheless, the above mechanisms and possibly still others all work together to maintain a normal extracellular fluid volume. The known mechanisms include (1) hormonal reflexes which can cause varying degrees of fluid retention or fluid loss, (2) direct effect of arterial pressure and renal blood flow on renal output, and (3) cardiovascular reflexes that effect increases or decreases in extracellular fluid volume. Utilizing all these mechanisms, *the extracellular fluid volume is normally regulated to almost exactly* that amount which barely keeps the interstitial fluid spaces filled. However, it is even more important that the blood volume be regulated very exactly than that the extracellular fluid volume be so regulated. When there is a conflict between these two, the blood volume continues to be regulated within narrow limits while the extracellular fluid volume can change greatly, sometimes resulting in very extensive edema. Some conditions that result in edema were discussed in Chapter

6, and further relationships between blood volume and extracellular fluid volume regulation will be discussed in Chapter 34.

THIRST

The phenomenon of thirst is equally as important for regulating the extracellular fluid volume as the renal mechanisms discussed above, for at least some water continues to be lost from the body all of the time and must be replenished. Indeed, even when the kidneys reduce their output of urine to the minimal amount required to rid the body of urea and other necessary excretory products, the urine volume still amounts to about 400 ml. per day, which is called the *obligatory urinary volume*. Therefore, persons who have deficient thirst mechanisms or who become unconscious or paralyzed and cannot respond to the desire for water will become progressively dehydrated. A definition of thirst is the *inner consciousness of the desire to drink*.

Causes of Thirst

Many of the same factors that promote fluid retention by the kidneys also cause thirst. These include especially *extracellular dehydration* and *cardiac failure*, but in addition to these two, *intracellular dehydration* and *dryness of the mouth* can also result in thirst.

Effect of Extracellular Dehydration on Thirst. In experiments designed to elucidate the mechanism of thirst, the extracellular fluid volume has been reduced in many different ways. Included among these have been hemorrhage, water deprivation until dehydration of all fluid compartments occurs, and administration of diuretic drugs to cause very rapid loss of extracellular fluid through the kidneys. In all these instances an animal greatly increases its rate of drinking or the human being develops an intense thirst, which also makes him seek water.

An especially interesting type of extracellular dehydration which causes thirst is that which occurs when an animal is maintained for long periods of time on a low salt intake. In such an instance the osmolar concentration of the extracellular fluids falls very low, and the extracellular fluid volume also decreases, sometimes to as little as two-thirds normal. In such instances the animal begins to drink large volumes of water, but unless sodium chloride is available in the water he will not restore normal extracellular fluid volume, and his excessive drinking continues on and on. Yet, it disappears immediately when an adequate amount of sodium chloride is placed in his water to return the extracellular fluid volume to normal. This illustrates that it is low extracellular fluid volume and not lack of water alone that is important for initiating thirst.

Effect of hemorrhage and cardiac failure on thirst. A small amount of hemorrhage ordinarily will not cause thirst, but this also almost never reduces the cardiac output and does not in any other way impair the circulatory system. However, when hemorrhage is sufficient that the circulation of blood is greatly embarrassed, experimental animals and human beings do experience intense desire for water. This same effect also occurs in *acute cardiac failure*, in which the circulatory system is compromised in much the same way as following hemorrhage.

Intracellular Dehydration as a Cause of Thirst. At times the extracellular fluid volume is completely normal, but the intracellular fluid volume is markedly decreased. This, too, will cause thirst. For instance, injection of hypertonic sodium chloride or hypertonic sucrose solution, which will cause osmotic removal of water from the intracellular fluid compartment, induces immediate and intense thirst within a matter of seconds. The subject normally drinks a sufficient amount of water to reduce the extracellular fluid osmolarity to normal, which allows normal amounts of water to return to the cells.

It should be noted particularly that thirst *is not caused by hyperosmolarity* of the extracellular and intracellular fluids unless a concomitant change occurs in one of the two volumes. This illustrates once again that thirst is concerned more with fluid volumes than with their osmolar concentrations.

Relation of Dryness of the Mouth to Thirst. Almost everyone is aware of the fact that a dry mouth is often associated with thirst. A partial explanation of this is that a dry mouth also is often associated with extracellular and intracellular dehydration. Yet, when a drug such as atropine is given to a person to prevent salivation, his extracellular and intracellular fluid volumes may remain entirely normal, and yet his mouth becomes dry. Under these conditions the dryness of the mouth can promote sensations in the mouth that cause the person to drink water. However, these sensations are not the same as thirst, though they do cause the same result.

The Relief of Thirst

Obviously, the way to relieve thirst is to correct the abnormality which is causing it. For instance, if the abnormality is extracellular dehydration, the correction would be to provide the subject with both water and sufficient salt to keep the water in the extracellular fluid compartment. If the thirst results from both extracellular and intracellular fluid dehydration, water alone will relieve the thirst. Since this is the usual cause of thirst in our normal daily life, the thirst mechanism ordinarily operates as a feedback control system for maintaining normal fluid volumes in both the extracellular and intracellular fluid compartments.

Temporary Relief of Thirst Caused by the Act of Drinking. A thirsty person receives relief from his thirst immediately after drinking water even before the water has been absorbed from the gastrointestinal tract. In fact, in persons who have esophageal fistulae (a condition in which the water never goes into the gastrointestinal tract) relief of thirst will still occur following the act of drinking, but this relief will be only temporary and will return after 15 minutes or more. If the water does enter the gut, however, distention of the upper gastrointestinal tract, particularly the stomach, provides still further temporary relief of thirst. For instance, simple inflation of a balloon in the stomach can relieve thirst for 5 to 30 minutes.

One might wonder what the value of this temporary relief of thirst could be, but there is a very good reason for its occurrence as follows: After a person has drunk water, as long as a half hour to an hour may be required for the water to be absorbed into the extracellular fluids. Were his thirst sensations not temporarily relieved following the drinking of water, he would continue to drink more and more. When all this water should finally become absorbed, his body

fluid volumes would be far greater than normal, and he would have created a condition opposite to that which he was attempting to correct. It is well known that a thirsty animal never drinks more than the amount of water needed to relieve his state of dehydration but ordinarily will drink almost exactly the right amount. Were he to overdrink, the extra water, on later passing into the urine, would carry a moderate amount of electrolytes out of his body fluids. For an animal with a very limited amount of electrolytes in its diet this might be catastrophic.

Neural Integration of Thirst—The "Drinking" Center

A very exact point called the *drinking center* has been localized in each side of the hypothalamus, lateral and caudal to the supraoptic nuclei. This center is illustrated in Figure 68. Electrical stimulation of the drinking center by implanted electrodes will cause an animal to begin drinking within a few seconds and to continue drinking until the electrical stimulus is stopped. Also, injection of hypertonic salt solutions into the area, which causes osmosis of water out of the neuronal cells and results in intracellular dehydration, will also cause drinking.

It is especially interesting that the drinking center is located in close proximity to the supraoptic nuclei that promote antidiuresis. That is, these closely associated areas of the brain promote simultaneously both increased intake of water and decreased output of water in the urine.

Basic Stimulus for Exciting the Drinking Center. In the above discussion of the many factors affecting thirst it was pointed out that *extracellular dehydration, intracellular dehydration,* and *circulatory failure* can all promote thirst. Furthermore, the *act of drinking* and *fullness of the gastrointestinal tract* can inhibit thirst. It is almost certain that the latter two of these, the act of drinking and fullness of the gastrointestinal tract, excite peripheral sensory receptors that transmit impulses into the drinking center to cause this reaction. However, the other three stimuli seem to affect the neurons of the drinking center directly, and it is possible to explain all their effects on the basis of one single stimulus, namely, *intracellular dehydration*. For instance, extracellular de-

drogen ion is secreted through the cell membrane into the tubule.

The precise mechanism by which hydrogen ions are finally secreted through the cell membrane is not known. However, this process can continue until the concentration of hydrogen ions in the tubules becomes as much as 800 times that in the extracellular fluid or, in other words, until the pH of the tubular fluids falls to approximately 4.5. This represents a limit to the ability of the tubular epithelium to secrete hydrogen ions.

To secrete hydrogen ions against such a tremendous concentration gradient requires large amounts of energy, as was explained in relation to the active transport of other substances through membranes in Chapter 3. For this reason, any poison that reduces the ability of the epithelial cells to utilize energy from nutrients can also reduce or totally block the secretion of hydrogen ions.

Exchange of Hydrogen Ions with Sodium and Other Cations. When a hydrogen ion is secreted into the tubule, a sodium ion or possibly one of the other cations in the tubular fluid, potassium, calcium, or magnesium, is usually absorbed into the epithelial cell and transported into the extracellular fluid. Here again, the precise mechanism by which the sodium is absorbed is not known, but *it is coupled with the secretion of hydrogen, one sodium ion being reabsorbed for every hydrogen ion* secreted. The coupling of these reactions is also illustrated in Figure 73.

Regulation of Hydrogen Ion Secretion by the Carbon Dioxide Concentration in the Extracellular Fluid. Since the chemical reactions for secretion of hydrogen ions begin with carbon dioxide, the greater the carbon dioxide concentration in the extracellular fluid, the more rapid will the reactions proceed, and the greater becomes the rate of hydrogen ion secretion. Therefore, any factor that increases the carbon dioxide concentration in the extracellular fluids, such as decreased respiration or increased metabolic rate, will also increase the rate of hydrogen ion secretion. Conversely, any factor that decreases the carbon dioxide, such as excess pulmonary ventilation or decreased metabolic rate, will decrease the rate of hydrogen ion secretion.

At normal carbon dioxide concentrations, the rate of hydrogen ion secretion is about 3.5 millimols per minute, but this rises or falls directly in proportion to any changes in extracellular carbon dioxide.

Interaction of Bicarbonate Ions with Hydrogen Ions in the Tubules

Bicarbonate ion is continually being filtered through the glomerular membrane into the glomerular filtrate, and this usually is in combination with sodium ions, or, to a less extent, with other cations of the extracellular fluid. When the sodium and bicarbonate ions reach the point in the tubules where hydrogen ions are being secreted, the sodium is absorbed in the interchange for hydrogen ions, and the hydrogen combines with the bicarbonate to form carbonic acid, as illustrated in Figure 73. This carbonic acid in turn dissociates into carbon dioxide and water; most of the carbon dioxide then diffuses through the epithelial cells back into the extracellular fluids while the water passes into the urine. Thus, *if plenty of hydrogen ions are available, the bicarbonate ion* is completely removed from the tubules so that none remains to pass into the urine. However, if we now note in Figure 73 the chemical reactions that are responsible for formation of hydrogen ions in the epithelial cells, we will see that along with the formation of hydrogen ions bicarbonate ions are also created. These diffuse out of the epithelial cells into the extracellular fluids in combination with the sodium ions that have been absorbed from the tubule.

The net effect of all these reactions is the following: For each bicarbonate ion that reacts with a hydrogen ion in the tubules, one sodium ion is absorbed and one bicarbonate ion is secreted into the extracellular fluid. This amounts simply to an absorption process for sodium bicarbonate, though the bicarbonate ion that enters the interstitial fluid with the sodium is not the same bicarbonate ion that had been in the tubular fluid.

Balance between Hydrogen Ion Secretion and Bicarbonate Ion Filtration by the Glomerulus

One of the factors that can affect the amount of bicarbonate ions entering the tubules each minute is the plasma bicarbonate concentration. Figure 74 illustrates the relative amounts of hydrogen ions and bicarbonate ions entering the tubules each minute when the carbon dioxide concentration of the body fluids remains normal but the bicarbonate concentration varies. The rate of hydrogen ion secretion is constant while, on the other hand, the bicarbonate ion entering the tubules changes in proportion to the plasma bicarbonate ion concentration. Any one of the following three conditions can prevail: (1) When the plasma bicarbonate concentration is 28 mM./l., hydrogen ion secretion and bicarbonate ion filtration normally exactly balance each other and neutralize each other. (2) When the plasma bicarbonate concentration is less than 28 mM./l., an excess of hydrogen ion secretion and hydrogen ion loss into the urine occurs, which is denoted by the area shaded with small dots. (3) When the bicarbonate concentration is greater than 28 mM./l., more bicarbonate than hydrogen ions will enter the tubules so that bicarbonate will be lost in the urine, which is denoted by the area shaded with heavy dots.

The significance of this balance between hydrogen ions and bicarbonate ions is the following: *In acidosis the ratio of carbon dioxide to bicarbonate ion concentration in the extracellular fluids is always greater than normal* (see the Henderson-Hasselbalch equation, Number 11), which means that in acidosis there will always be an excess of

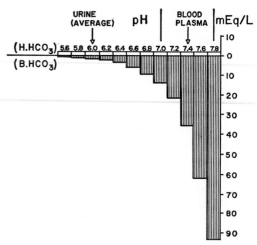

Figure 75. Relationship of bicarbonate ion concentration in the urine to the pH of the urine. (Redrawn from Gamble: Chemical Anatomy, Physiology and Pathology of Extracellular Fluid. Harvard University Press.)

hydrogen ions secreted, and these are carried into the urine. Since the extracellular fluid loses the hydrogen ions, this mechanism acts as an automatic system to decrease the hydrogen ion concentration whenever it rises too high.

Conversely, *in alkalosis, the ratio of dissolved carbon dioxide to bicarbonate ion in the extracellular fluids is always less than normal.* Therefore, bicarbonate ion will enter the tubules in excess of hydrogen ion, and this excess will be lost directly into the urine. In this way the alkaline half of the bicarbonate buffer system is reduced, allowing the body fluids to become more acidic. Here again, the mechanism acts as an automatic regulator of hydrogen ion concentration in the extracellular fluid, this time to increase the hydrogen ion concentration whenever it falls too low.

Figure 75 illustrates the rapid increase in bicarbonate excretion in the urine as the extracellular fluid becomes progressively more alkaline.

Transport of Excess Hydrogen Ions from the Tubules into the Urine

When excess hydrogen ions are secreted into the tubules, they must continually combine with other substances in the tubules; otherwise their concentration would soon

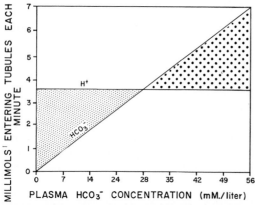

Figure 74. Relationship between hydrogen ion secretion and bicarbonate ion filtration. The area shaded with small dots represents excess hydrogen ions entering the tubules. The area shaded with large dots represents excess bicarbonate ions entering the tubules.

rise so high (the pH would fall below 4.5) that further secretion of hydrogen ions would cease. Two distinct mechanisms exist by which the hydrogen ions are transported from the tubules: first, by combination with the buffers of the tubular fluid and, second, by combination with ammonia secreted by the tubular epithelium.

Combination of Excess Hydrogen Ions with Tubular Buffers. The principal buffer in the tubular fluid (besides the bicarbonate buffer, which has already been discussed above) is the phosphate buffer. The quantity of Na_2HPO_4 in the glomerular filtrate is normally about four times as great as that of NaH_2PO_4. Excess hydrogen ions entering the tubules combine with the Na_2HPO_4, as illustrated in Figure 76, form-

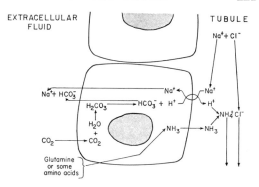

Figure 77. Secretion of ammonia by the tubular epithelial cells, and reaction of the ammonia with hydrogen ions in the tubules.

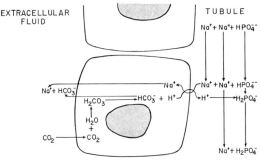

Figure 76. Chemical reactions in the tubules involving hydrogen ions, sodium ions, and the phosphate buffer system.

ing NaH_2PO_4, which passes on into the urine. Thus, sodium is liberated and is absorbed from the tubules in place of the hydrogen ion involved in the reaction. The sodium that is absorbed combines with the bicarbonate ion formed in the process of secreting hydrogen ions. Thus, the net effect of this reaction is to increase the amount of sodium bicarbonate in the extracellular fluids, which is the kidney's way of making the extracellular fluids more alkaline.

Ammonia Secretion by the Tubular Epithelium. Another mechanism for transporting hydrogen ions from the tubules to the exterior is to combine them with ammonia. The tubular epithelial cells continually synthesize ammonia and secrete this into the tubules. The ammonia then reacts with hydrogen ions, as illustrated in Figure 77, forming ammonium ions that are excreted into the urine in combination with chloride or other tubular anions.

This mechanism for removal of hydrogen ions from the tubules is especially important because most of the anions of the tubular fluid are chloride. Only a very few hydrogen ions could be transported into the urine in direct combination with chloride, because hydrochloric acid is a very strong acid, and the tubular pH would rapidly fall to the critical value of 4.5 so that further hydrogen ion secretion would cease. However, when hydrogen ions combine with ammonia and the resulting ammonium ions then combine with chloride, the pH does not fall significantly because ammonium chloride is a neutral salt.

Sixty per cent of the ammonia secreted by the tubular epithelium is derived from *glutamine,* and the remaining 40 per cent from asparagine or different ones of the amino acids. Ammonia is secreted continually as long as the tubular fluids are acidic. If the tubular fluids remain highly acidic for long periods of time, the secretion of ammonia steadily increases during the first two to three days, rising as much as 10-fold. For instance, immediately after acidosis begins, as little as 30 millimols of ammonia might be secreted each day, but after two days as much as 200 millimols can be secreted, illustrating that the ammonia-secreting mechanism can adapt very readily to handle greatly increased loads of acid elimination.

Summary of Renal Regulation of Hydrogen Ion Concentration

To summarize the net effects of the reactions discussed above, we find the follow-

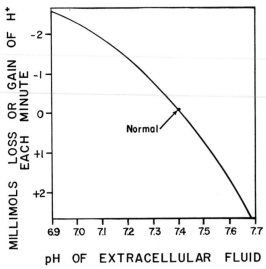

Figure 78. Effect of extracellular fluid pH on the rate of loss or gain of hydrogen ions in the body each minute.

ing: First, when the rate of hydrogen ion secretion into the tubules exactly equals the filtration of bicarbonate ion, the two neutralize each other, and nothing happens to the hydrogen ion concentration in the extracellular fluids. Second, when the hydrogen ion secretion is in excess of bicarbonate filtration, no bicarbonate ion will be lost at all into the urine, but hydrogen ions will be lost, which shifts the pH of the body fluids toward the alkaline side. Third, when the filtration of bicarbonate ions is greater than the secretion of hydrogen ions, large quantities of sodium bicarbonate fail to be reabsorbed by the tubules and are lost into the urine; this decreases the sodium bicarbonate concentration in the extracellular fluids and thereby shifts the pH toward the acidic side.

In turn, it is the pH of the extracellular fluid which determines the balance between hydrogen ion secretion and bicarbonate ion filtration into the tubules. The lower the pH, the greater becomes the ratio of dissolved carbon dioxide to bicarbonate ion in the extracellular fluids, which increases the relative ratio of hydrogen ion secretion to bicarbonate ion filtration, leading rapidly to correction of the acidotic condition. Conversely, in alkalosis, the ratio of bicarbonate filtration to hydrogen ion secretion becomes very great, causing very rapid sodium bicarbonate loss into the urine with consequent correction of the alkalosis.

Rapidity of Acid-Base Regulation by the Kidneys. Figure 78 illustrates the effect of extracellular fluid pH on the rate at which hydrogen ions will be lost or gained from the body fluids each minute, illustrating that at a pH of 7.0 approximately 2.3 millimols of hydrogen ions will be lost each minute, but as the pH returns toward normal the rate of loss falls off markedly. Then, when the pH becomes significantly greater than normal, hydrogen ions are gained by the extracellular fluids. For instance, at a pH of 7.6 about 1.5 millimols of hydrogen ions are gained each minute.

The total amount of buffers in the entire body is approximately 1,000 millimols. If all these should be suddenly shifted to the alkaline or acidic side by injecting an alkali or an acid, the kidneys would be able to return the pH of the body fluids back almost to normal in 10 to 20 hours. Though this mechanism is slow to act, it is different from the respiratory regulatory mechanism in that it continues acting until the pH reaches exact normal rather than a certain percentage of the way. Therefore, the real value of the renal mechanism for regulating hydrogen ion concentration is not its rapidity of action but instead its ability in the end to neutralize completely any excess acid or alkali that enters the body fluids.

Ordinarily, the kidneys can remove up to about 500 millimols of acid or alkali each day. If greater quantities of acid or alkali than this enter the body fluids each day, the kidneys will be unable to cope with the extra load, and severe acidosis or alkalosis will ensue.

Range of Urinary pH. In the process of adjusting the hydrogen ion concentration of the extracellular fluids, the kidneys often excrete urines with pH's as low as 4.5 or up to as high as 8.0. When acid is being excreted the pH falls, and when alkali is being excreted the pH rises. Even when the pH of the extracellular fluids is at the normal value of 7.4, a fraction of a millimol of acid is still lost each minute. The reason for this is that about 50 to 100 millimols more acid than alkali are formed in the body each day, and this acid must be continually removed. Because of the presence of this excess acid in the urine, the normal urine pH is about 6.0 instead of 7.4, which is the pH of the blood.

CLINICAL ABNORMALITIES OF ACID-BASE BALANCE

Respiratory Acidosis and Alkalosis

From the discussions earlier in the chapter it is quite obvious that any factor that decreases the rate of pulmonary ventilation will increase the concentrations of dissolved carbon dioxide, carbonic acid, and hydrogen ions, thus resulting in acidosis. Because this type of acidosis is caused by an abnormality of respiration it is called *respiratory acidosis*.

On the other hand, excessive pulmonary ventilation will reverse the process and decrease the hydrogen ion concentration, thus resulting in alkalosis; this condition is called *respiratory alkalosis*.

A person can cause respiratory acidosis voluntarily by simply holding his breath, which he can do until the pH of the body fluids falls to as low as perhaps 7.1. On the other hand, he can voluntarily overbreathe and cause alkalosis up to a pH of about 7.8.

However, respiratory acidosis and alkalosis more frequently result from pathological conditions. For instance, damage to the respiratory center in the medulla oblongata, obstruction of the passageways in the respiratory tract, pneumonia, decreased pulmonary surface area, and any other factor that interferes with the exchange of gases between the blood and alveolar air will result in respiratory acidosis. On the other hand, only rarely do pathological conditions cause respiratory alkalosis. However, an occasional psychoneurosis causes a person to overbreathe to such an extent that he becomes alkalotic. A physiological type of respiratory alkalosis occurs when a person ascends to a high altitude. The low oxygen content of the air stimulates respiration, which causes excess loss of carbon dioxide and development of mild respiratory alkalosis.

Metabolic Acidosis and Alkalosis

The terms *metabolic acidosis* and *metabolic alkalosis* refer to all other abnormalities of acid-base balance besides those caused by excess or too little carbon dioxide in the body fluids. Use of the word "metabolic" in this instance is unfortunate, because carbon dioxide most certainly is also a metabolic product. Yet, by convention, carbonic acid resulting from dissolved carbon dioxide is called a *respiratory acid* while any other acid in the body, whether it be formed by metabolism or simply ingested by the person, is called a *metabolic acid*.

Causes of Metabolic Acidosis. Metabolic acidosis can result from (1) the formation of metabolic acids in the body, (2) from the addition of metabolic acids intravenously, or (3) from addition of metabolic acids by way of the gastrointestinal tract. Metabolic acidosis can result also from (4) loss of alkali from the body fluids. Some of the specific conditions that cause metabolic acidosis are the following:

Severe diarrhea is one of the most frequent causes of metabolic acidosis for the following reasons: The gastrointestinal secretions normally contain large amounts of sodium bicarbonate. Therefore, excessive loss of these secretions during a bout of diarrhea is exactly the same as excretion of large amounts of sodium bicarbonate into the urine. In accordance with the Henderson-Hasselbalch equation, this results in a shift of the bicarbonate buffer system toward the acid side and results in metabolic acidosis. In fact, acidosis resulting from severe diarrhea can be so severe that it is one of the most common causes of death in young children.

A second cause of metabolic acidosis is *vomiting*. Vomiting of gastric contents alone, which occurs rarely, will cause a loss of acid and will lead to alkalosis, but vomiting of contents from deeper in the gastrointestinal tract, which often occurs, will cause loss of alkali and result in metabolic acidosis.

A third common type of acidosis is *uremic acidosis*, which occurs in severe renal disease. The cause of this is failure of the kidneys to rid the body of even the normal amounts of acids formed each day by the metabolic processes of the body.

A fourth and extremely important cause of metabolic acidosis is *diabetes mellitus*. In this condition, lack of insulin secretion by the pancreas prevents normal use of glucose for metabolism. Instead, the stored fats are split into acetoacetic acid, and this in turn is metabolized by the tissues for energy in place of glucose. Simultaneously, the concentration of acetoacetic acid in the extracellular fluids often rises very high, and large quantities of it are excreted in the urine, sometimes as much as 500 to 1,000 millimols per day. This condition unfortunately not only causes metabolic acidosis because of its presence in the blood stream but also because it carries large amounts of sodium with it into the urine. In an earlier discussion in this chapter it was noted that sodium loss can be prevented as long as sufficient ammonia secretion by the tubules is available to combine with hydrogen ions and thereby release sodium for reabsorption. But when the total amount of a strong acid entering the tubules exceeds the rate of ammonia secretion, the excess acid carries sodium with it into the urine rather than allowing it to reenter the extracellular fluids in the form of sodium bicarbonate. Therefore, in diabetes mellitus the acidosis results, first, from the presence of acetoacetic acid itself in the extracellular fluids, and, second, from the loss of large amounts of sodium bicarbonate, the alkaline half of the bicarbonate buffer system, from the extracellular fluids.

Causes of Metabolic Alkalosis. Metabolic alkalosis does not occur nearly so often as metabolic acidosis. It most frequently follows *excessive ingestion of alkaline drugs* such as sodium bicarbonate for the treatment of gastritis or peptic ulcer. However, metabolic alkalosis occasionally results from *excessive vomiting of gastric contents* without vomiting of lower gastrointestinal contents, which causes excessive loss of the hydrochloric acid secreted by the stomach mucosa. The net result is loss of acid from the extracellular fluids and development of metabolic alkalosis.

Effects of Acidosis and Alkalosis on the Body

Acidosis. The major effect of acidosis is depression of the *central nervous system*. When the pH of the blood falls below 7.0, the nervous system becomes so depressed that the person first becomes disoriented and, later, comatose. Therefore, patients dying of diabetic acidosis, uremic acidosis, and other types of acidosis usually die in a state of coma.

In metabolic acidosis the high hydrogen ion concentration causes increased rate and depth of respiration. Therefore, one of the diagnostic signs of *metabolic* acidosis is increased pulmonary ventilation. On the other hand, in *respiratory acidosis respiration is usually depressed*, which is opposite to the effect in metabolic acidosis.

Alkalosis. The major effect of alkalosis on the body is *overexcitability of the nervous system*. This effect occurs both in the central nervous system and in the peripheral nerves, but usually the peripheral nerves are affected before the central nervous system. The nerves become so excitable that they automatically and repetitively fire even when they are not stimulated by normal stimuli. As a result, the muscles go into a state of *tetany*, which means a state of tonic spasm. This tetany usually appears first in the muscles of the forearm, then spreads rapidly to the muscles of the face, and finally all over the body. Alkalotic patients may die from tetany of the respiratory muscles.

Only occasionally does an alkalotic person develop severe symptoms of central nervous system overexcitability. The symptoms may manifest themselves as extreme nervousness or, in susceptible persons, as convulsions. For instance, in persons who are predisposed to epileptic fits, simply overbreathing will often result in an attack. Indeed, this is one of the clinical methods for assessing one's degree of epileptic predisposition.

In metabolic alkalosis, the low hydrogen ion concentration decreases the excitability of the respiratory center and results in very shallow and slow breathing, which is opposite to the effect in metabolic acidosis. In respiratory alkalosis, the pulmonary ventilation is ordinarily markedly increased, as was explained above.

Respiratory Compensation of Metabolic Acidosis or Alkalosis

It was pointed out above that the high hydrogen ion concentration of metabolic acidosis causes increased pulmonary ventilation, which in turn results in rapid removal of carbon dioxide from the body fluids and reduces the hydrogen ion concentration. Thus, the respiratory effect helps to compensate for the metabolic acidosis. However, this compensation will occur only part-way. Ordinarily, the respiratory system is capable of compensating between 50 and 75 per cent. That is, if the metabolic factor makes the pH of the blood fall to 7.0 at normal pulmonary ventilation, the rate of pulmonary ventilation will normally increase sufficiently to return the pH of the blood to 7.2 to 7.3, as was pointed out earlier in the chapter.

The opposite type of respiratory compensation occurs in metabolic alkalosis. That is, alkalosis diminishes the pulmonary ventilation, which in turn causes increased hydrogen ion concentration. Here again the compensation can take place to about 50 to 75 per cent.

Renal Compensation of Respiratory Acidosis or Alkalosis

If a person develops respiratory acidosis that continues for a prolonged period of time, the kidneys will secrete an excess of hydrogen ions, resulting in an increase in sodium bicarbonate in the extracellular fluids. After half a day or more, the pH of the body fluids will have returned essentially to normal even though the person continues to breathe poorly. Thus, renal compensation of respiratory acidosis can be complete rather than only partial.

Exactly the converse effect occurs in respiratory alkalosis. Large amounts of sodium bicarbonate are lost into the urine, thereby decreasing the pH to normal. Here again the compensation goes almost to completion in about a half day or a little more.

Physiology of Treatment in Acidosis or Alkalosis

Obviously, the best treatment for acidosis or alkalosis is to remove the condition causing the abnormality, but, if this cannot be effected, different drugs can be used to neutralize the excess acid or alkali.

To neutralize excess acid, large amounts of sodium bicarbonate can be ingested by mouth. This is absorbed into the blood stream and increases the basic half of the bicarbonate buffer, thereby shifting the pH to the alkaline side. Sodium bicarbonate is occasionally used also for intravenous therapy, but this has such strong and often dangerous physiological effects that other substances are more often used, such as sodium lactate, sodium gluconate, or other organic compounds of sodium. The lactate and gluconate portions of the molecules are metabolized in the body, leaving the sodium in the extracellular fluids in the form of sodium bicarbonate, and thereby shifting the pH of the fluids in the alkaline direction.

For treatment of alkalosis, ammonium chloride is usually administered by mouth. When this is absorbed into the blood, the ammonia portion of the ammonium chloride is converted by the liver into urea; this reaction liberates hydrochloric acid, which immediately reacts with the buffers of the body fluids to shift the hydrogen ion concentration in the acid direction. Occasionally, ammonium chloride is infused intravenously, but the ammonium ion is highly toxic and this procedure can be dangerous.

Interrelationships of pH, Dissolved CO_2, and HCO_3^- Concentration

pH Measurements. In studying a patient with acidosis or alkalosis one needs preferably to know the pH of his body fluids. This can be determined quite easily by measuring the pH of the

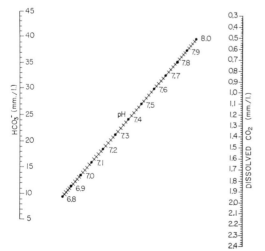

Figure 79.   Nomogram for the Henderson-Hasselbalch equation relating pH, carbon dioxide concentration, and bicarbonate ion concentration. (Redrawn from McLean: *Physiol. Rev.* 18:495, 1938.)

plasma with a glass electrode pH meter. However, extreme care must be exercised in removing the plasma and in making the measurement, because even the slightest diffusion of carbon dioxide out of the plasma into the air will shift the bicarbonate buffer system in the alkaline direction, resulting in a much elevated pH measurement.

The pH, CO_2, and HCO_3^- nomogram. Unfortunately, the pH measurement does not indicate whether a person has metabolic or respiratory acidosis or alkalosis. To determine this, one must measure both the carbon dioxide and bicarbonate concentrations in the plasma. Measurement of the dissolved carbon dioxide concentration is extremely difficult, but measurement of the bicarbonate ion concentration is a simple chemical procedure and can be accomplished in any clinical laboratory. Then the CO_2 concentration can be calculated in the following way: Referring once again to the Henderson-Hasselbalch equation (Number 11), if the concentrations of any two of the factors in the equation are known, the third can be calculated. Figure 79 illustrates a nomogram with three separate scales, one representing CO_2 concentration, another the bicarbonate concentration, and the third the pH of the extracellular fluid. Placing a straight edge across these scales at points representing the values for pH and bicarbonate concentration will allow one to find the CO_2 concentration.

The pH-Bicarbonate Diagram. The same relationship as that shown in Figure 79 between bicarbonate concentration, CO_2 concentration, and pH can be represented also by the so-called *pH-bicarbonate diagram*, which is illustrated in Figure 80. This diagram can be used to determine the type of acidosis or alkalosis a person has and its severity. Its use may be explained as follows:

The vertical lines of the diagram depict different CO_2 concentrations. The normal carbon dioxide concentration of 1.2 mM./liter is denoted by the heavy line. The points along this line represent the possible combinations of bicarbonate concentration and pH that can exist in the body fluids when the CO_2 concentration is normal.

The horizontal lines represent the concentrations of metabolic acids and bases in the body fluids. The heavy line, denoted by the numeral zero, indicates a balance between both of these. That is, the points on this line represent the possible combinations of bicarbonate concentration and pH that can occur as long as the metabolic acids and bases in the body fluids are normal. The upper two horizontal lines indicate respectively additions of 5 or 10 millimols per liter of extra metabolic base to the body fluids, and the two lower horizontal lines indicate additions of 5 to 10 extra millimols per liter of metabolic acid.

To use this diagram we simply find the pH of the blood and the bicarbonate concentration, then

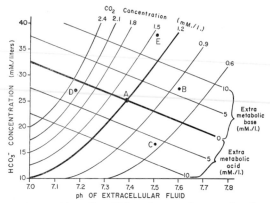

Figure 80. The pH-bicarbonate diagram for determining relative degrees of metabolic and respiratory acidosis or alkalosis in a patient.

plot the appropriate point on the diagram. For instance, if the pH is found to be the normal value of 7.4 and bicarbonate concentration the normal value of 26 mM./l., we plot point A, which represents the normal condition.

Now, using data obtained from another patient, we plot a new point with a pH of 7.63 and a bicarbonate concentration of 28 millimols per liter. This is point B on the diagram, which represents a CO_2 concentration of 0.8 millimols per liter and 7 millimols per liter extra metabolic base. Thus, this person has *metabolic alkalosis* because he has considerable extra metabolic base in his body fluids, but he also has *respiratory alkalosis* because he is overventilating to an extent that his CO_2 concentration is considerably less than normal.

Similarly, from other data, we can plot points C, D, and E. Point C represents 6 millimols per liter of *metabolic acidosis* and sufficient *respiratory alkalosis* to reduce the CO_2 concentration down to 0.7 millimols per liter. A person with such a finding as this could have respiratory alkalosis that has been partially compensated by metabolic acidosis produced by the kidneys. Or, conversely, it is possible that the metabolic acidosis was primary, and the person has overcompensated with respiratory alkalosis.

Point D represents *mild metabolic acidosis,* 2 millimols per liter, combined with *very severe respiratory acidosis.* A person could get into this state with severe primary respiratory acidosis and very mild metabolic acidosis resulting from some other cause.

Point E represents *very mild respiratory acidosis* and *very severe metabolic alkalosis.* Presumably, in this case the metabolic alkalosis was primary, and respiratory compensation caused mild respiratory acidosis in an attempt to compensate for the metabolic alkalosis.

In summary, by using the pH-bicarbonate diagram, one can determine both the degree of metabolic acidosis or alkalosis and the degree of respiratory acidosis or alkalosis in a patient at the same time.

The Carbon Dioxide–Combining Power of the Blood (Alkali Reserve). Unfortunately, it is almost impossible to determine the plasma CO_2 concentration in a clinical laboratory, and it is also somewhat difficult to determine the pH and the bicarbonate concentration because the blood must be removed from the patient and not be exposed to air before the appropriate measurements are made. Therefore, the usual clinical laboratory measures the so-called *carbon dioxide–combining power of the plasma,* which is also called the *alkali reserve.* This measurement is made as follows: Blood is removed from the patient, it is rendered incoagulable with potassium oxalate, and the plasma is separated from the cells. No special precautions are taken about exposure to air. Instead, in the laboratory the plasma is reexposed to 7 per cent carbon dioxide until it equilibrates. Then the total carbon dioxide in the plasma is determined chemically, including all the dissolved carbon dioxide as well as that which can be liberated from the bicarbonate in the plasma by the addition of acid. Since about $^{19}/_{20}$ is in the form of bicarbonate, this is principally a measure of plasma bicarbonate, and it is called the carbon dioxide–combining power of the plasma.

The normal carbon dioxide–combining power is 27 mM./l., but in very severe metabolic acidosis it may be reduced to as low as 5 to 10 mM./l. Conversely, in very severe metabolic alkalosis, it may rise to as high as 40 to 50 mM./l. Ordinarily, these concentrations are expressed in terms of the *volume* of carbon dioxide that can be released from each 100 ml. of plasma rather than in millimols. The normal amount is 58 volumes per cent (58 ml. per 100 ml. of plasma). In severe metabolic alkalosis this occasionally rises to as high as 80 to 90 volumes per cent, and in very severe metabolic acidosis it can fall to as low as 10 to 15 volumes per cent.

It should be noted that the carbon dioxide–combining power tells one nothing at all about *respiratory* acidosis or alkalosis, for the plasma is not equilibrated with the alveolar CO_2 of the patient prior to the test but with 7 per cent CO_2 provided in the laboratory.

REFERENCES

Brodsky, W. A.: Regulation of urine flow and solute excretion during acute acidosis induced by loading with strong mineral acids in hydropenic dogs. *Am. J. Physiol., 181:*616, 1955.

Davenport, H. W.: The ABC of Acid-Base Chemistry: The Elements of Physiological Blood-Gas Chemistry for Medical Students and Physicians. 2nd ed., Chicago, University of Chicago Press, 1950.

Deane, N., and Smith, H. W.: The apparent first dissociation constant, pK, of carbonic acid in the human erythrocyte. J. Biol. Chem., 227:101, 1957.

Dorman, P. J., Sullivan, W. J., and Pitts, R. F.: The renal response to acute respiratory acidosis. J. Clin. Invest., 33:82, 1954.

Fenn, W. O., Otis, A. B., and Suskind, M.: The accumulation of carbon dioxide in apneic dogs during intermittent oxygen insufflation. Am. J. Phys. Med., 33:299, 1954.

Giebisch, G., Berger, L., and Pitts, R. F.: The extrarenal response to acute acid-base disturbances of respiratory origin. J. Clin. Invest., 34:231, 1955.

Gottschalk, C. W., Lassiter, W. E., and Mylle, M.: Localization of urine acidification in the mammalian kidney. Am. J. Physiol., 198:581, 1960.

Grodins, F. S.: Respiration and the regulation of acid-base balance. Arch. Int. Med., 99:569, 1957.

Lotspeich, W. D., and Pitts, R. F.: The role of amino acids in the renal tubular secretion of ammonia. J. Biol. Chem., 168:611, 1947.

Menaker, W.: Buffer equilibria and reabsorption in the production of urinary acidity. Am. J. Physiol., 154:174, 1948.

Milne, M. D., Scribner, B. H., and Crawford, M. A.: Non-ionic diffusion and the excretion of weak acids and bases. Am. J. Med., 24:709, 1958.

Ogston, A. G.: The definition and meaning of pH. Physiol. Rev., 27:228, 1947.

Pitts, R. F.: Acid-base regulation of the kidney from seminars of renal physiology. Am. J. Med., 9:356, 1950.

Pitts, R. F.: Mechanisms for stabilizing the alkaline reserves of the body. Harvey Lect., 48:172, 1952–1953.

Pitts, R. F.: Modern concepts of acid-base regulation. Arch. Int. Med., 89:864, 1952.

Pitts, R. F.: Renal excretion of acid. Fed. Proc. 7:418, 1948.

Pitts, R. F., Ayer, J. L., and Schiess, W. A.: The renal regulation of acid-base balance in man. III. The reabsorption and excretion of bicarbonate. J. Clin. Invest., 28:35, 1949.

Pitts, R. F., and Lotspeich, W. D.: Bicarbonate and renal regulation of acid-base balance. Am. J. Physiol., 147:138, 1946.

Pitts, R. F., Lotspeich, W. D., Schiess, W. A., and Ayer, J. L.: The renal regulation of acid-base balance in man. I. The nature of the mechanism for acidifying the urine. J. Clin. Invest., 27:48, 1948.

Simmons, D. H., and Avedon, M.: Acid-base alterations and plasma potassium concentration. Am. J. Physiol., 197:319, 1959.

Swann, R. C., and Pitts, R. F.: Neutralization of infused acid by nephrectomized dogs. J. Clin. Invest., 34:205, 1955.

Van Slyke, D. D., Phillips, R. A., Hamilton, P. B., Archibald, R. M., Futcher, P. H., and Hiller, A.: Glutamine as a source material of urinary ammonia. J. Biol. Chem., 150:481, 1945.

Weisberg, H. F.: Water, Electrolyte, and Acid-Base Balance, Normal and Pathologic as a Basis for Therapy. Baltimore, Williams & Wilkins Co., 1953.

West, E. S.: Textbook of Biophysical Chemistry. New York, The Macmillan Co., 1956.

White, H. L., and Rolf, D.: Renal glutaminase and ammonia excretion. Am. J. Physiol., 169:174, 1952.

See also Chapter 8, Formation of urine; Chapter 9, Regulation of extracellular fluid; Chapter 11, Renal disorders.

Physiology of Renal Disease,

Diuresis, and Micturition

The physiology of renal disease can be classified into 4 different categories: (1) *acute renal shutdown,* in which the kidneys stop working entirely or almost entirely, (2) *renal insufficiency,* in which progressively more and more nephrons are destroyed until the kidneys simply cannot perform all the needed functions, (3) the *nephrotic syndrome,* in which the glomeruli have become far more permeable than normal so that large amounts of protein are lost into the urine, and (4) *specific tubular abnormalities,* including especially abnormal reabsorption or lack of reabsorption of certain substances by the tubules.

ACUTE RENAL SHUTDOWN

Causes of Acute Renal Shutdown

Tubular Necrosis. The most common cause of acute renal shutdown is *tubular necrosis,* which means destruction of epithelial cells in the tubules, as illustrated in Figure 81. The different causes of tubular necrosis are (1) *various poisons* that destroy the tubular epithelial cells, (2) *ischemia* of the kidneys, and (3) transfusion reactions.

Renal poisons. Among the different renal poisons are carbon tetrachloride and the heavy metals such as the mercuric ion. These substances have specific nephrotoxic action on the tubular epithelial cells, causing death of many of them. As a result, the epithelial cells slough away from the basement membrane and plug the tubules. In some instances the basement membrane also is destroyed, but, if not, new tubular epithelial cells can usually grow along the surface of the membrane so that the tubule becomes repaired within 10 days to two weeks.

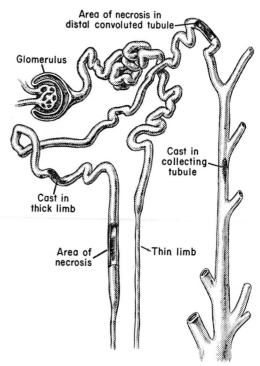

Figure 81. Damage to the distal tubules as a result of shock. (Modified from Maclean: Acute Renal Failure. Charles C Thomas.)

Renal ischemia. Ischemia of the kidney is very likely to result from *severe circulatory shock.* In shock, the heart simply fails to pump sufficient amounts of blood to supply adequate nutrition to the different parts of the body, and renal blood flow is particularly likely to suffer because of very strong sympathetic constriction of the renal vessels. Therefore, lack of adequate nutrition often destroys many tubular epithelial cells and thereby plugs many of the nephrons.

Transfusion reaction. Another important

other hand, moderate renal insufficiency may actually increase the urinary output as was described above in relation to over-function of the remaining nephrons when the majority have been destroyed.

A second factor frequently measured is the *specific gravity* of the urine. Depending on the types of substances being cleared, this can vary tremendously; its upper extreme can go as high as 1.045 and it can fall to as little as 1.0015. To test the ability of the kidneys to dilute the urine, the patient drinks large quantities of water and measurements are made of the minimal specific gravity that can be attained. Then, at another time, he goes without water from 12 to 24 hours, and the maximum concentration of the urine is measured. Referring back to Figure 86, it will be noted that the fewer the number of nephrons in the two kidneys, the nearer will the urine specific gravity approach 1.010 in both the dilution and the concentration tests. When the patient has *isosthenuria*—that is, when the urine fails either to concentrate or dilute—one can be sure that renal function has been decreased to a very low level, to lower than one-sixth normal maximal function in most instances.

DIURETICS AND MECHANISMS OF THEIR ACTIONS

A diuretic is a substance that increases the rate of urine output. Diuretics can act either by increasing the glomerular filtration rate or by decreasing the rate of reabsorption of fluid from the tubules.

The principal use of diuretics is to reduce the

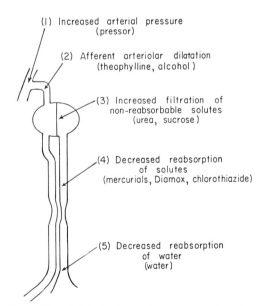

(1) Increased arterial pressure
(pressor)

(2) Afferent arteriolar dilatation
(theophylline, alcohol)

(3) Increased filtration of
non-reabsorbable solutes
(urea, sucrose)

(4) Decreased reabsorption
of solutes
(mercurials, Diamox, chlorothiazide)

(5) Decreased reabsorption
of water
(water)

Figure 87. Points in the nephron at which various diuretics act.

total amount of fluid in the body. They are especially important in treating edema resulting from conditions other than kidney disease, such as the edema of congestive heart disease and that caused by diminished plasma proteins or increased permeability of the capillaries. Diuretics normally are of little value in treating the edema caused by kidney disease, because the abnormal kidneys will rarely respond.

When using a diuretic it is usually important that the rate of sodium loss in the urine also be increased as well as the rate of water loss. The reason for this is the following: Whenever a person has edema, not only does his extracellular fluids contain water, but also greatly increased quantities of sodium chloride. If water alone were removed from these fluids, the fluids would in turn become hypertonic and elicit an osmoreceptor response, followed by marked secretion of antidiuretic hormone. Consequently, large amounts of water would immediately be reabsorbed from the tubules, which would nullify the effect of the diuretic. However, if sodium is lost along with the water, this nullification will not result. Therefore, all valuable diuretics cause marked *natruresis* (sodium loss) as well as diuresis.

Diuretics can be classified into three different physiologic types: (1) those that increase glomerular filtration, (2) those that increase the tubular osmotic load, and (3) those that inhibit the secretion of antidiuretic hormone. Figure 87 shows the points in the nephron where the different diuretics function.

Diuretics That Increase Glomerular Filtration. The glomerular filtration rate can be increased by *increasing the arterial pressure, by dilating the afferent arterioles, by constricting the efferent arterioles,* or *by decreasing the colloid osmotic pressure.* Some of the different agents that can increase the glomerular filtration rate in one of these ways are the following:

Agents that increase the arterial pressure include *nor-epinephrine,* other sympathomimetic drugs, and sometimes large infusions of fluid. However, the pressor drugs, such as nor-epinephrine, usually have a dual effect on fluid output. The increase in arterial presure caused by nor-epinephrine tends to increase the output, while direct constriction of the afferent arterioles tends to reduce urine output. In low and moderate pressure ranges the pressure effect is more important so that nor-epinephrine normally causes diuresis, whereas in high pressure ranges, above about 160 mm. Hg, the urine output begins to fall.

Administration of *digitalis* to a patient with congestive heart failure frequently benefits the circulation so greatly that the glomerular pressure increases. And this increases the glomerular filtration rate, resulting in diuresis.

Certain chemicals directly dilate the afferent

arterioles, including *theophylline, caffeine,* and *alcohol,* all of which increase the glomerular filtration rate and result in increased urinary output.

In general, the agents that increase glomerular filtration rate can increase the total urinary output only about two- to three-fold.

Diuretics That Increase the Tubular Osmotic Pressure

The Osmotic Diuretics. Injection into the blood stream of *urea, sucrose, mannitol,* or any other substance not easily reabsorbed by the tubules will cause a great increase in the osmotically active substances in the tubules. The osmotic pressure of these prevents water reabsorption, and large amounts of tubular fluid flush on into the urine.

The same effect occurs when the glucose concentration of the blood rises to very high levels in diabetes mellitus. Above a glucose concentration of about 250 mg. per cent, very little glucose is reabsorbed by the tubules; instead it acts as an osmotic diuretic and causes rapid loss of fluid into the urine. The name "diabetes" refers to the prolific urine flow.

Diuretics That Diminish Active Reabsorption—Mercurials, Carbonic Anhydrase Inhibitors, and Chlorothiazide. Any substance that will poison carrier systems in the tubular epithelial cells and thereby diminish active reabsorption of tubular solutes will increase the tubular osmotic pressure and cause an osmotic diuresis. The three most common drugs of this type are the mercurials, Diamox (acetazolamide), and chlorothiazide.

The *mercurial diuretics* are divalent organic mercurial compounds, and they have the property of combining with and inactivating sulfhydryl-containing enzymes which are important in several of the tubular transport systems. As a consequence, large doses of mercurial diuretics can decrease active reabsorption and active secretion of a number of different substances by the tubules. They have an especially important effect on active reabsorption of sodium in the distal portions of the proximal tubules; 20 to 30 per cent of the total tubular sodium load may fail to be reabsorbed. This leaves a tremendous amount of osmotically active sodium in the tubules, which prevents water reabsorption as well. Therefore, very large quantities of water and sodium are excreted. Because of this very high degree of effectiveness of mercurials, they are the most valuable of all the different diuretics used clinically. However, excessive usage of mercurial diuretics can sometimes destroy tubular epithelial cells, causing more harm than good.

Diamox *inhibits carbonic anhydrase,* and, therefore, when given in sufficient quantity can block hydrogen ion secretion by the tubular epithelial cells. This in turn decreases the reabsorption of both bicarbonate and sodium ions, again increasing the quantity of osmotically active substances remaining in the tubules and, therefore, causing diuresis—but also causing some degree of acidosis because of failure to excrete hydrogen ions.

Chlorothiazide both inhibits carbonic anhydrase and also inhibits sodium reabsorption. However, it is not so powerful a carbonic anhydrase inhibitor as Diamox, nor is it as powerful as the mercurials in inhibiting sodium reabsorption. It is a valuable diuretic when the combined qualities of both the other diuretics are desired. Furthermore, chlorothiazide seems to act at a different point in the tubules from the mercurials for reabsorption of sodium, because administration of mercurials and chlorothiazide at the same time causes additive effects.

Diuretics That Inhibit the Secretion of Antidiuretic Hormone

The single diuretic that is most important in inhibiting the secretion of antidiuretic hormone is water. This was discussed in Chapter 9. When large amounts of water are ingested, the body fluids become diluted, and antidiuretic hormone is no longer secreted by the supraoptico-hypophyseal system. As a result, water fails to be reabsorbed by the distal tubules and collecting ducts, and large amounts of dilute urine flow. In addition to water, various psychic factors as well as certain drugs that affect the central nervous system, such as narcotics, hypnotics, and anesthetics, can inhibit antidiuretic hormone secretion. For this reason, these can all cause bizarre increases in urinary output.

MICTURITION

Micturition is the process by which the urinary bladder empties itself when it becomes filled. Basically the bladder (1) progressively fills until the tension in its walls rises above a threshold value, at which time (2) a neurogenic reflex called the "micturition reflex" is elicited that (3) greatly exacerbates the pressure in the bladder and causes a conscious desire to urinate. The micturition reflex also initiates appropriate signals from the central nervous system to relax the external sphincter of the bladder, thereby allowing micturition.

Physiologic Anatomy of the Bladder and Its Nervous Connections. The uri-

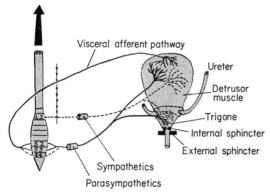

Figure 88.   The urinary bladder and its innervation.

nary bladder, which is illustrated in Figure 88, is composed of two principal parts: (a) the *body,* which is comprised mainly of the *detrusor muscle,* and (b) the *trigone,* a small triangular area near the mouth of the bladder through which both the *ureters* and the *urethra* pass. During bladder expansion it is the body of the bladder that stretches, and during the micturition reflex it is the detrusor muscle that contracts to empty the bladder. On the other hand, the trigonal muscle is interlaced around the opening of the urethra and maintains tonic closure of the urethral opening until the pressure in the bladder rises high enough to overcome the muscle tone. The trigonal muscle, therefore, is called the *internal sphincter of the bladder.* About two centimeters beyond the bladder, the urethra passes through the *urogenital diaphragm,* the muscle of which constitutes the *external sphincter* of the bladder. This muscle is a voluntary skeletal muscle controlled by the *perineal nerve.* Normally, this muscle remains tonically contracted all of the time, but it can be reflexly or voluntarily relaxed at the time of micturition.

Figure 88 also illustrates the basic nervous pathways for bladder control. Parasympathetic excitation causes constriction of the detrusor muscle and perhaps some relaxation of the trigonal area, while sympathetic stimulation causes exactly the opposite effects. The sympathetics are not believed to be involved in the micturition reflex, but they do help to control the degree of tone in the trigonal area and therefore determine to a great extent the pressure that must be built up in the bladder before urine can empty through the internal sphincter.

Tonus of the Bladder and the Cystometrogram during Bladder Filling.

When no urine at all is in the bladder, the intravesical pressure is approximately zero, as shown in Figure 89, but, by the time 100 ml. of urine have collected, the pressure will have risen to about 20 centimeters of water. Additional urine up to 400 to 600 milliliters can collect without significant further rise in pressure; the pressure still remains only 20 centimeters of water. Beyond this point, collection of more urine causes the pressure to rise very, very rapidly.

The curve of Figure 89 is called a *cystometrogram.* The initial portion of the curve —that is, the rise in pressure to 20 cms. of water—is called *segment I,* the plateau is called *segment II,* and the sharp rise above the 600 milliliters level is called *segment III.*

Superimposed on the tonic pressure changes during filling of the bladder are periodic acute increases in pressure which last from a few seconds to more than a minute. The pressure can rise only a few centimeters of water or it can rise to over 100 centimeters of water. These are *micturition waves* in the cystometrogram caused by the micturition reflex, which will be discussed below.

Mechanism of tone in the bladder.   The rapid rise of pressure in segment I of the cystometrogram presumably results from initial filling of the bladder up to a level at which the bladder wall can exert its tonic force against the fluid. The plateau in segment II is believed to result from tonic ac-

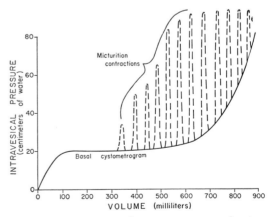

Figure 89.   A normal cystometrogram, showing also acute pressure waves (the dashed curves) caused by micturition reflexes.

tivity in the nerve plexus that lies over the surface of the bladder. However, this effect is not the result of control by the spinal cord, because it still occurs even after the extrinsic nerves to the bladder are cut. The plateau might also result to some extent from the effect of a physical law called Laplace's law in the following way: When a spherical vesicle begins to be filled, the increasing circumference of the vesicle causes an increase in the mechanical advantage of the fluid stretching the vesical wall, and the pressure required to cause additional filling may not increase at all. Everyone has experienced this effect in blowing up a balloon. After the initial start, the pressure then required to fill the balloon may be even less than that required to obtain the initial start.

The very rapid rise in pressure in segment III in the normal bladder presumably results from stretching the bladder to its physiological limit so that additional fluid will then be stretching connective tissue rather than muscle fibers. However, in the hypertonic bladder, this is not true because the rapid rise in pressure then occurs at a bladder volume much below that at which the connective tissue begins to be stretched. Therefore, it has been postulated that segment III might result from activation of a second type of smooth muscle in the vesical wall besides that which is normally tonically active.

The Micturition Reflex

Referring once again to Figure 89, it will be evident that as the bladder fills to the upper end of segment II in the cystometrogram, many superimposed *micturition contractions* begin to appear. These are the result of a stretch reflex initiated by stretch receptors in the bladder wall. Impulses are conducted to the sacral segments of the cord through the perineal nerves and then back again to the bladder through the parasympathetic nerves of the pelvic plexus.

Once a micturition reflex begins, it is "self-regenerative." That is, initial contraction of the bladder causes a further increase in afferent impulses from the bladder, which causes a further increase in reflex contraction of the bladder, the cycle thus repeating itself again and again until the bladder has reached a very strong degree of contraction.

Then, as the reflex begins to fatigue, the initial decrease in motor contraction reduces the afferent impulses, and this causes even more rapid reduction in bladder contraction. In other words, the micturition reflex is a single complete cycle of (a) progressive and rapid increase in pressure and (b) return of the pressure back to the basal tonic pressure of the bladder. Once a micturition reflex has occurred, the sacral portion of the spinal cord usually remains in an inhibited state for at least a few minutes or sometimes as long as an hour or more before another micturition reflex occurs. However, as the bladder becomes more and more filled, micturition reflexes occur more and more often, as illustrated in Figure 89.

Control of Micturition by the Brain. The micturition reflex is a completely automatic cord reflex, but it can be inhibited or facilitated by centers in the brain. These include: (1) a strong *facilitatory center in the upper pons*, (2) a strong *facilitatory center in the hypothalamus* (in the septum pellucidum and medial preoptic area), (3) a moderately strong *inhibitory center in the rostral mid-brain* at approximately the level of the superior colliculus, and (4) several *centers located in the cerebral cortex* that are mainly inhibitory but can at times become excitatory.

The fiber pathways through which micturition signals are transmitted to and from the brain are not known. However, some studies have indicated that the afferent fibers travel in or in close association with the lateral spinothalamic tracts. On the other hand, studies in cats show that transection of the posterior half of the spinal cord will cause loss of both the afferent and efferent tracts.

The micturition reflex is the basic cause of micturition, but the higher centers can facilitate this reflex and make it far more powerful than it would be with cord action alone, and the higher centers can inhibit the reflex. *Presumably, therefore, the normal mechanism for cortical control of the bladder is (1) to keep the micturition reflex partially inhibited all of the time except when it is desired to micturate and (2) to prevent micturition by continual tonic contraction of the external urinary sphincter until a convenient time presents itself. When the time to urinate arrives, the cortical centers can (a) facilitate the sacral micturition centers to initiate a micturition reflex and* (b) *inhibit the external urinary sphincter so that urination can occur.*

Abnormalities of Micturition

Tabetic Bladder. Syphilis in its late stages often invades the nervous system, causing constrictive fibrosis around the dorsal root nerve fibers as they enter the spinal cord. This condition is called *tabes dorsalis.* In addition to loss of many of the somatic sensations throughout the body, the afferent fibers that subserve the micturition reflex are also destroyed. As a result, periodic micturition contractions cannot occur, and the person loses all control of his bladder despite intact efferent fibers and despite intact neurogenic connections with the cerebrum. Therefore, instead of emptying periodically, the bladder fills to its capacity and then overflows a few drops at a time through the urethra. This is called "overflow dribbling."

Autonomous Bladder. When the motor fibers from the cord to the bladder are destroyed, the person loses all neurogenic control of bladder function. However, the condition is quite different from the tabetic bladder, for some local effect in the bladder wall itself or in the neuronal plexus on the surface of the bladder causes greatly increased bladder tone so that even slight filling increases the intravesical pressure to very high levels. Furthermore, periodic but very slight phasic contractions of the bladder occur, and these can cause emptying. Thus, the autonomous bladder rarely fills to a large volume, and the person has uncontrolled and often periodic micturition, this time not dribbling but discharge of 25 to 100 ml. of urine at a time.

The autonomous bladder becomes almost identical to the tabetic bladder if the sensory fibers are destroyed along with the motor fibers. The cause of this difference is not yet known.

The Automatic Bladder. If the spinal cord is damaged above the sacral region but the sacral segments are still intact, then typical micturition reflexes will still be able to occur. However, they are no longer controllable by the brain. During the first few days to several weeks after the damage to the cord has occurred, the micturition reflexes are either completely or almost completely suppressed. This is believed to result from sudden loss of facilitatory impulses from the brain stem and cerebrum. However, the excitability of the micturition centers in the sacral cord gradually increases until typical micturition reflexes return. Sometimes these reflexes are elicited by approximately normal amounts of urine in the bladder, whereas at other times the threshold for eliciting the reflex may be very slight or very large. The factor that causes this difference is the treatment of the patient during the early stages of the convalescent period. If the bladder is kept completely empty by continuous drainage, contracture of the bladder causes a low threshold for development of micturition reflexes. But, if the bladder is allowed to remain overly filled for long periods of time, it becomes progressively stretched, and large quantities of urine will then be necessary to elicit micturition reflexes.

It is especially interesting that scratching or otherwise stimulating the skin in the genital region can sometimes elicit a micturition reflex in this condition, thus providing a means by which some patients can still control the time of urination.

The Uninhibited Neurogenic Bladder. A fourth common abnormality of micturition is the so-called "uninhibited neurogenic bladder," which results in frequent and relatively uncontrollable micturition. This condition derives from damage in the spinal cord or brain stem that interrupts most of the inhibitory impulses. Therefore, facilitatory impulses passing continually down the cord keep the sacral centers so excitable that even a very small quantity of urine can elicit an uncontrollable micturition reflex and thereby promote urination.

REFERENCES

Aach, R. D., Rolf, D., and White, H. L.: Water losses and gains in fasting and nephrectomized rats. *Am. J. Physiol., 188:*156, 1957.

Allen, A. C.: *The Kidney—Medical and Surgical Diseases.* 2nd ed., New York, Grune & Stratton, Inc., 1960.

Baldwin, D. S., Berman, H. J., Heinemann, H. O., and Smith, H. W.: The elaboration of osmotically concentrated urine in renal disease. *J. Clin. Invest., 34:*800, 1955.

Bell, E. T.: Renal Diseases, 2nd ed., Philadelphia, Lea & Febiger, 1950.

Block, M. A., Wakim, K. G., Mann, F. C., and Bennett, W. A.: Renal lesions and function following prolonged experimental hypotension. *Surgery, 32:* 551, 1952.

Borghgraef, R. R., Kessler, R. H., and Pitts, R. F.: Plasma regression, distribution and excretion of radiomercury in relation to diuresis following the intravenous administration of Hg203 labeled chlormerodrin to the dog. *J. Clin. Invest., 35:*1055, 1956.

Boyd, R. I., and Commons, R. R.: The nephrotic syndrome: pathogenesis, diagnosis, and treatment. *M. Clin. North America, 36:*920, 1952.

Bradley, S. E.: The Pathologic Physiology of Uremia in Chronic Bright's Disease. Springfield, Illinois, Charles C Thomas, 1948.

Bradley, S. E., and Bradley, G. P.: Renal function during chronic anemia in man. *Blood, 2:*192, 1947.

Bradley, S. E., Bradley, G. P., Tyson, C. J., Curry, J. J., and Blake, W. D.: Renal function in renal diseases. *Am. J. Med., 9:*766, 1950.

Carter, N., Seldin, D. W., and Teng, H. C.: Effect of Diamox on plasma and urine acid-base composition during chronic respiratory acidosis. *Am. J. Physiol.*, 196:919, 1959.

Chinard, F. P., Lauson, H. D., Eder, H. A., Greif, R. L., and Hiller, A.: A study on the mechanism of proteinuria in patients with the nephrotic syndrome. *J. Clin. Invest.*, 33:621, 1954.

Corcoran, A. C., and Page, I. H.: The kidney; in Sodeman, W. A. (ed.): Pathologic Physiology. 2nd ed., Philadelphia, W. B. Saunders Co., 1956.

Di Luzio, N. R., and Houck, C. R.: The role of the kidney in the etiology of renal hyperlipemia. *J. Clin. Invest.*, 35:1381, 1956.

Eder, H. A., Lauson, H. D., Chinard, F. P., Greif, R. L., Cotzias, G. C., and VanSlume, D. D.: A study of the mechanisms of edema formation in patients with the nephrotic syndrome. *J. Clin. Invest.*, 33:636, 1954.

Fishberg, A.: Hypertension and Nephritis. 5th ed., Philadelphia, Lea & Febiger, 1954.

Greif, R. L., Sullivan, W. J., Jacobs, G. S., and Pitts, R. F.: Distribution of radio-mercury administered as labeled chlormerodrin (neohydrin) in the kidneys of rats and dogs. *J. Clin. Invest.*, 35:38, 1956.

Grollman, A.: Acute Renal Failure. Springfield, Illinois, Charles C Thomas, 1954.

Guyton, A. C.: The physiology of kidney disease. *Mississippi Doctor*, 30:68, 1952.

Hiatt, E. P.: Comparison of the diuretic effects of nitrate salts with other diuretic agents. *Am. J. Physiol.*, 189:173, 1957.

Keith, N. M.: Application of tests of renal function to renal disease. *M. Clin. North America*, 35:943, 1951.

Kessler, R. H., Lozano, R., and Pitts, R. F.: Studies on structure-diuretic activity relationships of organic compounds of mercury. *J. Clin. Invest.*, 36:656, 1957.

Kupfer, S., Thompson, D. D., and Pitts, R. F.: Isolated kidney and its response to diuretic agents. *Am. J. Physiol.*, 167:703, 1951.

Lauson, H. D., Forman, C. W., McNamara, H., Mattar, G., and Barnett, H. L.: The effect of corticotropin on glomerular permeability to albumin in children with the nephrotic syndrome. *J. Clin. Invest.*, 33:657, 1954.

Lippman, R. W.: Cation exchange resin in treatment of the nephrotic syndrome. *Arch. Int. Med.*, 88:9, 1951.

Marsh, D., Suzuki, G., and Meyers, F. H.: Role of afferent activity from the bladder in regulating its activity. *Am. J. Physiol.*, 196:351, 1959.

Merrill, J. P.: The Treatment of Renal Failure. New York, Grune & Stratton, Inc., 1955.

Mudge, G. H.: Clinical patterns of tubular dysfunction. *Am. J. Med.*, 24:785, 1958.

Munck, O.: Renal Circulation in Acute Renal Failure. Springfield, Illinois, Charles C Thomas, 1958.

Pitts, R. F.: The Physiological Basis of Diuretic Therapy. Springfield, Illinois, Charles C Thomas, 1959.

Relman, A. S., and Schwartz, W. B.: The kidney in potassium depletion. *Am. J. Med.*, 24:764, 1958.

Rhodin, J.: Electron microscopy of the kidney. *Am. J. Med.*, 24:661, 1958.

Toth, L. A.: Pseudo-water diuresis in man. *J. Urol.*, 76:206, 1956.

See also Chapter 8, Normal renal function; Chapter 9, Regulation of extracellular fluid; Chapter 10, Regulation of acid-base balance.

Part Three

BLOOD

Chapter 12

Red Blood Cells,
Anemia, and Polycythemia

The major function of red blood cells is to transport hemoglobin and thereby to transport oxygen from the lungs to the tissues. In some lower animals hemoglobin circulates as free protein in the plasma, not enclosed in red blood cells. However, when it is free in the plasma of the human being, approximately 3 per cent of it leaks through the capillary membrane into the tissue spaces or through the glomerular membrane of the kidney into Bowman's capsule each time the plasma passes through the capillaries. Therefore, in order for hemoglobin to remain in the blood stream, it must exist inside red blood cells.

The red blood cells have a few other functions besides simply transport of hemoglobin. For instance, they contain a large quantity of carbonic anhydrase, which catalyzes the reaction between carbon dioxide and water, increasing the rate of this reaction about 250 times. The rapidity of this reaction makes it possible for blood to react with large quantities of carbon dioxide and thereby transport it from the tissues to the lungs. Finally, because the red blood cells contain large quantities of hemoglobin and also normal quantities of electrolytes, the red blood cells are responsible for approximately 70 per cent of all the buffering power of whole blood. These specific functions are discussed elsewhere in the text and, consequently, are merely mentioned at the present time.

CHARACTERISTICS OF RED BLOOD CELLS

The Hematocrit. The term "hematocrit" means the percentage of the blood that is red blood cells. Ordinarily, when one expresses the hematocrit, the term per cent is not specifically stated. Thus, if one says that a patient has a hematocrit of 40, he actually means that 40 per cent of the volume of the blood is red blood cells. In the normal man the hematocrit averages 47 (± 7), and in the normal woman it averages 42 (± 5).

The Shape and Size of Red Blood Cells. Normal red blood cells are biconcave disks having a mean diameter of approximately 8 microns and a thickness at the thickest point of 2 microns and in the center of 1 micron or less. The average volume of the red blood cell is 87 (± 5) cubic microns.

The shapes of red blood cells can change tremendously as they pass through the capillaries. Actually, the red blood cell is a "bag" that can be deformed into almost any shape. Furthermore, when a red blood cell is deformed, because there is ordinarily a great excess of cellular membrane for the quantity of material inside, the deformation does not stretch the membrane and consequently does not rupture the cell.

The Concentration of Red Blood Cells in the Blood. In the normal man the average number of red blood cells per cubic millimeter is 5,400,000 ($\pm 600,000$) and in the normal woman it is 4,600,000 ($\pm 500,000$). The number of red blood cells varies in the different sexes and at different ages, as shown in Figure 90. Also, the altitude at which the person lives changes the number of red blood cells; this will be discussed later.

The Quantity of Hemoglobin in the Cells. The red blood cells have the ability to concentrate hemoglobin in the red cell fluid up to a value of approximately 34 grams per 100 ml. of red blood cells. Rarely does the concentration of hemoglobin rise above this value in each respective cell, for this limit apparently is a metabolic limit of the cell's hemoglobin-forming mechanism. Furthermore, in normal persons the percentage of hemoglobin is almost always near the maximum

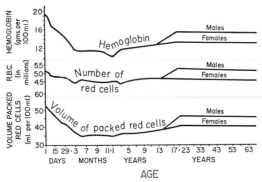

Figure 90. Relationship of age and sex to the hemoglobin content, red blood cell count, and hematocrit of the blood. (Redrawn from Wintrobe: Clinical Hematology. Lea & Febiger.)

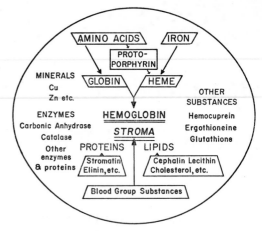

THE RED BLOOD CORPUSCLE

Figure 91. Constituents of the red blood cell and substances necessary for production of these constituents. (Redrawn from Wintrobe: Clinical Hematology. Lea & Febiger.)

level in each particular cell. However, when hemoglobin formation is deficient in the bone marrow, the percentage of hemoglobin in the cells may fall to as low as 15 grams per cent or less.

When the hematocrit and the quantity of hemoglobin in each respective cell are normal, the whole blood of men contains an average of 16 grams of hemoglobin per 100 ml. and of women an average of 14 grams per 100 ml. As will be discussed in connection with the transport of oxygen in Chapter 41, each gram of hemoglobin is capable of combining with approximately 1.3 ml. of oxygen. Therefore, in the normal man 21 ml. of oxygen can be carried in combination with hemoglobin in each 100 ml. of blood, and in the normal woman 18 ml. of oxygen can be carried.

The Membrane and Stroma of Red Blood Cells. The membrane and stroma of red blood cells represent approximately 2 to 5 per cent of the entire red blood cell by weight. This portion of the red blood cell is composed of approximately 50 per cent protein consisting of stromatin, elinin, and an "anti-sphering" protein. Another 10 per cent of the membrane and stroma is comprised of lipids, especially cephalin, lecithin, and cholesterol, though other lipids are also present. A large proportion of these lipids apparently is combined as lipoproteins with the protein of the stroma.

The thickness of the cell membrane is approximately 10 to 20 millimicrons.

PRODUCTION AND DESTRUCTION OF RED BLOOD CELLS

In discussing the production of red blood cells, two major factors must be considered: first, production of the cell itself and, second, production of hemoglobin in the cell. Figure 91 illustrates the complexity of red blood cell production, showing that many different substances are required for formation of the cell structure, that other substances are needed for formation of hemoglobin, and that still other substances are necessary to act as enzymes and catalysts during the processes of red cell formation. The importance of these various factors will be discussed in the following sections.

Areas of the Body That Produce Red Blood Cells. In the early few weeks of fetal life, primitive red blood cells are produced in the yolk sac. During the middle trimester of gestation the liver is the main organ for production of red blood cells, and at the same time a reasonable quantity of red blood cells is also produced by the spleen and the lymph nodes. Then, during the latter part of gestation and after birth, red blood cells are produced mainly by the bone marrow.

As illustrated by Figure 92, the bone marrow of essentially all bones produces red

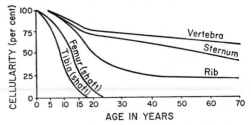

Figure 92. Relative rates of red blood cell production in the different bones at different ages. (Redrawn from Wintrobe: Clinical Hematology. Lea & Febiger.)

blood cells up until adolescence, but the marrow of the long bones becomes quite fatty and produces no more red blood cells after approximately the age of 20. Beyond this time only the marrow of the membranous bones such as the vertebrae, the sternum, and the ribs produces cells. Even in these bones the marrow becomes less productive as age increases; as a result, progressive, mild anemia usually develops in old age.

Sometimes when various factors stimulate the bone marrow to produce tremendous quantities of red blood cells, much of the marrow that has already stopped producing red blood cells can once again become productive, and that marrow which is still producing red blood cells can become greatly hyperplastic and produce far greater than normal quantities. Indeed, the spleen especially and occasionally even the liver may reestablish their hemopoietic functions long after birth when extreme stimuli persist for prolonged periods of time.

Genesis of the Red Blood Cell

The blood cells are derived from a primordial cell known as the *hemocytoblast*, which is illustrated in Figure 93. Also, new hemocytoblasts are continually being formed from *reticulum* cells located throughout the bone marrow.

As illustrated in Figure 93, the hemocytoblast first forms the *basophil erythroblast*, which begins the synthesis of hemoglobin. The erythroblast then becomes a *polychromatophil erythroblast*, so called because of a mixture of basophilic material and the red hemoglobin. Following this, the nucleus of the cell shrinks while still greater quantities of hemoglobin are formed, and the cell becomes a *normoblast*. During all these stages the different cells continue to divide so that greater and greater numbers of young red blood cells are formed. Finally, after the cytoplasm of the normoblast has become filled with hemoglobin up to a concentration of approximately 34 per cent, the nucleus of the normoblast disappears. It is generally believed that this nucleus is actually extruded from the cell, but it is possible that it undergoes autolysis and absorption. Nevertheless, the cell finally formed, the *erythrocyte*, usually contains no nuclear material when it passes by the process of diapedesis (squeezing through the pores of the membrane) into the blood capillaries. A few of the erythrocytes entering the blood still contain small amounts of basophilic proteins interspersed among the hemoglobin in the cytoplasm. These proteins are probably the remains of the hemoglobin-producing enzyme systems, for hemoglobin continues to be produced as long as they persist. They have the appearance of a delicate reticulum,

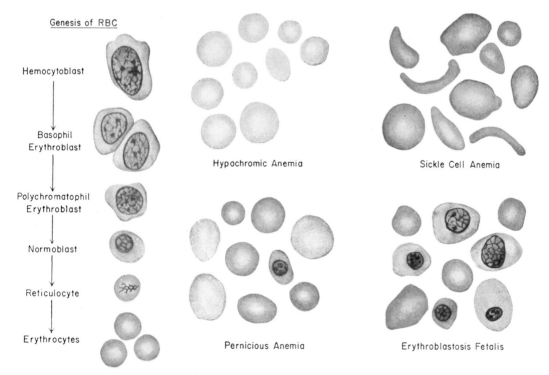

Genesis of RBC

Hemocytoblast

Basophil Erythroblast

Hypochromic Anemia

Sickle Cell Anemia

Polychromatophil Erythroblast

Normoblast

Reticulocyte

Erythrocytes

Pernicious Anemia

Erythroblastosis Fetalis

Figure 93.   Genesis of red blood cells, and red blood cells in different types of anemias.

and the cell, which is illustrated in Figure 93, is known as a *reticulocyte*. Ordinarily, the total proportion of reticulocytes in the blood is less than 0.5 per cent.

REGULATION OF RED BLOOD CELL PRODUCTION

The total mass of red blood cells in the circulatory system is regulated within very narrow limits so that an adequate number of red cells will always be available to provide sufficient tissue oxygenation and, yet, so that the cells will not be so concentrated that they impede blood flow. Yet, strangely enough we do not know the exact mechanism by which this regulation is effected even though it is one of the most important of all the regulatory systems of the body. What we do know is the following.

Maximal rate of red blood cell production. The normal rate of red blood cell production is approximately enough to form 1250 ml. of new blood per month, and this is also the normal rate of red cell destruction. The adult who has suffered severe hemorrhage can increase this to at least 4 times normal, and, in persons who have had to produce red blood cells rapidly for long periods of time because of blood diseases, extreme hyperplasia of the bone marrow and of hemopoietic tissue in the spleen and elsewhere might increase the rate of red blood cell production to as high as 10 to 15 times normal.

Tissue Oxygenation as the Basic Regulator of Red Blood Cell Production

Any condition that causes the quantity of oxygen transported to the tissues to decrease ordinarily increases the rate of red blood cell production. Thus, when a person becomes extremely *anemic* as a result of hemorrhage or any other condition, the bone marrow immediately begins to produce large quantities of red blood cells. Also, destruction of portions of the bone marrow by any means, especially x-ray therapy, causes hyperplasia of the remaining bone marrow, thereby supplying the demand for red blood cells in the body.

At very *high altitudes*, where the quantity of oxygen in the air is greatly decreased, insufficient oxygen is transported to the tissues,

and red cells are produced so rapidly that the number of red blood cells in the blood is considerably increased. Therefore, it is obvious that it is not the concentration of red blood cells in the blood that controls the rate of red cell production, but, instead, it is the functional ability of the cells to transport oxygen to the tissues that is the determinant of the rate of production.

Various diseases of the circulation that cause decreased blood flow through the peripheral vessels also increase the rate of red cell production. This is especially apparent in prolonged *cardiac failure,* for the anoxia resulting from sluggish flow of blood through the tissues in this condition increases the rate of red cell production, with resultant increase in the hematocrit and usually some increase in the total blood volume.

The Basic Mechanism by which Tissue Anoxia Increases Red Cell Production —Erythropoietic Stimulating Factor

Localized anoxia of the bone marrow *does not* increase the rate of red blood cell production even though generalized anoxia throughout the body does do so. Furthermore, blood plasma removed from an anoxic animal and injected into a normal animal causes very rapid red blood cell production. Therefore, it is quite certain that some *humoral factor* is present in the plasma of anoxic animals that has the capability of increasing the rate of red blood cell production. All the known general hormones, such as the adrenocortical hormones, thyroid hormone, etc., have been eliminated as possible causes of this effect. Therefore, the cause has been postulated to be a specific factor or group of factors called *erythropoietic stimulating factor, erythropoietin,* and *hemopoietin.*

No specific site in the body, with the possible exception of the kidneys, has been found in which erythropoietic stimulating factor is formed in greater abundance than in other parts of the body. Nephrectomized animals develop only small concentrations of erythropoietic stimulating factor, but this might result from toxicity caused by nephrectomy. Therefore, at present, it is believed that erythropoietic stimulating factor is formed generally throughout the body, possibly as a product of the blood cells themselves or more likely of all the anoxic tissues in the body.

Erythropoietic stimulating factor exerts its actions directly on the bone marrow, stimulating all phases of red cell production, including the rate of cell maturation as well as the rate of erythrocyte release from the bone marrow into the blood.

An excess of red blood cells in the circulation greatly diminishes the formation of erythropoietic stimulating factor, thereby decreasing the rate of red cell production and returning the total red cell mass to normal.

Other Factors That Affect the Rate of Red Blood Cell Production

When the rate of hemoglobin production is depressed in the tissues, a proportionate decrease in rate of red blood cell production does not necessarily occur. Therefore, the level of iron in the body *does not* directly affect the total number of red blood cells produced, but the level of iron does greatly alter the quantity of hemoglobin that is available to fill the red blood cells. Consequently, when iron is deficient, the newly formed cells enter the blood stream in a *hypochromic* state and are not capable of carrying normal amounts of oxygen.

Male sex hormones increase the rate of red blood cell production by approximately 10 per cent, while female sex hormones do not greatly affect the production. Also, lack of sufficient quantities of thyroid hormone, adrenocortical hormones, and some anterior pituitary hormones can depress the rate of red cell formation. On the other hand, excess adrenocortical hormones and perhaps excesses of other hormones can cause considerable increase in the rate of red blood cell production. Thus, in patients with adrenocortical tumors one of the features of the disease is often an excess of red blood cells.

Obviously, lack of any of the various accessory substances necessary for red blood cell production, which will be discussed later in the chapter, depresses the rate of red blood cell production.

Effect of Rate of Red Blood Cell Formation on the Type of Cell Released into the Blood

When the bone marrow produces red blood cells at a very rapid rate, many of the cells are released from the bone marrow into the blood before they are mature erythrocytes. Thus, marked increase in the rate of red cell production can cause the percentage of reticulocytes in the circulating blood to rise to as high as 30 to 50 per cent of the total number of red blood cells, and, if the rate of production is even greater, a large number of normoblasts may appear in the circulating blood. In some of the severe anemias, such as erythroblastosis fetalis and thalassemia, which will be discussed later in the chapter, the number of normoblasts may occasionally rise to as high as 5 to 20 per cent of all the circulating red blood cells. Finally, if the stimulus for production of red blood cells becomes extreme, a small number of erythroblasts and possibly even an occasional hemocytoblast may appear in the circulating blood.

CHEMICAL FACTORS NEEDED FOR FORMATION OF THE RED BLOOD CELL STROMA AND MEMBRANE

When certain constituents of the diet are missing or when an animal is incapable of utilizing these constituents, the red blood cell is formed abnormally or very slowly. For instance, many of the vitamins in the vitamin B complex are especially needed for appropriate production of red blood cells. Also, the substances choline and thymidine are necessary for production of the red blood cell stroma and membrane. The most important of the vitamin B compounds appear to be vitamin B_{12} and folic acid (pteroylglutamic acid). However, patients who have severe nicotinic acid deficiency and patients with severe thiamine deficiency may also develop moderate anemias. Also, deficiency of pyridoxine can cause a very severe anemia in animals, though this type of deficiency rarely if ever occurs in human beings because sufficient pyridoxine is usually present in the diet.

The Maturation Factor—Vitamin B_{12} (Cyanocobalamin)

Vitamin B_{12} is an essential nutrient for all cells of the body, and growth of tissues in general is greatly depressed when this vitamin is lacking. However, since red blood cell—forming tissues are among the most rapidly growing and proliferating of all the tissues, lack of vitamin B_{12} especially inhibits the rate of red blood cell production. Furthermore, the erythroblastic cells of the bone marrow, in addition to failing to proliferate rapidly, become larger than normal and, therefore, develop into so-called *mega-*

loblasts instead of erythroblasts. Their cell membranes are poorly formed and very fragile, and the stroma of the cell is probably also abnormal, for the adult erythrocyte, called a *macrocyte,* is often quite irregular, large, and oval instead of the usual biconcave disc. These poorly formed macrocytes, after entering the circulating blood, are quite capable of carrying oxygen, but their fragility causes them to have a short life, measured in weeks instead of in months, as is true of normal cells. Therefore, it is said that vitamin B_{12} deficiency causes *maturation failure* in the process of erythropoiesis.

The occurrence of maturation failure does not prevent normal formation of hemoglobin. Indeed, the hemoglobin *concentration* in the cell is approximately 34 grams per cent, the same as normal, and, moreover, the average *quantity* of hemoglobin in the macrocyte is considerably greater than normal because the average volume of each cell is greater than normal.

Maturation Failure Caused by Poor Absorption of Vitamin B_{12}—Pernicious Anemia. The usual cause of maturation failure is not a lack of vitamin B_{12} in the diet but instead failure to absorb the vitamin B_{12} from the gastrointestinal tract. This most commonly occurs in the disease called *pernicious anemia,* in which the basic abnormality is an *atrophic gastric mucosa* that fails to secrete normal gastric secretions. In the mucus secreted by the stomach is a mucoprotein (or some substance bound with the mucoproteins) that combines with the vitamin B_{12} in the diet and makes it much more soluble than usual, thereby allowing it to be absorbed from the lower gastrointestinal tract. Lack of this so-called *intrinsic factor* in the gastric secretions usually leads to a deficiency of vitamin B_{12} and subsequently to maturation failure and anemia. It also leads to poor growth of the body in the young person and to degenerative conditions in the central nervous system, which will be discussed at further length in Chapter 70.

Once vitamin B_{12} has been absorbed from the gastrointestinal tract it is stored in large quantities in the liver and then released slowly as needed to the bone marrow and other tissues of the body. The total amount of vitamin B_{12} required each day to maintain normal red cell maturation is less than 1 microgram.

Relationship of Folic Acid (Pteroylglutamic Acid) to Vitamin B_{12}. Occasionally a patient with maturation failure anemia responds equally as well to folic acid as to vitamin B_{12}, so that it has become apparent that this substance is also concerned with the maturation of red blood cells. Though the precise actions of both folic acid and vitamin B_{12} are not known, it is believed that they act as co-enzymes at different stages in the synthesis of nucleoproteins, folic acid and vitamin B_{12} both being required for the formation of deoxyribose nucleoprotein and vitamin B_{12} alone being necessary for the production of ribose nucleoprotein. Though folic acid can often substitute for vitamin B_{12} in the maturation process of red blood cells, it cannot act as a substitute for vitamin B_{12} in the maintenance of central nervous system integrity because here the major requirement is for production of ribose nucleoprotein rather than for deoxyribose nucleoprotein.

FORMATION OF HEMOGLOBIN

Synthesis of hemoglobin begins in the erythroblasts and continues throughout the normoblastic stage. Even when young red blood cells leave the bone marrow and pass into the blood stream, they continue to form hemoglobin for many days. Thus, hemoglobin formation does not depend upon a specific structure of the bone marrow but, instead, is an intrinsic ability of the early red blood cells themselves.

Figure 94 gives the basic steps in the formation of hemoglobin. All the chemical steps in this process are not known, but from tracer studies with isotopes it is known that hemoglobin is synthesized mainly from acetic acid and glycine. It is believed that the acetic acid is changed in Krebs' cycle, which will be explained in Chapter 65, into alpha-ketoglutaric acid, and then two molecules of this combine with one molecule of glycine to form a pyrrole compound. In turn, four pyrrole compounds combine to form a protoporphyrin compound. One of the protoporphyrin compounds, known as protoporphyrin III, then combines with iron to form the heme molecule. Finally, four heme molecules combine with one molecule of

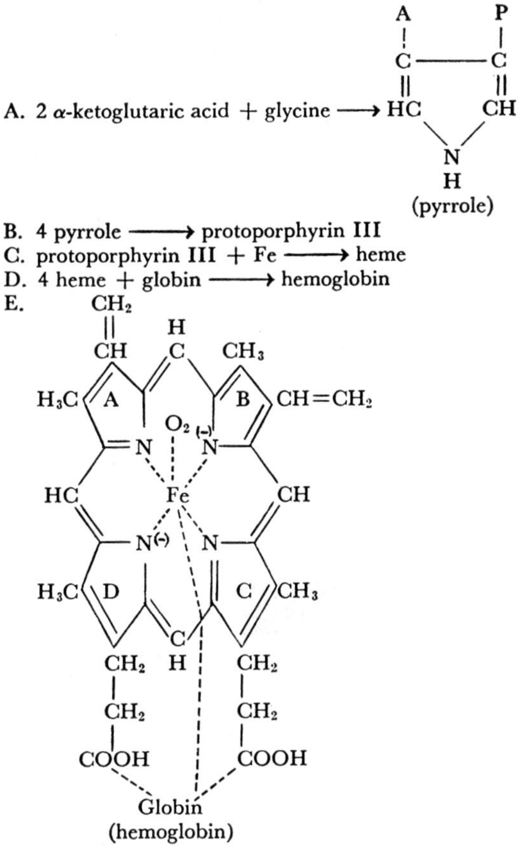

A. 2 α-ketoglutaric acid + glycine ⟶

$$\begin{array}{ccc} A & & P \\ | & & | \\ C & \!\!\!\!-\!\!\!\!- & C \\ \| & & \| \\ HC & & CH \end{array}$$

\N
H
(pyrrole)

B. 4 pyrrole ⟶ protoporphyrin III
C. protoporphyrin III + Fe ⟶ heme
D. 4 heme + globin ⟶ hemoglobin
E.

Globin
(hemoglobin)

Figure 94. Formation of hemoglobin.

globin, a globulin, to form hemoglobin, which has a molecular weight of 68,800. In Section *E* of Figure 94, the manner in which iron and globin combine with protoporphyrin III to form hemoglobin is illustrated.

Combination of Hemoglobin with Oxygen

The most important feature of the hemoglobin molecule is its ability to combine loosely and reversibly with oxygen. This ability will be discussed in detail in Chapter 41, for the entire function of hemoglobin in the body depends upon its ability to combine with oxygen in the lungs and then to release this oxygen readily in the tissue capillaries where the gaseous tension of oxygen is much lower than in the lungs.

It is illustrated in Figure 94 that oxygen *does not* combine with the two positive valences of the ferrous iron in the hemoglobin molecule. Instead, it binds very

loosely with two of the six "coordination" valences of the iron atom. This is an extremely loose bond so that the combination is easily reversible. Furthermore, the oxygen does not become ionic oxygen but is carried as molecular oxygen to the tissues where, because of the loose, readily reversible combination, it is released into the tissue fluids still in the form of dissolved molecular oxygen rather than ionic oxygen. It should be recalled at this point that each molecule of hemoglobin contains four molecules of heme. Therefore, one molecule of hemoglobin contains four iron atoms and can carry four molecules of oxygen.

Iron Metabolism

Because iron is a very important substance for the formation of hemoglobin and oxidative enzymes such as myoglobin, the cytochromes, cytochrome oxidase, peroxidase, and catalase, it is essential to understand the means by which iron is utilized in the body.

The total quantity of iron in the body averages about 4.5 grams, and approximately 65 per cent of this is present in the form of hemoglobin. Approximately 4 per cent is present in the form of myoglobin, approximately 1 per cent in the form of the various heme enzymes that control intracellular oxidation, approximately 0.1 per cent in the form of transferrin in the blood plasma, approximately 15 per cent stored in the form of ferritin or hemosiderin, and approximately 10 to 15 per cent probably in other forms.

Transport and Storage of Iron. Transport, storage, and metabolism of iron in the body is illustrated in Figure 95, which may be explained as follows: When iron is absorbed from the small intestine, it immediately combines with a beta globulin to form the compound *transferrin*, in which form it is transported in the blood plasma. The iron in this compound is very loosely combined with the globulin molecule, and, consequently, it can be released to any of the tissue cells at any point in the body. Excess iron present in the blood is deposited in the cells, especially in the liver cells, and there it combines with *apoferritin* to form *ferritin*. Apoferritin is a protein having a molecular weight of approximately 460,000, and varying quantities of iron can combine in clusters

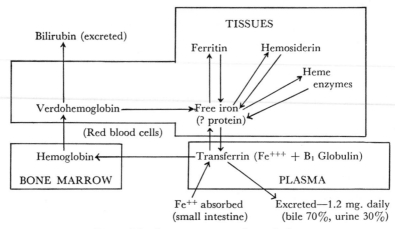

Figure 95. Iron transport and metabolism.

of iron radicals with the apoferritin molecule; therefore, ferritin may contain only a small amount of iron or a relatively large amount. Thus, most of the *storage iron* in the normal person is stored in the form of ferritin, which is present in all cells of the body, but to an extreme extent in the liver cells, and is spread diffusely throughout each cell.

When the total quantity of iron in the body is more than the apoferritin storage pool can accommodate, some of it is stored in the less soluble form of *hemosiderin.* Hemosiderin forms large clusters in the cells and consequently can be stained and observed in tissue slices by usual histologic techniques, whereas ferritin cannot.

When the quantity of iron in the plasma falls very low, iron is absorbed from ferritin quite easily but less easily from hemosiderin. The absorbed iron is then transported to the portions of the body where it is needed.

When the red blood cells have lived their life span and are destroyed, the hemoglobin released from the cells is ingested by the reticuloendothelial cells. There free iron is liberated, and it can then either be stored in the form of ferritin or hemosiderin or it can be transferred to other parts of the body for various uses.

Daily Loss of Iron. About 1.2 mg. of iron are excreted each day into the bile and urine—approximately 70 per cent into the bile and 30 per cent into the urine. In addition to this loss of iron, additional quantities are lost whenever bleeding occurs. Thus, in the female, the menstrual loss of blood

brings the average iron loss up to a value of approximately 2.1 mg. per day instead of the 1.2 mg. per day lost from the average male.

Obviously, the quantity of iron derived from the diet each day must at least equal that lost from the body. The dietary iron will be discussed in Chapter 70.

Regulation of Body Iron by the Mucosal Absorptive Process. The amount of iron absorbed from the gastrointestinal tract is automatically regulated by the amount of iron already present in the body. The mechanism of this is the following: The initial step in the absorption of iron is combination of the iron with *apoferritin* in the mucosal cells to form *ferritin.* The iron is then exchanged from the ferritin to *transferrin* that transports it away in the blood. If all the iron storage areas of the body are already saturated with iron, then little or no iron will be transported from the gastrointestinal mucosa. As a result, *the apoferritin of the mucosa becomes saturated with iron* so that no further iron can be absorbed. On the other hand, if the body has been depleted of iron, the rate of iron transport away from the gastrointestinal mucosa becomes very marked, and, consequently, the rate of absorption is also greatly increased.

Only ferrous iron can combine with apoferritin in the gastric mucosa to form ferritin. Fortunately, the acidity of the gastric contents, as well as the presence of a number of reducing agents in the foods causes reduction of a large portion of the ferric iron to the ferrous form. Yet, organic iron in the form of hemoglobin, myoglobin, and other heme compounds normally is not released from the food so that these substances are not adequate to supply the daily needs for iron.

Accessory Substances Needed for Formation of Hemoglobin

In addition to amino acids and iron, which are needed directly for formation of the hemoglobin molecule, a number of other substances act as catalysts or enzymes during different stages of hemoglobin formation. For instance, an average human adult requires approximately 2 mgs. of *copper* each day in his diet if normal hemoglobin formation is to take place, and addition of small quantities of copper to the diet of patients who have hypochromic anemia occasionally accelerates the rate of hemoglobin formation. This occurs even though copper is not one of the substances needed as a building stone in the formation of hemoglobin. Fortunately, the quantity of copper in the normal daily diet is sufficient that copper deficiency anemia is almost unknown in the human being.

Lack of *pyridoxine* in the diet of some animals not only decreases the rate of red blood cell formation but depresses the rate of hemoglobin formation to an even greater extent. Also, *cobalt* deficiency can greatly depress the formation of hemoglobin in some animals, whereas, strangely enough, a great excess of cobalt can cause formation of greater than normal numbers of red blood cells that contain normal quantities of hemoglobin. Finally, *nickel* has been found to take the place of cobalt to a moderate extent in aiding the synthesis of hemoglobin in the bone marrow.

Though the function of these different substances in the formation of hemoglobin is not known, the above listing of them serves mainly to emphasize the fact that hemoglobin formation results from a series of synthesis reactions, each one of which depends upon appropriate building materials and also upon appropriate controlling catalysts and enzymes.

Protoporphyrin III in Red Blood Cells. Approximately 40 micrograms of protoporphyrin III, one of the precursors of hemoglobin, is present in each 100 ml. of normal circulating red blood cells. When iron is deficient in the body, normal quantities of protoporphyrins are still produced by the erythroblasts in their attempt to form hemoglobin, but these protoporphyrins are not further synthesized into hemoglobin. Consequently, in patients who have chronic iron deficiency, the quantity of protoporphyrin III in the circulating red blood cells may rise to as high as 600 micrograms per 100 ml. On the other hand, in patients who have severe pernicious anemia, in which cells fail to mature, essentially all the protoporphyrin that is formed in the cells is synthesized into hemoglobin during the long period of quiescence before the cells are released into the blood stream. Therefore, the content of protoporphyrin III in the circulating red blood cells of pernicious anemia patients is only approximately 15 micrograms per cent. From these data, it is obvious that the quantity of protoporphyrin III in the cells is a measure of the ratio of the rate of cell formation to the rate of hemoglobin formation.

Porphyria. Occasionally, synthesis of protoporphyrin III is abnormal, and large quantities of one of the intermediate protoporphyrins, protoporphyrin I, is formed. What prevents the conversion of protoporphyrin I into protoporphyrin III is not known, but this condition frequently occurs in liver disease, and even more often in persons who have a hereditary tendency toward porphyria. When protoporphyrin I cannot change into protoporphyrin III, some automatic mechanism causes far greater than normal quantities of protoporhyrin I to be formed, and much of this is then excreted in the urine. Upon exposure to light, the protoporphyrin I develops a reddish black color, giving the urine a dark red or even black appearance if the quantity is sufficient.

The presence of porphyrins in the body fluids frequently causes the skin to become quite sensitive to light, exposure to sunlight often leading to bullous lesions.

DESTRUCTION OF RED BLOOD CELLS

Life Span of the Red Blood Cell in the Circulatory System

When the red blood cell is delivered from the bone marrow into the circulatory system, it normally circulates an average of 120 days before being destroyed.

The experimental method by which the life of red blood cells has been determined has been to tag them with one of many different radioactive materials and then to study the rate of loss of radioactive red blood cells from the circulatory system. By appropriate mathematical calculations one can then deduce the average life of the cells. The determinations made in this manner have ranged from approximately 90 days up to 140 days, but it appears from the best-controlled studies that the average life of the red cell is approximately in the range of 120 days. Figure 96 shows the progressive anemia that occurs during the few months following sudden cessation of red blood cell production by the bone marrow,

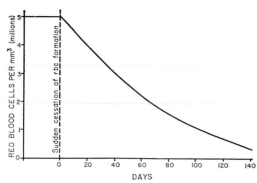

Figure 96. Effect of sudden cessation of red blood cell formation on subsequent red blood cell concentration in the circulatory system.

illustrating again how long some of the cells continue to live.

Insofar as is known, there are no factors that increase the life span of the red blood cell, but many factors can shorten the life span. One of the most important of these factors is malformation of the red blood cells in the bone marrow so that the shapes of the cells are abnormal or so that the cell membranes are fragile; as a result, the cells rupture quite easily when they are deformed in passing through the capillaries, resulting in one of the anemias which will be discussed later in the chapter.

Method of Red Blood Cell Destruction in the Body

No specific mechanism has been found in the body for destroying red blood cells. Instead, as the red blood cell becomes older and older, the cell membrane simply becomes more and more fragile, and then finally, during one of the periods of deformation as the cell squeezes through a capillary, it *fragments.* Such fragmentation takes place to a relatively large extent in the spleen—especially when the red blood cells enter the pulp of the spleen by the process of diapedesis and then pass by the same process into the splenic sinusoids. Obviously, such a procedure would have an intensely destructive action on any red blood cell that exhibits even a minor degree of fragility. However, removal of the spleen from the body does not materially affect the normal rate of red blood cell destruction. Consequently, probably the major proportion of the red blood cells, even under normal con-

ditions, is destroyed in other parts of the circulatory system rather than in the spleen.

Once the cells have fragmented, the hemoglobin immediately diffuses throughout the plasma, and the cell membrane becomes a crumbled shell and thereafter is known as a cell "ghost." These cell ghosts are probably removed from the blood within a few minutes by the reticuloendothelial cells lining many of the blood vessels and especially the sinusoids of the spleen, the liver, and the bone marrow. Presumably the cell ghosts are digested in the reticuloendothelial cells, and the proteins and lipids are used either for energy or are re-used by various portions of the body for building other structures. The hemoglobin that is released into the plasma leaks through the capillary membrane into the tissue spaces, where it is broken down by reticuloendothelial cells or other cells into component parts as follows.

Destruction of Hemoglobin

When a red cell fragments, its hemoglobin is immediately released into the plasma. Very soon, this is phagocytized by the reticuloendothelial cells, which split the heme portion from the globin molecule and open the porphyrin ring of the heme at one of the methene bridges. The result is a straight chain of four pyrrole nuclei, which is the basic structure of bile pigment. The first pigment formed is *biliverdin,* but this is rapidly reduced to *bilirubin.* These products are gradually released into the plasma.

Bilirubin is insoluble in water, but it combines firmly with plasma proteins and is transported in this form throughout the body. On reaching the liver, the liver cells remove the bilirubin from the protein and conjugate approximately 80 per cent of it with glucuronic acid to form *bilirubin glucuronide.* This is highly soluble in water and is normally secreted by the liver cells into the bile. An additional 10 per cent is conjugated with sulfate to form the soluble *bilirubin sulfate,* and the final 10 per cent is conjugated with other solubilizing substances, all of which are similarly excreted.

It is bilirubin in the bile that gives it its greenish-yellow color, and any failure of the liver to excrete bile causes increased quantities of bilirubin in the body fluids. These in turn produce a yellow color (jaundice) in the skin. Obviously, the more rapid the destruction of red blood cells the greater also will be the amount of bilirubin in the body fluids. This entire subject of bilirubin excretion by the liver will be discussed in detail in relation to liver function in Chapter 72.

In forming the bile pigments, the reticuloendothelial cells remove the iron from the heme, and this is immediately released by the reticuloendothelial cells into the iron pool of the body as discussed above. The iron then can be reused for formation of additional hemoglobin or other substances, or it may be stored temporarily until needed at a later date.

THE ANEMIAS

Anemia means a deficiency of red blood cells in the blood. Physiologically, the different types of anemia can be classified under four major headings: first, anemias caused by blood loss; second, anemias caused by bone marrow aplasia; third, anemias caused by maturation failure; and, fourth, anemias caused by hemolysis.

Anemias Caused by Blood Loss

After acute blood loss, the total quantities of circulating red blood cells and of circulating plasma are decreased. The plasma portion of the blood is replaced within approximately 24 hours; this replacement obviously dilutes the blood and decreases the hematocrit. The red blood cells are the same cells that had been in the blood prior to the hemorrhage, and, consequently, the anemia is said to be *normochromic, normocytic anemia* because the cells contain normal quantities of hemoglobin and are of normal size. During the ensuing three or four weeks new red blood cells are formed rapidly because of increased stimulus from the resulting tissue anoxia, and the condition is corrected.

Chronic Blood Loss Anemia. When blood is lost continually over long periods of time, not only are the actual red blood cells lost, but large proportions of the body iron are depleted. Furthermore, large quantities of iron usually cannot be obtained from the diet with ease because the dietary quantities are small. Yet, tissue anoxia causes the bone marrow to continue producing large numbers of red blood cells. Since these cells are not fully filled with hemoglobin when they are released into the blood, they are small in size and the concentration of hemoglobin is less than normal, ranging usually between 15 and 30 per cent instead of the normal 34 per cent. Thus, the person develops *hypochromic, microcytic anemia.*

Treatment of this type of anemia by oral administration of iron is usually completely effective.

Anemia Caused by Bone Marrow Aplasia

Bone marrow aplasia means simply lack of a functioning bone marrow. When the bone marrow is destroyed suddenly, those cells already present in the blood usually are normal cells, depending upon the condition of the bone marrow prior to cessation of red blood cell production. Consequently, these persons in general have *normochromic, normocytic anemia.*

Sudden bone marrow aplasia can result from excessive exposure to x-ray or gamma ray radiation. Many persons exposed to the blast of the atom bomb lived through the explosion but died a month or more later from aplastic anemia. However, gamma ray radiation does not destroy the primordial reticulum cells or hemocytoblasts to the same extent that it destroys the more differentiated cells. Consequently, if a person can live through the first few months of anemia, ordinarily his red blood cell count returns to normal or near normal after a few more months.

Aplastic anemia is also frequently caused by cancerous invasion of the bone marrow or by poisoning with different industrial chemicals or drugs, especially those derived from benzene or other aromatic organic compounds.

Anemia Caused by Maturation Failure

Several different types of maturation failure anemia occur. One of these is *pernicious anemia,* which is also known as *addisonian anemia.* It was pointed out above that the basic cause of pernicious anemia is an atrophic stomach mucosa which fails to secrete a mucoprotein called "intrinsic factor"; this factor must combine with vitamin B_{12} before it can be absorbed adequately from the gastrointestinal tract. Lack of vitamin B_{12} absorption results in failure of red blood cell maturation and greatly reduced output of cells by the bone marrow.

A number of other conditions besides pernicious anemia can also cause maturation failure. For instance, in *pregnancy* the infant frequently requires so many vitamins from the mother that not enough are left for the mother to produce normal red blood cells. Secondly, in *sprue* (a disorder of absorption in the intestinal tract) the absorption of vitamin B_{12}, even though sufficient "intrinsic factor" is available, is deficient, and maturation failure results. Finally, after *total gastrectomy* "intrinsic factor" is absent, and maturation failure will result if prophylactic therapy is not provided.

In maturation failure anemia the cells have very bizarre shapes because of the poor formation of the cells. Indeed, a few of the cells may be minute in size and are called "microcytes," but the average size is considerably larger than normal so that the anemia is often known as *macrocytic anemia*. Furthermore, all the cells are well filled with hemoglobin so that the percentage in the cells is approximately 34 per cent, the normal value. Because the cells are actually larger than normal and therefore contain a greater than normal quantity of hemoglobin, these cells are frequently said to be "hyperchromic," and the anemia occasionally is called by a fourth name, *hyperchromic anemia*.

In maturation failure anemia the red blood cell count may rarely fall as low as 1 million per cubic millimeter or, in other words, to about one-fifth the normal number of red blood cells. This decrease is caused both by decreased rate of cell production and also by rapid destruction of the cells that are formed.

Treatment of Maturation Failure Anemia. Figure 97 illustrates the effects that occur in the blood when a patient with pernicious anemia is treated with vitamin B₁₂. Immediately, the number of red blood cells produced and released into the blood stream increases, as is evidenced by the number of reticulocytes that appear. For the first few days of treatment, these reticulocytes may represent as much as 15 per cent of the circulating red blood cells. Within approximately 40 days the treated patient has a normal red blood cell count, and the new cells are normal cells rather than macrocytic cells, with the result that the individual cell volume returns to normal. However, treatment must be continued indefinitely in many of these patients, or relapse will occur.

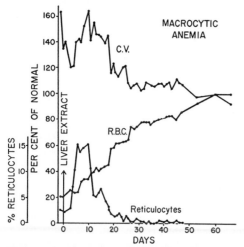

Figure 97. Treatment of maturation failure anemia with vitamin B₁₂. (Redrawn from Wintrobe: Clinical Hematology. Lea & Febiger.)

Anemias Caused by Hemolysis of the Red Blood Cells

Most of the hemolytic anemias are caused by hereditary abnormalities in the formation of the red blood cells that make them very fragile. One of these is *familial hemolytic anemia*, also known as *familial microcytosis* and *spherocytosis*, which results from production of very small red blood cells. The cells, instead of being flat and concave, are spherical. The volume of each cell may be nearly normal, but its shape is different from that of the normal cell, and when it attempts to squeeze through a small capillary, any lateral pressure on it can cause it to explode; the normal concave and flat cell is more like an unfilled bag which can squeeze into almost any shape. As a result of this likelihood of rupturing, the level of bilirubin in the body fluids is continually high, sometimes causing yellowness (jaundice) of the skin and particularly of the sclerae of the eyes. Obviously, the rapid destruction of the red blood cells also causes anemia. This condition is almost always greatly benefited by removal of the spleen, illustrating the sometimes importance of this organ in the process of red cell destruction.

In *sickle cell anemia*, which is present in a large percentage of the Negro population of the world, the cells in a blood smear appear to be long, new moon–like sickles instead of the normal biconcave cells. The process of sickling is caused by an inherited abnormality of the hemoglobin in the cells. The hemoglobin of the normal adult is called *hemoglobin A*, while that of patients with sickle cell anemia is quite different and is called *hemoglobin S*. The molecules of hemoglobin S tend to polymerize into long chains and to precipitate inside the cell, especially when the cell is exposed to low oxygen tension. It is this precipitation that causes the abnormal cellular shape, and this in turn makes the cells very fragile as they attempt to squeeze through the capillaries.

Patients with severe sickling tendencies often develop anemic "crises" in which the following sequence of events occurs: Some extrinsic factor causes a low oxygen tension in some peripheral circulatory bed, and this tension causes the hemoglobin of the cells passing through that bed to precipitate. As a result, the cells have difficulty passing through the capillaries, which impedes the flow of blood through the area. Extraction of oxygen by the tissues from the slowly moving blood further reduces the available oxygen so that still more cells become sickled, and the condition progresses by means of this vicious cycle from bad to worse. Once it starts large quantities of the person's cells are destroyed, always resulting in serious acute anemia that requires several weeks for repair or sometimes even causes death.

Thalassemia, which is also known as *Cooley's anemia* and, sometimes, as *Mediterranean anemia*, is another inherited type of anemia that occurs most commonly in Thailand and to less extents among the different Mediterranean races. The anemia results from 3 abnormalities of the red cells. First, the red cell membrane is very thin and fragile. Second, the cells are *microcytic* (very small) and contain low concentrations of hemoglobin. Third, most of the hemoglobin is of the *fetal type* called *hemoglobin F* instead of normal adult hemoglobin A. Because of the diminished hemoglobin content of the cells and also because of destruction of the fragile cells, tissue anoxia is often extreme. This causes very rapid hemopoiesis with tremendous numbers of early red blood cells appearing in the circulation, including sometimes as much as 10 to 15 per cent normoblasts and often even a few per cent erythroblasts.

Still other forms of hemolytic anemia occur. For instance, hemolysis often follows transfusion reactions. It occurs in malaria, and in some instances even syphilis can also cause hemolysis of the red blood cells. Physiologically, many of the same effects that occur in the hemolytic anemias described above also occur in these conditions.

Erythroblastosis Fetalis. Many babies are born with external signs of jaundice and with extreme anemia. When this occurs, the fetus usually has Rh positive blood, and the mother usually has Rh negative blood, as will be discussed in Chapter 15. Under these conditions the mother becomes immunized against the baby's Rh positive cells, and immune bodies from the mother pass through the placenta into the baby to destroy the baby's cells. For the first few weeks of life many of these immune bodies from the mother remain in the baby's body, destroying the red blood cells almost as rapidly as they are formed. This condition is known as *erythroblastosis fetalis* because of the characteristics of the blood, which can be explained as follows:

In erythroblastosis, as is also true in thalassemia, the bone marrow must produce red blood cells extremely rapidly to keep the person from dying of anemia. This rapid production of red blood cells by the bone marrow causes many early forms of red blood cells to be released into the blood, and the more rapidly the cells are produced, the younger are the cells released. In both thalassemia and erythroblastosis fetalis the young cells are produced so rapidly that an extremely high percentage of the red blood cells may be reticulocytes instead of mature erythrocytes, and as high as 5 to 15 per cent of the red blood cells may even be normoblasts. A few of the cells are still younger than normoblasts, going back to erythroblasts and hemocytoblasts. Consequently, the picture of the blood smear in erythroblastosis and in thalassemia is very striking, showing a large number of young nucleated red blood cells.

Effects of Anemia on the Circulatory System

The viscosity of the blood, which will be discussed in detail in Chapter 26, is dependent almost entirely on the concentration of red blood cells. In severe anemia the blood viscosity may fall to as low as 1.5 times that of water rather than the normal of approximately 3 times the viscosity of water. The greatly decreased viscosity of the blood decreases the resistance to blood flow in the peripheral vessels so that far greater than normal quantities of blood return to the heart. Consequently, the cardiac output is often increased to two or more times normal as a result of this decreased viscosity.

Probably, also, anoxia of the tissues can initiate reflex changes to cause additional increase in cardiac output. For instance, anoxia stimulates the carotid and aortic chemoreceptors, and possibly it even directly stimulates the vasomotor center of the medulla to a slight extent to increase the sympathetic activity throughout the body. Also, anoxia of the blood vessels themselves causes them to dilate, allowing increased return of blood to the heart. All these effects increase the cardiac output to a higher level than ever. Thus, one of the major effects of anemia is an *increased work load on the heart*.

The increased cardiac output in anemia offsets many of the symptoms of anemia, for, even though each unit quantity of blood carries only small quantities of oxygen, the rate of blood flow may be increased to an extent that almost normal quantities of oxygen are delivered to the tissues.

As long as an anemic person's rate of activity is low, he can live without fatal anoxia of the tissues, even though his concentration of red blood cells may be reduced to one-fourth normal. However, when he begins to perform exercise, his heart is not capable of pumping much greater quantities of blood than it is already pumping. Consequently, during exercise, which greatly increases the demands for oxygen, cardiac failure develops immediately, and extreme tissue anoxia results.

POLYCYTHEMIA

Physiologic Polycythemia. When one remains at high altitudes for weeks or months, his blood-forming organs automatically produce large quantities of red blood cells. This becomes so extreme at altitudes of 14,000 to 15,000 feet that all persons residing permanently at these levels have continued polycythemia, with blood cell counts of 6 million to 8 million per cubic millimeter, which are far above the normal 4½ million to 5½ million.

Polycythemia Vera (Erythremia). In addition to those persons who have physiologic polycythemia, others have a condition known as *polycythemia vera* in which the red blood cell count may be as high as 11 million and the hematocrit as high as 70 to 75 per cent. Polycythemia vera is a tumorous condition of the blood cell–producing organs that causes excess production of red blood cells in the same manner that a tumor of a breast causes excess production of a specific type of breast cell. It also causes excess production of white blood cells and platelets, but these are masked by the great overabundance of red cells.

In polycythemia vera not only does the hematocrit increase but the total blood volume occasionally also increases to as much as twice normal. As a result, the entire vascular system becomes intensely engorged. In addition to this many of the capillaries become plugged by the very viscous blood, for the viscosity of the blood in polycythemia vera sometimes increases from the normal of 3 times the viscosity of water up to 15 times the viscosity of water.

In polycythemia vera many of the red blood cells are very small. If they were of normal size, the maximum number of cells that could possibly occur in 1 cubic millimeter of blood would be approximately 11 million, even with no plasma at all left in the blood. However, blood cell counts as high as 11 million per cubic millimeter, and even higher in a few instances, have been recorded in polycythemia vera despite the fact that the hematocrits have been only about 70 to 75 per cent. Therefore, it is obvious that the red blood cells in such conditions must be only three-fourths normal size or smaller. This fact again illustrates that polycythemia vera results from production of abnormal cells.

Effect of Polycythemia on the Circulatory System

Because of the greatly increased viscosity of the blood in polycythemia, the flow of blood through the vessels is extremely sluggish. In accordance with the factors that regulate the return of blood to the heart as discussed in Chapter 35, it is obvious that increasing the viscosity tends to decrease the rate of venous return to the heart. On the other hand, the blood volume is greatly increased in polycythemia, which tends to increase the venous return. Actually, the cardiac output in polycythemia is not far from normal because these two factors more or less neutralize each other.

Because the total blood volume in polycythemia is sometimes twice normal, the circulation time through the body may also be increased to twice normal. In other words, the mean circulation time occasionally is as great as 120 seconds instead of the normal of approximately 60 seconds. Thus, the velocity of blood flow in any given vessel is considerably decreased in polycythemia.

The arterial pressure is normal in most persons with polycythemia, though in approximately one third of them the blood pressure is elevated. This means that the blood pressure regulating mechanisms can usually offset the tendency for increased blood viscosity to increase peripheral resistance and thereby increase arterial pressure. Yet, beyond certain limits, these regulations fail.

The color of the skin is dependent to a great extent on the quantity of blood in the subpapillary venous plexus. Obviously, in polycythemia vera the quantity of blood in this plexus is greatly increased. Furthermore, because the blood passes very sluggishly through the skin capillaries before entering the venous plexus, a larger than normal proportion of the hemoglobin is reduced before the blood enters the plexus. The blue color of this reduced hemoglobin is prepotent over the red color of oxygenated hemoglobin. Therefore, because a large quantity of blue, reduced hemoglobin is present in the subpapillary venous plexus, a person with polycythemia vera ordinarily has a cyanotic (blue) skin.

REFERENCES

Albritton, E. C.: Standard Values in Blood. Philadelphia, W. B. Saunders Co., 1952.

Behrendt, H.: Chemistry of Erythrocytes. Oxford, Blackwell Scientific Publications, 1957.

Berlin, N. I., Waldmann, T. A., and Weissman, S. M.: Life span of red blood cell. *Physiol. Rev.*, 39:577, 1959.

Castle, W. B.: Disorders of the blood; in Sodeman, W. A. (ed.): Pathologic Physiology. 2nd ed., Philadelphia, W. B. Saunders Co., 1956.

Cole, B. T., Penrod, K. E., and Hall, F. G.: The hematocrit and hemoglobin response of blood donors. *J. Aviation Med.*, 24:227, 1953.

Dacie, J. V.: The Hemolytic Anemias. 2nd ed., New York, Grune & Stratton, Inc., 1958.

Diggs, L. W.: The Morphology of Human Blood Cells. Philadelphia, W. B. Saunders Co., 1956.

Dougherty, T. F., and Dougherty, J. H.: Blood: formed elements. *Ann. Rev. Physiol.*, 15:195, 1953.

Drabkin, D. L.: Metabolism of the hemin chromoproteins. *Physiol. Rev.*, 31:345, 1951.

Eadie, G. S., and Brown, I. W., Jr.: Red blood cell survival studies. *Blood*, 8:1110, 1953.

Eadie, G. S., and Brown, I. W., Jr.: The potential life span and ultimate survival of fresh red blood cells in normal healthy recipients as studied by simultaneous Cr51 tagging and differential hemolysis. *J. Clin. Invest.*, 34:629, 1955.

Gordon, A. S.: Hemopoietine. *Physiol. Rev.*, *39*:1, 1959.

Grant, W. C., and Root, W. S.: Fundamental stimulus for erythropoiesis. *Physiol. Rev.*, *32*:449, 1952.

Hampton, J. K., Jr., and Mayerson, H. S.: Hemoglobin iron as stimulus for production of ferritin by kidney. *Am. J. Physiol.*, *160*:1, 1950.

Hartwig, Q. L., Melville, G. S., Jr., Leffingwell, T. P., and Young, R. J.: Iron-59 metabolism as an index of erythropoietic damage and recovery in monkeys exposed to nuclear radiations. *Am. J. Physiol.*, *196*: 156, 1959.

Heinrich, H. C.: Vitamin B_{12} and Intrinsic Factors. Stuttgart, Ferdanand Enke, 1957.

Jacobs, M. H.: Blood (formed elements). *Ann. Rev. Physiol.*, *20*:405, 1958.

Jonxis, J. H. P., and Delafresnaye, J. F. (eds.): Abnormal Haemoglobins. Springfield, Illinois, Charles C Thomas, 1959.

Lajtha, L. G.: Bone marrow cell metabolism. *Physiol. Rev.*, *37*:50, 1957.

Lawrence, J. H.: Polycythemia. New York, Grune & Stratton, Inc., 1955.

Linman, J. W.: Factors Controlling Erythropoiesis. Springfield, Illinois, Charles C Thomas, 1960.

Lipkin, M., and Hardy, J. D.: Differential diagnosis of hematologic diseases aided by mechanical correlation of data. *Science*, *125*:551, 1957.

Macfarlane, R. G. (ed.): The Functions of the Blood. New York, Academic Press, 1960.

Manwell, C.: Comparative physiology: blood pigments. *Ann. Rev. of Physiol.*, *22*:191, 1960.

Orahovats, P. D., and Root, W. S.: Effect of total sympathectomy on red cell and hemoglobin production in the chronically anemic dog. *Am. J. Physiol.*, *173*:324, 1953.

Pace, N., Meyer, L. B., and Vaughan, B. E.: Erythrolysis on return of altitude acclimatized individuals to sea level. *J. Appl. Physiol.*, *9*:141, 1956.

Pauling, L.: Abnormality of hemoglobin molecules in hereditary hemolytic anemias. *Harvey Lect.*, *49*:216, 1953–1954.

Piney, A.: A Clinical Atlas of Blood diseases. 7th ed., New York, Blakiston, 1952.

Root, W. S.: The stimulus for erythropoiesis. *J. Mt. Sinai Hosp.*, *20*:331, 1954.

Shemin, D.: The biosynthesis of porphyrins. *Harvey Lect.*, *50*:258, 1954–1955.

Shorr, E.: The intermediary metabolism and biological activities of ferritin. *Harvey Lect.*, *50*:112, 1954–1955.

Stroebel, C. F., and Fowler, W. S.: Secondary polycythemia. *Med. Clin. N. America*, *40*:1061, 1956.

Sturgis, C. C.: *Hematology.* 2nd ed., Springfield, Illinois, Charles C Thomas, 1955.

Talbot, G. D.: Blood and Bone Marrow Patterns. New York, Grune & Stratton, Inc., 1957.

Verloop M. C., Deenstra, H., and van der Hoeven, L. H.: Erythroblastosis and leukemia. *Blood, 7*: 453, 1952.

Weissman, S. M., Waldmann, T. A., and Berlin, N. I.: Quantitative measurement of erythropoiesis in the dog. *Am. J. Physiol.*, *198*:183, 1960.

Wilkinson, J. F.: Modern Trends in Blood Diseases. New York, Paul B. Hoeber, 1955.

Wintrobe, M. M.: Clinical Hematology. Philadelphia, Lea & Febiger, 1956.

Wintrobe, M. M.: Factors and mechanisms in the production of the red corpuscles. *Harvey Lect.*, *45*: 87, 1949–1950.

Witts, L. J.: Pathogenesis of the megaloblastic anemias. *Lancet*, *2*:367, 1951.

See also Chapter 13, The white blood cells.

Resistance of the Body to Infection; the Reticuloendothelial System; Leukocytes; Inflammation

The body is constantly exposed to bacteria. Some exist all the time in the mouth, the respiratory passageways, the colon, the mucous membrane of the eyes, and even the urinary tract, and many of these bacteria are actually capable of causing disease conditions if they invade the deeper tissues. In addition, a person is intermittently exposed to highly virulent bacteria and viruses from outside the body which can cause specific diseases such as pneumonia, streptococcic infections, typhoid fever, and so forth.

On the other hand, a group of tissues and cells collectively known as the *reticuloendothelial system* constantly combats any infectious agent that tries to invade the body. The reticuloendothelial system functions in two different ways to prevent disease: (1) by actually destroying any invading agent by the process of phagocytosis and (2) by forming immune bodies against the invading agent, the immune bodies in turn destroying the invader. The present chapter will be concerned with the first of these methods, while the following chapter will be concerned with the second.

THE RETICULOENDOTHELIAL SYSTEM

The reticuloendothelial system is comprised of those tissues and cells that are capable of phagocytizing bacteria, viruses, or other foreign agents or are capable of forming immune bodies against these. They include (1) the phagocytic cells of the bone marrow, spleen, liver, and lymph nodes, (2) the white blood cells in the circulatory system, and (3) phagocytic cells that wander through the tissues in constant quest of invading agents. All these cells are closely related to each other, and they have a common origin in the *reticulum cell.*

The Reticulum Cell. The reticulum cell is a primordial cell not greatly different from the original germinal epithelial cells. It is capable of differentiating into many other types of cells. For instance, reticulum cells in the bone marrow are continually forming (a) *hemocytoblasts,* which then form red blood cells, and (b) *myeloblasts,* which later become white blood cells. But equally as important is their capability to develop into *lymphocytes* in the lymph nodes and into *tissue histiocytes* which wander through the tissues to perform the function of phagocytosis.

Reticulum cells are found in great numbers in the red pulp of the spleen, and they line the sinuses of the spleen, the liver, and lymph nodes. At all these different points they exhibit the property of *phagocytosis*—that is, the ability to ingest foreign organisms or foreign particulate matter of any type.

Finally, reticulum cells in almost any part of the body can become *plasma cells* which, as will be discussed in great detail in the following chapter, are principally responsible for the formation of immune bodies. Therefore, the reticulum cell is the true basis of the reticuloendothelial system, which in turn provides the body with its resistance to infection.

General Organization of the Reticulo-endothelial System

The Lymph Nodes. The lymphatic system was discussed in Chapter 6, at which time it was pointed out that essentially no particulate matter nor even large molecular compounds can be absorbed directly through the capillary membranes into the blood stream. Instead, any invading organisms or even large molecules that enter the tissue spaces must pass by way of the lymphatic system into the blood. Lymph nodes are located intermittently along the course of the lymphatics. Figure 40 in Chapter 6 illustrates the general organization of a lymph node, showing lymph entering by way of the *afferent lymphatics,* flowing through the outer capsule of the lymph node into *subcapsular sinuses,* then gradually through the *medullary sinuses,* and finally out the *hilus* into the *efferent lymphatics.* Figure 98 illustrates the general meshwork of the medullary sinuses, with large numbers of reticulum cells lining the sinuses. If any proteins or particles foreign to the animal's own body are flowing in the

lymph, then these reticulum cells are capable of phagocytizing the foreign materials and preventing general dissemination throughout the body.

The Reticular Structures of the Circulatory System. If invading agents succeed in getting past the lymph nodes or if they should by chance enter the circulation directly without going through the lymph nodes, there is still a second line of defense for their removal even after they enter the circulation. Three special structures that contain large numbers of reticulum cells are responsible for this—the spleen, the liver, and the bone marrow.

Figure 99 illustrates the general structure of the *spleen,* with an artery entering the splenic capsule, then passing into the *splenic pulp,* and finally connecting through small capillaries with the large *venous sinuses.* The capillaries of certain parts of the spleen seem to be highly porous, allowing large quantities of whole blood cells to pass out of the capillaries into the *red pulp* and gradually to *squeeze* through the pulp and sinus walls back into the venous system. The red pulp is loaded with reticulum cells, and, in addition, the venous sinuses are also lined with reticulum cells. This peculiar passage of cells through the red pulp provides an exceptionally effective means for phagocytosis of unwanted debris in the blood, and the reticulum cells of the venous sinuses are additionally valuable.

The *sinuses of the liver* are also lined with reticulum cells, called *Kupffer cells,* which are illustrated in Figure 100. Though in any small portion of the liver the Kupffer cells may not be so numerous as the reticu-

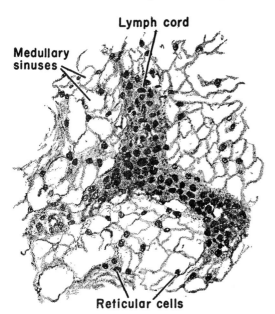

Figure 98. Magnified section of a lymph node, showing the *medullary sinuses* lined with *reticulum cells* and a *lymph cord* forming new lymphocytes.

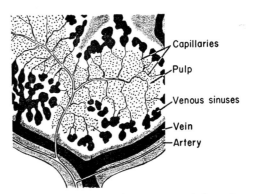

Figure 99. Functional structures of the spleen. (Modified from Maximow and Bloom: Textbook of Histology.)

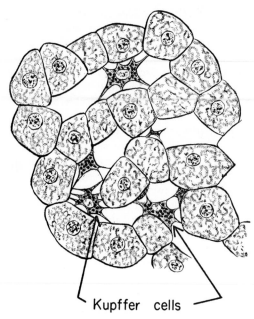

Kupffer cells

Figure 100. Kupffer cells lining the liver sinusoids, showing phagocytosis of India ink particles. (Redrawn from Copenhaver and Johnson: Bailey's Textbook of Histology. Williams and Wilkins Co.)

lum cells of the spleen, the total size of the liver is so much greater than that of the spleen that the liver ranks along with the spleen as an exceptionally important blood purifier. The reticulum system of the liver is especially valuable because all portal blood must pass through the liver before entering the general circulation. Large numbers of bacteria constantly pass by diapedesis through the gastrointestinal mucosa into the portal blood, but the liver filtration system is so effective that essentially none of these bacteria succeeds in passing from the portal blood into the general systemic circulation.

The reticulum cells of the *bone marrow* are of major importance as precursors of the red and white blood cells, but they are also capable of phagocytizing foreign substances that have entered the circulation. It is interesting that the reticulum cells of the bone marrow are even more capable than those of the spleen and liver for removing very fine particles such as protein toxins.

In summary, the different structures of the circulatory system which contain large numbers of reticulum cells operate continuously as a filtration system for removing unwanted materials from the circulation. Indeed, even

old blood cells which have ended their useful life span and have finally ruptured are removed by the reticulum cells—especially by those of the spleen.

Defense Functions of the Leukocytes in the Blood. The leukocytes, which flow freely in the blood and which will be discussed later in the chapter, are also capable of phagocytizing and removing foreign organisms from the blood; this is especially true of the polymorphonuclear neutrophils. However, the leukocytes probably perform most of their functions after they have passed out of the blood into the tissues, and it is primarily the reticulum cells that are responsible for direct cleansing of the blood.

The Tissue Histiocyte and Defense of the Tissues Against Infection. In virtually all tissues of the body are many cells called *histiocytes* or *clasmatocytes* that have properties almost identical with reticulum cells. These are always available to remove foreign substances, and they can even phagocytize necrotic tissue cells and any other debris that might enter the tissues.

In addition to their phagocytic ability, histiocytes in damaged tissues are also capable of changing into fibroblasts which then lay down collagen fibers to repair the damage. Furthermore, histiocytes can swell up and move by ameboid motion through the tissues, whereupon they are then called *macrophages*. These cells seek out areas of inflammation and help to devour the infectious agents or necrotic tissues. Several of the white blood cells, the monocytes and lymphocytes particularly, upon migrating into the tissues can become histiocytes. These aspects of histiocyte function and formation will be discussed further in connection with the functions of the leukocytes.

THE LEUKOCYTES (WHITE BLOOD CELLS)

The leukocytes are the *mobile units* of the reticuloendothelial system. They are formed partially in the bone marrow (the *granulocytes*) and partially in the lymph nodes (*lymphocytes* and *monocytes*), but after formation they are transported in the blood to the different parts of the body where they are to be used. The real value of the white blood cells is that their transport can be focused to areas of serious inflammation,

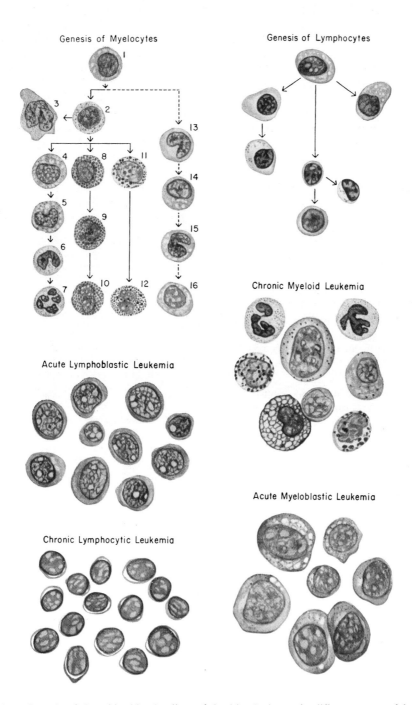

Figure 101. Genesis of the white blood cells, and the blood picture in different types of leukemia. The different cells of the myelogenous series are: *1*, myeloblast; *2*, promyelocyte; *3*, megakaryocyte; *4*, neutrophil myelocyte; *5*, young neutrophil metamyelocyte; *6*, "band" neutrophil metamyelocyte; *7*, polymorphonuclear neutrophil; *8*, eosinophil myelocyte; *9*, eosinophil metamyelocyte; *10*, polymorphonuclear eosinophil; *11*, basophil myelocyte; *12*, polymorphonuclear basophil; *13*, *14*, *15*, and *16*, stages of monocyte formation. (Redrawn in part from Piney: A Clinical Atlas of Blood Diseases. The Blakiston Co.)

thereby providing a rapid and potent defense against any infectious agent that might be present. Also, the number of white blood cells in the circulation as well as their characteristics can change rapidly and purposefully to aid the defense process. Thus, a study of the white cells in the blood provides a very valuable clinical tool for making diagnoses and for giving prognoses in disease conditions. For this reason, it is very important that the medical student understand the characteristics, the functions, and the abnormalities of different ones of the white blood cells.

General Characteristics of Leukocytes

The Types of White Blood Cells. Six different types of white blood cells are normally found in the blood. These are the *polymorphonuclear neutrophils,* the *polymorphonuclear eosinophils,* the *polymorphonuclear basophils,* the *monocytes,* the *lymphocytes,* and the *platelets,* which are fragments of *megakaryocytes.* The three types of polymorphonuclear cells have a granular appearance, as illustrated in Figure 101; therefore, these are distinguished from the other white blood cells by the term *granulocytes,* or in clinical terminology they are often called simply "polys."

The granulocytes and the monocytes protect the body against invading organisms by ingesting them—that is, by the process of *phagocytosis.* One of the functions of the lymph glands and lymphocytes is formation of monocytes which in turn destroy invading organisms. Finally, the function of platelets is to initiate the blood clotting mechanism. All these functions are protective mechanisms of one type or another.

The diameters of the different white blood cells in the circulating blood are approximately: polymorphonuclear neutrophils, eosinophils, and basophils, 10 to 12 microns; monocytes, 12 to 15 microns; small lymphocytes, 8 microns; large lymphocytes, 13 microns; and platelets, 1 to 3 microns. These diameters are often larger than the diameter of the capillaries; therefore, the cells deform greatly as they pass along the capillaries.

Concentrations of the Different White Blood Cells in the Blood. Figure 102 illustrates the variations in the blood concentrations of the different white blood cells from birth up to the age of 70. As noted in the figure, the adult has approximately 7000 white blood cells per cubic millimeter of blood, whereas a child usually has a somewhat greater number—especially a greater number of lymphocytes.

In many disease conditions one or more types of cells sometimes become especially prevalent with no change in the concentrations of the other cells. Therefore, it is often important to determine the so-called *differential count*—that is, the relative numbers of the different types of white blood cells. The average normal differential count in every 100 cells is the following:

Polymorphonuclear neutrophils	63.0
Polymorphonuclear eosinophils	1.6
Polymorphonuclear basophils	0.4
Monocytes	5.0
Lymphocytes	30.0

The number of platelets in each cubic millimeter of blood is normally about 400,-000. However, on using some methods for counting platelets, counts as low as 250,000 are often obtained, for platelets have a tendency to aggregate and to stick to any wettable surface, thus making it almost impossible to count all of them.

Genesis of the Leukocytes. Figure 101 illustrates the stages in the development of white blood cells. The polymorphonuclear cells are normally formed only in the bone marrow. On the other hand, lymphocytes and monocytes are produced in the various lymphogenous organs, including the lymph glands, the spleen, the thymus, the tonsils, and various lymphoid rests in the gut and elsewhere.

Some of the white blood cells formed in the bone marrow are stored within the marrow until they are needed in the circulatory system. Then when the need arises, various factors that will be discussed later cause them to be released.

Platelets almost certainly are fragments of megakaryocytes. As illustrated in Figure 101, megakaryocytes are formed in the bone marrow and are part of the myelogenous group of white blood cells. It is generally taught that these megakaryocytes fragment in the bone marrow, the small fragments known as platelets passing then into the blood, but it is possible that the large megakaryocytes are released directly into the blood and fragment later as they attempt to traverse the capillaries.

Materials needed for formation of white blood cells. In general, the white blood cells need essentially the same vitamins and amino

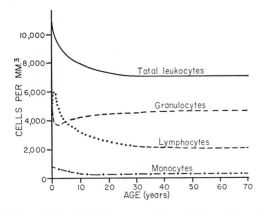

Figure 102. Relative proportions of the different white blood cells at different ages.

acids as most of the other cells of the body for their formation. Especially does lack of folic acid, a compound of the vitamin B complex, block the formation of white blood cells as well as prevent maturation of red blood cells, which was pointed out in the previous chapter. Also, in extreme debilitation the production of white blood cells may be greatly reduced, despite the fact that these cells are needed more during such a state than usually.

Life Span of the White Blood Cells. How long the various white blood cells remain in the blood stream is not known. Actually, the main reason white blood cells are present in the blood is simply to be transported from the bone marrow or lymphoid tissue to the areas of the body where they are needed. Therefore, it is to be expected that the life of the white blood cells in the blood would be short.

In patients who suddenly stop producing white blood cells, such as persons who have been irradiated by gamma rays from an atom bomb blast, the polymorphonuclear leukocytes disappear from the blood in three to six days. However, the life span of polys, including both their intravascular and intrastitial life, may be as long as 8 to 12 days in a person who is not being subjected to severe destructive processes.

The life span of the monocytes in the blood is a complete mystery, for monocytes apparently wander back and forth between the tissues and the blood. The monocytes possibly live for considerably longer periods of time, especially in the tissues, than do the polymorphonuclear cells, for they persist in infectious areas much longer than the polys.

Lymphocytes enter the circulatory system continually along with the drainage of fluid from the lymph nodes. The total number entering the blood from the thoracic duct in each 24 hours is usually several times as great as the total number of lymphocytes present in the blood stream at any given time. Therefore, the life of the lymphocytes

in the blood must be considerably less than 24 hours, and some estimations of the life of the lymphocytes in the blood stream have been as low as four hours.

The platelets in the blood are totally replaced approximately once every four days; in other words, about 100,000 platelets are formed each day for each cubic millimeter of blood.

Properties of White Blood Cells. *Diapedesis and ameboid motion.* The white blood cells can squeeze through the pores of the blood vessels by the process of *diapedesis.* That is, even though the pore is much smaller than the size of the cell, a small portion of the cell slides through the pore at a time, the portion sliding through being momentarily constricted to the size of the pore, as illustrated in Figure 103.

Once the cells have entered the tissue spaces, the polymorphonuclear leukocytes especially, and the monocytes to a slightly less degree, move through the tissues by ameboid motion, which was described in Chapter 2 for amebae. Such movement consists of forward projection of a pseudopodium followed by progressive movement of more and more of the cellular constituents into the pseudopodium, thus dragging forward the posterior portions of the cell. Then the cycle is repeated again and again. Some of the polymorphonuclear cells can move through the tissues by ameboid motion at a rate as great as 40 microns per minute—that is, they can move at least three times their own length each minute.

Chemotaxis as related to leukocytes. A number of different chemical substances in the tissues cause the leukocytes to move either toward or away from the source of the chemical. This phenomenon is known as *chemotaxis.* An especially important chemotactic agent seems to be *leukotaxine,* which attracts polymorphonuclear neutrophils to areas of inflammation. Also, a number of bacterial toxins can cause chemotaxis of some of the leukocytes. Some of these toxins cause *positive chemotaxis,* which means that they attract the white blood cells toward the source of the toxin, while others cause *negative chemotaxis,* which means that they repel the leukocytes from the source of the toxin.

As illustrated in Figure 103, chemotaxis depends on the existence of a concentration gradient of the chemotactic agent. The con-

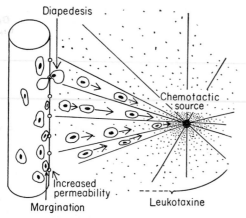

Figure 103. Liberation of leukotaxine by necrotic tissue, and the permeability, margination, and chemotactic properties of leukotaxine.

centration of the agent is greatest near its source, and as it spreads by diffusion away from the source its concentration decreases approximately in proportion to the square of the distance from the source. Therefore, on the side of the cell away from the source of the chemotactic agent the concentration is less than on the side facing the source. In positive chemotaxis, the greater concentration on one side of the cell causes pseudopodia to project toward the source of the agent, and in negative chemotaxis the opposite effect occurs.

Phagocytosis. The most important function of the neutrophils and monocytes is phagocytosis, which means ingestion of particulate matter by the cells. When phagocytic cells come in contact with appropriate extraneous particulate matter, either in the tissues or in the blood stream, the phenomenon of phagocytosis takes place extremely rapidly, for the particle passes through the cell membrane to the inside of the phagocyte within a few hundredths of a second.

Obviously, the phagocytes must be selective in the material that is phagocytized, or otherwise some of the structures of the body itself would be ingested. Whether or not phagocytosis will occur depends especially upon three selective procedures. First, if the surface of a particle is rough, the likelihood of phagocytosis is increased, whereas a smooth particle is very resistant to phagocytosis. Second, most natural substances of the body are electronegatively charged and therefore are repelled from the phagocytes,

which also are electronegative. On the other hand, dead tissues and foreign particles are frequently electropositive and are therefore subject to phagocytosis. Third, the body has a means for promoting phagocytosis of foreign materials by selectively coating foreign particles with globulin molecules called *opsonins.* After the opsonins have coated the particle, the enclosing globulin film allows adhesion of the phagocyte to the surface of the particle, which promotes phagocytosis. The special relationship of opsonization to immunity will be discussed in the following chapter.

The most phagocytic of all the white cells in the blood are the polymorphonuclear neutrophils. The eosinophils and monocytes are slightly phagocytic, while the basophils and lymphocytes exhibit almost no phagocytosis.

Once they have left the circulatory system and entered the tissues, the monocytes progressively swell during the next few hours and become *macrophages,* which then are much more powerful phagocytes than the neutrophils. They have the ability to engulf much larger particles and often 5 or more times as many particles as the neutrophils. And they can even phagocytize whole red blood cells or malarial parasites, whereas neutrophils are not capable of phagocytizing particles much larger than bacteria. Also, macrophages have much greater ability than neutrophils to phagocytize necrotic tissue, which is a very important function performed by these cells in chronic infection. Neutrophils are quite frequently called "microphages" in contradistinction to the term "macrophages," both these terms indicating not only an ability of the cells to ingest foreign matter but also that the macrophages are much larger and much more powerful than the neutrophils. Thus, the principal value of the neutrophils is their readiness for function, whereas the principal value of the macrophages derived from the monocytes is their prolonged and very powerful phagocytic activity.

If the inflammation becomes chronic and lasts for several weeks or months, such as in tuberculosis and chronic salpingitis (an infection of the fallopian tubes), the concentration of monocytes in the blood may rise from 5 per cent of the total leukocytes to as high as 30 to 50 per cent. The reason for this effect is not known, but presumably some of the inflammatory products cause progressive change of large numbers of lymphocytes, either while they are still in the lymph nodes or after they have entered the blood stream, into monocytes. This obviously makes large numbers of monocytes readily available to the inflamed areas and speeds the development of macrophages.

Enzymatic digestion in the phagocytes. Once a foreign particle has been phagocytized, the cell immediately begins digesting the particle. Neutrophils and macrophages both have *proteolytic enzymes* especially geared for digesting bacteria and other foreign protein matter. The macrophages also contain large amounts of *lipases,* which digest the thick lipoid membranes possessed by tubercle bacteria, leprosy bacteria, and others.

In addition to the enzymes that actually digest the ingested particles, phagocytic cells also contain bactericidal agents, which kill bacteria before they can multiply and destroy the phagocyte itself. The neutrophil, for instance, contains considerable quantities of lysozyme, an especially important bactericidal agent, in its cytoplasm.

Death of the phagocytes as a result of phagocytosis. Phagocytes continue to ingest and digest foreign particles until sufficient quantities of breakdown substances from the foreign particles accumulate within the cytoplasm of the phagocyte to kill the phagocyte itself. Thus, a polymorphonuclear neutrophil is usually capable of phagocytizing about 5 to 25 bacteria before death of the phagocyte itself occurs, but a macrophage sometimes engulfs as many as 100 bacteria before death.

INFLAMMATION AND THE FUNCTION OF LEUKOCYTES

The Process of Inflammation

Inflammation comprises the changes in the tissues in response to injury. When tissue injury occurs, whether it be caused by bacteria, trauma, chemicals, heat, or any other phenomenon, a substance known as *necrosin* is liberated by the damaged cells into the surrounding fluids. This destroys some of the adjacent cells but also increases the permeability of the adjacent capillaries, thus allowing large quantities of fluid and protein, including fibrinogen to leak into the tissues. Local extracellular edema results, and the extracellular fluid and lymphatic fluid both clot because of the coagulating effect of necrosin on the leaking fibrinogen. Thus, *brawny edema* develops in the spaces surrounding the injured cells.

The "Walling Off" Effect of Inflammation. It can be seen from the above discussion that the net result of inflammation is to "wall off" the area of injury from the remaining portions of the body. The tissue spaces and the lymphatics are blocked by fibrinogen clots so that fluid flows through the spaces very slowly. Therefore, if the injury has occurred as a result of bacterial invasion, very few bacteria are transported from the area of inflammation into other regions of the body, and, if the inflammation is caused by mechanical, chemical, or other types of local cellular damage, then walling off the area of injury delays the spread of toxic breakdown products from the degenerating cells.

The intensity of the inflammatory process is proportional to the degree of tissue injury. For instance, staphylococci invading the tissues liberate extremely lethal cellular toxins. As a result, very large quantities of necrosin are liberated, and the process of inflammation develops rapidly — indeed, much more rapidly than the staphylococci themselves can multiply and spread. Therefore, staphylococcal infection is "walled off" very rapidly. On the other hand, streptococci do not cause such intense local destruction of the cells. Therefore, relatively small quantities of necrosin are liberated, and the walling off process develops slowly while the streptococci reproduce and migrate. As a result, streptococci have far greater tendency to spread through the body than do staphylococci, even though staphylococci are far more destructive to the tissues.

Attraction of Polymorphonuclear Leukocytes to the Area of Inflammation— Leukotaxine. When tissues are damaged, a second substance in addition to necrosin, a chemotactic polypeptide known as *leukotaxine,* is liberated. Leukotaxine diffuses away from the area of tissue necrosis and increases the permeability of the local capillaries, adding to the increased permeability already caused by necrosin. Then polymorphonuclear leukocytes stick to the walls of the damaged capillary, resulting in a process known as "margination," which is shown in Figure 103. Gradually the cells pass by diapedesis into the tissue spaces, are drawn chemotactically and migrate toward the source of the leukotaxine. Thus, within an hour or more after tissue damage the area of necrosis becomes well supplied with polymorphonuclear leukocytes.

Essentially all the leukocytes attracted immediately to an area of inflammation are neutrophils. The reason for this is two-fold: first, the neutrophils exhibit far more chemotactic response to leukotaxine than do any of the other leukocytes and, second, the number of polymorphonuclear neutrophils in the blood is greater than that of any of the other leukocytes.

Leukocytosis during Inflammation— Leukocytosis Promoting Factor. The term *leukocytosis* means an increase above normal in the total number of white blood cells in the circulatory system.

A globulin substance known as *leukocytosis promoting factor* is liberated by most inflamed tissues concurrently with the release of necrosin and leukotaxine. This factor diffuses away from the area of necrosis, into the blood, and finally to the bone marrow where it has two actions: First, it causes large numbers of polymorphonuclear cells, especially neutrophils, to be released into the blood within a few minutes from the storage areas of the bone marrow, thus increasing the total number of leukocytes per cubic millimeter of blood sometimes to as high as 20,000 to 30,000. Second, it increases the rate of leukocyte production by the bone marrow. Within a day or two after onset of the inflammation, the bone marrow becomes hyperplastic and then continues to produce large numbers of white blood cells as long as leukocyte promoting factor is formed in the inflamed tissues. Yet, it is only the stored white blood cells that provide the polymorphonuclear cells for the first day or so of inflammation until the bone marrow has had time to become hyperplastic.

Effect of Production Rate on the Morphology of Polymorphonuclear Neutrophils. Figure 104 illustrates the forms of neutrophils beginning with the myelocyte, then the juvenile form, and progressively the older forms. In the usual blood smear one finds mainly the trilobulated forms of neutrophils, a few "stab"

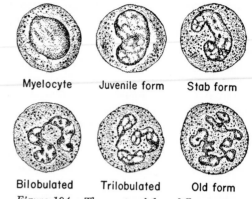

Myelocyte   Juvenile form   Stab form

Bilobulated   Trilobulated   Old form

Figure 104. The neutrophil at different ages.

forms, and a few many-lobulated forms. Neutrophils first liberated into the blood are usually in the stab stage, but after they have circulated for several days they progress to an old form with 5 or more lobules until finally they become very fragile and disintegrate.

During leukocytosis, the character of the neutrophil usually shifts toward that of the earlier forms. The reasons for this are, first, that infection causes the neutrophils to flow into the area of infection so rapidly that the only cells left in the blood are those recently liberated from the bone marrow, and second, that bone marrow actually releases earlier and earlier forms of white blood cells the more rapidly these cells are produced. Therefore, when a large quantity of leukocytosis promoting factor is formed, the neutrophils become mainly stab forms, and even some myelocytes may enter the blood.

When the bone marrow becomes aplastic so that very few new white blood cells are being liberated, those granulocytes still in the blood are mainly the few hardy cells that have remained there for many days—the many-lobulated cells.

The Monocytic Response in Chronic Inflammation

If the neutrophils are not capable of combating the cause of inflammation, then gradually over a period of several days very large numbers of macrophages appear in the localized region of inflammation.

First, the tissue histiocytes change into macrophages, develop ameboid motion, and migrate chemotactically toward the area of inflammation. Then, monocytes begin to enter the tissues from the blood. They change their characteristics drastically during the first few hours; they start to swell, to exhibit increased ameboid motion, and even become chemotactic. Finally, the largest source of

In actuality, therefore, it is probable that almost all if not all the different cells of the body are capable of forming antibodies. Yet, most of the cells will not release the antibodies into the circulating body fluids. For this reason, the immunity that develops is called *tissue immunity* in contradistinction to *humoral immunity*. Immune bodies appear in the plasma simply because plasma cells, lymphocytes, reticulum cells, and some others are capable of extruding them from their cytoplasm.

Mechanism of Antibody Formation. The precise means by which cells form antibodies has not been determined. Yet, some general principles of antibody formation appear to be the following: First, on entering the cell the antigen seems to act as a "template," which causes some of the protein molecules in the cell to arrange their polar forces so that they are the cast image of those on the antigen. (A template is a mold against which another object is fitted to exact dimensions.) Once the new type of protein is formed, it is then autocatalytically reproduced again and again, and the products are the antibodies.

Continued Production of Antibodies. Once the antigen has acted as a template for starting the production of antibodies in the cell the antigen itself can then be removed from the cell, and the cell will still continue to produce the specific antibodies. Indeed, inheritance of the altered cellular proteins from one cell generation to the next causes continued production of specific antibodies for long periods of time thereafter. Histochemical studies show that the original antigen usually does not remain in the cells more than two to three weeks, though continued production of humoral antibodies often continues for as long as six months to a year.

The Antigen-Antibody Reaction

In Figure 106 the antibody is designated by a small white rectangle with a black spot at each end. Each of these spots is considered to be a reactive point on the antibody. Some antibodies have only one reactive point, whereas others have two reactive points. The antigen is illustrated in Figure 106 as a stippled, bone-shaped structure having 5 reactive points, for antigens character-

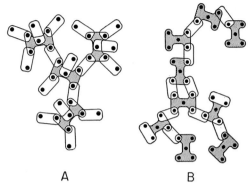

Figure 106. Reactions between antigens and antibodies. The antibodies are represented by rectangular structures, and the antigens are represented by stippled structures. *A*, Reaction when excess antibody is present. *B*, Reaction when excess antigen is present. (Redrawn from Raffel: Immunity. Appleton-Century-Crofts, Inc.)

istically have far more reactive points than do antibodies, sometimes as many as 30 to 50.

In section *A* of Figure 106 every reactive point on the four molecules of antigen has reacted with antibodies. Thus, all the reactive forces on the surfaces of the antigen molecules are blocked by this reaction. In section *B* of Figure 106 an excess of antigen is available for the quantity of antibody in the solution. Consequently, the antibody molecules have reacted with as many points on the antigen molecules as possible, but a considerable number of reactive portions of the antigens are still uncovered. Such a reaction as this leaves the antigen still capable of further antigenicity in the host, and, if the antigen is a toxin, such an incomplete reaction may also leave the antigen still capable of certain degrees of toxicity.

Several different specific reactions can take place between antigens and antibodies for combating the toxic or invasive qualities of antigenic agents. These processes are *neutralization, precipitation, agglutination, lysis,* and *opsonization.* These processes are described in the following paragraphs.

Neutralization of the Antigen by Antibodies. When the antigen is a toxin to the body, combination of this toxic antigen with antibody "neutralizes" the toxin. Because the molecule of toxin becomes covered with antibodies, the prosthetic groups on the toxin that are responsible for the toxicity are prevented from acting on the body. After the antibody has reacted with the toxin, this combined antibody and antigen is engulfed by cells of the reticuloendothelial system, whereupon both the antigen and antibody are digested and thereby destroyed.

Viruses as well as toxins can be neutralized, for viruses contain mainly nucleoprotein molecules, and the human body often develops antibodies against these nucleoproteins. Then, on second exposure to the virus, the antibodies attach themselves to the surfaces of the virus particles and prevent their invading the tissues. After the virus has been thus neutralized, it too is engulfed and digested by the reticuloendothelial system.

Antigen-Antibody Precipitation. Immune bodies, obviously, are soluble in water, and many antigenic proteins are also soluble, but, once the antigen combines with the antibody, the combination often precipitates. The reason for this is the following: The ability of proteins to remain in solution depends to a great extent upon the electrical charges on the surfaces of the protein molecules. When antibodies and antigens are free in solution or react incompletely, they remain in solution because a large number of unneutralized polar electrostatic charges are present on their surfaces. However, when the quantity of antigen is exactly right for complete reaction with the amount of available antibody, then the antigen-antibody mixture has greatly reduced polar forces still exposed to the fluid; as a result, precipitation occurs. Such precipitation probably depends upon the formation of lattices, as shown in Figure 106, the antibodies and antigens aggregating to form large particles that settle to the bottom of the solution.

The curve of Figure 107 illustrates that maximum precipitation occurs when an exact quantity of antigen is mixed with a standard quantity of antibody. Too much antigen or too little depresses the degree of precipitation. This precipitation reaction is extremely important, for it is a very useful means for quantitating the amount of immune bodies that develop in the plasma in response to specific antigens.

Agglutination. Many of the invading agents of the body are not soluble proteins but instead are particulate objects such as bacteria. When bacteria enter the body, immune bodies develop against the bacterial proteins. Then, when the same bacteria enter the body a second time, one of the means by which the body is protected against the bacteria is by bacterial agglutination. Immune bodies that have developed against the bacterial proteins immediately attach themselves to the surfaces of the bacteria, some of the immune bodies attaching at only one reactive point so that the second reactive points remain available to attach to the surfaces of other bacteria of the same type. As a result, large numbers of antibodies bridge the gaps between adjacent bacteria and thereafter hold them together. Then these

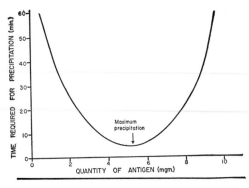

Figure 107. Effect of antigen quantity in a solution on the rapidity of antigen-antibody precipitation. (The antibody quantity remains constant.)

combine with still other bacteria until a heavy, non-invasive aggregate forms.

Even red blood cells may agglutinate, because antibodies against the proteins of red blood cells cause the cells to adhere to each other. This is the basis of transfusion reactions, which will be discussed in Chapter 15.

Lysis of Cellular Structures as a Result of the Antigen-Antibody Reaction. Another means by which the antigen-antibody reaction can protect the body against invading bacteria is by causing cellular lysis. For this to occur, many antibodies are believed to attach one of their reactive points to the surface of the bacterium, and then the second reactive points of the antibodies combine with a substance of the plasma known as *complement*. Until complement combines with the antibodies nothing happens to the membrane of the invading organism, but complement, in combination with the antibody, reacts with the membrane to cause its dissolution. When this occurs the organism spills its contents into the fluid of the body, and thereafter it is no longer effective as an invading agent.

Complement. Complement is not an immune body but is a complex protein compound probably formed by at least three different globulins and one lipid or lipoprotein compound. Occasionally, the quantity of complement in the human body becomes slight enough that appropriate destruction of bacteria cannot take place. An example of this occurs when the spinal canal is invaded by the influenza bacterium, for the quantity of complement in the spinal fluids is insufficient to allow bacterial destruction. Consequently, in the absence of complement, influenza bacteria invade the meninges very rapidly, but intraspinal injection of sufficient quantities of complement and antibodies against the influenza bacterium can result in a dramatic cure of the patient.

Complement is extremely labile. Even moderate heat for short periods of time can destroy it, and most of the complement in blood removed from the human body is often autocatalytically destroyed within 24 hours. This is of importance when blood is transfused for its complement value.

Opsonization. Antibodies and complement attached to bacteria often do not destroy the bacteria but make them more susceptible than normally to phagocytosis. This phenomenon is known as *opsonization*, and the immune bodies that cause this response are called *opsonins*. Thus, even though antibodies in many instances cannot directly destroy bacteria, they often lead the bacteria into the mouths of reticuloendothelial phagocytes. The presence of specific opsonizing antibodies and complement may increase the rate of phagocytosis by as much as 5- to 100-fold.

The mechanism of opsonization seems to be based on the chemical structure of complement. In opsonization, when the phagocyte comes in contact with the opsonized bacterium, the phagocytic membrane immediately becomes miscible with the complement covering the surface of the opsonized bacterium; once this occurs the bacterium finds itself inside the phagocyte.

Tissue Immunity

Many times the human being becomes immune to invading agents even though no antibodies can be demonstrated in his body fluids. This occurs frequently in virus infections; it seems that the cells themselves develop intracellular antibodies which are not released into the body fluids. This makes the cells thenceforth resistant to the same agent despite the lack of humoral immunity. Since viruses cannot live outside cells, reinfection is thus prevented.

Relative Persistence of Humoral and Tissue Immunity. The term *humoral immunity* applies to immunity resulting from the presence of circulating antibodies in the body fluids, in contradistinction to the term *tissue immunity*, which means immunity in the cells. Obviously, humoral immunity lasts only as long as specific antibodies persist in the body fluids, which is usually about 3 months to 3 years. On the other hand, tissue immunity may last for the entire remaining life of the individual. This is especially true when a person has had an attack of a virus disease such as yellow fever or smallpox, both of which are generalized virus infections.

The difference in the persistence of humoral immunity and tissue immunity might be explained on the basis of the origin of the two types of immunity. The humoral antibodies are probably derived mainly from the reticuloendothelial, lymphoid, and plasma cells. Because these cells are constantly dying and regenerating, many generations of new cells develop within a few months. As the cells pass through hundreds of generations, it is quite easy to understand that the newer generations might well produce new types of antibodies rather than the type produced a year previously. On the other hand, because most of the other tissues of the body do not renew their cells rapidly, it is also easy to understand how development of antibodies in these cells might well cause persistence of immunity for many years.

In general, it is much more difficult to develop tissue immunity than to develop humoral immunity. For instance, simply injecting dead virus proteins into the circulatory system will very rarely cause any tissue immunity to develop. Ordinarily, the virus must actually grow in the body and probably must enter the cells themselves before tissue immunity develops.

Cross Immunity

Antibodies that have been formed against specific antigens sometimes react with still other antigens because of the existence of similar polar forces on the two respective antigens. Yet, the second antigen usually does not have exactly the same arrangement of polar forces as that on the first antigen; therefore, reaction of the antibody with the second antigen is not nearly so firm as the reaction with the primary antigen.

As the human being becomes older he becomes progressively more immune to foreign substances to which he has never been exposed. This progressive immunity probably results in part from cross immunity between the different antigens.

The Number of Antigens to Which the Body Can Become Immune—Interference. The body can form 50 or even more different types of immune bodies at the same time, provided that the administered antigens are in approximately equal concentrations. However, whenever one or more of the antigens are present in even slightly excessive quantities, almost all the immune bodies are formed against the most abundant antigens, thus exhibiting the phenomenon of *interference* between the antigens.

The Acquisition of Immunity

From the day the human being is born he begins developing acquired immunity. One of the first antigenic substances to which the baby becomes immune is egg albumin, for egg albumin molecules diffuse to a considerable extent through the gastrointestinal membrane into the body fluids. Later the child is exposed to the proteins of various meat extracts, to respiratory infections, to large numbers of bacteria in the gastrointestinal tract, and to various types of internal infection. It is obvious, therefore, how the human being develops progressive immunity through the years to many different types of antigens.

Specific Immunization with Vaccines.

The term "vaccine" originated from vaccination with vaccinia virus for immunization against smallpox. To vaccinate one against smallpox the subject is infected with vaccinia virus by scratching some of the virus into the skin. Following the infection, specific immunity against vaccinia develops, and, because this virus has almost exactly the same antigenic properties as smallpox virus, immunity against smallpox also results.

Live virus vaccines have also been developed for yellow fever, rabies, etc. The necessary characteristics of live virus vaccines are (1) the virus must be sufficiently similar to the pathogenic virus to cause immunity, and (2) the virus must be "non-virulent"—that is, unable to cause significant disease symptoms. Ordinarily, a virus is made non-virulent by passing it many times from one animal to another until the virus mutates sufficiently that it is no longer virulent.

In contradistinction to the live virus vaccines, the type of vaccine used most frequently for specific immunization is composed of dead products of the virulent organisms. Thus, typhoid vaccine may be prepared by simply heating tremendous numbers of typhoid bacilli until all the bacteria are dead. Vaccines may also be prepared by killing the organisms with x-ray irradiation, neutron irradiation, destructive grinding, destructive disintegration with sonic or ultrasonic sound waves, and by killing with various chemical agents. Any one of these different procedures sometimes alters the chemical structure of the antigens in the bacteria and therefore prevents satisfactory development of immunity. In searching for a vaccine for a particular disease, one simply tries all of the different methods of destroying bacteria or viruses until he empirically derives a satisfactory vaccine for establishing specific immunity.

Also, one can be immunized against toxins such as tetanus or diphtherial toxin by injecting "toxoids." These are toxins that have been chemically changed so that they are *still antigenic but are no longer toxic.*

The antibody response to vaccination.

Figure 108 illustrates the response of the host to vaccination with a dead antigen. After the primary injection of antigen, no antibodies enter the body fluids for about a week, for presumably the antigen must be ingested by appropriate cells, and then the protein-reproducing mechanisms of these cells must be specifically altered before gamma globulins can be produced. Then, suddenly, at the end of approximately a week, the blood concentration of antibodies rises rapidly, reaching a peak in approximately 10 to 14 days. Following this response, the immune bodies initially released into the blood begin to deteriorate, and the cells taper off their production of antibodies so that significant concentrations of antibodies persist only a few weeks.

When a *secondary* injection of antigen is given after the primary response has ceased, the body begins producing new antibodies within a day or so, as illustrated by the top curve of Figure 108. The concentration of antibodies rises much higher this time than following the primary injection, even though exactly the same dose of antigen is used. Also, the antibodies persist for many months in the body fluids instead of for only a few weeks.

After several additional injections of antigen, the response reaches maximum intensity and no further increment of increase can be expected thereafter.

The reason that the secondary and tertiary

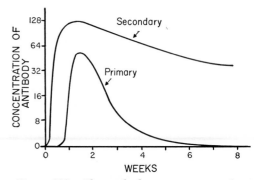

Figure 108. The antibody response to a primary injection of antigen and to a secondary injection of antigen several weeks later.

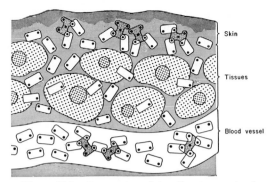

Figure 110. Prevention of the allergic reaction by the presence of excessive quantities of bivalent antibodies in the circulating body fluids. The antigens entering through the skin or by way of the circulatory system are neutralized before they can reach the vital cells.

be the following: The more a person is exposed to an antigen the greater becomes the ratio of complete antibodies to incomplete antibodies, and since complete antibodies are capable of circulating freely in the body fluids, as illustrated in Figure 110, out of contact with the cells, it is presumed that any antigen entering the body is neutralized by the circulating antibodies before they can ever reach the vicinity of the cells where univalent antibodies are still attached.

Treatment of Allergies with ACTH and Glucocorticoid Hormones. Administration of glucocorticoids such as *cortisone* and *hydrocortisone* will reduce the severity of almost any allergic reaction. Furthermore, injection of ACTH (adrenocorticotropic hormone) causes the adrenal cortex to produce large quantities of glucocorticoids, which then give the same effect. Glucocorticoids in extreme quantities depress the formation of antibodies, and it has been postulated that this might suppress the allergies. However, the glucocorticoids also have an "anti-inflammatory" effect that could also explain their beneficial effect in allergy. This effect will be discussed in Chapter 74.

Possible Value of Allergic Reactions in the Body

Most people think of allergic reactions as being only detrimental. However, occasionally a person is born without the ability to form gamma globulins, and consequently has essentially no complete antibodies in his fluids. It has been shown that these persons, nevertheless, are still capable of developing localized hypersensitive states; spread of viruses and perhaps of other infective agents will be prevented as a result of the local allergic response. The swelling and the brawny edema associated with the allergic response immobilize the fluids and prevent their spread. Perhaps this is a very valuable effect even in the normal person because it can delay body-wide invasion by infective agents until the reticuloendothelial system and the immune process can collect their resources to combat the disease.

REFERENCES

Bean, W.: Physical and toxic agents; in Sodeman, W. A. (ed.): Pathologic Physiology. 2nd ed., Philadelphia, W. B. Saunders Co., 1956.

Boyd, W. C.: Fundamentals of Immunology. New York, Interscience Publishers, 1956.

Brocklehurst, W. E., Humphrey, J. H., and Perry W. L. M.: Cutaneous Antigen-Antibody Reactions in the Rat. *J. Physiol.*, 150:489, 1960.

Carpenter, P. L.: Immunology and Serology. Philadelphia, W. B. Saunders Company, 1956.

Ciba Foundation, Symposia Volumes: Cellular Aspects of Immunity. Boston, Little, Brown and Co., 1960.

Ciba Foundation: Symposia Volumes. Histamine. Boston, Little, Brown and Co., 1956.

Code, C. F.: Histamine in blood. *Physiol. Rev.*, 32:47, 1952.

Cooke, R. A., and Sherman, W. B.: Allergy; in Sodeman, W. A. (ed.): Pathologic Physiology. 2nd ed., Philadelphia, W. B. Saunders Co., 1956.

Doan, C. A.: The spleen and reticulo-endothelial system; in Sodeman, W. A. (ed.): Pathologic Physiology. 2nd ed., Philadelphia, W. B. Saunders Co., 1956.

Dulbecco, R.: Interaction of viruses and animal cells. A study of facts and interpretations. *Physiol Rev.*, 35:301, 1955.

Dworetzky, M.: Role of histamine or other released substances in anaphylaxis in isolated guinea pig ileum. *Am. J. Physiol.*, 197:31, 1959.

Guyton, A. C.: The physiological basis of allergy. *South. M. J.*, 46:73, 1953.

Hare, R.: Bacteriology and Immunity. New York, Longmans, Green & Co., 1956.

Hayes, S. P.: The effect of cortisone on local antibody formation. *J. Immunol.*, 70:450, 1953.

Heidelberger, M.: Lectures in Immunochemistry. New York, Academic Press, 1956.

Henry Ford Hospital Symposium: Mechanisms of Hypersensitivity. Boston, Little Brown and Co., 1959.

Kabat, E. A., and Mayer, M. M.: Experimental Immunochemistry. Springfield, Illinois, Charles C Thomas, 1958.

Pappenheimer, A. M., Jr.: Hypersensitivity of the delayed type. Harvey Lect., 52:100, 1956–1957.

Raffel, S.: Immunity; Hypersensitivity; Serology. New York, Appleton-Century-Crofts, 1953.

Smith, D. T., and Conant, N. F.: Zinsser Bacteriology. 11th ed., New York, Appleton-Century-Crofts, 1957.

Talmage, D. W., and Cann. J. R.: The Chemistry of

Immunity in Health and Disease. Springfield, Illinois, Charles C Thomas, 1960.

Thorbecke, G. J., and Keuning, F. J.: Antibody formation in vitro by haemopoietic organs after subcutaneous and intravenous immunization. *J. Immunol., 70:*126, 1953.

Walford, R. L.: Leukocyte Antigens and Antibodies. New York, Grune & Stratton, 1959.

Wilson, G. S., and Miles, A. A.: Topley and Wilson's Principles of Bacteriology and Immunity. 4th ed., Baltimore, Williams & Wilkins Co., 1955.

Yoffey, J. M., and Courtice, F. C.: Lymphatics, Lymph and Lymphoid Tissue. Cambridge, Harvard University Press, 1956.

See also Chapter 13, White blood cells; Chapter 15, Transfusion.

Blood Groups; Transfusion; Tissue and Organ Transplantation

Antigenicity and Immune Reactions of Blood

When blood transfusions from one person to another were first attempted the transfusions were successful in some instances, but, in many more, immediate or delayed agglutination and hemolysis of the red blood cells occurred. Soon it was discovered that the bloods of different persons usually have different antigenic and immune properties so that antibodies in the plasma of one blood react with antigens in the cells of another. Furthermore, the antigens and the antibodies are almost never precisely the same in one person as in another. For this reason, it is very easy for blood from a donor to be mismatched with that of a recipient. Fortunately, if proper precautions are taken, one can determine ahead of time whether or not appropriate antibodies and antigens will be present in the donor and recipient bloods to cause a reaction, but, on the other hand, lack of proper precautions will often result in varying degrees of red cell agglutination and hemolysis, resulting in a typical transfusion reaction that can often lead to death.

Multiplicity of Antigens in the Blood. Figure 111 illustrates the surface structure of the red blood cell, showing by the different symbols different types of protein antigens in the cell membrane. As pointed out in the previous chapter, a person does not form immune bodies against the antigens in his own cells, but if cells from one person are transfused into another person, antibodies will be developed against all the antigens not in the recipient's own blood. Fortunately, many of the antigens are common

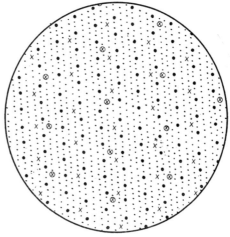

Figure 111. Antigenic structure of the cell membrane. Each symbol represents a different type of antigen.

from one person to another, and bloods are grouped and typed on the basis of the major types of antigens appearing in the cells.

At least 30 commonly occurring antigens, each one of which can at times cause antigen-antibody reactions, have been found in human blood cells. In addition to these, many hundreds of others of less potency or occurring in individual families rather than having widespread occurrence are known to exist. Among the 30 or more common antigens, certain ones are highly antigenic and regularly cause transfusion reactions if proper precautions are not taken, while others are of importance principally for studying the inheritance of genes and therefore, for establishing parentage, race, and so forth. However, even though these less important antigens do not normally cause

187

serious transfusion reaction, they do cause reactions in transplanted tissues and organs, as will be discussed later in the chapter.

Two particular groups of antigens are more likely than the others to cause blood transfusions. These are the so-called *O-A-B* system of antigens and the *Rh-Hr* system. Bloods are divided into different *groups* and *types* in accordance with the types of antigens present in the cells.

THE BLOOD GROUPS

The O, A, and B Antigens—"Group Specific Substances"

Three different but related antigens—type O, type A, and type B—occur in the cells of different persons. Because of the way these antigens are inherited, a person may have one of them in his blood at a time, or he may have two simultaneously, but never all three. These three antigens are sometimes called *group specific substances*, because the different blood groups are determined by their presence or absence in the cells.

The Agglutinogens. Type O group specific substance is a very poor antigen, and therefore "anti-O" antibodies only very rarely develop in the plasma of any person. For this reason Type O group specific substance is almost never a cause of agglutination or hemolysis of the red blood cells. On the other hand, types A and B group specific substances are strongly antigenic and cause severe agglutinative and hemolytic reactions. For this reason they are called the *agglutinogens*.

The Four Major Blood Groups. In transfusing blood from one person to another, the bloods of donors and recipients are normally classified into four major groups, as illustrated in Table 9, depending on the presence or absence of the two agglutino-

gens. When neither A nor B agglutinogen is present, the blood group is *group O*. When only type A agglutinogen is present, the blood is *group A*. When only type B agglutinogen is present, the blood is *group B*. And when both A and B agglutinogens are present, the blood is *group AB*.

Relative frequency of the different blood types. The prevalence of the different blood types among white persons is approximately as follows:

O	47 per cent
A	41 per cent
B	9 per cent
AB	3 per cent

It is obvious from these percentages that the O and A genes occur frequently but the B gene is very infrequent.

A_1 and A_2 subgroups. The A blood group can be divided into subgroups A_1 and A_2. A_1 red blood cells react very strongly with alpha agglutinins, but A_2 cells react rather weakly with alpha agglutinins. Furthermore, A_1 cells are agglutinated by a second agglutinin called *apha$_1$ agglutinin*, whereas A_2 cells are agglutinated by anti-O agglutinins. A_1 red cells probably contain a type A group specific substance, while A_2 red cells probably contain a modified type A group specific substance and also type O group specific substance. Approximately 80 per cent of group A blood or group AB blood is of the A_1 type and approximately 20 per cent is A_2.

Splitting group A blood into the subtypes is usually unnecessary from a practical point of view because transfusion reactions between bloods of these subgroups have rarely occurred.

Inheritance of the Group Specific Substances. Figure 112*A* illustrates on two adjacent chromosomes the genes that determine the

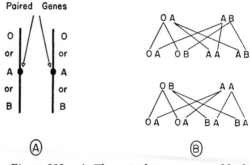

Figure 112. *A,* The paired genes responsible for the different blood group genotypes. *B,* Two examples of father and mother matings and the genotypes of their offspring.

Table 9. The Blood Groups, with Their Genotypes and Their Constituent Agglutinogens and Agglutinins

Genotypes	Blood Groups	Agglutinogens	Agglutinins
OO	O	—	α and β
OA or AA	A	A	β
OB or BB	B	B	α
AB	AB	A and B	—

blood groups. These are allelomorphic genes that can be any one of three different types: type O, type A, or type B. There is no dominance among the three different allelomorphs. Therefore, if either of the two genes in the two respective chromosomes is type O, type O group specific substance will be present in the red blood cells. If either of the two genes is type A, the red blood cells will contain type A group specific substance, and, likewise, if either of the two genes is group B, the red blood cells will contain group B specific substance. The six possible combinations of genes, as shown in Table 9, are OO, OA, OB, AA, BB, and AB. These different combinations of genes are known as the *genotypes,* and each person is one of the six different genotypes. In section *B* of Figure 112 is shown how mating fathers and mothers of different genotypes can cause inheritance of the different group specific substances in the offspring. Only two different types of matings are shown in Figure 112*B,* but 21 different matings of genotypes are possible between the male and the female.

One can observe from Table 9 that a person with genotype OO produces no agglutinogens at all, and, therefore, his blood group is O, while a person with either genotype OA or AA produces type A agglutinogens and, therefore, has blood group A. Genotypes OB and BB give group B blood, and genotype AB gives group AB blood.

The Agglutinins

When type A agglutinogen *is not present* in a person's red blood cells, antibodies known as *alpha agglutinins* or "anti-A" agglutinins develop in his plasma. Also, when type B agglutinogen *is not present* in the red blood cells, antibodies known as *beta agglutinins* or "anti-B" agglutinins develop in the plasma.

Thus, referring once again to Table 9 it will be observed that group O blood, though containing no agglutinogens, does contain both *alpha* and *beta agglutinins,* while group A blood contains type A agglutinogens and beta agglutinins, and group B blood contains type B agglutinogen and alpha agglutinins. Finally, group AB blood contains both A and B agglutinogens but no agglutinins at all.

Titer of the Agglutinins at Different Ages. Immediately after birth the quantity of agglutinins in the plasma is almost always zero. Two to eight months after birth,

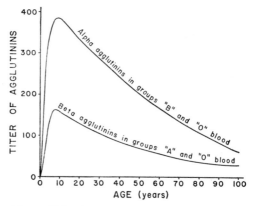

Figure 113. Average titer of alpha and beta agglutinins in the blood of persons in group B and group A at different ages.

the infant begins to produce agglutinins—alpha agglutinins when type A agglutinogens are not present in the cells and beta agglutinins when type B agglutinogens are not in the cells. Figure 113 illustrates the changing titer of alpha and beta agglutinins in the average population at different ages. A maximum titer is usually reached at 8 to 10 years of age, and this gradually declines throughout the remaining years of life.

Origin of the Agglutinins in the Plasma. The agglutinins are gamma globulins, as are other immune bodies, and are produced by the same cells that produce immune bodies to infectious diseases.

It is difficult to understand how agglutinins are produced in individuals who do not have the respective group specific substance in their red blood cells. Perhaps small amounts of group A and B substances enter the body in the food or by some other means, and these substances in turn initiate the development of alpha and beta agglutinins. One of the reasons for believing this to be true is that injection of a group specific substance into a recipient of another blood type causes a typical immune response with formation of greater quantities of agglutinins than ever, as will be discussed below. Also, the newborn baby has few if any agglutinins, showing that their formation occurs after birth.

Immune Response of a Recipient after Administration of a Foreign Group Specific Substance. Figure 114 illustrates the effect of transfusing a type B recipient with 300 ml. of type A red blood cells. Immediately after

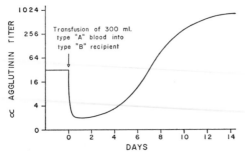

Figure 114. Effect of administering 300 ml. of type A blood to a type B recipient, showing, first, absorption of alpha agglutinins from the recipient's plasma, and second, an immune response in the recipient to produce a very high titer of alpha agglutinins approximately a week later.

transfusion, the alpha agglutinin titer of the recipient's plasma falls considerably. This decrease is due to absorption of the agglutinins by the type A group specific substance in the transfused cells. However, a week or more later the titer of alpha agglutinins in the recipient rises to approximately 30 times the original titer of these agglutinins. This indicates that the recipient has been previously "sensitized" to group A specific substance, for such a rapid and intense immune response does not occur without previous exposure. Therefore, the agglutinins are formed in the same manner as are other immune bodies.

The Agglutination Process in Transfusion Reactions

When bloods are mismatched so that alpha or beta agglutinins are mixed with red blood cells containing A or B agglutinogens, respectively, the red cells agglutinate by the following process: The agglutinins attach themselves to the red blood cells, and, because they are bivalent, a single agglutinin can attach to two different red blood cells at the same time, thereby causing them to adhere to each other. This causes the cells to clump and then plug up small blood vessels throughout the circulatory system. During the ensuing few hours to few days, the reticuloendothelial system destroys the cells, releasing hemoglobin into the blood.

Hemolysis in Transfusion Reactions. Sometimes alpha and beta hemolysins as well as agglutinins develop in the plasma. Usually hemolysins are present when the titer of agglutinins is very high, but the hemolysins are actually different antibodies from the agglutinins. The hemolysins, instead of causing the blood cells to clump, cause lysis

of the red blood cells by the immune process described in Chapter 14. Because hemolysins are less commonly present in plasma than are agglutinins, the immune reaction that occurs between bloods of different groups is usually agglutination rather than hemolysis. However, even agglutination eventually causes hemolysis of the cells because the reticuloendothelial system destroys the agglutinated cells.

Blood Typing

Prior to giving a transfusion to a recipient, it is necessary to determine the blood group of the recipient and the group of the donor blood so that the bloods will be appropriately matched. This "typing" of blood is performed as follows:

Occasionally, a type A person has extremely strong beta agglutinins in his plasma, and, also occasionally, a type B person has extremely strong alpha agglutinins in his plasma. When such persons are found, they are used as donors for laboratory "typing sera." In other words, two sera are prepared, the first containing a very strong titer of alpha agglutinins and the second a very strong titer of beta agglutinins.

The usual method of blood typing is the slide technique. In using this technique a drop or more of blood is removed from the person to be typed. This is then diluted approximately 10 times with saline so that clotting will not occur. This leaves essentially a suspension of red blood cells in saline. Two drops of this suspension are placed on a microscope slide, and a drop of alpha agglutinin serum is mixed with one of the drops of cell suspension while a drop of beta agglutinin serum is mixed with the second drop of cell suspension. After allowing several minutes for the agglutination process to take place, the slide is observed under a microscope to determine whether or not the cells have clumped. If they have clumped, one knows that an immune reaction has resulted between the serum and the cells.

Table 10 illustrates the reactions that occur with each of the four different types of blood. Group O red blood cells have no agglutinogens and, therefore, will not react with either the alpha or the beta serum. Group A blood has A agglutinogens and therefore agglutinates with alpha agglu-

Table 10. Blood Typing—Showing Agglutination of Cells of the Different Blood Groups with α and β Agglutinins

Red Blood Cells	Sera	
	α	β
O	−	−
A	+	−
B	−	+
AB	+	+

tinins. Group B blood has B agglutinogens and agglutinates with the beta serum. Group AB blood has both A and B agglutinogens and agglutinates with both types of serum.

Cross-matching

If a patient's life depends on immediate transfusion, it is not absolutely essential to type the bloods of the donor and the recipient, for one can simply test the bloods against each other to determine whether or not agglutination will occur. To do this, one prepares, first, a suspension of red cells from the donor, and, second, a small quantity of defibrinated serum from the recipient. Then he mixes the serum from the recipient with the cells from the donor to determine whether or not agglutination occurs. In a second test, the cells of the recipient are "cross-matched" against the serum of the donor. If no agglutination of either the donor's or the recipient's cells occurs, it can be assumed that the two bloods are of the same type, and it is safe to proceed with a transfusion even though the actual blood type is unknown.

The Rh and Hr Factors

In addition to type O, A, and B antigens, red blood cells of any one of the major blood groups can contain other antigenic proteins, including the so-called "Rh factor." Several different types of Rh proteins exist in human red blood cells, but they all react similarly. Therefore, the Rh factor will be discussed first as if it were one single antigenic protein.

Blood containing Rh factor is called *Rh positive blood,* and blood not containing Rh factor is called *Rh negative blood.*

Development of Anti-Rh Agglutinins. A difference between Rh factor and A and B

agglutinogens is that anti-Rh agglutinins do not develop without prior exposure to reasonable quantities of Rh proteins. In other words, anti-Rh agglutinins do not spontaneously appear in the blood of Rh negative persons but, instead, develop only after Rh antigen has entered the person's body in large quantities, such as by transfusion.

When red blood cells containing Rh factor, or even when protein breakdown products of such red cells, are injected into an Rh negative person, anti-Rh agglutinins develop very slowly, the maximal titer of agglutinins occurring after approximately two to four months. However, once the Rh negative person has been "sensitized" by this initial exposure to Rh factor, a second exposure causes rapid development of a high titer of anti-Rh agglutinins in 10 to 14 days.

Characteristics of Rh Agglutination. Anti-Rh agglutinins are similar to the alpha and beta agglutinins discussed above, for they attach to Rh positive red blood cells and cause these to form clumps. However, the agglutination reaction is usually a very weak one and cannot be detected by the usual methods of blood typing discussed above. Usually for agglutination to take place the red blood cells must be suspended in an albumin solution, and the mixture of cells and anti-Rh agglutinins must be incubated at 37° C. The weakness of this agglutination reaction is one of the reasons for failure to recognize the importance of the Rh factor until 1941.

Anti-Rh immune bodies do not cause hemolysis, but, whenever agglutination occurs in the body, the clumped blood cells plug the capillaries in the peripheral circulatory system, and the cells are gradually destroyed by the reticuloendothelial system during the next few hours to few days so that the final effect of the agglutination reaction is actually hemolysis.

The Rh "Types" in Blood. Three major and several other minor Rh factors have been discovered. The major ones are the Rh_0, Rh', and Rh'' factors. The red blood cells of approximately 85 per cent of white persons contain Rh_0 factor, 70 per cent contain Rh'' factor, and 30 per cent contain Rh' factor.

The Rh_0 antigen is the only one of all the Rh factors that is strongly antigenic, and, therefore, it is also the only one that often causes transfusion reactions. Unfortunately, it also is the most prevalent of the Rh factors. Because of its extreme importance and because of the lack of importance of most of the other Rh factors, bloods are usually typed on the basis of the Rh_0 antigen only, totally neglecting the other Rh factors.

The Rh positive state. If a person's red blood cells contain any one of the 3 different Rh factors, his blood is said to be Rh positive, for any one of the 3 different factors can cause immune responses and agglutination. When a person has one of the Rh factors he is also likely to have one or more of the other Rh factors. Therefore, the total percentage of Rh positive persons among the white population averages approximately 87 per cent; all except 2 per cent of these have Rh_0 factor, all except 17 per cent have Rh″ factor, and when Rh′ factor is present in the blood, it almost never occurs alone but occurs in about one third of the persons who possess Rh_0 factor, Rh″ factor, or both.

The Rh negative state. A person is considered to be Rh negative when his red blood cells contain *none* of the different Rh factors. Approximately 13 per cent of the white population is Rh negative.

Many individuals who are called Rh positive can still develop anti-Rh immune bodies, for they *may be Rh positive for only one or two of the Rh factors and Rh negative for the other Rh factors*. Therefore, persons who are classified as "Rh positive" are not absolutely safe against Rh immune reactions. To avoid confusion, subjects are sometimes typed for each of the three different types of Rh factor, though more often they are typed for all of them at once, or for the Rh_0 factor alone as explained above.

Prevalence of Rh factor among the races. Rh negativity occurs principally in the white races, for the different colored races tend to be almost entirely Rh positive. In the parts of the world where the races have mixed, the population has an Rh percentage somewhere between the white percentage of 87 per cent and the colored percentage of 100 per cent. American Negroes are approximately 95 per cent positive, thus demonstrating probable admixture of large amounts of white blood.

The Hr Factor. The Hr factor, like the Rh factor, is actually many separate protein antigens. For each type of Rh factor there is a corresponding Hr type of factor—that is, an Hr_0 factor, an Hr′ factor, and an Hr″ factor, and several still less important Hr factors which correspond to the respective Rh factors.

The Hr factor is almost never strongly antigenic and, therefore, rarely causes serious transfusion reactions, though on occasion the transfusion of Hr positive blood into a sensitized Hr negative person will cause a mild reaction.

The major importance of the Hr factor lies in its relationship to the inheritance of the Rh factor, as will be explained below. Whenever any one of the Rh factors is lacking, the corresponding Hr factor will be present, and, on the contrary, whenever the Hr factor is missing the corresponding Rh factor will always be present. Also, it is possible for both the Rh and the Hr factors of the same type to be present in the same individual, which is explained by the following relationships.

Inheritance of the Rh and Hr Factors. A theory that explains the inheritance of the major Rh and Hr factors is the following: Figure 115 illustrates portions of 2 chromosomes lying side by side with 3 paired, allelomorphic genes. Each of the 2 top genes may be an Rh′ or an Hr′ gene; each of the second pair of genes may be an Rh_0 or an Hr_0 gene; and each of the third pair of genes may be an Rh″ or an Hr″ gene. It is obvi-

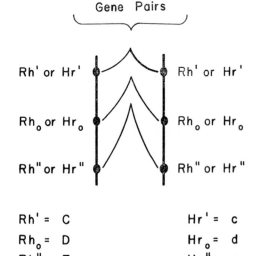

Figure 115. Theoretical arrangement of three allelomorphic pairs of genes in the chromosomes, these determining Rh and Hr heredity. At the bottom of the figure, it is noted that the Rh and Hr designations are frequently designated by the letters C, D, E, c, d, and e.

ous, therefore, that persons can have many different combinations of Rh and Hr genes—36 such combinations in all.

It is noted in Figure 115 that the Rh' gene is frequently called a C gene, the Rh0 gene is frequently called a D gene, etc., with C, D, and E representing the Rh factors and c, d, and e representing the Hr factors. Using these designations the 36 different *genotypes* of individuals for the major Rh and Hr factors are frequently represented as follows: $\dfrac{CDe}{cDe}$, $\dfrac{cDe}{Cde}$, $\dfrac{CDE}{CDE}$, etc.

No one of the Rh or Hr genes is dominant over the others. Therefore, whenever any of these genes is present in either one of the chromosomes, the corresponding factor occurs in the red blood cells. When both chromosomes contain Rh' genes and contain no Hr' genes, then the blood contains only Rh' factor and contains no Hr' factor, but, when the gene on one chromosome is Rh' and the corresponding gene on the other chromosome is Hr', the red blood cells contain both the factors.

Erythroblastosis Fetalis.

Erythroblastosis fetalis is a disease of the newborn infant characterized by progressive agglutination and hemolysis of the red blood cells. In most instances of erythroblastosis fetalis the mother is Rh negative, the father is Rh positive, the baby has inherited the Rh positive characteristic from the father, and the mother has developed anti-Rh agglutinins that have diffused into the baby to cause red blood cell agglutination.

Formation of anti-Rh agglutinins in the mother. The Rh protein is present in the fetal tissues from the earliest stages of development, and, as is true of most of the different cellular proteins, the Rh protein is present in all the cells of the body rather than in only the red blood cells. Therefore, when any portion of the fetal tissues or fetal red blood cells degenerates, some of the Rh antigen is released into the fluids of the baby, and these then diffuse through the membrane of the placenta into the mother. Once in the mother they elicit the usual formation of anti-Rh agglutinins.

Prevalence of the disease. An Rh negative mother having her first Rh positive child usually does not develop sufficient anti-Rh agglutinins to cause any harm. However, an Rh negative mother having her second Rh positive child will have become "sensitized" by the first child and therefore will often develop anti-Rh agglutinins very rapidly upon becoming pregnant with the second

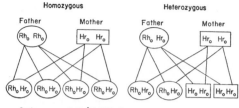

Homozygous   Heterozygous

Figure 116. Some representative matings of father and mother, showing that all offspring of the homozygous Rh positive father will be Rh positive if the mother is Rh negative.

child. Approximately 3 per cent of these second babies exhibit some signs of erythroblastosis fetalis; approximately 10 per cent of the third babies exhibit the disease; and the incidence rises progressively with subsequent pregnancies.

The Rh negative mother develops anti-Rh agglutinins only when the fetus is Rh positive. As illustrated in Figure 116, many of the Rh positive fathers are heterozygous (about 55%), causing about one fourth of the offspring to be Rh negative. Therefore, after an erythroblastotic child has been born, it is not certain that future children will also be erythroblastotic for some of them could be Rh negative and not susceptible. Also, it is probable that the anti-Rh immune response in the mother becomes less and less intense the longer she waits between pregnancies; as a result, long intervals between pregnancies might be considerably safer than short intervals when the mother is Rh negative and the father is positive.

Effect of the mother's immune bodies on the baby. After anti-Rh antibodies have formed in the mother, they diffuse very slowly through the placental membrane into the baby's blood. There they cause slow agglutination of the baby's blood, and clumps of blood cells occlude small blood vessels. The red blood cells of these clumps gradually hemolyze, releasing hemoglobin into the blood. The reticuloendothelial system then converts the hemoglobin into bilirubin, which causes yellowness (jaundice) of the skin. The antibodies probably also attack and damage many of the other cells of the body.

Clinical picture of erythroblastosis. The newborn, jaundiced, erythroblastotic baby is usually anemic at birth, and the anti-Rh agglutinins from the mother usually circulate in the baby's blood for one to two months after birth, destroying more and more red blood cells. Therefore, the hemoglobin level of the erythroblastotic baby often falls for approximately the first 45 days after birth, and, if the level falls below 6 to 8 grams per cent, the baby usually dies.

The hemopoietic tissues of the baby attempt to replace the hemolyzing red blood cells. The liver and the spleen become greatly enlarged and produce red blood cells in the same manner that they normally produce red blood cells during the middle of gestation. Because of the very rapid production of cells, many early forms are emptied into the circulatory system, and it is because of the presence of many erythroblasts in the circulatory system that the disease has been called "erythroblastosis fetalis."

Though the severe anemia of erythroblastosis fetalis is usually the cause of death, it is not the only cause, for severely erythroblastotic children are very likely to have many other degenerative abnormalities throughout the body, including especially damage to the brain. Many children who barely survive from the anemia still exhibit permanent mental impairment or permanent damage to the motor areas of the brain. This damage may result from the anemia or high level of bilirubin in the body fluids, but more likely it is caused by direct reaction of the anti-Rh agglutinins with the Rh protein of the brain cells.

Treatment of the erythroblastic baby. The usual treatment for erythroblastosis fetalis is to replace the newborn infant's blood with Rh negative blood. Approximately 400 ml. of Rh negative blood is infused over a period of 1½ or more hours while the baby's own Rh positive blood is being removed. Once the Rh negative blood is in the baby, very little further destruction of red blood cells occurs, and second transfusions are usually unnecessary. By the time the Rh negative blood is replaced with the baby's own blood, the remaining anti-Rh agglutinins will have been destroyed.

Erythroblastosis fetalis occurring in babies of Rh positive mothers. Approximately 7 per cent of the babies who have erythroblastosis fetalis are born of Rh positive mothers rather than Rh negative mothers. A very few cases are caused by alpha or beta agglutinins diffusing from the mother into the baby to agglutinate the baby's red blood cells. Some of the other instances result from the fact that the so-called "Rh positive" mother is sometimes Rh positive for only one or two of the Rh factors and yet Rh negative for the other Rh factors. Finally, similar reactions have also been noted as a result of the Hr factor or other less well-known antigenic factors in the baby's blood, some of which will be discussed in the following section.

Other Blood Factors

Many antigenic proteins besides the O, A, B, Rh, and Hr factors are present in red blood cells of different people, but these other factors very rarely cause transfusion reactions and, therefore, are mainly of academic and legal importance. Some of these different blood factors are the M, N, S, s, P, Kell, Lewis, Duffy, Kidd, Diego, and Lutheran factors. Occasionally, transfusion of red cells containing one of these factors will cause specific agglutinins to develop in the recipient, and immune reactions can then occur when the same type of blood is infused a second time. However, these different antigenic factors do not exhibit extreme degrees of antigenicity and, therefore, usually cause very weak transfusion reactions or no reactions at all.

Inheritance of most of the different blood factors follows almost the same principles as those observed for inheritance of the major group specific substances and for the Rh and Hr factors. The genes for the different factors are almost all dominant, and whenever any one of the genes is inherited from a parent the factor will usually be present in the child's blood.

Method for Studying Obscure Blood Factors. One of the means by which different blood factors, including the Rh factor, have been studied in the human being has been to immunize lower animals such as rabbits with human red blood cells. Specific antibodies develop in the animal against the different antigens of the human cells, and specific immune sera prepared from the plasma of these animals can then be used for determining the presence or absence of the same antigens in red blood cells of other persons.

Use of Blood Typing in Forensic Medicine. In the past two decades the use of blood typing has become an important legal procedure in cases of disputed parentage. There are 3 different genes in the OAB system of blood groups and 6 major ones in the Rh-Hr system. Including all the other blood types as well, more than 30 different blood group genes can be determined for each person by blood-typing procedures. After the mother's and child's genes have been determined, many of the father's genes are then known immediately, because any gene present in a child but not present in the mother must be present in the father. Using all possible blood factors, the father of a particular child can often be picked out of as many as a hundred or more male suspects.

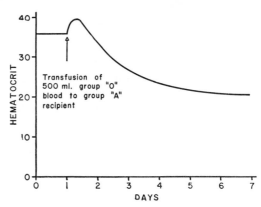

Figure 117. Delayed destruction of a recipient's red blood cells following infusion of "universal donor" group O blood into a group A recipient.

TRANSFUSION

Indications for Transfusion. The most common reason for transfusion is decreased blood volume, which will be discussed in detail in Chapter 37 in relation to shock. Also, transfusions are often used for treating anemia or to supply the recipient with some other constituent of whole blood besides red blood cells, such as to supply a thrombocytopenic patient with new platelets. Also, hemophilic patients can be rendered temporarily non-hemophilic by plasma transfusion, and, occasionally, the quantity of "complement" in a recipient must be supplemented by fresh plasma infusions before certain antigen-antibody reactions can take place.

Transfusion Reactions Resulting from Mismatched Blood Groups

If blood of one group is transfused to a recipient of another group, a transfusion reaction is likely to occur in which the red blood cells of the donor blood are agglutinated. However, even though the bloods might be mismatched, it is very rare that the transfused blood ever causes agglutination of the *recipient's cells* for the following reason: The plasma portion of the donor blood immediately becomes diluted by all the plasma of the recipient, thereby decreasing the titer of the infused agglutinins to a level too low to cause agglutination. On the other hand, the infused blood does not dilute the agglutinins in the recipient's plasma to a major extent. Therefore, they can still agglutinate the donor cells.

Universal Donor Blood. Because the cells of group O blood contain neither of the two agglutinogens, small quantities of this blood can be transfused into almost any recipient without immediate agglutination occurring. For this reason group O blood is sometimes called *universal donor blood*. It must be noted, however, that transfusion of especially large amounts of group O blood

into a mismatched recipient can cause either immediate or delayed agglutination of the recipient's own cells, as illustrated in Figure 117, because the infused agglutinins then are not diluted sufficiently to prevent the reaction.

Nevertheless, for use in extreme emergencies, when sufficient time is not available for blood typing or cross-matching, many blood banks keep small quantities of group O blood specially available.

The Universal Recipient. Group AB persons are sometimes called *universal recipients* because their plasma contains neither alpha nor beta agglutinins, and small quantities of all other blood groups can be infused without causing a transfusion reaction. However, here again, if large quantities of these mismatched bloods should be administered, the agglutinins in the donor blood might accumulate in sufficient quantities to agglutinate the recipient's type AB cells.

Hemolysis of Red Cells Following Transfusion Reactions. All transfusion reactions resulting from mismatched blood groups eventually cause hemolysis of the red blood cells. Occasionally, specific *hemolysins* are present in the plasma of the recipient along with the agglutinins and therefore cause immediate hemolysis, but more frequently the cells agglutinate first and then are entrapped in the peripheral vessels. Over a period of hours to days the entrapped cells degenerate and hemolyze, liberating hemoglobin into the circulatory system.

When the rate of hemolysis is rapid, the concentration of hemoglobin in the blood can rise to extremely high values. A small quantity of this remains attached to other proteins in the circulating blood so that in mild transfusions essentially none of the hemoglobin will leave the circulation. However, above a threshold value, the excess hemoglobin becomes unattached from the other proteins and diffuses out of the circulation into the tissue spaces or through the renal glomeruli into the kidney tubules, as will be discussed below. The hemoglobin remaining in the circulation or passing into the tissue spaces is gradually ingested by reticuloendothelial cells and converted into bilirubin, which was discussed in Chapter 12. During very rapid hemolysis the concentration of bilirubin in the body fluids can sometimes rise high enough to cause *jaundice*—that is, the person's tissues become tinged with yellow pigment. But jaundice usually does not appear unless 300 to 500 ml. of blood is hemolyzed in less than a day.

Acute Kidney Shutdown Following Transfusion Reactions. One of the most lethal effects of transfusion reactions is acute kidney shutdown, which can begin within a few minutes or hours and continue until the person dies of renal failure.

The kidney shutdown seems to result from two different causes: First, the antigen-antibody reaction of the transfusion reaction releases toxic substances from the hemolyzing blood that cause very powerful renal vasoconstriction. Second, if the total amount of free hemoglobin in the circulating blood is greater than that quantity which can bind with the plasma proteins, the excess will leak through the glomerular membranes into the kidney tubules. If this amount is still slight, it can be reabsorbed through the tubular epithelium into the blood and will cause no harm, but, if it is great, then only small portions are reabsorbed. Yet, water continues to be reabsorbed, causing the tubular hemoglobin concentration to rise so high that it precipitates and blocks many of the tubules. Thus, renal vasoconstriction and tubular block add together to cause the acute renal shutdown. If the shutdown is complete, the patient dies a renal death within a week to 12 days, as explained in Chapter 11.

Physiological Principles of Treatment Following Transfusion Reactions. A transfusion reaction can cause considerable degrees of fever and certain amounts of general toxicity, but these effects, in the absence of renal shutdown, are almost never lethal. Therefore, treatment is usually directed toward preventing renal damage, especially by preventing hemoglobin precipitation in the kidney tubules, as follows: (1) rapid infusion of dilute intravenous fluids to cause water diuresis, (2) administration of diuretics to prevent reabsorption of water by the tubules and also to overcome the renal vasoconstriction, and (3) alkalinization of the body fluids because alkaline tubular fluid can dissolve more hemoglobin than can acid tubular fluid.

If a transfusion is stopped at the earliest sign of a transfusion reaction, usually the patient will not die. In the days prior to blood typing and cross-matching, donor blood was usually given to a recipient at a relatively slow rate, but the transfusion was stopped immediately if the patient complained of pain in his kidney regions. Such pain usually would occur after 100 to 200 ml. of mismatched blood had been administered, and, if the transfusion was stopped just at that point, the patient usually did not die.

Transfusion Reactions Occurring When Rh Factors Are Mismatched

If the recipient has previously received a blood transfusion containing a strongly antigenic Rh factor not present in his own blood, then he may have built up appropriate anti-Rh antibodies that can cause an immediate transfusion reaction on subsequent exposure to the same type of Rh blood. Since the Rh_0 antigen is the only Rh factor with strong antigenicity, this is almost always the cause of transfusion reactions of this type. If the titer of anti-Rh antibodies is very high, the characteristics of the reaction are almost identical with those described above for mismatched blood groups.

On the other hand, if the recipient has never received an Rh positive transfusion before, he will have no immediate reaction at all. Instead, the antibodies will require 10 days or more to build up. Then slow agglutination and hemolysis of the infused cells result, causing jaundice but no renal damage.

Other Types of Transfusion Reactions

Pyrogenic Reactions. Pyrogenic reactions occur more frequently than either agglutination or hemolysis. These reactions cause fever in the recipient but do not destroy red blood cells. Most pyrogenic reactions probably result from the presence in the donor plasma of proteins to which the recipient is allergic, or they result from the presence of breakdown products in old, deteriorating donor blood. If the donor has eaten certain foods to which the recipient is allergic, reagins from these foods can sometimes be transmitted to the recipient, thereby causing allergic reactions. The usual pyrogenic reaction causes severe chills, and occasionally the blood pressure falls, but ordinarily no dire results follow the reaction.

Transfusion Reactions Resulting from Anticoagulants. The usual anticoagulant used for transfusion is citrate. As discussed in the following chapter, citrate operates as an anticoagulant by combining with the calcium ions of the plasma so that these become nonionizable. Without the presence of ionizable calcium the coagulation process cannot take place. Normal nerve, muscle, and heart function also cannot occur in the absence of calcium ion. Therefore, if blood containing large quantities of citrate anticoagulant is administered rapidly, the recipient is likely to experience typical tetany due to low calcium, which is discussed in detail in Chapter 77. Such tetany can kill the patient within a few minutes because of respiratory muscular spasm.

Ordinarily the liver can remove citrate from the blood within a few minutes and polymerize this citrate into glycogen or utilize it directly for energy. Therefore, when blood transfusions are given at slow rates, the citrate type of reaction is not likely to occur. On the other hand, if the patient has liver damage, the rate of transfusion must be decreased even more than usually to prevent this type of reaction.

The Blood Bank

Blood can be stored for several weeks at a temperature of 4° C. Then, after warming and straining out the numerous small clots that usually will have developed, the blood may be readministered to a recipient. To keep the red blood cells viable, the stored blood must be fortified with an adequate quantity of added dextrose, and, to prevent clotting, a citrate anticoagulant is usually used. An acid citrate solution preserves the red blood cells longer than does an alkaline citrate solution. Ordinarily, therefore, the solution for mixing with blood to be stored is such that, after mixing with the blood, the concentration of dextrose in the mixture is 0.5 per cent and the concentration of disodium acid citrate 0.5 per cent.

Effect of Duration of Storage on the Red Blood Cells. Because stored red blood cells still contain viable enzymes, a certain amount of metabolism continues even during storage. The rate of destruction of red blood cells during storage is approximately equal to the normal rate of destruction of red blood cells in the body—that is, approximately 10 per cent every 8 to 12 days. Therefore, the older the blood becomes, the less valuable is it for transfusion. Figure 118 illustrates the effect of blood storage on its physiological value. It will be noted that blood stored for 28 days loses approximately 25 per cent of the red blood cells before it is administered to the recipient. Furthermore, those cells that have not been destroyed are already relatively old cells and do not last as long in the recipient as do fresh blood cells.

Use of "Washed" Red Blood Cells for Transfusion. After blood has been stored in the blood bank for 2 to 4 weeks it is usually centrifuged, and the plasma is removed for future plasma infusions. The cells can be resuspended in saline or other appropriate solution and injected into patients who are in need of red blood cells. Such

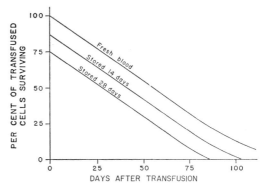

Figure 118. Effect of prolonged storage of blood in a blood bank on the viability of the red blood cells.

treatment is quite satisfactory for anemic patients who have poor hemopoietic systems. Also, it is a relatively inexpensive procedure because the red blood cells are a by-product of plasma manufacture.

Plasma Transfusions

Plasma is sometimes equally as satisfactory as whole blood for transfusion and occasionally even preferable. For instance, when a person is bleeding severely, death often results from circulatory collapse caused by diminished blood volume but not from diminished red blood cell concentration. To supply blood would require considerable lost time in blood typing and other precautions against transfusion reactions. However, plasma can usually be administered in very large quantities without reactions. Furthermore, plasma can be stored for many years instead of the few weeks that blood can be stored. Also, it can be administered to patients for its protein nutrient value as well as because of a need for whole blood. Use of plasma for blood volume replacement and as a nutrient will be discussed in Chapter 37.

Storage of Plasma. Plasma can be stored in the refrigerator in a *liquid* form at approximately 4° C. for several months. As long as the plasma remains in the liquid phase, slow autolysis of the plasma proteins continues, with production of pyrogens. Therefore, pyrogenic reactions are more and more likely to occur in the recipient the older the plasma becomes.

To prevent autolytic destruction, plasma is usually *frozen* and maintained at a temperature of about −20° C. In this state it can be stored for years without any harmful effects.

Pooling of plasma to reduce agglutinin titers. Before freezing plasma or even before using it as a replacement fluid, plasma from approximately 10 different donors is usually mixed together to form "pooled" plasma. This is done to reduce the agglutinin titer in those units of plasma that may have high titers. A few type A persons have very high titers of beta agglutinins, a few type B persons have very high titers of alpha agglutinins, and an occasional type O person may have high titers of both alpha and beta agglutinins. On the other hand, the majority of

people have very low titers of these two agglutinins. Should a recipient receive plasma from blood having a high titer of agglutinins, the recipient's red blood cells might all be agglutinated as the result. Yet, it is very difficult to determine the titer of all units of plasma from the different donors. Therefore, the different units of plasma are mixed together so that the high and low titers will average out to a low value.

One can usually inject into a recipient a small quantity of pooled plasma without causing any harm, because the agglutinins in the plasma will be diluted by the recipient's blood. However, administration of large quantities of pooled plasma may agglutinate the recipient's blood with disastrous results, or delayed transfusion reactions, which were discussed above, may occur to cause gradual destruction of the red blood cells. When it is realized that many patients, particularly those with severe burns, must receive several liters of plasma a day, this problem is of considerable concern.

In recent years, *purified A and B group specific substances* have been mixed with plasma to neutralize the alpha and beta agglutinins. Thereafter, considerably larger quantities of pooled plasma can be administered to recipients without the possibility of agglutinating the recipient's blood.

Lyophilized Plasma. A method that has been used for commercial preparation and storage of plasma is the so-called "lyophilizing process." Plasma is placed in a strong glass flask and frozen on the inner walls of this flask while the flask is being rotated. Then the flask is connected to a very high vacuum. It will be recalled from the physics of evaporation that, when the pressure surrounding frozen water is extremely low, the ice can be evaporated directly into the gaseous phase without passing through the liquid phase. This is the basis of the lyophilizing process, for the frozen water is evaporated, leaving behind a very fluffy, powdery mixture of plasma proteins and plasma salts. When the flask containing these is stored, it is left in the same evacuated state. Then, when it is desired to use the plasma, all one needs to do is to replace the water that has been removed by evaporation. The evacuated flask is connected by means of a small rubber tube and syringe needle to another flask containing distilled, sterilized water. The syringe needle punctures the rubber seal of the evacuated flask, and the water from the second flask flows into the evacuated one. Because a vacuum exists even between the minute particles of proteins and salts, water flows immediately into all of the interstices of the protein and salt mass. This allows an immediate and very diffuse mixing of the lyophilized plasma with the new water. As a consequence, the plasma is returned to the liquid phase approximately 20 to 30 seconds after introduction of the water.

If the vacuum is lost from the flask of lyophilized plasma, air entrapped within the powder prevents water from flowing into the interstices. As a consequence, it becomes almost impossible to redissolve the plasma under these conditions.

Lyophilized plasma can be stored at normal room temperature or even at slightly elevated temperatures for years without any harm. This, therefore, is the commercial and the military method for preparing plasma.

Reactions Following Plasma Administration. *Citrate reactions.*

Most plasma is prepared from citrated blood that has been kept in blood banks. Therefore, the plasma itself still contains citrate, and its use is subject to the same precautions as for blood that has citrate anticoagulant. Because plasma is frequently used as a life-saving measure in patients who have suffered severe hemorrhage, it is always necessary to be on the constant lookout for citrate tetany. One might expect that the citrate ion would be removed from plasma before its use; however, it must be recalled that it is the plasma that clots and not the red blood cells. Therefore, citrate is just as important in plasma as an anticoagulant as it is in whole blood. Occasionally, the action of citrate is neutralized by administering to the patient through a second syringe needle an extra quantity of calcium simultaneously with the administration of plasma.

Serum infusions and reactions. Sometimes calcium is added to plasma to neutralize the citrate anticoagulant, and then the plasma is allowed to clot. When the clot retracts, it extrudes the water, the salts, and the other plasma proteins besides the fibrinogen that forms the clot. This material is known as *serum* rather than plasma. Because it contains both the albumin and the globulins of normal plasma, it can be used in place of whole plasma for substitutive therapy. The clotting process liberates into serum certain toxic products that have not yet been elucidated but that can cause hyperthermia and allergic shock. Therefore, the toxic products of serum are often more dangerous to the recipient than is the citrate that is ordinarily used to prevent clotting of the plasma.

Serum hepatitis caused by pooled plasma. A virus disease known as *serum hepatitis* frequently spreads from one person to another by means of plasma infusions. One person out of every few hundred has this type of hepatitis. Therefore, when plasma from many different recipients is pooled, it is very likely that the entire mixture of pooled plasma will become infected. Consequently, the pooling process, even though necessary to keep the titer of agglutinins low, increases the spread of serum hepatitis. Therefore, specific precautions are taken to avert passage of this disease: First, a bilirubin test is performed on all blood that comes into the blood bank. If the bilirubin level is high, the donor is possibly suffering from liver disease, and this liver disease might be serum hepatitis. Therefore, such blood is rejected before it is given to a recipient or before it is made into plasma. Second, various anti-viral agents have been placed in plasma in an attempt to control serum hepatitis. However, these have not been universally successful, and the disease is still frequently transmitted from donor to recipient by means of blood transfusions and, much more frequently, pooled plasma infusions. Third, by pooling only a few units of plasma, usually about 10, the likelihood of severe hepatitis is kept at a minimum.

Plasma reactions due to preservatives. Reactions have occurred in the recipient owing to the presence of preservatives placed in plasma. This occurred particularly in World War II when Merthiolate was used in relatively high concentration as a plasma preservative. Ordinarily, the quantity of Merthiolate used did not hurt the recipient, but, when the recipient needed 10 to 30 pints of plasma, then the quantity of mercury in the Merthiolate was sufficient to cause tubular necrosis in the kidney with resulting complete kidney shutdown in many persons. More recently antibiotic preservatives have been used with far less likelihood of reaction in the recipient.

TRANSPLANTATION OF TISSUES AND ORGANS

Relation of Genotypes to Transplantation.

In the modern age of surgery, many attempts are being made to transplant tissues and even organs from one person to another, or, occasionally, from lower animals to the human being. All the different antigenic proteins of red blood cells that cause transfusion reactions and possibly still many more are also present in the other cells of the body. Consequently, any foreign cells transplanted into a recipient can cause immune responses and immune reactions. The alpha and beta agglutinins of a recipient can destroy grafted cells containing, respectively, type A and B antigens, or the Rh and Hr antigens in the graft can cause antibodies to develop in the recipient, these antibodies later destroying the graft. And, in addition, there are probably hundreds of additional antigens which can cause similar effects. In other words, most recipients are just as able to resist invasion by foreign cells as to resist invasion by foreign bacteria.

Autologous, Homologous, and Heterologous Transplants. A transplant of tissue or an organ from one part of a person's body to some other part of his body is called an *autologous transplant*. Such transplants can be skin grafts, bone grafts, cartilage grafts, and so forth. A transplant from one human being to another or from any animal to another member of the same species is called a *homologous transplant*. Finally, a transplant from a lower animal to a human being or from an animal of one species to one of another species is called a *heterologous transplant*.

Cellular Transplants. In the case of autologous transplants, cells in the transplant will almost always live indefinitely if an adequate blood supply is provided, but, in the case of homologous and heterologous transplants, immune reactions almost always occur, causing death of all the cells in the transplant 3 to 10 weeks after transplantation. The cells of homologous transplants usually persist slightly longer than those of heterologous transplants because the antigenic structure of the homologous transplant is more nearly the same as that of the recipient's tissues than is true of the heterologous transplant. The greater the difference in antigenic structure, the more rapid and the more severe also are the immune reactions to the graft.

Transplants from one identical twin to another are the one exception in which homologous transplants of cellular tissues are often successful. The reason for this is that the antigenic proteins of both twins are determined by identical genes derived originally from the same single fertilized ovum.

Some of the different cellular tissues and organs that have been transplanted either experimentally or for temporary benefit from one person to another have been skin, kidneys, glandular tissue, and bone marrow. In animals, even hearts and lungs have been

transplanted and have survived in a functional capacity for at least 18 hours.

Transplantation of Noncellular Tissues. Certain tissues that have no cells or in which the cells are unimportant to the purpose of the graft, such as the cornea, tendon, fascia, and bone, can usually be grafted from one person to another with considerable success. In these instances the grafts act merely as a supporting latticework into which or around which the surrounding living tissues of the recipient grow. Indeed, some such grafts—bone and fascia—are occasionally successful even when they come from a lower animal rather than from another human being.

A special problem arises in the case of a corneal transplant from one human eye to another, for, not only must it maintain structural continuity, but it must also remain transparent. About 50 to 90 per cent of the corneas remain transparent, the exact percentage depending principally on the preliminary condition of the recipient's eye. The remainder will suddenly become cloudy at the end of two weeks to two years. This cloudiness is the result of an antigen-antibody reaction. It is believed that those corneas which do not become cloudy fail to do so for any of three different reasons: First, their antigenicity might be low enough that they fail to cause the production of sufficient immune bodies to elicit the response. Second, the vascularity of the cornea is so slight that the antigens of the cornea may never infuse the host in sufficient quantities to elicit an immune response. Or, third, it is possible that, if the reaction is delayed long enough, the corneal proteins will adapt to the antigenic structure of the recipient so that a reaction can no longer occur against the corneal tissue.

Attempts to Overcome the Antigen-Antibody Reactions in Transplanted Tissue

Because of the extreme importance of transplanting certain tissues and organs, such as skin and kidneys, very serious attempts have been made to prevent the antigen-antibody reactions associated with transplants. The following three specific procedures have met with certain degrees of success in experimental animals:

Glucocorticoid Therapy (Cortisone, Hydrocortisone, and ACTH). The glucocorticoid hormones from the adrenal gland greatly suppress the formation of antibodies. Therefore, administration of large quantities of these, or of ACTH, which causes the adrenal gland to produce glucocorticoids, will often allow transplants to persist much longer than usual in the recipient. However, this is only a delaying process rather than a preventive one, though it can be used in rare instances to prolong grafts long enough to save the life of the recipient until other therapeutic procedures can be instituted.

Adaptation of the Grafted Tissues to the Animal's Body. Embryonic tissues transplanted from a human fetus less than 5 months old usually will not cause antibodies to develop in the host and, therefore, will grow in the human being indefinitely. The cause of this is an inherent ability of embryonic cells to adapt themselves to the antigenic structure of the host in such a way that the host will not produce antibodies against the cells. Therefore, especially in experimental animals, it has been possible to effect valuable embryonic transplants, and it is probable that this procedure will have some usefulness in the human being in the future.

Suppression of Antibody Formation by Irradiation. Occasionally, a human being has naturally suppressed antibody formation resulting from (a) congenital aglobulinemia in which the person is simply unable to produce gamma globulins and (b) destructive diseases of his reticuloendothelial system such as result occasionally in multiple myeloma. Transplants of homologous tissues into these individuals are occasionally successful, or at least their destruction is delayed. Also, irradiative destruction of most of the reticuloendothelial system by either x-rays or gamma rays will render an animal susceptible to a homologous transplant. Unfortunately, this procedure leaves the animal unprotected from disease and also unable to form blood cells. To get around this, experiments are now under way to transplant embryonic bone marrow into these animals after irradiation, hoping to solve the problem of the destroyed reticuloendothelial system.

REFERENCES

Albert, F., and Medawar, P. B.: Biological Problems of Grafting. Springfield, Illinois, Charles C Thomas, 1959.

Andresen, P. H.: Human Blood Groups Utilized in Disputed Paternity Cases and Criminal Proceedings. Springfield, Illinois, Charles C Thomas, 1952.

Brown, J. B., and Fryer, M. P.: Postmortem Homografts. Springfield, Illinois, Charles C Thomas, 1960.

Ciba Foundation Symposium: Preservation and transplantation of normal tissues. Boston, Little, Brown and Co., 1954.

Converse, J. M.: The relation of immunology to tissue homotransplantation. New York, *Ann. N. Y. Acad. of Sc.*, 1955.

Discombe, G.: Blood Transfusion. London, William Heinemann, 1955.

Finerly, J. C.: Parabiosis in physiological studies. *Physiol. Rev.*, 32:277, 1952.

James, J. D.: Practical Blood Transfusion. Oxford, Blackwell Scientific Publications, 1958.

Kabat, E. A.: Blood Group Substances. New York, Academic Press, 1956.

Kabat, E. A.: Immunochemistry of the blood group substances. *Harvey Lect.*, 46:252, 1950–1951.

Kerr, D. J. A.: Forensic Medicine. 6th ed., New York, The Macmillan Co., 1958.

Keynes, G.: Blood Transfusion. Baltimore, Williams & Wilkins Co., 1949.

Lawler, S. D., and Lawler, L. J.: Human Blood Groups and Inheritance. Cambridge, Harvard University Press, 1957.

Lawrence, H. S.: Homograft sensitivity. *Physiol. Rev.*, 39:811, 1959.

Medawar, P. B.: The immunology of transplantation. *Harvey Lect.*, 52:144, 1956–57.

Merrill, J. P.: Transplantation of normal tissues. *Physiol. Rev.*, 39:860, 1959.

Mollison, P. L.: Blood Transfusion in Clinical Medicine. 2nd ed., Springfield, Illinois, Charles C Thomas, 1957.

Noel, J., and Schull, W. J.: Human Heredity. Chicago. University of Chicago Press, 1954.

Pollak, O. J.: Grouping, Typing, and Banking of Blood. Springfield, Illinois, Charles C Thomas, 1951.

Race, R. R., and Sanger, R.: Blood Groups in Man. 3rd ed., Springfield, Illinois, Charles C Thomas, 1958.

Soulier, J. P.: Transfusion reaction. *Blood*, 7:664, 1952.

Wiener, A. S.: An Rh-Hr Syllabus. 2nd ed., New York, Grune & Stratton, Inc., 1958.

Wiener, A. S.: An Rh-Hr Syllabus—The Types and Their Applications. 2nd ed., New York, Grune & Stratton, Inc., 1960.

Winchester, A. M.: Genetics. 2nd ed., Boston, Houghton, Mifflin Co., 1958.

See also Chapter 14, Immunity; Chapter 16, Blood coagulation.

Hemostasis and Blood Coagulation

The term *hemostasis* means prevention of blood loss. Whenever a vessel is severed or ruptured in any way, the adjacent portions of the damaged vessel automatically contract, causing local vascular spasm. This helps to prevent blood loss but usually is not sufficient to stop the bleeding entirely. Instead, the ultimate stoppage of bleeding is generally accomplished by blood coagulation. Indeed, if the blood coagulation mechanism were totally non-functional, one would bleed to death within two to three days from internal hemorrhages, for many minute capillaries and arteries rupture continually, and the blood coagulation mechanism is necessary to block these minor leaks.

BASIC THEORY OF BLOOD COAGULATION

As much as the basic problem of blood coagulation has been studied and as important as this mechanism is to normal function of the body, the precise mechanism by which blood coagulates is still unknown. Over 30 different substances that affect blood coagulation, have been found in the blood and related tissues, some promoting coagulation, called the *procoagulants*, and others inhibiting coagulation, called the *anticoagulants*. Whether or not the blood will coagulate depends on a balance between these two groups of substances. Normally the anticoagulants are in the ascendancy and the blood does not coagulate, but when a blood vessel is ruptured the activity of the procoagulants in the area of damage becomes much greater than that of the anticoagulants, and a blood clot does develop.

Figure 119 is a diagram drawn by Seegers to show some of the interrelationships of the different anticoagulants and procoagulants in the process of fibrin formation, which is the basis of clot formation. The number alone of these different substances illustrates the complexity of the problem, especially since the means by which most of the substances enter into the coagulation process are yet completely unknown.

Yet, on the other hand, some of the most important of the procoagulants and anticoagulants have been delineated fairly successfully, and their functions in the coagulation process have been at least partially described. Therefore, in the first part of this discussion we will make an attempt to point out the functions and mechanisms of action of some of the more important substances in the schema.

Basic Mechanism of Coagulation

In general, most research workers in this field are agreed that the coagulation process takes place in three essential steps:

First, *a substance called thromboplastin is released from the injured tissue area.*

Second, *the thromboplastin initiates a series of chemical reactions in the plasma which eventually converts prothrombin into thrombin.*

Third, *thrombin then acts as an enzyme to convert fibrinogen into fibrin threads that enmesh red blood cells, platelets, and plasma to form the clot itself.*

Each of these stages will be discussed separately, though it must be recognized that they all occur in sequence with each other, new thromboplastin often being formed continually while part of the blood clot has already been formed.

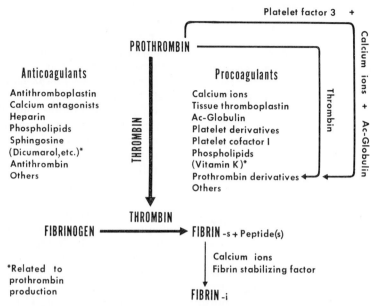

Figure 119. Interrelationships between the procoagulants and anticoagulants in causing the process of clotting. (Courtesy of Dr. Walter H. Seegers.)

Initiation of the Coagulation Process—the Formation and Release of Thromboplastin

Thromboplastin, which initiates the chemical processes that lead to blood coagulation, is any one of several different lipid or lipoprotein compounds that can be derived from essentially all tissues of the body. A special type of thromboplastin is present in the circulating platelets of the blood which has characteristics slightly different from those of thromboplastin derived from tissues. Both of these types of thromboplastin, *tissue thromboplastin* and *platelet thromboplastin,* are of considerable importance in the coagulation process.

The Fixed Tissues as the Major Source of Thromboplastin—Tissue Thromboplastin. Simply macerating almost any tissue of the body and extracting the tissue juice will provide a very powerful thromboplastin solution which, when injected intravenously, will often cause such severe clotting throughout the circulatory system that death will ensue within a few minutes. Since platelet thromboplastin is not nearly so powerful as this, it is believed that the fixed tissues themselves are the major source of the thromboplastin that normally initiates the clotting process. That is, whenever a blood vessel is broken, whether this be caused by a cut, some other type of traumatic rupture or even spontaneous rupture, the damaged blood vessel wall and perhaps contiguous tissues release tissue thromboplastin to initiate the blood coagulation process in the local area.

Platelet Thromboplastin and Plasma Cofactors Necessary To Activate Platelet Thromboplastin. Pure platelet thromboplastin usually cannot initiate clotting by itself. Instead, it must first combine with or be acted upon by a number of factors in the plasma called *plasma cofactors.* Three of the plasma cofactors that are especially important to activate platelet thromboplastin are (1) *anti-hemophilic factor,* (2) *plasma thromboplastin component,* and (3) *plasma thromboplastin antecedent.* Lack of any one of these plasma cofactors will prevent the activation of platelet thromboplastin and, therefore, prevent clotting as a result of platelet disintegration.

Though thromboplastin from platelets is rarely a major factor in initiating the clot for repairing a damaged vessel, nevertheless, platelet thromboplastin seems to be important for promoting progress of the clotting process once it has begun. It was pointed out above that one of the major steps in clotting is the conversion of prothrombin into thrombin. Once thrombin begins to form at a local site of vascular damage, the damaged surfaces become very sticky to platelets so that large numbers of platelets begin to adhere and distintegrate, releasing their thromboplastin into the plasma. It is believed that this thromboplastin then immediately reacts with the three plasma cofactors plus the thrombin that has already formed to give an *activated platelet thromboplastin,* which has almost exactly the same characteristics as tissue thromboplastin. The activated thromboplastin then accelerates the clotting process, making it go to completion much more rapidly than would otherwise have been the case.

Conversion of Prothrombin to Thrombin

After tissue thromboplastin has been released into the blood, or after platelet thromboplastin has been activated by the cofactors, the next major step in the clotting process is the conversion of prothrombin to thrombin.

Prothrombin. Prothrombin is a plasma globulin present in the blood in a normal concentration of about 15 mg. per 100 ml. Purified preparations have been obtained having a molecular weight of 62,700. Under very special conditions prothrombin can be changed in the laboratory directly into thrombin without the addition of any other substances from the plasma. Therefore, it is believed that the prothrombin molecule contains all the necessary constituents for formation of thrombin itself. However, in the normal circulatory system conditions are such that conversion of prothrombin to thrombin does not occur without intervention of thromboplastin and several other chemical factors of the blood.

Prothrombin is formed continually by the liver, and it is continually being used throughout the body for blood clotting. If the liver fails to produce prothrombin, its concentration in the plasma falls too low within 24 hours to provide adequate blood coagulation. Vitamin K is required by the liver for normal formation of prothrombin. Therefore, either lack of vitamin K or any liver disease that prevents normal prothrombin formation can often decrease the prothrombin level so low that bleeding tendencies result.

Prothrombin Conversion Factors and Their "Prothrombinase" Activity. When thromboplastin is liberated into the plasma it immediately combines with calcium and several other substances in the plasma called *prothrombin conversion factors* to form a combination that has the ability to convert prothrombin into thrombin. This combination is said to have *prothrombinase activity,* which means that it acts enzymatically to convert prothrombin into thrombin.

Many different prothrombin conversion factors have been postulated, and the relative importance of the different ones that are generally agreed upon is unknown. The following two prothrombin conversion factors seem to be the ones most necessary to the blood coagulation process: (1) *accelerator globulin,* and (2) *proconvertin* (also known as *factor VII*). Both these substances are proteins formed by the liver. Therefore, any liver condition that prevents their formation can block or delay the coagulation process, as is also true in the case of prothrombin, as was noted above.

Effect of Calcium on Prothrombinase Activity. Calcium enters into the reaction between thromboplastin, accelerator globulin, and proconvertin to give prothrombinase activity. The calcium must be available in the ionic form to cause the reactions. Therefore, any agent that precipitates calcium from the blood or binds the calcium so that it is not available in the ionic form will block the coagulation mechanism.

In the normal body, however, lack of calcium probably never causes failure of the coagulation mechanism for the following reason: When the calcium ion concentration falls below approximately one-half normal, the peripheral nerve fibers become so irritable that they begin to fire spontaneously, and the person develops tetany, as was explained in Chapter 9. A further fall in calcium ion concentration will make the tetany so severe that spasm of the respiratory muscles will kill the person. Even at this level the amount of calcium ion in the blood is still far greater than the amount needed to activate the prothrombinase system. Therefore, the person would always die of tetany long before low calcium could be a significant cause of bleeding.

The Chemical Effect of Prothrombinase Activity on Prothrombin. Once all the appropriate factors have reacted, thromboplastin, accelerator globulin, proconvertin, calcium ions, and perhaps still other poorly delineated substances, this combination will convert prothrombin into thrombin within a matter of seconds. The amount of thrombin produced is approximately proportional to the amount of prothrombinase activity that has developed, and in turn the amount of prothrombinase activity depends on the quantities of thromboplastin and prothrombin conversion factors available. Except in certain rare hemorrhagic diseases, there are excesses of all the necessary factors besides thromboplastin itself. Therefore, *normally, the amount of thrombin that is finally formed is directly proportional to the original amount of thromboplastin released from the damaged tissues and disintegrating platelets.*

Conversion of Fibrinogen to Fibrin; Formation of the Clot

Fibrinogen. Fibrinogen is a very large molecular weight (400,000) protein occurring in the plasma in quantities of 100 to 800 mg. per 100 ml. Most, if not all, of the fibrinogen in the circulating blood is formed in the liver, and liver damage decreases the total quantity of circulating fibrinogen exactly as it does the quantities of prothrombin, accelerator globulin, and proconvertin. Yet, ordinarily, liver damage decreases the other factors far more than fibrinogen. Therefore, only rarely does the level of fibrinogen in the circulatory system fall low enough, even under pathological conditions, to interfere with normal blood coagulation.

Because of its large molecular weight, fibrinogen normally does not leak into the interstitial fluids to any significant extent, and, since it is one of the major factors in the coagulation process, interstitial fluids ordinarily do not coagulate. Yet, when the permeability of the capillaries becomes pathologically increased, fibrinogen does then appear both in the tissue fluids and in lymph in sufficient quantities to cause clotting if the tissues become damaged.

Action of Thrombin on Fibrinogen to Form Fibrin. Thrombin is a protein enzyme with esterase activity. It acts on fibrinogen to remove two low molecular weight peptides from each molecule of fibrinogen, forming molecules of *activated fibrin,* which is also called *fibrin monomer.* These molecules rapidly *polymerize into long fibrin threads,* which form the *reticulum* of the clot.

During the polymerization process, calcium ions and another factor called *protein-stabilizing factor* combine with the activated fibrin; these two substances add to the stability of the fibrin threads.

The Blood Clot, Clot Retraction, and Serum. The clot itself is composed of a meshwork of fibrin threads running in all directions and entrapping blood cells, platelets, and plasma. Within a few minutes after the clot is formed it begins to contract and usually expresses most of the plasma from the clot within 30 to 60 minutes. The plasma extruded from the clot is called *serum,* for all its fibrinogen and much of the other clotting factors will have been removed. Therefore, serum itself cannot clot because of lack of these factors.

For reasons not completely understood, large numbers of platelets are necessary for clot retraction to occur. Electron micrographs of platelets in blood clots show that they form nidi for development of more and more new fibrin threads. Therefore, it is possible that the platelets entrapped in the clot continue to form thromboplastin, which promotes more and more of the coagulation process. The newly forming fibrin threads probably act as elastic bands (or become kinked in some way) to pull the clot into a smaller and smaller volume. Regardless of the exact means by which platelets effect clot retraction, lack of clot retraction is an especially valuable clinical test for demonstrating diminished numbers of platelets in the blood.

Fibrin threads have the ability to adhere to damaged surfaces of blood vessels. Therefore, the blood clot as it forms also becomes adherent to any vascular opening, and as the clot retracts this pulls the edges of the opening together, thus contributing to the ultimate state of hemostasis.

The Vicious Cycle of Clot Formation

Once a blood clot has actually started to develop, it normally extends within a matter of seconds or minutes into much of the surrounding blood. In other words, the clot itself initiates a *positive feedback mechanism, or vicious cycle,* to promote more clotting. Probably the most important cause of this is thrombin itself, for thrombin is a very powerful procoagulant resulting in the conversion of still more prothrombin into thrombin. The precise means by which the thrombin promotes this action is not known, though it has been suggested that it (1) causes disintegration of platelets, (2) activates thromboplastin, or (3) has a direct effect on prothrombin to form prothrombin derivatives, which in turn promote prothrombin conversion into thrombin. Regardless of the precise means by which thrombin acts as a procoagulant, it is a very powerful one and results in the rapid formation of still more thrombin and consequently rapid growth of the clot.

Failure of Clot Growth in Flowing Blood. A clot that develops in a blood vessel in which the blood is not flowing usually stops growing when it reaches an intersection with another blood vessel in which blood is flowing. The flowing blood carries the thrombin and other procoagulants away so rapidly that their concentrations cannot rise high enough to promote further clotting. Thus, extension of the clot usually stops when it comes in contact with blood that is flowing faster than a certain critical velocity.

Prevention of Blood Clotting in the Normal Vascular System—The Intravascular Anticoagulants

Probably the two most important factors for preventing clotting in the normal vascular system are, first, the smooth endothelium that prevents adherence of platelets and therefore prevents the release of thromboplastin from the platelets and, second, a monomolecular layer of negatively charged protein adsorbed to the inner surface of the endothelium that also prevents adherence of the negatively charged platelets. In other words, in the normal vascular system the conditions simply are not propitious for initiation of the clotting process.

However, even normal blood contains a small amount of procoagulants because a small number of platelets and other tissues containing procoagulants are constantly releasing these. Therefore, a tendency always exists for a small quantity of thrombin to be formed. But, if the concentration of thrombin does not increase above a critical value, fibrinogen cannot be converted into fibrin. Several different anticoagulants are always present in the blood to block the co-

agulation process at different points in the clotting mechanism. Though all these anticoagulant factors are not known and their relative importance has not been determined, at least three of them seem to be of considerable physiological importance. These are *antithromboplastin*, the *antithrombins*, and *heparin*.

Antithromboplastin. Thromboplastin, once released into the blood, loses its activity within a few minutes to an hour, and this even occurs when prothrombin has been removed from the plasma so that the thromboplastin cannot be consumed in the process of converting prothrombin. Therefore, it is said that plasma has an "antithromboplastin" activity, though the exact substance that is responsible for this is yet unknown. Obviously, then, thromboplastin released into the blood cannot continue to promote more and more clotting indefinitely.

Antithrombin Effects. Since thrombin is an enzyme it is not used up chemically during the conversion of fibrinogen into fibrin, and theoretically it could remain in the circulatory system indefinitely and cause continual conversion of more and more fibrinogen into fibrin until all the blood in the body should become clotted. However, in actuality, the thrombin is removed from the blood very rapidly in three different ways as follows:

First, the major portion of the thrombin is *adsorbed by the fibrin threads* as they develop in the clot. This prevents diffusion of the thrombin into the still uncoagulated blood.

Second, a constituent of the plasma proteins called *antithrombin* directly inactivates thrombin.

Third, small amounts of thrombin are destroyed by the anticoagulant action of *heparin*, which will be discussed below.

Thus, even when thrombin is formed in the circulation, there are three means for removing it; one method removes the very large quantities formed during the actual coagulation process and the other two are capable of removing minute quantities of thrombin even before they can initiate an actual clot.

Heparin. Heparin, which is a powerful anticoagulant, is a conjugated polysaccharide found in the cytoplasm of many types of cells, including even the cytoplasm of unicellular animals. Therefore, heparin probably is produced by many different cells of the human body, though especially large quantities are formed by the basophilic *mast cells* located in the pericapillary connective tissue throughout the body. It is believed that these mast cells continually secrete small quantities of heparin and that the heparin then diffuses into the circulatory system. The *basophil cells* of the blood, which seem to be identical with the mast cells, possibly also release minute quantities of heparin into the plasma, but the number of basophils is so slight that their importance for heparin secretion is probably negligible.

Mast cells are extremely abundant in the tissue surrounding the capillaries of the lungs and to a less extent the capillaries of the liver. It is easy to understand why large quantities of heparin might be needed in these areas, for the capillaries of the lungs and liver receive many embolic clots formed in the slowly flowing venous blood; sufficient formation of heparin might prevent further growth of the clots.

The concentration of heparin in normal blood is not known, but on the basis of yet inaccurate methods of measurement it has been estimated to be as much as 0.01 mg. per 100 ml. of blood. Though this concentration is 10 to 100 times less than that often used clinically to prevent blood clotting, it, nevertheless, is probably sufficient to aid in preventing blood coagulation in the normal circulatory system, for only very minute quantities of procoagulants are normally formed, and only minute amounts of heparin are therefore needed to prevent clotting.

Mechanism of heparin action. When large quantities of heparin are present in blood, the formation of thrombin is blocked. Therefore, probably the best explanation of the action of heparin is that it *blocks the change of prothrombin into thrombin.* One of the ways in which heparin blocks this change is by forming a complex consisting of heparin, accelerator globulin, and antithrombin, in this way reducing the amount of accelerator globulin available to activate prothrombin. It has also been claimed that heparin dissolutes some of the plasma lipoproteins and in the process releases an anticoagulant. Indeed, very low concentrations of sphingosine, a lipid normally found in

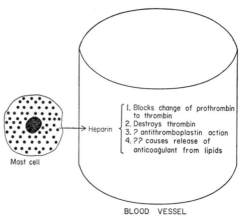

Figure 120.   Possible actions of heparin in the blood.

small quantities in lipoproteins, inhibits the conversion of prothrombin to thrombin, but it does not become an anticoagulant until it is freed from the lipoprotein combination. The different possible methods of heparin action are summarized in Figure 120.

COURSE OF EVENTS THAT PROVIDE HEMOSTASIS IN A RUPTURED VESSEL

Vascular Spasm. Damage to a blood vessel ordinarily causes local myogenic spasm. Also, in the case of large vessels, sympathetic reflexes transmitted by nerve fibers to the spinal cord and back again result in vascular spasm for many centimeters along its course in both directions. Both these processes aid the clotting mechanism in decreasing blood loss. When the damage to the vessel is a smooth cut, the spasm is likely to be relatively slight, and bleeding will then be much more severe than occurs when the vessel is traumatized very widely at the time of rupture. Indeed, persons whose legs have been severed by a crushing type of trauma sometimes have such intense spasm in vessels even as large as the anterior tibial artery that serious loss of blood does not ensue.

The local vascular spasm at first results simply from myogenic contraction induced by the trauma itself. However, once a clot has begun to form and platelets to disintegrate, a substance called *serotonin* (5-hydroxytryptamine) is released from the disintegrating platelets, and it in turn is believed to cause the smooth muscle to contract still more, thus intensifying the local contraction.

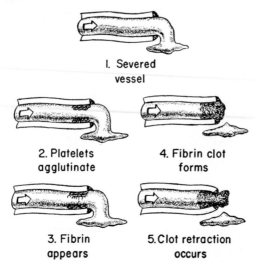

1. Severed
vessel

2. Platelets
agglutinate

4. Fibrin clot
forms

3. Fibrin
appears

5. Clot retraction
occurs

Figure 121. The clotting process in a traumatized blood vessel. (Redrawn from Seegers: Hemostatic Agents. Charles C Thomas.)

Clotting in a Ruptured Vessel. Figure 121 illustrates the clotting process at the end of a ruptured blood vessel. At first the blood flows freely from the vessel, but, owing to trauma near the end of the vessel, platelets adhere to the damaged endothelial wall, and then small shreds of fibrin develop. These shreds of fibrin entrap red blood cells and more platelets, and then still more fibrin is formed. Finally, the entire vessel at the ruptured end is filled with a clot; blood loss stops; and after 30 minutes to an hour the clot retracts, closing the vessel walls to some extent.

Fibrous organization of the blood clot in a vessel. After a blood clot has formed, it is invaded very rapidly by large numbers of macrophages and more slowly by fibroblasts. The macrophages phagocytize the red blood cells, releasing the hemoglobin into the body fluids and digesting the cell membranes. The fibroblasts, on the other hand, *organize* the clot so that after 2 to 3 weeks the clot becomes mainly a fibrous mass. Then, after several more months the fibrous tissue contracts, leaving the vessel a small fibrous band.

Occasionally, organized clots *recanalize—* that is, smaller blood vessels grow through the organized clots to form new, though smaller, blood channels along the occluded vessels.

Lysis of Clots. Though clots in blood vessels ordinarily organize, some of the smaller clots dissolve, and the vessels that have been occluded again become capable of carrying blood. Also, when blood is removed from the body and placed in a test tube it clots within a few minutes, but after 24 to 48 hours lysis of the clot ordinarily occurs.

The mechanism of lysis is probably the following: Among the plasma proteins is a protein known as *profibrinolysin,* which is activated a few hours after blood clotting to become *fibrinolysin,* though the means by which this activation occurs is totally unknown. Fibrinolysin causes active lysis of fibrin threads and also destroys any fibrinogen remaining in the clot to prevent further formation of fibrin. As the fibrin is destroyed the clot dissolves unless it has already been "organized" by fibroblasts.

CONDITIONS THAT CAUSE EXCESSIVE BLEEDING IN HUMAN BEINGS

Excessive bleeding can result from deficiency of any one of the many different coagulation factors. Among those that have been specifically implicated in different bleeding diseases have been (1) prothrombin, (2) accelerator globulin, (3) proconvertin, (4) antihemophilic factor, (5) plasma thromboplastin component, (6) whole platelets, and (7) several other poorly described factors about which almost nothing is yet known. Almost any one of these deficiencies can be inherited because, in the final analysis, it is the genes that determine whether or not and how much of a specific factor will be present. Also, disease conditions, especially of the liver or of the bone marrow, often affect the coagulation process.

Three particular types of bleeding tendencies that have been studied to the greatest extent will be discussed: (1) proconvertin and prothrombin deficiency, (2) hemophilia, and (3) thrombocytopenia (platelet deficiency).

Decreased Proconvertin or Prothrombin —Vitamin K Deficiency

Hepatitis, cirrhosis, acute yellow atrophy, and other diseases of the liver, can all depress the rate of proconvertin and prothrombin formation so greatly that the patient develops a severe tendency to bleed.

Another cause of depressed proconvertin and prothrombin level is vitamin K deficiency. Vitamin K is necessary for some of the intermediate stages in the formation of both of these substances, particularly of proconvertin. Fortunately, vitamin K is continually synthesized in the gastrointestinal tract by bacteria so that vitamin K deficiency rarely if ever occurs because of absence from the diet. However, vitamin K deficiency does often occur as a result of poor absorption of fats from the gastrointestinal tract because vitamin K is fat soluble and ordinarily is absorbed into the blood along with the fats.

One of the most prevalent causes of vitamin K deficiency is failure of the liver to secrete bile into the gastrointestinal tract (which occurs either as a result of obstruction of the bile ducts or as a result of liver disease), for lack of bile prevents adequate fat digestion and absorption. Therefore, liver disease often causes decreased proconvertin and prothrombin production both because of poor vitamin K absorption and because of dysfunctional liver cells. As a result of this, vitamin K is injected into all patients with liver disease or obstructed bile ducts prior to performing any surgical procedure. Ordinarily, if vitamin K is given to a deficient patient 4 to 8 hours prior to operation and the liver parenchymal cells are at least one-half normal, sufficient proconvertin and prothrombin will be produced to prevent excessive bleeding during the operation.

Hemophilia

The term *hemophilia* is loosely applied to several different hereditary deficiencies of coagulation, all of which cause bleeding tendencies hardly distinguishable one from the other. The three most common causes of the hemophilic syndrome are deficiency of (1) antihemophilic factor (classical hemophilia)—about 75 per cent of the total, (2) plasma thromboplastin component—about 15 per cent, and (3) plasma thromboplastin antecedent—about 5 to 10 per cent. If normal plasma containing the missing factor is transfused into a hemophilic patient, normal coagulation takes place, and his bleeding tendency is temporarily relieved. Unfortunately, there is no satisfactory long-term treatment for hemophilia, but, when an operation is to be performed, or during a bleeding crisis, transfusion of normal plasma or injection of purified globulin will revert the patient's blood coagulation system to normal for a few days.

Many patients with hemophilia die in early life, though still many others with less severe bleeding live out a normal life span. Very commonly, the patient's joints become severely damaged because of repeated joint hemorrhage following exercise.

Genetics of Classical Hemophilia. Hemophilia resulting from lack of antihemophilic factor is called *classical hemophilia*, while hemophilia caused by deficiencies of other factors is only loosely classified as *non-classical hemophilia*. The genetics of classical hemophilia and of plasma thromboplastin component deficiency are very much the same, both being sex-linked, while other

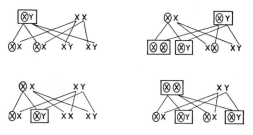

○ Circles = Abnormal recessive gene causing Hemophilia
▢ Rectangles = Individuals with Hemophilia

Figure 122. The genetics of hemophilia.

types of hemophilia have completely different methods of inheritance.

Hemophilia is actually a very rare disease, occurring in only one person out of every 3,000, but, because of its prevalence in some of the royal families of Europe, and because of in-breeding within these families, the genetics of hemophilia have become well known. As illustrated in Figure 122, the encircled "X" chromosomes denote female chromosomes that either contain recessive genes that cause hemophilia or, more likely, are lacking the gene normally responsible for forming antihemophilic factor in the blood. Both X chromosomes must be of the hemophilic type in order for hemophilia to occur in a female, but, because the male has only one X chromosome, if this chromosome is of a hemophilic type, then hemophilia is certain to result. It is further obvious from Figure 122 that a hemophilic male married to a normal female will have no hemophilic children, but, because the father's X chromosome passes into all of his daughters, these daughters will all be hemophilic "carriers." Half of his daughters' daughters in turn will be hemophilic carriers, and half of their sons will actually be hemophilic. For a female offspring to have hemophilia, the father must be a hemophiliac himself and the mother must be a hemophilic carrier, which is an extremely rare situation.

Thrombocytopenia

Thrombocytopenia is the presence of a very low quantity of platelets in the circulatory system. Patients with thrombocytopenia have a tendency to bleed as do hemophiliacs. Also, many minute blood vessels, including the capillaries, continually rupture in this condition. As a result, small punctate hemorrhages occur throughout all of the body tissues. The skin of such a patient displays many small, purplish blotches, giving the disease the name *thrombocytopenia purpura*. The tendency for small blood vessels to rupture does not occur in hemophilia, indicating that platelets are possibly especially important for repair of minute breaks in capillaries and other small vessels. Indeed, it has been claimed that platelets can agglutinate to fill such ruptures without actually causing clots.

Ordinarily, excessive bleeding does not occur until the number of platelets in the blood falls below a critical value of approximately 50,000 per cubic millimeter rather than the normal of 400,000.

Even without making specific platelet counts on the blood, one can sometimes demonstrate the existence of thrombocytopenia by simply noting whether or not a clot of the patient's blood retracts, for, as pointed out above, clot retraction is dependent upon the presence of large numbers of platelets entrapped in the fibrin mesh of the clot.

Most patients with thrombocytopenia have the disease known as *idiopathic thrombocytopenia*, which means simply "thrombocytopenia of unknown cause." In this disease the number of megakaryocytes in the bone marrow is normal, but either the ability of these megakaryocytes to release platelets into the blood is greatly depressed or the platelets that are released into the blood are removed much more rapidly than normally. It has been taught for many years that the spleen possibly removes platelets from the blood much more rapidly than normally in idiopathic thrombocytopenia. On the basis of this idea, the spleen of such patients is often removed in an attempt to treat the condition. However, splenectomy usually is of almost no benefit, indicating that splenic destruction of platelets is certainly not the primary cause of idiopathic thrombocytopenia.

In addition to idiopathic thrombocytopenia, the number of thrombocytes (platelets) in the blood may be greatly depressed by any abnormality that causes aplasia of the bone marrow. For instance, irradiation injury to the bone marrow, aplasia of the bone marrow resulting from drug sensitivity, and even pernicious anemia, can all cause sufficient decrease in the total number of platelets that thrombocytopenic bleeding results.

Relief from bleeding for 1 to 4 days can often be effected in the thrombocytopenic patient by giving him *whole blood transfusions*. To do this, the blood must be removed from the donor into a siliconized chamber and then rapidly placed in the recipient so that the platelets are damaged as little as possible. Obviously, the quantity of platelets that can be administered to the patient in a reasonable quantity of transfused blood cannot cause tremendous benefit.

THROMBOEMBOLIC CONDITIONS IN THE HUMAN BEING

Thrombi and Emboli. An abnormal clot that develops in a blood vessel is called a *thrombus*. Once a clot has developed, continued flow of blood past the clot is likely to break it away from its attachment, and such freely flowing clots are known as *emboli*. Emboli generally do not stop flowing until they come to a narrow point in the circulatory system. Thus, emboli originating in large arteries or in the left side of the heart eventually plug either smaller arteries or arterioles. On the other hand, emboli originating in the venous system or in the right side of the heart flow into the vessels of the lung to cause pulmonary embolism.

Causes of Thromboembolic Conditions. The causes of thromboembolic conditions in the human being are usually two-fold: First, any *roughened surface of a vessel*—as may be caused by arteriosclerosis, infection, or trauma—is likely to attract platelets and thereby initiate the clotting process. Second, blood often clots *when it flows very slowly* through blood vessels, for a few platelets are always disintegrating and forming thromboplastin. If the blood is flowing too slowly, the concentration of thromboplastin in local areas often rises high enough to initiate clotting, but when the blood flows rapidly the thromboplastin is rapidly mixed with large quantities of blood and never reaches a sufficient concentration to cause clotting.

Femoral Thrombosis and Massive Pulmonary Embolism

Because clotting almost always occurs when blood flow is blocked in any vessel of the body, the immobility of bed patients plus the practice of propping the knees up with pillows often causes stasis of blood in one or more of the leg veins for as much as an hour, and this stasis initiates the clotting process. Then the clot grows in all directions, especially in the direction of the slowly moving blood, sometimes growing the entire length of the leg veins and occasionally even into the common iliac vein and the inferior vena cava. Then, about 1 time out of every 10, the clot disengages from its attachments to the vessel wall and flows freely with the venous blood into the right side of the heart and thence into the pulmonary arteries to cause *massive pulmonary embolism*. If the clot is large enough to occlude both the pulmonary arteries, immediate death of the patient ensues. If only one of the pulmonary arteries or a smaller branch is blocked, death may not occur, or the embolism may lead to death in a few hours to several days because of further growth of the clot within the pulmonary vessels.

Arterial Thrombosis and Embolism

Thrombi and emboli in the coronary arteries are discussed in Chapter 30; thrombi and emboli also frequently block small and medium-sized peripheral arteries. Large clots ordinarily do not develop in the large arteries because of the rapid blood flow, but the left atrium, particularly the auricular appendix of a dilated left atrium such as occurs in mitral valvular disease, is a favorite site for thrombus formation. When a clot breaks away from the wall of the left atrium, it passes through the left ventricle and into one of the systemic arteries.

An embolus plugging an artery of the central nervous system can cause immediate death or serious central nervous system symptoms such as paralysis, dementia, blindness, etc. Also, thrombi developing in cerebral vessels as a result of arteriosclerotic plaques are the cause of approximately 1 to 2 per cent of all deaths.

When an embolus lodges in the brachial artery, sufficient collateral circulation is usually present that the patient will not lose his arm, but embolism of a femoral or iliac artery usually causes almost complete ischemia of the entire leg, and gangrene is often the result. Also, the patient is very likely to die of plasma-loss shock even before gangrene takes place, for the following reasons: The small amount of blood that does flow into the limb loses much of its plasma into the leg tissues because of increased capillary permeability resulting from the ischemia. Also, toxic products are elaborated from the ischemic tissues of the leg, and these toxic products further debilitate the circulatory system.

ANTICOAGULANTS FOR CLINICAL USE

In some thromboembolic conditions, it is desirable to delay the coagulation process to a certain degree. Therefore, various anticoagulants have been developed for treatment of these conditions. The ones most useful clinically are heparin and Dicumarol.

Heparin as an Intravenous Anticoagulant

Commercial heparin is extracted from animal tissues, especially the lungs of animals, and is prepared in almost pure form. Injection of relatively small quantities, approximately ½ to 1 mg. per kilogram of body weight, causes the blood clotting time to increase from a normal of approximately 6 minutes up to 30 or more minutes. Furthermore, this change in clotting time occurs instantaneously, thereby immediately preventing further development of the thromboembolic condition.

The action of heparin lasts approximately 3 to 4 hours. It is believed that the injected heparin is destroyed by an enzyme in the blood known as *heparinase*. Also, much of the injected heparin diffuses into the interstitial fluids and therefore becomes unavailable as a blood anticoagulant.

In the treatment of a patient with heparin, too much heparin is sometimes given, and serious bleeding crises occur. In these instances, *protamine* and *toluidine blue* act specifically as antiheparins, and the clotting mechanism can be reverted to normal by administration of these substances. These substances probably combine with heparin and inactivate it because they carry positive electrical charges while heparin carries negative charges.

Dicumarol as an Anticoagulant

When dicumarol is given to a patient, the plasma levels of prothrombin, proconvertin, and still other procoagulants formed by the liver begin to fall, indicating that Dicumarol has a potent depressant effect on liver formation of all these compounds. Dicumarol causes this effect by competing with vitamin K for reactive sites in the intermediate processes for formation of the procoagulants, thereby blocking the action of the vitamin K.

In the past it has been believed that the major effect of Dicumarol was to decrease the amount of prothrombin available for conversion to thrombin, and some coagulationists still believe this to be true. However, proconvertin seems to be decreased much more than prothrombin, indicating that Dicumarol might act principally by reducing proconvertin activity rather than prothrombin activity.

After administration of an effective dose of Dicumarol, the coagulant activity of the blood decreases to approximately 50 per cent of normal by the end of 12 hours, and it falls to approximately 20 per cent of normal by the end of 24 hours. In other words, the coagulation process is not blocked immediately, but must await the consumption of the proconvertin and prothrombin already present in the plasma.

After Dicumarol therapy is discontinued, the Dicumarol already in the liver must first be destroyed before the coagulation factors can be formed again: thus an additional one to three days is required before normal clotting will return. However, administration of large quantities of vitamin K accelerates the return of normal blood clotting.

In addition to Dicumarol many other similar anticoagulants have been synthesized all of which interfere with the production of prothrombin and related coagulation factors. They differ, however, in respect to (1) their potency, (2) the time interval for them to produce anticoagulation, and (3) the time interval required for recovery of coagulation at the end of therapy.

Prevention of Blood Coagulation Outside the Body

Though blood removed from the body normally clots in 3 to 6 minutes, blood collected in *paraffinized containers* often does not clot for as long as 30 minutes, and blood collected in containers coated with a thin layer of some of the *silicones* sometimes will not clot for even longer periods of time. The reason for this delay in clotting is that preparing the surfaces of the containers with these substances prevents adherence of platelets and consequently prevents their disintegration. On the other hand, untreated glass containers allow almost immediate adherence of platelets and rapid development of clots.

Heparin can be used for preventing coagulation of blood outside the body as well as in the body, and heparin is occasionally used as an anticoagulant when blood is removed from a donor to be transfused later into a recipient. Also, heparin is used in almost all animal experiments in which the blood is passed through external tubes and then back into the animal. In this instance, the quantity of heparin that must be administered to the animal is 3 to 5 mg. per kilogram of body weight.

Various substances that *decrease the quantity of calcium ion* in the blood can be used for preventing blood coagulation outside the body. For instance, soluble *oxalate* compounds mixed in very small quantity with a sample of blood precipitate calcium oxalate from the plasma and thereby decrease the ionic calcium level so much that blood coagulation is blocked.

A second calcium deionizing agent used for preventing coagulation is *sodium, ammonium,* or *potassium citrate.* The citrate ion combines with calcium in the blood to cause an un-ionized calcium compound, and the lack of ionic calcium prevents coagulation. Citrate anticoagulants have a very important advantage over the oxalate anticoagulants, for oxalate is toxic to the body, whereas small quantities of citrate can be injected intravenously. After injection, the citrate ion is removed from the blood within a few minutes by the recipient's liver and is polymerized into glucose, then metabolized in the usual manner. Consequently, 500 ml. of blood that has been rendered incoagulable by sodium citrate can ordinarily be injected into a recipient within a few minutes without any dire consequences. In order to be on the safe side, however, 500 ml. of blood is usually administered over a period of 30 or more minutes, for, if the liver is damaged or if large quantities of citrated blood or plasma are given too rapidly, the citrate ion may not be removed quickly enough, and the citrate can then greatly depress the level of calcium ion in the blood with resultant tetany and convulsive death of the patient.

HEMOSTATIC AGENTS

Hemostatic agents are substances that cause rapid clotting. Recently, commercial preparations of *thrombin* have been used to accelerate coagulation. When thrombin is injected into a bleeding area or is placed on a bleeding surface, it causes fibrinogen to change into fibrin in a matter of seconds, thereby greatly speeding the process of coagulation. Such an agent has a number of clinical uses in patients who are oozing blood from diffuse areas.

Purified fibrinogen is also commercially available. This has been used mainly for adhering skin grafts to recipient areas of a patient. The fibrinogen solution is painted on the area, a graft is placed over the solution, the fibrinogen changes into fibrin as a result of the action of tissue enzymes, and the skin graft is then stuck. Other than this one major use, purified fibrinogen has not proved to be of special significance, mainly because the level of fibrinogen in the plasma is rarely if ever greatly depressed.

Because foams present a large surface area, which promotes coagulation upon contact with blood, several such materials have been employed clinically to hasten clotting. For instance, *oxidized cellulose sponge, fibrin foam,* and *sponge made of gelatin* have all been used for this purpose. These substances are used especially in neurosurgery, in which very small blocks of the foam material are placed over bleeding points and then compressed for several minutes. This pressure stops the bleeding, and a clot develops in the foam material. The foam is left in the wound and is absorbed during the few days following the operation.

BLOOD COAGULATION TESTS

Bleeding Time

When a sharp knife is used to pierce the tip of the finger, bleeding ordinarily lasts approximately three minutes. However, the time depends largely upon the depth of the wound and upon the degree of hyperemia in the finger at the time of the test. Consequently, "bleeding times" are not very significant in studying the ability of the blood to coagulate. Bleeding time tests are sometimes performed on blood removed from the lobe of the ear, in which case the bleeding usually lasts between three and six minutes; interpretation is as equivocal as in bleeding time tests performed on the finger.

Clotting Time

Capillary Tube Test. Many methods have been devised for determining clotting times. One of the simplest of these is to allow blood from the pierced finger to flow by capillary into a small glass capillary tube. Then, approximately every half minute the capillary tube is broken. When, after breaking the tube, the ends adhere to each other because of a clot in the blood, the time that has elapsed is noted. The clotting time by this method is approximately three minutes, but the time depends to a great extent on the size of the glass capillary tube, because close contact with glass itself increases the rate of clotting.

Test Tube Methods. A second method for determining clotting times is to collect blood in a chemically clean glass test tube and then to tip the tube back and forth approximately every 30 seconds until the blood has clotted. By this method, the clotting time ranges between five and eight minutes in the normal subject.

Procedures using multiple test tubes have been devised for determining clotting time, and these methods are more accurate than either of the above. However, they require more blood, and when numerous tests of clotting time are to be performed the single test tube method is probably the preferable one. Obviously, none of the clotting times is very accurate because they are dependent to a high degree on the condition of the glass itself and even on the size of the tube.

Prothrombin Time

The prothrombin time gives an indication of the total quantity of prothrombin in the blood. Figure 123 shows the relationship of prothrombin concentration to prothrombin time. The means for determining prothrombin time is the following:

Blood removed from the patient is immediately oxalated so that none of the prothrombin can change into thrombin. At any time later, a large excess of calcium ion and thromboplastin is suddenly mixed with the oxalated blood. These substances nullify the effect of the oxalate and also catalyze the prothrombin-to-thrombin reaction. The time required for coagulation to take place is known as the "prothrombin time." The normal prothrombin time is approximately 12 seconds, though this depends to a certain extent on the exact procedure employed. In each laboratory a curve relating concentration to prothrombin time, such as that shown in Figure 123, is ordinarily drawn for the method used so that the significance of the prothrombin time can be evaluated.

Methods are also available for direct measurement of the total quantity of prothrombin in the blood. These are based on various empirical methods similar to those used for determining prothrombin time, but the reagents and the blood are prepared in such a manner that the total quantity of prothrombin may be quantitated. (One unit of prothrombin is that quantity which, when changed to thrombin, will coagulate 1 ml. of fibrinogen solution at normal plasma concentration in 15 seconds. The normal blood concentration of prothrombin is 300 to 375 units per 100 ml. of plasma.)

Other Tests Relating to Coagulation

In Chapter 13 it was pointed out that the normal *platelet count* in the blood as measured by most platelet-counting techniques ranges between approximately 250,000 and 400,000 per cubic mm. Obviously, if a decreased platelet count is found, thrombocytopenia exists.

Another factor of importance insofar as platelets are concerned is *clot retraction.* Once a clot has formed in the bottom of a test tube, clot retraction normally occurs in 30 to 60 minutes. If clot retraction does not occur, the number of platelets in the blood may be greatly reduced.

Tests very similar to that for prothrombin time have been devised to determine the relative quantities of accelerator globulin and proconvertin in the blood. These tests are not often used because deficiency of these factors rarely occurs without simultaneous deficiency of prothrombin. In performing the tests excesses of all the factors besides the one being tested are added to oxalated blood all at once, and then the time of coagulation is determined in the same manner as the usual prothrombin time. If the factor is deficient, the time will be considerably prolonged. It should be pointed out that in determining the usual prothrombin time, a deficiency of either of these other

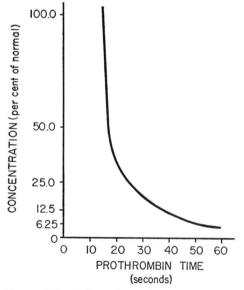

Figure 123. Relationship of prothrombin concentration in the blood to the prothrombin time. (Redrawn from Marple: Thromboembolic Conditions and Their Treatment with Anticoagulants. Charles C Thomas.)

factors can also prolong the measured time. Therefore, an increased prothrombin time as performed in the usual hospital laboratory does not always mean decreased quantity of prothrombin but may mean decreased quantity of some other factor.

REFERENCES

Biggs, R.., and MacFarlane, R. G.: Human Blood Coagulation. 2nd ed., Springfield, Illinois, Charles C Thomas, 1957.

Biggs, R., and MacFarlane, R. G.: Human Blood Coagulation and Its Disorders. Springfield, Illinois, Charles C Thomas, 1953.

Brinkhouse, K. M.: Blood clotting: the plasma procoagulants. Ann. Rev. Physiol., 21:271, 1959.

Celander, R. and Guest, M. M.: Assay of canine pro-fibrinolysin (plasminogen). Am. J. Physiol., 197: 391, 1959.

de Nicola, P.: The Laboratory Diagnosis of Coagulation Defects. Springfield, Illinois, Charles C Thomas, 1956.

De Takats, G.: Thromboembolic Disease. Springfield, Illinois, Charles C Thomas, 1955.

Deutsch, E., Johnson, S. A., and Seegers, W. H.: Differentiation of certain platelet factors related to blood coagulation. Circ. Res., 3:110, 1955.

Fenichel, R. L., and Seegers, W. H.: Studies on human clot retraction. J. Appl. Physiol., 10:71, 1957.

Ferguson, J. H., Johnston, C. L., Jr., and Howell, D. A.: Anti-AcG: specific circulating inhibitor of the labile clotting factor. Proc. Soc. Exp. Biol., & Med., 95:567, 1957.

Ferguson, J. H., and Patch, M. J.: Determinants of the so-called prothrombin time. Proc. Soc. Exp. Biol. & Med., 93:193, 1956.

Ferry, J. D.: Polymerization of fibrinogen. Physiol. Rev., 34:753, 1954.

Fishman, J. B., and Kline, D. L.: Isolation of partially purified human plasmin (fibrinolysin). Proc. Soc. Exp. Biol. & Med., 91:323, 1956.

Fresh, J. W., Ferguson, J. H., Stamey, C., Morgan, F. M., and Lewis, J. H.: Blood prothrombin, proconvertin and proaccelerin in normal infancy: questionable relationships to vitamin K. Pediatrics, 19:241, 1957.

Fulton, G. P., Maynard, F. L., Riley, J. F., and West, G. B.: Humoral aspects of tissue mast cells. Physiol. Rev., 37:221, 1957.

Guest, M. M.: Profibrinolysin, antifibrinolysin, fibrinogen and urine fibrinolytic factors in the human subject. J. Clin. Invest., 33:1553, 1954.

Horvath, S. M., Hamilton, L. H., Spurr, G. B., Allbaugh, E. B., and Hutt, B. K.: Plasma expanders and bleeding times. J. Appl. Physiol., 7:617, 1955.

Jaques, L. B.: The physiology of the anticoagulants. Rev. hemat., 10:412, 1955.

Kalsberg, P., and Shulman, S.: Electron microscopic observation of intermediate polymers in the conversion of fibrinogen to fibrin. J. Biol. Chem., 200: 293, 1953.

Laki, K.: Chemistry of prothrombin and some of its reactions. Physiol. Rev., 34:730, 1954.

Lamu, F., and Waugh, D. F.: Transformation of prothrombin into thrombin. Physiol. Rev., 34:722, 1954.

Landaburu, R. H., and Seegers, W. H.: Generation of proteolytic activity during activation of prothrombin. Am. J. Physiol., 197:1178, 1959.

Lewis, J. H., Ferguson, J. H., and Arends, T.: Hemorrhagic disease with circulating inhibitors of blood clotting: anti-AHF and anti-PTC in eight cases. Blood, 11:846, 1956.

Lewis, J. H., Ferguson, J. H., Fresh, J. W., and Zucker, M. B.: Primary hemorrhagic diseases. J. Lab. & Clin. Med., 49:211, 1957.

Lorand, L.: Interaction of thrombin and fibrinogen. Physiol. Rev., 34:742, 1954.

Lozner, E. L.: Differential diagnosis, pathogenesis and treatment of the thrombocytopenic purpuras. Am. J. Med., 14:459, 1953.

Macfarlane, R. G.: Blood coagulation, with particular reference to the early stages. Physiol. Rev., 36: 479, 1956.

Mann, F. D.: Blood clotting. Ann. Rev. Physiol., 19: 205, 1957.

Morawitz, P.: The Chemistry of Blood Coagulation. Springfield, Illinois, Charles C Thomas, 1958.

Penner, J. A., and Seegers, W. H.: Activities of prothrombin. Am. J. Physiol., 186:343, 1956.

Quick, A. J.: Hemophilia, Am. J. Med., 14:349, 1953.

Quick, A. J.: Hemorrhagic Diseases. Philadelphia, Lea & Febiger, 1957.

Quick, A. J., Shanberg, J. N., and Stefanini, M.: The role of platelets in the coagulation of the blood. Am. J. M. Sc., 217:198, 1949.

Riley, J. F.: Pharmacology and functions of the mast cells. Pharmacol. Rev., 7:267, 1955.

Roskam, J.: Arrest of Bleeding. Springfield, Illinois, Charles C Thomas, 1954.

Seegers, W. H.: A modern theory of blood clotting. J. Mich. M. Soc., 55:272, 1956.

Seegers, W. H.: Coagulation of the blood. Harvey Lect., 47:180, 1951–1952.

Seegers, W. H.: Initiation of the blood coagulation mechanisms. Circ. Res., 4:126, 1956.

Seegers, W. H.: Introduction: prothrombin and fibrinogen related to the blood clotting mechanisms. Physiol. Rev., 34:711, 1954.

Sherry, S., Fletcher, A. P., and Alkjaersig, N.: Fibrinolysis and fibrinolytic activity in man. Physiol. Rev., 39:343, 1959.

Sherry, S., Troll, W., and Glueck, H.: Thrombin as a proteolytic enzyme. Physiol. Rev., 34:736, 1954.

Stefanini, M., and Damashek, W.: The Hemorrhagic Disorders. New York, Grune & Stratton, Inc., 1955.

Tocantins, L. M.: The Coagulation of Blood: Methods of Study. New York, Grune & Stratton, Inc., 1955.

Ware, A. G., and Lanchantin, G. F.: Purification of fibrinogen, prothrombin, and thrombin. Physiol. Rev., 34:714, 1954.

White, S. G., Aggler, P. M., and Glendening, M. B.: Plasma thromboplastin component. A hitherto unrecognized blood coagulation factor. Blood, 8:101, 1953.

See also Chapter 13, White blood cells; Chapter 15, Transfusion.

Part Four

PERIPHERAL NERVOUS AND

MUSCULAR SYSTEMS

Electrical Characteristics of Excitable Cells—Membrane Potentials, Action Potentials, Excitation, and Rhythmicity

The excitable cells of the body are those cells that are capable of transmitting electrochemical impulses along their membranes. These include especially the nerve and muscle fibers. Electrochemical impulses probably can spread also along the membranes of glandular cells and perhaps almost all the other cells of the body under special conditions. However, the present discussion will be concerned principally with electrical potentials generated both at rest and during action by nerve and muscle cells.

THE MEMBRANE POTENTIAL

Electrical Characteristics of the Membrane; Nature of the Membrane Potential. Referring back to Chapter 2 it will be recalled that all cellular membranes are composed mainly of lipid materials supported by a protein matrix. This membrane is extremely thin, only a few hundred Angstroms in thickness, and is porous to many small molecules and ions in the surrounding fluids.

Except under special circumstances, the number of negative ions in a solution will equal the number of positive ions. However, Figure 124 illustrates a condition in which the number of negative and the number of positive ions on each side of a membrane are not equal. Instead, an excess of positive ions is present on one side, while an excess of negative ions is present on the other side,

thus causing a *membrane potential* between the two sides.

The cause of these ionic imbalances is the following: The membrane is semipermeable, its pores large enough for the positive ions to flow through while the negative ions are blocked. On the right hand side the total concentration of both negative and positive ions is very great, while on the left hand side it is very slight. The ions in both portions of the solution are continually moving because of kinetic motion of the molecules and dissolved substances. When positive ions

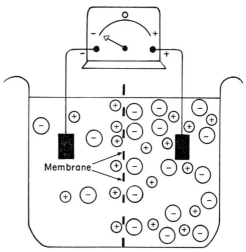

Figure 124. Development of a membrane potential as a result of (1) a concentration gradient and (2) selective permeability to positive ions but not to negative ions.

217

strike the semiporous membrane, some of them pass on through to the opposite side, but the negative ions cannot because they are too large. Yet, the positive ions do not travel far into the other solution because of lack of negative charges to go along with them. Instead, they line up to the left of the membrane while the excess negative ions left behind line up to the right of the membrane. Thus, a membrane potential has developed across a membrane with positivity to the left and negativity to the right. If electrodes are placed into the solutions on the two sides of the membrane, this electrical potential will be recorded by an appropriate meter as illustrated in the figure.

Concentration Gradients and Their Relationship to the Resultant Potential. A necessary condition for the development of the membrane potential in Figure 124 is a greater concentration of diffusible positive ions on one side of the membrane than on the other side. Were this not true, the same number of positive ions would diffuse in each direction and no net potential would develop. In other words, *the potential is proportional to the difference in tendency of the ions to diffuse in one direction versus the other direction.* These tendencies are proportional to the logarithms of the concentrations of the diffusible ions in accordance with the following formula (at body temperature, 37° C.):

$$\text{EMF (In millivolts)} = 61 \times \log \frac{\text{concentration 1}}{\text{concentration 2}}$$

Thus, when the concentration of the positive ions to the right in Figure 124 is 10 times that to the left, the log of 10 is 1, and the potential difference is 61 millivolts.

In summary, the two conditions necessary for a membrane potential to develop are:

(1) *The membrane must be semipermeable, allowing ions of one charge to diffuse through the pores more readily than ions of the opposite charge.*

(2) *The concentration of the diffusible ions must be greater on one side of the membrane than on the other side.*

Potentials Across the Membrane of Excitable Cells

Concentration Gradients Responsible for Membrane Potentials. The active transport mechanisms of the cell membrane,

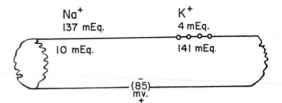

Figure 125. Differential concentrations of sodium and potassium across a resting nerve membrane. The membrane is 20 to 100 times as permeable to potassium as to sodium, and potassium diffusion through the pores generates a resting potential of approximately 85 millivolts.

discussed in Chapter 3, continually transport sodium from inside the cell to the outside and probably also potassium from the outside to the inside. Consequently, concentration gradients of these ions develop across the membrane as illustrated in Figure 125, with a high sodium concentration developing on the outside and a high potassium on the inside. Once these concentration gradients have developed, the conditions are appropriate for diffusion of large quantities of one or the other of the two ions through the membrane pores, thereby creating a potential between the two sides of the membrane.

The negative ions do not play any important role in the causation of resting cellular membrane potentials. However, once the positive ions have created such a potential, the potential itself displaces chloride ions to the outside of the cell while only a few chloride ions remain on the inside. But, it must be reemphasized that this concentration gradient of chloride is the *result of rather than the cause of* cellular membrane potentials.

Differential Permeability of the Resting Membrane to Sodium and Potassium. Under resting conditions the membranes of nerve and muscle fibers are 20 to 100 times as permeable to potassium as to sodium. However, when the membrane becomes excited and an electrochemical impulse is transmitted along it, the mebrane momentarily becomes more permeable to sodium than to potassium. It is this rapid change in permeability of the membrane to the two ions that causes an electrochemical impulse to be transmitted along nerve and muscle fibers.

Potassium Ions as the Major Determinant of the Resting Membrane Potential. In the resting state, potassium passes with relative ease through the membrane, while sodium is impeded. Therefore, it is principally the potassium that is responsible for the *resting membrane potential*. And, because the potassium concentration inside the membrane is very high in relation to the outside of the membrane, there will be far greater tendency for *positive charges to diffuse outward* through the membrane than inward. Consequently, a state of positivity develops outside the membrane and negativity inside, which is illustrated by the plus and minus signs in the nerve segment illustrated in Figure 126. Thus, a membrane potential has developed across the fiber membrane.

Formula for the membrane potential. The rate of diffusion of potassium ions outward through the membrane will depend on the concentration gradient of potassium times the permeability of the membrane to potassium. On the other hand, the rate of diffusion of sodium ions to the inside is determined by the sodium concentration gradient times the permeability of the membrane to the sodium. Combining these two together, the voltage that will be generated when both these concentration gradients are considered will be the following:

$$\text{EMF (In mV)} = 61 \cdot \log \frac{K_i P_k + Na_i P_{Na}}{K_o P_k + Na_o P_{Na}}$$

in which P_k is the permeability to potassium, P_{Na} is the permeability to sodium, K_i is the potassium concentration inside the cell, K_o is potassium on the outside, Na_i is sodium on the inside, and Na_o is sodium on the outside. Obviously, since the resting permeability to sodium is very small compared to that of potassium, then the measured resting potential will approach that which would develop if only potassium were diffusible through the membrane. That is,

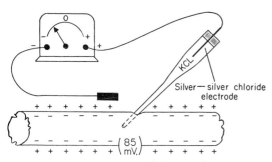

Figure 126. Measurement of the membrane potential of a nerve fiber by means of a microelectrode.

$$\text{EMF (In mV)} = 61 \cdot \log \frac{K_i}{K_o}$$

Using the values for potassium concentrations given in Figure 125, the membrane potential calculates to be 94 millivolts, with negativity inside the membrane and positivity outside.

Measured potentials in nerve and muscle fibers. The resting potentials of different nerve and muscle fibers usually range between 80 and 90 millivolts. Figure 126 illustrates the method used for measuring the resting membrane potential. A micropipette is formed from a capillary glass tube so that the tip of the pipette has a diameter of only ½ to 2 microns. Inside this pipette is a strong solution of potassium chloride which acts as a conductor. The fiber whose membrane is to be measured is pierced with the pipette, and appropriate connections are made from the pipette to a meter, as illustrated in the figure. The resting membrane potential measured in the figure is shown to be 85 millivolts, which compares admirably with the value of 94 millivolts calculated above.

This illustrates that the calculated "potassium potential" across the membrane is slightly greater than the actually measured potential. The difference is caused by the continual diffusion of small quantities of sodium ions inward through the membrane, but, as a first approximation, the resting membrane potential is very nearly equal to the "potassium potential."

THE ACTION POTENTIAL

When an excitable membrane is stimulated in any one of many different ways— by breaking the surface of the membrane. by crushing it, by placing certain chemicals on it, or by electrical stimuli—the membrane potential at the stimulus site undergoes a sequence of changes called the *action potential*. The *resting* membrane potential is positive on the outside and negative on the inside, but when the membrane becomes excited, the potential momentarily decreases almost to zero or, more frequently, actually reverses so that negativity appears on the outside and positivity inside. This reversal lasts only about one-half millisecond in large nerve fibers, and then the normal resting potential reappears. This rapid decrease or reversal of potential followed immediately by reestablishment of a normal resting potential is the action potential. Note especially that an action potential is not a single potential at all but is a *sequence of potentials* that completes its course rapidly during a very small fraction of a second.

An action potential causes electrical currents to flow momentarily along the inner and outer surfaces of the fiber membrane, and these usually excite the fiber further down its length, initiating an action potential that travels along the fiber and causes propagation of an electrochemical impulse along the membrane. For this reason, it is now important to consider the electrical events that take place during the action potential.

Characteristics of the Action Potential. Figure 127 illustrates a very small segment of a nerve fiber, showing the resting membrane potential prior to beginning of an action potential, then reversal of potential during the action potential, and finally return to the resting potential. The meters to the right show the changes in potential. Figure 128 illustrates graphically the precise potentials that are recorded during the complete sequence of the action potential. Figure 128 shows the resting potential across the membrane to be 85 millivolts, but immediately after stimulation the voltage reverses and becomes −50 millivolts. This sudden change in voltage across the membrane

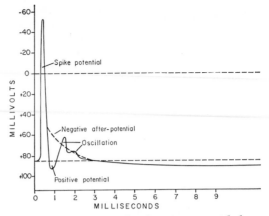

Figure 128. An idealized action potential showing the initial spike followed by (1) a positive potential, (2) oscillation, (3) a negative after-potential, and (4) a positive after-potential.

is called a *spike potential*. Then the voltage again reverses and reapproaches the resting level. However, in doing so it sometimes overshoots the resting level, and the excess above 85 millivolts is called the *positive potential*. Immediately after the positive potential the voltage becomes less than 85 millivolts again and oscillates slightly for a few milliseconds. Sometimes the positive potential and the oscillations are not present; instead, the potential simply follows the dashed line shown at the base of the spike potential. The difference between this dashed line and the resting voltage of 85 millivolts represents a *negative after-potential* that may last from 2 to 15 milliseconds. After this interval is over, the membrane potential becomes even more positive than the normal 85 millivolts and remains positive thereafter for 50 milliseconds or longer. This is called the *positive after-potential*. A complete understanding of the action potential now requires a discussion of the events that cause each of the phases shown in Figure 128.

The Spike Potential

The spike potential constitutes the most conspicuous portion of the action potential complex, and its generation can be divided into two phases, the depolarization phase and the repolarization phase. *Depolarization* means the loss of the resting potential, and *repolarization* means reattainment of the resting potential.

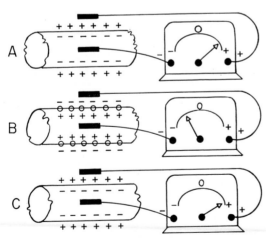

Figure 127. Sequential events in an action potential, showing in (A) the normal resting potential, in (B) sudden development of a reversal potential, and in (C) reestablishment of the normal resting potential.

The Depolarization Process—"Activation" of the Membrane. Earlier in the chapter it was pointed out that the resting membrane is 20 to 100 times as permeable to potassium as to sodium. Any stimulus capable of evoking an action potential must increase the membrane permeability to sodium. However, once a slight increase in sodium permeability has occurred, the process is thereafter self-perpetuating in the following way: Flow of small quantities of sodium inward through the membrane, for reasons not yet understood, causes the membrane to become even more permeable to sodium. Therefore, more sodium flows inward; this in turn makes the pores even more permeable to sodium, and this cycle of events continues over and over again until the sodium permeability of the membrane becomes several times as great as the potassium permeability. This progressive cycle of increasing sodium permeability is called *activation* of the membrane.

After activation, because of the very large concentration gradient of sodium at the membrane, 137 milliequivalents to 10 milliequivalents, extreme amounts of sodium flow to the inside of the fiber. Now, if we reapply the formula above for calculating the membrane potential, assuming this time that the sodium permeability is several times the potassium permeability, we find that the potential has actually reversed. That is, the "sodium potential" at the membrane is now dominant over the "potassium potential," so that the potential will have become negative on the outside and positive inside, as illustrated by the spike in Figure 128. This negative potential, also called the *reversal potential*, may rise to as high as minus 50 millivolts, showing the dominance of sodium over potassium.

Repolarization Caused by "Inactivation" of the Membrane and Outward Flow of Potassium. When the membrane potential has reversed and negativity has developed on the outside of the membrane, the reversed potential slows up the diffusion of sodium ions to the inside. This, then, sets off a reverse process to that which caused depolarization. That is, a decrease in the inward flow of sodium allows the membrane to become less permeable to sodium; this further decreases the flow of sodium to the inside, making the membrane still less per-meable; and the cycle repeats itself again and again until the membrane redevelops its resting state of almost complete impermeability to sodium. This process of decreasing sodium permeability is called *inactivation* of the membrane.

It must be noted that inactivation of the membrane decreases only its sodium permeability while potassium continues to diffuse through the membrane with great ease. Therefore, potassium once again becomes the ion dominating the membrane potential. Because of the concentration gradient of potassium—high inside, low outside—a very great outward flux of potassium ions carries large numbers of positive charges to the outside, causing within a few ten-thousandths of a second a large excess of positivity outside the membrane while leaving negativity inside. Thus, the membrane has become *repolarized*, and the normal resting potential has been recreated.

Summary of the Ionic Fluxes during the Action Potential

Figure 129 illustrates the inward flux (influx) of sodium and the outward flux (efflux) of potassium at various times during the action potential. This figure shows a progressive increase in sodium flow to the inside during the rise of the spike potential. It also shows a decrease in sodium influx along with increasing potassium efflux during the decline of the action potential. Thus, the rise of the spike potential is caused by progressive increase in permeability of the membrane to sodium with an excess of positive charges (sodium ions) flowing inward, and the decline results from diminished perme-

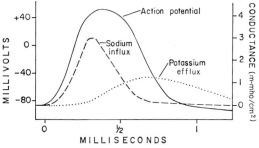

Figure 129. Relationship of sodium influx and potassium efflux to the different phases of the action potential. (Modified from Hodgkin and Huxley: Movement of sodium and potassium ions during nervous activity. *Symp. Quant. Biol.,* 17:43, 1952.)

ability of the membrane to sodium and an excess of positive charges (potassium ions) flowing to the outside.

Mechanism of the Changes in Membrane Permeability during the Action Potential

The great mystery in the whole process of the action potential is the manner in which permeability can change from microsecond to microsecond during the action potential. However, this might be explained in the following way: Experiments have shown that excessive amounts of calcium ions in the body fluids will make the membrane less permeable to sodium. Based principally on this fact, a theory has been proposed for explaining the successive changes in membrane permeability during the action potential. First, it is assumed that the passage of sodium and calcium ions through the membrane occurs only at certain sites and that the ions are likely to become temporarily bound with the substance of the membrane at these sites. Furthermore, the nature of calcium ions makes them have a far higher binding power than sodium. Therefore, under normal circumstances the permeable sites of the membrane are filled with calcium. Yet, if sodium can push these calcium ions away from their binding sites toward the interior of the cell, then still more sodium can move inward, and the momentum of the first sodium will push additional calcium ions inward, thus resulting in a progressive increase in sodium flow to the interior as the sodium develops more and more momentum. This would explain the "activation" phase of the action potential.

Inflow of sodium then begins to cease because of development of the reversal potential which opposes the flow of sodium. As a result, calcium again occupies the binding sites in the membrane, and the membrane becomes once again far less permeable to sodium; this explains the process of "inactivation." Then, in a fraction of a millisecond, potassium efflux reestablishes the resting membrane potential.

The Positive Potential and the Oscillations following the Spike

Referring once again to Figure 129 one notes that very rapid efflux of potassium continues for a considerable period of time after the spike potential is over. This is believed to be caused by an aftermath of the membrane activation process as follows: The membrane, toward the end of the spike potential and slightly thereafter, becomes even more permeable to potassium than normally, thus allowing more dominance of the "potassium potential" than ever and creating a brief interval of *positive potential*.

Immediately after the positive potential the membrane voltage oscillates back and forth a few cycles, and the oscillations then die out. These have been postulated to result from the following effect: The high positive potential supposedly *decreases* the permeability of the membrane to potassium, which decreases potassium efflux. The membrane potential, therefore, falls, and this *increases* the membrane permeability to potassium, allowing increased potassium efflux once more. As a result, the potential becomes greater again, and the process continues through several cycles of damped oscillation until it dies away.

The Negative After-potential

At least three different factors are known to contribute to the negative after-potential shown in Figure 128. These are the following: (1) Because of potassium efflux during the action potential, the potassium concentration builds up immediately outside the membrane; this causes the concentration gradient of potassium to be temporarily less than normal and, therefore, reduces the amount of voltage that will develop across the membrane. The potassium gradually diffuses away from the outside of the membrane as the negative after-potential disappears. (2) The membrane permeability to sodium may also remain slightly higher than normal during this period of time, allowing the "sodium potential" to reduce the membrane potential a slight amount. (3) A shift of chloride ions through the membrane during the spike potential and slow return of these to their normal state create a slight negative potential that decreases the membrane potential.

The Positive After-potential

During the spike potential a large quantity of sodium ions flows to the inside of the fiber, and a large quantity of potassium ions flows to the outside. Consequently, the concentration gradients across the membrane at the end of the spike potential are slightly less than they are under normal conditions. The active transport mechanisms immediately begin transporting sodium back out of the cell and possibly potassium back to the interior. However, the outward transport of sodium is greater than the inward transport of potassium, resulting in an excess of positive charges moving to the outside. This creates the *positive after-potential*.

The positive after-potential normally is only a fraction of a millivolt or at most a few millivolts greater than the normal membrane potential, but it lasts from 50 milliseconds to as long as many seconds in different excitable tissues. If the active transport processes have been poisoned, all portions of the action potential besides the positive after-potential will still be present, but the positive after-potential disappears.

Plateau in the Action Potential

In some instances the excitable membrane does not repolarize immediately after depolarization, but, instead, the potential remains on a *plateau* near the peak of the spike sometimes for many milliseconds before repolarization begins. Such a plateau is illustrated in Figure 130, from which one can readily see that the plateau greatly prolongs the period of depolarization. It is this type of action potential that occurs in the heart, where the plateau lasts for as long as two to three tenths of a second and causes contraction of the heart muscle during this entire period of time.

The cause of the plateau is not completely known, but the following theory has been offered as an explanation: The membranes of some fibers are undoubtedly different from others, and in some of these the mechanism discussed earlier that causes membrane inactivation is slow to develop,

and, consequently, repolarization is very slow to get started. It has been postulated that the efflux of potassium at the end of the spike potential remains too low at first to set off the process of inactivation. Yet, when the process does begin, the membrane rapidly becomes repolarized, as illustrated in Figure 130 by the rapid decline of the potential at the end of the plateau.

Relation of Active Metabolism to the Action Potential

From the foregoing discussion it is obvious that no membrane potentials could exist across the cell membranes were it not for the concentration gradients of potassium and sodium. These gradients are caused by active transport of sodium to the exterior and probably some active transport of potassium to the interior, as shown in Figure 131. This figure also shows an additional mechanism in the nerve membrane for transport of sodium out of the membrane even before it can leak all the way to the interior of the cell.

In addition to establishing the initial concentration gradients, these same transport mechanisms reestablish the concentration gradients when they are partially lost during action potentials. The quantity of ions lost through the membrane with each action potential is actually very minute—indeed, so slight in certain nerves that 10,000 to 100,000 action potentials can occur before nerve action ceases. Therefore, once the concentration gradients have been fully developed,

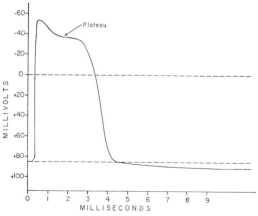

Figure 130. The presence of a plateau following the spike potential. This is the type of action potential that occurs in heart muscle.

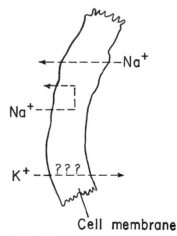

Figure 131. The active transport processes of the cell membrane.

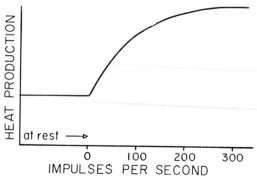

Figure 132. Heat production in a nerve at rest and at progressively increasing rates of stimulation.

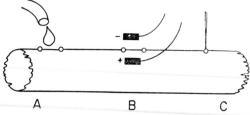

Figure 133. Different methods for depolarizing the nerve membrane: (A) chemical depolarization with acid or acetylcholine, (B) electrical depolarization, (C) mechanical depolarization with a needle.

the active metabolic processes of the cell can be poisoned, and many thousands of impulses can still be transmitted.

It is obvious, then, that the action potential itself, including both the depolarization and the repolarization processes, occurs without any immediate active metabolic process in the fiber, but establishment of the prerequisite concentration gradients does require active metabolic processes. The establishment of sodium and potassium concentration gradients, either as a result of sodium transport alone or as a result of both sodium and potassium transport, was discussed in detail in Chapter 3.

Figure 132 illustrates the rate of heat production (which is a measure of the rate of metabolism) in a nerve fiber during the resting condition and then later during the transmission of progressively increasing numbers of action potentials. This figure illustrates that activity increases the rate of metabolism in the nerve. It is this increased metabolic activity that reestablishes the concentration gradients.

EXCITATION—THE PROCESS OF ELICITING THE ACTION POTENTIAL

Chemical Stimulation. Basically, any factor that causes sodium ions to begin to diffuse inward through the membrane in sufficient numbers will set off the automatic "activation" mechanism noted above that eventuates in the action potential. Figure 133 illustrates some of the means by which this can be accomplished. At point A *a chemical solution which makes the membrane more permeable than usual to sodium ions* is placed on the fiber. Because of the

high gradient of sodium ions between the exterior and interior of the cell, the increase in permeability allows a sudden surge of sodium ions inward, and this sets off the action potential.

The different chemicals that can stimulate a nerve fiber include acids, bases, almost any salt solution of very strong concentration, and, most importantly, the substance *acetylcholine.* In the body many nerve endings when stimulated secrete acetylcholine at their endings where they synapse with other neurons or where they end on muscle fibers. The acetylcholine in turn stimulates the successive neuron or muscle fiber. This will be discussed in much greater detail in the following chapter. This is probably the most important means in the body by which nerve and muscle fibers are stimulated. Under some conditions *nor-epinephrine* secreted by sympathetic nerve endings can stimulate smooth or cardiac muscle fibers, and it is possible that still other hormonal substances are secreted in the central nervous system that can stimulate successive neurons.

Mechanical Stimulation. Point C in Figure 133 illustrates a nerve fiber being pricked with a pin. This, too, can cause a sudden surge of sodium inward and for obvious reasons can elicit an action potential.

Electrical Stimulation. Point B in Figure 133 illustrates that electrical stimulation also can initiate an action potential. An electrical charge artificially induced across the membrane can cause an excess flow of ions through the membrane, and, therefore, can upset the normal concentration gradients. This then initiates an action potential. However, not all methods of applying electrical stimuli will result in excitation, and, since this is the usual means by which nerve fibers are excited when they are studied in the

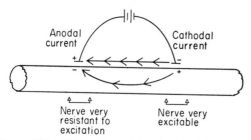

Figure 134. Effects of anodal and cathodal currents on the excitability of the nerve membrane.

laboratory, the process of electrical excitation deserves more detailed comment.

Cathodal versus anodal currents. Figure 134 illustrates a battery connected to two electrodes on the surface of a nerve fiber. At the cathode, or negative electrode, the potential outside the membrane is negative with respect to that on the inside, and the current that flows through the membrane at this point is called *cathodal current*. At the anode, the electrode is positive with respect to the potential immediately inside the membrane, and the current flow at this point is called *anodal current*.

A cathodal current excites the fiber while an anodal current actually makes the fiber more resistant to excitation than normal. Though this difference between the two types of current cannot be explained completely, it has been postulated to result from the following effects: The normal impermeability of the membrane to sodium results partially from the high resting membrane potential across the membrane, and any condition that lessens this potential causes the membrane to become progressively more permeable to sodium. Obviously, at the cathode the applied voltage is opposite to the resting potential of the membrane, and this reduces the net potential. As a result, the membrane becomes far more permeable than usual to sodium with the subsequent development of an action potential.

On the other hand, at the anode the applied potential actually enhances the membrane potential. This makes the membrane less permeable to sodium than ever, resulting in increased resistance of the membrane to stimulation by other means.

Though an anodal current will not stimulate an excitable membrane, sudden removal of the anodal current usually will excite it in the following way: As long as the anodal current continues, the membrane

potential remains much higher than the fiber can maintain. Therefore, removal of the current allows the potential to fall very suddenly initiating oscillations in the membrane potential similar to those observed following spike potentials, as explained earlier in the chapter. If one of these oscillations carries the membrane potential low enough that it reaches threshold, then excitation will result. For this reason, any sudden flow of current through an excitable membrane, whether it be cathodal or anodal, usually excites the membrane, the cathodal current causing excitation when it is applied and the anodal current causing excitation when it is removed.

Threshold for excitation and "acute subthreshold potential." A very weak cathodal current will not excite the fiber. But, when this cathodal current is progressively increased, there comes a point at which excitation will take place. Figure 135 illustrates the effects of successively applied cathodal stimuli of progressing strength. A very weak stimulus at point A causes the membrane potential to decrease from 85 millivolts to 80 millivolts, but this is not a sufficient decrease for the automatic processes of the action potential to develop. At point B the stimulus is greater, but, here again, the intensity is not enough to set off the automatic action potential. Nevertheless, the membrane voltage is disturbed for as long as a millisecond or more after both of the weak stimuli; the potential changes during this small interval of time are called *acute subthreshold potentials*, as illustrated in the figure.

At point C in Figure 135, the stimulus elicits an acute membrane potential that is

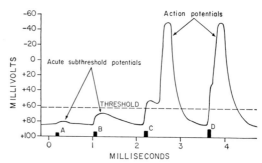

Figure 135. Effect of graded stimuli on an excitable membrane, showing the development of "acute subthreshold potentials" when the stimulus is not equal to the threshold value required for eliciting an action potential.

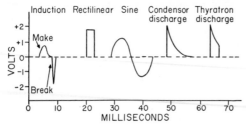

Figure 136. Graphic representation of different types of commonly used electrical stimuli.

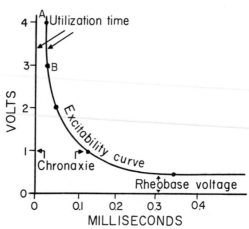

Figure 137. Excitability curve of a large myelinated nerve fiber.

not subthreshold but slightly more than the threshold value, and, after a short "latent period," it initiates an action potential. At point D the stimulus is still stronger, and the acute membrane potential initiates the action potential even sooner. Thus, this figure shows that even a very weak stimulus always causes a local potential change at the membrane, but that the intensity of the *local potential* must rise to a *threshold value* before the automatic action potential will be set off.

Usual types of electrical stimuli. Figure 136 illustrates graphically a number of different types of electrical stimuli often used to excite nerves. In general, each of these is a pulse of electrical voltage, and they stimulate either as a result of induced cathodal currents or as a result of induced anodal currents followed by sudden removal. The most important of these types of stimuli is the *rectilinear stimulus.* It can be used for making many physiological measurements of the excitability of nerve and muscle cells because it can be characterized in terms of *voltage* and *duration.*

Excitability curve. An example in which the rectilinear stimulus is of value in characterizing excitability of tissues is provided by the so-called "excitability curve" shown in Figure 137. To obtain this curve a high voltage stimulus (4 volts in this instance) is first applied to the fiber, and the minimum duration of stimulus required to excite the fiber is found. The voltage and minimal time are plotted as point A. Then a stimulus voltage of 3 volts is applied, and the minimal time required is again determined; the results are plotted as point B. The same is repeated at 2 volts, at 1 volt, at ½ volt, and so forth, until the least voltage possible at which the membrane will be stimulated has been reached. On connecting these points, the so-called excitability curve of the excitable tissue is determined.

The excitability curve of Figure 137 is approximately that of a large myelinated nerve fiber. This curve illustrates that 4 volts of cathodal current properly applied to the nerve fiber will stimulate it in approximately 1/50,000 second. Yet, 1 volt requires about 1/8,000 second. The least possible time required for stimulation even with very high voltage of stimulus is called the *utilization time*. On the other hand, the least possible voltage at which it will fire however long the stimulus is applied to the fiber is called the *rheobase*. Then, if the voltage is increased to twice the rheobase voltage, the time required to stimulate the fiber is called the *chronaxie*, and this is often used as a means of expressing relative excitabilities of different excitable tissues. For instance, the chronaxie of a large type A fiber is about 0.0001 to 0.0002 second; of smaller myelinated nerve fibers approximately 0.0003; of unmyelinated fibers 0.0005 second; skeletal muscle fibers 0.00025 to 0.0001 second; and heart muscle 0.001 to 0.003 second.

Clinical Use of the Chronaxie To Determine Innervation of Muscle. A muscle that still has an intact nerve supply has many large myelinated nerve fibers within its substance. Nerve fibers are more excitable than muscle fibers. Therefore, an electrical impulse passing through an innervated muscle will first excite the nerves, and these in turn will excite the muscle. Therefore, if a needle electrode is inserted into a normal muscle, the chronaxie determined will be approximately that of a large type A nerve fiber. However, if the muscle has lost its nerve supply as a result of poliomyelitis, nerve trauma, or any other condition, the chronaxie will be that of the muscle itself—that is, much longer. This procedure is sometimes used as a diagnostic test when other methods of determining the presence or absence of innervation have failed.

"Accommodation" to stimuli. When a cathodal current is applied suddenly to a nerve fiber, the threshold voltage required to cause firing is considerably less than that required when the cathodal current increases very slowly. This

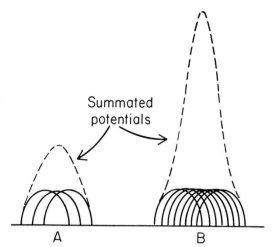

Summated potentials

Figure 152. Summated action potentials recorded from a nerve trunk.

potassium solution or by burning the nerve and then placing an electrode on the affected area.

When only a single fiber in a nerve trunk fires, most of the electrical current generated around the nerve will be dissipated in "eddy currents" within the nerve trunk before they can reach the recording electrodes on the outside of the nerve. Therefore, the actual voltage recorded by the oscilloscope is far below that which was discussed in the previous chapter for single fiber recordings. However, when many fibers fire simultaneously the currents mutually support each other and the recorded voltage can then equal or nearly equal that recorded directly on the membrane of a single fiber. Figure 152A illustrates by the solid curves individual monophasic action potentials that would be recorded from single fibers in a nerve trunk if they should fire singly, showing that the potential would be very weak. However, when three fibers fire in rapid succession the summated potential that will actually be recorded from the surface of the entire nerve trunk is the dashed curve. In Figure 152B still many more impulses occur in rapid succession, and the summated potential is still greater. Note, also, that the duration of the recorded action potential may be considerably greater than that recorded from a single fiber.

Physiologic Demonstration of the Different Types of Nerve Fibers in a Nerve Trunk. Referring once again to Figure 151, we see a characteristic summated monophasic action potential recorded from a nerve trunk containing fibers of all sizes. Because the alpha type A fibers carry impulses much more rapidly than the other fibers, the summated action potential caused by these fibers appears first in the record. Then when the impulses in the beta fibers reach the recording electrode a second elevation occurs in the record.

A third elevation is caused by impulses from the gamma fibers, and finally a fourth by the delta fibers. The time interval between the stimulus artifact in the recording and the appearance of the delta action potential is approximately 10 times that for the alpha fibers.

CONDUCTION OF IMPULSES BY SKELETAL MUSCLE FIBERS

Almost everything said in the previous and present chapters regarding the excitation of nerve fibers and conduction of impulses in nerve fibers applies equally as well, except for quantitative differences, for skeletal muscle fibers. However, several specific qualities of skeletal muscle excitation and impulse transmission must be mentioned.

The Resting Potential and Action Potential in Skeletal Muscle. The normal resting potential of skeletal muscle fibers is essentially the same as that of nerve fibers—that is, about 80 to 90 millivolts. Likewise, the spike potential generated by excitation of a skeletal muscle fiber has essentially the same voltage as that in large nerve fibers, but it lasts 5 to 10 milliseconds instead of ½ millisecond—that is, a duration of about 10 times as long. Because of this prolonged duration, the maximum number of impulses that can be transmitted in skeletal muscle fibers is between 100 and 250 per second. However, as will be discussed in the following chapter, this is a sufficient rate of stimulation to cause maximum contraction.

Excitability of Skeletal Muscle. Skeletal muscle is somewhat less excitable to electrical stimuli than large, myelinated nerve fibers, but its degree of excitability is not far different from that of many small, unmyelinated fibers. That is, the stimulus voltage must either be higher or last longer to stimulate muscle fibers than to stimulate the larger nerve fibers.

A muscle fiber can be stimulated much more easily when the stimulus is applied at the neuromuscular junction than at other points on the fiber. This fact is used clinically to determine the presence or absence of muscular innervation. An electrode is moved back and forth on the skin overlying the muscle in question, and, if a particular point can be found at which the muscle is much more strongly stimulated than at other points, one can reasonably expect that this is the locus of viable neuromuscular junctions. These points of excessive excitability are called *motor points.*

Velocity of Conduction in Skeletal Muscle Fibers. The average velocity of conduction in skeletal muscle fibers is approximately 5 meters per second, about the same as that in very small myelinated nerve fibers. However, skeletal muscle fibers, like nerve fibers, vary greatly in size from one part of the body to another, and the velocity of conduction is considerably less than this value in some muscles and considerably greater in other muscles.

Transmission of Impulses from Nerves to Skeletal Muscle Fibers: the Neuromuscular Junction

Figure 153 illustrates the nueromuscular junction between a large myelinated nerve fiber and a skeletal muscle fiber. The nerve fiber branches at its end to form the complicated structure called the *end-plate,* which adheres very tightly to the muscle fiber but lies entirely outside the muscle fiber membrane. At the tips of the many nerve branches in the end plate are *sole feet,* and a fine granular substance known as *granules of Kühne* is dispersed in the spaces between the sole feet. These granules are believed to be small vesicles of *acetylcholine,* a hormone that can be released by the end-plate to excite the muscle fiber.

Secretion of Acetylcholine by the End-plate. When a nerve impulse reaches the neuromuscular junction, a small amount of acetylcholine is released by the end-plate into the minute space between the end-plate and the muscle fiber. It has been postulated that the nerve impulse causes calcium ions to move from the interstitial fluids into the end-plate and that these ions in turn rupture the vesicles of acetylcholine and release the acetylcholine to excite the muscle fiber.

Destruction of the released acetylcholine by cholinesterase. Within approximately 1/500 second after acetylcholine is released by the end-plate, it is destroyed by an enzyme called *cholinesterase,* which is present in great abundance in the neuromuscular apparatus. Therefore, the acetylcholine acts on the muscle fiber for only a few milliseconds and then is gone.

The End-plate Potential and Excitation of the Skeletal Muscle Fiber. Even though the acetylcholine released into the space between the end-plate and the muscle membrane lasts for only a minute fraction of a second, nevertheless, even during this period of time it can affect the muscle membrane sufficiently to make it very permeable to sodium ions, allowing rapid influx of sodium into the muscle fiber. As a result, the membrane becomes more positive on the inside and more negative on the outside, creating a potential called the *end-plate potential.*

A typical end-plate potential is illustrated at point A in Figure 154. This potential was recorded after the muscle had been poisoned with curare, which prevented an action potential in the muscle fiber. However, in the normal muscle fiber, the effect shown at point B occurs: At this point, the end-plate potential begins, but before it can complete its course the electrical charges created by this potential stimulate the adjacent portions of the muscle fiber and initiate an action potential. In other words, the end-plate potential is analogous to the "local potential" dis-

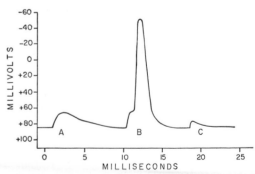

Figure 154. End-plate potentials: (A) normal end-plate potential recorded in a curarized muscle so that the muscle fiber itself could not generate an action potential, (B) end-plate potential eliciting a muscle action potential, and (C) end-plate potential too weak to elicit a muscle action potential.

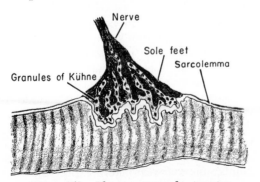

Figure 153. The neuromuscular junction.

cussed in the previous chapter, which occurs at a conductive membrane when an electrical stimulus is applied. At point C, only a small quantity of acetylcholine is released at the end-plate, causing the end-plate potential to be much less than the threshold value required to cause an action potential. In this case the end-plate potential is analogous to the "acute subthreshold potential" that follows a subthreshold electrical stimulus.

"Amplifier" Characteristics of the Neuromuscular Junction. The neuromuscular junction actually functions as an "amplifier" to increase the very small currents generated by terminal nerve fibers into currents with sufficient strength to excite the muscle fibers. Electrical studies show that the current generated by the nerve fiber itself is far less than the threshold value required to stimulate the muscle fiber. However, by causing the release of acetylcholine, an end-plate potential is generated that is a much stronger stimulus than the nerve potential itself and can therefore excite the muscle fiber.

"Safety Factor" for Transmission at the Neuromuscular Junction; Fatigue of the Junction. Ordinarily, each impulse that arrives at the neuromuscular junction creates a sufficiently large end-plate potential to stimulate the muscle fiber every time. Therefore, the normal neuromuscular junction is said to have a high *safety factor*. However, stimulation of the nerve fiber at rates greater than 150 times per second is likely to diminish the quantity of acetylcholine released with each impulse so greatly that many of the impulses then fail to pass into the muscle fiber.

Prolonged stimulation of a motor nerve at high rates will progressively diminish the quantity of acetylcholine secreted by the end-plate, which causes more and more diminishment of transmission into the muscle fibers. This is called *fatigue* of the neuromuscular junction. This effect is quite different from transmission of impulses in nerve fibers, for fatigue of nerve fibers to the extent that conduction is impaired is almost unknown under physiological conditions.

Drugs Affecting Transmission at the Neuromuscular Junction. *Drugs that stimulate the muscle fiber by an acetylcholine-like action.* Many different compounds, including *methacholine, carbachol,* and *nicotine,* have exactly the same effect on the muscle fiber

as does acetylcholine. The difference between these drugs and acetylcholine is that they are not destroyed by cholinesterase or are destroyed very slowly, and when once applied to the muscle fiber the action persists for many minutes to several hours. Moderate quantities of the above three drugs applied to a muscle fiber cause localized areas of depolarization, and every time the muscle fiber becomes repolarized elsewhere these depolarized areas, by virtue of their leaking ions, cause new depolarization waves. Consequently, following moderate dosages of methacholine, carbachol, and nicotine the muscle fibers often exhibit a state of spasm. On the other hand, when extreme dosages of these three drugs are used, so much of the membranes becomes depolarized that the fibers can no longer pass impulses at all, and a state of flaccid paralysis exists instead of the spasm that occurs with moderate dosages.

Drugs that block transmission at the myoneural junction—curariform drugs. An entire group of drugs, known as the *curariform drugs,* can prevent passage of impulses from the end-plate into the muscle. Exactly how curare works at the myoneural junction is not known, but it is believed to affect the membrane in such a way that acetylcholine cannot increase the permeability of the membrane sufficiently to initiate a depolarization wave. It has been suggested that curare might destroy an *acetylcholine receptor substance* at the end-plate, which substance is necessary for the action of acetylcholine on the membrane. Very infrequent impulses arriving at the end-plate can stimulate the curarized muscle fiber, but rapidly repeated impulses arriving at the end-plate are mostly blocked, thus indicating that it might be possible for the muscle fiber to generate sufficient quantities of the receptor substance between widely spaced end-plate discharges but not between rapidly repeated end-plate discharges.

Regardless of the method by which curare and other curariform drugs work, they all oppose the action of acetylcholine, and, when given to an animal in sufficient quantity, the normal quantity of acetylcholine liberated at the end-plate is not enough to depolarize the muscle membrane.

Drugs that stimulate the myoneural junction by inactivating cholinesterase. Three particularly well known drugs, *neostigmine, physostigmine,* and *di-isopropylfluorophosphate,* inactivate cholinesterase so that the cholinesterase normally in the muscle fibers will not hydrolyze acetylcholine released at the end-plate. Therefore, acetylcholine increases in quantity with successive nerve impulses so that extreme amounts of acetylcholine accumulate and repetitively stimulate the muscle fiber. This causes muscular spasm when even a few impulses are reaching the muscle.

Neostigmine and physostigmine merely combine with cholinesterase to inactivate it, but after several hours they are displaced from the cholinesterase so that the cholinesterase once again becomes active. On the other hand, di-isopropylfluorophosphate, which has military potential as a very powerful "nerve" gas, actually destroys cholinesterase, and it takes several weeks for the body to replace the cholinesterase that has been destroyed.

Myasthenia Gravis

A disease known as myasthenia gravis occurs in human begins, probably as a result of the inability of the end-plate to secrete normal quantities of acetylcholine. (Other possible causes would be the presence of excessive quantities of cholinesterase at the nerve endings or non-responsiveness of the muscle fiber to acetylcholine.) As a result, the end-plate potentials developed at the nerve endings are too weak to stimulate the muscle fibers adequately. If the disease is intense enough, the patient dies of paralysis—in particular, of paralysis of the respiratory muscles. However, the disease can usually be ameliorated with several different drugs, as follows:

Treatment of Myasthenia Gravis with Drugs. When a patient with myasthenia gravis is treated with a drug such as neostigmine that is capable of inactivating or destroying cholinesterase, the acetylcholine secreted by the end-plate will not be destroyed immediately. If a sequence of nerve impulses arrives at the end-plate, the quantity of acetylcholine present at the membrane increases progressively until finally the end-plate potential caused by the acetylcholine rises above the threshold value for stimulating the muscle fiber. Thus, it is possible by diminishing the quantity of cholinesterase in the body of a patient with myasthenia gravis to allow even the inadequate quantities of acetylcholine secreted at his end-plates to effect almost normal muscular activity.

EXCITATION OF SMOOTH MUSCLE

Excitation of smooth muscle and transmission of action potentials in smooth muscle have not been studied nearly so extensively as in large nerve fibers and skeletal muscle fibers, principally because of the extreme difficulty of making accurate membrane potential measurements between the inside and outside of the very small smooth muscle cells. Yet, in the few measurements that have been made, the resting membrane potential of smooth muscle cells has measured about 50 millivolts.

Characteristics of the Action Potential in Smooth Muscle Fibers. When excited electrically or with certain drugs such as

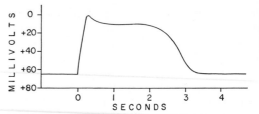

Figure 155. Monophasic action potential from a smooth muscle fiber of the rat uterus. (Drawn from a recording by Woodbury, J. W., and McIntyre, D. M.: *Am. J. Physiol.,* 187:338, 1956.)

acetylcholine or histamine, a true action potential develops in smooth muscle. However, the voltage recorded from these action potentials is only 60 millivolts instead of the 120 to 135 millivolts recorded from large nerve and muscle fibers. It is probable, however, that the recorded potential is considerably lower than the true value because of the difficulty in making accurate measurements in smooth muscle cells.

The duration of these action potentials is often similar to that in skeletal muscle fibers (5 to 10 milliseconds), but more often is of very long duration, up to 1 to 3 seconds. But, since there are many different types of smooth muscle in the body, operating under many varying conditions, it is reasonable to find different characteristics of action potentials in different smooth muscle fibers.

Figure 155 illustrates a typical monophasic action potential recorded from a smooth muscle fiber of the rat uterus, showing that the action potential develops rapidly and then remains on a plateau for as long as 1 to 3 seconds, returning gradually to a normal resting membrane potential at the end of this time. The smooth muscle fiber remains refractory as long as the action potential persists—that is, 1 to 3 seconds.

In most smooth muscle tissues, rhythmical action potentials are spontaneously generated sometimes as often as once every 5 seconds but sometimes with periodicities as long as once every few minutes. These are probably responsible for the *rhythmical contractions* of smooth muscle organs, which will be described in the following chapter.

Means of Exciting Smooth Muscles. The smooth muscle cell can be excited by *stretching the muscle,* by *cathodal currents,* and, in the case of some smooth muscles, by *application of acetylcholine, histamine,* or *nor-epinephrine.* In general, electrical stimuli required to activate smooth muscle fibers must be considerably stronger than those for stimulating either large nerve fibers or skeletal muscle fibers.

Slow Potential Changes in Smooth Muscle. In addition to true action potentials, the resting membrane potential of smooth muscle can vary up or down under different conditions. For instance, any one of the methods for exciting smooth muscle noted above can cause the resting membrane potential to fall a small amount without necessarily falling to the threshold level required to initiate an action potential. On the other hand, other substances cause the resting membrane potential to rise.

Prolonged diminishment of the membrane potential, without actually causing an action potential, could possibly cause the *tonic contractions* that are so characteristic of smooth muscle. Likewise, increased membrane potential could inhibit contraction, which is also a characteristic of smooth muscle at times.

It should also be noted that very small spike potentials of about 8 millivolts at a frequency of about 10 per second occur continually at the membranes of some smooth muscle cells. Though the function of these is not known, they possibly also help to maintain tonic contraction in smooth muscle fibers.

Conduction of Action Potentials by Smooth Muscles. Histological studies indicate that membrane continuity does not exist between adjacent smooth muscle fibers. However, physiological studies show that action potentials can usually spread from one smooth muscle fiber to another. This explains how it is possible to stimulate a smooth muscle organ in one region and excite a contraction that spreads over the entire organ. The rate of transmission of the action potential can be as slow as 5 millimeters per second or as rapid as five centimeters per second, depending on the type of smooth muscle fiber.

NERVE DESTRUCTION AND REGENERATION

Peripheral Nerve Degeneration

When a peripheral nerve is cut, the portion of the nerve peripheral to the cut will still conduct

impulses for approximately 2 to 3 days. After that the entire nerve fiber peripheral to the section becomes inactive and begins to degenerate, exhibiting fatty necrosis of the myelin sheaths and fibrotic invasion of the entire nerve fiber. This fatty degeneration is commonly called "Wallerian degeneration." The neuronal bodies in the spinal cord that had been supplying the peripheral nerve fibers also undergo changes known as "chromatolysis." The chromophilic elements of these large neuronal cells of the anterior horns break up into very finely divided material. These chromophilic elements of the neuronal cells are probably enzyme systems that elaborate substances needed by the peripheral nerve fiber. Therefore, when the nerve is cut the flow of material from the cell body outward toward the periphery cannot proceed normally, and this possibly causes the changes in the neuronal cells. Regardless of what the actual mechanism is, this process of chromatolysis is frequently used in histologic studies to trace the backward connections of nerve fibers that have been cut.

Peripheral Nerve Regeneration

After a nerve has been sectioned, the central stump of the nerve elaborates many branches from each fiber, giving rise to at least 10 and perhaps as many as 50 to 100 new fibers from each of the cut fibers. If these new fibers can find the sheath of the peripheral end of the cut nerve they will grow along the nerve sheath, but more usually the cut ends of the nerve trunks will have pulled fairly far apart, and the new axons branch in all directions in trying to find a pathway for growth. Oftentimes this causes a *neuroma*, which is a great mass of axons grown into a tumor. If the fibers of the neuroma are sensory fibers, compression of the neroma is extremely painful. In persons who have lost legs or arms, painful neuromas at the stump often make it impossible to apply a prosthesis to the stump.

Rate of Nerve Regrowth. If nerve fibers do cross the gap in the sectioned nerve and grow back down the peripheral nerve sheath, the axons regrow at rates between 0.4 and 4.5 mm. per day, averaging perhaps 1 mm. per day. Thus section of a nerve at the spinal cord causes a muscle in the foot to be without a nerve fiber for at least 250 days and often for as long as four years.

Conductive Properties of New Axons. During axon regrowth, the tips of budding axons will not conduct impulses, but the slightly older portions do conduct impulses, though they do so slowly. The young fiber is quite small in size, and the axon regrows before the myelin sheath is reformed. The older portions of the new growing axon continue to grow in thickness and continue to develop thicker and thicker myelin sheaths while the peripheral end of the axon is growing forward. Consequently, the velocity of conduction in the older portions of the axon is faster than in the peripheral portions.

Arborization Method of Recovery in Poliomyelitis

After selective destruction of some of the anterior roots of the spinal cord in experimental animals, the terminal endings of remaining, live fibers have the ability to branch like limbs of trees and then resupply the muscle fibers that have lost their innervation. This establishment of new innervation begins within 5 to 8 days after loss of the original innervation, and it can continue for several years. In rabbits at least four fifths and perhaps as much as nine tenths of the motor fibers can be destroyed, and still muscular function may return to normal—presumably as a result of this process of arborization.

When poliomyelitis virus invades the spinal cord it destroys anterior horn cells, but usually a few anterior horn cells are spared in any given area. If this happens, a few remaining nerve fibers will still innervate each area of muscle supplied by any given segment of the cord. Consequently, it is argued that patients with poliomyelitis also recover from the intense paralysis existing immediately after the disease by progressive arborization which continues for a few months to a year or more.

It is quite interesting that the muscles of patients who are recovering from poliomyelitis fatigue very rapidly, probably because of an inability of the end-plates of recovered muscles to secrete sufficient quantities of acetylcholine. This indicates that it might be more difficult than usual for each neuron to maintain proper metabolism in all the newly formed end-plates of patients recovered from poliomyelitis, probably because one anterior horn cell under these conditions would be innervating perhaps as many as 5000 end-plates rather than the normal average of approximately 1500 end-plates.

REFERENCES

Acheson, G. H.: Neuro-muscular junctions. *Fed. Proc.*, 7:447, 1948.

Adriani, J.: Nerve Blocks. Springfield, Illinois, Charles C Thomas, 1954.

Botelho, S. Y.: Comparison of simultaneously recorded electrical and mechanical activity in myasthenia gravis patients and in partially curarized normal humans. *Am. J. Med.*, 19:693, 1955.

Coers, C., and Woolf, A. L.: The Innervation of Muscle. Oxford, Blackwell Scientific Publications, 1959.

Cohen, L. A.: Nerve electrodes for in vivo studies. *J. Appl. Physiol.*, 9:135, 1956.

Dun, F. T.: The blockage of motor impulses in an asynchronized volley at the neuromuscular junction. *J. Cell. Physiol.*, 46:348, 1955.

Eaton, L. M., and Lambert, E. H.: Electromyography and electric stimulation of nerves in diseases of motor unit; observations on myasthenic syndrome associated with malignant tumors. *J. Am. Med. Assoc.*, 163:1117, 1957.

Gasser, H. S., and Grundfest, H.: Axon diameters in relation to the spike dimensions and the conduction velocity in mammalian A fibers. *Am. J. Physiol.*, 127:393–414, 1939.

Guth, I.: Regeneration in the mammalian peripheral nervous system. *Physiol. Rev.*, 36:441, 1956.

Guyton, A. C., and MacDonald, M. A.: Physiology of botulinus toxin. *Arch. Neurol. & Psychiat.*, 57: 578–592, 1947.

Guyton, A. C., and Reeder, R. C.: The dynamics of curarization. *J. Pharmacol. & Exper. Therap.*, 97: 322–330, 1949.

Holmstedt, B.: Pharmacology of organophosphorus cholinesterase inhibitors. *Pharmacol. Rev.*, 11:567, 1959.

Hunt, C. C., and Kuffler, S. W.: Motor innervation of skeletal muscle: multiple innervation of individual muscle fibres and motor unit function. *J. Physiol.*, 126:293, 1954.

Huxley, A. F., and Stampfli, R.: Evidence for saltatory conduction in peripheral myelinated nerve fibers. *J. Physiol.*, 108:315, 1949.

Larrabee, M. G., and Edwards, C.: Excitation and conduction in the nervous system. *Ann. Rev. Physiol.*, 15:283, 1953.

McIntyre, A. R.: Curare: Its History, Nature and Clinical Use. Chicago, University of Chicago Press, 1947.

Miledi, R.: Junctional and extra-junctional acetylcholine receptors in skeletal muscle fibres. *J. Physiol.*, 151:24, 1960.

Norris, F. H., Jr., and Chatfield, P. O.: Some electrophysiological aspects of muscular dystrophy. *Electroencephalography*, 7:391, 1955.

Norris, F. H., Jr., and Gasteiger, E. L.: Action potentials of single motor units in normal muscle. *Electroencephalography*, 7:115, 1955.

Ooyama, H., and Wright, E. B.: Effect of anodal and cathodal pulses applied during action potential at a single Ranvier node. *Am. J. Physiol.*, 197:1247, 1959.

Osserman, K. E.: Myasthenia Gravis, New York, Grune & Stratton, Inc., 1958.

Rosenblueth, A.: The Transmission of Nerve Impulses at Neuroeffector Junctions and Peripheral Synapses. New York, John Wiley and Sons, 1950.

Stampfi, R.: Saltatory conduction in nerve. *Physiol. Rev.*, 34:101, 1954.

Tasaki, I., and Bak, A. F.: Current-voltage relations of single nodes of Ranvier as examined by voltage clamp technique. *J. Neurophysiol.*, 21:124, 1958.

Van, H. A.: Innervation of mammalian muscle. *Phys. Ther. Rev.*, 35:67, 1955.

Wagman, I. H., and Lesse, H.: Maximum conduction velocities of motor fibers of ulnar nerve in human subjects of various ages and sizes. *J. Neurophysiol.*, 15:235–244, 1952.

Werner, G.: Neuromuscular facilitation and antidromic discharges in motor nerves: their relation to activity in motor nerve terminals. *J. Neurophysiol.*, *23*:171, 1960.

Windle, W. F.: Regeneration of axons in the vertebrate central nervous system. *Physiol. Rev.*, *36*: 427, 1956.

Woodhall, B.: *Peripheral Nerve Regeneration.* Washington, U. S. Gov't. Printing Office, 1956.

Wright, G. P.: The neurotoxins of *Clostridium botulinum* and *Clostridium tetani. Pharmacol Rev.*, *7*: 413, 1955.

See also Chapter 17, Membrane potentials; Chapter 47, Central nervous system synapse.

Chapter 19

Contraction of
Skeletal and Smooth Muscle

Approximately one half of the body is skeletal muscle, and the smooth muscle and cardiac muscle add an additional several pounds. Many of the same principles of contraction apply to all these different types of muscle, but in the present chapter the function of skeletal and smooth muscle will be considered specifically, while cardiac muscle and its specialized functions will be discussed in Chapter 21.

Physiologic Anatomy of Skeletal Muscle

The Skeletal Muscle Fiber. All skeletal muscles of the body are made up of numerous muscle fibers ranging between 10 and 100 microns in diameter. In most muscles the fibers extend the entire length of the muscle and usually are each innervated by one or more neuromuscular junctions located somewhere on the middle third of the fiber.

Each muscle fiber contains several hundred to several thousand myofibrils, which are illustrated by the small dots in the cross-sectional view of Figure 156. Each myofibril in turn has, lying side by side, about 2500 *myosin* and *actin-tropomyosin filaments*, which, as will be explained later, are large polymerized protein molecules that are responsible for muscle contraction.

All skeletal muscle fibers, as well as cardiac muscle fibers, exhibit *cross-striations* when viewed with the ordinary light microscope (see Figure 156), for which reason these types of muscle are often called *striated muscle*. The light bands are *isotropic* to polarized light and are known as "I" bands. The dark bands are *anisotropic* to polarized light and are known as "A" bands. The combination of an "A" band and an "I" band is called a *sarcomere*, and the total length of this is usually slightly more than 2 microns.

Figure 157 illustrates an enlarged segment of a myofibril, showing that each fibril is also separated into sarcomeres. Furthermore,

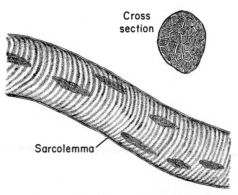

Figure 156. Side and cross-sectional views of a skeletal muscle fiber.

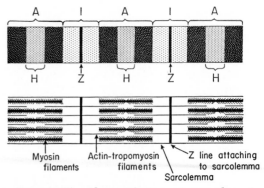

Figure 157. Above: Electron micrographic picture of a myofibril. *Below:* Arrangement of the myosin and actin-tropomyosin filaments in the sarcomeres.

All or Nothing Law. In Chapter 17, it was pointed out that, following stimulation of a nerve fiber, the action potential either travels over the entire neuron or fails to travel at all. This is called the *all or nothing law*. The same principle applies in muscle— that is, a stimulus to a muscle fiber causes an action potential to travel over the entire fiber or fails to stimulate it at all, except at the local point of the stimulus. Yet, the force of contraction that results when the muscle does become excited can vary, depending on the contractile state of the fiber when it is stimulated. That is, if appropriate nutrients are not available, the contraction might well be weak, or the same will be true if the fiber is already fatigued. On the other hand, the fiber might be in a highly contractile state, such as occurs when the muscle is warmed, and will contract even more strongly than normally.

Treppe (staircase effect). If a resting muscle is suddenly stimulated with successive stimuli a few seconds apart, the contractions will become progressively stronger and stronger for about 30 contractions because the contractile state of the muscle myofibrils becomes greater and greater with the succesive contractions. This effect, which is called *treppe*, is associated with, first, diminution in potassium inside the muscle fiber and, second, increase in calcium inside the fiber. It is possible that diminution of the potassium allows greater reversal of membrane potential during excitation and, therefore, greater contraction. But, on the other hand, a more likely suggestion is that the increasing calcium ion concentration inside the fiber activates the myofibrils more and more strongly with succesive contractions, which is in accord with the belief that it is calcium ions that initiate the contractile process.

CONTRACTION OF SKELETAL MUSCLE IN THE BODY

The Motor Unit

Each motor neuron that leaves the spinal cord usually innervates many different muscle fibers, the number of fibers depending on the type of muscle. All the muscle fibers innervated by a single motor nerve fiber are called a *motor unit*. In general, those muscles which react very rapidly and whose control is very exact have very few muscle fibers (as few as 10 to 25 in ocular muscles) in each motor unit but have a large number of nerve fibers to each muscle. On the other hand, the slowly acting postural muscles, which do not require excessively fine degree of control, may have as many as 2000 to 3000 muscle fibers in each motor unit. An average figure for all the muscles of the body can be considered to be about 1500 muscle fibers to the motor unit.

The muscle fibers of a single motor unit usually lie reasonably close to each other, but not always exactly adjacent. They make up a mass in the muscle belly sometimes as large as one quarter of an inch in diameter, though at other times only a fraction of a millimeter in diameter. Usually muscle fibers of adjacent motor units overlap each other, with some of the fibers from one motor unit lying within the second motor unit and some of the fibers from both of these lying within still additional motor units. This interdigitation allows the separate motor units to contract in support of each other rather than as individual segments.

In the past it has been believed that each muscle fiber receives only one nerve ending. However, more recent studies have shown that two or more nerve endings exist on most muscle fibers, and these very frequently originate from different motor neurons. In other words, a single muscle fiber may be part of two and possibly even more different motor units. This multiple innervation protects the fiber against loss of function when part of a motor nerve is destroyed, and since these endings are usually far apart on the muscle fiber, it increases the rapidity of the muscle response to nerve stimuli.

Macro-motor Units. From the preceding chapter it will be recalled that loss of a large percentage of the nerve fibers to a muscle belly causes the remaining nerve fibers to sprout forth and innervate many of the paralyzed muscle fibers. When this occurs, such as following poliomyelitis, one occasionally develops *macro-motor units,* which can contain several times the normal number of muscle fibers. This obviously decreases the degree of control that one has over his muscles, but, nevertheless, allows the muscle to regain function.

Summation of Muscle Contraction

Summation means the adding together of individual muscle twitches to make strong

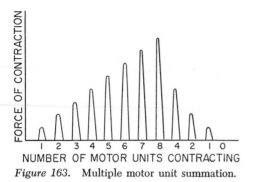

Figure 163. Multiple motor unit summation.

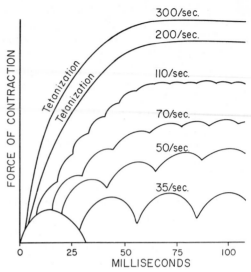

Figure 164. Wave summation and tetanization.

and concerted muscle movements. In general, summation occurs in 2 different ways: (1) by increasing the number of motor units contracting simultaneously and (2) by increasing the rapidity of contraction of individual motor units. These are called, respectively, *multiple motor unit summation* and *wave summation.*

Multiple Motor Unit Summation. Figure 163 illustrates multiple motor unit summation, showing that the force of contraction increases progressively as the number of contracting motor units increases from 1 to 8. This is comparable to spatial summation in a motor nerve. That is, as more and more muscle fibers are stimulated simultaneously, the greater becomes the strength of contraction.

Wave Summation. Figure 164 illustrates the principles of wave summation, showing in the lower left hand corner a single muscle twitch followed by successive muscle twitches at various frequencies. When the frequency is 35 per second, the first muscle twitch is not completely over by the time the second one begins. Therefore, since the muscle is already in a partially contracted state when the second twitch begins, the degree of muscle shortening this time is slightly greater than that which occurs with the single muscle twitch. The third, fourth, and additional twitches add still more shortening.

At more rapid rates of contraction, the degree of summation of successive contractions becomes greater and greater, because the successive contractions appear at earlier times following the preceding contraction.

Tetanization. When a muscle is stimulated at progressively greater rates, a frequency of stimulation is finally reached at which the successive contractions fuse together and cannot be distinguished one from the other. This state is called *tetanization,* and the lowest frequency at which it occurs is called the *critical frequency.*

Tetanization results from the viscous properties of muscle. That is, the muscle fibers themselves are actually filled with a viscous fluid, and the fibers in turn are encased in muscle sheaths and fasciae that resist change in length. Therefore, rapidly succeeding contractions will not allow sufficient muscle relaxation between contractions for the individual contractions to be observed. Therefore, the muscle remains in a continual state of contraction.

Once the critical frequency for tetanization is reached, further increase in rate of stimulation does not increase the force of contraction more than a few per cent. The reason for this is the following: By the time the critical frequency of each type of muscle has been reached, the contractile process is by then activated almost all the time; therefore, additional stimuli cannot increase the degree of activation a significant amount.

Asynchronous Summation of Motor Units. Actually it is rare for either multiple motor unit summation or wave summation to occur separately from the other in normal muscle function. Instead, special neurogenic mechanisms in the spinal cord normally increase both the impulse rate and the number of motor units firing at the same time. If a motor unit fires at all, it usually fires at least 5 times per second, but this can increase up to as high as 100 or more times per second in fast muscles and 30 to 50 times per second in slow muscles—always to frequencies sufficient to cause complete tetanization.

Yet, even when tetanization of individual motor units of a muscle is not occurring, the tension exerted by the whole muscle is still continuous and non-jerky because *the different motor units fire asynchronously.* That is, while one is contracting another is relaxing; then another fires, followed by still another, and so forth. Consequently, even when motor units fire as infrequently as 5 times per second, the muscle contraction, though weak, will nevertheless be very smooth.

Gradation of Contraction. *Gradation of contraction* means the different degrees of force that can be exerted by a muscle. Ordinarily, the gradation of contraction of almost any muscle of the body is almost infinite. A muscle contraction can be almost infinitesimal, then slightly stronger, then still slightly stronger, increasing in very small increments up to maximal contraction. That is, nervous control of a muscle can be so well graded by the neuronal circuits in the spinal cord that almost any degree of contraction can be called forth from a muscle. However, the rapidly acting muscles such as the ocular muscles and finger muscles can be controlled even more critically than can the slow postural muscles because of fewer fibers in the motor units and because of their more rapidly acting muscle fibers. Therefore, it is said that the ocular and finger muscles have better gradation of contraction than do the postural muscles.

Relation of Muscle Length to Force of Contraction

If a muscle is already shortened before it is stimulated to contract, the force that will be exerted between its two ends will be less than normal. On the other hand, if a muscle is overly stretched prior to contraction, the force exerted by the contraction will also be less than normal. Figure 165 shows these effects, illustrating that maximum force of contraction occurs when the muscle length is approximately normal, and either preliminary shortening of the muscle or preliminary stretching is harmful to the contractile process.

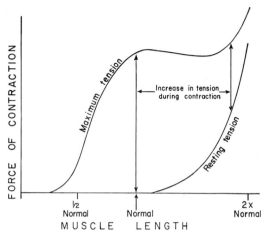

Figure 165. Relation of muscle length to force of contraction.

Accommodation of Muscle Length to the Length of the Lever System—Physical Contracture. If a bone is broken and then heals in a shortened state, the force of contraction of the muscles lying along this broken bone would obviously become decreased because of the shortened lengths of muscles. However, muscles shortened in this manner undergo *physical contracture* during the next few weeks. That is, the muscle fibers actually shorten and reestablish new muscle lengths approximately equal to the maximum length of the lever system itself, thus reestablishing optimum force of contraction by the muscles.

The same shortening process also occurs in muscles of limbs immobilized for several weeks in casts if the muscles during this time are in a shortened position. When the cast is removed, the muscles must often be restretched over a period of weeks before full mobility is restored.

Maximum Strength of Contraction. The maximum strength of tetanic contraction of a muscle operating at normal muscle length is about 3 kilograms per square centimeter of muscle or 42 pounds per square inch. Since a quadriceps muscle can at times have as much as 16 square inches of muscle belly, as much as 600 to 700 pounds of tension may at times be applied to the patellar tendon. One can quite readily understand, therefore, how it is possible for muscles sometimes to pull their tendons out of the insertions in bones. This often occurs where the patellar tendon inserts in the tibia and even more frequently where the achilles tendon of the gastrocnemius muscle inserts at the heel.

Relation of Velocity of Contraction to Load

Contraction of a muscle may occur very rapidly when it is contracting against no load—as rapidly as 10 times its own length in one second. However, when loads are applied, the velocity of contraction becomes progressively less as the load increases, and when the load equals the maximum isometric force of contraction of a muscle, then the velocity of contraction becomes zero and no contraction at all results. Figure 166 illustrates this relationship, showing progressive diminution in velocity with increasing load.

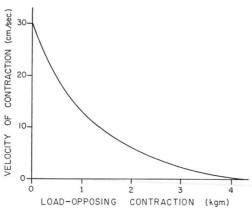

Figure 166. Relation of load to velocity of contraction in a skeletal muscle eight centimeters long.

This decreasing velocity with increasing load is partially explained by the viscous properties of the muscle fiber itself. However, the effect seems to be associated even more with the rate at which energy can be released from adenosine triphosphate to the contractile elements of the muscle. That is, to contract against a load the muscle must perform work, and to do this it must also obtain the required amount of energy. Since muscle can remove energy from adenosine triphosphate at only a certain rate, then the greater the load the less, presumably, must be the velocity of movement while the muscle obtains the required amount of energy.

Skeletal Muscle Tone

Even when muscles are at rest, a certain amount of tautness usually remains, and the degree of this tautness varies from time to time and from person to person. This resid-

ual degree of contraction in skeletal muscle is called *muscle tone*. Since skeletal muscle fibers are not known to contract without an actual action potential to stimulate the fiber, it is believed that skeletal muscle tone results entirely from muscle action potentials. A few spontaneous impulses arise in individual muscle fibers without any nerve excitation, and it is possible that impulses of this type might be partly responsible for basal skeletal muscle tone. However, most skeletal muscle tone is caused by nerve impulses coming from the spinal cord. These in turn are controlled partly by impulses transmitted from the brain to the appropriate anterior motor neurons and partly by impulses that originate in *muscle spindles* located in the muscle itself. Muscle spindles are sensory receptors that exist throughout essentially all skeletal muscles to detect the degree of muscle contraction. They will be discussed in detail in Chapter 50, but, briefly, they transmit impulses almost continually through the posterior roots into the spinal cord, where they excite the anterior motor neurons. Simply cutting the posterior roots, thereby blocking the muscle spindle impulses, will usually reduce muscle tone to such a low level that the muscle becomes almost completely flaccid. Still many other neurogenic factors that enter into the control of muscle tone will be discussed in detail in relation to muscle spindle and spinal cord function in Chapters 50 and 56.

Muscle Fatigue

Prolonged and strong contraction of a muscle leads to the well-known state of muscle *fatigue*. This results from an inability of the contractile and metabolic processes of the muscle fibers to continue supplying the same work output. The nerve continues to function properly, the nerve impulses pass normally through the neuromuscular junction into the muscle fiber, and even normal potentials spread over the muscle fibers, but the contraction becomes weaker and weaker.

Interruption of blood flow through a muscle leads to very severe muscle fatigue in a minute or more because of the obvious loss of nutrient supply.

Physiological Contracture. If a muscle becomes fatigued to an extreme extent, it is likely to become continually contracted, re-

hormone, growth hormone, and even insulin. Unfortunately, the precise means by which each of these factors affects smooth muscle contraction has not been adequately studied, though it is well known that the contractile state of smooth muscle does vary tremendously in different metabolic states.

Excitation of Smooth Muscle by Nerve Impulses. Smooth muscle in almost all areas of the body is innervated by either the sympathetic or the parasympathetic nervous system and often by both. Any smooth muscle fiber usually responds exactly oppositely to sympathetic stimulation as it does to parasympathetic stimulation. A large proportion of the smooth muscle fibers contract when excited by sympathetic stimulation, while these same fibers relax when excited by parasympathetic stimulation. In other organs the smooth muscle fibers respond exactly oppositely; that is, they contract when stimulated by the parasympathetics but relax when stimulated by the sympathetics. It is believed that these opposite reactions are caused by the presence or absence of specific receptor substances in the membranes of the muscle cells, though their exact nature is yet unknown. This reciprocal relationship will be discussed further in the following chapter on the autonomic nervous system.

Excitation of smooth muscle by nerve stimuli can cause either an increase or decrease in tonic contraction or rhythmic contraction or both simultaneously. If the chemical mediator liberated at the nerve endings is sufficient only to reduce the membrane potential, a tonic contraction presumably will occur. However, if the mediator is liberated in sufficient quantities to cause an action potential, a rhythmic contraction that spreads through the muscle mass presumably will result.

Plasticity of Smooth Muscle

A very important characteristic of smooth muscle is its ability to change length greatly when the change occurs slowly, with very little change in force of tonic contraction. This phenomenon has been called *plasticity* of smooth muscle or *stress-relaxation*. If a segment of smooth muscle one inch long is suddenly stretched to two inches, the tension between the two ends of the muscle will increase instantaneously, but the extra tension begins to disappear immediately, and within a minute or more the tension will have returned almost to the value prior to the stretch. Thus, after the adaptative process is over, the smooth muscle still will not have increased its tension very much despite the elongation. The converse occurs when the muscle is shortened, the tension at first decreasing but rising almost back to the control value within another few minutes.

If we apply this same principle to hollow organs, when an organ is in a contracted state a certain amount of pressure will be exerted against the internal contents. But when the organ fills to a greater degree, if this filling occurs slowly, the pressure remains almost constant despite the enlarged size. Thus, this plasticity characteristic of smooth muscle allows a hollow viscus to "accommodate" either small or large amounts of material without greatly altering the internal pressure.

REFERENCES

Alexander, R. S.: Immediate effects of stretch on muscle contractility. Am. J. Physiol., 196:807, 1959.

Bourne, G. H.: (ed.): The Structure and Function of Muscle. 3 Volumes. New York, Academic Press, 1960.

Bozler, E.: The effect of polyphosphates and magnesium on the mechanical properties of extracted muscle fibers. J. Gen. Physiol., 39:789, 1956.

Burnstock, G., and Prosser, C. L.: Responses of smooth muscles to quick stretch; relation of stretch to conduction. Am. J. Physiol., 198:921, 1960.

Coers, C., and Woolf, A. L.: The Innervation of Muscle. Springfield, Illinois, Charles C Thomas, 1959.

Ederstrom, H. E., Vergeer, T., Rohde, R. A., and Ahlness, P.: Quantitative changes in foot blood flow in the dog following sympathectomy and motor denervation. Am. J. Physiol., 187:461, 1956.

Feigen, G. A.: Muscle. Ann. Rev. Physiol., 18:89. 1956.

Gelfan, S.: Muscle. Ann. Rev. Physiol., 20:67, 1958.

Gerard, R. W., and Taylor, R. E.: Muscle and nerve; physiological orientation. Am. J. Med., 15:83, 1953.

Gilson, A. S., Jr.: Twitch summation in genesis of isometric tetanus of skeletal muscle. Am. J. Physiol., 170:363, 1952.

Guyton, A. C.: Reaction of the body to poliomyelitis and the recovery process. Arch. Int. Med., 83:27–47, 1949.

Guyton, A. C., and Reeder, R. C.: Pain and contracture in poliomyelitis. Arch. Neurol. & Psychiat., 63:954–963, 1950.

Hill, A. L., and others: Physiology of voluntary muscle. British Medical Bulletin, 12:1956 (Sept.).

Hill, A. V.: The heat of shortening and the dynamic constants of muscle. Proc. Roy. Soc., 126:136, 1938.

Hill, A. V.: The heat production of muscle and nerve, 1848–1914. *Ann. Rev. Physiol., 21:*1, 1959.

Hines, H. M., and Thomson, J. D.: Changes in muscle and nerve following motor neuron denervation. *Am. J. Phys. Med., 35:*35, 1956.

Hober, R.: Physical Chemistry of Cells and Tissues. Philadelphia, Blakiston, 1945.

Hodes, R.: The innervation of skeletal muscle. *Ann. Rev. Physiol., 15:*139, 1953.

Huxley, H. E.: The contraction of muscle. *Scient. Am., 199:*67, 1958.

Kao, C. Y.: Long-term observations of spontaneous electrical activity of the uterine smooth muscle. *Am. J. Physiol., 196:*343, 1959.

Karpovich, P. V.: Physiology of Muscular Activity. 4th ed., Philadelphia, W. B. Saunders Co., 1953.

Kranz, L. G.: Kinesiology Manual. 3rd ed., St. Louis, C. V. Mosby Co., 1956.

Leonard, E., and Sarnoff, S. J.: Effect of aramine-induced smooth muscle contraction on length-tension diagrams of venous strips. *Circ. Res., 5:*169, 1957.

Lind, A. R.: Muscle fatigue and recovery from fatigue induced by sustained contractions. *J. Physiol., 147:*162, 1959.

Morales, M. F., Botts, J., Blum, J. J., and Hill, T. L.: Elementary processes in muscle action: an examination of current concepts. *Physiol. Rev., 35:*475, 1955.

Nachmansohn, D. (ed.): Molecular Biology. (Elementary Processes of Nerve Conduction and Muscle Contraction.) New York, Academic Press, 1960.

Prosser, C. L., Smith, C. E., and Melton, C. E.: Conduction of action potentials in the ureter of the rat. *Am. J. Physiol., 181:*651, 1955.

Ramsey, R. W.: Analysis of contraction of skeletal muscle. *Am. J. Physiol., 181:*688, 1955.

Remington, J. W. (ed.): Tissue Elasticity. Am. Physiol. Soc., 1957.

Remington, J. W., and Alexander, R. S.: Relation of tissue extensibility to smooth muscle tone. *Am. J. Physiol., 185:*302, 1956.

Sleator, W., Jr., and Butcher, H. R., Jr.: Action potentials and pressure changes in ureteral peristaltic waves. *Am. J. Physiol., 180:*261, 1955.

Steindler, A.: Kinesiology. Springfield, Illinois, Charles C Thomas, 1955.

Sten-Knudsen, O.: Is muscle contraction initiated by internal current flow? *J. Physiol., 151:*363, 1960.

Sutfin, D. C., Thomson, J. D., and Hines, H. M.: Kinetics of denervation atrophy in the skeletal muscle of the rat. *Am. J. Physiol., 179:*535, 1954.

Taylor, C. L.: The biomechanics of control in upper-extremity prostheses. *Artificial Limbs, 2:*4, 1955.

Thomson, J. D.: Stress-relaxation in mammalian gastrocnemius muscle. *Am. J. Physiol., 196:*1088, 1959.

Wakim, K. G., and Krusen, F. H.: Comparison of effects of electric stimulation with effects of intermittent compression on the work output and endurance of denervated muscle. *Arch. Phys. Med., 38:*21, 1957.

Weber, H. H.: The biochemistry of muscle. *Ann. Rev. Biochem., 26:*667, 1957.

Woodbury, J. W., and McIntyre, D. M.: Transmembranal action potentials from pregnant uterus. *Am. J. Physiol., 187:*338, 1956.

See also Chapter 17, Membrane potentials; Chapter 18, Neuromuscular junction; Chapter 68, Energetics.

Chapter 20

The Autonomic Nervous System

The portion of the nervous system that controls the visceral functions of the body is called the *autonomic nervous system*. This system helps to control arterial pressure, gastrointestinal motility and secretion, urinary output, sweating, body temperature, and many other bodily activities, some of which are controlled almost entirely by the autonomic nervous system and some of which are controlled only partially.

GENERAL ORGANIZATION OF THE AUTONOMIC NERVOUS SYSTEM

The autonomic nervous system is activated mainly by centers located in the *spinal cord,* the *brain stem,* and the *hypothalamus.* However, even portions of the cerebral cortex can transmit impulses to the lower centers and in this way effect autonomic control. Often the autonomic nervous system operates by means of *visceral reflexes.* That is, sensory signals from appropriate parts of the body send impulses into the centers of the cord, brain stem, or hypothalamus, and these in turn transmit appropriate reflex responses back to the visceral organs to control their activities.

The autonomic impulses are transmitted to the body through two major subdivisions called respectively the *sympathetic* and *parasympathetic systems,* the characteristics and functions of which follow.

Physiologic Anatomy of the Sympathetic Nervous System

Figure 171 illustrates the general organization of the sympathetic nervous system, showing one of the two *sympathetic chains* on the side of the spinal column and nerves extending to the different internal organs. The sympathetic nerves originate in the spinal cord between the segments T-1

and L-2. They begin in the *sympathetic motor neurons* of the *intermediolateral horns* of the spinal gray mattter. No sympathetic nerves originate in the neck segments of the cord nor in the lumbar and sacral segments below L-2, but nerve fibers travel upward or downward from the sympathetic chains to supply the head and leg regions, as will be explained below.

Preganglionic and Postganglionic Sympathetic Neurons. The sympathetic nerves are different from skeletal motor nerves in the following way: Each motor fiber to a skeletal

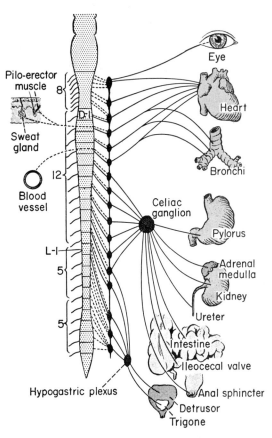

Figure 171. Anatomy of the sympathetic nervous system.

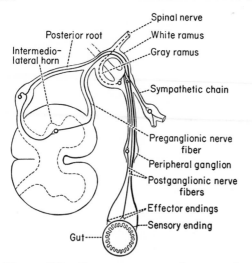

Figure 172. Nerve connections between the spinal cord, the sympathetic chain, the spinal nerves, and the peripheral sympathetic nerves.

muscle is composed of a single fiber originating in the cord. Each sympathetic pathway is composed of a *preganglionic neuron* and a *postganglionic neuron*. The cell body of the preganglionic neuron lies in the spinal cord, and its fiber passes, as illustrated in Figure 172, through an *anterior root* of the cord into a *spinal nerve* and finally through the *white ramus* from the spinal nerve to the *sympathetic chain*. Here the fiber either synapses with postganglionic neurons in the *sympathetic ganglia* or often passes on through the chain into one of its radiating nerves to synapse with postganglionic neurons in one of the outlying sympathetic ganglia. The fiber of each postganglionic neuron then travels through an additional nerve to its destination in one of the organs.

Sympathetic Nerve Fibers in the Skeletal Nerves. Many of the fibers from the postganglionic neurons in the sympathetic chain pass back into the spinal nerves through *gray rami* at all levels of the cord. These pathways are made up of type C fibers that extend throughout the entire body in the skeletal nerves to control the blood vessels, the sweat glands, and the piloerector muscles of the hairs. Approximately 8 per cent of the fibers in the average skeletal nerve are sympathetic fibers, a fact that indicates their importance.

A few of the preganglionic neurons do not pass first into the sympathetic chain but instead enter the spinal nerves directly from the spinal cord and synapse with postganglionic neurons located in the spinal nerves themselves. Therefore, destruction of the sympathetic chain does not remove all sympathetic activity, though it does remove at least 90 per cent of it.

Segmental Distribution of Sympathetic Nerves. The sympathetic pathways originating in the different segments of the spinal cord are not necessarily distributed to the same part of the body as the somatic nerve fibers from the same segments. Instead, *the sympathetic fibers from T-1 generally pass up the sympathetic chain into the head, from T-2 into the neck, T-3, T-4, T-5 and T-6 into the thorax, T-7, T-8, T-9, T-10 and T-11 into the abdomen, T-12, L-1 and L-2 into the legs.* This distribution is only approximate and has a tremendous amount of overlap.

The distribution of sympathetic nerves to each organ is determined by the position in the embryo at which the organ originates. For instance, the heart receives many sympathetic nerves from the neck portion of the sympathetic chain, because it is in the neck that the heart originates in the embryo. Likewise, the abdominal organs receive their sympathetic innervation from the lower thoracic segments because the primitive gut originates in the lower thoracic area.

Special Nature of the Sympathetic Nerve Endings in the Adrenal Medullae. Preganglionic sympathetic nerve fibers pass all the way from the intermediolateral horn cells of the spinal cord, through the sympathetic chains, through the splanchnic nerves, and finally into the adrenal medullae. There they end directly on special cells that secrete nor-epinephrine and epinephrine. These secretory cells are embryologically derived from nervous tissue and are analogous to postganglionic neurons; indeed, they even have rudimentary nerve fibers.

Control of the Sympathetics by the Central Nervous System. Figure 173 illustrates the location of different centers in the brain stem and hypothalamus for control of different visceral functions. These centers receive impulses from other parts of the brain and also from sensory nerve fibers originating in all parts of the body. In turn they transmit impulses to the intermediolateral horn cells through tracts that lie anterolaterally in the spinal cord. The interrelationships of the different autonomic centers with each other and with other functional areas of the brain will be discussed in numerous chapters throughout the text, especially Chapter 60. For the present suffice it to say that these centers are

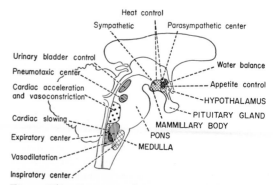

Figure 173. Parasympathetic and sympathetic centers in the brain stem and hypothalamus.

heart and by resistance to flow of this blood through the vascular system. In general, sympathetic stimulation increases both propulsion by the heart and resistance to flow, which can cause the pressure to increase very greatly.

On the other hand, parasympathetic stimulation decreases the pumping effectiveness of the heart, which lowers the pressure a moderate amount, though not nearly so much as the sympathetics can increase the pressure.

Effects of Sympathetic and Parasympathetic Stimulation on Other Functions of the Body. Because of the great importance of the sympathetic and parasympathetic control systems, these will be discussed many times in this text in relation to a myriad of body functions that will not be considered in detail at the present time. In general, most of the endodermal structures, such as the ducts of the liver, the gallbladder, the ureter, and the bladder, are inhibited by sympathetic stimulation but excited by parasympathetic stimulation. Sympathetic stimulation also has metabolic effects, causing the release of glucose from the liver, increase in the blood glucose concentration, increase in basal metabolic rate, and an increase in mental activity. Finally, the sympathetics and parasympathetics are involved in regulating the male and female sexual acts, as will be explained in Chapters 78 and 79.

Function of the Adrenal Medullae

Stimulation of the sympathetic nerves to the adrenal medullae causes large quantities of both nor-epinephrine and epinephrine to be released into the circulating blood, and these two hormones in turn are carried in the blood to all tissues of the body. On the average, approximately 25 per cent of the secretion is nor-epinephrine and 75 per cent epinephrine, though the relative proportions of these change considerably under different physiological conditions.

The circulating nor-epinephrine has almost the same effects on the different organs as those caused by direct sympathetic stimulation. For instance, nor-epinephrine causes vasoconstriction of essentially all the blood vessels of the body; it causes increased activity of the heart, inhibition of the gastrointestinal tract, dilatation of the pupil of the eye, and so forth.

Epinephrine, also, causes almost the same effects as those caused by nor-epinephrine, but the effects differ in the following respects: First, epinephrine has a greater effect on cardiac activity than nor-epinephrine. Second, epinephrine causes only weak constriction of the blood vessels of the muscles in comparison to a much stronger constriction that results from nor-epinephrine. Since the muscle vessels represent about half of all the vessels of the body, this difference is of special importance because nor-epinephrine greatly increases the total peripheral resistance and thereby elevates the arterial pressure a corresponding amount, while epinephrine raises the arterial pressure to a much less extent but increases the cardiac output considerably because of its effect on the heart.

A third major difference between the action of epinephrine and nor-epinephrine relates to their effects on tissue metabolism. Epinephrine has about 10 times as great a metabolic effect as nor-epinephrine. That is, epinephrine increases the metabolic rate of the body, often to as much as 150 per cent above normal, in this way increasing the activity and excitability of the whole body. It also enhances other metabolic activities such as the rate of glycogenolysis in the liver and the rate at which glucose is released into the blood.

In summary, stimulation of the adrenal medullae causes the release of hormones that have almost the same effects throughout the body as direct sympathetic stimulation. The only significant differences are caused by the epinephrine in the secretion, which increases the rate of metabolism and cardiac output to a greater extent than is caused by direct sympathetic stimulation.

"Alpha" and "Beta" Adrenergic Receptors. To explain the differences in action of nor-epinephrine and epinephrine on different sympathetic effector organs, it has been postulated that two different types of receptor substances exist in the membranes of different effector cells, one called *alpha receptor substance* and the other *beta receptor substance. Supposedly, nor-epinephrine can affect only those effector cells that contain the alpha receptor, while epinephrine can affect both.* Table 13 gives the postulated distribution of alpha and beta receptors in organs that are controlled by the sympathetics. It must

Table 13. Relationships of Adrenergic Receptors to Function

Alpha Receptor	Beta Receptor
Vasoconstriction	Vasodilation (muscle)
Cardioacceleration	Cardioacceleration
Increased myocardial strength	Increased myocardial strength
Iris dilatation	Myometrial relaxation
Intestinal relaxation	Bronchial relaxation
Pilomotor contraction	
Glycogenolysis	

be noted that certain alpha functions are excitatory while others are inhibitory. Likewise, certain beta functions are excitatory and others inhibitory. Therefore, alpha and beta receptors are not necessarily associated with excitation or inhibition but simply with the affinity of the hormone for the effector organ.

Another hormone closely similar to epinephrine and nor-epinephrine, *isopropyl nor-epinephrine*, has an extremely strong action on beta functions but almost no action on alpha functions. Furthermore, small amounts of this third hormone have been reported to be present in the adrenal medullae and possibly are secreted into the blood along with nor-epinephrine and epinephrine.

Unfortunately, the alpha and beta receptor concept has not been able to explain all the differences between the actions of the different sympathomimetic hormones. Therefore, it is probably best for the present simply to recognize that each respective organ reacts slightly differently to nor-epinephrine, epinephrine, isopropyl nor-epinephrine, and other similar compounds.

Value of the Adrenal Medullae to the Function of the Sympathetic Nervous System. Usually, when any part of the sympathetic nervous system is stimulated the entire system or at least major portions of it are stimulated at the same time. Therefore, nor-epinephrine and epinephrine are almost always released by the adrenal medullae at the same time that the different organs are being stimulated directly by the sympathetic nerves. Therefore, the organs are actually stimulated in two different ways simultaneously, directly and indirectly, by the medullary hormones. The two means of stimulation support each other, and either one of the two can actually substitute for the other. For instance, destruction of the direct sympathetic pathways to the organs does not abrogate excitation of the organs, because nor-epinephrine and epinephrine are still released

into the circulating fluids and indirectly cause stimulation. Likewise, total loss of the two adrenal medullae usually has very little significant effect on the operation of the sympathetic nervous system because the direct pathways can still perform almost all the necessary duties. In summary, the dual mechanism of sympathetic stimulation provides a safety factor, one mechanism being able to substitute for the other when the second is missing.

Another important value of the adrenal medullae is the capability of nor-epinephrine and epinephrine to stimulate structures of the body that are not innervated by direct sympathetic fibers. For instance, the metabolic rate of every cell of the body is increased by these hormones, especially by epinephrine, even though only a small proportion of all the cells in the body are innervated by sympathetic fibers. Therefore, one of the especially important functions of the adrenal medullae is their role in increasing the activity of cells not directly stimulated by the sympathetics.

Change in the ratio of nor-epinephrine and epinephrine secretions under special conditions. Recent experiments indicate that epinephrine and nor-epinephrine might be secreted by two different types of cells in the adrenal medullae. Furthermore, certain types of stimulation of the sympathetic nervous system, such as that which occurs following insulin hypoglycemia, seems to result in a greatly increased ratio of epinephrine to nor-epinephrine secretion. This effect supposedly provides the extra amounts of epinephrine needed to cause release of glucose from the liver into the blood stream. Yet, reflexes associated with pain are believed to increase the ratio of nor-epinephrine to epinephrine, the nor-epinephrine supposedly elevating the arterial pressure much more than would be caused by epinephrine. This differential secretion of the two hormones is not yet proved, though one can readily understand how such a functional difference could be of great value to the body.

Relationship of Number of Stimuli to the Degree of the Sympathetic and Parasympathetic Activity

A special difference between the autonomic nervous system and the skeletal nervous system is the very low frequency of stimulation required for full activation of the autonomic system. In general, only one impulse every few seconds suffices to maintain normal sympathetic or parasympathetic tone, and full activation occurs when the nerve fibers are stimulated 10 to 20 times per second. This compares with full activation in the skeletal nervous system at about 100 to 250 impulses per second.

Sympathetic and Parasympathetic "Tone"

The sympathetic and parasympathetic systems are continually active, and this basal rate of activity is known respectively as *sympathetic tone* and *parasympathetic tone.*

The value of tone is that it allows a single nervous system both to increase and decrease the activity of a stimulated organ. For instance, sympathetic tone normally keeps almost all the blood vessels of the body constricted to approximately one-half their maximum diameter. By increasing the degree of sympathetic stimulation the vessels can be constricted even more, but, on the other hand, by inhibiting the normal tone the vessels can be dilated. If it were not for the continual sympathetic tone, the sympathetic system could only cause vasoconstriction but could never cause vasodilatation.

Figure 175 illustrates the effect of tone on the heart rate. The normal heart rate of the animal represented by this experiment was approximately 130 beats per minute. Then the sympathetic fibers to the heart were suddenly cut, thereby removing the sympa-

thetic tone. This caused the heart rate to fall to 122 beats per minute. Then the parasympathetics were cut, and the loss of parasympathetic tone allowed the heart rate to return to approximately the original value. From this experiment it is obvious that sympathetic and parasympathetic tone both are normally active on the heart.

Another interesting example of tone is that of the parasympathetics in the gastrointestinal tract. Surgical removal of the parasympathetics can cause very serious and prolonged gastric and intestinal "atony," thus illustrating that in normal function the parasympathetic tone to the gut is very strong. This tone can be decreased by the brain, thereby inhibiting gastrointestinal motility, or, on the other hand, it can be increased, thereby promoting increased gastrointestinal activity.

Tone caused by basal secretion of nor-epinephrine and epinephrine by the adrenal medullae. The normal resting rate of secretion by the adrenal medullae is about 0.2 μgm./kgm./min. of nor-epinephrine and about 0.07 μgm./kgm./min. of epinephrine. These quantities are quite considerable—indeed, enough to maintain the blood pressure almost up to the normal value even though all direct sympathetic pathways to the cardiovascular system should be removed. Therefore, it is obvious that much of the overall tone of the sympathetic nervous system results from basal secretion of nor-epinephrine and epinephrine in addition to that which results from direct sympathetic stimulation.

Effect of loss of sympathetic or parasympathetic tone following denervation. Immediately after a sympathetic or parasympathetic nerve is cut, the innervated organ loses its sympathetic or parasympathetic tone. In the case of the blood vessels, for instance, cutting the sympathetic nerves results immediately in almost maximal vasodilatation of the vessels. However, over a period of several days or weeks, the *intrinsic tone* in the smooth muscle of the vessels increases, usually restoring almost normal vasoconstriction.

Essentially the same events occur in any organ whenever sympathetic or parasympathetic tone is lost. That is, compensation soon develops to return the function of the organ almost to its normal basal level.

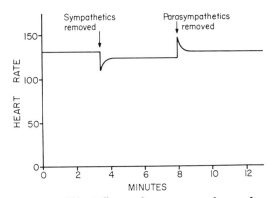

Figure 175. Effects of transecting the cardiac sympathetic and the parasympathetic nerves on the heart rate, illustrating the existence of tone in both systems.

Part of this compensation results from the phenomenon of sensitization which will be described below.

"Sensitization" of Sympathetic and Parasympathetic Organs Following Denervation

During the first week or so after a sympathetic or parasympathetic nerve is destroyed, the innervated organ becomes more and more sensitive to injected nor-epinephrine or acetylcholine, respectively. This effect is illustrated in Figure 176; the blood flow in the forearm before removal of the sympathetics was 200 ml. per minute, and a test dose of nor-epinephrine caused only a slight depression in flow. Then the stellate ganglion was removed, and normal sympathetic tone was lost. At first, the blood flow rose markedly because of the lost vascular tone, but over a period of days to weeks the blood flow returned almost to normal because of progressive increase in intrinsic tone of the vascular musculature itself, thus compensating for the loss of sympathetic tone. Another test dose of nor-epinephrine was then administered and the blood flow decreased tremendously, illustrating that the blood vessels had become some 10 times as responsive to nor-epinephrine as previously. This phenomenon is called *sensitization.*

Sensitization occurs to a very great extent when the postganglionic neurons are removed, but to less extent when the preganglionic neurons are removed. The reason for this seems to be continued slow firing of the postganglionic neurons even when they are

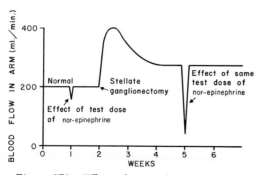

Figure 176. Effect of sympathectomy on blood flow in the arm, and the effect of a test dose of nor-epinephrine before and after sympathectomy, showing sensitization of the vasculature to nor-epinephrine.

not supplied by preganglionic fibers. That is, continued secretion of adrenergic or cholinergic substances at the nerve endings keeps the effector organs from becoming sensitized, but, whenever these substances are no longer secreted, sensitization begins to develop.

The Mechanism of Sensitization. The precise means by which sensitization develops is not known, though several suggestions have been made. First, it has been suggested that prolonged lack of nerve stimulation allows the quantity of "receptor substances" in the membranes of the effector cells to increase, thereby increasing the responsiveness of the cells to the circulating nor-epinephrine and epinephrine. A second suggestion has been that effector cells, when stimulated repetitively by the nerves, build up resistance to the neurohumors. Therefore, prolonged lack of stimulation could allow the effector cells to lose even their normal resistance, thus resulting in sensitization. Possible causes of this resistance are an increase in cell membrane thickness, reduction in active enzymes of the cell membrane or internal structures of the cell, or so forth.

AUTONOMIC REFLEXES

It is mainly by means of *autonomic reflexes* that the autonomic nervous system regulates visceral functions. Throughout this text the function of different ones of these reflexes will be discussed in detail in relation to individual organs, but, to illustrate their importance, a few of them are presented here briefly.

Cardiovascular Autonomic Reflexes. Several reflexes in the cardiovascular system help to control the arterial blood pressure, cardiac output, and heart rate. One of these is the so-called *pressoreceptor reflex.* Stretch receptors called *pressoreceptors* are located in the walls of the major arteries, including the carotid arteries and the aorta. When these become overstretched by high pressure, impulses are transmitted to the brain stem, where they inhibit the sympathetic centers. This results in decreased sympathetic impulses to the heart and blood vessels, which allows the arterial pressure to fall back toward normal. This reflex and other cardiovascular reflexes will be discussed in Chapter 32.

of the entire action potential to about 0.3 seconds in the ventricles and about 0.15 seconds in the atria.

The resting membrane potential of cardiac muscle is approximately 80 to 85 millivolts in atrial and ventricular muscle and approximately 90 to 100 millivolts in Purkinje fibers but only 50 to 60 millivolts in the S-A node. This low resting potential of the S-A node is characteristic of spontaneously discharging fibers such as those found in this node.

The action potential recorded in cardiac muscle is usually about 105 millivolts, which means that there is a *reversal potential,* or "overshoot," beyond the resting potential of about 20 millivolts. These relationships between resting potential, action potential, and reversal potential are all illustrated in Figure 179, and the basic principles of their genesis were discussed in Chapter 17.

Velocity of Conduction of the Cardiac Impulse. The velocity of conduction of the action potential in both atrial and ventricular muscle fibers is about 0.3 meter per second, which is 300 times slower than the velocity in very large nerve fibers and about 10 times slower than in skeletal muscle fibers.

Purkinje fibers, on the other hand, conduct impulses three to seven times as rapidly as the contractile cardiac muscle, i.e., 1 to 3 meters per second. This more rapid conductivity of the Purkinje fibers allows the action potential to be distributed throughout the ventricles much more rapidly than could possibly occur by muscle conduction alone.

Finally, the velocity of conduction in the A-V *junctional fibers* is only 0.03 meter per second, which is important in allowing the delay between atrial and ventricular contraction, which was discussed above.

Duration of Contraction. When an action potential occurs in cardiac muscle, the muscle continues to contract as long as the membrane remains depolarized, presumably because of continued influx of calcium ions during this entire period of time. The calcium ions are believed to keep the actomyosin complex in a contracted state. Thus, the duration of contraction of atrial muscle is about 0.15 second and of ventricular muscle about 0.3 second. This prolonged contraction is essential to the function of the heart as a pump, for it allows time for the heart chambers to empty most of their blood with each contraction.

Effect of heart rate on duration of contraction. When the heart rate is increased, the duration of the action potential and the duration of contraction decreases almost as much as the rate increases. Therefore, the ratio of contractile period (systole) to the period of relaxation (diastole) remains nearly constant. This decrease in systole prevents fast heart rates from keeping the heart contracted all the time and, therefore, allows adequate filling of the heart during diastole even when the heart rate is increased to as much as two and one-half times normal.

Refractory Period of Cardiac Muscle. Cardiac muscle, like skeletal muscle, is "refractory" to restimulation for a short period of time after it has been excited. With extremely strong electrical stimuli it can sometimes be restimulated only a few milliseconds later. However, the normal cardiac impulse does not have the extreme stimulatory power of a high voltage electrical stimulus. Therefore, the refractory period of the heart is usually stated in terms of the *functional refractory period,* which is the interval of time in which an action potential from another part of the heart will fail to reexcite an already excited area of cardiac muscle. The normal functional refractory period of the ventricles is approximately 0.25 second, and there is an additional *relative refractory period* of about 0.05 second during which the muscle is more difficult than normal to excite but nevertheless can be excited.

The All or Nothing Principle as Applied to the Heart. Each cardiac muscle fiber responds to an electrical stimulus in much the same manner as a skeletal muscle fiber. If the electrical stimulus is strong enough to stimulate any single part of the fiber, the impulse will spread in all directions. However, if the stimulus is too weak to stimulate even a single portion of the fiber, then no action potential will occur at all. In other words, cardiac muscle fibers obey the all or nothing principle exactly as do skeletal muscle fibers and nerve fibers.

However, the heart is composed of two major syncytiums, the atrial and ventricular syncytiums, and the cellular membranes of all fibers in each syncytium connect with the membranes of all the other fibers. Therefore, a stimulus strong enough to stimulate any single fiber stimulates the entire respective syncytium, and, if the excitation

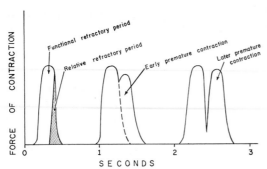

Figure 180. Contraction of the heart, showing: (1) the durations of the functional refractory period and the relative refractory period, (2) the effect of an early premature contraction, and (3) the effect of a later premature contraction. Note that the premature contractions do not cause wave summation as occurs in skeletal muscle.

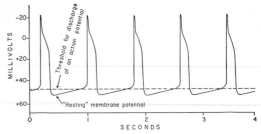

Figure 181. Rhythmical discharge of an S-A nodal fiber.

originates in the atria, it usually spreads also into the ventricles.

Lack of Summation in Cardiac Muscle. The action potential of cardiac muscle usually lasts so long that the muscle fibers have plenty of time to contract maximally every time they are stimulated. This is different from skeletal muscle fibers whose action potentials last only about 0.005 second. Because as much as 0.03 second may be required for development of maximum tension, skeletal muscle fibers usually become only partially contracted before the action potential is over, and many rapidly succeeding impulses are usually needed to produce complete contraction. This is called wave summation. In cardiac muscle even a single action potential lasts long enough to cause complete contraction. Therefore, even when action potentials are initiated in cardiac muscle, one rapidly succeeding the other, no summation results. This lack of summation, illustrated in Figure 180, is quite different from the wave summation that occurs in skeletal muscle. Indeed, as shown in the figure, the second contraction is often depressed because of lack of time to recover from the previous contraction.

RHYTHMICAL EXCITATION OF THE HEART

Rhythmicity of Cardiac Muscle

Cardiac muscle, unlike skeletal muscle but like most smooth muscle, undergoes continuous rhythmical contraction. The precise cause of this rhythmicity has not been determined, though it is believed to result from greater membrane permeability of cardiac muscle than of skeletal muscle, which results in continual leakage of sodium ions inward through the membrane. This in turn causes a continual tendency for the resting membrane potential to decrease. When it decreases beyond a critical threshold value, an action potential begins, spontaneously exciting the entire muscle mass.

Figure 181 illustrates a typical transmembrane recording from an S-A nodal fiber, showing a membrane potential of approximately 55 millivolts immediately after recovery from an action potential. However, because of membrane leakage, the resting membrane potential slowly decreases from 55 millivolts to about 45 millivolts. At approximately this point the threshold for stimulation is reached, and a new action potential is spontaneously generated. When the muscle has recovered from this, the leakage phenomenon begins anew to produce still another cycle.

Rate of Rhythm of the Various Portions of the Heart. Spontaneous rhythmicity also occurs in all other types of cardiac muscle, but the rhythmical rates are different for the different areas of the heart. Ordinarily, the natural rate of rhythm of the S-A fibers (when under the influence of vagal tone) is about 72 to 80 contractions per minute, while that of the A-V node is about 60 to 65 per minute, of the atrial muscle about 20 to 40 per minute, and of the ventricular muscle about 10 to 30 per minute.

The Sino-Atrial Node as the Pacemaker of the Heart; the Normal Heart Rate

Whenever a spontaneous action potential occurs in the S-A node, it spreads to the atria and then through the A-V bundle into the ventricles, causing all parts of the heart to contract at the rhythmical rate of the S-A node, which is normally about 72 to 80 beats per minute. For this reason the S-A node is called the *pacemaker* of the heart.

But why is the rhythm of the heart not controlled by the spontaneous rhythm of the atrial, Purkinje, or ventricular fibers rather than by the S-A node? The reason for this is the following: Every time the S-A node causes the other areas of the heart to depolarize, a certain interval of time must elapse before each type of muscle can repolarize and then spontaneously discharge again. The S-A node, because of its very fast basic rhythm, repolarizes and spontaneously discharges a second time before any of the other types of cardiac muscle can discharge on its own. This occurs repetitively so that the other parts of the heart must keep on beating as fast as the S-A node instead of establishing their own intrinsic rhythms.

Other Areas of the Heart as the Pacemakers. On occasion the S-A node fails to generate impulses. In such a case some point in the Purkinje system, most often the A-V node, usually becomes the pacemaker because these fibers have the second most rapid rhythmical rate in the heart. Also, a small area of muscle anywhere in the heart can at times become very irritable and develop a rate of rhythm greater than that of the S-A node. The irritable focus then becomes the pacemaker because it discharges more rapidly than the S-A node.

Spread of Depolarization Through the Heart

Before discussing the spread of depolarization through the heart, it should be recalled from Chapter 17 that *depolarization* occurs at the onset of the action potential when the membrane potential suddenly reverses polarity. Since the action potential is very prolonged in cardiac muscle, we usually speak of the spread of depolarization through the heart rather than of the spread of the action potential.

Figure 182 shows the time sequence for spread of depolarization through the heart. This begins in the S-A node and radiates in all directions through the atria, reaching the farthest point in the left atrium in about

0.10 second. One can observe a wavelike contraction spreading from the S-A node over the two atria during this process of depolarization.

There is no special system for conduction of the depolarization process through the atria other than the slowly conducting muscle fibers themselves. This results in very slow transmission from the S-A node to the A-V node, approximately 0.08 second elapsing before the impulse reaches the A-V node.

Delay of the Impulse at the A-V Node. Even after the impulse reaches the A-V node, still another 0.08 second elapses before it enters the A-V bundle because of the extremely slow transmission through the A-V *junctional fibers* that connect the atrial muscle fibers with the Purkinje fibers of the A-V node. Impulse transmission in these fibers is some 10 times slower than that in the atrial musculature itself.

The total lapse of time from the origin of the impulse in the S-A node until it finally passes through the A-V bundle into the ventricular septum averages about 0.16 second. This prolonged delay increases the effectiveness of the heart as a pump, for it allows the atria to pump their blood into the ventricles before the ventricles contract.

Conduction of the Impulse through the Ventricles. Once the impulse has passed through the A-V bundle into the ventricular septum, it then spreads through the two *bundle branches* of the Purkinje system

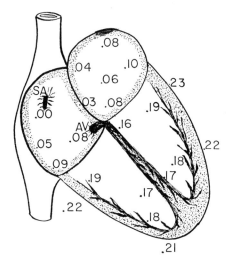

Figure 182. Transmission of the cardiac impulse through the heart, showing the time of appearance (in fractions of a second) of the impulse in different parts of the heart.

along the endocardial walls of each ventricle, passing first down to the apex of each ventricle and then back along a sub-endocardial network of Purkinje fibers up to the base of the heart, as shown in Figure 182. The total lapse of time for transmission of the impulse through the entire Purkinje system of the ventricles is approximately 0.03 to 0.04 second, which is very rapid compared to the transmission of the impulse elsewhere in the heart.

From the endocardial surface of the ventricles Purkinje fibers penetrate only about one-third to one-half the thickness of the ventricular walls. After leaving the Purkinje fibers, the impulse must then travel the rest of the way to the outer surface of the ventricles through ordinary cardiac muscle, requiring another 0.03 second. Thus, the impulse travels over the entire endocardial surface of the heart very rapidly but then spreads much more slowly through the ventricular walls to the exterior.

The total elapsed time between the origin of the impulse at the S-A node and the termination of the impulse on the outside of the ventricles at the base of the heart averages approximately 0.23 second, and the interval from the time the impulse enters the septum of the ventricles until it has finally completed its course through the ventricles is approximately 0.07 second. These exact time intervals for passage of the depolarization wave (the impulse) through the human heart are extremely important in analyzing electrocardiograms, which will be discussed in the following three chapters.

Value of the Purkinje System. For the ventricles to be effective as pumps, all parts of each ventricle must contract almost simultaneously. Therefore, it is desirable that the depolarization process travel throughout the ventricles rapidly; otherwise, large portions of the ventricles might be contracting while other portions are still relaxed. This obviously decreases the effectiveness of the ventricles as pumps. The Purkinje system, which conducts impulses three to seven times as rapidly as the cardiac muscle itself, has been estimated to increase the effectiveness of the heart as a pump about 25 per cent.

Another value of the Purkinje system is that it helps to prevent cardiac fibrillation, which will be discussed later in the chapter.

ABNORMAL RHYTHMS OF THE HEART

Abnormal cardiac rhythms can be caused by (1) abnormal rhythmicity of the pacemaker itself, (2) shift of the pacemaker from the S-A node to other parts of the heart, (3) blocks at different points in the transmission of the impulse through the heart, (4) abnormal pathways of impulse transmission through the heart, and (5) spontaneous generation of abnormal impulses in almost any part of the heart. Some of these will be discussed in Chapter 24 in relation to electrocardiographic analysis of cardiac arrhythmias, but the major disturbances and their causes will be presented here to illustrate some of the aberrations that can occur in the rhythmicity and conducting system of the heart.

Premature Contractions—Ectopic Foci

Often, a small area of the heart becomes much more excitable than normal and causes an occasional abnormal impulse to be generated in between the normal impulses. A depolarization wave spreads outward from the irritable area and initiates a *premature contraction* of the heart. The focus at which the abnormal impulse is generated is called an *ectopic focus*.

The usual cause of an ectopic focus is an irritable cardiac muscle resulting from overuse of stimulants such as caffeine or nicotine, or resulting from lack of sleep, anxiety, or other debilitating states. When an ectopic beat originates in one of the two atria, the contraction usually spreads from the atria into the ventricles, and the whole heart contracts prematurely. However, if the ectopic focus is in the Purkinje system or in the ventricles, the impulse normally spreads only over the ventricles, resulting in ventricular premature contraction but no atrial premature contraction.

Shift of the Pacemaker to an Ectopic Focus

Sometimes an ectopic focus becomes so irritable that it establishes a rhythmical contraction of its own at a more rapid rate than that of the S-A node. When this occurs the ectopic focus becomes the pacemaker of the heart. Essentially the same conditions that cause premature beats can also result in an ectopic pacemaker. The most common point for development of an ectopic pacemaker is the A-V node itself or the A-V bundle. The second most common is some point in the atria and, third, some point in the ventricular wall. Obviously, the sequence of contraction of the different parts of the heart becomes quite abnormal when the pacemaker shifts away from the S-A node. Fortunately, as will be discussed in Chapter 25, contraction of the atria prior to contraction of the ventricles is not absolutely essential for pumping by the heart. Consequently, even with the most abnormal pacemaker, the heart usually still pumps with as much as 70 per cent normal effectiveness.

Heart Block

Occasionally, transmission of the impulse through the heart is blocked at critical points in the conductive system. One of the most common of these points is between the atria and the ventricles; this condition is called *atrioventricular block*. Another common point is in one of the *bundle branches* of the Purkinje system. Rarely, a block also develops between the S-A node and the atrial musculature.

Atrioventricular Block. In the human being, block from the atria to the ventricles can result from localized damage or depression of the A-V *junctional* fibers or of the A-V *bundle*. The causes include different types of infectious processes, excessive stimulation by the vagus nerves (which depresses conductivity of the junctional fibers), localized destruction of the A-V bundle as a result of a coronary infarct, pressure on the A-V bundle by arteriosclerotic plaques, or depression caused by various drugs.

Figure 183 illustrates a typical record of atrial and ventricular contraction while the A-V bundle was being progressively compressed to cause successive stages of block. During the first three contractions of the record, ventricular contraction followed in orderly sequence approximately 0.16 second after atrial contraction. Then, A-V bundle compression was begun, and the interval of time between the beginning of atrial contraction until the beginning of ventricular contraction increased steadily during the next five heart beats from 0.16 second to 0.32 second. Beyond this point further compression completely blocked impulse transmission. Thereafter, the atria continued to beat at their normal rate of rhythm, while the ventricles failed to contract at all for approximately 7 seconds. Then, a rhythmical focus in the ventricles suddenly began to act as a ventricular pacemaker, causing ventricular contractions at a rate of approximately 30 per minute; these were completely dissociated from the atrial contraction.

Stokes-Adams syndrome. Very often in heart disease, conduction from the atria to the ventricles becomes only barely adequate to maintain normal cardiac rhythmicity. Then, additional stress on the heart causes conduction to become suddenly inadequate. Each time this happens the ventricles fail to beat for 4 to 10 seconds but then usually assume their own intrinsic rhythm, as illustrated in the record of Figure 183. During the 4 to 10 seconds while the ventricles fail to beat, the brain receives no blood flow, and the patient faints for a few seconds. This is known as *Stokes-Adams* syndrome.

The cause of the prolonged ventricular asystole is believed to be that the natural ventricular rate of rhythmicity remains very low as long as the S-A node is driving the ventricles. During the few seconds after ventricular asystole begins, the cardiac muscle becomes progressively more anoxic be-

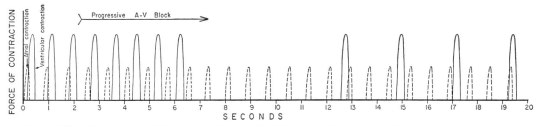

Figure 183. Contraction of the atria and ventricles of a heart, showing the effect of progressive A-V block. Note the progressive increase in the interval between the onset of atrial contraction and the onset of ventricular contraction. Note also the final complete asynchronism between atrial and ventricular contraction.

cause of failure to receive an adequate blood supply through the coronary system. This results in a rapidly increasing rate of rhythmicity which causes the ventricular muscle to begin beating after several seconds. Also, several autonomic reflexes initiated by decreased pressures and decreased blood flow in the circulatory system result in ventricular stimulation; this, too, helps the ventricles to assume their own rhythm. Occasionally, though, the ventricles fail to pick up a spontaneous rhythm, and the patient dies.

Block of the Purkinje System in the Ventricles. Block of the Purkinje system can occur not only in the A-V bundle but also in any of the ventricular branches. Major blocks very frequently occur in an entire bundle branch supplying one whole ventricle, but even more common are minor blocks in small branches more distal in the ventricles. Indeed, either a major or a minor block occurs in almost all patients with coronary infarcts. When such a block occurs, the impulse then spreads through the ventricles by way of the muscle fibers themselves, a route that transmits the signal only about one fourth as rapidly as the Purkinje system. As a consequence, the pumping effectiveness of the heart beat is often decreased by as much as 20 to 30 per cent because all the fibers of the ventricles do not contract coordinately.

Flutter and Fibrillation—the Circus Movement

Frequently, either the atria or the ventricles begin to contract extremely rapidly and often incoordinately. The lower frequency and more coordinate contractions up to 200 to 300 beats per minute are generally called *flutter* and the very high frequency and incoordinate contractions *fibrillation*. In fibrillation the contractions are so rapid and spread in so many directions at once that one must look carefully to distinguish the individual contraction waves.

Two basic theories of flutter and fibrillation have been proposed; these are (1) a *single or multiple ectopic foci* emitting many impulses one after another in rapid succession and (2) a *circus movement*, in which the impulse travels around and around through the heart muscle, never stopping.

The first of these theories, the ectopic focus theory, is quite easy to understand. That is, an area of the heart simply becomes so irritable that it keeps sending very rapid impulses in all directions, resulting in rapid rates of contraction. There is reason to believe that at least some instances of atrial flutter may result from this cause, but there is also reason to believe that many instances of atrial flutter result from circus movements around the atria. Since only the circus movement theory has been able to explain adequately the course of events in atrial and ventricular fibrillation, we will discuss it in detail.

The Circus Movement. Figure 184 illustrates several small cardiac muscle strips cut in the form of circles. If such a strip is stimulated at the twelve o'clock position *so that the impulse travels in only one direction*, the impulse will spread progressively around the circle until it returns to the twelve o'clock position. If the originally stimulated muscle fibers are still in a refractory state, the impulse will then die out, for refractory muscle cannot transmit a second impulse. However, there are three different conditions that could cause this impulse to continue to travel around the circle:

First, if the *length of the pathway around the circle is long*, by the time the impulse returns to the twelve o'clock position the originally stimulated muscle will no longer be refractory, and the impulse will continue around the circle again and again.

Second, if the length of the pathway re-

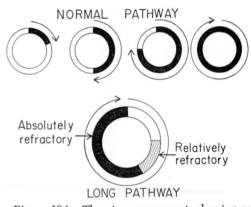

Figure 184. The circus movement, showing annihilation of the impulse in the short pathway and continued propagation of the impulse in the long pathway

mains constant but the *velocity of conduction becomes decreased* enough, an increased interval of time will elapse before the impulse returns to the twelve o'clock position. By this time the originally stimulated muscle might be out of the refractory state and the impulse can continue around the circle again and again.

Third, *the refractory period of the muscle might become greatly shortened.* In this case, the impulse could also continue around and around the circle.

All three of these conditions occur in different pathological states of the human heart as follows: (1) A long pathway frequently occurs in dilated hearts. (2) Decreased rate of conduction frequently results from blockage of the Purkinje system. (3) A shortened refractory period frequently occurs in response to various drugs such as epinephrine, or following intense vagal stimulation. Thus, in many different cardiac disturbances circus movements can cause abnormal cardiac rhythmicity that completely ignores the pacesetting effects of the S-A node.

Atrial Flutter Resulting from a Circus Pathway. Figure 185 illustrates a circus pathway around and around the atria from top to bottom, the pathway lying to the left of the superior and inferior venae cavae. Such circus pathways have been initiated experimentally in the atria of dogs' hearts, and electrocardiographic records, which will be discussed in Chapter 24, indicate that this type of circus pathway also occasionally develops in the human heart when the atria become greatly dilated as a result of valvular heart disease. The rate of flutter is usually about 200 to 350 times per minute.

Partial block at the A-V node during atrial flutter. The functional refractory period of the Purkinje fibers and ventricular muscle is approximately 1/200 minute so that not over 200 impulses per minute can be transmitted into the ventricles. Therefore, when the atrium contracts as rapidly as 300 times per minute, only 1 out of every 2 of the impulses will pass into the ventricles, thus causing the atria to beat at a rate two times that of the ventricles. The heart is then said to have a 2 to 1 rhythm. Occasionally, a 3 to 1 and, rarely, a 4 to 1 rhythm of the heart develops in the same manner.

The "Chain Reaction" Mechanism of Fibrillation. Fibrillation, whether it occurs in the atria or in the ventricles, is a very different condition from flutter. One can see many separate contractile waves spreading in different directions over the cardiac muscle at the same time in either atrial or ventricular fibrillation. Obviously, then, the circus movement in fibrillation is entirely different from that in flutter. One of the best ways to explain the mechanism of fibrillation is to describe the initiation of fibrillation by stimulation with 60 cycle alternating electrical current.

Fibrillation caused by 60 cycle alternating current. At a central point in the ventricles of heart A in Figure 186 a 60 cycle electrical stimulus is applied through a stimulating electrode. The first cycle of the electrical stimulus causes a depolarization wave to spread in all directions, leaving all the muscle beneath the electrode in a refractory state. After about 0.25 second, this muscle begins to come out of the refractory state, some portions of the muscle coming out of refractoriness prior to other portions. This state of events is depicted in heart A by many light patches, which represent excitable cardiac muscle, and dark patches, that

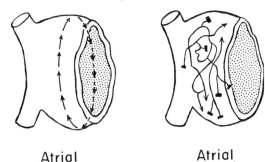

Atrial
flutter

Atrial
fibrillation

Figure 185. Pathways of impulses in atrial flutter and atrial fibrillation.

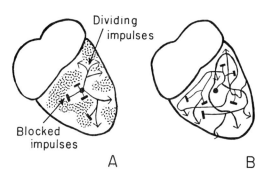

Figure 186. (A) initiation of fibrillation in a heart when patches of refractory musculature are present, (B) continued propagation of fibrillatory impulses in the fibrillating ventricle.

represent refractory muscle. Stimuli from the electrode can now cause impulses to travel in certain directions through the heart but not in all directions. It will be observed in heart A that certain impulses travel for short distances until they reach refractory areas of the heart and then are blocked. Other impulses, however, pass between the refractory areas and continue to travel in the excitable patches of muscle. Now, several events transpire in rapid succession, all occurring simultaneously and eventuating in a state of fibrillation. These are:

First, block of the impulses in some directions but successful transmission in other directions creates one of the necessary conditions for a circus movement to develop— that is, *transmission of at least some of the depolarization waves around the heart in only one direction.* As a result, these waves do not annihilate themselves on the opposite side of the heart but can continue around and around the ventricles.

Second, the rapid stimulation of the heart causes two changes in the cardiac muscle itself, both of which predispose to a circus movement: (1) *The velocity of conduction through the heart becomes decreased,* which allows a longer time interval for the impulses to travel around the heart. (2) The *refractory period of the muscle becomes shortened,* allowing reentry of the impulse into previously excited heart muscle within a much shorter period of time than normally.

Third, one of the most important features of fibrillation is the *division of impulses,* as illustrated in heart A. When a depolarization wave reaches a refractory area in the heart it travels to both sides around the area. Thus, a single impulse becomes two impulses. Then when each of these reaches another refractory area it, too, divides to form still two more impulses. In this way many different impulses are continually being formed in the heart by a progressive *chain reaction* until, finally, there are many impulses traveling in many different directions at the same time. Furthermore, this irregular pattern of impulse travel causes a continual irregular pattern of patchy refractory areas in the heart. One can readily see that a vicious cycle has been initiated: more and more impulses are formed; these cause more and more patches of refractory muscle; and the refractory patches cause more and

more division of the impulses. Therefore, any time a single area of cardiac muscle comes out of refractoriness, an impulse is always close at hand to reexcite the area.

Heart B in Figure 186 illustrates the final state that develops in fibrillation. Here one can see many impulses traveling in all directions, some dividing and increasing the number of impulses while others are blocked entirely by refractory areas. In the final state of fibrillation, the number of new impulses being formed exactly equals the number of impulses that are being blocked by refractory areas. Thus, a steady state has developed with a certain average number of impulses traveling all the time in all directions through the cardiac syncytium.

As is the case with many other cardiac arrhythmias fibrillation is usually confined to either the atria or the ventricles alone and not to both syncytial masses of muscle at the same time.

Demonstration of the chain reaction mechanism of ventricular fibrillation in the "iron heart." In the human heart the chain reaction mechanism is difficult to demonstrate for two reasons: (1) It is impossible to follow exactly the wave fronts of the electrical impulses traveling through the heart muscle and (2) there are so many minute waves of contraction spreading at the same time that the eyes cannot follow these continually. An *iron heart model* has been developed in our laboratory that does show very easily the chain reaction mechanism. This is a large iron bob suspended in nitric acid. Under appropriate conditions an oxide film develops on the surface of the iron. Then, a single electrical stimulus to the surface will cause a single reaction wave to travel over the entire surface comparable to normal stimulation of the heart. But multiple stimuli either all at once or in rapid succession will cause the typical chain reaction as described above, with resultant fibrillation. One can easily see the chain reaction, and it can be recorded electrically. Also, typical fibrillatory electrocardiographic patterns are recorded.

Atrial Fibrillation. Atrial fibrillation is a completely different story from atrial flutter because the circus movement does not travel in a regular pathway. Instead, many different excitation waves can be seen to travel over the surface of the atria at the same time. Atrial fibrillation occurs very frequently when the atria become greatly over-dilated—in fact, many times as frequently as flutter. When flutter does occur, it usually becomes fibrillation after a few days or weeks. To the right in Figure 185 are illustrated the pathways of fibrillatory impulses traveling through the atria. Obviously, atrial fibrillation results in complete incoordination of atrial contraction so that atrial pumping ceases entirely.

Effect of atrial fibrillation on the overall pumping effectiveness of the heart. The normal function of the atria is only to help fill the ventricles. However, the atria are probably responsible for not more than 25 to 30 per cent of the normal ventricular filling, which will be explained in Chapter 25. Therefore, even when the atria fail to act as primer pumps, the ventricles can still fill enough that the effectiveness of the heart as a pump is reduced only 25 to 30 per cent, which is well within the "cardiac reserve" of all but severely weakened hearts. For this reason, atrial fibrillation can continue for many years without profound cardiac debility.

Irregularity of ventricular rate during atrial fibrillation. When the atria are fibrillating, impulses arrive at the A-V node very rapidly but also very irregularly. Since the A-V bundle will not pass a second impulse for approximately 0.3 second after a previous one, at least 0.3 second must elapse between one ventricular contraction and the next, and an additional interval of 0 to 0.6 second usually occurs before one of the irregular fibrillatory impulses happens to arrive at the A-V node. Thus, the interval between successive ventricular contractions varies from 0.3 second up to about 0.9 second, causing a very irregular heart beat. In fact, this irregularity is one of the clinical findings used to diagnose the condition.

Ventricular Fibrillation. Ventricular fibrillation is extremely important because at least one quarter of all persons die in ventricular fibrillation. For instance, the hearts of most patients with coronary infarcts fibrillate shortly before death. In only a few instances on record have fibrillating human ventricles been known to return of their own accord to a rhythmic beat.

The likelihood of circus movements and, consequently, of ventricular fibrillation in the ventricles is greatly increased when the ventricles are dilated or when the rapidly conducting *Purkinje system is blocked* so that impulses cannot be transmitted rapidly. Also, *electrical stimuli*, as noted above, or *ectopic foci*, which will be discussed below, are common initiating causes of ventricular fibrillation.

Inability of the heart to pump blood during ventricular fibrillation. When the ventricles begin to fibrillate, the different parts of the ventricles no longer contract simultaneously. For the first few seconds the ventricular muscle undergoes rather coarse contractions which may pump a few milliliters of blood with each contraction. However, the impulses in the ventricles rapidly become divided into many much smaller impulses, and the contractions become very fine rather than coarse, pumping no blood whatsoever. The ventricles dilate because of failure to pump the blood that is flowing into them, and within 60 to 90 seconds the ventricular muscle becomes too weak, because of lack of coronary blood supply, to contract strongly even if coordinate contraction should return. Therefore, death is immediate when ventricular fibrillation begins.

Irritable foci as the usual cause of ventricular fibrillation. The cause of ventricular fibrillation is most often an irritable focus in the ventricular muscle caused by coronary insufficiency or by compression from an arteriosclerotic plaque. Most impulses originating in an irritable focus travel around the heart in all directions, meet on the opposite side of the heart, and annihilate themselves. However, when impulses from a focus become very frequent the refractory period of the stimulated muscle becomes shortened, impulse conduction becomes slowed, and patchy areas of refractoriness develop in the ventricles. These are the essential conditions for initiating the chain reaction mechanism, and fibrillation begins in the same manner as that described above for stimulation with a 60 cycle electrical current. Thus, any ectopic focus that emits rapid impulses is very likely to initiate fibrillation.

Electrical defibrillation of the ventricles. Though a weak alternating current will almost invariably throw the ventricles into fibrillation, a very strong electrical current passed through the ventricles for a short interval of time can stop fibrillation by throwing all the ventricular muscle into refractori-

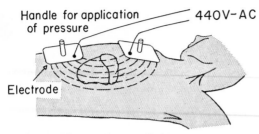

Handle for application
of pressure   440V-AC

Electrode

Figure 187. Application of alternating current to the chest of a patient to stop ventricular fibrillation.

ness simultaneously. This is accomplished by passing intense current through electrodes placed on two sides of the heart. The current penetrates most of the fibers of the ventricles, thus stimulating essentially all parts of the ventricles simultaneously and causing them to become refractory. All impulses stop, and the heart then remains quiescent for 3 to 5 seconds, after which it begins to beat again, with the S-A node or, often, some other part of the heart becoming the pacemaker. Occasionally, however, the same irritable focus which had originally thrown the ventricles into fibrillation is still present, and fibrillation begins again immediately.

When electrodes are applied directly to the two sides of the heart, fibrillation can usually be stopped with 70 to 100 volts of 60 cycle alternating current at 1 to 2 amperes of current flow. When applied through the chest wall, as illustrated in Figure 187, approximately 440 volts, 60 cycle alternating current at 4 to 5 amperes are required.

Defibrillation of the human heart has been performed many times during surgical operations by direct application of electrodes to the heart, but defibrillation through the chest wall has been accomplished in the human being in only a dozen or more instances because the defibrillatory current must be applied within less than a minute after fibrillation begins; otherwise, the heart will be so weak from lack of coronary blood flow that it cannot return to a normal rhythm even when defibrillated. In our laboratory the heart of a single anesthetized dog, however, was defibrillated 130 times through the chest wall, and the animal remained in perfectly normal condition.

Hand pumping of the heart ("cardiac massage") as an aid to defibrillation. Even though one fails to defibrillate the heart within 1 minute after fibrillation begins, it is still possible to revive the heart by preliminarily pumping the heart by hand. Small quantities of blood are delivered in this way into the aorta, and a renewed coronary blood supply develops. After a few minutes of replenishing the nutrient supply to the heart, electrical defibrillation then often becomes possible. Indeed, fibrillating hearts have been pumped by hand as long as 90 minutes before defibrillation.

Lack of blood flow to the brain for more than 5 to 10 minutes usually results in permanent mental impairment or even total destruction of the brain. Even though the heart should be revived, the patient might yet die from the effects of brain damage or live with permanent mental impairments.

Cardiac Arrest

When cardiac metabolism becomes greatly disturbed as a result of any one of many possible conditions, the rhythmic contractions of the heart occasionally stop. One of the most common causes of cardiac arrest is anoxia of the heart, for severe anoxia prevents the muscle fibers from maintaining normal ionic differentials across their membranes. Therefore, polarization of the membranes become reduced, and the excitability may be so affected that the automatic rhythmicity disappears.

Occasionally, patients with severe myocardial disease suddenly develop cardiac arrest, which obviously can lead to death. In a few cases, however, the condition has been diagnosed soon enough that rhythmical electrical impulses applied to the chest wall from an electronic cardiac "pacemaker" have been successful in reviving the patient and keeping him alive for days at a time, sometimes until the natural rhythm of the heart has resumed.

EFFECT OF AUTONOMIC STIMULATION ON THE BEAT OF THE HEART

In the previous chapter it was noted that the heart is innervated by both sympathetic and parasympathetic nerves. Anatomically these nerves enter the *cardiac plexus,* which entwines around the great vessels leading from the superior part of the heart. The fibers then spread over the heart as illustrated schematically in Figure 188.

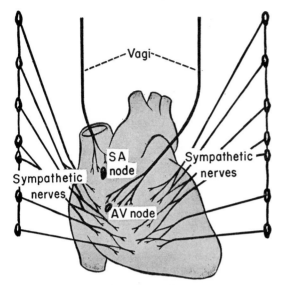

Figure 188.   The cardiac nerves.

Effect of Sympathetic Stimulation on the Heart

Sympathetic stimulation causes essentially the opposite effects on the heart to those caused by vagal stimulation. First, this *increases the rate of the S-A node*. Second, it *increases very greatly the force of contraction* of all the cardiac musculature, both atrial and ventricular. And, third, it *increases the excitability* of all portions of the heart, thus making the heart much more excitable to any extraneous stimulus.

In summary, sympathetic stimulation increases the overall activity of the heart. Maximal sympathetic stimulation can almost triple the rate of heart beat and can increase the strength of the heart contraction as much as two- to three-fold.

The parasympathetic nerves (the vagi) supply few, if any, nerve fibers to the ventricular musculature, but they innervate the atrial musculature very strongly.

The sympathetic nervous system supplies fibers to essentially all areas of both the atria and the ventricles, traveling principally along the coronary blood vessels.

Effect of Vagal (Parasympathetic) Stimulation on the Heart

Acetylcholine secreted at the vagal endings has two major effects on the heart. First, it *decreases the rate of rhythm of the S-A node*. Second, it *decreases the excitability* of the A-V junctional fibers between the atrial musculature and the Purkinje system, thereby *slowing the transmission of impulses into the ventricles,* and sometimes even blocking impulse transmission between the atria and the ventricles.

Very strong stimulation of either one or both of the vagi usually completely stops the rhythmic contraction of the S-A node or blocks transmission of impulses through the A-V junction. In either case, rhythmic impulses are no longer transmitted into the ventricles. The ventricles stop beating for about 4 to 10 seconds, but then begin contracting at their own intrinsic rhythm of 10 to 30 beats per minute. This is called *ventricular escape.*

EFFECT OF VARIOUS IONS ON THE MAMMALIAN HEART

In the discussion of membrane potentials in Chapter 17 it was pointed out that three particular cations, *potassium, sodium,* and *calcium,* have very marked effects on action potential transmission, and in Chapter 19 it was noted that calcium ion has an additional stimulatory effect on muscle contraction. These same effects apply to the heart.

The action of individual ions on the heart can be studied by adding these to fluids used to perfuse the heart in a preparation such as that illustrated in Figure 189. In making this preparation the heart is removed rapidly from the animal's body, and its aorta is cannulated immediately. The cannula is connected to a perfusion bottle located approximately three feet higher than the heart itself so that the fluid in the aorta will be under pressure. The pressure causes the aortic valve to close and the fluid to flow through the coronary vessels. When essential ions are present in the perfusion fluid, plus glucose and oxygen for nutrition, and the heart is kept appropriately warm, the perfused mammalian heart will beat for many hours.

Effect of Potassium on the Heart

Excess potassium in the extracellular fluids causes the heart to become extremely *dilated and flaccid with slowing of the heart rate.* Very large quantities can also cause atrio-

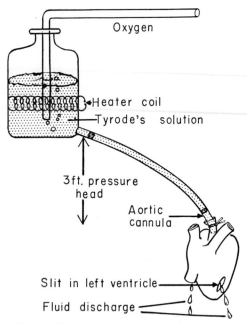

Oxygen

Heater coil

Tyrode's solution

3ft. pressure head

Aortic cannula

Slit in left ventricle

Fluid discharge

Figure 189. System for perfusing the heart.

ventricular block and slowing of impulse conduction throughout the heart, resulting in a very abnormal electrocardiogram. Finally, elevation of the potassium to only 10 to 15 mEq. per liter—2 to 3 times the normal value—will usually cause such weakness of the heart that the person dies.

All these effects of potassium excess are believed to be caused by decreased membrane potentials resulting from high potassium levels in the extracellular fluids. This effect on membrane potentials was discussed in Chapter 17.

Effect of Calcium on the Heart

Calcium ions cause almost exactly the opposite effects to those of potassium ions, resulting in markedly increased strength and duration of contraction. These effects probably result partly or entirely from a direct stimulatory effect of calcium ions on the contraction of actomyosin in the cardiac muscle fibers. On the contrary, greatly diminished calcium concentration in the extracellular fluid can result in an extremely weakened heart, similar to that which results from excess potassium.

Since calcium and potassium have opposite effects on the heart, each of these can nullify most of the effects of the other. Thus, it is said that the *calcium to potassium ratio*

in the body fluids must remain relatively constant for normal heart function.

Effect of Sodium Ions

For reasons not yet understood, low sodium ion concentration decreases the strength of cardiac contraction. It is possible that this effect comes from diminished action potentials resulting from a decreased sodium potential across the membrane, as explained in Chapter 17. At times the sodium ion concentration in human patients can fall to as low as two-thirds normal, which is probably enough to reduce the strength of heart contraction by as much as 20 to 30 per cent. Excess sodium, within known physiological ranges, has little cardiac effect.

EFFECT OF TEMPERATURE ON THE HEART

The direct effect of temperature on the heart can also be studied using the perfusion system of Figure 189. Increased temperature causes a greatly increased heart rate, and decreased temperature greatly decreases the rate. If the sinus is kept cool while the ventricle is heated far above normal, the intrinsic rhythmic rate of the ventricle may become greater than that of the S-A node, causing the ventricle to become its own pacemaker. A 10° F. rise in temperature approximately doubles the heart rate.

Experiments in dogs have shown that cooling the heart from the normal value of 99° F. down to about 85° F. actually increases stroke volume output of the heart. This partially compensates for the diminished heart rate, allowing the heart to continue to pump adequate quantities of blood. However, at still lower temperatures, the cardiac output finally becomes insufficient to keep the person alive.

At higher than normal temperatures, the stroke volume output decreases slightly, but the greatly increased rate of beat still progressively increases the total cardiac output up to a body temperature of about 106° F.

REFERENCES

Alanis, J., Lopez, E., and Pulido, J.: The H potential and the conduction velocity of the bundle of His. *J. Physiol.*, 147:315, 1959.

Anzola, J., and Rushmer, R. F.: Cardiac responses to sympathetic stimulation. *Circ. Res., 4:*302, 1956.

Briggs, A. H., and Holland, W. C.: Antifibrillatory effects of electrolyte-regulating steroids on isolated rabbit atria. *Am. J. Physiol., 197:*1161, 1959.

Brooks, C. M.: Auricular fibrillation: relationship of vulnerables period to "dip" phenomenon of auricular excitability curve. *Am. J. Physiol., 164:*301, 1951.

Brooks, C. M., Cranefield, P. F., Hoffman, B. F., and Siebens, A. A.: Anodal effects during the refractory period of cardiac muscle. *J. Cellul. Physiol., 48:* 237, 1956.

Brooks, C. M., Hoffman, B., Suckling, E. E., and Orias, O.: Excitability of the Heart. New York, Grune & Stratton, Inc., 1955.

Brown, E. B., Jr.: Role of hyperkalemia in production of ventricular fibrillation following hypercapnia. *Proc. Soc. Exp. Biol. & Med. 90:*319, 1955.

Burn, J. H., and Rand, M. J.: The relation of circulating nor-adrenaline to the effect of sympathetic stimulation. *J. Physiol., 150:*295, 1960.

Carlsten, A., Folkow, B., and Hamberger, C. A.: Cardiovascular effects of direct vagal stimulation in man. *Acta Physiol. Scandinav., 41:*68, 1957.

Coffman, J. D., and Gregg, D. E.: Ventricular fibrillation during uniform myocardial anoxia due to asphyxia. *Am. J. Physiol., 198:*955, 1960.

Covino, B. G., and Hegnauer, A. H.: Ventricular excitability cycle: its modification by pH and hypothermia. *Am. J. Physiol., 181:*553, 1955.

Cranefield, P. F., and Hoffman, B. F.: Electrophysiology of single cardiac cells. *Physiol. Rev., 38:*41, 1958.

Cranefield, P. F., Hoffman, B. F., and Carvalho, A. P. de: Effects of acetylcholine on single fibers of the atrioventricular node. *Circ. Res., 7:*19, 1959.

Crowell, J. W., Sharpe, G. P., and Lambright, R. L.: Prolonged massage of the fibrillating heart. *Surgery, 42:*701, 1957.

de Carvalho, A. P., de Mello, W. C., and Hoffman, B. F.: Electrophysiological evidence for specialized fiber types in rabbit atrium. *Am. J. Physiol., 196:* 483, 1959.

Folkow, B., Frost, J., Haeger, K., and Uvnas, B.: Cholinergic fibers in sympathetic outflow to heart in dog and cat. *Acta. Physiol. Scandinav., 15:*421, 1948.

Folkow, B., Lofving, B., and Mellander, S.: Quantitative aspects of the sympathetic neuro-hormonal control of the heart rate. *Acta Physiol. Scandinav., 37:*363, 1956.

Guyton, A. C.: Resuscitation in respiratory and circulatory arrest. *Mississippi Doctor, 29:*35, 1951.

Guyton, A. C., and Satterfield, J.: Factors concerned in electrical defibrillation of the heart, particularly through the unopened chest. *Am. J. Physiol., 167:*81, 1951.

Hoffman, B. F., Bindler, E., and Suckling, E. E.: Postextrasystolic potentiation of contraction in cardiac muscle. *Am. J. Physiol., 185:*95, 1956.

Hoffman, B. F., de Carvalho, A. P., Mello, W. C., and Cranefield, P. F.: Electrical activity of single fibers of the atrioventricular node. *Circ. Res., 7:*11, 1959.

Hoffman, B. F., and Cranefield, P. F.: Electrophysiology of the Heart. New York, Blakiston, 1960.

Hoffman, B. F., and Kelly, J. J., Jr.: Effect of rate and rhythm on contraction of rat papillary muscle. *Am. J. Physiol., 197:*1199, 1959.

Hoffman, B. F., Siebens, A. A., Cranefield, P. F., and Brooks, C. M.: The effect of epinephrine and norepinephrine on ventricular vulnerability. *Circ. Res. 3:*140, 1955.

Hurst, J. W.: Cardiac Resuscitation. Springfield, Illinois, Charles C Thomas, 1960.

Mendez, C., Gruhzit, C. C., and Moe, G. K.: Influence of cycle length upon refractory period of auricles, ventricle, and A-V node in the dog. *Am. J. Physiol., 184:*287, 1956.

Mitchell, C. A. G.: Cardiovascular Innervation. Baltimore, Williams & Wilkins, 1956.

Moe, G. K.: Cardiac arrhythmias; introductory remarks. *Ann. N. Y. Acad. Sc., 64:*540, 1956.

Moe, G. K., Preston, J. B., and Burlington, H.: Physiologic evidence for a dual A-V transmission system. *Circ. Res., 4:*357, 1956.

Randall, W. C., and Kelso, A. F.: Dynamic basis for sympathetic cardiac augmentation. *Am. J. Physiol., 198:*975, 1960.

Randall, W. C., and Rohse, W. G.: The augmentor action of the sympathetic cardiac nerves. *Circ. Res., 4:*470, 1956.

Rohse, W. G., Kaye, M., and Randall, W. C.: Prolonged pressor effects of selective stimulation of the stellate ganglion. *Circ. Res., 5:*144, 1957.

Scher, A. M., Rodriquez, M. I., Liikane, J., and Young, A. C.: The mechanism of atrioventricular conduction. *Circ. Res., 7:*54, 1959.

Scher, A. M., and Young, A. C.: The pathway of ventricular depolarization in the dog. *Circ. Res., 4:*461, 1956.

Siebens, A. A., Hoffman, B. F., Cranefield, P. F., and Brooks, C. McC.: Regulation of contractile force during ventricular arrhythmias. *Am. J. Physiol., 197:*971, 1959.

Siebens, A. A., Hoffman, B. F., Farrell, J. E., and Brooks, C. M.: Effects of *l*-epinephrine and *l*-norepinephrine on cardiac excitability. *Am. J. Physiol., 175:*1, 1953.

Sperelakis, N., Hoshiko, T., and Berne, R. M.: Nonsyncytial nature of cardiac muscle: membrane resistance of single cells. *Am. J. Physiol., 198:*531, 1960.

Teorell, T.: A contribution to the knowledge of rhythmical transport processes of water and salts. *Exp. Cell. Res.,* Supplement 3:339, 1955.

Teorell, T.: On oscillatory transport of fluid across membranes. *Acta. Soc. Med. Upsal., 62:*60, 1957.

Teorell, T.: Rhythmical potential and impedance variations in isolated frog skin induced by lithium ion. *Acta Physiol.. Scandinav., 31:*268, 1954.

Wiggers, C. A.: Defibrillation of the ventricles. *Circ. Res., 1:*191, 1953.

Woodbury, J. W., Lee, J., Brady, A. J., and Merendino, K. A.: Transmembranal potentials from the human heart. *Circ Res., 5:*179, 1957.

See also Chapter 22, The electrocardiogram; Chapter 38, General bibliography for the cardiovascular system.

The Normal Electrocardiogram

Immediately prior to each contraction of the heart, an electrical impulse initiated in the S-A node travels through the atria, through the A-V bundle and the Purkinje system, and finally through the ventricular muscle. The transmission of this impulse has already been discussed in detail in Chapter 21. As the impulse passes through the heart, electrical currents spread into the tissues surrounding the heart, and a small proportion of these currents spreads all the way to the surface of the body. If electrodes are placed on the body on opposite sides of the heart, the electrical potentials generated by the heart can be recorded; the recording is known as an

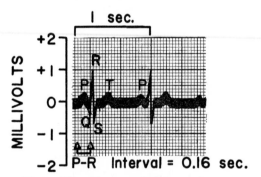

Figure 190. The normal electrocardiogram.

electrocardiogram. A normal electrocardiogram is illustrated in Figure 190.

CHARACTERISTICS OF THE NORMAL ELECTROCARDIOGRAM

The normal electrocardiogram is composed of a P wave, a QRS wave, and a T wave. The QRS wave is actually three separate waves, the Q wave, the R wave, and the S wave. All these waves are caused by passage of the cardiac impulse through the ventri-

cles, and they are usually known simply as the QRS complex. In the normal electrocardiogram, the Q and S waves are usually much less prominent than the R wave and sometimes actually absent, but, even so, the wave is still known as the QRS complex or simply QRS wave.

The P wave is caused by electrical currents generated as the atria depolarize prior to contraction, and the QRS complex is caused by currents generated when the ventricles depolarize prior to contraction. Therefore, both the P wave and the components of the QRS complex are *depolarization waves.* The T wave is caused by currents generated as the ventricles recover from the state of depolarization, and this wave is known as a *repolarization wave.* Thus, the electrocardiogram is composed of both depolarization and repolarization waves. The principles of depolarization and repolarization were discussed in Chapter 17. However, the distinction between depolarization waves and repolarization waves is so very important in electrocardiography that further clarification is needed, as follows:

Depolarization Waves versus Repolarization Waves

Figure 191 illustrates a muscle fiber in four different stages of depolarization and repolarization. The term "depolarization" might be misleading. It means loss of the normal resting membrane potential resulting from increased membrane permeability when an action potential occurs. Usually the membrane potential actually reverses, that is, becomes positive inside and negative outside during depolarization, as is illustrated in Figure 191.

In section A of Figure 191, the process of

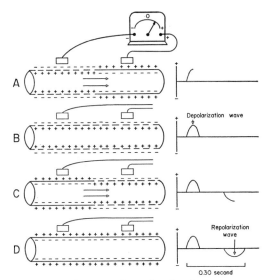

Figure 191. Recording the *depolarization wave* and the *repolarization wave* from a cardiac muscle fiber

depolarization is traveling from the left to right, and the first half of the fiber is already depolarized while the remaining half is still polarized. Therefore, the left electrode on the fiber is in an area of negativity, while the right electrode is in an area of positivity, which causes the meter to record positively. To the right of the muscle fiber in section A is illustrated a record of the potential between the electrodes as recorded by a high-speed recording meter at this particular stage of depolarization. It will be noted that, when depolarization has reached this halfway mark, the record has risen to a maximum positive value. In section B of Figure 191, depolarization has extended over the entire muscle fiber, and the recording to the right has returned to the zero base line because both electrodes are now in areas of equal negativity. The completed wave is a *depolarization wave* because it is due to the spread of the depolarization process down the extent of the muscle fiber.

Section C of Figure 191 illustrates the repolarization process in the muscle fiber, repolarization having proceeded halfway along the extent of the fiber from left to right. At this point, the left electrode is in an area of positivity, while the right electrode is in an area of negativity. This is opposite to the polarities in section A of this figure. Consequently, the recording, as illustrated to the right, becomes negative. Fi-

nally, in section D of Figure 191, the muscle fiber has completely repolarized, and both electrodes are in areas of positivity so that no potential is recorded between them. Thus, in the recording to the right, the potential returns once more to the zero level. This completed negative wave is a *repolarization wave* because it results from spread of the repolarization process over the muscle fiber.

Relationship of the Monophasic Action Potential of Cardiac Muscle to the QRS and T Waves. The monophasic action potential of ventricular muscle, which was discussed in the preceding chapter, normally lasts between 0.25 and 0.30 second. The top part of Figure 192 again illustrates a monophasic action potential recorded from a microelectrode inserted into a ventricular muscle fiber. The upsweep of this action potential is the depolarization process, and the return of the potential to the base line is the repolarization process. Note below the simultaneous recording of the electrocardiogram from this same ventricle, which shows the QRS wave appearing at the beginning of the monophasic action potential and the T wave appearing at the end. Actually, repolarization begins immediately after depolarization is complete. However, during the *plateau* stage of repolarization, the *rate* of repolarization is too slow for a large amount of electrical current to be generated around the heart. But during the *rapid phase* of repolarization at the end of the action poten-

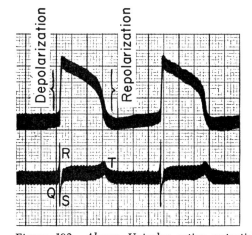

Figure 192. *Above:* Unipolar action potential from a ventricular muscle fiber during normal cardiac function, showing rapid depolarization and then repolarization occurring very slowly during the plateau stage but very rapidly toward the end. *Below:* Electrocardiogram recorded simultaneously.

tial, large amounts of current are again generated, and the T wave appears.

Relationship of Atrial and Ventricular Contraction to the Waves of the Electrocardiogram

Before contraction of muscle can occur, a depolarization wave must spread through the muscle to initiate the chemical processes of contraction. The P wave results from spread of the depolarization wave through the atria, and the QRS wave from spread of the depolarization wave through the ventricles. Therefore, the P wave occurs at the *beginning of contraction of the atria,* and the QRS wave occurs at the *beginning of contraction of the ventricles.*

The atria repolarize approximately 0.10 to 0.20 second after the depolarization wave. However, this is just at the moment that the QRS wave is being recorded in the electrocardiogram. Therefore, the atrial repolarization wave, known as the *atrial T wave,* is usually totally obscured by the much larger QRS wave. For this reason, an atrial T wave is rarely observed in the electrocardiogram.

On the other hand, the ventricular repolarization wave is the T wave of the normal electrocardiogram. Ordinarily, ventricular muscle begins to repolarize approximately 0.15 second after the beginning of the depolarization wave and completes its repolarization approximately 0.30 second after onset of depolarization. Thus, the process of repolarization extends over a fairly long period of time, about 0.15 second. For this reason the T wave in the normal electrocardiogram is a fairly prolonged wave, but the voltage of the T wave is considerably less than the voltage of the QRS complex partly because of its prolonged length.

Voltage and Time Calibration of the Electrocardiogram

All recordings of electrocardiograms are made with appropriate calibration lines on the recording paper. Either these calibration lines are already ruled on the paper, as is the case when the pen recorder is used, or they are recorded on the paper at the same time that the electrocardiogram is recorded, which is the case with the optical types of electrocardiograph.

As illustrated in Figure 190, the horizontal calibration lines are arranged so that 10 small divisions (1 cm.) in the vertical direction in the standard electrocardiogram represents 1 millivolt.

The vertical lines on the electrocardiogram are time calibration lines. Each inch of the standard electrocardiogram is 1 second. Each inch in turn is usually broken into 5 segments by dark vertical lines, the distance between which represents 0.20 second. The intervals between the dark vertical lines are broken into 5 smaller intervals by thin lines, and the distance between each two of the smaller lines represents 0.04 second.

Normal voltages in the electrocardiogram. The voltages of the waves in the normal electrocardiogram depend on the manner in which the electrodes are applied to the surface of the body. When one electrode is placed directly over the heart and the second electrode is placed elsewhere on the body, the voltage of the QRS complex may be as much as 3 to 4 millivolts. When electrocardiograms are recorded from electrodes on the two arms or on one arm and one leg, the voltage of the QRS complex usually ranges approximately 1 millivolt from the top of the R wave to the bottom of the S wave, the voltage of the P wave between 0.1 and 0.3 millivolt, and that of the T wave between 0.2 and 0.3 millivolt.

The P-Q Interval. The duration of time between the beginning of the P wave and the beginning of the QRS wave is the interval between the beginning of contraction of the atrium and the beginning of contraction of the ventricle. This period of time is called the P-Q interval. Ordinarily, the P-Q interval is approximately 0.16 second or slightly less. This interval is sometimes also called the P-R interval because the Q wave frequently is absent.

The Q-T Interval. Contraction of the ventricle lasts essentially between the Q wave and the end of the T wave. This interval of time is called the Q-T interval and ordinarily is approximately 0.30 second.

The Rate of the Heart as Determined from Electrocardiograms. The rate of heart beat can be determined very easily from electrocardiograms because the time interval between two successive beats is the reciprocal of the heart rate. If the interval between two beats as determined from the time calibration lines is 1 second, the heart rate is 60 beats per minute. The normal interval between two successive QRS complexes is approximately 0.8 second. This is a heart rate of 60/0.8 times per minute, or 75 beats per minute.

METHODS FOR RECORDING ELECTROCARDIOGRAMS

The electrical currents generated by the cardiac muscle during each beat of the heart sometimes change potentials and polarity in less than 1/100 of a second. Therefore, it is essential that any apparatus for recording electrocardiograms be capable of responding very rapidly to these changes in electrical potentials. In general, four different types of recording apparatuses are used for this purpose, as follows:

The String Galvanometer Electrocardiograph

The string galvanometer is illustrated in Figure 193. The main body of the string galvanometer is composed of a large magnet, the north and south poles of which are illustrated in the figure. A small gap exists between these poles and a very thin "string" is suspended along the length of the gap. The string is ordinarily made of a quartz thread plated on its surface with a thin layer of gold. Quartz is extremely elastic and is one of the strongest materials known, and the gold on its surface is an excellent conductor of electricity. Consequently, the string is in reality a very elastic wire with a diameter of approximately four microns, approximately one half the diameter of a red blood cell.

Application of an electrical potential to the two ends of the string causes current to flow through the string. It will be recalled that when current flows through a wire suspended in a strong magnetic field, the wire moves at right angles to the lines of magnetic force. In other words, in Figure 193 the string moves crosswise through the gap between the magnets. When current flows in one direction, the string moves forward proportionally to the potential on the two ends of the string, and when current flows in the opposite direction it moves backward. Therefore, the movement of the string is an indicator of the electrical potential applied to the two ends of the string.

To record these string movements, a special camera system is arranged so that light passes through holes in the poles of the magnet and thence onto a moving strip of photographic paper. Light from the lamp is first collimated and then projected onto the string. A telescope focuses the shadow of the string on the paper camera which is shown to the left. A large field of light covers the outside of the camera, and the string shadow is oriented vertically on this field of light. Across the middle of the field is a small slit that allows a line of light to pass into the camera. Therefore, as the paper moves beneath this line of light all of the paper becomes exposed except at that particular point where the string shadow lies across the slit of the camera. Consequently, after the paper is developed, it is black over its entire surface except for the white line where the shadow of the string plays back and forth along the camera slit.

The usual string galvanometer is capable of responding to changes in electrical potentials as rapidly as 300 to 400 cycles per second and, with special design, to frequencies higher than these. In general, such response is perfectly satisfactory for recording all desirable information from the electrical potentials of the heart.

The Moving Coil Galvanometer Electrocardiograph

Figure 194 illustrates the moving coil type of galvanometer, which may be described as follows: A very strong magnetic field is developed between the north and south poles of a strong permanent

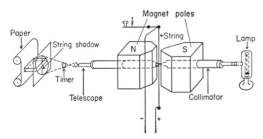

Figure 193. A string galvanometer type of electrocardiograph. (Redrawn from Katz: Electrocardiography. Lea and Febiger.)

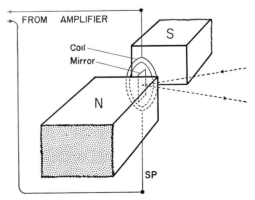

Figure 194. The moving coil type of electrocardiograph. (Redrawn from Katz: Electrocardiography. Lea & Febiger.)

magnet or electromagnet. Suspended in the magnetic field between these two poles is a coil of wire, one end of which is connected to the wire suspending the coil from above and the other end of which is connected to the wire beneath the coil. A mirror is attached to the middle of the coil so that it rotates when the coil rotates. Passage of an electric current through the coil of wire causes one side of the coil to move backward in the magnetic field while the other side, in which the current flows in the opposite direction, moves forward. Flow of current in the opposite direction causes the coil also to rotate in the opposite direction. If a beam of light is played on the mirror as the coil rotates to right or left the reflected beam of light moves a very long distance from side to side with even the slightest movement of the mirror. This reflected beam of light then can be recorded on a moving photographic paper in a manner similar to that described for the string galvanometer.

A mirror galvanometer type of recorder usually requires an amplifier to make the potentials recorded from the surface of the body strong enough to move the coil through a sufficient arc. Such galvanometers can be built capable of recording changes in electrical potentials occurring as rapidly as 100 cycles per second; therefore, this type of galvanometer will record essentially all the information necessary for electrocardiographic studies. Because of the simplicity of this type of recorder, it is used quite frequently in electrocardiographic equipment.

The Pen Recorder

Because all of the above types of apparatus require photographic development of a film or paper before the recording can be viewed, in recent years apparatus has been designed which is capable of writing the electrocardiogram with a pen directly on a moving sheet of paper. The pen is often a thin tube connected at one end to an inkwell, and its recording end is connected to a powerful magnet system that is capable of moving the pen back and forth at high speed. As the paper moves forward, the pen records the electrocardiogram by moving across the paper first in one direction and then in the other direction. The movement of the pen in turn is controlled by means of appropriate amplifiers connected to the electrocardiographic electrodes on the patient.

Other pen recording systems use special paper that does not require ink in the recording stylus. One such paper turns black when it is exposed to heat; the stylus itself is made very hot by electric current flowing through its tip. Another type of recording paper turns black when electric current flows from the tip of the stylus through the paper to an electrode at its back. This leaves a black line at every point on the paper that the stylus touches.

Recording Electrocardiograms with the Oscilloscope

Electrocardiograms can also be recorded on the screen of an oscilloscope by the method discussed for nerve potentials in Chapter 17, or they can be photographed from the oscilloscopic screen. However, because of the cost of the oscilloscope, and because extremely high frequency electrical potentials do not need to be recorded, the three less complicated and less expensive recorders described above are ordinarily used in clinical electrocardiography.

FLOW OF CURRENT AROUND THE HEART DURING THE CARDIAC CYCLE

Recording Electrical Potentials from a Partially Depolarized Mass of Syncytial Cardiac Muscle

Figure 195 illustrates a syncytial mass of cardiac muscle that has been stimulated at its centralmost point. Prior to stimulation, all of the exterior of the muscle cells had been positive and the interior negative. However, for reasons presented in Chapter 17 in the discussion of membrane potentials, as soon as an area of the cardiac syncytium becomes depolarized, negative charges leak to the outside of the depolarized area, making this particular surface area electronegative with respect to the remaining surface of the heart, which is still polarized in the normal manner. Therefore, a meter connected with its negative terminal on the area of depolarization and its positive terminal on one of the still-polarized areas, as illustrated by the

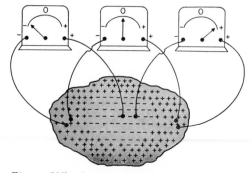

Figure 195. Instantaneous potentials developed on the surface of a cardiac muscle mass that has been depolarized in its center.

meter to the right in the figure, will record positively. Two other possible electrode placements and meter readings are also illustrated in Figure 195. These should be studied carefully. Obviously, since the process of depolarization spreads in all directions through the heart, the potential differences shown in the figure last for only a few milliseconds, and the actual recordings can be accomplished only with high-speed recording apparatus.

Flow of Electrical Currents through the Extracellular Fluids Surrounding a Mass of Cardiac Muscle

Figure 196 illustrates a mass of cardiac muscle that is depolarized at one end, still normally polarized at the other end, and is surrounded by extracellular fluid. Current flowing between the two areas of opposite potential in an electrolytic solution flows in large elliptical pathways such as those illustrated in the figure.

If one electrode is placed directly on the negative portion of the muscle and another on the positive portion of the muscle, the total potential difference between the two areas will be recorded. Also, electrodes placed at point A and point B, well away from the cardiac muscle itself but within the field of this flowing electrical current, will still record a potential difference. This can be understood very easily by consider-

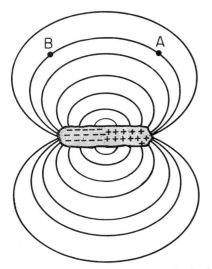

Figure 196. Current flow through the fluids surrounding a strip of cardiac muscle that has been depolarized at one end.

ing the line through points A and B as an electrical resistor, for electrolytic solutions are actually large volumes of conductive material that have a reasonable amount of resistance to the flow of current. Point B is positive with respect to the depolarized area, point A is positive with respect to B, and the polarized area of the muscle is positive with respect to point A.

Indeed, one could shift the electrodes A and B all along this line of current flow, and a potential difference would still be recorded. If the electrodes are brought closer together, the potential difference becomes less and less. On the other hand, as the electrodes approach respectively the depolarized and polarized areas of the cardiac muscle, the potential difference progressively increases.

Effect of the Size of the Areas of Depolarization and Polarization on the Recorded Potentials. Another factor that determines the amount of potential difference between the electrodes A and B of Figure 196 is the *total quantity of depolarization and polarization* existing in the muscle mass. When the areas of depolarization and polarization are both large, a much larger quantity of current flows through this resistance than flows when the areas of polarization and depolarization, or either of these areas, are small. Therefore, the potentials recorded at all points in the electrical field surrounding the heart are greater the greater the areas of depolarization and polarization.

The highest potentials are recorded in the surrounding fluids *when approximately one half of the cardiac muscle is depolarized* and *the other half is still polarized*. The reason for this is that the total surface area of the heart that is negative is then approximately equal to the total surface area that is positive, and this allows maximal flow of current.

Flow of Electrical Currents around the Heart in the Chest

Figure 197 illustrates the cardiac ventricles within the chest. Even the lungs, though filled with air, conduct electricity to a surprising extent, and fluids of the other tissues surrounding the heart conduct electricity even more easily. Therefore, the heart is actually suspended in a conductive medium. When one portion of the ventricles becomes

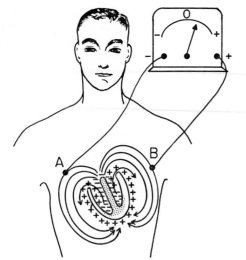

Figure 197. Flow of current in the chest around a partially depolarized heart.

electronegative with respect to the remainder, electrical current flows from the depolarized area to the polarized area in large circuitous routes, as noted in the figure.

It will be recalled from the discussion of the Purkinje system in Chapter 21 that the cardiac impulse first arrives in the ventricles on the walls of the septum so that this area is the first portion to become depolarized. That is, the septum becomes electronegative with respect to the rest of the ventricles; the lines of current flow pass from the endocardial surfaces to the positive portions of the ventricles as shown in Figure 197. If one algebraically adds all of these lines of current flow from the septum to other parts of the heart, he finds that the average direction in which current flows is from the base of the heart toward the apex of the heart.

After the walls of the septum have become depolarized, the next part of the heart to become depolarized is the lateral endocardium of both ventricles, which are stimulated directly by the Purkinje system. This provides electronegativity on the insides of the ventricles and electropositivity on the outer walls of the ventricles. Here again the algebraic average of the current flow is from the base of the heart toward the apex, and, during most of the remainder of the cycle of depolarization, the current continues to flow from the base toward the apex. However, immediately before the depolarization wave has completed its course through the

ventricles, the direction of current flow usually reverses for a split second, flowing then from apex toward the base. This change in direction of current flow will be discussed in detail in the following chapter, and the alterations in direction of current flow in different disease conditions will also be discussed.

However, in the normal heart it may be considered that current flows from the base toward the apex during the entire cycle of depolarization except at the very end. Therefore, if a meter is connected with its positive electrode toward the apex and its negative electrode toward the base, the meter will record positively during almost the entire cycle. But, if the negative electrode is nearer to the apex and its positive electrode nearer the base, then the meter will record negatively. In making electrocardiographic recordings, various standard positions for placement of electrodes are used, and whether the polarity of the recording during each cardiac cycle is positive or negative is determined by the orientation of electrodes with respect to the current flow in the heart. Some of the conventional electrode systems, commonly called *electrocardiographic leads,* will be discussed below.

The Arms and Legs as Electrodes

If two electrodes are placed on the surface of the body (points A and B in Fig. 197), the flow of current around the heart will cause a potential difference between the two electrodes because point A is nearer to the negative part of the ventricles than is point B. This potential difference is shown on the meter. For practical purposes, however, it is not desirable always to place the electrodes actually on the chest wall. Therefore, each of the arms is usually considered as an electrode, and the left leg is considered as another electrode. Each arm connects to one corner of the upper part of the chest and, therefore, makes direct electrical connection with some of the circuitous routes of current flow around the heart. The left leg connects with the current flowing at the bottom of the heart. Therefore, a wire connected to the left leg is usually considered to be a direct electrical connection to the lower end of a triangle around the heart, whereas wires connected to the two arms

Chapter 23

Electrocardiographic Interpretation in Cardiac Myopathies—Vectorial Analysis

From the preceding discussion of impulse transmission through the heart, it is obvious that many changes in the function of the heart can cause abnormal electrical currents in the extracellular fluids around the heart and, consequently, can alter the shape of the waves in the electrocardiogram. For this reason, almost all serious abnormalities of the heart muscle can be detected by analyzing the contours of the different waves in the different electrocardiographic leads. The purpose of the present chapter is to discuss the various alterations in the electrocardiograms when the muscle of the heart, especially of the ventricles, functions abnormally.

PRINCIPLES OF VECTORIAL ANALYSIS OF ELECTROCARDIOGRAMS

Use of Vectors to Represent Electrical Potentials

Before it is possible for one to understand how cardiac abnormalities affect the contours of waves in the electrocardiogram, he must first become familiar with the concept of vectors and vectorial analysis as applied to electrical currents flowing around the heart.

Several times in the preceding chapter it was pointed out that currents from the heart flow in a particular direction at each instant in the cardiac cycle. A vector is an arrow that points in the direction of current flow *with the arrowpoint in the positive direction*. Also, by convention, the length of the arrow is drawn *in proportion to the voltage generated by the current flow*.

In Figure 204 at point A is shown a vector that lies on a syncytial mass of cardiac muscle and points from an area of only a few negative charges toward an area of a few positive charges. Because there are so few negative and positive

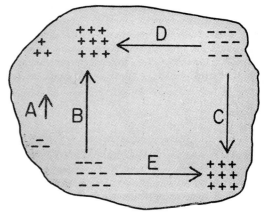

Figure 204. Vectors depicting current flow within a mass of cardiac muscle. Discussed in the text.

charges, very little current flows, and the potential between these areas is only slight; therefore, the vector is drawn very short to represent the weak potential. Also, the direction of the vector is always drawn from the negative area toward the positive area to indicate the direction of current flow.

At the ends of vector B are far greater numbers of positive and negative charges than at the ends of vector A. Consequently, this vector is considerably longer than vector A. At the ends of vector C are a large number of negative charges and a large number of positive charges, but this time the negative charges are above while the positive charges are below, and the vector extends from above downward. Likewise, vector D shows that current flows along this axis from right to left, and vector E shows that current flows along its axis from left to right. In other words, a number of different vectors are illustrated in Figure 204. The length of each vector indicates the strength of the electrical potential between each pair of negative and positive areas, and this potential in turn depends upon the total amount of depolarization and polarization that is present, which was explained in detail in the previous chapter. The direction of each vector indicates the direction of current flow. It should be noted again that the point of the arrow, by convention, always represents the positive end of the vector.

The Summated Vector in a Mass of Partially Depolarized Cardiac Muscle

Figure 205 represents a mass of cardiac muscle that is partially depolarized and still partially polarized. Most of the depolarized areas are to the left and most of the polarized areas are to the right. Therefore, the general direction of current flow is from left to right, and a large vector has been drawn through the muscle mass to represent this sum of current flow in this direction. Actually, some of the current flows in the direction opposite to the vector because some negative charges are located to the right of some of the positive charges. This neutralizes part of the potential that would have otherwise been recorded, and thereby also shortens the vector.

In summary, when currents flow around a mass of cardiac muscle, a summated vector can be drawn through the cardiac muscular mass to represent the average direction of current flow and at the same time to represent by its length the net electrical potential that develops in the direction of the vector.

The Summated Vector in the Heart at Any Given Instant. Figure 206 shows depolarization of the ventricular septum and parts of the lateral endocardial walls of the two ventricles. Electrical currents flow from the septum and from the lateral endocardial walls to the outside of the heart as indicated by the elliptical arrows. Current also flows inside the heart chambers directly from the depolarized areas toward the polarized areas. Even though this small amount of current flows upward inside the heart, a con-

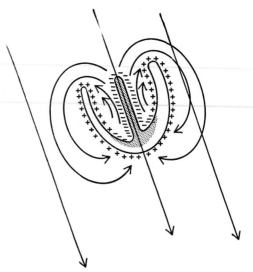

Figure 206. A summated vector through the partially depolarized heart. Two additional vectors are also shown, one to each side of the heart. These have the same significance as the vector through the center of the heart (discussed in text).

siderably greater quantity of current on the outside of the ventricles flows downward toward the apex at the same time. Therefore, the summated vector of currents at this particular instant is drawn through the center of the ventricles in a direction from the base of the heart toward the apex. Furthermore, because these currents are considerable in quantity, the length of the vector is relatively long.

Transposition of Vectors in Space

Two other vectors besides the one through the center of the heart are shown in Figure 206. These vectors extend in exactly the same direction as that through the center of the heart, and they are exactly the same length as the vector through the heart. They also have exactly the same meaning as the single vector drawn through the center of the heart, because a vector indicates only two things: (1) the direction of current flow, and (2) the potential caused by the current. Therefore, the vector can be drawn to pass directly through the center of the heart, or it can be drawn to the side of the heart or at one end of the heart. As long as the direction is appropriate and as long as the length of the vector is appropriate, its meaning remains exactly the same regardless of its position with respect to the heart.

Denoting the Direction of a Vector in Terms of Degrees

When a vector is horizontal and directed toward the subject's left side, it is said that the

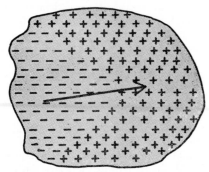

Figure 205. A summated vector in a mass of cardiac muscle.

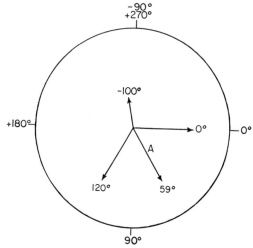

Figure 207. Vectors drawn to represent directions of current flow and potentials between several areas of depolarized heart muscle.

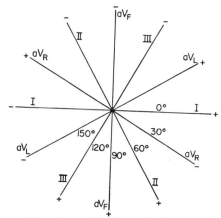

Figure 208. Axes of the three standard leads and of the three unipolar leads.

vector extends in the direction of 0 degrees, as is illustrated in Figure 207. From this zero reference point, the directional scale of vectors rotates in a clockwise manner: when the vector extends from above downward, it has a direction of 90 degrees; when it extends from the subject's left to his right, it has a direction of 180 degrees; and, when it extends upward, it has a direction of −90 or +270 degrees.

In a normal heart the average direction of the vector of the heart during spread of the depolarization wave is approximately 59 degrees, which is illustrated by vector A drawn from the center of Figure 207 in the 59 degree direction. This means that during most of the depolarization wave, the apex of the heart remains positive with respect to the base of the heart as will be discussed later in the chapter.

The above system for representing vectors in terms of degrees applies only to the *frontal plane* of the heart. Systems for representing anteroposterior orientation of the cardiac vector have also been devised, but these are not used to a great extent in conventional electrocardiography except in the chest leads. The same general principles of vectorial analysis as those described here for single plane electrocardiography can easily be applied to third dimensional analysis.

"Axis" of Each of the Standard and Unipolar Leads

In the previous chapter the three standard leads and the three unipolar leads were de-

scribed. Each lead is actually a pair of electrodes placed on opposite sides of the heart, and the direction from the negative to the positive electrode is called the *axis of the lead.* A horizontal axis from right to left is said to be 0 degrees, and the degrees are then recorded in the clockwise direction. Lead I is recorded from two electrodes placed respectively on the two arms. Since the electrodes lie in the horizontal direction with the positive electrode to the left, the axis of lead I is 0 degrees.

In recording lead II, electrodes are placed on the right arm and left leg. The right arm connects to the torso in the upper right-hand corner and the left leg to the lower left-hand corner. Therefore, the direction of this lead is approximately 60 degrees.

By a similar analysis it can be seen that lead III has an axis of approximately 120 degrees, lead aVR 30 degrees, aVF 90 degrees, and aVL 150 degrees. The directions of the axes of all these different leads are shown in Figure 208. Also, the polarities of the electrodes are illustrated by the plus and minus signs.

Vectorial Analysis of Potentials Recorded in Different Leads

Now that we have discussed, first, the conventions for representing current flow and potentials across the heart by means of vectors and, second, the axes of the leads, it becomes possible to put these two together and determine the potential that will be recorded in each lead for a given vector in the heart.

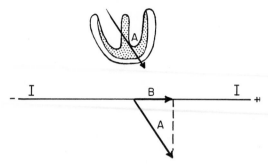

Figure 209. Determination of a resultant vector B along the axis of lead I when vector A represents the current flow in the ventricles.

Figure 209 illustrates a partially depolarized heart; vector A represents the direction of current flow in the heart and its potential. In this instance the direction of current flow is 55 degrees, and the potential will be assumed to be 2 millivolts. This vector A is now moved to a convenient point below the heart, but its direction and length remain exactly the same. Through its base is drawn the axis of lead I in the 0 degree direction. From the tip of vector A a perpendicular is dropped to the lead I axis, and a so-called *resultant vector* B is drawn along the axis. The head of this vector is in the positive direction, which means that the record momentarily being recorded in the electrocardiogram of lead I will be positive. The voltage recorded will be equal to the ratio of the lengths of vector B to vector A times 2 millivolts, or in other words, approximately 1 millivolt.

In Figure 210, vector A represents the current flow in another heart during ventricular depolarization in which the left side of

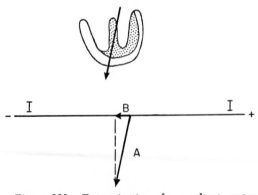

Figure 210. Determination of a resultant vector B along the axis of lead I when vector A represents the current flow in the ventricles.

the heart becomes depolarized somewhat more rapidly than the right. In this instance the vector has a direction of 100 degrees, and the voltage is still 2 millivolts. To determine the potential in lead I, we drop a perpendicular to the lead I axis and find the resultant vector B. Vector B is very short and this time in the negative direction, indicating that at this particular instant the recording in lead I will be negative (below the zero line), and the voltage recorded will be very slight. This figure illustrates especially that when the vector in the heart is in a direction almost perpendicular to the axis of the lead, the voltage recorded in the lead is very small. If the vector has almost exactly the same axis as the lead, essentially the entire voltage of the vector will be recorded.

Vectorial Analysis of Potentials in the Three Standard Leads. Figure 211 illus-

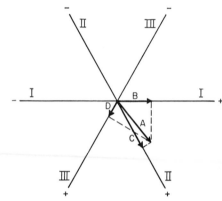

Figure 211. Determination of resultant vectors in leads I, II, and III when vector A represents the current flow in the ventricles.

trates vector A in a partially depolarized ventricle. To determine the potential recorded at this instant in each one of the three standard leads, perpendiculars are dropped to all the different leads as illustrated in the figure. The resultant vector B depicts the potential recorded in lead I, vector C depicts the potential in lead II, and vector D in lead III. In each of these the record is positive. The potential in lead I is approximately one half that of the vector through the heart; in lead II it is almost exactly equal that in the heart; and in lead III it is about one third that in the heart.

Vectorial Analysis of Potentials in the Augmented Limb Leads. Figure 212 shows vector A in a ventricle about half-way

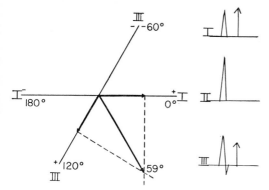

Figure 217. Plotting the mean electrical axis of the heart from two electrocardiographic leads.

tracting the negative portion of the QRS wave in leads I and III from the positive portions, each net vector is plotted on the axes of the respective leads as illustrated in Figure 217.

If the resultant vector of lead I is positive, its base is placed at the point of intersection, and it is plotted in a positive direction along the line depicting lead I. On the other hand, if this vector is negative, it is plotted in a negative direction. Also, for lead III, the resultant vector is placed with its base at the point of intersection, and, if it is positive, it is plotted in the positive direction along the line depicting lead III. If it is negative it is plotted in the negative direction.

In order to determine the actual vector of current flow in the heart, one draws perpendicular lines from the apex of each of the two vectors of leads I and III, respectively. The point of intersection of these two perpendicular lines represents, by vectorial analysis, the apex of the actual vector in the heart, and the point of intersection of the two lead axes represents the negative end of the actual vector as shown in the figure. The average potential generated in the direction of current flow is represented by the length of the vector, and the mean electrical axis is represented by the direction of the vector. Thus, the vector of the mean electrical axis of the heart as determined in Figure 217 is 59 degrees.

It should be emphasized that the vector of current flow through the ventricles determined by this method does not determine the vector at any given instant in the depolarization process of the ventricles but, instead, determines approximately how much and in what direction the average current flows during the entire depolarization period.

Ventricular Conditions That Cause Axis Deviation

Though the mean electrical axis of the ventricles averages approximately 59 degrees, this average can swing to the left to approximately 20

degrees or it can swing to the right to approximately 90 degrees and still be normal. Yet, a number of cardiac conditions can cause axis deviation even beyond these normal limits, as follows:

Change in the Position of the Heart. Obviously, if the heart itself is angulated to the left, the mean electrical axis of the heart will also shift to the left. Such shift to the left occurs during expiration, it occurs when a person lies down, because the abdominal contents press upward against the diaphragm, and it occurs quite frequently in stocky, fat persons whose diaphragms normally press upward against the heart.

On the other hand, shift of the mechanical axis of the heart to the right will cause the mean electrical axis of the ventricles to shift to the right. This condition occurs during inspiration, it occurs when a person stands up, and it occurs normally in tall, lanky persons whose hearts hang downward.

In general, changes in position of the heart cannot cause more than approximately 20 to 30 degrees shift of the axis either to the left or to the right, whereas many pathologic conditions of the heart shift the axis much more than this.

Hypertrophy of One Ventricle. When one ventricle greatly hypertrophies, the axis of the heart shifts because of two reasons: First, far greater quantity of heart muscle then exists on the hypertrophied side of the heart than on the other side, and this allows excess generation of electrical currents on that side of the heart. Second, and more important, more time is required for the depolarization wave to travel through the hypertrophied ventricle than through the normal ventricle. Consequently, the normal ventricle be-

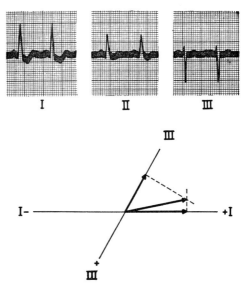

Figure 218. Left axis deviation in hypertensive heart disease. Note also the slightly prolonged QRS complex.

comes depolarized considerably in advance of the hypertrophied ventricle, and this causes a strong vector from the normal side of the heart toward the hypertrophied side. Thus the axis deviates in the direction of the hypertrophied ventricle.

Left axis deviation resulting from hypertrophy of the left ventricle. Figure 218 illustrates the three standard leads of an electrocardiogram in which an analysis of the axis direction shows left axis deviation with the mean electrical axis pointing in the −20 degree direction. This is a typical electrocardiogram resulting from increased muscular mass of the left ventricle. In this instance the axis deviation was caused by *hypertension,* which caused the left ventricle to hypertrophy in order to pump blood against the elevated systemic arterial pressure. However, a similar picture of left axis deviation occurs when the left ventricle hypertrophies as a result of aortic valvular stenosis, aortic valvular regurgitation, or any of a number of congenital heart conditions in which the left ventricle enlarges while the right side of the heart remains relatively normal in size.

Right axis deviation resulting from hypertrophy of the right ventricle. The electrocardiogram of Figure 219 illustrates intense right

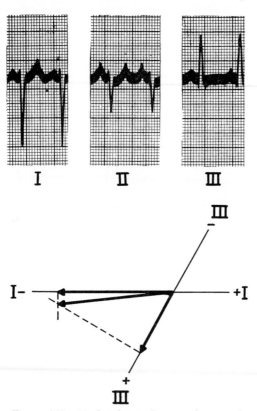

Figure 219. High-voltage electrocardiogram due to pulmonary stenosis with right ventricular hypertrophy. Also, there is intense right axis deviation.

axis deviation with an electrical axis of approximately 170 degrees, which is 111 degrees to the right of the normal mean electrical axis of the ventricles. The right axis deviation illustrated in this figure was caused by hypertrophy of the right side of the heart as a result of pulmonary stenosis. However, right axis deviation may also occur in other congenital heart conditions such as tetralogy of Fallot, interventricular septal defect, etc. Also, hypertrophy of the right ventricle as a result of increased pulmonary vascular resistance, and even *massive pulmonary embolism* with excessive dilatation of the right side of the heart, can cause right axis deviation.

Bundle Branch Block. Ordinarily the depolarization wave spreads through the septum to the apex of the heart and then simultaneously through the lateral walls of both ventricles. Therefore, the two lateral walls of the ventricles depolarize at almost the same time, the right usually very slightly ahead of the left, and the currents flowing from one ventricle almost neutralize the currents flowing from the other ventricle. If one of the major bundle branches is blocked in the ventricular muscular system, depolarization of the two ventricles does not occur even nearly simultaneously, and the depolarization currents do not neutralize each other. As a result, axis deviation results, as follows:

Left bundle branch block. When the left bundle branch is blocked, cardiac depolarization spreads through the right ventricle approximately three times as rapidly as through the left ventricle. Consequently, much of the left ventricle remains polarized for a long time after the right ventricle has become totally depolarized. Thus, the right ventricle is electronegative with respect to the left ventricle during most of the depolarization process, and a very strong vector projects from the right ventricle toward the left ventricle. In other words, there is intense left axis deviation because the positive end of the vector points toward the left ventricle. This is illustrated in Figure 220, which shows typical left axis deviation resulting from left bundle branch block. It will be observed that the axis is approximately −50 degrees.

Because of slowness of impulse conduction when the Purkinje system is blocked, axis deviation resulting from bundle branch block greatly increases the duration of the QRS complex, as will be discussed in greater detail later in the chapter. It is the prolonged QRS complex that differentiates this condition from axis deviation occurring with hypertrophy.

Right bundle branch block. When the right bundle branch is blocked, the left ventricle depolarizes far more rapidly than the right ventricle so that the left becomes electronegative while the right remains electropositive. A very

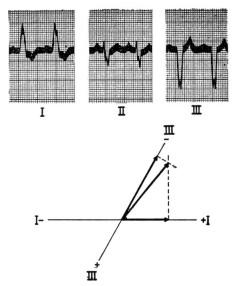

Figure 220. Left axis deviation due to left bundle branch block. Note also the greatly prolonged QRS complex.

strong vector develops with its negative end toward the left ventricle and its positive end toward the right ventricle. In other words, intense right axis deviation occurs.

Right axis deviation caused by right bundle branch block is illustrated in Figure 221, which shows an axis of approximately 105 degrees and a prolonged QRS complex because of blocked conduction in the heart.

Axis Deviation Caused by Muscular Destruction. Following heart attacks which result in destruction of part of the cardiac muscle and replacement of this muscle with fibrous tissue, very abnormal deviations of the axis of the ventricles can occur. The cause of the axis deviation is probably two-fold: First, part of the muscular mass itself is destroyed and is replaced by scar

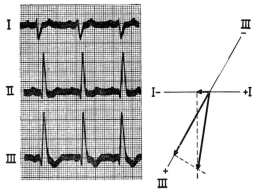

Figure 221. Right axis deviation due to right bundle branch block. Note also the greatly prolonged QRS complex.

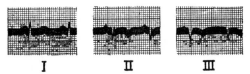

Figure 222. Low-voltage electrocardiogram with evidences of local conduction blocks throughout the ventricles.

tissue so that a smaller quantity of muscle may then be available on one side of the heart than on the other side to generate electrical currents. Second, and probably more important, is blockage of the conduction of depolarization at one or more local points in the ventricles. When blockage of the impulse occurs, the impulse beyond the block flows through the muscle itself rather than through the Purkinje system, allowing the muscular tissue beyond the block to remain electropositive for long periods of time after other portions of the heart have already become totally depolarized. Thus, even local blocks in the ventricles can cause considerable shift of the axis of the heart.

Muscular destruction causes the axis to shift in the direction opposite to the side of destruction, but conduction block causes the axis to shift toward the side of destruction. Thus, the two effects may or may not neutralize each other. Consequently, old infarctions in the heart do not produce consistent changes in axis deviation. Therefore, when other signs of old infarction are present in the electrocardiogram, such as low voltage, as shown in Figure 222, increased duration of the QRS complex, and bizarre spiking patterns of the QRS complex it is probably unimportant to determine the axis of the heart.

CONDITIONS THAT CAUSE ABNORMAL VOLTAGES OF THE QRS COMPLEX

Increased Voltage in the Standard Leads

Normally, the voltages in the three standard electrocardiographic leads, as measured from the peak of the R wave to the bottom of the S wave, vary between 0.5 millivolt and 2.0 millivolts, with lead III usually recording the lowest voltage and lead II usually recording the highest voltage. However, these relationships are not invariably true in even the normal heart. In general, when the sum of the voltages of all the QRS complexes of the three standard leads is greater than 4 millivolts, one considers the patient to have a high-voltage electrocardiogram.

The cause of high-voltage QRS complexes is increased muscular mass of the heart, and this ordinarily results from hypertrophy of the muscle caused by excess load on one part of the heart or the other. The right ventricle hypertrophies when it must pump blood through a stenotic pulmonary valve, and the left ventricle hypertrophies in hypertension. The increased quantity of muscle allows generation of increased quantities of current around the heart. As a result, the electrical potentials recorded in the electrocardiographic leads are considerably greater than normal, as shown in Figures 218 and 219.

Increased Voltage in Chest Leads

The voltage recorded in chest leads depends to a great extent on the exact position of each lead on the chest and on the exact position of the heart inside the chest. Therefore, it is difficult to set special limits on high or low voltage for chest leads. Yet, when the total voltage between the peak of the R wave and the peak of the S wave in any single chest lead is more than 2½ millivolts, one can consider this voltage to be above normal. The usual cause of voltage increased above normal in chest leads is also hypertrophy of the heart.

Decreased Voltage in the Standard Leads

There are three major causes of decreased voltage in the electrocardiograms of the three standard electrocardiographic leads. These are, first, abnormalities of the cardiac muscle itself that prevent generation of large quantities of currents; second, abnormal conditions around the heart so that currents cannot be conducted from the heart to the surface of the body with ease; and, third, rotation of the apex of the heart anteriorly so that the electrical currents of the heart flow mainly anteroposteriorly in the chest rather than up and down the body.

Decreased Voltage Caused by Cardiac Myopathies. One of the most usual causes of decreased voltage of the QRS complex is a series of local intraventricular blocks to the conduction of the cardiac impulse. This causes electrical currents to flow through the ventricles relatively slowly and prevents major portions of the heart from becoming massively depolarized all at once. Consequently, this condition causes moderate prolongation of the QRS complex along with decreased voltage. Figure 222 illustrates the typical low-voltage electrocardiogram with very slight prolongation of the QRS complex, which one often finds after multiple small infarctions of the heart that have resulted in local blocks throughout the ventricles.

Beriberi heart disease frequently causes decreased electrical potentials in the standard electrocardiographic leads. Presumably, beriberi de-

presses the metabolism of the cardiac muscle and therefore prevents each portion of the muscle from generating normal quantities of current. Consequently the overall voltages recorded by the electrocardiographic leads are considerably reduced.

Many different toxic conditions of the heart can also decrease the voltages in the electrocardiogram, either by blocking the rate of spread of the depolarization wave in the heart or by depressing the cardiac muscle so that the quantity of current generated during depolarization is diminished.

Decreased Voltage Caused by Conditions Surrounding the Heart. One of the most important causes of decreased voltage in the electrocardiographic leads is fluid in the pericardium. Because extracellular fluid conducts electrical currents with great ease, currents flowing out of the heart are conducted with great ease from one part of the heart to another through the pericardial effusion, and the quantity of current reaching the surface of the body is greatly diminished. Pleural effusion to a lesser extent can also "short out" the currents around the heart so that the voltages at the surface of the body and in the electrocardiograms will be decreased.

Pulmonary emphysema can also decrease the electrocardiographic potentials but by a different method from that of pericardial effusion. In pulmonary emphysema, conduction of electrical current through the lungs is considerably depressed because of the excessive quantity of air in the lungs. Also, the chest cavity enlarges, and the lungs tend to envelop the heart to a greater extent than normally. Therefore, the lungs act as an insulator to prevent spread of currents from the heart to the surface of the body, and this in general results in decreased electrocardiographic potentials in the various leads.

Decreased Voltage Resulting from Anteroposterior Direction of Current Flow. Under certain conditions, such as in patients with very thick chests, the apex of the heart may point almost directly toward the sternum. In this instance, most of the currents in the ventricles, instead of flowing up and down the chest, flow backward and forward along the axis of the heart. For this reason, the voltages in the standard electrocardiographic leads are greatly decreased, but the voltages in the chest leads are greatly increased.

PROLONGED AND BIZARRE PATTERNS OF THE QRS COMPLEX

Prolonged QRS Complex as a Result of Cardiac Hypertrophy

The QRS complex lasts as long as the process of depolarization continues to spread through the ventricles—that is, as long as part of the ventricles is depolarized and part is still polarized. Therefore, the cause of a prolonged QRS complex is always *delayed conduction* of the impulse through the ventricles. Such delayed conduction often occurs when one or both ventricles are hypertrophied or dilated, owing to the longer pathway that the impulse must then travel. The normal QRS complex lasts about 0.06 to 0.07 second, whereas in hypertrophy or dilatation of the left or right ventricle the QRS complex may be prolonged to 0.09 second or occasionally 0.10 second.

Prolonged QRS Complex Resulting from Purkinje System Blocks

Block of the Purkinje system decreases the rate of impulse conduction through the heart to approximately one-third to one-fourth normal. Therefore, if complete block of one of the bundle branches occurs, the duration of the QRS complex is increased to a value of approximately 0.16 to 0.18 second.

In general a QRS complex is considered to be abnormally long when it lasts more than 0.09 second, and when it lasts more than 0.12 second the prolongation is almost certain to be caused by pathologic block of the conduction system somewhere in the ventricles, as illustrated in Figures 220 and 221.

Local block of the Purkinje system in the walls of the ventricles can prolong the QRS complex to a mild or moderate extent, though not greatly. Such local blocks prevent passage of the impulse into small areas of the ventricles, but, because the impulse does pass rapidly into adjacent areas, it can flow by muscular conduction into the blocked areas with only a slight delay. Therefore, local blocks, unless they affect relatively large bundles of Purkinje fibers, will usually prolong the QRS complex only a few hundredths of a second.

Conditions Causing Bizarre QRS Complexes

The same factors that cause axis deviations, decreased voltage of the QRS complex, and prolonged QRS complexes can cause very bizarre patterns of the complex. These factors include, mainly, destruction of cardiac muscle in various areas throughout the ventricular system with replacement of this muscle by scar tissue, and secondly, local or major blocks in the conduction of impulses by the Purkinje system.

Sometimes local blocks occur in both the right ventricle and the left ventricle. If the blocks are such that the impulse reaches the blocked area in the right ventricle much later than it reaches the blocked area in the left ventricle, but the total quantity of blocked muscle in the left ventricle is greater than the total quantity in the right ven-

tricle, then a situation occurs in which the axis of the heart first shifts very strongly to the left and then—when the left ventricle has become totally depolarized but a small portion of the right ventricle still remains polarized—rapidly shifts diametrically oppositely toward the right ventricle. This effect causes double or even triple peaks in some of the standard electrocardiographic leads, such as those illustrated in Figure 220.

CURRENT OF INJURY

Many different cardiac abnormalities, especially those that damage the heart muscle itself, often cause part of the heart to remain depolarized all the time. When this occurs, current will flow between the pathologically depolarized and the normal polarized areas. This is called the *current of injury.*

Some of the abnormalities that can cause current of injury are: (1) mechanical trauma, which makes the membranes remain excessively permeable so that repolarization cannot take place, (2) infectious processes that damage the muscle membranes, and (3) ischemia of the muscle caused by coronary occlusion, which is by far the most common cause of current injury in the heart; during ischemia appropriate energy simply is not available to repolarize the membranes.

Effect of Current of Injury on the QRS Complex

In Figure 223 a shaded area in the base of the left ventricle is newly infarcted. Therefore, during the T-P interval—that is, when the normal ventricular muscle is polarized—current flows from the base of the left ventricle toward the rest of the ventricles, or, in other words, in a direction of approximately 125 degrees. As illustrated in the lower portions of the figure, even before the QRS

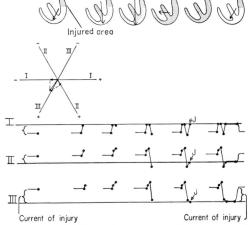

Figure 223. Effect of a current of injury on the electrocardiogram.

complex begins, this current flow causes an initial record in lead I below the zero potential line because the resultant vector of the current of injury points toward the negative terminal of lead I. In lead II the record is above the line because the resultant vector points toward the positive terminal of lead II. In lead III the vector of the current flow is in the same direction as the polarity of lead III so that the record is positive. Furthermore, because the vector of the current of injury lies almost exactly along the axis of lead III, the potential of the current of injury in lead III is much higher than in either of the other two records.

As the heart then proceeds through its normal wave of depolarization, part of the septum first becomes depolarized, and the process of depolarization spreads down to the apex and back toward the bases of the ventricles. The last portion of the ventricles to become totally depolarized is the base of the right ventricle because the base of the left ventricle is already totally and permanently depolarized. By vectorial analysis, as illustrated in the figure, the electrocardiogram generated by the depolarization wave traveling through the ventricles may be constructed graphically.

When the heart becomes totally depolarized at the end of the depolarization process, as noted at the right in Figure 223, all of the ventricular system is in a negative state. Therefore, at this instant in the electrocardiogram, absolutely no current flows around the musculature of the ventricles, and the current of injury is abolished.

As repolarization then takes place, all of the heart finally repolarizes except the area of permanent depolarization in the injured base of the left ventricle. Thus, the repolarization wave (the T wave) causes a return of the current of injury in each lead, as noted at the far right in Figure 223.

The J Point—The Zero Reference Potential of the Electrocardiogram

One would think that the electrocardiograph machines for recording electrocardiograms could determine when no currents are flowing around the heart. However, many stray currents exist in the body, such as currents resulting from "skin potentials," currents resulting from differences in ionic concentrations in different parts of the body, etc. Therefore, when two electrodes are connected between the arms or between an arm and a leg, these stray currents make it impossible for one to predetermine the exact zero reference level in the electrocardiogram. To determine a zero potential line in the record of the electrocardiogram one notes *the exact point at which the wave of depolarization just completes its passage through the heart,* which obviously occurs at the very end

of the QRS complex. This point is known as the "J point" in the electrocardiogram, as illustrated in Figures 223 and 224. For further analysis of the electrical axis of the current of injury a horizontal line is drawn through the electrocardiogram at the level of the J point, and this horizontal line is the zero potential line in the electrocardiogram.

Use of the J Point in Plotting the Axis of a Current of Injury. Figure 224 illustrates

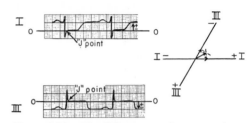

Figure 224. The "J" point as the zero reference voltage of the electrocardiogram. Also, method for plotting the axis of a current of injury.

electrocardiograms recorded from leads I and III, both of which show currents of injury. In other words, the J point and the S-T segment of each of these two electrocardiograms are not on the same line as the T-P segment. A horizontal line has been drawn through the J point to represent the zero potential level in each of the two recordings. The potential of the current of injury in each lead is the difference between the level of the T-P segment of the electrocardiogram and the zero potential line, as illustrated by the arrows. In lead I the recorded current of injury is above the zero potential line and is, therefore, positive. On the other hand, in lead III the T-P segment is below the zero potential line; therefore, the current of injury in lead III is negative.

To the right in Figure 224, the potentials of the current of injury in leads I and III are plotted on the coordinates of these leads, and the vector of the current of injury is determined by the method already described. In this instance, the vector of the current of injury extends from the right side of the body toward the left and slightly in the upward direction, with an axis of approximately −30 degrees.

If one places the vector of the current of injury directly over the ventricles, *the negative end of the vector points toward the depolarized area of the ventricles.* In the instance illustrated in Figure 224, the damaged area would be in the lateral wall of the right ventricle.

Coronary Ischemia as a Cause of Current of Injury

Insufficient blood flow to the cardiac muscle depresses metabolism of the muscle for three different reasons: oxygen lack, excess carbon dioxide, and lack of sufficient transport of nutrients. Consequently, polarization of the membranes cannot occur in areas of severe myocardial ischemia. Often, the heart muscle does not die because the blood flow is sufficient to maintain life of the muscle even though it is not sufficient to cause repolarization of the membranes. As long as this state exists, a current of injury continues to flow.

Obviously, extreme ischemia of the cardiac muscle occurs following coronary occlusion, and strong currents of injury flow from the infarcted area of the ventricles during diastole, as is illustrated in Figures 225 and 226. Therefore, one of the most important diagnostic features of electrocardiograms recorded following acute coronary thrombosis is the current of injury.

Acute Anterior Wall Infarction. Figure 225 illustrates the electrocardiogram in the three standard leads and in one chest lead recorded from a patient with acute anterior wall cardiac infarction. The most important diagnostic feature of this electrocardiogram is the current of injury in the chest lead. If one draws a zero potential line through the J point of this lead, he finds a strong negative current of injury during diastole. In other words, the negative end of the current of injury vector is against the chest wall. This means that the current of injury is emanating from the anterior wall of the ventricles, which is the main reason for diagnosing this condition as anterior wall infarction.

If one analyzes the currents of injury in leads I and III, he finds a negative vector for the current of injury in lead I and a positive vector for the current of injury in lead III. This means that the resultant vector of the current of injury in the heart is approximately +150 degrees, with the negative end of the vector pointing toward the left ventricle and the positive end of the vector pointing toward the right ventricle. Thus, in this particular electrocardiogram the current of injury appears to be coming mainly from the left ventricle and from the anterior wall of the heart. Therefore, one would suspect that this anterior wall infarction is probably caused by thrombosis of the descending limb of the left coronary artery.

Posterior Wall Infarction. Figure 226 illustrates the three standard leads and one chest lead from a patient with posterior wall infarction. The major diagnostic feature of this electrocardiogram is also in the chest lead. If a zero potential reference line is drawn through the J point of this lead, it is readily apparent that during diastole the vector of the current of injury is positive. This means that the positive end of the vector is at the chest wall and the negative end of the vector is away from the chest wall. In other words, the current of injury is coming from the opposite side of the heart from that portion adjacent to the chest wall, which is the reason why this type of electrocardiogram is the basis for a diagnosis of posterior wall infarction.

If one analyzes the currents of injury in leads II and III of Figure 226, it is readily apparent that the current of injury is negative in both leads. By vectorial analysis as shown in the figure, it is evident that the vector of the current of injury is approximately −95 degrees with the negative end of the vector pointing downward and the positive end of the vector pointing upward. Thus, because the infarct, as illustrated by the chest

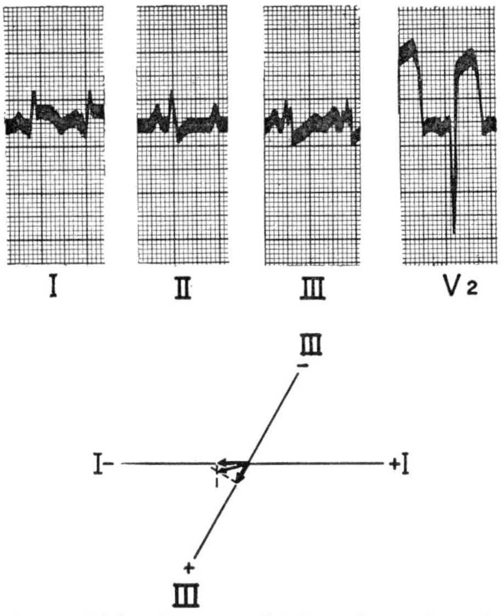

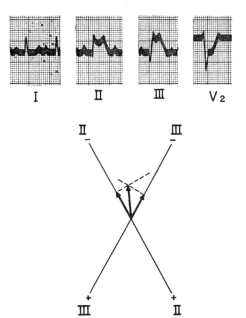

Figure 225. Current of injury in acute anterior wall infarction. Note the intense current of injury in lead V₂.

Figure 226. Current of injury in acute posterior wall, apical infarction.

lead, is on the posterior wall of the heart and, as illustrated by the currents of injury in leads II and III, is in the downward portion of the heart, one would suspect that this infarct is close to the apex on the posterior wall of the left ventricle, possibly spreading over the septum into the wall of the right ventricle to a slight exent.

Infarction in Other Parts of the Heart.
By the same procedures as those illustrated in the above two discussions of anterior and posterior wall infarctions, it is possible to determine the locus of an infarcted area emitting a current of injury regardless of which part of the heart is involved. In making such vectorial analyses, it must always be remembered that *the positive end of the vector points toward the normal cadiac muscle and the negative end of the vector points toward the abnormal portion of the heart that is emitting the current of injury.*

Recovery from Coronary Thrombosis.
Figure 227 illustrates the chest lead from a patient with posterior infarction, showing the change in this chest lead from the day of the attack to one week later, then three weeks later, and finally one year later. From this electrocardiogram it can be seen that the current of injury is very strong immediately after the acute attack, but after approximately one week the current of injury has diminished considerably, and after three weeks it is completely gone. After that, the electrocardiogram does not change greatly during the following year. This is the usual recovery pattern following cardiac infarction of moderate degree when the collateral coronary blood flow is sufficient to reestablish appropriate nutrition to the infarcted area. On the other hand, when all the coronary vessels throughout the heart are fairly well sclerosed, it may not be possible for the adjacent coronary vessels to supply sufficient blood to the infarcted area for recovery. Therefore, in some patients with coronary infarction the infarcted area never redevelops an adequate coronary blood supply, and relative coronary insufficiency persists in this area of the heart indefinitely. If the muscle does not die and become replaced

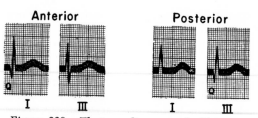

Figure 228. Electrocardiograms of old anterior and posterior wall infarctions, illustrating the Q wave in lead I in old anterior wall infarction and the Q wave in lead III in old posterior wall infarction.

by scar tissue, it will continually emit current of injury as long as the relative ischemia exists.

Old recovered myocardial infarction. Figure 228 illustrates leads I and III in anterior infarction and posterior infarction as these leads appear approximately a year after the acute episode. These are what might be called the "ideal" configurations of the QRS complex in these types of recovered myocardial infarction. It is illustrated in these figures that usually a Q wave develops at the beginning of the QRS complex in lead I in anterior infarction, whereas in posterior infarction a Q wave develops at the beginning of the QRS complex in lead III. These types of configurations are certainly not those found in all cases of old anterior and posterior cardiac infarction. As has been pointed out above, local loss of muscle and local areas of conduction block can cause many bizarre patterns of the QRS complex, decreased voltage of the QRS complex, and prolongation of the QRS complex.

Current of Injury in Angina Pectoris.
"Angina pectoris" means simply pain in the pectoral regions of the upper chest, this pain usually radiating down the left arm and into the neck. The pain is caused by relative ischemia of the heart, for no pain may be felt as long as the person is perfectly quiet, but, just as soon as he overworks his heart, the pain appears.

A current of injury often occurs during an attack of severe angina pectoris, for the relative coronary insufficiency occasionally becomes great enough to prevent adequate repolarization of the membranes in some areas of the heart during diastole.

Other Causes of Currents of Injury

Pericarditis. When the parietal pericardium becomes infected, the infection may invade the surface of the heart to a moderate extent, causing a tendency for the myocardium along the surface of the pericardial cavity not to repolarize. Furthermore, it is possible for pericarditis to affect the myocardium on one side of the heart but not on the other side, in which case currents of injury flow around the heart. Thus, pericarditis can

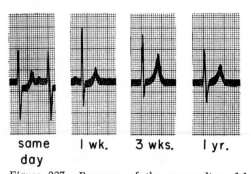

Figure 227. Recovery of the myocardium following moderate posterior wall infarction, illustrating disappearance of the current of injury (lead V_3).

cause electrocardiograms simulating those that occur in almost any type of myocardial infarction. The difference between the electrocardiograms that occur in pericarditis and those that occur in myocardial infarction is not immediately apparent, but the course of additional changes in the electrocardiogram is quite different. Usually, after the pericardial infection is over, the electrocardiogram returns to normal, whereas in myocardial infarction, after the acute phase of the infarction is over, various conductive or muscular deficiency abnormalities still persist as were detailed above.

Myocarditis.   Myocarditis—that is, inflammation of the myocardium—can be caused by a number of different conditions, including especially toxic inflammation of the myocardium as the result of diphtheria toxin or inflammation of the myocardium during acute rheumatic fever. In these instances, inflammation of areas of the myocardium may prevent normal repolarization of the heart and consequently result in currents of injury.

Here again, as in pericarditis, the myocarditis may be localized mainly on one side of the heart, in which case the electrocardiograms in the various leads can simulate all the different types of myocardial infarction. However, myocarditis can eventually be differentiated from cardiac infarction because a normal electrocardiogram is usually re-established after recovery from myocarditis, whereas a normal electrocardiogram is almost never re-established after recovery from infarction.

Mechanical Trauma of the Heart.   Very rarely the heart can be bruised or otherwise mechanically traumatized. In such conditions the membranes of the muscle fibers do not polarize satisfactorily during diastole and currents of injury are emitted from the bruised areas. Here again, electrocardiograms simulating myocardial infarction may be recorded.

ABNORMALITIES IN THE T WAVE

Earlier in the chapter it was pointed out that the T wave is normally positive in all the standard leads and that this is caused by repolarization of the apex of the heart ahead of the endocardial surfaces of the ventricles. This is backwards to the direction in which depolarization takes place.

If the student does not by now understand the basic principles of the upright T wave in the standard leads, he should become familiar with the earlier more detailed discussion of this before proceeding to the following few sections.

The T wave becomes abnormal when the normal sequence of repolarization does not occur. Several factors can change this sequence of repolarization, as follows:

Effect of Slow Conduction of the Depolarization Wave on the T Wave

Referring back to Figure 220, it will be observed that the QRS complex is considerably prolonged. The reason for this prolongation is delayed conduction in the left ventricle as a result of left bundle branch block. The left ventricle becomes depolarized approximately 0.10 second after depolarization of the right ventricle. The refractory periods of the right and left ventricular muscle masses are not greatly different from each other. Therefore, the right ventricle begins to repolarize long before the left ventricle; this causes positivity in the right ventricle and negativity in the left ventricle. In other words, the mean axis of the T wave is from left to right, which is opposite to the mean electrical axis of the QRS complex. Thus, when conduction of the impulse is greatly delayed through the ventricles, the T wave is almost always of opposite polarity to that of the QRS complex.

In Figure 221 and in several figures in the following chapter, conduction also does not occur through the Purkinje system. As a result, the rate of conduction is greatly slowed, and in each instance the T wave is of opposite polarity to that of the QRS complex, whether the condition causing this delayed conduction happens to be left bundle branch block, right bundle branch block, ventricular extrasystole, or otherwise.

Prolonged Refractory Period of Portions of the Ventricular Muscle as a Cause of Abnormalities in the T Wave

If the apex of the left ventricle should have an abnormally long refractory period, then repolarization of the ventricle would not begin at the apex as it normally does. Instead, the base of the heart would repolarize ahead of the apex, and the vector of repolarization would point from the apex toward the base of the heart. This is opposite to the usual vector of repolarization, and, consequently, the T wave in all three standard leads would be negative rather than the usual positive. Thus, the simple fact that the apical muscle of the heart has a prolonged refractory period is sufficient to cause marked changes in the T wave, even to the extent of changing the entire polarity, as is illustrated in Figure 229.

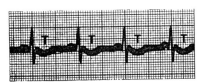

Figure 229.   Inverted T wave resulting from mild ischemia of the apex of the ventricles.

Many different portions of the ventricular muscle can have abnormally long refractory periods. For instance, the refractory period can be prolonged in the base of the left ventricle, in the side of the right ventricle, in the septum, at the apex, or in any other area. Prolongation of the refractory period in any one of these areas will cause some abnormality in the T wave, and it is usually possible to calculate by vectorial analysis what the abnormality will be.

Ischemia is by far the most common cause of increased refractory period of cardiac muscle, and, when the ischemia occurs in only one area of the heart, the refractory period of this area increases out of proportion to that in other portions. As a result, very definite changes in the T wave may take place. The ischemia may result from chronic, progressive coronary occlusion, acute coronary occlusion, or relative coronary insufficiency occurring during exercise.

One means for detecting mild coronary insufficiency is to have the patient exercise and then record the electrocardiogram immediately thereafter, noting whether or not changes occur in the T waves. The changes in the T waves need not be very specific, for any change in the T wave in any lead—inversion, for instance, or a biphasic wave—is evidence enough that some portion of the ventricular muscle has increased its refractory period out of proportion to the rest of the heart, and this is probably due to relative coronary insufficiency.

All the other conditions that can cause currents of injury, including pericarditis, myocarditis, and mechanical trauma of the heart, can also cause changes in the T wave. A current of injury occurs when the refractory period of the muscle is so long that some of the muscle fails to repolarize before the next cardiac contraction. Therefore, a current of injury is actually an exacerbated form of abnormal T wave, for current of injury and abnormal repolarization of the heart distorting the T wave both result from increased refractory period of one or several portions of cardiac muscle, and the difference is only a matter of degree.

Effect of Digitalis on the T Wave. As discussed in Chapter 36, digitalis is a drug that can be used during relative coronary insufficiency to increase the strength of cardiac muscular contraction. However, digitalis also decreases the refractory period of cardiac muscle. It usually decreases the refractory period of most of the cardiac muscle of the heart in approximately the same proportion, but, when overdosages of digitalis are given, the refractory period of one part of the heart may be decreased out of proportion to the refractory period of other portions of the heart. As a result, non-specific changes such as T wave inversion or biphasic T waves may occur in one or more of the electrocardiographic leads. A biphasic T wave due to excessive administration

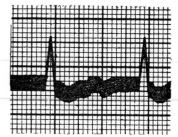

Figure 230.   Biphasic T wave due to digitalis toxicity.

of digitalis is illustrated in Figure 230. There is a slight amount of current of injury, too. This probably results from still another effect of digitalis, greatly increased permeability of the muscle membranes.

Changes in the T wave during digitalis administration are one of the earliest signs of digitalis toxicity. If still more digitalis is given to the patient, strong currents of injury may develop, and, as noted in the preceding chapter, digitalis can also block conduction of the cardiac impulse to various portions of the heart so that various arrhythmias result. It is desirable clinically to prevent digitalis excess from going beyond the stage of T wave abnormalities. Therefore, the electrocardiograph is used routinely in following digitalized patients.

Effect of Various Toxic Conditions on the T Wave. Because changes in the T wave can result from even the slightest change in the refractory period of one portion of the heart or another, the T wave is one of the most important indicators in the electrocardiogram of mild abnormality of the cardiac muscle. Many different toxic conditions of the body can cause changes in the T wave. These include excess administration of almost any drug that depresses or overstimulates cellular metabolism, infectious processes that cause high fever or other toxic manifestations throughout the body, abnormalities of metabolism resulting from various glandular dysfunctions such as thyrotoxicosis, toxicity resulting from uremia, toxicity resulting from changes in acid-base balance in the body, abnormal ionic constituents of the extracellular fluids, and many other conditions.

Though the various toxicities that cause generalized abnormalities in the body tend to affect the T wave of the electrocardiogram before they affect other portions of the electrocardiogram, if these toxicities become severe enough they can cause currents of injury and finally can distort the QRS complex.

REFERENCES

See Chapter 22, General bibliography on electrocardiography; Chapter 30, Coronary disease; Chapter 38, Cardiac abnormalities.

Chapter 24

Electrocardiographic Interpretation of Cardiac Arrhythmias

The rhythmicity of the heart and some of the abnormalities of rhythmicity were discussed in Chapter 21. The major purpose of the present chapter is to discuss still other abnormalities of rhythm and to describe the various types of electrocardiograms that are recorded in these conditions known clinically as "cardiac arrhythmias."

ABNORMAL SINUS RHYTHMS

Tachycardia

The term "tachycardia" means a fast heart rate; an electrocardiogram recorded from a patient with tachycardia is illustrated in Figure 231.

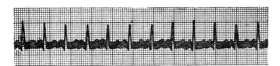

Figure 231. Sinus tachycardia (lead I).

This electrocardiogram is perfectly normal except that the rate of heart beat, as determined from the time interval between QRS complexes, is approximately 150 per minute instead of the normal 72 beats per minute.

The three general causes of tachycardia are first, *increased body temperature*, second, *stimulation of the heart by the sympathetics*, and third, *toxic conditions of the heart*.

The rate of the heart increases approximately 10 beats per minute for each degree Fahrenheit increase in body temperature up to a body temperature of about 105°, but beyond this the heart rate may actually decrease owing to progressive weakening of the heart muscle as a result of the fever. Fever causes tachycardia because increased temperature increases the rate of metabolism of the cardiac muscle, which in turn directly increases the excitability and the rate of rhythm of the heart.

The various factors that can cause the sympathetics to excite the heart have already been discussed in relation to the reflexes of the circulatory system. For instance, when a patient loses blood and passes into a state of shock or semi-shock, reflex sympathetic stimulation of the heart increases its rate to as much as 150 to 180 beats per minute. Also, simple weakening of the myocardium sometimes increases the heart rate because the weakened heart does not pump blood into the arterial tree to a normal extent, and this elicits sufficient sympathetic reflexes to increase the rate of the heart. It is possible, too, that pathologic processes that weaken the heart might in some manner directly increase the excitability of the S-A node, increasing the heart rate in this manner.

Various toxic conditions, such as myocarditis, ischemia of the heart, etc., can change the degree of excitability of the cardiac muscle by directly affecting the membranes of the muscle fibers. Consequently, these conditions occasionally cause sinus tachycardia by directly increasing the excitability of the S-A node.

Bradycardia

The term "bradycardia" means, very simply, a slowed heart rate; the condition is caused by factors opposite to those that cause tachycardia. Figure 232 illustrates an electrocardiographic record

Figure 232. Sinus bradycardia (lead III).

from a patient with bradycardia, whose heart rate is approximately 40 beats per minute, as is evident from the time calibration lines.

Bradycardia in Athletes. The well-trained athlete ordinarily has a considerably slower heart

319

rate than the untrained person. The reason for this is that the athlete's heart is considerably stronger than that in a normal person, and this in turn allows the athlete's heart to pump a greater stroke volume output per beat. Thus, the large quantities of blood pumped into the arterial tree with each beat initiate sufficient circulatory reflexes to cause bradycardia.

Vagal Stimulation as a Cause of Bradycardia. Obviously, any circulatory reflex that stimulates the vagus nerve can cause the rate of the heart to decrease considerably. Perhaps the most striking example of this occurs in patients with the *carotid sinus syndrome.* In these patients an arteriosclerotic process in the carotid sinus region of the carotid artery causes excessive sensitivity of the pressure receptors located in the arterial wall; as a result mild pressure on the neck elicits a strong pressoreceptor reflex, causing intense vagal stimulation of the heart and extreme bradycardia. Indeed, such pressure may actually stop the heart.

Bradycardia Resulting from Myocardial Weakening. Though mild weakness of the myocardium may cause increased heart rate owing to compensatory circulatory reflexes, when the various weakening factors, such as ischemia, toxicities, etc., develop to an extreme extent, the natural excitability of the cardiac muscle becomes more and more depressed until finally the natural rhythm of the heart is greatly slowed. Thus in the late stages of various toxic conditions, such as acidosis, uremia, different types of poisonings, etc., the heart rate becomes very slow.

Sinus Arrhythmia

Figure 233 illustrates a cardiotachometer recording of the heart rate during normal and deep respiration. A cardiotachometer is an instrument that records by the height of successive spikes the duration of the interval between each two QRS complexes in the electrocardiogram. It will be noted from this record that the heart rate increases and decreases approximately 5 per cent during the various phases of the respiratory cycle. However, during deep respiration, as is shown to the right in Figure 233, the heart rate increases and decreases by as much as 30 per cent.

Sinus arrhythmia is a result of several circulatory reflexes that will be described in detail in

Chapter 32. First, when the blood pressure rises and falls during each cycle of respiration, the pressoreceptors are alternately stimulated and depressed, causing reflex slowing and speeding up of the heart rate. Second, during each respiratory cycle, the negative intrapleural pressure increases and decreases, which increases and decreases the effective pressure in the veins of the chest. This elicits a waxing and waning Bainbridge reflex that also increases and decreases cardiac rate. Finally, when the respiratory center of the medulla is excited during each respiratory cycle, some of the impulses "spill over" from the respiratory center into the vasomotor center, causing alternate increase and decrease in the number of impulses transmitted to the heart through the sympathetics and vagi. Thus, a number of different reflexes probably combine to cause sinus arrhythmia, and it is well known that sinus arrhythmia is normally present in every person. However, it is very pronounced in some persons, possibly as a result of excessive depth of respiration or excessive sensitivity of the various reflexes which cause the arrhythmia.

ABNORMAL RHYTHMS RESULTING FROM BLOCK IN IMPULSE CONDUCTION

Sinoatrial Block

In rare instances the impulse from the S-A node is blocked before it enters the atrial muscle. This phenomenon is illustrated in Figure 234, which shows the sudden cessation of P waves due to standstill of the atrium. However, the ventricle picks up a new rhythm, the impulse originating presumably in the A-V node or in the A-V bundle so that the ventricular QRS-T complex is not altered. At times after sinoatrial block the pacemaker of the heart will be a point in the atrial muscle rather than in the A-V node or ventricles. In this instance, an abnormal P wave will occur before each QRS-T complex and the rate of heart beat will usually be considerably greater.

Atrioventricular Block

The only means by which impulses can ordinarily pass from the atria into the ventricles is through the A-V bundle, which is also known as the bundle of His. The different conditions that

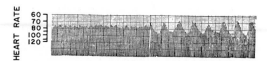

Figure 233. Sinus arrhythmia as detected by a cardiotachometer. To the left the subject is breathing normally and to the right very deeply.

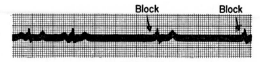

Figure 234. S-A nodal block with ventricular "escape" (lead III).

can either decrease the rate of conduction of the impulse through this bundle or can totally block the impulse are:

1. *Ischemia of the A-V bundle (or A-V junction)* often delays or blocks conduction from the atria to the ventricles. Coronary insufficiency can cause ischemia of the bundle in the same manner that it can cause ischemia of the myocardium. If the ischemia is mild, the rate of conduction may be depressed but not blocked, but, if the ischemia is very severe, conduction may be totally blocked.

2. *Compression of the A-V bundle* by scar tissue or by calcified portions of the heart can depress conduction or block conduction from the atria to the ventricles. In old age, the fibrous rings around the valves of the heart sometimes become calcified, and these calcified rings can at times press against the A-V bundle sufficiently to alter conduction.

3. *Inflammation of the A-V bundle or fibers of the A-V junction* can depress conductivity between the atria and the ventricles. Inflammation results frequently from different types of myocarditis such as occur in diphtheria and rheumatic fever. The toxin from the diphtheria bacilli specifically injures the myocardium and the Purkinje system so that portions of the Purkinje fibers may be destroyed or sufficient edema may develop around the fibers to depress their rate of conduction or even totally block their conduction. Rheumatic fever also causes inflammation and edema, most of the pathology occurring in the connective tissues surrounding the Purkinje fibers rather than in the Purkinje fibers themselves. Consequently, depressed conduction in rheumatic fever is probably due mainly to edema and connective tissue reactions around the A-V bundle and A-V junction rather than in the bundle itself.

4. *Extreme stimulation of the heart by the vagi* in rare instances will block impulse conduction through the A-V junctional tissue. This, too, can result in atrioventricular block. Such vagal excitation occasionally results from strong stimulation of the pressoreceptors in persons with the *carotid sinus syndrome*, which is discussed in Chapter 32.

Incomplete Heart Block. *Prolonged P-R (or P-Q) interval—"first degree block."* The normal lapse of time between the *beginning* of the P wave and the *beginning* of the QRS complex is approximately 0.16 second when the heart is beating at a normal rate. This P-R interval decreases in length with faster heartbeat and increases with slower heartbeat. In general, when the P-R interval increases above a value of approximately 0.20

second, the P-R interval is said to be prolonged, and the patient is said to have *first degree incomplete heart block.* That is, the rate of conduction through the A-V bundle is slowed. Figure 235 illustrates an electrocardiogram with a prolonged P-R interval, the interval in this instance being approximately 0.30 second.

The P-R interval rarely increases above 0.35 to 0.50 second, for by the time the rate of conduction through the A-V bundle is depressed to this extent, the intensity of the action potentials along the Purkinje fibers is usually so depressed that conduction stops entirely. Thus, when a patient's P-R interval is approaching these limits, additional slight increase in the severity of the condition will completely block the impulse conduction rather than simply delaying conduction further. Therefore, one of the means for determining the severity of some heart diseases—rheumatic fever, for instance—is to measure the P-R interval.

Second degree block. When conduction through the A-V bundle is slowed until the P-R interval is 0.25 to 0.50 second, the action potentials traveling through the bundle fibers are sometimes strong enough to pass on through the bundle and at other times are not strong enough. Often the impulse passes into the ventricles on one heartbeat and fails to pass on the next one or two beats, thus alternating between conduction and non-conduction. In this instance, the atria beat at a considerably faster rate than the ventricles, and it is said that there are "dropped beats" of the ventricles. This condition is called *second degree incomplete heart block.*

Figure 236 illustrates P-R intervals as long as 0.45 second, and it also illustrates one dropped beat as a result of failure of conduction between the atria and ventricles through the A-V bundle.

At times every other beat of the ventricles will be dropped so that a "2:1 rhythm" develops in the heart, with the atria beating twice for every single beat of the ventricles. Sometimes other rhythmns, such as 3:2 or 3:1, also develop.

Complete Atrioventricular Block. When the condition causing poor conduction in the A-V bundle becomes extremely severe, complete block of the impulse from the atria into the ventricles occurs. In this instance the P waves become completely dissociated from the QRS-T complexes, as illustrated in Figure 237. It will be noted that the rate of rhythm of the atria in this electrocardio-

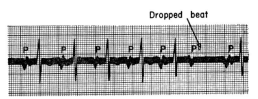

Dropped beat

Figure 236. Partial atrioventricular block (lead **V₈**).

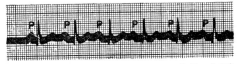

Figure 235. Prolonged P-R interval (lead II).

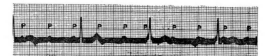

Figure 237. Complete atrioventricular block (lead II).

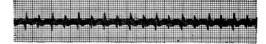

Figure 238. Partial intraventricular block—electrical alternans (lead III).

gram is approximately 100 beats per minute, while the rate of ventricular beat is less than 40 per minute. Furthermore, there is no relationship whatsoever between the rhythm of the atria and that of the ventricles, for the ventricles have "escaped" from control by the atria, and they are beating at their own natural rate.

Stokes-Adams syndrome. In some patients with atrioventricular block, total block comes and goes—that is, all impulses are conducted from the atria into the ventricles for a period of time, and then suddenly no impulses at all are transmitted. The ventricles "escape" and beat at their own rate until suddenly once again conduction through the A-V bundle returns. The duration of dissociation between the atria and the ventricles may be a few seconds, a few minutes, a few hours, or even weeks or more before conduction returns. Particularly does this condition occur in hearts with borderline ischemia.

Immediately after conduction through the A-V bundle is first blocked, the ventricles usually will not pick up their own rhythm for about 5 to 10 seconds. Because the brain cannot remain active for more than 3 to 5 seconds without blood supply, such patients usually faint between block of conduction and "escape" of the ventricles. These periodic fainting spells are known as Stokes-Adams syndrome.

Occasionally the interval of ventricular standstill is so long that it either becomes detrimental to the health of the patient or causes death. Consequently, many of these patients would be better off with total heart block than constantly shifting back and forth between total heart block and atrial control of the ventricles. Such patients are frequently treated with drugs that depress conduction in the A-V bundle so that total heart block will persist all of the time. Commonly, digitalis is the drug used for this purpose, but quinidine or barium ion can also convert a Stokes-Adams syndrome into total heart block.

Incomplete Intraventricular Block— Electrical Alternans

The same factors that can block impulse conduction in the A-V bundle, except vagal stimulation, can also block impulse conduction in peripheral portions of the Purkinje system. At times, *incomplete* block occurs so that the impulse is sometimes transmitted and sometimes not transmitted, causing slowing of the impulse during some heart cycles and not during others. The QRS complex may be considerably abnormal during those cycles in which the impulse is slowed, for even the slightest delay in conduction may allow an area of the heart to remain electropositive longer than normally, and this will alter the QRS complex. Figure 238 illustrates the condition known as *electrical alternans* which results from intraventricular block every other heartbeat. This electrocardiogram illustrates rather extreme tachycardia, which is probably the reason incomplete conduction block somewhere in the ventricles has occurred, for, when the rate of the heart is very rapid, it may be impossible for portions of the Purkinje system to recover rapidly enough to respond during each succeeding heartbeat. Also, many conditions that depress the heart, such as ischemia, myocarditis, and digitalis toxicity, can cause incomplete intraventricular block and electrical alternans.

PREMATURE BEATS

A premature beat is a contraction of the heart prior to the time when normal contraction would have been expected. This condition is also frequently called *extrasystole*.

Causes of Premature Beats. Most premature beats probably result from *ectopic foci* in the heart, which emit abnormal impulses at odd times during the cardiac rhythm. The possible causes of ectopic foci—that is, irritable foci in cardiac muscle—are (1) local areas of ischemia, (2) small calcified plaques at different points in the heart, which press against the adjacent cardiac muscle so that some of the fibers are irritated, and (3) toxic irritation, inflammation, or mechanical pressure against portions of the myocardium. Mechanical initiation of ectopic foci is frequent during cardiac catheterization, large numbers of premature beats occurring when the catheter enters the right ventricle and presses against the endocardium.

Atrial Premature Beats

Figure 239 illustrates an electrocardiogram showing a single atrial premature beat. The P wave of this beat is relatively normal and the QRS complex is also normal, but the interval between the preceding beat and the premature beat is shortened. Also, the interval between the

Premature beat

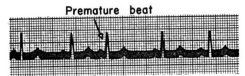

Figure 239.   Atrial premature beat (lead I).

premature beat and the next succeeding beat is slightly prolonged. The reason for this is that the premature beat originated in the atrium some distance from the S-A node, and the impulse of the premature beat had to travel through a considerable amount of atrial muscle before it discharged the S-A node. Consequently, the S-A node probably discharged at approximately the same time that the QRS-T complex began, and the duration of time from this point to the next succeeding P wave is approximately the interval between two normal beats of the heart.

When the heart beats ahead of schedule, the ventricles will not have filled normally, and the stroke volume output of the heart during that beat is depressed. The succeeding beat of the heart, which occurs after a longer than normal diastolic filling period, then pumps a greater than normal stroke volume output. Therefore, the pulse wave passing to the periphery after a premature beat may be so weak that the pulse cannot be felt at all in the radial artery, whereas the succeeding pulse may be extra strong. Thus, a *pulse deficit* results in the radial pulse in relation to the number of beats of the heart.

At times every other beat of the heart may be a premature beat. This causes the patient to have a *bigeminal pulse*—that is, a strong pulse alternating with a weak pulse. Occasionally, one premature beat occurs for every two normal beats, or two premature beats for every one normal beat, and these cause a *trigeminal pulse*.

Atrial premature beats occur frequently in healthy persons and, indeed, are often found in athletes and others whose hearts are certain to be in healthy condition. Yet, mild toxic conditions resulting from such factors as excess smoking, lack of sleep, too much coffee, alcoholism, and use of various drugs can frequently initiate such beats.

A-V Nodal or A-V Bundle Premature Beats

Figure 240 illustrates a premature beat originating either in the A-V node or in the A-V bundle.

Premature beat

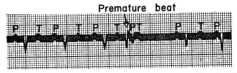

Figure 240.   A-V nodal premature beat (lead III).

The P wave is missing from the record of the premature beat. Instead, the P wave occurs in its normal sequence, the rhythm of the atria being undisturbed because impulses normally do not pass backward from the A-V node into the atria. This unidirectional transmission at the A-V node is extremely important in analyzing electrocardiograms, for impulses can pass quite easily from the atria into the A-V node and thence into the ventricles, but very rarely do impulses pass backward from the A-V node into the atria. As noted in Figure 240, the P wave is superimposed on the QRS-T complex of the premature beat; this distorts the complex.

In general, A-V nodal premature beats have the same significance and causes as atrial premature beats.

Ventricular Premature Beats

The electrocardiogram of Figure 241 illustrates a series of ventricular premature beats alternating with normal beats. Ventricular premature beats cause several special effects in the electrocardiogram, as follows: First, the QRS complex is usually considerably prolonged. The reason for this is that the impulse is conducted mainly through the muscle of the ventricles rather than through the Purkinje system. Second, the QRS complex has a very high voltage, for the following reason: When the normal impulse passes through the heart, it passes through both ventricles approximately simultaneously; consequently, the depolar-

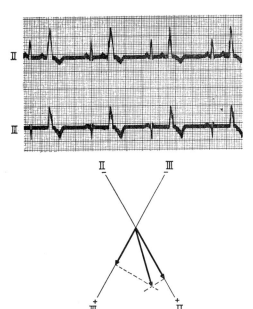

Figure 241.   Ventricular premature beats (leads II and III). Axis of the premature beats is plotted in accord with the principles of vectorial analysis explained in the preceding chapter.

ization waves of the two sides of the heart partially neutralize each other. However, when an ectopic beat occurs, the impulse travels in only one direction so that there is no such neutralization effect, and one entire side of the heart is depolarized while the other entire side is still polarized; this causes very intense electrical potentials.

Following almost all ventricular premature beats the T wave has a potential opposite to that of the QRS complex because the *slow conduction of the impulse* through the cardiac muscle causes the area first depolarized also to repolarize first. As a result, the direction of current flow in the heart during repolarization is opposite to the direction of current flow during depolarization. This is not true of the normal T wave, as was explained in the preceding chapter.

Many ventricular premature beats are relatively benign in their origin and result from simple factors such as cigarettes, coffee, lack of sleep, various mild toxic states, and even emotional irritability. On the other hand, some ventricular premature beats result from actual pathology of the heart. For instance, many ventricular premature beats occur following coronary thrombosis because of stray impulses originating around the borders of the infarcted area of the heart.

Plotting the Origin of an Ectopic Ventricular Premature Beat. In the preceding chapter, the principles of vectorial analysis were explained. Applying these principles one can determine from the electrocardiogram in Figure 241 the point of origin of the ventricular premature beat as follows: From the figure, it is seen that the vectors of the premature beats in leads II and III are both strongly positive. Plotting these vectors on the axes of leads II and III, one finds that the vector of the ectopic beat has its negative end at the base of the heart and its positive end toward the apex. Thus, the first portion of the heart to become depolarized during the premature beat lies near the base of the heart, and the last portion to become depolarized is the apex of the heart.

PAROXYSMAL TACHYCARDIA

Mild abnormalities in any portion of the heart, including the atria, the Purkinje system, and the ventricles, can sometimes cause rapid rhythmic discharge of impulses which spread in all directions throughout the heart. Because of the rapidity of the rhythm of the irritable focus, this focus becomes the pacemaker of the heart.

The term "paroxysmal" means that the heart rate usually becomes very rapid in paroxysms, the paroxysms beginning suddenly and lasting for a few seconds, a few minutes, a few hours, or some-

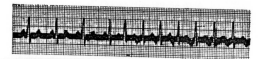

Figure 242. Atrial paroxysmal tachycardia (lead I).

times much longer. Then the paroxysms usually end as suddenly as they begin, the pacemaker of the heart shifting back to the S-A node.

The different types of paroxysmal tachycardias can often be stopped by eliciting a vagal reflex. A strange type of vagal reflex sometimes used for this purpose is one that occurs when painful pressure is applied to the eyes. Also, pressure on the carotid sinuses can sometimes elicit enough of a vagal reflex to stop the tachycardia. Various drugs may also be used to stop paroxysmal tachycardia. The one most frequently used is quinidine, which depresses cardiac muscle and often blocks the rhythmic discharge of the irritable focus that is causing the paroxysmal attack.

Atrial Paroxysmal Tachycardia

Figure 242 illustrates a sudden increase in the rate of heart beat from approximately 95 beats per minute up to approximately 150 beats per minute. On close observation of the electrocardiogram it will be seen that an inverted P wave occurs before each of the QRS-T complexes during the paroxysm of rapid heart beat, though this P wave is partially superimposed on the normal T wave of the preceding beat. This indicates that the origin of this paroxysmal tachycardia is in the atrium, but, because the P wave is abnormal, the origin is not near the S-A node.

A-V Nodal Paroxysmal Tachycardia. Paroxysmal tachycardia sometimes results from an irritable focus either in the A-V node or in the A-V bundle. This initiates normal impulses in the ventricles, thereby causing normal QRS-T complexes. However, P waves usually do not appear along with the QRS-T complexes.

Atrial and A-V nodal paroxysmal tachycardia usually occurs in young, otherwise healthy persons for reasons totally unknown. Yet, factors that irritate the heart such as coffee, lack of sleep, etc., can all predispose to the condition. In general, atrial paroxysmal tachycardia frightens the individual tremendously and may cause him to be weak during the paroxysm, but ordinarily no permanent harm comes from the attacks.

Ventricular Paroxysmal Tachycardia

Figure 243 illustrates a typical short paroxysm of ventricular tachycardia. The electrocardiogram of ventricular paroxysmal tachycardia has the ap-

traction. Ordinarily, the right atrial pressure rises approximately 4 to 6 mm. Hg during atrial contraction, while the left atrial pressure rises about 7 to 8 mm. Hg.

The *c wave* is caused partly by reflux of blood out of the ventricles into the atria during ventricular contraction and partially by two other factors: First, even after the A-V valves have closed they bulge still further toward the atria because of increasing pressure in the ventricles, and this further elevates the atrial pressure. Second, contraction of the ventricular musculature reduces the sizes of the atrioventricular rings, which places tension on the atrial musculature attached to the rings, and this too increases the pressure.

The *v wave* results from a slow buildup of blood in the atria during ventricular systole. Because the A-V valves are closed during systole and blood continues to flow from the veins into the atria, the atrial pressure continues to rise until the end of systole, thereby creating the v wave. Then the A-V valves open, allowing blood to flow rapidly into the ventricles and causing the v wave to disappear.

Function of the Ventricles as Pumps

Diastasis. During diastole the A-V valves remain open, and, because the normal A-V valves are so large that they offer almost no resistance to blood flow, the pressures in the ventricles are only a fraction of a millimeter of mercury less than the pressures in the respective atria.

Furthermore, the A-V valves are so large that one can actually consider each side of the heart during diastole to be a single large chamber rather than being divided into an atrium and a ventricle. For this reason it is said that the heart is in a state of *diastasis* when the A-V valves are wide open.

When the atria contract, the pressure not only rises in the atria but also in the ventricles at the same time. This slight surge of pressure in the ventricles causes additional distention of the ventricles before they contract.

Pressure Changes in the Ventricles. Immediately after ventricular contraction begins the ventricular pressure rises suddenly, as shown in Figure 247, to approximately 120 mm. Hg in the left ventricle

and to approximately 26 mm. Hg in the right ventricle. The pressure in each of the two ventricles remains elevated throughout systole, which lasts about 0.3 second. At the end of this time the pressure falls precipitously back to slightly less than the atrial pressure and remains at this level, except for minor variations, throughout diastole, which lasts another 0.5 second.

Function of the Valves. The *A-V valves* obviously prevent backflow of blood from the ventricles to the atria during systole, and the *semilunar valves* prevent backflow from the aorta and pulmonary arteries into the ventricles during diastole. The different valves of the heart, which are illustrated in Figure 248, close and open *passively*. That is, they close when a backward pressure gradient pushes blood backward, and they open whenever a forward pressure gradient forces blood in the forward direction. For obvious anatomical reasons, the thin, filmy A-V valves require almost no backflow to cause closure while the much heavier semilunar valves require rather rapid back-flow.

The A-V valves usually close almost completely even before ventricular contraction begins for the following reason: When the atria contract, blood forced into the ventricles immediately raises the ventricular pressure. However, atrial contraction also

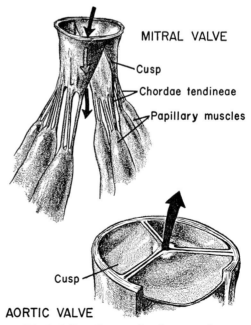

MITRAL VALVE

Cusp

Chordae tendineae

Papillary muscles

Cusp

AORTIC VALVE

Figure 248. The mitral and aortic valves.

causes blood to flow backwards into the great veins, which allows the pressure in the atria to decrease very rapidly. As a result, the atrial pressure usually falls below ventricular pressure even before ventricular contraction takes place, resulting in backward flow of blood and either closure or almost closure of the A-V valves. Closure of the valves prior to ventricular contraction undoubtedly increases the effectiveness of the ventricles as pumps, for little or no blood will then be lost from the ventricles after the onset of ventricular systole.

Function of the papillary muscles. Figure 248 also illustrates the papillary muscles attached to the vanes of the A-V valves by the *chordae tendineae.* The papillary muscles contract when the ventricular walls contract, and, contrary to what might be expected, they *do not* help to close the valves. Instead, they pull the vanes of the valves inward toward the ventricles to prevent them from bulging too far backward toward the atria during ventricular contraction. Their degree of contraction is just sufficient to allow adequate closure of the valves and yet to prevent excessive backward bulging. If a chorda tendinea becomes ruptured or if one of the papillary muscles becomes paralyzed as a result of ischemia or other effects, the valve will bulge very far backwards, sometimes so far that it leaks severely and results in very severe cardiac incapacity.

Opening and Closing of the Aortic and Pulmonary Valves. When the pressures in the ventricles rise, the semilunar valves do not open until the ventricular pressures become slightly greater than the pressures in the arteries. The semilunar valves then open passively in response to pressure differentials, as do the A-V valves; they are not controlled by any intrinsic muscles connected to the valves themselves. When the ventricles relax, the pressures in the ventricles fall precipitously. Some of the blood that has been pushed forward into the elastic arteries flows backward, but only a few milliliters of blood reenter the ventricles before the backward flow swings the semilunar valves closed.

There are some differences between the operation of the aortic and pulmonary valves and the operation of the A-V valves. First, the high pressure in the arteries causes the semilunar valves to close very rapidly in comparison with the closure of the A-V valves. Second, the velocity of blood ejection through the aortic and pulmonary valves is far greater than the velocity of blood flow through the A-V valves. Because of the rapid closure and rapid ejection, the edges of the semilunar valves are subjected to greater mechanical abrasion than are the A-V valves, which are supported by the chordae tendineae. It is obvious from the anatomy of the aortic and pulmonary valves, as illustrated in Figure 248, that they are well adapted to withstand considerable physical trauma.

The Aortic Pressure Curve

The pressure that develops in the aorta depends upon many factors besides contraction of the heart. This pressure curve will be discussed in detail in Chapter 27, but it is desirable now simply to point out those features of the aortic pressure curve that relate especially to the cardiac cycle.

When the left ventricle contracts, the ventricular pressure rises rapidly until the aortic valve opens. Then the pressure in the ventricle rises only a little thereafter, as is illustrated in Figure 247, for blood immediately flows out of the ventricle into the aorta. While the blood is flowing outward, the pressure in the aorta remains a millimeter or more of mercury lower than the pressure in the left ventricle because of the resistance to flow of blood through the aortic ring.

The blood entering the arteries causes the walls of these arteries to stretch, and the pressure in the arterial system rises. Then, at the end of systole even after the left ventricle stops ejecting blood, the elastic tension of the arterial walls maintains high pressure in the arteries while the ventricular pressure falls. This creates a pressure differential backward across the aortic valve, and the aortic valve closes.

A so-called *incisura* occurs in the aortic pressure curve when the aortic valve suddenly closes. This probably can be explained as follows: When blood flows backward from the aorta into the left ventricle, some of the pressure in the arteries is converted into kinetic energy to cause the backward momentum of the blood; therefore, the aortic pressure itself falls slightly while the blood is flowing backward. Just as soon as the aortic valve closes, this kinetic energy of backward flow is suddenly converted back into pressure which again stretches the aortic wall. This is analogous to pressure exerted against a wall when a stream of water from a nozzle is turned against the wall. Thus, backward flow of even a few milliliters of blood can cause first a fall in aortic pressure and then a rise, creating the incisura.

After the aortic valve is closed, pressure in the aorta falls slowly throughout diastole because blood stored in the elastic arteries flows continually through the peripheral vessels back to the veins. By the time the ventricle contracts again, the aortic pressure usually has fallen to approximately 80 mm. Hg (diastolic pressure), which is two thirds the maximal pressure of 120 mm. Hg (systolic pressure) occurring in the aorta during ventricular contraction.

Obviously, the pressure curve in the pulmonary artery is similar to that in the aorta except that the pressures are much less, as will be discussed in Chapter 29.

The Ventricular Volume Curve

Also shown in Figure 247 is a curve depicting the relative changes in ventricular volume from moment to moment. Such a curve as this can be recorded by placing a cylinder, called an "oncometer," around the ventricle. The cylinder is closed at one end and has a snug rubber gasket between the other end of the cylinder and the atrioventricular junction of the heart. Every time the ventricles increase in size, they displace air from the cylinder. If the cylinder is connected by means of a rubber tube to a tambour recording system, the increase and decrease in ventricular volume can be recorded.

Systolic Changes in Ventricular Volume. Just as soon as the aortic and pulmonary valves open, the blood in the ventricles begins to flow outward, and, during the first third of ventricular systole, approximately two thirds of the blood to be ejected leaves the ventricles. This is the *period of rapid discharge*. During the latter two thirds of ventricular systole the flow of blood from the ventricles is relatively slow because of increased back pressure in the arteries. This is the *period of slow discharge*. Then suddenly the period of cardiac contraction is over, the aortic and pulmonary valves close,

and the ventricular volumes remain constant for a very short interval until the ventricular pressures fall low enough for the A-V valves to open.

Diastolic Changes in Ventricular Volume. When the A-V valves open, the pressures that have built up in the atria because of continued return of blood from the veins cause sudden inflow of blood into the ventricles. Therefore, during the first third of ventricular diastole the ventricles fill approximately two thirds, which is known as the *period of rapid filling*.

Effect of atrial contraction on ventricular filling. After the period of rapid filling, the ventricular volumes do not increase greatly until the atria suddenly begin to contract in the latter part of diastole. At this point the blood that has been stored in the atria is suddenly placed under additional pressure as a result of atrial contraction, and much of it flows into the ventricles, increasing the ventricular volume even more, as shown in Figure 247. Some of the atrial blood flows backward into the veins. However, it is claimed by anatomists that the arrangement of muscle fibers around the openings of the veins is such that atrial contraction causes the openings of these vessels to decrease. Therefore, even though no actual valves exist at the inlets into the atria, such an arrangement of the musculature may possibly aid the atria in propelling larger quantities of blood into the ventricles than would otherwise occur.

End-diastolic and End-systolic Volumes of the Ventricles. When the ventricles contract, they do not empty completely, but, instead, each ventricle still has a remaining blood volume of about 80 ml., which is called the *end-systolic* volume.

During diastole, filling of the ventricles normally increases their volumes up to an average of approximately 150 to 160 ml.; this volume is known as the *end-diastolic volume*. This difference between end-diastolic volume and end-systolic volume—that is, the amount of blood ejected from the heart with each heartbeat—is called the *stroke volume output*, which will be discussed at length later in the chapter.

When the heart contracts very strongly, the end-systolic volume can fall to as little as 20 to 30 ml. On the other hand, when large amounts of blood flow into the ventricles during diastole, their end-diastolic volumes can become as great as 200 or more ml. Thus, by increasing the end-diastolic volume and decreasing the end-systolic volume, the stroke volume output can be increased to more than double normal. On the contrary, decreasing the cardiac contractility or diastolic filling of the ventricles can lessen the stroke volume output to zero.

Periods of the Ventricular Cycle

For the sake of clarity the periods of ventricular systole and diastole are sometimes further subdivided. Observing Figure 247 once again, it will be noted that there is a short interval between the closure of the A-V valves and the opening of the aortic and pulmonary valves. During this interval the ventricle increases its tension but does not decrease its volume. Therefore, the muscle fibers maintain constant length, for which reason this interval is known as the *period of isometric contraction*.

Between the opening of the semilunar valves and their closure, blood flows from the ventricles. The pressures in the ventricles do not change to a great extent though the muscle fibers of the ventricles change their lengths tremendously. Therefore, the muscle contracts almost isotonically, and this period of ventricular contraction is called the *period of isotonic contraction* or the *period of ejection*.

Immediately after the semilunar valves close and before the A-V valves open, the ventricles are relatively small because they have emptied a large portion of their blood. Furthermore, the lengths of the ventricular muscle fibers do not change until the A-V valves open, but their tension does continue to decrease. This period is called the *period of isometric relaxation* because the ventricular muscle is relaxing isometrically.

Some physiologists consider diastole to begin when the heart stops ejecting blood. Therefore, the period between the end of ejection and closure of the semilunar valves is called the *protodiastolic period*.

After the A-V valves open, all the ventricular musculature remains in a state of relaxation up to the point of A-V valve closure, though the ventricles dilate owing to the influx of blood from the atria. This is a *period of ventricular filling* or *isotonic relaxation* of the ventricles.

RELATIONSHIP OF THE HEART SOUNDS TO THE CARDIAC PRESSURE CYCLES

When one listens to the heart with a stethoscope, he does not hear the opening of the valves, for this is a relatively slowly developing process that makes no noise. However, when the valves close, the vanes of the valves and the surrounding fluids vibrate under the influence of the sudden pressure differentials which develop. Therefore, when the ventricles first contract, one hears a sound that is probably caused by the closure of the A-V valves. The vibration is low in pitch and relatively long continued and is known as the *first heart sound*. When the aortic and pulmonary valves close, one hears a relatively rapid snap, for these valves close extremely rapidly and vibrate for only a short period of time. This sound is known as the *second heart sound*. The precise causes of these sounds will be discussed in Chapter 38, which relates to auscultation.

Occasionally, one can hear an *atrial sound* when the atria beat, presumably because of vibrations associated with the flow of blood into the ventricles. Also, a *third heart sound* sometimes occurs at the end of the first third of diastole or in the middle of diastole. This is said to be due to blood flowing with a rumbling motion into the almost-filled ventricle. The atrial sound and the third heart sound can usually be recorded with special recording instruments but can be heard with the stethoscope only with great difficulty.

Systole and Diastole in Clinical Usage. Strictly speaking, systole means "contraction." Therefore, physiologically it is probably best that systole be considered to begin approximately with the closure of the A-V valves and to end approximately with the opening of the A-V valves.

Clinically, it is not possible to determine when the A-V valves open, but it is very easy to determine when the A-V valves and the aortic and pulmonary valves close by listening to the heart sounds. Because only a short interval elapses between the closure of the aortic and pulmonary valves and the opening of the A-V valves, the clinician measures systole as the time interval between the first heart sound and the second heart sound or, in other words, the time interval between closure of the A-V valves and closure of the semilunar valves. Diastole is considered to be the interval between closure of the aortic and pulmonary valves and closure of the A-V valves.

Stroke Volume Output of the Heart

The stroke volume output of the heart is the quantity of blood pumped from each ventricle with each heart beat. Normally this is about 70 ml., but under conditions compatible with life it can decrease to as little as a few ml. per beat and can increase to about 160 ml. per beat.

Relationship of Cardiac Output and Heart Rate to Stroke Volume Output. The cardiac output is the amount of blood pumped by the heart each minute and obviously is equal to the amount pumped by each heartbeat times the number of beats per minute in accordance with the following formula:

Cardiac output = Stroke volume output
× Heart rate

This formula shows that if the heart rate increases while the cardiac output remains normal, the stroke volume output obviously will decrease. On the contrary, a decrease in heart rate must be offset by an increase in stroke volume output if the cardiac output remains normal. Following athletic training, the normal heart rate decreases considerably, sometimes to as low as 45 beats per minute, but this is offset by an increase in the stroke volume output to as much as 120 ml. per beat. On the other hand, in the very asthenic person, the normal stroke volume output may be as little as 45 to 50 ml. per beat while the heart rate is elevated to 90 to 100 beats per minute.

The different factors that can cause the stroke volume output to change during physical stress or disease will be discussed later in the chapter.

Work Output of the Heart

The *work output of the heart* is the amount of energy that the heart transfers to the blood while pumping it into the arteries. Energy is transferred to the blood in two forms: First, by far the major proportion is used to move the blood from the low pressure veins to the high pressure arteries. This is *potential energy of pressure*. Second, a minor proportion of the energy is used to accelerate the blood to its velocity of ejection through the aortic and pulmonary valves. This is *kinetic energy of blood flow*.

Energy Expended to Create Potential Energy of Pressure. The work performed by the left ventricle to raise the pressure of the blood during each heart beat is equal to *stroke volume output × (aortic systolic pressure minus left atrial pressure)*. Likewise, the work performed by the right ventricle to raise the pressure of the blood is equal to *stroke volume output × (pulmonary systolic pressure minus right atrial pressure)*. When pressure is expressed in *dynes per square centimeter* and stroke volume output in *milliliters*, the work output is in *ergs*. Right ventricular work output is usually about one-fifth the work output of the left ventricle because of the difference in systolic pressure against which the two ventricles must pump.

The Kinetic Energy of Blood Flow. The work output of each ventricle required to create kinetic energy of blood flow is proportional to the mass of the blood ejected times the square of the velocity of ejection. That is,

$$\text{Kinetic energy} = \frac{mv^2}{2}$$

When the mass is expressed in *grams* of blood ejected and the velocity in *centimeters per second* the work output is in *ergs*.

Ordinarily, the work output required to create kinetic energy of blood flow is less than 1 per cent of the total work output of the heart. However, in certain abnormal conditions such as aortic stenosis, in which the blood flows with great velocity through the stenosed valve, as much as 50 per cent of the total work output may be required to create kinetic energy of blood flow.

Efficiency of Cardiac Contraction

Heart muscle, like skeletal muscle, utilizes chemical energy to provide the work of contraction. This energy is derived mainly from the metabolism of glucose and, to a less extent, of other nutrients. The different reactions that liberate this energy will be discussed in detail in Chapters 65 to 68.

During muscular contraction most of the chemical energy is converted into heat and a much smaller portion into work output. The ratio of work output to chemical energy expenditure is called the *efficiency of cardiac contraction* or simply *efficiency of the heart*. The efficiency of the normal heart, beating under normal load, is usually very low, some 5 to 10 per cent. However, during maximum work output it rises to as high as 15 to 25 per cent in the normal heart and rarely to as high as 30 per cent in the well-trained athlete's heart.

REGULATION OF CARDIAC FUNCTION

When a person is at rest, the heart is called upon to pump only 4 to 6 liters of blood each minute. However, during severe exercise it may be required to pump as much as five or more times this amount. The present section will discuss the means by which the heart can adapt itself to such extreme increases in cardiac output.

The two means by which the heart can increase its output are, first, by *increasing the heart rate* and, second, by *increasing the stroke volume output*. Under different conditions each of these two methods of increasing cardiac output can take place, and even more often both of them operate simultaneously. Therefore, they must be discussed separately.

Regulation of Cardiac Function by Regulating the Heart Rate

Obviously, any increase in heart rate, if the stroke volume output remains constant, causes a proportional increase in cardiac output. Therefore, any means for regulating the heart rate is likewise a means for regulating the cardiac output.

Neurogenic Control of Heart Rate. Aside from the intrinsic basic rhythm of the heart, which was discussed in Chapter 21, the heart rate is controlled mainly by the autonomic nervous system. Vagal stimulation slows the heart while sympathetic stimulation speeds it. Furthermore, almost all stressful conditions of the body, including exercise especially, increase the activity of the sympathetic nervous system while decreasing the activity of the parasympathetics, thereby usually causing the heart rate to increase greatly and in this way increasing the cardiac output. The specific autonomic reflexes that regulate the heart rate will be discussed in Chapter 32 in association with the reflexes that also help to regulate arterial pressure.

Upper Limit of Heart Rate for Optimal Pumping by the Heart. When the heart rate rises above about 150 beats per minute, ventricular filling begins to be compromised because of too short diastolic filling periods, and, when the rate rises above about 200 beats per minute, ventricular filling during diastole is by then so severely depressed that further increase in rate actually decreases the cardiac output rather than further increasing it. Therefore, the upper limit of the heart rate for effectively increasing the cardiac output is about 200 beats per minute.

Regulation of Cardiac Function by Changing the Stroke Volume Output —the "Law of the Heart"

The second means by which cardiac function is regulated—that is, by changing the stroke volume output—though equally as important as changes in heart rate, is not nearly so easily understood and requires detailed discussion. We can begin by presenting the *"law of the heart,"* which describes an automatic mechanism by which the stroke volume output can adjust to the amount of blood required of the heart to pump.

Principle of the "Law of the Heart." The law of the heart is frequently called "Starling's law" in honor of the physiologist who more than half a century ago enunciated its general principles. Basically, Starling's law states that *the greater the heart is filled during diastole the greater will be the force of cardiac contraction* and consequently the greater also will be the amount of blood pumped. This can be applied to the overall pumping function of the heart in the following way: Even when the heart rate remains constant, all the blood that returns to the heart from the peripheral veins up to a certain limit is immediately pumped on through the lungs and into the aorta without excessive damming of blood in the peripheral or pulmonary veins. The heart, therefore, acts simply as an automatic pumping station to pump all the blood that flows into it from the veins regardless of how great or small this might be so long as it is within the physiological limits of the heart. Therefore, stating this law in another way: *within physiological limits, the heart pumps all the blood that comes to it without allowing an excessive rise in venous pressure.*

Relationship of the Law of the Heart to the Stroke Volume Output—"Ventricular Function Curve." Figure 249 illustrates the relationship of the end-diastolic volume of the heart to the stroke volume output in a completely denervated heart, showing that the greater the volume of blood in each ventricle immediately before contraction, the greater also will be

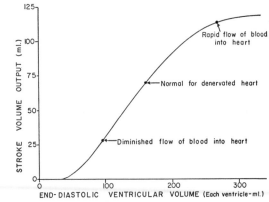

Figure 249. Effect of ventricular filling on stroke volume output, illustrating increased stroke volume output when blood flow into the heart is rapid and reduced stroke volume output when blood flow into the heart is reduced. (The values in the figure are extrapolated from the dog to the human being.)

the stroke volume output. This curve is called a *ventricular function curve*. As illustrated in the figure, the normal amount of blood pumped by the heart is about 70 to 75 ml. However, if a larger quantity of blood than normal enters the ventricles during diastole, a larger amount will also be pumped because the stroke volume output adjusts to the degree of distention of the heart. When excess quantities of blood enter the heart during diastole, the stroke volume output simply becomes greater and relieves the heart of this extra blood. Thus, the heart acts very much like a sump pump; whatever amount of blood enters, that also is the amount of blood that will be pumped on through into the arteries.

The Heart-Lung Preparation. A method frequently used to demonstrate the law of the heart is the heart-lung preparation, which is illustrated in Figure 250. In this preparation, the blood leaving the heart by way of the aorta is diverted into an external system of tubes and then back again into the right atrium so that the blood circulates around and around through the artificial circulatory system. The only parts of the animal's body that remain alive are the heart and lungs. The blood is oxygenated by artificial respiration of the lungs, and a glucose solution is added periodically to the blood to supply appropriate nutrition for cardiac contraction.

As blood flows through the external circuit, right atrial pressure, aortic pressure, and blood flow are measured. Also, an adjustable venous reservoir allows the pressure in the right atrium to be increased or decreased, and a heater coil is

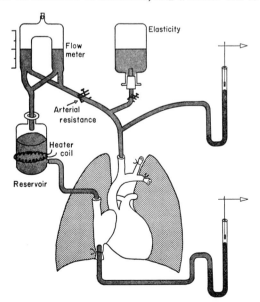

Figure 250. The heart-lung preparation.

wound around the reservoir to maintain normal blood temperature. A screw clamp is provided on the main outflow tube from the heart so that the arterial resistance can be increased or decreased. Finally, a special reservoir containing air in its upper part and blood in its lower part is used as an "elastic buffer" so that the blood pressure will not rise and fall excessively with each contraction of the heart. Some of the principles of cardiac function that can be demonstrated with the heart-lung preparation are the following:

First, the *relationship of end-diastolic volume to stroke volume output,* as shown in Figure 249, can be demonstrated by raising and lowering the venous reservoir. When the reservoir is raised, blood flows into the heart very rapidly, distending the cardiac chambers and causing increased stroke volume output, thus demonstrating the law of the heart.

Second, one can show that *increasing the arterial resistance does not greatly decrease the stroke volume output so long as the right atrial pressure remains constant.* This illustrates that the aortic pressure, within physiological limits, has rather little effect on the output, though very high pressures can overload the heart so much that the stroke volume output does then become greatly reduced.

Third, it can be demonstrated that the *rate of heart beat is independent of either right atrial pressure or arterial pressure* if the nerves to the heart are cut. The heart continues to beat at its natural rate of rhythmicity regardless of how these two factors are changed. On the other hand, increasing the temperature of the heart increases the rate, and decreasing the temperature decreases the rate, as was explained in Chapter 21. The heart-lung preparation is also frequently used to demonstrate the effects of drugs, electrolytes, and various nutrients on cardiac contraction.

Cardiac Contractility—"Families" of Ventricular Function Curves

The term "cardiac contractility" means the vigor with which the heart muscle contracts in each beat. The contractility of one person's heart is often quite different from that of another person's heart, but, more important to the present discussion, the contractility of any one person's heart can change drastically from time to time. Therefore, the ventricular function curve shown in Figure 249 applies only when cardiac contractility remains constant.

Nervous Regulation of Cardiac Contractility. The most important factor that can change cardiac contractility is stimulation of the heart by the sympathetic nervous system. Figure 251 illustrates the effects of

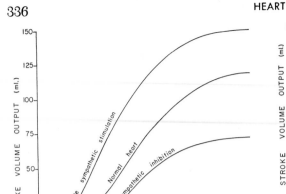

Figure 251. A family of ventricular function curves, illustrating the effect of different degrees of sympathetic activity on cardiac contractility.

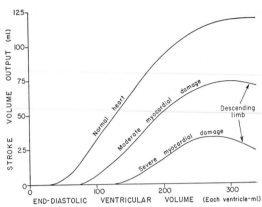

Figure 252. A family of ventricular function curves, illustrating the effect of different degrees of myocardial damage on cardiac contractility.

sympathetic stimulation or sympathetic inhibition on the ventricular function curve, showing that sympathetic stimulation increases the stroke volume output at each level of cardiac filling, while sympathetic inhibition decreases the stroke volume output at each level of filling. In summary, the vigor of heart action as a pump is regulated to a very great extent by the degree of sympathetic stimulation.

The group of curves in Figure 251 is called a *family of curves*, each curve depicting the function of the heart under a different condition of contractility. Obviously, extreme sympathetic stimulation would give a curve even higher than the highest one in the figure, and very slight sympathetic stimulation would give another curve between the top and middle one. Thus, a different curve describes the functional capabilities of the heart for each degree of sympathetic stimulation, the curves *rising very orderly* with progressively higher levels of stimulation.

The importance of neurogenic regulation of cardiac contractility is that it provides a means for controlling cardiac pumping capability separately and independently from the control of heart rate. Therefore, even though the heart rate should remain constant, sympathetic stimulation can still increase the cardiac output by increasing the stroke volume output.

Effect of Myocardial Damage on Cardiac Contractility. One of the most common abnormalities of the heart is myocardial

damage caused by occlusion of a coronary artery, but also valvular damage, cardiac fatigue, poor cardiac nutrition, and other factors can all result in diminished effectiveness of the heart as a pump. Figure 252 shows a family of ventricular function curves that depicts the effects of myocardial damage of varying degrees on cardiac contractility. With moderate cardiac damage the stroke volume output is reduced at each end-diastolic ventricular volume, and with severe cardiac damage the stroke volume output at each volume is further reduced. Here again, a different function curve applies for each degree of cardiac damage, and these function curves become depressed more and more in an orderly manner as the degree of damage progresses.

The descending limb of the cardiac function curve in severe myocardial damage. An especially interesting effect of severe myocardial damage on the ventricular function curve is a "descending limb" of the curve as illustrated to the far right in Figure 252. That is, *when the weakened heart is stretched beyond certain limits, instead of the stroke volume output continuing to increase, it decreases.* The cause of this effect is elongation of the muscle fibers beyond their physiological operating range. This "descending limb" will be discussed further in Chapter 36 in relation to decompensation of the heart in cardiac failure.

Regulation of Cardiac Function in Exercise

In the above discussions two different means by which the pumping ability of the

Chapter 26

General Organization of the Circulatory System: Hemodynamics

The Circulatory System as a "Circuit"

At the outset of this discussion, the most important feature of the circulation that must always be kept in mind is that it is a circuit. That is, the blood flows continuously around and around through the heart and vessels, and, if a given amount of blood is pumped by the heart, this same amount must also flow through each respective subdivision of the circulation. Furthermore, if blood is displaced from one segment of the circulation, some other segment of the circulation must expand.

Figure 253 illustrates the general plan of the circulation, showing the two major subdivisions, the *systemic circulation* and the *pulmonary circulation*. In turn, each of these subdivisions is divided into *arteries, small arteries, arterioles, capillaries, venules, small veins,* and *large veins.* In the figure all the arteries are shown to be a single large distensible chamber and all the veins to be another even larger distensible chamber, while the arterioles and capillaries represent very small connections between the arteries and veins. Blood flows easily in essentially all parts of the circulation except in the arterioles and capillaries. Consequently, it is said that all the vessels except the small vessels offer very little resistance. To cause blood to flow through the small "resistance" vessels, the heart pumps the blood into the arteries under high pressure—up to a systolic pressure of about 120 mm. Hg in the systemic circulation and up to a systolic pressure of about 26 mm. Hg in the pulmonary system.

In this short introduction to the general organization of the circulatory system, we have already delineated several of the major problems that must be understood if one wishes to comprehend the overall function of the circulatory system. These are: (1) What factors affect the flow of blood through the circulatory system? (2) What factors are responsible for the pressure differences throughout the circulation? (3)

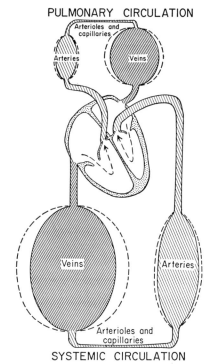

PULMONARY CIRCULATION

SYSTEMIC CIRCULATION

Figure 253. Schematic representation of the circulation, showing the distensible and the resistive portions of the systemic and pulmonary circulations.

What determines the resistances to blood flow in different parts of the circulation? (4) How is resistance to blood flow regulated? (5) How distensible are the different vessels of the circulation, and under what conditions is this distensibility important? And (6) what can make large volumes of blood shift from one segment of the circulation to another segment such as from the arteries to the veins or from the systemic circulation to the pulmonary circulation?

The remainder of this chapter and several of the chapters yet to come will be devoted to answering these questions. As a first step, the characteristics of blood flow through vessels will be described, including especially the interrelationships between pressure, flow, and resistance. The study of all these interrelationships and other basic principles of blood circulation is called *hemodynamics.*

INTERRELATIONSHIPS BETWEEN PRESSURE, FLOW, AND RESISTANCE

Figure 254 illustrates a blood vessel segment anywhere in the circulatory system. Blood is flowing through the vessel; P_1 represents the pressure at the origin of the segment. At the other end of the segment the pressure is P_2. Since the vessel is relatively small, the blood is experiencing difficulty in flowing. This is called *resistance.* Stated another way, a *pressure gradient* between the two ends of the vessel causes *blood* to *flow* from the high pressure area to the low pressure area while *resistance* impedes the flow. This can be expressed mathematically as follows:

$$BF = \frac{P_1 - P_2}{R} \qquad (1)$$

in which BF is blood flow, P_1 is the higher pressure, P_2 the lower pressure, and R the resistance.

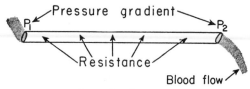

Figure 254. Relationship between pressure, resistance, and blood flow.

It should be noted especially that it is the *difference* in pressure between the two ends of the blood vessel segment that determines the rate of flow and not the absolute pressure in the vessel. For instance, if the pressure at both ends of the segment were 100 mm. Hg and yet no difference existed between the two ends, there would be no pressure gradient to cause flow, and consequently no flow would occur despite the presence of the 100 mm. Hg pressure.

The above formula expresses the most important of all the relationships that the student needs to understand to comprehend the hemodynamics of the circulation. This formula can be further simplified as follows:

$$BF = \frac{P}{R} \qquad (2)$$

Here P simply represents the pressure gradient between the two ends of the vessel. Because of the extreme importance of this formula the student should also become familiar with its other two algebraic forms:

$$P = BF \times R \qquad (3)$$

$$R = \frac{P}{BF} \qquad (4)$$

Blood Flow in Different Vessels of the Circulation

Blood flow means simply the quantity of blood that passes a given point in the circulation in a given period of time. Ordinarily, blood flow is expressed in milliliters or liters per minute, but it can be expressed in milliliters per second or any other unit of flow.

The overall blood flow in the circulation of an adult person at rest is about 5,000 ml. per minute. This is called the *cardiac output* per minute because it is the amount of blood pumped by each ventricle of the heart in that period of time. It is also quite obvious that this same amount of blood must pass through both the systemic and pulmonary circulations.

Methods for Measuring Blood Flow. Many different mechanical or mechanoelectrical devices can be inserted in series with blood vessels to measure flow through the vessel. These are called simply *flowmeters.*

Figure 255 illustrates two of the common types

of flowmeters used for measuring blood flow in vessels. Figure 255A shows the so-called *stromuhr*. When tubes 2 and 3 are compressed simultaneously, blood flows up tube 1, causing the level of blood to rise in the left chamber and to fall in the right chamber. When the interfaces of the blood and mineral oil have shifted upward and downward respectively in the two chambers, then tubes 2 and 3 are opened and tubes 1 and 4 are closed. This causes the blood–mineral oil interfaces to flow in the opposite direction. The flow of blood can be determined by timing the rate at which the interface moves along the scale as shown in the figure.

Figure 225B illustrates a *rotameter*. Blood enters from the bottom and flows upward through a cone-shaped cavity. In this cavity is a small float. When no blood at all is flowing, the float falls to the bottom of the cavity, but as blood flows faster and faster, the float rises higher and higher. By appropriately designing the slope of the cone-shaped cavity, it is possible to make the float rise in a linear relationship to the rate of blood flow. In using the rotameter, one can measure the blood flow by measuring the height to which the float rises, or, if he wishes to record the blood flow continuously, an arrangement such as that shown in the figure can be made with a small steel shaft projecting upward from the float into a coil of wire. The inductance of the coil increases as the steel shaft moves farther up into the coil, and by using appropriate electronic apparatus the blood flow can be recorded continuously.

The plethysmograph. Figure 256 illustrates an apparatus known as a "plethysmograph," which is used for estimating the quantity of blood flow through the forearm. This apparatus operates as follows: The forearm is placed in an airtight

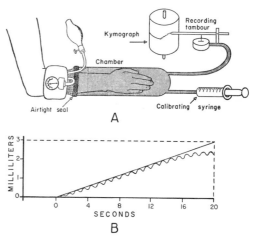

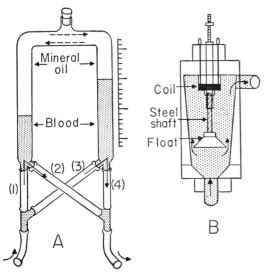

Figure 255. Apparatuses for measuring blood flow.

Figure 256. (A) the plethysmograph, (B) a plethysmographic record.

chamber, and an airtight seal is made between the proximal portion of the chamber and the forearm near the elbow. The chamber is connected to a tambour recorder so that a writing lever rises and falls as the membrane of the tambour is stretched or relaxed. Any increase or decrease in the volume of the arm inside the airtight chamber increases or decreases the pressure in the chamber and causes the membrane of the tambour to rise or fall, respectively. In order to determine the quantity of blood flowing through the forearm, a blood pressure cuff placed on the arm above the plethysmograph is suddenly inflated to a pressure somewhat above venous blood pressure and somewhat below arterial blood pressure—40 mm. Hg, for instance. The pressure in the cuff occludes the veins so that blood cannot return from the forearm into the general circulatory system, but blood does continue to flow through the unoccluded arteries into the forearm. Therefore, when the blood pressure cuff is first inflated, the forearm swells, and the quantity of blood flowing into the forearm is recorded on the kymograph as illustrated in Figure 256 A and B. The plethysmograph is then calibrated by injecting into the chamber standard volumes of air or fluid from the syringe which is noted in the diagram.

In making measurements of blood flow from the plethysmograph, a tangent is drawn to the plethysmographic recording at the very onset of the rise, as illustrated in Figure 256 B. The reason for this is that, after a few seconds of blood flow into the arm, all the blood vessels of the forearm become distended and exert a considerable amount of back pressure, which opposes further inflow of blood. Thus it is only immediately after the cuff pressure is elevated that the recording actually represents the normal rate of blood flow into the forearm. In the recording of the figure, measurements from the tangent show that the initial rate

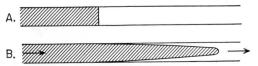

Figure 257. An experiment illustrating laminar blood flow, showing (A) two separate fluids before flow begins and (B) the same fluids one second after flow begins.

of blood flow is 30 milliliters in 20 seconds or 90 ml. per minute.

Obviously, plethysmographs can be used for recording blood flow through a leg, a toe, a finger, or even through a number of different internal organs of the body, for plethysmographs known as "oncometers" can be placed around the spleen, the kidney, the liver, various glands, and even the heart. Unfortunately, technical difficulties in the use of plethysmographs are likely to make their recordings very inaccurate—sometimes 50 per cent or more.

Measurement of cardiac output. In experimental animals flowmeters can be inserted directly into the arterial or venous system near the heart to measure the cardiac output. However, these procedures require extensive surgical procedures and, therefore, cannot be used in the human being. Instead, several *indirect procedures* involving the rate of dilution of injected dye or rate of oxygen uptake by the blood flowing through the lungs have been developed for measuring cardiac output. These procedures will be described in detail in Chapter 35 in connection with the discussion of cardiac output and its regulation.

Laminar Flow of Blood in Vessels. When blood flows at a continuous rate through a long, smooth vessel, the velocity of flow in the center of the vessel is far greater than that toward the outer edges. This is illustrated by the experiment shown in Figure 257. In vessel A are two different fluids, the one to the left colored by a dye and the one to the right a clear fluid, but there is no flow in the vessel. Then the fluids are made to flow, and a parabolic interface between these two fluids one second later is shown in vessel B, illustrating that the portion of fluid adjacent to the walls has hardly moved at all while that slightly away from the wall has moved a small distance and that in the center of the vessel has moved very far. This effect is called *laminar flow* or *streamline flow.*

The cause of laminar flow is the following: The fluid molecules touching the wall move essentially not at all because of close adherence to the vessel wall. The next layer of molecules slips over these, the third layer over the second, the fourth layer over the third, and so forth. Therefore, the fluid in the middle of the vessel can move very rapidly because many layers of molecules exist between the middle of the vessel and the vessel wall, all of these capable of slipping over each other, while those portions of fluid near the wall do not have this advantage.

Laminar flow of blood occurs in all the large vessels of the body to at least some extent. However, in most parts of the circulation there is also a reasonable amount of *turbulence* caused by the blood hitting obstructions and therefore forming whorls in the blood called *eddy currents.* When these are present, blood does not flow along the vessel nearly so easily as it does when the flow is streamlined because the eddies add to the overall resistance of flow in the vessel.

Blood Pressure

The pressure at different points in the circulation is determined by three different important factors: first, the amount of blood available in the circulation to distend the vessels, second, the pumping activity of the heart to force the blood along the vessels and, third, the resistance to flow from one segment of the vascular tree to the next. The interrelationships of these factors in the regulation of arterial pressure are so important that the whole subject of pressure regulation will be discussed in detail in Chapter 32.

The Standard Unit of Pressure. Blood pressure is almost always measured in *millimeters of mercury* (*mm. Hg*) because the mercury manometer (shown in Figure 258) has been used as the standard reference for measuring blood pressure for many years. Actually, blood pressure means the *force exerted by the blood against any unit area of the vessel wall,* and when one says that the pressure in a vessel is 50 mm. Hg, this means that the force exerted would be sufficient to push a column of mercury up to a level of 50 mm. If the pressure were 100 mm. Hg, it would push the column of mercury up to 100 mm.

Occasionally, pressure is measured in *centimeters of water.* A pressure of 10 cm. of

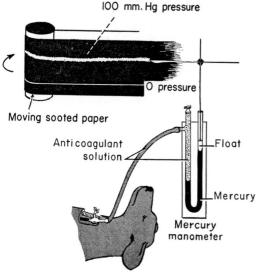

Figure 258. Recording arterial pressure with a mercury manometer.

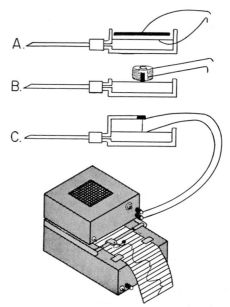

Figure 259. Principles of three different types of electronic transducers for recording rapidly changing blood pressures.

water means a pressure sufficient to raise a column of water up to a height of 10 cm. *One millimeter of mercury equals 1.36 centimeters of water* because the density of mercury is 13.6 times that of water, and 1 cm. is 10 times as great as 1 mm. Dividing 13.6 by 10 we derive the factor 1.36.

Measurement of Blood Pressure with the Mercury Manometer. Figure 258 illustrates a standard mercury manometer for measuring blood pressure. A cannula is inserted into an artery, a vein, or even into the heart, and the pressure from the cannula is transmitted to the left-hand side of the manometer where it pushes the mercury down while raising the right-hand mercury column. The difference between the two levels of mercury is approximately equal to the pressure in the circulation in terms of millimeters of mercury. (To be more exact, it is equal to 104 per cent of the pressure because of the weight of the water on the left-hand column of mercury.)

High-Fidelity Methods for Measuring Blood Pressure. Unfortunately, the mercury in the mercury manometer has so much *inertia* that it cannot rise and fall very rapidly. For this reason the mercury manometer, though excellent for recording steady pressures, cannot respond to pressure changes that occur more rapidly than approximately one cycle every 2 to 3 seconds. Whenever it is desired to record rapidly changing pressures, some other type of pressure recorder is needed. Figure 259 demonstrates the basic prin-

ciples of three electronic pressure *transducers* commonly used for converting pressure into electrical signals and then recording the pressure on a high speed electrical recorder. Each of these transducers employs a very thin and highly stretched membrane which forms one wall of the fluid chamber. The fluid chamber in turn is connected through a needle or a *hard walled* tube with the vessel in which the pressure is to be measured. Pressure variations in the vessel cause changes of pressure in the chamber beneath the membrane. When the pressure is high, the membrane bulges slightly outward and when low it returns toward its resting position. In Figure 259A a simple metal plate is placed a few thousandths of an inch above the membrane. When the membrane bulges outwards the *capacitance* between the plates increases, and this change in capacitance can be recorded appropriately by means of an electronic system. In Figure 259B a small iron slug rests on the membrane and this can be displaced upward or downward in a surrounding coil. Movement of the iron changes the *inductance* of the coil, and this, too, can be recorded. Finally, in Figure 259C a very thin and stretched resistance wire is connected with the membrane. When this wire is greatly stretched its resistance increases, and when less stretched the resistance decreases. These changes also can be recorded by means of an electronic system.

It is possible also to connect a mirror to the edge of the membrane so that it angulates as the membrane bulges. A beam of light reflected from the mirror reflects a moving spot of light that can record pressure changes on a moving photographic paper.

Using some of these high fidelity types of recording systems, pressure cycles up to 500 cycles per second have been recorded accurately, and in very common use are recorders capable of registering pressure changes as rapidly as 20 to 100 cycles per second.

Resistance to Blood Flow

Units of Resistance and Total Peripheral Resistance. Resistance is the impediment to blood flow in a vessel, but it cannot be measured by any direct means. Instead, resistance must be calculated from measurement of blood flow and pressure gradient in the vessel. If the pressure gradient along a vessel is 1 mm. Hg and the flow is 1 ml./sec., then the resistance is said to be 1 *peripheral resistance unit,* usually abbreviated *PRU.*

The rate of blood flow through the circulatory system when a person is at rest is close to 100 ml./sec., and the pressure gradient from the systemic arteries to the systemic veins is about 100 mm. Hg. Therefore, in round figures the resistance of the systemic circulation, called the *total peripheral resistance,* is approximately 1 PRU. In some conditions in which the blood vessels throughout the body become strongly constricted, the total peripheral resistance rises to as high as 4 PRU, and when the vessels become greatly dilated it can fall to as little as one-fourth PRU.

In the pulmonary system the mean arterial pressure averages 16 mm. Hg and the mean left atrial pressure averages 4 mm. Hg, giving a net pressure gradient of 12 mm. Therefore, in round figures the *total pulmonary resistance* at rest calculates to be about 0.12 PRU. This can increase in disease conditions to as high as 1 PRU and can fall in certain physiological states such as exercise to as low as 0.03 PRU.

Expression of resistance in CGS units. Occasionally, a basic physical unit called the CGS unit is used to express resistance. This unit is *dyne seconds/centimeters⁵*. Resistance in these units can be calculated by the following formula:

$$R\left(\frac{\text{dynes sec.}}{\text{cm.}^5}\right) = \frac{1333 \times \text{mm. Hg}}{\text{ml./sec.}} \quad (5)$$

Effect of Vascular Diameter on Resistance. In the discussion above of laminar blood flow it was pointed out that the fluid molecules in contact with a vessel wall hardly move because of adherence to the walls of the vessel. Most of the movement of blood occurs by slippage of successive molecular layers over each other, with the centralmost portion of the blood in the vessel flowing rapidly and that nearest to the wall flowing very slowly. However, a large amount of friction occurs between the layers of molecules so that the process of slippage is greatly impeded. Unfortunately, those portions of fluid nearest the wall are impeded severely because the number of layers for slippage is very few, while those portions farthest from the wall—in the center of the vessel—are impeded the least. Therefore, blood flow in small vessels is very greatly impeded because none of the blood is a great distance from the wall, while in very large vessels most of the flowing blood is a significant distance away from the walls and flows with very little impediment.

But there is still another cause for greater resistance in small vessels than in large vessels: Because of their small cross-sectional area, the velocity of flow must increase greatly if the same quantity of blood is to pass through the small vessel each minute as through the larger vessel. Combining this effect with the laminar effect one finds that the resistance of a vessel increases inversely with the diameter according to the following formula:

$$\text{Resistance} \propto \frac{1}{\text{Diameter}^4} \quad (6)$$

This effect is illustrated very forcefully in Figure 260, which shows three vessels all having the same pressure at their proximal ends but having diameters of 1, 2, and 4 units respectively. If 1 ml. of blood flows through the first vessel, then 16 ml. will flow through the second, *and 256 ml. through the third.*

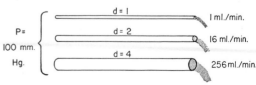

Figure 260. Effect of vascular diameter on blood flow.

This extreme dependence of resistance on diameter is especially important in the arterioles because the inside diameters of arterioles can change as much as three- to four-fold, which means that the resistance of individual arterioles can change many hundred-fold under different physiological conditions.

Effect of Vascular Length on Resistance. Obviously, the longer a vessel the greater is the distance along the vascular wall that the blood must slip to reach its destination, and, therefore, the greater will be the total friction. Consequently, the resistance of a vessel is directly proportional to its length in accordance with the following formula:

$$\text{Resistance} \infty \text{ Length} \qquad (7)$$

Figure 261 illustrates this effect of vascular length, showing three vessels of three different lengths but with the same pressure gradient. The flow through the top vessel is 1 ml. per minute, and that through the second vessel, which is one half as long, is 2 ml. per minute and through the third (one third as long as the first and two thirds as long as the second) 3 ml. per minute.

Effect of Blood Viscosity on Resistance. Viscosity is basically the force required to cause one layer of blood to slip past the next adjacent layer, and the viscosity does not always remain exactly the same. Obviously, the greater the viscosity the greater will be the friction engendered in the vessel and also the greater will be the resistance to flow. Thus,

$$\text{Resistance} \infty \text{ Blood viscosity} \qquad (8)$$

Effect of red blood cell concentration on blood viscosity. The major factor affecting blood viscosity is the concentration of red blood cells; the greater the number of cells, the greater is the friction between successive layers of blood. Another factor that affects blood viscosity is the concentration of proteins in the plasma, but this affects resist-

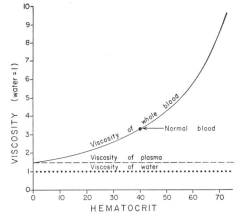

Figure 262.   Effect of hematocrit on viscosity.

ance to a much less extent than the red cells and is not a significant consideration in most hemodynamic studies.

If the viscosity of water is arbitrarily considered to be a value of 1, then the viscosity of normal plasma is about 1.5, and the viscosity of normal blood is about 3.0. Figure 262 illustrates the effect of hematocrit on viscosity, showing that in the low range the hematocrit affects the viscosity only to a slight extent, while in the high range it affects the viscosity tremendously. Obviously, the resistance to blood flow can become tremendous when the hematocrit is very high, while the resistance to blood flow in an anemic person is relatively slight.

Summary of the Factors That Cause Resistance in Vessels. The following formula summarizes the effects of vascular diameter, vascular length, and blood viscosity on resistance:

$$R \ \infty \ \frac{L \cdot V}{D^4} \qquad (9)$$

Poiseuille's Law

By substituting the value of R in the above formula into formula 2, which relates blood flow, resistance, and blood pressure, one derives the following composite formula for blood flow known as *Poiseuille's law:*

$$BF = \frac{P \cdot D^4}{V \cdot L} \cdot C \qquad (10)$$

in which C is a constant that relates the specific units used for the different factors of the formula.

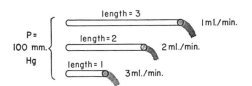

Figure 261.   Effect of vessel length on blood flow.

To emphasize once again the importance of vascular diameter in the control of blood flow, one should note that it affects blood flow in proportion to its fourth power, causing tremendous changes in flow for very slight changes in diameter, while changes in vessel length, blood viscosity, or pressure affect blood flow to a far less extent.

Failure of Poiseuille's law to apply in all instances of blood flow in vessels. Now that we have discussed the different factors that affect resistance, pressure, and blood flow we must point out that the experiments leading to the derivation of Poiseuille's law were performed in rigid tubes—usually glass tubes—in which streamline flow occurs. However, there is an essential difference between blood flow in rigid tubes and in most blood vessels: In vessels the walls are broken by bifurcations or bends so that considerable turbulence, instead of streamline flow, occurs. This causes greater resistance than would otherwise be expected. Therefore, rigid application of all the principles of Poiseuille's law to blood flow in the circulation is not warranted other than as a first approximation. Yet, one is still quite safe in remembering that changes in vascular diameter affect blood flow tremendously, while the other factors affect blood flow to a much less extent.

Resistance to Blood Flow Through Series Vessels. In Figure 263 A are two vessels, connected in series, having resistances of R_1 and R_2. It is immediately evident that the total resistance is equal to the sum of the two, or

$$R \text{ (total)} = R_1 + R_2 \quad (11)$$

Furthermore, it is equally evident that any number of resistances in series with each other must be added together. For instance, the total peripheral resistance is equal to the resistance of the arteries plus that of the arterioles plus that of the capillaries plus that of the veins.

Resistance of Vessels in Parallel. Shown in Figure 263B are four vessels, *connected in parallel,* with respective resistances of R_1, R_2, R_3, and R_4. However, the diameters of these vessels are not exactly the same. It is obvious that for a given pressure differential far greater amounts of blood can flow through this system than through any one of the vessels alone. Therefore, the total

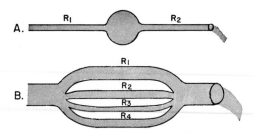

Figure 263. Vascular resistances: (A) in series and (B) in parallel.

resistance is far less than the resistance of any single vessel.

To calculate the total resistance in 263B one first determines the *conductance* of each of the vessels, which is equal to the reciprocal of the resistance, or $\dfrac{1}{R_1}$, $\dfrac{1}{R_2}$, $\dfrac{1}{R_3}$, and $\dfrac{1}{R_4}$. The total conductance of all the vessels, $\dfrac{1}{R_{(total)}}$, is equal to the sum of the individual conductances:

$$\frac{1}{R_{(total)}} = \frac{1}{R_1} + \frac{1}{R_2} + \frac{1}{R_3} + \frac{1}{R_4} \quad (12)$$

And resistance though the parallel circuit is the following:

$$R_{(total)} = \cfrac{1}{\dfrac{1}{R_1} + \dfrac{1}{R_2} + \dfrac{1}{R_3} + \dfrac{1}{R_4}} \quad (13)$$

Thus, one can see that the summation of parallel resistances is much more complicated than that of series resistances. However, for a first approximation one can simply remember that the resistance of vessels in parallel is far less than that of any single vessel, and, if these vessels are of approximately the same size, the total resistance is equal to the resistance of a single vessel divided by the number of vessels in parallel. This principle is extremely important in understanding the resistances through vascular beds where very large numbers of vessels of approximately equal diameter are connected in parallel.

Effect of Pressure on Vascular Resistance —Critical Closing Pressure

Since all blood vessels are distensible, increasing the pressure inside the vessels causes the vascular diameters also to increase. This in turn reduces the resistance of the vessel. Conversely, reduction in vascular pressures increases the resistance. Figure 264 illustrates the effect of changing the arterial pressure on blood flow through a local area of the peripheral vascular system. As the arterial pressure falls from 120 mm. Hg downward, the flow at first decreases linearly with the decrease in pressure. However, as the pressure falls into low ranges the relationship becomes nonlinear, and at 20 mm. Hg blood flow ceases entirely. This point at which the blood stops flowing is called the *critical closing pressure* of the arterioles. The pressure level at which "critical closure" occurs rises with increased vasomotor tone, and it can be explained as follows:

Mechanism of Critical Closing Pressure. The vasomotor tone of the arterioles is always attempting to constrict these vessels to smaller diameters, while on the other hand the pressure inside the arterioles is tending to dilate them. When the pressure falls progressively lower and lower, it finally reaches a point at which the pressure inside the vessel is no longer capable of keeping the vessel open; this pressure is called the *critical closing pressure.*

A physical law, the *law of Laplace,* helps to explain the closure of vessels at a very exact critical pressure level. This law states that the force tending to stretch the muscle fibers in the vascular wall is proportional to *the diameter of the vessel* times *the pressure.* Therefore, as the pressure in the vessel falls,

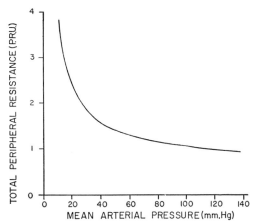

Figure 265.   Effect of arterial pressure on the total peripheral resistance.

thus allowing the vascular diameter also to decrease, the force tending to keep the vascular wall stretched decreases extremely rapidly, much more rapidly than would be accounted for by the decrease in pressure alone.

Another factor that contributes to the cessation of blood flow when the arterial pressure falls low is the size of the blood cells themselves, for, when the arteriolar diameter falls below a certain critical diameter, the red cells cannot pass through, and they will actually block the flow of plasma as well. The average critical closing pressure is about 20 mm. Hg when whole blood is flowing through the vessels and about 5 mm. Hg when only plasma is flowing through.

Effect of Arterial Pressure on Total Peripheral Resistance.   Figure 265 illustrates the effect of mean arterial pressure on total peripheral resistance of the entire systemic circulatory system, showing that the higher the pressure the less becomes the resistance. Furthermore, as the mean arterial pressure approaches the critical closing pressure at about 20 mm. Hg, the total peripheral resistance rises very rapidly because of rather abrupt closure of most of the vessels in the body.

VASCULAR DISTENSIBILITY—PRESSURE VOLUME CURVES

The diameter of blood vessels, unlike that of metal pipes and glass tubes, increases as the internal pressure increases, because blood vessels are *distensible.* However, the

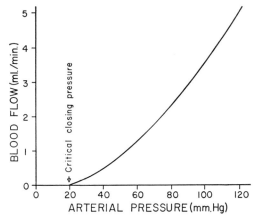

Figure 264.   Effect of arterial pressure on blood flow through a peripheral vascular bed. This figure shows that blood flow normally ceases at about 20 mm. Hg, a level called the "critical closing pressure."

vascular distensibilities differ greatly in different segments of the circulation, and, as we shall see, this affects very significantly the operation of the circulatory system under many changing physiological conditions.

Units of Vascular Distensibility. Vascular distensibility is normally expressed as the fractional increase in volume for each millimeter mercury rise in pressure in accordance with the following formula:

$$\text{Vascular distensibility} = \frac{\text{Change in volume}}{\text{Change in pressure} \times \text{Original volume}} \quad (14)$$

That is, if one mm. Hg causes a vessel originally containing 10 ml. of blood to increase its volume by 1 ml., then the distensibility would be 0.1 per mm. Hg or 10 per cent per mm. Hg.

Difference in distensibility of the arteries and the veins. Anatomically, the walls of arteries are far stronger than those of veins. Consequently, the veins, on the average, are about six times as distensible as the arteries. That is, a given rise in pressure will cause about six times as much extra blood to fill a vein as an artery of comparable size.

In the pulmonary circulation the veins are very similar to those of the systemic veins. However, the pulmonary artery, which normally operates under pressures about one fifth those in the systemic arterial system, has a distensibility only about one half that of veins, rather than one sixth, as is true of the systemic arteries.

Vascular "Capacitance"

Usually in hemodynamic studies it is much more important to know the *total quantity of blood* that can be stored in a given portion of the circulation for each mm. Hg pressure rise rather than the distensibility of the individual vessels. This value is sometimes called the *overall distensibility* or *total distensibility,* or it can be expressed still more precisely by the term *capacitance,* which is a physical term meaning the increase in volume caused by a given increase in pressure as follows:

$$\text{Vascular capacitance} = \frac{\text{Increase in volume}}{\text{Increase in pressure}} \quad (15)$$

It should be pointed out very distinctly that capacitance and distensibility are quite different. A highly distensible vessel which has a very slight volume may have far less capacitance than a much less distensible vessel which has a very large volume. Thus, *capacitance is equal to distensibility times the volume.*

The capacitance of a vein is about 24 times that of its corresponding artery because (a) it is about six times as distensible and (b) it has a volume about four times as great (6 × 4 = 24).

Pressure-Volume Curves of the Arterial and Venous Circulations

A very convenient method for expressing the relationship of pressure to volume in a vessel or in a large portion of the circulation is the so-called *pressure-volume curve.* The two solid curves of Figure 266 represent respectively the pressure-volume curves in the normal arterial and venous systems, showing that the arterial system, including the large arteries, small arteries, and arterioles, contains approximately 750 ml. of blood when the mean arterial pressure is 100 mm. Hg but only 300 to 400 ml. when the pressure has fallen to zero.

The volume of blood normally in the entire venous tree is about 2500 ml., but only a slight change in venous pressure changes this volume tremendously.

Difference in Capacitance of the Arterial and Venous Systems. Referring once again to Figure 266, one can see that a

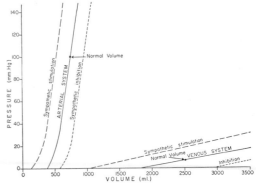

Figure 266. Pressure-volume curves of the systemic arterial and venous systems, showing also the effects of sympathetic stimulation and sympathetic inhibition.

change of 1 mm. Hg increases the venous volume a very large amount but increases the arterial volume only slightly. That is, the *capacitance of the venous system is far greater than the capacitance of the arteries* —about 24 times as great.

This difference in capacitance is particularly important when the heart suddenly becomes a stronger or a weaker pump. For instance, sudden increase in pumping activity increases the amount of blood in the arteries but reduces that in the veins an equal amount. Because of the difference in capacitances of these two segments of the circulation, the arterial pressure rises about 24 mm. for each 1 mm. Hg fall in the venous system. The same effect also occurs when the arteriolar resistance becomes greatly increased; blood then is dammed in the arterial tree and impeded in its passage to the veins. For each mm. Hg rise in the arteries, the mean pressure in the veins falls only 1/24 mm. Hg.

Because of the tremendous amounts of blood that can be stored in the veins with only slight changes in pressure, the veins are frequently called the *storage areas* of the circulation.

Effect of Sympathetic Stimulation or Sympathetic Inhibition on the Pressure-Volume Relationships of the Arterial and Venous Systems. Also shown in Figure 266 are the pressure-volume curves of the arterial and venous systems during moderate sympathetic stimulation and also during sympathetic inhibition. It is quite evident that sympathetic stimulation, with its concomitant increase in smooth muscle tone in the vascular walls, increases the pressure at each volume of the arteries or veins while, on the other hand, sympathetic inhibition decreases the pressure at each respective volume. Obviously, control of the vessels in this manner by the sympathetics can be very valuable for diminishing or enhancing the dimensions of one segment of the circulation, thus transferring blood to or from other segments. For instance, an increase in vascular tone throughout the systemic circulation without a similar increase in the pulmonary circulation often causes large volumes of blood to shift out of the systemic vessels into the lungs.

Sympathetic control of vascular volume is also especially important during hemorrhage.

Enhancement of the sympathetic tone of the vessels, especially of the veins, simply reduces the dimensions of the circulatory system, and the circulation continues to operate almost normally, even when as much as 25 per cent of the total blood volume has been lost.

"MEAN CIRCULATORY PRESSURE" AND PRESSURE-VOLUME CURVES OF THE ENTIRE CIRCULATORY SYSTEM

The Mean Circulatory Pressure

The *mean circulatory pressure* is the pressure that would be measured in the circulation if one could instantaneously stop all blood flow and could bring all the pressures in the circulation immediately to equilibrium. In our laboratory, the mean circulatory pressure has been measured reasonably accurately in dogs within 2 to 3 seconds after the heart has been stopped. To do this the heart is thrown into fibrillation by an electrical stimulus, and blood is pumped very rapidly from the systemic arteries to the veins to cause equilibrium between the two major chambers of the circulation.

The mean circulatory pressure measured in the above manner is almost exactly 7 mm. Hg and almost never varies more than 1 mm. from this value in the normal resting animal. However, many different factors can change the mean circulatory pressure, including (1) change in blood volume, (2) increased or decreased sympathetic stimulation, (3) changes in tissue fluid volume outside the circulation, and (4) any other factor that changes the dimensions of the circulatory system, such as positive pressure in the lungs, pressure on the abdomen, dilatation of the heart, and so forth.

The importance of the mean circulatory pressure is that it is *one of the major factors that determine the rate at which blood flows from the vascular tree into the right atrium of the heart and, therefore, help to control the cardiac output itself.* This is so important that it will be explained in detail in Chapter 35.

Another important aspect of the mean circulatory pressure is that the mechanisms for regulating blood volume normally perform this function so precisely as to keep the mean circulatory pressure almost exactly constant. Since the mean circulatory pressure is actually a measure of the degree of "filling" of the circulation, one can see the logic of this. The mechanisms for regulating blood volume will be explained in detail in Chapter 34.

Pressure-Volume Curves of the Entire Circulation

Figure 267 illustrates the changes in mean circulatory pressure as the total blood volume increases (1) under normal conditions, (2) during strong sympathetic stimulation, and (3) during complete sympathetic inhibition. The point marked by the arrow is the operating point of the normal circulation. However, *if blood is lost from the circulatory system* and the loss is not compensated by sympathetic constriction of the vessels, then the mean circulatory pressure will fall to a lower value. If increased amounts of blood are added, the mean circulatory pressure will rise accordingly.

The *capacitance* of the entire circulatory system in the human being, as estimated from experiments in dogs, is approximately 200 ml. for each 1 mm. rise in mean circulatory pressure.

Sympathetic stimulation and inhibition affect the pressure-volume curves of the entire circulatory system in the same way that they effect the pressure-volume curves of the individual parts of the circulation, as illustrated by the two dashed curves of Figure 267. That is, for any given blood volume, the mean circulatory pressure rises very markedly with strong sympathetic stimulation and falls markedly when the sympathetics are inhibited. This is an extremely important factor in the regulation of blood flow into the heart and thereby for regulating the cardiac output. For instance, during exercise, sympathetic activity increases the mean circulatory pressure and correspondingly helps to increase the cardiac output.

Relationship between Mean Circulatory Pressure, Mean Systemic Pressure, and Mean Pulmonary Pressure

The term *mean circulatory pressure* refers to the pressure that would be measured in the entire circulatory system if all pressures were instantaneously brought to equilibrium. *Mean systemic pressure* is the pressure that would be measured in the systemic vessels if the root of the aorta and the great veins entering the heart were suddenly clamped and all pressures in the systemic system were brought instantaneously to equilibrium. Finally, *mean pulmonary pressure* is the pressure that would be measured in the pulmonary system if the pulmonary artery and large pulmonary veins were suddenly clamped and all pulmonary pressures brought instantaneously to equilibrium.

In preliminary measurements made in dogs in our laboratory, mean systemic pressure and mean pulmonary pressure have been approximately equal to the mean circulatory pressure under normal conditions. However, this is not always true in pathological conditions for the following reasons:

First, if the right heart is much weaker than the left heart, blood becomes dammed in the systemic circulation while it is pumped out of the pulmonary system. As a consequence, the mean systemic pressure becomes greater than the mean pulmonary pressure. Yet, because of the small volume of the pulmonary system compared with that of the systemic system, the decrease in mean pulmonary pressure is about seven times as great as the rise in mean systemic pressure.

Second, damage to the left heart causes blood to dam in the lungs while decreasing the quantity of blood in the systemic circulation. For each decrease of 1 mm. Hg in mean systemic pressure, the mean pulmonary pressure rises about 7 mm. Hg.

STRESS RELAXATION OF VESSELS

The term *stress relaxation* as applied to blood vessels means that a vessel exposed to increased pressure becomes progressively

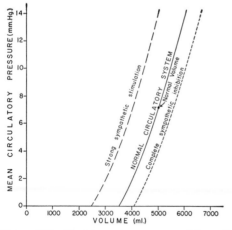

Figure 267. Pressure-volume curves of the entire circulation, illustrating the effect of strong sympathetic stimulation and complete sympathetic inhibition.

enlarged over a period of many minutes. Figure 268 illustrates diagrammatically one of the effects of stress relaxation, showing its importance to the function of the circulation. In this figure, the pressure is being recorded in a small segment of a vein that is occluded at both ends. Then, an extra volume of blood is suddenly injected into the segment until the pressure rises from 5 to 12 mm. Hg. Even though none of the blood is removed after it is injected, the pressure nevertheless begins to fall immediately and approaches approximately 6 mm. Hg after several minutes. In other words, the volume of blood injected caused immediate *elastic* distention of the vein, but then the smooth muscle fibers of the vein actually began to adjust themselves to new lengths as a result of the intravascular force imposed on them. This is a characteristic of all smooth muscle tissues, called *plasticity*, which was explained in Chapter 19.

After stress relaxation had taken place in the experiment illustrated in Figure 268, the extra blood volume was then suddenly removed, and the pressure immediately fell to a very low value. Subsequently, the smooth muscle fibers began to readjust their tensions back to their initial values, and after a number of minutes the normal vascular pressure of 5 mm. Hg had returned. This effect is called *reverse stress relaxation*.

Stress relaxation occurs only slightly in the arteries but to an extreme extent in the veins. As a result, prolonged elevation of venous pressure can often double or even triple the blood volume in the venous tree. This is a very valuable mechanism by which the circulation can accommodate much extra blood when this might be required, and reverse stress relaxation is a very valuable means by which the circulation automatically adjusts itself to diminished blood volume after serious blood loss.

REFERENCES

Barcroft, H.: Peripheral circulation. *Ann. Rev. Physiol.*, 16:215, 1954.

Burton, A. C.: On physical equilibrium of small blood vessels. *Am. J. Physiol.*, 164:319, 1951.

Burton, A. C.: Relation of structure to function of the tissues of the wall of blood vessels. *Physiol. Rev.*, 34:619, 1954.

Burton, A. C., and Rosenberg, E.: Effects of raised venous pressure in the circulation of the isolated perfused rabbit ear. *Am. J. Physiol.*, 185:465, 1956.

Denison, A. B., Jr., Spencer, M. P., and Green, H. D.: A square wave electromagnetic flowmeter for application to intact blood vessels. *Circ. Res.*, 3:39, 1955.

Dodd, A. W., and Daniel, E. E.: Vascular muscle reactivity. *Circ. Res.*, 8:446, 1960.

Folkow, B.: A study of the factors influencing the tone of denervated blood vessels perfused at various pressures. *Acta Physiol. Scandinav.*, 27:99, 1952.

Folkow, B., and Lofving, B.: The distensibility of the systemic resistance blood vessels. *Acta Physiol. Scandinav.*, 38:37, 1956.

Green, H. D.: Circulation: physical principles; in Glasser, O. (ed.): Medical Physics. Chicago, Year Book Publishers, 1944.

Guyton, A. C.: Peripheral circulation. *Ann. Rev. Physiol.*, 21:239, 1959.

Guyton, A. C., Armstrong, G. G., and Chipley, P. L.: Pressure-volume curves of the entire arterial and venous systems in the living animal. *Am. J. Physiol.*, 184:253, 1956.

Guyton, A. C., and Greganti, F. P.: A physiologic reference point for measuring circulatory pressures in the dog—particularly venous pressure. *Am. J. Physiol.*, 185:137, 1956.

Guyton, A. C., Lindsey, A. W., and Armstrong, G. G.: Relationship of total peripheral resistance to the pressure gradient from the arteries to the veins. *Am. J. Physiol.*, 186:294, 1956.

Haynes, R. H., and Burton, A. C.: Role of the non-Newtonian behavior of blood in hemodynamics. *Am. J. Physiol.*, 197:943, 1959.

Hinshaw, L. B., and Day, S. B.: Tissue pressure and critical closing pressure in the isolated denervated dog foreleg. *Am. J. Physiol.*, 196:489, 1959.

Holt, J. P.: Flow of liquids through "collapsible" tubes. *Circ. Res.*, 7:342, 1959.

Levy, M. N.: Influence of anomalous blood viscosity on resistance to flow in the dog's hind limb. *Circ. Res.*, 4:533, 1956.

Levy, M. N., Phillips, F. A., Jr., and Brind, S. H.: The static limit of arterial blood pressure in the dog's hind limb. *Circ. Res.*, 2:509, 1954.

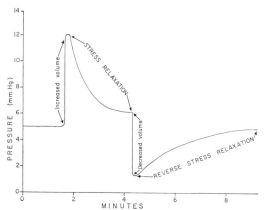

Figure 268. Effect on the intravascular pressure of injecting a small volume of blood into a venous segment, illustrating the principles of stress relaxation.

Levy, M. N., and Share, L.: The influence of erythrocyte concentration upon the pressure-flow relationships in the dog's hind limb. *Circ. Res., 1:*247, 1953.

McDowall, R. J. S.: The Control of the Circulation of the Blood. London, Dawson and Sons, 1956.

McDowall, R. J. S.: The Control of the Circulation of the Blood (Suppl. vol.), London, Dawson and Sons, 1956.

Pappenheimer, J. R.: Peripheral circulation, *Ann. Rev. Physiol., 14:*259, 1952.

Phillips, F. A., Jr., Brind, S. H., and Levy, M. N.: The immediate influence of increased venous pressure upon resistance to flow in the dog's hind leg. *Circ. Res., 3:*357, 1955.

Richardson, T. Q., and Guyton, A. C.: Effects of polycythemia and anemia on cardiac output and other circulatory factors. *Am. J. Physiol., 197:*1167, 1959.

Yamada, S. I., and Astrom, A.: Critical closing presure and vasomotor tone in the hind leg and the kidney of the cat. *Am. J. Physiol., 196:*213, 1959.

See also Chapters 27 and 28, The systemic circulation; Chapter 29, Pulmonary circulation; Chapter 5, Capillary circulation; Chapter 38, General bibliography for the cardiovascular system.

Chapter 27

The Systemic Circulation: I. General Characteristics and Pressure Pulses

When blood is pumped from the heart, it distends the arteries and develops pressure in the arterial system. Because of this pressure, the blood in the arterial system then flows through the peripheral blood vessels back into the right atrium of the heart, thus completing a circuit. The purpose of the present chapter is to discuss the flow of blood through this peripheral circuit, which is called the "systemic circulatory system" or sometimes the "peripheral circulatory system" or the "greater circulatory system."

GENERAL CHARACTERISTICS OF THE SYSTEMIC CIRCULATORY SYSTEM

Physiologic Anatomy

Figure 269 illustrates diagrammatically the systemic circulatory system beginning at the

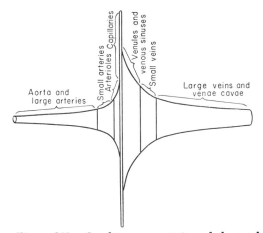

Figure 269. Graphic representation of the total diameters of the vascular beds in each portion of the systemic circulatory system.

aorta, extending to the venae cavae, and emptying into the right atrium. This figure is a graph showing the diameter of each bed of vessels as it would be if all the vessels of each type were placed side by side and coalesced into one major vessel. It is apparent from this diagram that the total diameter of all the capillaries is far greater than that of the aorta—actually 25 to 30 times as great.

Cross-sectional Areas. The total cross-sectional area of the aorta is approximately 2.5 sq. cm., and the combined cross-sectional area of all the capillaries coalesced together is approximately 1700 sq. cm. In other words, the cross-sectional area of the capillaries is approximately 700 times as great as that of the aorta. The cross-sectional area of the veins, which have a diameter about twice that of the arteries, is about four times the cross-sectional area of the corresponding arteries in most portions of the body. The cross-sectional areas of the venules and small veins are especially tremendous, for many of the venules and small veins form extensive venous sinuses beneath the skin, in the liver, in the spleen, and in other portions of the body. Referring once again to Figure 269, and recalling that the cross-sectional area of any particular vessel is proportional to the square of the diameter of the vessel, it becomes obvious that the relative ratios of the cross-sectional areas of the various portions of the vascular system are approximately as follows: aorta, 1; small arteries, 8; arterioles, 15; capillaries, 700; venules, 150; small veins, 30; venae cavae, 4.

Length of the Various Vessels. The total length of the aorta is approximately 50 cm. and the length of the more distal arteries varies from a few centimeters up to 50 cm. before they empty into the arterioles. The arterioles, however, have a length of only a few millimeters before emptying into the capillaries, and the capillaries have an average length of approximately 0.5 to 1.0

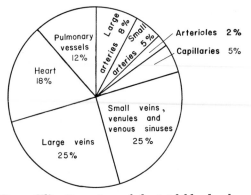

Figure 270. Percentage of the total blood volume in each portion of the circulatory system.

mm. The venules are quite variable in many parts of the body, but where they form plexuses of venous sinuses their lengths may be several centimeters. The small veins are approximately the same length as the small arteries, and the same is true of the large veins and venae cavae.

Quantities of Blood in the Different Parts of the Circulatory System. Figure 270 illustrates diagrammatically the quantity of blood in the different portions of the circulatory system. Beginning with the large arteries, it has been estimated that the quantity of blood in these vessels, including all vessels down to the size of one quarter inch, is approximately 8 per cent of the total blood volume. The small arteries, smaller in size than one quarter inch, have been estimated to contain approximately 5 per cent of the total blood, and the total quantity of blood in the arterioles is probably no more than 2 per cent of the total blood volume.

The quantity of blood in the capillaries is probably no greater than 5 per cent of the total blood volume when the human being is resting, for the following reason: The total time that blood remains in the peripheral capillaries is usually not over 1 to 2 seconds, and the total quantity of blood passing through the capillaries each minute is about 5000 ml. Calculating from this, one would obtain a blood volume in the capillaries of approximately 1.5 to 3.0 per cent of the total blood volume. However, it is probable that many capillaries are inactive and that blood is "sequestered" in them—that is, not flowing. Therefore, in Figure 270 the quantity of blood in the peripheral capillaries is estimated to be 5 per cent of the blood volume.

It is readily apparent from Figure 270 that approximately one half of all the blood in the body is in the peripheral venous system with 25 per cent ascribed to the venules, small veins, and venous sinuses, and 25 per cent ascribed to the large veins. Therefore, the veins represent the main storage area of the body for blood, and these veins have the ability to expand and contract, thereby delivering blood or removing blood from the remainder of the circulatory system when such transfer is needed.

In addition to the blood in the peripheral circulatory system, approximately 30 per cent of the blood is in the heart and lungs.

Velocity of Blood Flow

Relationship of Velocity of Blood Flow to Cross-sectional Area of the Vessels. If the quantity of blood flow remains constant and the diameter of a vessel through which it is flowing increases, the velocity of blood flow decreases inversely in proportion to the square of the increase in diameter of the vessel or inversely in proportion to the increase in area of the vessel, as shown in the formula $V = BF/A$, where V is the velocity, and A is the cross-sectional area. As an example, a vessel one half the diameter of another vessel which has the same length will hold only one fourth as much blood as will the larger vessel. Consequently, in order for the same quantity of blood to flow through the small vessel as through the large vessel, the velocity of blood flow must be four times that in the large vessel.

Velocity of Blood Flow in the Various Portions of the Circulatory System. Because the cross-sectional area of the aorta is approximately 2.5 sq. cm. and the quantity of blood flow from the heart into the aorta at rest is approximately 5000 ml. per minute, one can calculate from these figures that blood flows through the aorta at a mean velocity of 33 cm. per second or slightly more than 1 foot per second. This means that if the aorta were cut wide open and the blood were projected horizontally 3 feet above the floor, the blood would travel only 3 inches horizontally before it would hit the floor. This illustrates that the mean velocity of blood flow in the aorta is not very great under basal conditions. During strenuous activity the heart can pump as much as seven to eight times normal blood flow, which increases the velocity of blood flow in the aorta to as great as 8 feet per second. Furthermore, the velocity of blood flow in the aorta and in all the large arteries is pulsatile because of the intermittent action of the heart as a pump. Consequently, the velocity of blood flow even when the individual is at rest is several feet per second during systole but almost nothing during diastole, these values averaging to a mean of about 1 foot per second.

Because the velocity of blood flow varies inversely with the total cross-sectional area of all the vessels of each type, one can readily calculate that the velocity of blood flow decreases progressively in the small and smaller arteries, and it reaches a value of *about 0.5 mm. per second in the capillaries.* The capillaries have a length of only 0.5 to 1 mm.; this means, therefore, that blood remains in most of the capillaries only 1 to 2 seconds.

The velocity of blood flow in the veins is about four times slower than in the arteries. Indeed, the flow of blood along the two venae cavae, which together have a cross-sectional area some four times as great as that of the aorta, is only about 8 cm. per second under basal conditions and approximately 60 cm. per second with maximal cardiac pumping.

In summary, the velocity of blood flow in the aorta is the most rapid of that in any part of the body, but even there the velocity is not great.

Partial Circulation Time. Clinically, it is very difficult to determine the cardiac output, but it is very easy to determine the so-called partial circulation time, which gives one a crude estimation of the average circulation time.

The method for determining the partial circulation time is the following: Assume that a substance such as *fluorescein* is injected into an arm vein of the subject. This passes through the veins of the arm, through the right side of the heart, through the lungs, through the left side of the heart, and finally into the arterial system. When the fluorescein enters the capillaries of the conjunctivae while they are under examination with ultraviolet light, one suddenly observes a greenish yellow glow. It is obvious that one can time the interval required for fluorescein to flow from the arm to the eye. Likewise, one can time the interval required for some other substance such as *dulcin* or *Decholin* to flow from the arm to the taste buds, for the subject will suddenly

taste sweetness or bitterness, respectively, when the substance gets to these buds. Third, *cyanide* can be injected, the end point being determined when the cyanide suddenly reaches the aortic and carotid bodies and causes a respiratory gasp. Fourth, a *radioactive material* can be injected into a vein of one arm, and, when this arrives in the arteries of the opposite arm, an appropriately placed Geiger counter will detect the radioactivity. Fifth, *ether* injected into an arm vein causes the patient to cough or show a facial grimace when the ether reaches the lungs.

In other words, there are numerous different methods for determining the partial circulation time. These vary slightly in the intervals recorded, but on the average this partial circulation time is approximately 14 seconds in the normal human being under basal conditions, except for the arm-to-lung ether test, which is about one half this long. Obviously, the partial circulation time does not represent the average length of time required for blood to flow from the arm to one of the receptors in the arterial system. Instead, it represents the length of time for the fast-moving portion of blood to travel this distance. Much more of the blood is delayed in its passage through the lungs and elsewhere. Therefore, the partial circulation time, even though a valuable clinical test, is not a mathematically valid measure of the mean velocity of circulation.

The partial circulation time during exercise decreases tremendously and may become as little as 2 to 3 seconds. On the other hand, the partial circulation time may be as great as 60 or more seconds in cardiac failure.

Pressures in the Various Portions of the Vascular Tree

The pressure in the aorta is pulsatile, as is illustrated in Figure 271. It fluctuates between a systolic level of 120 mm. Hg and a

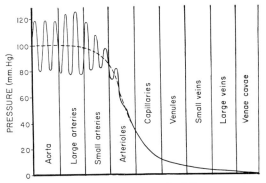

Figure 271. Blood pressures in the different portions of the systemic circulatory system.

diastolic level of 80 mm. Hg, with a mean level of approximately 100 mm. Hg. These pulsations extend into the large and small arteries, but in the very small arteries and arterioles they are damped out. The pulsations are of especial diagnostic importance in some circulatory diseases, as will be discussed in detail later in the chapter, but they have little effect on the mean blood flow in different parts of the circulatory system.

Because the resistance to blood flow from the aorta to the origin of the large arteries is almost zero, the difference between mean pressure at the beginning of the aorta and at the end of the aorta can hardly be measured with ordinary blood pressure–measuring apparatus. Therefore, the mean arterial pressure at the beginning of the large arteries is almost equal to that in the proximal part of the aorta, perhaps falling from 100 mm. Hg to 99 mm. Hg. By the time the blood flows through the large arteries, which also offer little resistance, the mean pressure has fallen not over a few mm. so that the mean pressure at the origin of the small arteries of about one eighth inch caliber is still about 97 mm. Hg. The resistance to blood flow increases tremendously in the small arteries, and the mean pressure at the end of these and at the beginning of the arterioles is about 85 mm. Hg.

The normal pressure drop in the arterioles is approximately from 85 mm. Hg at the beginning of the arterioles down to 35 mm. Hg at the end of the arterioles. Thus, about one half of the total pressure drop from the left ventricle to the right atrium normally occurs in the arterioles.

The pressure at the beginning of the capillary is normally about 35 mm. Hg and at the venous end of the capillary, as illustrated in Figure 271, is approximately 15 mm. Hg. The mean pressure throughout the extent of the capillaries ranges about 25 mm. Hg under normal conditions.

Because there is very little resistance to the flow of blood in the venous system, the pressure ordinarily falls from about 15 mm. Hg at the origin of the venules to approximately 6 mm. Hg at the origin of the small veins, then to 2 mm. Hg at the beginning of the large veins, to 1 mm. Hg at the beginning of the venae cavae, and, finally, to 0 mm. Hg where the venae cavae empty into the right atrium.

Table 14. Blood Flow to Different Organs and Tissues Under Basal Conditions. (Based mainly on data compiled by Dr. L. A. Sapirstein.)

	Per cent	ml./min.
Brain	14	700
Heart	3	150
Bronchial	3	150
Kidneys	22	1100
Liver	27	1350
Portal	(21)	(1050)
Arterial	(6)	(300)
Muscle	15	750
Bone	5	250
Skin (cool weather)	6	300
Thyroid gland	1	50
Adrenal glands	0.5	25
Other tissues	3.5	175
Total	100.0	5000

Blood Flow to Different Areas of the Body

Table 14 gives the rate of blood flow to different tissues and organs of the body, illustrating that it varies tremendously from one organ to another. In general, the flow is proportional to the need of the tissues for oxygen and other nutrients transported in the blood. Special regulatory mechanisms which will be discussed in detail in the next chapter exist locally in each part of the circulation to adjust blood flow to the need for nutrients. For the present it should be pointed out that certain glandular tissues, such as the thyroid gland and the adrenal cortex, have very rapid rates of blood flow in proportion to the mass of tissue–as much as 200 ml./min./100 gm. This in general correlates with the very rapid rates of metabolism of these two glands. In the case of muscle the normal resting blood flow is only about 3 ml./min./100 gm., but this can increase as much as 20-fold in very heavy exercise.

PRESSURE PULSES IN THE ARTERIES

Since the heart is a pulsatile pump, blood enters the arteries, intermittently causing *pressure pulses* in the arterial system. In the normal young adult the pressure at the height of a pulse, the *systolic pressure*, is about 120 mm. Hg and at its lowest point, the *diastolic pressure*, is about 80 mm. Hg.

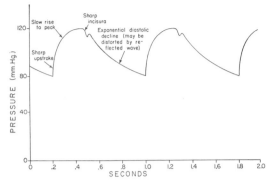

Figure 272. A normal pressure pulse contour recorded from the ascending aorta. (From Opdyke: *Fed. Proc.* 11:734, 1952.)

The difference between these two pressures, about 40 mm. Hg, is called the *pulse pressure.*

Figure 272 illustrates a typical pressure pulse curve recorded in the ascending aorta of a human being, showing a very rapid rise in arterial pressure during ventricular systole, followed by a maintained high level of pressure for 0.2 to 0.3 second. This is terminated by a sharp *incisura* at the end of systole, followed by a slow decline of pressure back to the diastolic level. The incisura occurs at the same time that the aortic valve closes and is caused as follows: During systole the pressure in the arteries rises to a high value. When the ventricle relaxes the intraventricular pressure begins to fall rapidly, and backflow of blood from the aorta into the ventricle allows the aortic pressure also to begin falling. The backflow suddenly snaps the aortic valve closed. However, the momentum that has been built up in the backflowing blood brings still a little more blood into the root of the aorta, raising the pressure again and thus giving the incisura in the record.

After systole is over, the pressure in the central aorta decreases rapidly at first but progressively more and more slowly as diastole proceeds. The reason for this difference is that blood flows through the peripheral vessels much more rapidly when the pressure is high than when it is low.

Factors That Affect the Pulse Pressure

There are two major factors that affect the pulse pressure. These are (1) the *stroke volume output* of the heart and (2) the *capacitance (total distensibility)* of the arterial tree.

In general, the greater the stroke volume output the greater is the amount of blood that must be accommodated in the arterial tree with each heart beat and, therefore, the greater will the pressure rise during systole and the greater will it fall during diastole, thus causing a greater pulse pressure. On the other hand, the greater the capacitance of the arterial system the less will be the rise in pressure for a given stroke volume of blood pumped into the arteries. In effect, then, the pulse pressure is determined approximately by the *ratio of stroke volume output to capacitance* of the arterial tree. Therefore, any condition of the circulation that affects either of these two factors will also affect the pulse pressure.

Factors that Affect the Pulse Pressure by Changing the Stroke Volume Output. So many different circulatory conditions change the stroke volume output that only a few of these can be mentioned:

An increase in heart rate while the cardiac output remains constant will cause the stroke volume output to decrease in inverse proportion to the increased rate, and, as a consequence, the quantity of blood that must be accommodated in the arterial tree with each beat of the heart is correspondingly reduced, and the pulse pressure also decreases accordingly. In many instances, however, the cardiac output increases coincidentally with an increase in heart rate so that the stroke volume output remains unchanged or even actually rises. When this happens, the pulse pressure changes approximately in the same direction as the stroke volume output.

A decrease in total peripheral resistance allows rapid flow of blood from the arteries to the veins. This usually increases the venous return to the heart and increases the stroke volume output. Here, again, the pulse pressure is greatly increased.

An increase in mean circulatory pressure, if all other circulatory factors remain constant, will increase the rate of venous return to the heart and consequently increase the stroke volume output. Here again the pulse pressure is accordingly increased. Still other conditions that increase venous return will be discussed in Chapter 35. Whenever the venous return is increased while the heart rate remains constant, the stroke volume output and pulse pressure correspondingly increase. Therefore, the student is referred to this chapter for still other factors that can increase the pulse pressure.

Estimation of stroke volume output from the pressure pulse curve. Since the pulse pressure is roughly proportional to the stroke volume output, one can actually estimate the stroke volume output from the pulse pressure. In general, the greater the pulse pressure, the greater the stroke volume output. However, for this to be accurate, one must assume that the capacitance (total distensibility) of the arterial tree remains constant from one person to another. Furthermore, the correspondence between stroke volume output and pulse pressure is not completely linear for the following reasons: First, a large amount of blood flows out of the arterial tree while the heart is actually ejecting blood into the arteries during systole. If the duration of ejection is prolonged, this quantity of runoff may be very great, resulting in less pulse pressure than might otherwise be expected. Second, the arterial capacitance is slightly greater in low pressure ranges than in high pressure ranges; therefore, a given stroke volume output will cause the pressure to change more at high pressures than at low pressures, which will cause a nonlinear relationship between stroke volume output and the pulse pressure. Nevertheless, appropriate formulas have been devised to correct for these considerations so that reasonably accurate estimations of stroke volume output can be made from the pressure pulse curve.

Factors That Affect the Pulse Pressure by Altering the Arterial Capacitance. In contrast to the many different conditions that can cause changes in stroke volume output, there are only two major factors that often alter the arterial capacitance. These are (1) change in mean arterial pressure and (2) pathological changes that affect the distensibility of the arterial walls.

In the preceding chapter it was pointed out that the capacitance of a vascular segment is the volume of blood that can be accommodated for a given rise in pressure. As the arterial pressure rises from low to high values, the capacitance decreases slightly. Therefore, in the low pressure range

considerably more blood can be accommodated for a given rise in pressure than in the high pressure range. For this reason, *in a person who has high blood pressure but a normal stroke volume output, the pulse pressure will be considerably increased.*

In old age, the arterial walls lose much of their elastic and muscular tissues, and these are replaced by fibrous tissue and sometimes even calcified plaques that cannot stretch a significant amount. These changes greatly decrease the capacitance of the arterial system, which in turn causes the arterial pressure to rise very high during systole and to fall greatly during diastole as blood runs off from the arteries to the veins.

Abnormal Pressure Pulse Contours

Some conditions of the circulation cause abnormal *contours* to the pressure pulse wave in addition to altering the value of the pulse pressure. Especially distinctive among these are arteriosclerosis, patent ductus arteriosus, and aortic regurgitation.

Arteriosclerosis. In arteriosclerosis the arteries become fibrous and sometimes calcified, thereby resulting in greatly reduced arterial distensibility and also resulting in markedly increased pulse pressure. Usually a mild degree of hypertension also accompanies arteriosclerosis so that not only does the pulse pressure rise but the mean pressure also. The middle curve of Figure 273 illustrates a characteristic aortic pressure pulse contour in arteriosclerosis, showing a markedly elevated systolic pressure, a slightly elevated diastolic pressure, and also a great increase in pulse pressure. The curve is more peaked than that of the normal curve, and the incisura lies at

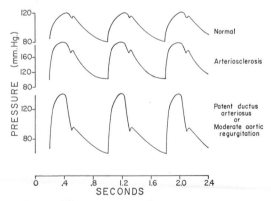

Figure 273. Pressure pulse contours in arteriosclerosis, patent ductus arteriosus, and moderate aortic regurgitation.

a lower point on the down slope of the curve than in the normal.

Patent Ductus Arteriosus. In patent ductus arteriosus blood flows from the aorta through the open ductus into the pulmonary artery, allowing very rapid runoff of blood from the arterial tree after each heart beat. However, this is compensated by a greater than normal stroke volume output, giving the pressure pulse contour shown by the lowest curve in Figure 273. Here one finds an elevated systolic pressure, a greatly depressed diastolic pressure, a greatly increased pulse pressure, and the incisura occurring again at a very low point on the downslope because an excessively large amount of blood runs off from the arteries even before systole is over.

Aortic Regurgitation. In aortic regurgitation much of the blood that is pumped into the aorta during systole flows back into the left ventricle during diastole. However, this backflow is compensated by a much greater than normal stroke volume output during systole. Thus, the condition is very similar to that of patent ductus arteriosus but not always identical, for in aortic regurgitation the valve sometimes fails entirely to close. When this is true the incisura illustrated in the lower curve of Figure 273 will be entirely absent.

Transmission of the Pressure Pulse to the Periphery

When the heart ejects blood into the aorta during systole, only the proximal portion of the aorta becomes distended at first, and it

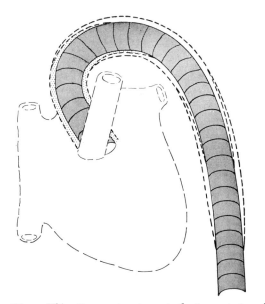

Figure 274. Progressive stages in the transmission of the pressure pulse along the aorta.

is only in this portion of the arterial tree that the pressure rises immediately. The cause of this is the inertia of the blood in the aorta, which prevents its sudden movement away from the central arteries into the peripheral arteries.

However, the rising pressure in the central aorta gradually overcomes the inertia of the blood to cause beginning movement of the blood toward the periphery. This compresses the blood in the more peripheral arteries, causing the pressure to rise progressively farther and farther out in the arterial tree. Figure 274 illustrates this *transmission of the pressure pulse* from the proximal portion of the aorta toward the distal portion, the aorta becoming distended as the pressure wave moves forward.

The velocity of transmission of the pressure pulse along the normal aorta is 3 to 5 meters per second, along the large arterial branches about 7 to 10 meters per second, and in the smaller arteries 15 to 35 meters per second. In general, the greater the distensibility of the artery, the slower will be the rate of transmission of the pressure pulse, which explains the slowness of transmission in the aorta versus the rapidity of transmission in the more distal arteries.

It should be noted particularly that the *velocity of transmission of the pressure pulse is much greater than the velocity of blood flow,* which was discussed earlier in the chapter. In transmission of the pressure pulse, only a small amount of blood entering the proximal aorta pushes the more distal blood forward sufficiently to elevate the pressure in the very distal arteries. Therefore, the blood ejected by the heart may have traveled only a few centimeters in the aorta by the time the pressure wave has already reached the distal ends of the arteries. In the aorta, the velocity of the pressure pulse is approximately 15 times that of blood flow, while in the more distal arteries the velocity of the pressure pulse may be as great as 100 times the velocity of blood flow.

Augmentation of the Peripheral Pulse Pressure. An interesting phenomenon that very often occurs in transmission of pressure pulses to the periphery is an increase in pulse pressure. This effect is illustrated in Figure 275, which shows considerable enhancement of the pulse pressure more and more peripherally.

All the precise causes of pulse pressure augmen-

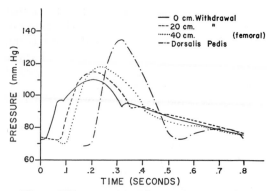

Figure 275. Pressure pulse contours in different segments of the arterial tree in man, showing (1) the delay in the pressure pulse as it spreads more and more peripherally and (2) augmentation of the pulse pressure especially in the dorsalis pedis artery. (Modified from Remington and Wood: *J. Applied Physiol.* 9:440, 1956.)

tation have not been determined, though at least the following three different factors are known to play a significant role in this effect: (1) Pressure waves are reflected to some extent by the peripheral arteries. That is, when a pressure pulse enters the peripheral arteries and distends them, the pressure in these peripheral arteries causes the pulse wave to begin traveling backward. This is analogous to a wave traveling in a bowl of water until it hits the edge. On striking the edge, the wave turns around and travels back onto the surface of the water. Furthermore, if the returning wave strikes an oncoming wave, the two "summate," causing a much higher wave than would otherwise occur. Such is the case in the arterial tree. The first portion of the pressure wave is reflected before the latter portion of the same wave ever reaches the peripheral arteries. Therefore, the first portion summates with the latter portion, causing higher pressures than would otherwise be recorded. (2) Part of the augmentation undoubtedly results from the progressive decrease in distensibility more peripherally in the arterial tree. Transmission of the pressure pulse in the aorta and large arteries is characterized by a high level of momentum of the blood in the advancing edge of the pressure wave. When this wave suddenly reaches the small arteries, which have less distensibility than the large arteries, much of the kinetic energy of this momentum is changed into pressure, resulting in augmentation of the pressure. (3) The pulse pressure is also augmented by transmission of certain parts of the pulse wave at more rapid rates than other parts. For instance, the high pressure portion is transmitted more rapidly than the low pressure portion because the arterial distensibility is less at high pressure than at low pressure. This causes crowding together of certain portions of the wave

and, therefore, "peaking" of the pressure pulse as illustrated for the dorsalis pedis in Figure 275.

Regardless of the relative significance of the different causes of augmentation of the pulse pressure, this phenomenon must be remembered whenever pressure measurements are made in peripheral arteries, for systolic pressure is sometimes as much as 20 to 30 per cent above that in the central aorta, and diastolic pressure is often reduced as much as 10 to 15 per cent.

Damping of the Pressure Pulse in the Small Arteries and Arterioles.

The pressure pulse becomes less and less intense as it passes through the small arteries and arterioles, until it becomes either totally or almost totally absent in the capillaries. This was illustrated in Figure 271 and is called *damping* of the pressure pulse.

Damping of the pressure pulse is probably caused mainly by a combined effect of vascular distensibility and vascular resistance. That is, for a pressure wave to travel from one area of an artery to another area, a small amount of blood must flow between the two areas. The resistance in the small arteries and arterioles is great enough that the flow of blood, and consequently the transmission of pressure, is greatly impeded. On the other hand, the distensibility of the vessels is great enough that the extra blood that does flow during a pressure pulse causes progressively less and less pressure rise in the more distal vessels. Therefore, even though the pressure rises and falls quite significantly in the large arteries, the combined resistance-distensibility effects cause the pressure pulse to become progressively smaller and smaller as it proceeds farther and farther into the small vessels. Figure 276 illustrates the effect of resistance on damping. The curve to the left is a normal pressure pulse contour recorded from the dorsalis pedis artery in a dog. To the right

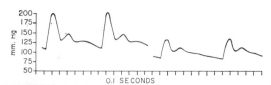

Figure 276. Pressure pulse contour in the dorsalis pedis artery of a dog recorded, first, under normal conditions and, second, during stimulation of the sympathetic nerves supplying the femoral artery. (Modified from Alexander and Kantowitz: *Surgery.* 33:42, 1953.)

is the same pressure pulse contour recorded during spasm of the femoral artery. The damping effect of the increased resistance is readily apparent.

Capillary pulsation. Occasionally pressure pulses are not completely damped by the time they reach the capillaries, and *capillary pulsations* result which can be readily demonstrated by pressing on the anterior portion of the fingernail so that the blood is pressed out of the anterior capillaries of the nail bed. This causes blanching anteriorly while the posterior half of the nail remains red because of blood still in the capillaries. If significant pulsation is occurring in the capillaries, the border between the red and white areas will shift forward as more capillaries become filled during the high pressure phase and backward during the low pressure phase.

Two major factors can cause capillary pulsation: (1) It occurs when the central pressure pulse is greatly exacerbated, as occurs when the heart rate is very slow or when the stroke volume output is greatly increased as a result of *aortic regurgitation, patent ductus arteriosus,* or even *extreme increase in venous return.* (2) Another cause of capillary pulsation is extreme dilatation of the small arteries and arterioles, which reduces the damping qualities of these vessels.

The Radial Pulse

Clinically, it has been the habit for many years for a physician to feel the radial pulse of each patient. This is done to determine the rate of the heartbeat or, frequently, because of the psychic contact that it gives the doctor with his patient. Under certain circumstances, however, the character of the pulse can also be of value in the diagnosis of circulatory diseases.

Weak Pulse. A weak pulse at the radial artery often indicates that the quantity of blood emitted into the arterial tree with each beat of the heart is less than normal. This occurs as a result of many different conditions: First, *a rapid rate of heartbeat* causes lessened stroke volume output even though the cardiac output is normal, and this results in a weak pulse. Second, a low cardiac output but normal heart rate decreases the stroke volume output and, consequently, weakens the radial pulse.

On the other hand, the cardiac output and rate of heartbeat may be perfectly normal, and yet the patient can still have a weak pulse due to local conditions in the hand and forearm. Whenever the hand and forearm are very cold, the arteries tend to become vasospastic so that pulse waves are not transmitted to the radial artery with ease; in this instance, a week pulse develops even though there is no abnormality of the circulation. Occasionally, hardening of the radial artery itself decreases the pulse strength though generalized arteriosclerosis everywhere besides the radial artery causes a bounding pulse.

Pulsus Paradoxus. Often the strength of the pulse becomes strong, then weak, then strong, continuing in coordination with the phases of respiration. This is due to alternate increase and decrease in cardiac output with each respiration. During inspiration all the blood vessels of the lungs are increased in size because of increased negative pressure in the thorax. Therefore, blood collects in the lungs and the quantity of blood that flows to the left ventricles during inspiration is decreased. As a result the stroke volume output and the pulse strength decrease. During expiration, an increased quantity of blood flows into the left ventricle, and the pulse strength increases. This is a normal effect in all persons, but it becomes extremely distinct in some conditions such as cardiac tamponade and very deep breathing.

Pulse Deficit. The rhythm of the heart is very irregular in atrial fibrillation, the cause for which was explained in Chapter 21. Irregular rhythms also occur frequently when aberrant pacemakers develop either in the atria or in the ventricles to cause beats of the heart at abnormal times in the cardiac cycle. In all these arrhythmias, two beats of the heart often come so close together that the second beat expels no blood or very little blood into the arterial tree because the left ventricle has no time to fill between the two beats. In this circumstance, one can hear the second beat of the heart with a stethoscope applied directly over the heart, but one does not feel a pulsation in the radial artery.

Determination of the *pulse deficit* furnishes a means of assessing the degree of disability caused by atrial fibrillation or by other arrhythmias. The physician counts the rate of the heart each minute by listening to it, and then he counts the rate of the radial pulse. The difference between these two is the pulse deficit, and the more severe the disability, the greater is the pulse deficit—that is, the greater is the number of heart contractions that do not pump blood.

Pulsus Alternans. In a few conditions the heart beats strongly with one beat and then weakly with the next beat, continually alternating in this manner. This alternation is frequently caused by intoxication with overdosage of digitalis, and it occurs occasionally in partial block of the Purkinje system. In such conditions, every other radial pulsation is strong while the intermittent pulsations are weak.

Clinical Methods for Measuring Systolic and Diastolic Pressures and the Pulse Pressure

Obviously, it is impossible to use the various rapid response needle recorders described in the previous chapter for making routine pressure measurements in human patients, although they are used on occasion when special studies are necessary. In general, the clinician determines systolic and diastolic pressures by indirect means. By definition, the systolic pressure is the pressure at the maximum level in the pulse pressure curve, and the diastolic pressure is the pressure at its lowest point. Clinically, the systolic pressure is written as the numerator of a fraction and the diastolic pressure as the denominator. Thus the normal pressure of an adult is $120/80$. *The pulse pressure is the difference between systolic pressure and diastolic pressure,* and the normal pulse pressure of an adult is 120 − 80, or 40 mm. Hg.

The Auscultatory Method.   Figure 277 illustrates the auscultatory method for determining systolic and diastolic blood pressures. A stethoscope is placed over the antecubital artery while a blood pressure cuff around the upper arm is inflated. As long as the cuff presses against the arm with so little pressure that the artery remains distended with blood, no sounds whatsoever are heard by the stethoscope despite the fact that the blood pressure within the artery is pulsating. When the cuff presses sufficiently that the artery collapses during the diastolic part of the arterial pressure cycle, a sound is heard

in the stethoscope. Most experimenters believe that the sound is caused by a sudden, vibrating rush of blood down through the artery when blood begins to flow once again after the collapse is over. Regardless of what causes the sounds to occur, it is an experimental fact that they do occur in the artery when the vessel collapses and opens during each pressure cycle.

In determining blood pressure by the auscultatory method, the pressure in the cuff is first elevated well above arterial systolic pressure. Then the pressure in the cuff is gradually reduced. As long as the pressure in the cuff is higher than systolic pressure, the brachial artery remains collapsed and no blood whatsoever flows into the lower artery during any part of the pressure cycle. Therefore, no sounds are heard in the lower artery. Just as soon as the pressure in the cuff falls below systolic pressure, blood slips through the artery beneath the cuff during systole, and one begins to hear sounds in the antecubital artery. As soon as these sounds are heard, the level of the manometer is noted, and this is approximately equal to the systolic blood pressure.

As the pressure in the cuff is lowered still more, the sounds in the lower artery, due to its alternate collapse and refilling, continue to be heard until the artery remains filled throughout the entire cycle of the pressure pulse. When the pressure in the cuff falls so low that the artery no longer collapses at all (because the pressure in the artery is then greater than that in the cuff, even during diastole), the pressure in the manometer is approximately equal to the diastolic pressure.

The auscultatory method for determining systolic and diastolic pressures is not entirely accurate, but it usually gives values within 10 per cent of those determined by direct measurements from the arteries.

Radial   Pulsation   and   Oscillometric Methods for Estimating Arterial Pressure. Arterial blood pressure can also be estimated by feeling the radial pulse or by recording the pulsation in the lower arm with an oscillometer while a cuff is inflated and deflated over the upper arm. An oscillometer consists of a partially inflated blood pressure cuff and a recording apparatus that can register pulsations in the cuff resulting from pulsations in the forearm. Indeed, a blood pressure recorder of the aneroid type

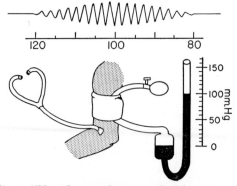

Figure 277.   The auscultatory method for measuring systolic and diastolic pressures.

makes an excellent oscillometer for estimating arterial pressure.

In applying these methods, the pressure in the cuff on the upper arm is raised well above the systolic level and then it is progressively reduced. No pulsation will be felt in the radial artery or registered by the oscillometer until the cuff pressure falls below the systolic pressure level. But, just as soon as this point is reached, a distinct radial pulse can be felt, or a distinct oscillation will be recorded by the oscillometer. Further decrease in the upper arm cuff pressure results, at first, in progressive increase in the intensity of radial or oscillometer pulsation. Then there is a slight decrease in these pulsations at approximately the diastolic level of pressure, but this change is so indistinct that estimation of diastolic pressure is very likely to be in severe error.

The oscillometric method is very valuable for measuring pressures when distinct sounds cannot be heard from the forearm arteries. This often results (1) in very young children or (2) in adults when the arteries are in a state of spasm, such as when a patient is in *shock*. These instances are often among the most important in which it is essential to have at least some estimation of arterial pressure, thus illustrating the value of knowing this accessory method for measuring systolic arterial pressure in addition to the auscultatory method.

Pressure Pulses in the Veins

The pressure pulses from the arteries are almost always damped out completely before they pass through the capillaries into the systemic veins. However, right atrial pulsations are sometimes transmitted backward along the veins to cause pressure pulses of an entirely different character. This usually does not occur to a significant extent in the normal circulation because most of the veins leading into the thoracic cavity are compressed by surrounding tissues, thereby causing sufficient resistance to damp out the pulsations before they can enter the peripheral veins. However, whenever the mean right atrial pressure is high, especially in heart failure, the veins are then well filled with blood and can easily transmit the pulsations. The atrial pulsations were discussed in Chapter 25. Briefly, they are (1) the *a wave*, caused by contraction of the atrium, (2) the *c wave*, caused by contraction of the ventricle, and (3) the *v wave*, caused by continued inflow of blood into the atrium when the A-V valves are closed during ventricular systole.

Backward transmission of the a, c, and v waves in the venous system probably has very little functional significance, though some research workers believe that these pulsations actually help blood to flow along the veins toward the heart by momentarily opening compressed veins. This, however, is yet unproved, and blood flow along the veins to the heart still occurs quite adequately even when the pulsations are experimentally removed.

In severe cardiac failure the venous pressure waves are often prominent enough that one can see the veins of the patient's neck pulsating. Indeed, this is a very important diagnostic point in severe congestive failure. In earlier days these pulsations were recorded for diagnostic purposes. The *a-c interval* in the recording is approximately equal to the P-Q interval of the electrocardiogram, and, before the days of electrocardiography, this was often used as a measure of the delay between atrial excitation and ventricular excitation. These waves, therefore, were then of considerable value in diagnosing different degrees of heart block.

REFERENCES

Alexander, R. S.: The genesis of the aortic standing wave. *Circ. Res.*, 1:145, 1953.

Alexander, R. S., and Kantrowitz, A.: Reduction of the peripheral arterial pulse by spasm of large arteries. *Surgery*, 33:42, 1953.

Altman, P. L.: Handbook of circulation. Philadelphia, W. B. Saunders Co., 1959.

Bordley, J., III, Connor, C. A. R., Hamilton, W. F., Kerr, W. J., and Wiggers, C. J.: Recommendations for human blood pressure determinations by sphygmomanometers. *Circulation*, 4:503, 1951.

Ciba Foundation: Peripheral circulation in man. Boston, Little, Brown, and Co., 1954.

Feitelbergs, S., Nabatoff, R. A., and Touroff, A. S. W.: An apparatus to measure the elasticity of blood vessels. *Ann. Surg.*, 137:141, 1953.

Folkow, B.: Peripheral circulation. *Ann. Rev. Physiol.*, 18:159, 1956.

Grodins, F. S., Stuart, W. H., and Veenstra, R. L.: Performance characteristics of the right heart bypass preparation. *Am. J. Physiol.*, 198:552, 1960.

Guyton, A. C.: Peripheral circulation. *Ann. Rev. Physiol.*, 21:239, 1959.

Hamilton, W. F.: The patterns of the arterial pulse. *Am. J. Physiol.*, 141:233, 1944.

Hamilton, W. F., and Brown, W. J., Jr.: Positive pulse reflection in an elastic model from a wider segment with higher resistance. *Am. J. Physiol.*, 197:730, 1959.

Hamilton, W. F., and Dow, P.: An experimental study of the Starling waves in the pulse propagated through the aorta. *Am. J. Physiol.*, 125:48, 1939.

Hamilton, W. F., and Remington, J. W.: Some factors in the regulation of stroke volume. *Am. J. Physiol.*, *153*:287, 1948.

Hamilton, W. F., Remington, J. W., and Dow, P.: Determination of propagation velocity of arterial pulse wave. *Am. J. Physiol.*, *144*:521, 1945.

Heath, C., and Brown, K. B., Jr.: Posthypercapnic hemodynamic changes in dogs. *J. Appl. Physiol.*, *8*:495, 1956.

Jensen, R. E., and Parnell, J.: Mechanical properties of arteries in vivo. *Circ. Res.*, *8*:622, 1960.

Kroeker, E. J., and Wood, E. H.: Comparison of simultaneously recorded central and peripheral arterial pressure pulses during rest, exercise and tilted position in man. *Circ. Res.*, *3*:623, 1955.

Lawton, R. W.: Measurements on the elasticity and damping of isolated aortic strips of the dog. *Circ. Res.*, *3*:403, 1955.

Luisada, A. A.: Cardiac Pressures and Pulses. New York, Grune & Stratton, Inc., 1956.

Malcolm, J. E.: Blood Pressure Sounds and Their Meanings. Springfield, Illinois, Charles C Thomas, 1957.

Nyboer, J.: The Electrical Resistive Measure of the Blood Pulse Volume, Peripheral and Central Blood Flow. Springfield, Illinois, Charles C Thomas, 1959.

Opdyke, D. F., and others: Panel Discussion: Interpretation and significance of alterations in central pulse form. *Fed. Proc.*, *11*:732, 1952.

Peterson, L. H.: Peripheral circulation. *Ann. Rev. Physiol.*, *19*:255, 1957.

Randall, J. E., and Stacy, R. W.: Mechanical impedance of the dog's hind leg to pulsatile blood flow. *Am. J. Physiol.*, *187*:94, 1956.

Randall, J. E., and Stacy, R. W.: Pulsatile and steady pressure-flow relations in the vascular bed of the hind leg of the dog. *Am. J. Physiol.*, *185*:351, 1956.

Remington, J. W.: Hysteresis loop behavior of the aorta and other extensible tissues. *Am. J. Physiol.*, *180*:83, 1955.

Remington, J. W.: Relation between length of diastole and stroke index in intact dog. *Am. J. Physiol.*, *162*:273, 1950.

Remington, J. W., and Alexander, R. S.: Stretch behavior of the bladder as an approach to vascular distensibility. *Am. J. Physiol.*, *181*:240, 1955.

Remington, J. W., and Hamilton, W. F.: The construction of a theoretical cardiac ejection curve from the contour of the aortic pressure pulse. *Am. J. Physiol.*, *144*:546, 1945.

Remington, J. W., Noback, C. R., Hamilton, W. F., and Gold, J. J.: Volume elasticity characteristics of the human aorta and prediction of the stroke volume from the pressure pulse. *Am. J. Physiol.*, *153*: 298, 1948.

Remington, J. W., and Wood, E. H.: Formation of peripheral pulse contour in man. *J. Appl. Physiol.*, *9*:433, 1956.

Rushmer, R. R.: Pressure-circumference relations in the aorta. *Am. J. Physiol.*, *183*:545, 1955.

Ryan, J. M., Stacy, R. W., and Watman, R. N.: Role of abdominal aortic branches in pulse wave contour genesis. *Circ. Res.*, *4*:676, 1956.

Spencer, M. P., and Denison, A. B.: The aortic flow pulse as related to differential pressure. *Circ. Res.*, *4*:476, 1956.

Stacy, R. W., and Giles, F. M.: Computer analysis of arterial properties. *Circ. Res.*, *7*:1031, 1959.

Steele, J. M.: Interpretation of arterial elasticity from measurements of pulse wave velocities. *Am. Heart J.*, *14*:452, 1937.

Warner, H. R.: A study of the mechanism of pressure wave distinction by arterial walls using an electrical analog. *Circ. Res.*, *5*:79, 1957.

Warner, H. R., Swan, H. J. C., Connolly, D. C., Tompkins, R. G., and Wood, E. H.: Quantitation of beat-to-beat changes in stroke volume from the aortic pulse contour in man. *J. Appl. Physiol.*, *5*: 495, 1953.

Wood, E. H., Leusen, I. R., Warner, H. R., and Wright, J. L.: Measurement of pressures in man by cardiac catheters. *Circ. Res.*, *2*:294, 1954.

See also Chapter 26, Hemodynamics; Chapter 28, Other aspects of the systemic circulation; Chapter 31, Special circulatory systems; Chapter 38, General bibliography for the cardiovascular system.

The Systemic Circulation: II. Regulation of Blood Flow by the Arterioles; Special Functions of the Venous System; Regulation of Capillary Pressure

REGULATION OF BLOOD FLOW BY THE ARTERIOLES

About one half of the resistance in the systemic circulation normally occurs in the arterioles, and another major share of the resistance occurs in the small arteries leading to the arterioles. Therefore, even slight changes in the diameters of these vessels can markedly alter the blood flow to areas that they supply. It should be remembered particularly that, in accordance with Poiseuille's law, halving the diameter of the arterioles can increase their resistance up to as much as 16-fold, and four-fold constriction can increase their resistance as much as 256 times.

The arterioles and small arteries are supplied with strong muscular coats that are certainly capable of changing the vessel diameters at least four to six times. Furthermore, these vessels are exceptionally well supplied with sympathetic nerves. These attributes of the arterioles and small arteries make them highly suited to the important role that they play in regulating blood flow to the individual tissues of the body.

Local "Autoregulation" of Blood Flow by the Individual Tissues

If blood flow to a leg or an arm is stopped for as long as a minute and then reinstituted, the flow immediately increases two to six times more than it had originally been, and the rapid flow continues until the metabolic deficit caused by lack of flow is made up. This phenomenon is called *local autoregulation of blood flow* or *reactive hyperemia,* and it is one of the most powerful of all the factors that control blood flow in most of the tissues of the body, including especially the muscles which make up almost one half of the body mass.

It should be emphasized that blood flow need not be stopped entirely to invoke local autoregulation, for decreasing it to one half normal, such as by reducing the arterial pressure, immediately institutes the mechanism, and within approximately one minute the flow will have returned to about five sixths of its original value. This illustrates that ischemia automatically promotes vasodilation of the arterioles, resulting in return of almost normal blood flow.

Furthermore, local autoregulation is not a nervous reflex phenomenon, for it occurs even when the nerves have been completely destroyed.

Thus, the tissues have their own intrinsic mechanism for "protecting" their blood flow. If any extraneous factor decreases the flow, the vessels respond to the local ischemia by dilating, thereby almost correcting the deficit in flow. On the other hand, if some other extraneous factor causes excess flow to the tissues, the vessels automatically constrict and thereby conserve the cardiac output for use elsewhere in the body.

Relationship of Local Metabolic Rate to Local Autoregulation. In addition to ischemia, increased metabolism of tissues also causes vasodilatation, and this is usually of sufficient degree to supply the amounts of oxygen and nutrients required for the extra activity. In other words, the local autoregulation mechanism operates in response to the requirements of the tissues, varying the blood flow in proportion to the tissues' needs.

Mechanism of Local Autoregulation. The precise mechanism by which local autoregulation occurs has not yet been determined, but two major suggestions have been offered: First, too little blood flow to a particular tissue could so greatly reduce the amount of oxygen and other nutrients carried to the tissues that the arterioles themselves might suffer a metabolic deficit, which weakens them and allows vasodilatation. Second, it has been suggested that ischemic tissues might release a vasodilator substance that in turn causes the arterioles to dilate.

Experiments in our laboratory have shown that simple oxygen lack in the blood flowing to tissues can cause marked vasodilatation. This is illustrated in Figure 278, which shows that the rate of blood flow in an isolated dog leg progressively increases as the oxygen saturation of the arterial blood decreases. Furthermore, the amount of increase in blood flow is enough to compensate for 70 per cent of the decreased oxygen saturation. These experiments indicate that the local autoregulatory mechanism could be explained very simply on the basis of oxygen lack as follows: The arteriolar walls might well be in competition with the tissue cells for oxygen, and, if the tissue cells are using so much oxygen that they deplete the available interstitial fluid oxygen to a very low value, then the vessels could automatically dilate, simply because their own muscle cells might not be receiving adequate amounts of oxygen to maintain contraction. This would allow increased flow of blood and would again supply adequate amounts of oxygen and other nutrients.

Importance of Local Autoregulation of Blood Flow. In persons whose entire

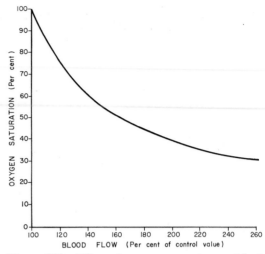

Figure 278. Effect of oxygen saturation on blood flow through an isolated dog leg.

sympathetic nervous systems have been removed, or in persons who have broken necks and, therefore, no cerebral control of their peripheral nervous system, or in animals in which the nervous control of the circulation has been completely blocked by drugs, blood flow to the different local areas of the body is still controlled very accurately in proportion to the degree of activity of each area. Therefore, the local autoregulation mechanism seems to be especially important to insure a continual supply of adequate nutrition to the tissues, both normally and in times of excessive activity. On the other hand, local autoregulation has nothing to do with the control of blood flow for other purposes besides nutrition. For instance, blood flow through the skin is to a great extent controlled for the purpose of cooling the surface of the body, and this control is mediated entirely through the nerves, as will be discussed below. Likewise, most of the renal blood flow under normal circumstances is not for supply of nutrients to the renal tissues but instead for the control of urinary output. Here again, very little of the regulation of blood flow is under the control of the local factors in the kidneys.

In skeletal muscle, which constitutes about 40 per cent of the weight of the body, as well as in cardiac and smooth muscle, the local autoregulatory mechanism under most conditions accounts for 80 to 100 per cent of all the regulation of local blood flow.

Long-term Regulation of Local Blood Flow by Changes in Tissue Vascularity

Tissues have still another intrinsic ability to regulate their own blood flow by changing their degree of "vascularity"; anoxia, in addition to causing local vasodilatation, also causes an *increased number of vessels* to grow into the anoxic tissue. This effect occurs in all tissues of the body when it is exposed to chronically low levels of oxygen in the atmosphere. Also, it occurs in any local area of the body, such as the heart, when one of the nutrient arteries becomes blocked. Finally, it occurs in any tissue that becomes very active.

This long-term mechanism usually requires four weeks to half a year to develop fully. Yet, it constitutes still another mechanism, in addition to the local autoregulatory mechanism discussed above, by which the tissues can regulate their own blood supply.

Regulation of Blood Flow by the Sympathetic Nerves

Besides the intrinsic mechanism for regulation of local blood flow, essentially all the blood vessels of the body are controlled also by sympathetic nerve fibers, as illustrated in Figure 279. A few of the vessels of the body are controlled, too, by parasympathetic nerve fibers, though these are of relatively little significance in the overall circulation with the possible exception of two areas of the body, the coronary vessels and the cerebral vessels, which will be discussed respectively in Chapters 30 and 31.

Control of the systemic circulation by the sympathetic nerves is mediated through two distinct regulatory systems: (1) the *vasoconstrictor system* and (2) the *vasodilator system*.

The Sympathetic Vasoconstrictor System. Essentially all vessels of the body are supplied by sympathetic vasoconstrictor nerve fibers. These are *adrenergic* nerves, which secrete principally the hormone norepinephrine at their endings. In many physiological states, such as (1) when low blood pressure stimulates the carotid sinus pressoreceptors and (2) when excess carbon dioxide in the body fluids stimulates the sympathetic vasoconstrictor center of the medulla, the vasoconstrictor fibers to all the blood vessels throughout the body might be stimulated at once, resulting in generalized vasoconstriction. At other times, local vasoconstriction occurs in response to spinal cord reflexes that regulate local temperature of individual parts of the body or in response to spinal cord reflexes that are initiated by local injury to the tissues.

The sympathetic vasoconstrictor system is so powerful in many vascular areas of the body that it can totally, or almost totally, block blood flow for many minutes at a time. It has especially powerful control over blood flow to the kidneys, the gastrointestinal system, and to the skin of the hands and feet.

Vasodilatation and the Sympathetic Vasodilator System. Vasodilatation occurs principally by *release of sympathetic vasoconstrictor tone*—that is, simply reducing the sympathetic impulses allows the vessels to dilate. However, in addition to this, sympathetic *vasodilator fibers* supply the arterioles in many areas of the circulation such as in the coronaries, all the vessels of the skeletal muscles, and all the vessels of the skin besides those in the hands and feet.

The vasodilator fibers to the muscles are cholinergic, and those to the skin are also believed to be cholinergic because they are activated at the same time that the cholinergic sweat fibers are activated. Therefore, it is rapidly becoming apparent that the sympathetic nervous system is not composed entirely of adrenergic nerve fibers as was once thought, but that it is actually a composite of both adrenergic and cholinergic fibers.

Furthermore, the sympathetic vasodilator system is activated in response to different physiological stimuli from those that activate

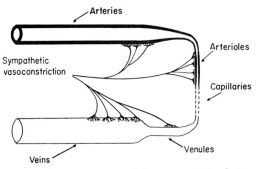

Figure 279. Innervation of the systemic circulation.

the vasoconstrictor system. For instance, stimulation of the motor region of the brain causes sympathetic vasodilatation in the muscles at the same time that it causes the muscles to contract. Also, too high a body temperature activates the vasodilators to the skin throughout most of the body to cause heat loss.

In summary, sympathetic vasodilatation occurs in two ways: first, by decreasing the vasoconstrictor tone throughout the circulatory system, and, second, by stimulating the vasodilator system. The second of these mechanisms does not function in all parts of the body, but is important in the control of blood flow to certain localized vascular areas.

Conditions Under Which Sympathetic Regulation is Important. In the above discussion of local autoregulation of blood flow by the tissues themselves, it was pointed out that adequate regulation for maintaining nutritional supply to the tissues can be achieved without nervous control of the vessels. However, many other functions of the circulatory system besides the nutritional function often require (1) *generalized vasoconstriction* or *vasodilatation* throughout the entire body or (2) *shifts of blood flow* from one area of the body to other areas even though this might be accomplished at the expense of the nutritional blood supply. It is the sympathetic nervous system that accomplishes these effects; some of the most important ramifications of these effects are the following:

Maintenance of normal arterial pressure. If any abnormality of the circulation, such as blood loss or a weakened heart, decreases the arterial pressure even a slight amount, this initiates a reaction in the "pressoreceptors" in the arterial walls. These in turn promote strong stimulation of the sympathetic vasoconstrictor system and thereby cause the pressure to return almost to normal. Fortunately, the vasoconstrictor system does not constrict the vessels of the brain and heart; most of the other tissues of the body can well afford decreased nutrition for several hours, though decreased nutrition to these vital areas might cause precipitous death. This reflex mechanism for control of arterial pressure is so important that it will be discussed in detail in Chapter 32.

Prevention of cerebral hypotension in the standing position. When one is in a lying position, blood from the caudal end of the body drains to the heart very readily. But, on standing, blood tends to pool in the lower part of the body, and the arterial pressure falls in the head. However, the pressoreceptors mentioned above fortunately are located in the walls of the neck and upper thoracic arteries, and they are affected by the falling pressure. Therefore, the same pressoreceptor reflexes as those mentioned above initiate vasoconstriction everywhere in the body, except in the brain vessels and coronaries, thereby preventing significant fall in cerebral arterial pressure as a person assumes the standing position.

Shift of blood flow from the internal areas of the body to the skin for regulation of body temperature. When a person becomes overheated, his skin vasodilator system, along with release of sympathetic vasoconstriction of the skin, causes intense vasodilatation of his skin vessels. As a result, much of the blood flow shifts from the internal areas of the body to the skin; the skin is thus heated, which promotes loss of the excess heat to the surroundings. This very important mechanism for regulation of body temperature will be discussed in detail in Chapter 71.

Function of the sympathetic nervous system during exercise. Even when all autonomic nerves to the muscles have been completely removed, the local autoregulatory mechanism still maintains adequate blood flow in proportion to the degree of activity in the muscle. However, the vasodilator nerves help in this regulation of muscle blood flow as follows: When the motor centers of the brain send impulses to the muscles to cause movements, they send impulses also through the sympathetic vasodilators to increase the muscle blood flow. This increase occurs almost instantly, not requiring a delay of several seconds to respond, as is the case with the autoregulation mechanism. Therefore, sympathetic vasodilator activity makes the nutrition required for muscular contraction available at the very onset of exercise rather than after a period of delay.

Also, other impulses from the motor centers of the brain stimulate the sympathetic vasoconstrictor system. And, after the mus-

slightly above normal, then the right ventricle fills to a greater extent than usual, causing the heart to pump blood more rapidly than usual and thereby decreasing the pressure at the tricuspid valve toward the normal mean value. On the other hand, if the pressure at this point falls, the right ventricle fails to fill adequately, its pumping decreases, and blood dams up in the venous system until the tricuspid pressure again rises to a normal value. In other words, *the heart acts as a servoregulator of pressure* at the tricuspid valve.

The reference point, as illustrated in Figure 283, lies *anterior to the back approximately 61 per cent of the thickness of the chest.* Furthermore, it lies almost *exactly in the midline* and approximately *one quarter of the distance above the lower end of the sternum.* A person can be in the standing or lying or even head-down position, and his central venous pressure referred to this reference point will remain almost exactly constant regardless of the position of the body. This does not mean that the pressure at this point is always zero. It may be as low as —4 mm. Hg or as high as 20 mm. Hg, but, whatever its value, changing the position of the body does not alter it significantly.

In making arterial pressure measurements, the precise hydrostatic point to which pressures are referred normally matters very little because percentagewise a hydrostatic error of as much as 10 or more centimeters (equivalent to 7.4 mm. Hg error) still does not affect the arterial pressure reading to a great extent. However, in venous pressure measurements the reference level must be very exact if the measurements are to be significant, for abnormalities of venous pressure as small as 1 mm. Hg can result in changes in cardiac output as great as 14 to 30 per cent.

Measurement of Venous Pressure. Clinical estimation of venous pressure. The venous pressure can often be estimated by simply observing the distention of the peripheral veins—especially the neck veins. For instance, in the sitting position the neck veins are never distended in the normal person. However, when the right atrial pressure becomes increased to as much as 10 mm. Hg, the lower veins of the neck begin to protrude even when one is sitting; when the right atrial pressure is elevated to as high as 15 mm. Hg, essentially all the veins in the neck become greatly distended, and the venous pulse becomes very prominent in these veins.

Rough estimates of the venous pressure can also be made by raising or lowering an arm while observing the distention of the antecubital, or hand, veins. As the arm is progressively raised, the veins suddenly collapse, and the level at which they collapse, when referred to the level of the heart, is a rough measure of the pressure.

Direct measurement of venous pressure. Venous pressure can be measured with ease by inserting a syringe needle connected to a water manometer directly into a vein. The venous pressure is expressed in relation to the level of the tricuspid valve, i.e., the height in centimeters of water above the level of the tricuspid valve; this can be converted to mm. Hg by dividing by a factor of 1.36.

Measurement of venous pressure in a peripheral vein usually is not an accurate estimate of the right atrial pressure because of the collapsed veins between the periphery and the heart, as discussed above. However, if the person is placed on his right side with his right arm hanging down, then most of the veins between the hanging arm and the heart will become distended. Under these conditions measurement of the antecubital pressure (with appropriate correction for hydrostatic level) will give a reasonable estimation of right atrial pressure, the measured pressure usually remaining about 3 mm. Hg above right atrial pressure because of resistance to flow toward the heart.

The only means by which right atrial pressure can be measured absolutely accurately in the human being is by inserting a catheter through the veins into the right atrium. This catheter can then be connected to a water manometer and the pressure measured in relation to the level of the tricuspid valve as noted above. Although passage of such a catheter is relatively safe, if it is passed on into the right ventricle, it occasionally causes cardiac arrhythmias, and, in one patient out of many thousands, can even result in ventricular fibrillation and death.

Blood Reservoir Function of the Veins

In discussing the general characteristics of the systemic circulation in the previous chapter it was pointed out that approximately 50 per cent of all the blood in the circulatory system is in the systemic veins. For this reason it is frequently said that the systemic veins act as a *blood reservoir* for the circulation. Also, relatively large quantities of blood are present in the veins of the lungs so that these, too, are considered to be blood reservoirs.

When blood is lost from the body to the extent that the arterial pressure begins to fall, pressure reflexes are elicited from the carotid sinuses and other pressure sensitive areas of the circulation, as will be detailed in Chapter 32; these in turn cause sympathetic constriction of the veins. This automatically helps to take up the slack in the circulatory system caused by the lost blood. Indeed, even after as much as 20 to 25 per cent of the total blood volume has been lost, the circulatory system will often still function almost normally because of this variable reservoir system of the veins.

Variations in Tone of the Venous Reservoir—Effect on Cardiac Output. An extremely important function of the venous reservoir is its ability to increase or decrease the rate at which blood is returned from the peripheral vessels to the heart. Sympathetic stimulation of the venous reservoir increases the pressures everywhere in the veins, this effect alone increasing the rate of venous return up to as much as two and one-half fold. During exercise, for instance, a major part of the increase in cardiac output results from sympathetic stimulation of the veins. This effect is very important in the regulation of cardiac output and, therefore, will be discussed in detail in Chapter 35.

Specific Blood Reservoirs. Certain portions of the venous system are so extensive that they are specifically called "blood reservoirs." These include (1) the *spleen*, which can sometimes decrease in size sufficiently to release as much as 150 ml. of blood into other areas of the circulation, (2) the *liver*, the sinuses of which can release several hundred ml. of blood into the remainder of the circulation, (3) the *large abdominal veins*, which can contribute as much as 300 ml., and (4) the *venous plexus beneath the skin*, which can probably contribute several hundred ml. The *heart* itself and the *lungs*, though not parts of the systemic venous reservoir system, nevertheless must be considered to be blood reservoirs. The heart, for instance, becomes reduced in size during sympathetic constriction and in this way can contribute about 100 ml. of blood, and the lungs can contribute another 100 to 200 ml. when the pulmonary pressures fall to low values.

When blood is transfused into the circulation, the effects are exactly opposite to those that occur following hemorrhage; the extra blood is stored principally in the venous tree and more particularly in the blood reservoirs.

EFFECT OF ARTERIAL AND VENOUS FACTORS ON CAPILLARY PRESSURE

Details of the capillary circulation were discussed in Chapter 5, which was concerned principally with the interchange of fluid between the blood and the interstitial spaces. However, now that we have discussed the basic hemodynamics of the systemic circulation, it is necessary to return to the capillaries and discuss the effect of arterial and venous dynamics on capillary pressure. In Chapter 5 it was pointed out that the average capillary pressure over a long period of time is controlled by the *law of the capillaries*—that is, by the interchange of fluid back and forth through the capillary membranes until equilibrium exists between the *capillary pressure,* the *plasma colloid osmotic pressure,* the *tissue pressure,* and the *tissue colloid osmotic pressure.* However, in some instances it takes several hours for equilibrium to be established, and in the meantime alterations in the pressures and resistances of the arteries and veins can make the capillary pressure rise temporarily to very high values or fall to very low values. This present discussion, therefore, will show how these different factors in the systemic circulation can raise or lower the capillary pressure.

Acute Effects on Capillary Pressure of Changes in Venous or Arterial Pressure

Changes in Arterial Pressure. An increase in arterial pressure occurring throughout the entire body increases the blood flow into the small vessels and consequently elevates the capillary pressure. On the average, the capillary pressure rises approximately one fourth as much as does the arterial pressure if other factors in the circulation do not change concurrently. When the capillary pressure remains elevated any length of time, even for a few seconds, fluid begins to leak from the blood into the interstitial spaces. Within a few minutes to a few hours, the blood volume decreases sufficiently to drop the arterial pressure and the capillary pressure to normal.

On the other hand, a fall in arterial pressure causes the opposite effect, the capillary pressure falling approximately one fourth as much as the fall in arterial pressure. Figure 284 illustrates the effect of a fall in arterial pressure on capillary pressure. The solid curve of this figure shows the normal mean pressures in all the different vessels of the systemic criculation, while curve 1 illustrates the changes in these pressures when the aortic pressure falls from a mean value of 100 mm. Hg to 80 mm. Hg. Here, again, it must be emphasized that the effect is only temporary, for fluid absorption into the capillaries automatically returns the pressures to normal within a few hours.

Changes in Venous Pressure. When the venous pressure rises, blood backs up in the capillaries and arteries, thereby elevating the pressures throughout the systemic circulation. This effect is illustrated by curve 2 in Figure 284, which shows that the pressure in the capillaries rises about three fourths as much as the venous pressure rises. Thus, it is evident that venous pressure changes can cause marked changes in capillary pressure. But, again, the effect can last for only a few hours because rapid loss of fluid from the capillaries greatly reduces the arterial pressure and returns the capillary pressure to equilibrium in accordance with the law of the capillaries.

Relative Importance of Changes in Arterial Pressure and Venous Pressure on Capillary Pressure. In the discussions above it was noted that capillary pressure changes only about one fourth as much as the arterial pressure changes and about three fourths as much as the venous pressure changes. Therefore, it is evident that capillary pressure is affected to a much greater extent by venous pressure changes than by arterial pressure changes. Yet, in physiological states of the circulation, changes in arterial and venous pressures are probably about equally important in their effects on capillary pressure for the following reason: The central venous pressure is normally 0 mm. Hg, and this rises even in pathological states rarely above 15 mm. Hg. On the other hand, the arterial pressure in circulatory shock may fall as low as 30 mm. Hg or, during excitement, may rise to as high as 200 mm. Hg mean pressure. Thus, the tremendous variations that occur in arterial pressure can actually cause as much or more variation in capillary pressure than can the most extensive changes in venous pressure. For this reason, it is quite wrong to state that capillary pressure is mainly determined by the venous pressure because, within pressure ranges that are often experienced in the human being, both arterial pressure and venous pressure affect capillary pressure in equally important ways.

Acute Effect of Changes in Arterial and Venous Resistances on Capillary Pressure

Obviously, an increase in arterial resistance will decrease the blood flow into the capillaries, resulting in reduced capillary pressure. On the other hand, an increase in venous resistance will impede the flow of blood out of the capillaries and result in elevated capillary pressure. Therefore, as a very general approximation it can be stated that the capillary pressure is regulated by the *ratio of venous to arterial resistance.* That is, the greater the venous resistance the higher the capillary pressure, and the greater the arterial resistance the lower becomes the capillary pressure.

Yet, the exact degree to which the capillary pressure will change is complicated by several factors, and the effect is quite different when the resistance change occurs only in a local area of the body rather than everywhere in the body at the same time. These differences are the following:

Generalized Changes in Resistance throughout the Body. *Arterial resistance.* When the arterial resistance increases everywhere in the systemic circulation, this ob-

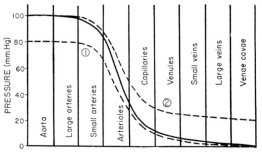

Figure 284. Normal pressures in different parts of the systemic circulation (solid curve), and the effects of decreasing the arterial pressure (curve 1) and of increasing the right atrial pressure (curve 2).

viously impedes the flow of blood out of the arteries into the capillaries. However, it also causes the arterial pressure to rise very greatly—almost as much as it impedes blood flow into the capillaries. Therefore, the capillary pressure falls only very slightly.

Venous resistance. When the venous resistance is increased throughout the circulation, this obviously impedes the blood flow out of the capillaries and tends to elevate capillary pressure. Yet, an increase in venous resistance also impedes blood flow into the heart so that the cardiac output is greatly reduced, resulting in diminished flow of blood from the arteries into the capillaries. Sometimes the diminution of blood flow into the capillaries is even greater than the tendency for blood to accumulate in the capillaries, often *causing the capillary pressure actually to decrease rather than to increase.*

Thus, it is evident that generalized changes in arteriolar or venous resistance are likely to have relatively little effect or sometimes even paradoxical effects on the capillary pressure because of the simultaneous effects of these resistance changes on arterial pressure or cardiac output.

Local Changes in Resistance. *Local arterial resistance.* When the arterial resistance increases in a local area of the circulation, this does not affect either the arterial pressure or the cardiac output to a significant extent, but it does greatly impede the flow of blood into the capillaries, causing the expected fall in capillary pressure. Reduction in arterial resistance likewise causes the expected rise in capillary pressure. Complete dilatation of the arterioles can cause the capillary pressure to rise in the normal person to as high as 60 to 70 mm. Hg while complete constriction can cause it to fall to zero, as illustrated in Figure 285.

Local venous resistance. Local constriction of the veins has very little effect on either arterial pressure or cardiac output, but it does impede the flow of blood out of one area of capillaries. Complete constriction of a vein can cause the capillary pressure in a local area to rise almost to equal the arterial pressure—that is, up to 90 mm. Hg or more—thus resulting in very rapid transudation of fluid out of the capillaries into the tissues:

Formulas for Capillary Pressure

Three different formulas which are valuable in predicting the effects of different factors on capillary pressure are the following:

$$P_c = P_{ra} + (P_a - P_{ra}) \frac{R_v}{R_v + R_a} \qquad (1)$$

$$P_c = \frac{P_a}{1 + R_a/R_v} \quad (\text{when } P_{ra} = 0) \qquad (2)$$

$$P_c = P_{ra} + FR_v \qquad (3)$$

In these formulas P_c is mean capillary pressure, R_v is venous resistance from the midpoint of the capillaries to the heart, R_a is arterial resistance from the heart to the midpoint of the capillaries, P_a is arterial pressure, P_{ra} is right atrial pressure, and F is blood flow. Note in formulas 1 and 2 that capillary pressure is dependent on the *ratio* of venous resistance to arterial resistance, on arterial pressure, and right atrial pressure. It is evident from formula 3 that capillary pressure is determined by the *venous resistance* times the *flow of blood* from the capillaries to the heart. These different relationships are especially valuable in analyzing circulatory dynamics in cardiac failure.

REFERENCES

Alexander, R. S.: The influence of constrictor drugs on the distensibility of the splanchnic venous system, analyzed on the basis of an aortic model. *Circ. Res.,* 2:140, 1954.

Barcroft, H., and Swan, H. J. C.: Sympathetic Control of Human Blood Vessels. Baltimore, Williams & Wilkins Co., 1953.

Barger, A. C., and others: Venous pressure and cutaneous reactive hyperemia in exhausting exercise and certain other circulatory stresses. *J. Appl. Physiol.,* 2:81, 1949.

Blair, D. A., Glover, W. E., and Roddie, I. C.: The abolition of reactive and post-exercise hyperaemia in the forearm by temporary restriction of arterial inflow. *J. Physiol.,* 148:648, 1959.

Celander, O., and Folkow, B.: A comparison of the sympathetic vasomotor fiber control of the vessels within the skin and the muscles. *Acta Physiol. Scand.,* 29:241, 1953.

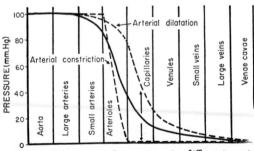

Figure 285. Normal pressures in different parts of the systemic circulation, and the effects of extreme arterial constriction and dilatation.

Crawford, D. G., Fairchild, H. M., and Guyton, A. C.: Oxygen lack as a possible cause of reactive hyperemia. *Am. J. Physiol.*, 197:613, 1959.

Davis, D. L., and Hamilton, W. F.: Small vessel responses of the dog paw. *Am. J. Physiol.*, 196:1316, 1959.

Edholm, O. G., Moreira, M. F., and Werner, A. Y.: The measurement of forearm blood flow during a raised venous pressure. *J. Physiol.*, 125:41P, 1954.

Fairchild, H. M., Crawford, D. G., and Guyton, A. C.: Oxygen deficiency as a cause of reactive hyperemia. *Fed. Proc.*, 18:43, 1959.

Folkow, B.: Nervous control of the blood vessels. *Physiol. Rev.*, 35:629, 1955.

Folkow, B., Haeger, K., and Kahlson, G.: Observations on reactive hyperemia as related to histamine, on drugs antagonizing vasodilation induced by histamine, and on vasodilator properties of adenosinetriphosphate. *Acta Physiol. Scandinav.*, 15:264, 1948.

Green, H. D., Deal, C. P., Jr., Bardhanabaedya, S., and Denison, A. B., Jr.: The effects of adrenergic substances and ischemia on the blood flow and peripheral resistance of the canine mesenteric vascular bed before and during adrenergic blockade. *J. Pharm. Exp. Ther.*, 113:115, 1955.

Green, H. D., Howard, W. B., and Kenan, L. F.: Autonomic control of blood flow in hind paw of the dog. *Am. J. Physiol.*, 187:469, 1956.

Green, H. D., and Kepchar, J. H.: Control of peripheral resistance in major systemic vascular beds. *Physiol. Rev.*, 39:617, 1959.

Guyton, A. C.: La circulation veineuse. *Symposia from the IIIrd World Congress of Cardiology*, p. 109, 1958.

Guyton, A. C.: Peripheral Circulation. *Ann. Rev. Physiol.*, 21:239, 1959.

Guyton, A. C.: The venous system and its role in the circulation. Modern Concepts of Cardiovascular Disease, 27:483, 1958.

Guyton, A. C., Farish, C. A., and Williams, J. W.: An improved arteriovenous oxygen difference recorder. *J. Appl. Physiol.*, 14:145, 1959.

Guyton, A. C., and Greganti, F. P.: A physiologic reference point for measuring circulatory pressures in the dog—particularly venous pressure. *Am. J. Physiol.*, 185:137, 1956.

Haddy, E. J.: Effect of histamine on small and large vessel pressures in the dog foreleg. *Am. J. Physiol.*, 198:161, 1960.

Haddy, F. J., Fleishman, M., and Emanuel, D. A.: Effect of epinephrine, norepinephrine, and serotonin upon systemic small and large vessel resistance. *Circ. Res.*, 5:247, 1957.

Haddy, F. J., and Gilbert, R. P.: The relation of a venous-arteriolar reflex to transmural pressure and resistance in small and large systemic vessels. *Circ. Res.*, 4:25, 1956.

Patel, D. J., and Burton, A. C.: Reactive hyperemia in the human finger. *Circ. Res.*, 4:710, 1956.

Uvnas, B.: Sympathetic vasodilator outflow. *Physiol. Rev.*, 34:608, 1954.

Yonce, L. R., and Hamilton, W. F.: Oxygen consumption in skeletal muscle during reactive hyperemia. *Am. J. Physiol.*, 197:190, 1959.

See also Chapter 26, Hemodynamics; Chapter 27, Other aspects of the systemic circulation; Chapter 31, Special circulatory systems; Chapter 38, General bibliography for the cardiovascular system.

Chapter 29

The Pulmonary Circulatory System

Except for a minute quantity of blood which flows through the bronchial arteries and returns to the left atrium instead of the right atrium, the quantity of blood flowing through the lungs is equal to that flowing through the systemic circulation. The present discussion is concerned specifically with the peculiarities of blood flow in the pulmonary circuit and the function of the right side of the heart in maintaining this flow.

PHYSIOLOGIC ANATOMY OF THE PULMONARY CIRCULATORY SYSTEM

The Right Side of the Heart. As illustrated in Figure 286, the right ventricle is wrapped half-way around the left ventricle. The cause of this is the difference in pressures developed by the two ventricles during systole. Because the left ventricle contracts with extreme force in comparison with the right ventricle, the left ventricle assumes a globular shape, and the septum protrudes into the right side of the heart. Yet, each side of the heart pumps the same quantity of blood; therefore, the external wall of the right ventricle bulges far outward and extends around a large portion of the left ventricle, in this way accommodating the same quantity of blood as the left ventricle. The semi-lunar shape of the right ventricle allows it to pump large quantities of blood with very little shortening of its muscle fibers.

The muscle of the right ventricle is little more than one third as thick as that of the left ventricle; this also results from the differential in pressures pumped by the two sides of the heart. Indeed, the wall of the right ventricle is only about three times as thick as the atrial walls, whereas the left ventricular muscle is some eight times as thick.

The Pulmonary Vessels. The pulmonary artery extends only about 1½ inches beyond the apex of the right ventricle and then divides into

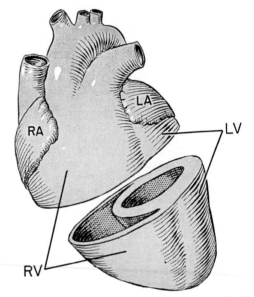

Figure 286. The anatomic relationship of the right ventricle to the left ventricle, showing the globular shape of the left ventricle and the half-moon shape of the right ventricle as it drapes around the left ventricle.

the right and left main branches, which supply blood to the two respective lungs. The pulmonary artery is also a thin structure with a wall thickness approximately twice that of the venae cavae and ⅓ to ¼ the thickness of the aorta. The pulmonary arterial branches are all very short and accommodate very small quantities of blood in comparison with the very large amounts that can be stored in the systemic arterial system.

The pulmonary veins, like the pulmonary arteries, are also short and do not accommodate nearly so much blood as do the counterpart veins in the systemic circulation.

The blood in the pulmonary arteries is not completely oxygenated, and even though it is flowing in arteries it is still called *venous blood*. On the other hand, the blood in the pulmonary veins has become oxygenated, and it is called *arterial blood*.

The Bronchial Vessels. A minor accessory arterial blood supply to the lungs exists directly from the aorta through usually one bronchial artery to the right lung and two bronchial arteries to the left lung. The blood flowing in the bronchial arteries is oxygenated or "arterial" blood, and it supplies the supporting tissues of the lungs, including the connective tissue, the septa, and the large and small bronchi. After this bronchial arterial blood has passed through the supporting tissues, it empties into the pulmonary arteries and veins and enters the left atrium rather than passing back to the right atrium. Therefore, an average of about 1 per cent (but on rare occasions as high as 10 to 50 per cent) more blood flows through the left side of the heart than through the right side.

The Lymphatics. Lymphatics extend from all the supportive tissues of the lung to the hilus pulmonis and thence into the thoracic duct. Particulate matter entering the alveoli is usually removed very rapidly via these channels, and protein is also removed from the lung tissues, thereby preventing edema.

PRESSURES IN THE PULMONARY SYSTEM

The Pressure Pulse Curve in the Right Ventricle

The pressure pulse curve of the right ventricle is illustrated in the lower portion of Figure 287. Approximately 0.16 second prior to ventricular systole, the atrium contracts, pumping a small quantity of blood into the right ventricle, and thereby causing about 4 mm. Hg initial rise in the right ventricular

diastolic pressure even before the ventricle contracts. Immediately following priming by the right atrium, the right ventricle contracts, and the right ventricular pressure rises rapidly until it equals the pressure in the pulmonary artery. The pulmonary valve opens, and for approximately 0.3 second blood flows from the right ventricle into the pulmonary artery. When the right ventricle relaxes, the pulmonary valve closes, and the right ventricular pressure falls to its previous diastolic level.

The systolic pressure in the right ventricle of the normal human being averages approximately 22 mm. Hg, and the diastolic pressure averages about 0 to 1 mm. Hg.

Pressures in the Pulmonary Artery

The pulmonary arterial pressure pulse curve is also shown in Figure 287, and it is contrasted with the aortic pressure pulse curve. During systole the pressure in the pulmonary artery remains essentially equal to the pressure in the right ventricle. However, after the pulmonary valve closes at the end of systole, the ventricular pressure falls but the pulmonary arterial pressure remains temporarily elevated, then falls gradually as blood flows through the capillaries of the lungs.

As shown in Figure 288, the systolic pulmonary arterial pressure averages approximately 22 mm. Hg in the normal human being, the diastolic pulmonary arterial pressure approximately 8 mm. Hg, and the mean pulmonary arterial pressure 13 mm. Hg.

The Pulmonary Arterial Pulse Pressure. The pulse pressure in the pulmonary arteries is approximately 14 mm. Hg, which is almost

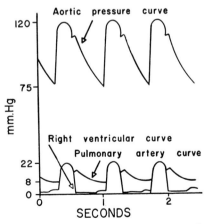

Figure 287. Pressure pulse contours in the right ventricle, pulmonary artery, and aorta. (Redrawn from Cournand: *Circulation.* 2:641, 1950.)

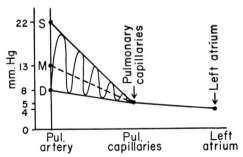

Figure 288. Pressures in the different vessels of the lungs. (Redrawn from Cournand: *Circulation.* 2:641, 1950.)

two thirds as much as the systolic pressure. This contrasts with a systemic arterial pulse pressure only one third the systolic pressure. The reason for this difference is the very small volume of blood that can be contained in the pulmonary arterial tree. In previous discussions of pulse pressure, it has been pointed out that the smaller the volume of an elastic reservoir that receives pulsatile injections of blood, the greater will be the pulse pressure. If it were not for the extreme distensibility of the thin pulmonary arteries, the pulmonary arterial pulse pressure would be even greater than it is.

Left Atrial and Pulmonary Venous Pressure

The mean pressure in the left atrium and in the major pulmonary veins averages approximately 4 mm. Hg in the human being. However, the pressure in the left atrium varies, even among normal individuals, from as low as 1 mm. Hg. to as high as 8 to 10 mm. Hg.

The pulse pressures in the left atrium with each beat of the heart are several times as great as the pulse pressures in the right atrium, for two reasons: First, the left ventricle contracts with far greater force than the right ventricle, resulting in far greater ventricular thrust against the blood in the left atrium than in the right. Second, part of the pulse pressures in the pulmonary artery are transmitted through the capillaries into the pulmonary veins, because the mean pulmonary vascular resistance is very low (only about one tenth that of the systemic circulation).

Backward Transmission of Increased Pressure from the Left Side of the Heart to the Pulmonary Artery

The normal pressure gradient between the mean pulmonary arterial pressure and the left atrial pressure is only 9 mm. Hg, and when the left atrial pressure rises, the pulmonary arterial pressure also rises almost an equal amount, the pressure gradient falling only slightly. Therefore, whenever the left ventricle fails or obstruction develops at the mitral valve, blood is dammed up in the pulmonary circuit; the left atrial pressure rises; and the pressures in the pulmonary veins,

capillaries, and arteries all experience a similar rise.

Right Ventricular Compensation in Response to Increased Pressure. Any increase in the pulmonary arterial pressure as a result of back pressure from the left ventricle or of increased resistance of the pulmonary circuit places a greater than normal work load on the right ventricle. The right ventricle, as does the left ventricle, obeys Starling's law of the heart and compensates for the increased load as follows: For the first beat or so after the load is increased, less than the normal quantity of blood is ejected into the pulmonary circuit. The blood remaining in the ventricle increases its volume and stretches the ventricular musculature. As a result, the ventricle contracts with increased force so that it then pumps a normal or almost normal quantity of blood into the pulmonary circuit despite the increased load.

If the pulmonary load becomes greater than the heart can overcome, the right ventricle fails, and blood becomes dammed in the right atrium and in the systemic veins. Ordinarily, the load on the right ventricle must be increased to approximately four times normal before the right ventricle fails, as is illustrated in Figure 289. Therefore, the pulmonary arterial pressure often rises to as high as four times normal before any significant rise occurs in the systemic venous pressure.

Sympathetic impulses to the heart often aid the right ventricle in compensating for increased load. For instance, whenever the

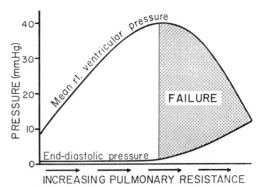

Figure 289. Effect of increasing pulmonary resistance on the mean right ventricular pressure and on the right ventricular "end-diastolic" pressure, which is approximately equal to the right atrial pressure. Note that when the ventricle fails, the ventricular pressure falls and the right atrial pressure rises.

termined. The two principal possibilities that have been suggested are: (1) that decreased oxygen tension in the cardiac tissues reduces the amount of oxygen available to the coronary vessels themselves and that this causes the coronaries to become weakened and, therefore, to dilate automatically and (2) that oxygen lack causes vasodilating substances such as adenosine phosphate compounds or lactic acid to be released by the tissues. (But thus far, it has not been shown that these substances are released in sufficient quantities to cause the extreme degree of vasodilatation that results.) Therefore, for the present we can simply say that oxygen lack is followed by coronary vasodilatation and in this way autoregulates blood flow to the cardiac musculature in proportion to the metabolic need for oxygen by the muscle fibers.

Nervous Control of Coronary Blood Flow. Stimulation of the parasympathetic fibers of the vagus nerve reduces the blood flow in the coronary vessels; and conversely, stimulation of the sympathetics to the heart increases the flow. Yet, it is believed that these results occur secondarily to other effects of nerve stimulation as follows: Sympathetic stimulation greatly increases the vigor of cardiac contraction, and because of local autoregulation, as discussed above, the blood flow automatically increases. On the other hand, parasympathetic stimulation reduces the vigor of cardiac contraction and thereby reduces the rate of cardiac metabolism, thus resulting in diminished coronary blood flow.

In support of the thesis that nerve stimulation has little direct action on the coronaries are the following facts. First, acetylcholine, which is the parasympathetic transmitter substance, vasodilates isolated coronary vessels, which is *opposite* to the effect observed in the beating heart. Second, nor-epinephrine, the sympathetic transmitter substance, has no significant effect on the coronaries in the nonbeating heart, so that here again one cannot ascribe the increased blood flow in the beating heart to a direct action of sympathetic stimulation.

In summary, coronary blood flow is controlled almost entirely by local autoregulation, but any factor, including nerve stimulation, that affects the vigor of cardiac contraction (which in turn affects the rate of

metabolism) will also change coronary blood flow because of the local autoregulatory mechanism which keeps blood flow in step with the rate of metabolism.

Effect of Drugs on Coronary Blood Flow. A number of vasodilator drugs, including the nitrites, the xanthines, and papaverine, act directly on the coronary blood vessels to cause vasodilatation. Therefore, these drugs are used to a great extent in the treatment of coronary insufficiency.

Pitressin and ergot alkaloids act directly on the coronary blood vessels to cause constriction. For this reason, the use of these drugs is always avoided in patients having any possibility of coronary heart disease.

CORONARY OCCLUSION

The coronary blood vessels sometimes become occluded very rapidly—within a few minutes or a few hours—as a result of blood clots or other abnormalities that can plug the lumina of the vessels. At other times the vessels are slowly and progressively occluded over a period of years, in which case a collateral blood supply can often develop to take over the function of the primary coronary blood supply. Unfortunately, the collateral blood supply usually does not become well developed until after the coronaries are occluded. Therefore, whether or not the heart is greatly damaged by coronary occlusion depends mainly upon the rapidity with which the occlusion occurs.

Collateral Circulation in the Heart. Relatively few communications exist between the larger coronary arteries, but there are many anastomoses between the arteries of approximately 50 to 100 microns diameter, as shown in Figure 293.

When a sudden occlusion occurs in one of the larger coronary vessels, the sizes of the minute anastomoses increase tremendously during the next several weeks to several months so that a new blood supply to the ischemic area grows inward from all sides. It is because of these developing collateral channels that a patient recovers from the various types of coronary occlusion.

The coronary arteries also anastomose through very minute channels with the arteries of the parietal pericardium, these anastomoses traveling along the pericardial reflections around the major vessels of the

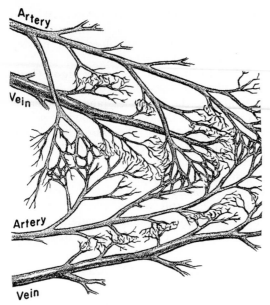

Figure 293.   Minute anastomoses of the coronary
arterial system.

heart. It will be recalled that the heart floats
within the pericardial cavity, and the only
possible communication between the coronary vessels and other vessels outside the
pericardium would be by way of these reflections. A few patients at autopsy have
been found to have both major coronary
arteries totally occluded, and yet the small
anastomotic vessels in the pericardial reflections have become large enough to supply
the entire heart with blood.

Causes of Coronary Occlusion

The most frequent cause of coronary occlusion
is *thrombosis* resulting from atherosclerosis. The
atherosclerotic process will be discussed in connection with lipid metabolism in Chapter 66, but,
to summarize this process, in various diseases affecting lipid metabolism and also in old age,
lipids containing mainly cholesterol and cholesterol salts are deposited beneath the intima of the
major arteries. These deposits become calcified
over a period of years, and considerable fibrous
tissue also invades the walls of the degenerating
arteries. Furthermore, "atherosclerotic plaques"
occasionally break through the intima of the
blood vessel and protrude into the lumen. The
presence of such a rough surface inside a vessel
causes blood platelets to deposit and to dissolute,
thus initiating the clotting process. When a small
clot has developed, more platelets become entrapped, and more clot develops until the vessel is

plugged. It is this mechanism that causes most
coronary thromboses.

Occasionally a coronary vessel is occluded by a
subintimal hemorrhage into the wall of the coronary vessel. It will be recalled that all large blood
vessels have small blood vessels, the *vasa vasorum*,
penetrating their walls to supply the walls themselves. The vascular supply of the coronary arteries in the form of vasa vasorum is not very great,
but occasionally those vasa that are present rupture and hemorrhage beneath the intima, thus
protruding the intima into the coronary vessel and
plugging it. Hypertensive patients develop coronary occlusions approximately two to three times
more often than normal persons, and it is suspected that the high blood pressure in the vasa
vasorum probably initiates subintimal hemorrhages, thus causing many of the occlusions in
these patients.

Very rarely, coronary occlusion occurs as a result of an *embolism* of clotted blood that has
formed in the left chambers of the heart and then
has passed into the aorta and finally into one of
the coronary arteries.

Sudden coronary occlusion ocurs almost always
in one of the larger coronary arteries, usually
within 3 to 6 cm. of the ostium of one or the other
of the two major coronary vessels. Also, the left
coronary artery is far more prone to coronary occlusion than the right coronary. An especially
frequent site for occlusion is in the anterior descending branch of the left coronary artery.

Progressive Coronary Sclerosis. Occasionally, the coronary arteries are not blocked
suddenly by thrombosis, by embolism, or by subintimal hemorrhage, but instead are slowly constricted by the atherosclerotic process. The
plaques themselves can grow all the way around
the artery, and this in turn causes progressive
growth of fibrous tissue, which becomes thicker
and thicker until it gradually constricts the artery.

The arteriosclerotic process is not limited to
old age. Indeed, atheromatous plaques in the
coronary vessels have been demonstrated even in
infants, and such plaques can be demonstrated in
the coronary arteries of approximately one half of
all persons between the ages of 45 and 50. At
the ages of 65 to 70 or older, pathologic study of
almost any heart shows not only atherosclerotic
plaques beneath the intima of the coronaries but
usually also plugging of at least some of the
major branches of the coronary vessels, which is
illustrated in Figure 294. As a consequence of
this plugging, blood flows backward in many of
the epicardial arteries because these arteries have
been plugged at their origins and anastomotic
channels supply blood backwards to them. This
phenomenon is also illustrated in Figure 294. Because most of these blocks develop slowly, many

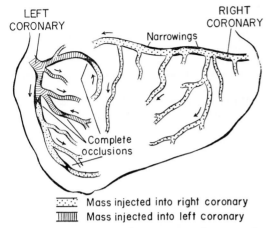

LEFT CORONARY

RIGHT CORONARY

Narrowings

Complete occlusions

▒▒▒ Mass injected into right coronary
▓▓▓ Mass injected into left coronary

Figure 294. Points of coronary occlusion in the coronary arteries of an aged patient. (Redrawn from Blumgart: *Am. Heart J. 19:*41, 1940.)

such hearts show no evidence of muscle damage from ischemia despite the fact that some of the major channels have been completely or almost completely plugged.

Effects of Ischemia on Cardiac Muscle

Conduction of the Depolarization Wave in the Ischemic Heart. Metabolic energy is needed to build up ionic differentials across the membranes of the Purkinje fibers and muscle fibers. If this metabolic energy is not available, appropriate polarization of the conductive membranes cannot occur, and cardiac impulses cannot be transmitted. Thus, ischemia of cardiac muscle can cause local failure of impulse conduction in the areas of the heart made ischemic by coronary occlusion.

Strength of Contraction of Ischemic Cardiac Muscle. Obviously, muscular contraction requires energy, which must be derived from various nutrients in the blood. When the supply of these nutrients is diminished, even though a depolarization wave may be conducted over the cardiac muscular fibers, there will not be sufficient available energy to cause normal contraction of the actomyosin filaments.

Thus, ischemia of cardiac muscle may totally abrogate muscular contraction as a result of failure to conduct the impulse, or it may simply weaken contraction of the muscle as a result of deficient contractile energy.

Death of Cardiac Muscle Fibers in Coronary Ischemia. In order for cardiac muscle to live, a certain amount of basal metabolism must take place. If the blood flow to cardiac muscle is diminished beyond a critical level, the muscle not only becomes non-functional but actually begins to die.

Value of rest in treating coronary occlusion. The degree of cellular death is determined by the *ratio of the degree of ischemia to the degree of metabolism* of the heart muscle. When the metabolism of the heart muscle is greatly increased, such as during exercise, in severe emotional strain, and as a result of fatigue; the heart musculature needs increased oxygen and other nutrients for sustaining its life. Furthermore, anastomotic blood vessels which supply blood to ischemic areas of the heart must still supply the areas of the heart that they normally supply. When the heart becomes excessively active, the vessels of the normal musculature become greatly dilated, and this allows most of the blood flowing into the coronary vessels to flow through the normal muscle tissue, thus leaving little blood to flow through the small anastomotic channels supplying the ischemic areas. Consequently, one of the most important factors in the treatment of a patient with coronary ischemia is observance of absolute rest. The greater the degree of rest during the first few months following sudden coronary occlusion, the less will be the death of the cells.

Causes of Death in Severe Coronary Ischemia

There are four major causes of death following coronary occlusion. These include decreased cardiac output, damming of blood in the pulmonary or systemic veins with death resulting from edema, especially pulmonary edema, fibrillation of the heart, and, occasionally, rupture of the heart.

Decreased Cardiac Output. When some of the cardiac muscular fibers are not functioning at all and others are too weak to contract with great force, the overall pumping ability of the affected ventricle is proportionately depressed. Indeed, the overall pumping strength of the heart is often decreased more than one might expect because of the phenomenon of *systolic stretch,* which is illustrated in Figure 295. When the normal portions of the ventricular muscle contract, the ischemic muscle, whether this be dead or simply non-functional, instead of contracting is actually forced outward by the pressure that develops inside the ventricle. If this area did not stretch, the pumping force of the ventricle would be directly proportional to the strength of contraction of the remainder of the ventricle. However, owing to stretch of the ischemic area, much of the pumping force of the ventricle is dissipated by bulging of the area of non-functional cardiac muscle.

When the heart becomes incapable of contracting with sufficient force to pump enough blood into the arterial tree, cardiac failure and death of

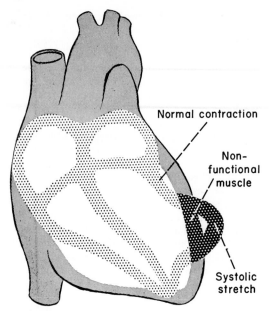

Figure 295. Systolic stretch in an area of ischemic cardiac muscle.

to become very thin. If this happens, the degree of systolic stretch becomes greater and greater until finally the heart ruptures. In fact, one of the means used in assessing the progress of a severe myocardial infarction is to record by x-ray whether the degree of systolic stretch is getting worse or better.

When a ventricle does rupture, the loss of blood into the pericardial space causes rapid development of *cardiac tamponade*—that is, compression of the heart from the outside by the blood collecting in the pericardial cavity. Because the heart is compressed, blood cannot flow into the right atrium with ease. The patient dies of decreased cardiac output if the pressure in the pericardial cavity rises rapidly above approximately 10 to 15 mm. Hg. However, if the pericardial pressure rises slowly—over a period of several days—it can rise to as high as 20 to 25 mm. Hg before death occurs, because the blood volume increases, causing increased mean circulatory pressure which forces blood to return to the heart.

the peripheral tissues ensue as a result of peripheral ischemia. The precise dynamics of this will be discussed in Chapter 36.

Damming of Blood in the Venous System. When the heart is not pumping blood forward, it must be damming blood in the venous systems of the lungs or the systemic circulation. In the early stages of coronary thrombosis this is not usually as serious as it is later, for, as will be discussed in Chapter 36 in relation to cardiac failure, during the first few days after a coronary occlusion fluid collects in the body and adds progressively to the venous congestive symptoms. When the congestion becomes intense, death frequently results from pulmonary congestion or rarely from systemic congestive symptoms.

Fibrillation of the Heart Following Coronary Occlusion. The hearts of many patients with even mild coronary occlusion develop ventricular fibrillation that causes death. This tendency to develop ventricular fibrillation usually lasts for about 24 hours following acute occlusion of a coronary vessel and probably results from excessive loss of potassium from the ischemic heart muscle into the surrounding tissue fluids. This apparently initiates large numbers of abnormal, ectopic impulses in the ventricular muscle, eventually resulting in a circus movement and fibrillation as explained in Chapter 21.

Rupture of the Ischemic Area. During the first day of an acute coronary infarct there is very little danger of rupture of the ischemic portion of the heart, but a few days after a large infarct occurs, the dead muscle fibers begin to degenerate, and the dead heart musculature is likely

The Stages of Recovery from Acute Coronary Thrombosis

The upper part of Figure 296 illustrates to the left the effects of acute coronary thrombosis in a patient with a small area of muscle ischemia and to the right in a patient with a large area of ischemia. It will be noted that when the area of ischemia is small, very little or no death of the muscle cells may occur, but part of the muscle often does become temporarily non-functional because of failure of polarization of the muscle membrane. When the area of ischemia is large, some of the muscle fibers in the very center of the area die very rapidly, perhaps within a few hours in an area of total cessation of coronary blood supply. Immediately around the dead area is an area that is non-functional because of failure of conduction. Then, extending circumferen-

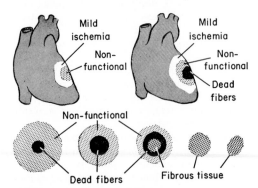

Figure 296. Top: small and large areas of coronary ischemia. *Bottom:* stages of recovery from myocardial infarction.

tially around the non-functional area, is an area that is still contracting, but weakly so because of mild ischemia. In this mildly ischemic area the small arterial anastomoses from other epicardial arteries are sufficient to supply the cardiac musculature provided that the patient is kept at rest, but even this area may become non-functional when the coronary blood flow is diverted to normal musculature during exercise. This again illustrates the necessity for rest in patients following coronary heart attacks.

In the lower part of Figure 296, the various stages of recovery following a coronary occlusion are illustrated. Shortly after the occlusion, the muscle fibers die only in the very center of the ischemic area, but during the ensuing few days this area of dead fibers grows because many of the marginal fibers finally succumb to the prolonged ischemia. At the same time, owing to the enlargement of the collateral arterial channels, the non-functional area of the heart muscle becomes smaller and smaller. After approximately 2 to 3 weeks most of the non-functional area of muscle will have become functional again along its outer margins, or it will have died in its central portions. In the meantime, fibrous tissue begins developing among the dead fibers, for ischemia stimulates growth of fibroblasts and promotes development of greater than normal quantities of fibrous tissue. Therefore, the dead muscular tissue is gradually replaced by fibrous tissue. Then, because it is a general property of fibrous tissue to undergo progressive elastomeric contraction and dissolution, the size of the fibrous scar becomes smaller and smaller over a period of several months to a year.

During progressive recovery of the infarcted area of the heart, the development of a strong, fibrous scar which becomes smaller and smaller finally stops the original systolic stretch, and the functional musculature once again becomes capable of exerting its entire force for pumping blood rather than for stretching the dead areas of the heart. Furthermore, the non-functional but not dead areas of the heart gradually become functional again as the collateral blood supply develops. It is by these means that the heart recovers.

Function of the Heart Following Recovery from Coronary Occlusion

Figure 297 illustrates the cardiac response curve of a normal heart and two abnormal hearts to changing right atrial pressure. When the right atrial pressure in the normal heart is zero, the cardiac output is approximately 5 liters per minute. As the right atrial pressure rises to approximately +2

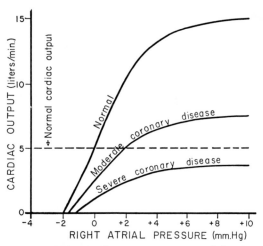

Figure 297. Cardiac response curves of the normal heart and of hearts with moderate and severe coronary disease.

mm. Hg, the cardiac output becomes approximately 10 liters a minute.

On the other hand, when some of the cardiac muscle is destroyed, the overall response of the heart may be decreased to that illustrated in the two lower curves of Figure 297. Thus, in moderate coronary heart disease, as illustrated by the middle curve, the cardiac output may be only 2.5 liters per minute instead of the normal 5 liters when right atrial pressure is 0 mm. Hg, and, in order for a normal cardiac output of 5 liters to exist with this heart of depressed responsiveness, the right atrial pressure must rise to approximately 2 mm. Hg. In very severe coronary disease, the response of the heart, as illustrated by the lower curve, is so weak that even though the right atrial pressure rises to very high values, the total cardiac output can never rise to a normal value.

Thus, when a heart becomes moderately weakened, a normal cardiac output of 5 liters or more per minute can still be maintained if the right atrial pressure rises, but, when very severe coronary heart disease develops, no amount of increase in right atrial pressure can possibly cause a normal cardiac output.

Pain in Coronary Disease

Normally, one cannot "feel" his heart, but ischemic cardiac muscle does exhibit pain sensation. Exactly what causes this pain is not known, but it is believed that ischemia causes the muscle to release acidic or other pain-promoting products that are not removed rapidly enough by the slowly moving blood. The high concentrations of these abnormal products then stimulate the pain endings in the cardiac muscles, and pain impulses are conducted through the sympathetic afferent nerve fibers into the central nervous system. The pain is usually referred to surface areas of the body, mainly the left arm and left shoulder; this will be discussed in detail in Chapter 49.

Collectively, the ischemic, referred pains from the heart are known as *angina pectoris*, and they occur whenever the load on the heart becomes too great in relation to the quantity of blood flowing through the coronary vessels. In general, most patients with heart disease who have angina pectoris do not feel the pain until they exercise or experience emotions and thereby increase the work load on the heart. However, some patients have such severe and lasting cardiac ischemia that the pain is present all of the time.

Surgical Treatment of Coronary Disease

For treating intractable angina pectoris the sympathetic chain is frequently removed from T-2 through T-5 to block the pathway of cardiac pain fibers into the spinal cord. Such an operation occasionally is successful when performed only on the left side, but often it is necessary to remove the sympathetic chain on both sides of the vertebral column.

Various attempts have been made to create additional collateral channels of blood flow into the heart. One method has been simply to denude, either by chemical means or by mechanical means, the surfaces of the visceral and parietal pericardium so that the heart will adhere and grow to the parietal pericardium. Then, new vessels can grow from the chest wall into the heart muscle. A second method has been to open the diaphragm between the abdomen and the pericardial cavity and to pull the greater omentum up over the heart muscle. After this procedure, some collateral blood vessels grow into the heart.

Finally, in experimental animals it has been shown that high pressure in the coronary veins will cause the collateral vessels in the heart to enlarge. Therefore, a surgical procedure that shows some promise has been simply to constrict the coronary sinus down to a size of about 3 mm.; this elevates the coronary venous pressure and results in some increase in collateral circulation.

The various surgical procedures designed to aid coronary circulation have not been satisfactory. One of the reasons has been simply that the patient who needs such an operation often cannot live through the surgical procedure. Also, proof that any of the operations truly benefits the coronary blood supply is not yet established.

REFERENCES

Alella, A., Williams, F. L., Bolene-Williams, C., and Katz, L. N.: Interrelation between cardiac oxygen consumption and coronary blood flow. *Am. J. Physiol.,* 183:570, 1955.

Alella, A., Williams, F. L., Bolene-Williams, C., and Katz, L. N.: Role of oxygen and exogenous glucose and lactic acid in the performance of the heart. *Am. J. Physiol.,* 185:487, 1956.

Bargeron, L. M., Jr., Ehmke, D., Gonlubol, F., Castellanos, A., Siegel, A., and Bing, R. J.: Effect of cigarette smoking on coronary blood flow and myocardial metabolism. *Circulation,* 15:251, 1957.

Berne, R. M., Blackmon, J. R., and Gardner, T. H.: Hypoxemia and coronary blood flow. *J. Clin. Invest.,* 36:1101, 1957.

Bing, R. J.: Coronary circulation in health and disease as studied by coronary sinus catheterization. *Bull. N. Y. Acad. Med.,* 27:407, 1951.

Bing, R. J.: Myocardial metabolism in diabetes. *Diabetes,* 6:95, 1956.

Bing, R. J.: The metabolism of the heart. *Tr. Am. Coll. Card.,* 5:8, 1955.

Bing, R. J., Castellanos, A., Gradel, E., Lupton, C., and Siegel, A.: Experimental myocardial infarction; circulatory, biochemical and pathologic changes. *Am. J. Med. Sc.,* 232:533, 1956.

Bliss, H. A., Sherrod, T. R., Whitehorn, W. V., and Winzler, R. J.: Biochemistry of the heart muscle. *Illinois M. J.,* 109:135, 1956.

Boas, E. P., and Adlersberg, D.: Genetic studies on coronary atherosclerosis developing after the age of sixty years. *Arch. Int. Med.,* 90:347, 1952.

Cole, D. R., Singian, E. B., and Katz, L. N.: The long-term prognosis following myocardial infarction, and some factors which affect it. *Circulation,* 9:321, 1954.

Denison, A. B., Jr., Bardhanabaedya, S., and Green, H. D.: Adrenergic drugs and blockade on coronary arterioles and myocardial contraction. *Circ. Res.,* 4:653, 1956.

Donald, D. E., and Essex, H. E.: Massive destruction of the myocardium of the canine right ventricle; a study of the early and late effects. *Am. J. Physiol.,* 177:477, 1954.

Donald, D. E., and Essex, H. E.: Studies on chronic effects of ligation of the canine right coronary artery. *Am. J. Physiol.,* 176:431, 1954.

Eckstein, R. W.: Coronary interarterial anastomoses in young pigs and mongrel dogs. *Circ. Res.,* 2:460, 1954.

Eckstein, R. W.: Development of interarterial coronary anastomoses by chronic anemia; disappearance following correction of anemia. *Circ. Res.,* 3: 306, 1955.

Eckstein, R. W.: Effect of exercise and coronary artery narrowing on coronary collateral circulation. *Circ. Res.,* 5:230, 1957.

Folkow, B., Frost, J., and Uvnas, B.: Action of acetylcholine, adrenaline anl nor-adrenaline on coronary blood flow of dog. *Acta Physiol. Scandinav.,* 17: 201, 1949.

Gerola, A., Feinberg, H., and Katz, L. N.: Myocardial oxygen consumption and coronary blood flow in hypothermia. *Am. J. Physiol.*, *196:*719, 1959.

Gofman, J. W.: Coronary Heart Disease, Springfield, Illinois, Charles C Thomas, 1959.

Gregg, D. E.: Coronary Circulation in Health and Disease. Philadelphia, Lea & Febiger, 1950.

Harris, A. S., Aguirre, Y., Guerra, C., Liptak, R. A., and Brigham, J. C.: Effects of certain local anesthetic drugs upon ventricular tachycardia resulting from myocardial infarction. *J. Appl. Physiol.*, *8:* 499, 1956.

Harris, A. S., and Bisteni, A.: Effects of sympathetic blockade drugs on ventricular tachycardia resulting from myocardial infarction. *Am. J. Physiol.*, *181:*559, 1955.

Jelliffe, R. W., Wolf, C. R., Berne, R. M., and Eckstein, R. W.: Absence of vasoactive and cardiotropic substances in coronary sinus blood of dogs. *Circ. Res.*, *5:*382, 1957.

Karmen, A., and Ladue, J. S.: Serum transaminase levels in experimental myocardial infarction. *Circulation*, *11:*711, 1955.

Katz, A. M., Katz, L. N., and Williams, F. L.: Regulation of coronary flow. *Am. J. Physiol.*, *180:*392, 1955.

Katz, L. N., Katz, A. M., and Williams, F. L.: Metabolic adjustments of alterations of cardiac work in hypoxemia. *Am. J. Physiol.*, *181:*539, 1955.

Keys, A., and White, P. D. (eds.): World Trends in Cardiology. I. Cardiovascular Epidemiology. New York, Paul B. Hoeber, 1956.

Laurent, D., Bolene-Williams, C., Williams, F. L., and Katz, L. N.: Effects of heart rate on coronary flow and cardiac oxygen consumption. *Am. J. Physiol.*, *185:*355, 1956.

Lombardo, T. A., Rose, L., Taeschler, M., Tuluy, S.,

and Bing, R. J.: The effect of exercise on coronary blood flow, myocardial oxygen consumption, and cardiac efficiency in man. *Circulation*, *7:*71, 1953.

McKeever, W. P., Gregg, D. E., and Canney, P. C.: Oxygen uptake of the nonworking left ventricle. *Circ. Res.*, *6:*612, 1958.

Master, A. M., and Jaffe, H. L.: Factors in the onset of coronary occlusion and coronary insufficiency. *J.A.M.A.*, *148:*795, 1952.

Morgan, A. D.: The Pathogenesis of Coronary Occlusion. Springfield, Illinois, Charles C Thomas, 1957.

Michal, G., Naegle, S., Danforth, W. H., Ballard, F. B., and Bing, R. J.: Metabolic changes in heart muscle during anoxia. *Am. J. Physiol.*, *197:*1147, 1959.

Plotz, M.: Coronary Heart Disease. New York, Paul B. Hoeber, 1957.

Read, R. C., Johnson, J. A., and Lillehei, C. W.: Coronary flow and resistance in the dog during total body perfusion. *Surg. Forum*, *7:*286, 1957.

Sabiston, D. C., Jr., and Gregg, D. E.: Effect of cardiac contraction on coronary blood flow. *Circulation*, *15:*14, 1957.

Wiggers, C. J.: The interplay of coronary vascular resistance and myocardial compression in regulating coronary flow. *Circ. Res.*, *2:*271, 1954.

Wolf, M. M., and Berne, R. M.: Coronary vasodilator properties of purine and pyrimidine derivatives. *Circ. Res.*, *4:*343, 1956.

Wright, I. S.: Myocardial Infarction. New York, Grune & Stratton, Inc., 1954.

Zao, Z. Z., Yen, M., and Herrmann, G. R.: Relation between S-T segment elevation and experimental myocardial oxygen gradient. *Am. J. Physiol.*, *196:* 207, 1959.

See also Chapter 38, General bibliography for the cardiovascular system.

Chapter 31

Blood Flow Through

Special Areas of the Body

The blood flow in many special areas of the body, such as the lungs, the kidneys, and the heart, has already been discussed in previous chapters, and uterine and fetal blood flow during reproduction will be discussed later in the text. In the present chapter the characteristics of blood flow in some of the other important circulatory systems, such as the brain, the splanchnic system, the muscles, and the skin, will be presented.

CEREBRAL CIRCULATION

The Physiologic Anatomy of the Blood Flow through the Brain

Blood flows into the brain through the two carotid arteries and, to a lesser extent, through the two vertebral arteries. The vertebral arteries coalesce to form the basilar artery of the hindbrain, and the basilar artery and the two internal carotid arteries connect with each other by way of the circle of Willis. Therefore, a very adequate collateral circulation exists among the large vessels to the brain.

Both carotid arteries can usually be occluded in young persons without any detrimental effects whatsoever to the function of the cerebrum. In older subjects it is sometimes possible also to occlude both carotid arteries without damage, though at times the vascular anastomoses between the large arteries at the base of the brain are so sclerotic that blocking both common carotids results in considerably diminished blood supply, thus causing temporary or permanent impairment of cerebral function.

The normal volume of blood flow through brain tissue averages 50 to 55 ml. per 100 grams of brain per minute. For the entire brain of the average adult, this is approximately 750 ml. per minute or 15 per cent of the total cardiac output under resting conditions. This total quantity of blood flow through the brain, even under extreme conditions, usually does not vary greatly from the normal value because the control systems are especially geared to maintain constant cerebral blood flow.

Collateral Circulation among the Smaller Arteries of the Brain. Though very adequate collateral channels exist between the large vessels of the brain, this is not true of the intermediate-size arteries. Consequently, when one of the major branch arteries of the brain, such as an anterior cerebral artery or a middle cerebral artery, becomes totally plugged, the result can be immediate death, total unilateral paralysis, or marked impairment of mentality.

If one of the major arteries of the brain becomes slowly sclerosed and occluded, the very small arterial or arteriolar anastomoses can gradually enlarge to take care of the needed blood supply. Also, immediately after a severe and sudden occlusion of one of the major arteries occurs, there is always an area of approximately a centimeter or more along the edges of the ischemic tissue that receives sufficient blood from the small anastomotic channels to maintain life of the neurons but not to maintain normal function. Consequently, during the ensuing few days or few weeks after a cerebral vascular occlusion, the anastomotic channels develop sufficiently to restore function in this marginal area, thus allowing the patient to recover at least some of his lost cerebral function.

Cerebral Hemorrhage and Cerebral Thrombosis

In patients with high blood pressure or with arteriosclerosis, "cerebral vascular accidents" are very likely to occur. Three fourths of these result from arterial hemorrhage and one fourth from arterial thrombosis. In either case the area of the brain supplied by the hemorrhaging or thrombosed artery becomes greatly damaged, for thrombosis causes damage simply as the result of the almost total ischemia that results, and pressure of hemorrhaging blood inside the cranial vault can cause ischemic death of nervous tissue by compressing the vascular supply. Also, clotting in the hemorrhaging vessel is very likely to cause thrombosis of the vessel. Obviously, either of these two types of accidents may cause paralysis, blindness, dementia, and so forth, depending on which part of the brain is destroyed.

Regulation of Cerebral Circulation— Autoregulation in Response to Excess Carbon Dioxide and Oxygen Lack

The rate of blood flow through the brain is regulated principally by the concentration of carbon dioxide and oxygen in the cerebral blood. Either excess carbon dioxide or diminished oxygen causes marked vasodilatation. Therefore, any time the cerebral blood flow becomes sluggish, causing a buildup of carbon dioxide and diminishment of oxygen in the cerebral blood, the blood flow automatically increases, thereby correcting these two conditions. Here again, then, one finds a very important local autoregulatory mechanism for maintenance of blood flow to the brain in proportion to its metabolism.

Value of Carbon Dioxide Control of the Cerebral Blood Flow. Studies on the function of the brain have shown that the excitability of neurons is greatly influenced by carbon dioxide concentration in the cerebral fluids; an increased carbon dioxide concentration depresses neuronal activity and a diminished carbon dioxide concentration increases neuronal activity. Therefore, it is very fortunate that an increase in carbon dioxide concentration increases the blood flow, which in turn carries carbon dioxide away from the brain tissues at an increased rate. Conversely, decreased carbon dioxide reduces the blood flow and allows the carbon dioxide concentration to rise toward normal.

Breathing air with a carbon dioxide concentration of 6 per cent increases cerebral blood flow approximately 100 per cent. This is the most powerful single stimulus known to affect cerebral blood flow.

Value of Oxygen Lack as a Regulator of Cerebral Blood Flow. The rate of metabolism and also the rate of oxygen utilization by the brain is extremely constant under many different conditions, varying very little even during intense mental activity, during muscular exercise, or even during sleep. Also, the rate of oxygen utilization by brain tissue remains within a few per cent of 3.5 ml. of oxygen per 100 gm. of brain tissue per minute. If ever the blood flow to the brain becomes insufficient to supply this amount of oxygen, then the oxygen lack mechanism immediately causes vasodilatation, allowing the transport of oxygen to the cerebral tissues to return toward normal. Thus, this autoregulatory mechanism is much the same as that which exists in the coronary and muscle circulations and in many other circulatory areas of the body. The need for very constant excitability of the neurons—never depressed and never overly excited—makes this mechanism of special importance in the cerebral circulation.

A decrease in the oxygen saturation of the arterial blood to about 75 per cent increases the cerebral blood flow approximately 40 per cent, thus showing that oxygen lack within the physiological range is perhaps one half as potent as carbon dioxide excess in increasing cerebral blood flow.

Effect of Cerebral Activity on Blood Flow. Only rarely does neuronal activity increase sufficiently to increase the overall rate of metabolism in the brain. However, in those few instances in which this does occur, the cerebral blood flow automatically increases a very moderate amount. For instance, an epileptic attack, which causes extreme activity throughout the entire brain, can result in an overall increase in cerebral blood flow of as much as 50 per cent. Likewise, epinephrine can increase the flow slightly. On the other hand, administration of anesthetics sometimes reduces brain metabolism and also cerebral blood flow as much as 30 to 40 per cent.

Local blood flow in even normally active portions of the brain can also increase as much as 40 to 50 per cent as a result of

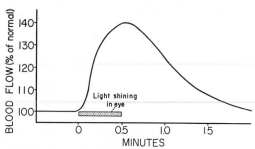

Figure 298. Increase in blood flow to the occipital regions of the brain when a light is flashed in the eyes of an animal.

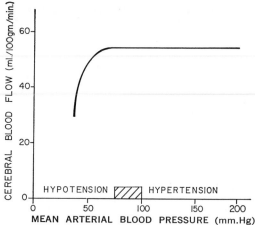

Figure 299. Relationship of mean arterial pressure to cerebral blood flow in normotensive, hypotensive, and hypertensive persons.

localized neuronal activity even though the total cerebral flow is hardly affected. This is illustrated in Figure 298, which shows the effect of shining an intense light into one eye of a cat; this results in increased blood flow in the corresponding area of the brain that becomes excited.

Effect of Arterial Pressure on Cerebral Blood Flow. Figure 299 shows cerebral blood flow measured in human beings having different blood pressures as a result of different clinical abnormalities. This figure shows especially the extreme constancy of cerebral blood flow in different persons between the limits of 60 mm. Hg and 180 mm. Hg mean arterial pressure. Cerebral blood flow suffers only when the arterial pressure falls below approximately the 60 mm. Hg mark. This, however, is not the effect observed when the arterial pressure is changed acutely from one pressure to another, for under these conditions the flow changes almost linearly with pressure. Fortunately, the arterial pressure control systems are especially organized to prevent drastic decreases in cerebral arterial pressure. These systems—especially the pressoreceptor reflex and the CNS ischemic reflex—will be discussed in detail in the following chapter.

Lack of Importance of Autonomic Nerves in Regulating Cerebral Blood Flow. Sympathetic nerves from the cervical sympathetic chain pass upward along the cerebral arteries to supply at least some of the cerebral vasculature. Also, parasympathetic fibers from the great superficial petrosal and facial nerves supply some of the vessels. However, transection of either the sympathetic or parasympathetic nerves causes no measurable effect on cerebral blood flow. On the other hand, stimulation

does affect blood flow slightly, the sympathetics causing mild vasoconstriction of the large vessels but not of the small vessels, and the parasympathetics causing mild vasodilatation. It remains yet to be proved that either of these has any functional importance in regulation of cerebral blood flow.

Measurement of Cerebral Blood Flow in Man

Obviously, it would be almost impossible to insert a flowmeter into the cerebral circulatory system of man. However, a satisfactory indirect method for making such a measurement has been achieved, the principles of which are the following:

The blood flow through any organ of the body can be determined by means of the so-called Fick principle. That is, if a constituent of the blood is removed from the blood as it flows through an organ, then the blood flow can be determined from two measurements: first, the amount removed from each ml. of blood as it goes through the organ and, second, the total quantity of the substance that is removed by the organ in a given period of time. The total blood flow during the period of measurement can be calculated by dividing the amount of substance removed from each ml. of blood into the total quantity removed.

In measuring blood flow through the brain the subject suddenly begins to breathe nitrous oxide of a given concentration. Samples of arterial blood are removed from any artery in the body and samples of venous blood are obtained directly from the internal jugular vein as it drains blood from the brain. The concentrations of the nitrous oxide in both of these bloods are then plotted for

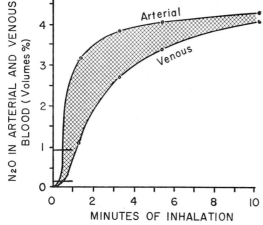

Figure 300. Method for measuring cerebral blood flow in man as explained in the text. (Modified from Kety: Methods in Medical Research, 1948.)

10 minutes, as shown in Figure 300. The quantity of nitrous oxide lost to the brain by each ml. of blood as it passes through the brain at each instant of the experiment can be determined from the difference in height of the two curves. This is called the *A-V difference*. The A-V difference is determined each minute for a period of 10 minutes and then averaged.

Now, to determine the amount of nitrous oxide that is removed from the blood by the brain tissue, one proceeds as follows: It will be noted from the curve of Figure 300 that the concentrations of nitrous oxide are reaching an equilibrium level toward the end of the 10 minute experiment. It is also known that the total amount of nitrous oxide absorbed by the brain tissue is directly proportional to the concentration in the arterial blood at the end of the 10-minute run. A *proportionality factor* has been determined in experiments on isolated brain tissue so that at the end of 10 minutes the total quantity of nitrous oxide in each 100 grams of brain tissue can be determined by multiplying the arterial concentration of nitrous oxide times the proportionality factor.

Once the average A-V difference and the amount of nitrous oxide absorbed per minute by the brain have been determined, the cerebral blood flow is then calculated by dividing the A-V difference into the quantity absorbed. As an example, if 5 ml. of nitrous oxide is absorbed by 100 grams of brain tissue in 10 minutes and the average A-V difference during this period of time is 1 ml. for each 100 cc. of blood, then a total of five 100 ml. portions of blood would have passed through the 100 grams of brain tissue during the 10-minute interval. In other words, the blood flow would be 50 ml. per 100 grams of brain tissue per minute. Assuming a brain size of 1400 grams, the blood flow would be 700 ml. per minute.

THE SPLANCHNIC CIRCULATION

Under basal conditions, as much as one sixth to one fourth of the cardiac output flows through the vessels of the intestines and through the spleen, finally coursing back into the portal venous system and then through the liver as illustrated in Figure 301. This is called the portal circulatory system, and it, plus the arterial blood flow into the liver, is called the *splanchnic circulation*.

Blood Flow through the Liver

When portal blood enters the liver it first flows through the venous sinuses in very close contact with the cords of liver parenchymal cells. Then it enters the central veins of the liver and from there flows into the vena cava.

In addition to the portal blood flow about one third as much blood flows into the liver from the hepatic artery. This arterial blood flow maintains nutrition in the connective tissue and especially in the walls of the bile ducts. Therefore, loss of hepatic arterial blood flow can be lethal because it causes necrosis of the basic liver structures. The blood from the hepatic artery, after it supplies the structural elements of the liver, empties into the liver sinuses to mix with the portal blood.

A Reservoir Function of the Liver. Be-

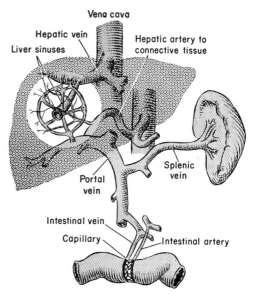

Figure 301. The portal and hepatic circulation.

cause the liver is an expandable and contractile organ, very large quantities of blood can be stored in its blood vessels. High pressure in the right atrium causes back pressure in the liver, the liver expands, and as much as one liter of blood occasionally is thereby stored in the large hepatic veins and venous sinuses. This occurs especially in cardiac failure with peripheral congestion, which will be discussed in Chapter 36.

Effect of Venous Pressure on the Storage of Blood in the Liver. The only significant factor regulating the volume of blood stored in the liver is the hepatic venous pressure. That is, when this pressure rises, the liver enlarges, and, when it falls, blood is soon returned from the liver into the other portions of the circulation. Thus, in effect, the liver is a large expansile venous organ capable of acting as a very valuable blood reservoir in time of excess blood volume and capable of supplying extra blood in times of diminished blood volume.

Permeability of the Venous Sinuses of the Liver. The venous sinuses of the liver are lined with an endothelium similar to that of the capillaries, but its permeability is extreme in comparison with that of the capillaries—so much so that even the proteins of the blood diffuse into the extravascular spaces of the liver almost as easily as the fluids of the blood. Fortunately, the pressure in the sinuses is only 2 to 7 mm. Hg so that most of these proteins also diffuse back into the blood. Yet, a large amount does pass into the liver lymphatics so that liver lymph normally contains almost as great a protein concentration as that of the plasma itself.

This extreme permeability of the liver sinuses brings the fluids of the hepatic blood into extremely close contact with the liver parenchymal cells, thus facilitating very rapid exchange of nutrient materials between the blood and the liver cells.

Measurement of Blood Flow through the Liver in Man. Several indirect methods for measuring blood flow through the liver similar to those used for measuring blood flow through the brain have been developed. The most important of these is the following: The substance *Bromsulphalein* is removed from the blood and excreted into the gut by the liver, and almost no Bromsulphalein is lost from the blood in

any other way. This material is injected continuously into the circulation and blood samples are removed from two points in the circulation: (1) from a catheter inserted into a peripheral vein and (2) from another catheter inserted through a peripheral vein all the way into the hepatic vein. The difference between the concentrations of Bromsulphalein in a usual peripheral vein and the hepatic vein represents the quantity of Bromsulphalein removed by each unit of blood passing through the liver. To determine the quantity of Bromsulphalein removed by the liver each minute, the substance is injected into the circulation continuously and its rate of injection is adjusted until the concentration of Bromsulphalein in the blood is neither increasing nor decreasing. When this is achieved the amount being injected is equal to the rate of liver excretion. On dividing the A-V difference into the rate being secreted, one determines the total liver blood flow per minute.

The total liver blood flow per minute in man averages 1440 ml. per minute, which represents about 29 per cent of the total cardiac output. Approximately 22 per cent of this is portal blood flow and 7 per cent hepatic artery flow.

The Filtration Function of the Liver. Blood flowing in the intestinal capillaries picks up many bacteria from the intestines. Indeed, a sample of blood from the portal system will almost always grow colon bacilli when cultured, whereas growth of colon bacilli from blood in the systemic circulation is extremely rare. Special high-speed motion pictures of the action of Kupffer cells, which line the liver sinuses, have demonstrated that these cells can cleanse blood extremely efficiently as it passes through the sinuses of the liver; when a bacterium comes into momentary contact with a Kupffer cell, in less than 0.01 of a second the bacterium passes inward through the wall of the Kupffer cell to become permanently lodged therein until it is digested. Probably not over 1 per cent of the bacteria absorbed into the portal blood from the intestines succeeds in passing through the liver into the systemic circulation.

The Metabolic "Buffering" Function of the Liver. The purpose of blood flow through the intestines is to absorb into the body fluids the

acts on the distal tubules of the kidney to decrease loss of sodium chloride and water into the urine. Because of the retention of salt and water, the extracellular fluid of the body increases in quantity, the blood volume increases, *and the blood pressure increases.* Therefore, this is possibly a second instance in which the kidney regulates blood pressure as a result of water and electrolyte retention.

Arguments against Fluid and Electrolyte Retention as the Usual Means by Which the Kidney Controls Blood Pressure. One of the reasons against believing fluid and electrolyte retention to be an important factor in usual blood pressure control by the kidneys is that constriction of the renal artery does not usually cause a very significant increase in the blood volume. For this reason, many physiologists have completely given up the idea that fluid and electrolyte retention is the normal means by which the kidney controls blood pressure. Others believe that it is not the retention of fluid that causes increased pressure following decreased kidney output but, instead, that it is *abnormal retention of electrolytes* or perhaps an *abnormal ratio of electrolytes* developing in the body fluids that increases the pressure.

Coincident with the rise in systemic arterial pressure after the renal artery is constricted, the cardiac output does not rise. Therefore, the increase in blood pressure, however it comes about, is generally believed to result from an increase in peripheral resistance. This is another reason for believing that decreased kidney output normally increases the blood pressure by some other mechanism besides fluid retention, for such retention should increase the blood volume and cardiac output rather than increase the peripheral resistance.

Yet, another perplexing problem must also be presented: It is possible that the original cause of the hypertension is increased cardiac output. But since each respective tissue regulates its own blood flow in accord with its need, after a few hours to days the resistances in all the tissues would be expected to rise and the flows to return to normal. Thus the cardiac output would fall to normal, and the experimenter would be deluded into believing the pressure to be elevated because of increased resistance. The point of this is that the kidneys could conceivably regulate arterial pressure by primarily altering cardiac output, rather than by altering peripheral resistance.

The Possible Importance of Sodium Ion in Blood Pressure Regulation. If the rise in blood pressure following decreased kidney output is not caused by an increase in cardiac output but instead by arteriolar constriction, then some mechanism must be postulated for constriction of the arterioles. Many who believe in the electrolyte theory as the means by which the kidney is capable of regulating blood pressure feel that elevation in sodium ion concentration in the body fluids, which is a common result of depressed kidney function, might directly affect the arterioles to increase their resistance. It has been postulated that sodium causes the smooth muscle fibers of the arteriolar walls to swell, in this manner increasing the resistance and elevating the pressure.

Kidney Secretion of Vasoconstrictor Substances as a Possible Means by Which the Kidney Controls Blood Pressure

When the renal artery is constricted, the kidney tissue becomes ischemic and releases a small amount of vasoconstrictor substances into the venous blood. Therefore, it has been postulated that the kidney automatically protects itself against ischemia by releasing a vasoconstrictor hormone, thereby causing arteriolar constriction throughout the remainder of the body and elevating the blood pressure.

One vasoconstrictor substance in particular, renin, has been isolated from the venous blood leaving an ischemic kidney. However, the amount is so small that it is still questionable whether or not it is of importance as a blood pressure regulator. Yet, because such a substance might be the cause of the yet unexplained disease essential hypertension, renin will be discussed in detail in the following chapter.

Effect of Other Factors on Kidney Regulation of Blood Pressure

Continuous stimulation of the sympathetic nerves to the kidneys over a period of several weeks causes the mean arterial pressure in an animal to rise to as high as 150 mm. Hg. Then when the stimulation is stopped the mean arterial pressure falls back to normal in a day or more. Therefore, whenever the various vasomotor regulatory systems elevate blood pressure by sympathetic stimulation, they not only elevate this pressure by arteriolar constriction but also by affecting the kidney mechanism for blood pressure regulation.

Posterior pituitary hormone, which is secreted almost continually by the posterior pituitary gland, causes the distal tubules of the kidney to absorb larger quantities of water than they would otherwise. Posterior pituitary hormone has never been definitely implicated in blood pressure control; however, when normal quantities of this hormone are not secreted, the human being becomes excessively susceptible to low blood pressure, which indicates that failure of the kidneys to reabsorb normal quantities of water causes the blood pressure regulatory mechanisms to operate at the lower limit of normal, and any additional factor that then tends to lower the blood pressure cannot be overcome by the regulatory systems.

Many other aspects of renal regulation of arterial pressure will be discussed in the following chapter in relation to hypertension.

CONTROL OF MEAN ARTERIAL PRESSURE BY THE NERVOUS SYSTEM

The Vasomotor Center and Its Control of the Circulation

Location of the Vasomotor Center. Figure 309 illustrates the vasomotor center and its connections with the heart and blood vessels through the vagus and sympathetic nerves. Actually it is wrong to say that a definite vasomotor "center" exists because many *different* areas of the medulla and other areas of the brain help to control arterial pressure. However, a very powerful sympathetic response causing vasoconstriction and cardioacceleration occurs when the floor of the fourth ventricle is stimulated approximately in the region of the inferior fovea, as shown in Figure 309. And stimulation of the dorsal motor nucleus of the vagus nerve elicits a powerful parasympathetic response, causing principally a decrease in heart rate.

The sympathetic and vagal portions of the vasomotor center usually *reciprocally inhibit each other*. In other words, when one of these becomes stimulated, the opposing center, because of special neuron circuits in the medulla, automatically becomes less active.

The Efferent Neuronal Pathways from the Vasomotor Center. Stimulation of the sympathetic area of the vasomotor center

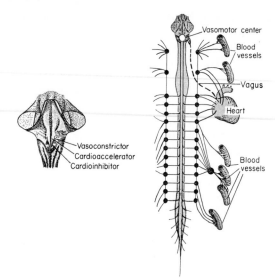

Figure 309. The vasomotor center and its control of the circulatory system through the sympathetic and vagus nerves.

sends impulses to the entire circulatory system and also to the heart by way of the sympathetic nervous system, while stimulation of the vagal area sends impulses by way of the vagus nerves to the heart. Through these pathways, the vasomotor center can increase or decrease the peripheral vascular resistance, it can increase or decrease the heart rate, and it can increase or decrease the strength of heart contraction. The connections of both the sympathetics and the vagus nerves with the circulatory system were discussed in detail in Chapter 20, The Autonomic Nervous System.

Tonic Activity of the Vasomotor Center. Normally, the vasomotor center is continually active, transmitting impulses both through the sympathetic and vagus nerves at all times. The impulses passing through the sympathetic nerves maintain a moderate degree of vasoconstriction in most areas of the circulation as well as a mild degree of cardiac stimulation. On the other hand, impulses transmitted through the parasympathetics maintain a moderate degree of cardioinhibition, which opposes the action of the sympathetics on the heart and keeps the heart rate at a lower level than it would naturally assume without these impulses.

The tonic activity of the sympathetics normally maintains an arterial pressure approximately twice that which would occur without this tonic activity. Figure 310 illustrates this effect, showing that administration of a

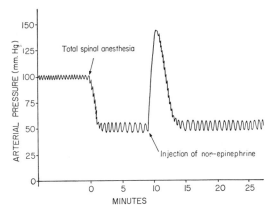

Figure 310. Effect of total spinal anesthesia on the arterial pressure, showing a marked fall in pressure resulting from loss of vasomotor tone.

total spinal anesthesia, which blocks all sympathetic nerve impulses to the circulatory system, reduces the arterial pressure immediately to 40 to 50 mm. Hg. Note, however, that injection of norepinephrine, which simulates sympathetic activity throughout the body, raises the pressure temporarily up to high values only to fall again back to the low "spinal level" as soon as the effect has worn off.

The significance of the tonic activity of the sympathetic stimulation of the circulation is the following: Arterial pressure can be raised above normal by increasing the degree of sympathetic tonic activity, or, on the other hand, it can be decreased below normal by inhibition of the tonic activity. Likewise, the heart rate can be increased by decreasing the tonic activity of the vagus nerve or can be decreased by increasing the tonic activity of the vagus nerve.

It should be noted particularly that so far as arterial pressure is concerned, by far *the dominant activity of the vasomotor center is the sympathetic vasoconstrictor effect.* The vagi can be completely sectioned, and hardly any change results in the regulation of the pressure. Therefore, when we speak of tonic activity of the vasomotor center, we almost always are referring to its sympathetic functions and not to its vagal functions.

Mechanism by Which Sympathetic Stimulation Elevates the Arterial Pressure. Sympathetic stimulation brings about three major effects that cause the arterial pressure to rise: First, it constricts the majority of the arteries of the circulation, especially the arterioles, which increases the total peripheral resistance and consequently elevates the pressure. Second, it increases the vascular tone of all the veins of the body, which in turn increases the flow of blood into the heart and, therefore, increases the force of cardiac pumping. Third, sympathetic stimulation of the heart directly increases its strength of contraction, which also helps to elevate the arterial pressure. It is a combination of these three effects that causes the increase in arterial pressure when the sympathetic nervous system is activated.

Effect of Carbon Dioxide on the Activity of the Vasomotor Center

The intensity of sympathetic activity of the vasomotor center increases almost directly in proportion to the concentration of carbon dioxide in the extracellular fluids. Therefore, carbon dioxide is one of the most powerful of all stimuli affecting the activity of the vasomotor center—a very high carbon dioxide concentration can increase the mean arterial pressure from a normal of 100 mm. Hg up to as high as 200 to 270 mm. Hg.

The exact mechanism by which carbon dioxide affects the vasomotor center is not known. However, it is presumed that carbon dioxide has a direct stimulatory effect on the neuronal cells. Some of the theories for this effect will be discussed in Chapter 42 in connection with the regulation of respiration, for the respiratory center reacts to carbon dioxide in very much the same manner as the vasomotor center.

Importance of Carbon Dioxide as a Regulator of Arterial Pressure. The amount of carbon dioxide produced by the tissues of the body increases in direct proportion to the rate of metabolism of the tissues. And, when the metabolism increases, the amount of blood flow required by the tissues to meet the metabolic needs is correspondingly increased. It is valuable, then, that the elevated carbon dioxide concentration increases the arterial pressure and that this in turn forces increased quantities of blood through the vascular system.

Effect of Ischemia on the Activity of the Vasomotor Center—the CNS Ischemic Reflex

Ischemia means lack of sufficient blood flow to maintain normal metabolic function of the cells. When ischemia of the vasomotor center occurs as a result of occluding the arteries to the brain, systemic arterial pressure rises markedly. It is believed that this is caused mainly by failure of the slowly flowing blood to carry carbon dioxide away from the vasomotor center; the local concentration of carbon dioxide supposedly increases greatly and elevates the arterial pressure. Or perhaps other factors, such as the buildup of lactic acid in the vasomotor center, might also contribute to the marked elevation in pressure. This elevation of arterial pressure in response to cerebral ischemia is known as the *central nervous system ischemic reflex* or simply *CNS ischemic reflex*.

The magnitude of the ischemic effect on vasomotor activity is almost identical to that caused by excess carbon dioxide; both elevate the arterial pressure sometimes to as high as 270 mm. Hg mean arterial pressure, with systolic and diastolic pressures of 330 and 230 mm. Hg respectively. Furthermore, the degree of sympathetic vasoconstriction caused by intense cerebral ischemia is often so great that some of the peripheral vessels become totally or almost totally occluded. The kidneys, for instance, will entirely cease their production of urine because of arteriolar constriction in response to the sympathetic discharge. No factor that affects vasomotor activity, other than carbon dioxide, has yet been shown to have nearly so powerful an effect on kidney secretion of urine. *Therefore, the CNS ischemic reflex is one of the most powerful of all the factors that can affect arterial pressure.*

Importance of the CNS Ischemic Reflex as a Regulator of Arterial Pressure. It will be recalled from the discussion of the cerebral circulation in Chapter 31 that decreasing the arterial pressure to as low as 60 mm. Hg normally does not decrease the blood flow to the brain because of local autoregulatory mechanisms that cause the blood vessels simply to dilate when the blood pressure falls. However, when the blood pressure falls below 60 mm. Hg, and especially below 30 to 50 mm. Hg, the cerebral tissues do then become ischemic, and the CNS ischemic reflex occurs.

Therefore, despite the extremely powerful nature of the CNS ischemic reflex, it does not become active until the arterial pressure falls far below normal. Therefore, it is not believed to be one of the major mechanisms for regulating normal arterial pressure. Instead, it operates principally as an emergency arterial pressure control system that acts rapidly and extremely powerfully to prevent further decrease in arterial pressure whenever blood flow to the brain decreases dangerously close to the lethal level.

The Cushing Reflex. The so-called *Cushing reflex* is a special type of CNS ischemic reflex that results from increased pressure in the cerebrospinal fluid system. When the cerebrospinal fluid pressure rises to equal the arterial pressure, it compresses the arteries in the cranial vault and cuts off the blood supply to the brain. Obviously, this initiates a CNS ischemic reflex, which causes the arterial pressure to rise. When the arterial pressure has risen to a level higher than the cerebrospinal fluid pressure, blood then flows once again into the vessels of the brain to relieve the ischemia. Ordinarily, the blood pressure comes to a new equilibrium level slightly higher than the cerebrospinal fluid pressure, thus allowing blood to continue flowing to the brain at all times. A typical Cushing reflex is illustrated in Figure 311.

Obviously, the Cushing reflex helps to

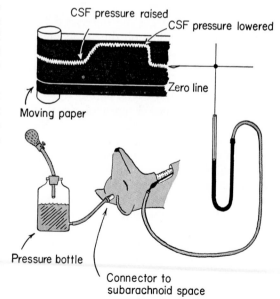

Figure 311. The Cushing reflex, showing a rise in arterial pressure resulting from increased cerebrospinal fluid pressure.

vessels of the heart itself; this presumably results from the excessive work load on the heart muscle and failure of the coronary vessels to enlarge to the same extent that the muscle hypertrophies. Approximately 70 per cent of all persons who die of hypertension die of myocardial failure resulting from coronary arteriosclerosis.

Cerebral Hemorrhage. The high pressure in the arteries of hypertensive patients, and especially the high pressure that occurs during exercise or emotional strain, can cause blood vessels throughout the body to rupture. Arteriosclerotic vessels are weaker than normal, and the likelihood of rupture is great. One area of the body that is extremely susceptible to hemorrhaging vessels is the brain, and when hemorrhage occurs in this area it causes paralysis, mental impairment, or perhaps death because of loss of some vital function of the nervous system. Hemorrhage in the brain is commonly called a "cerebral vascular accident," and is even more commonly known as a "stroke." Approximately 20 per cent of all persons who die from hypertension die of cerebral hemorrhage.

Kidney Disease. Widespread hemorrhages often occur throughout the abdominal organs in hypertension for the same reasons that they occur in the brain. One of the organs in which such hemorrhages are very prevalent is the kidney. After hemorrhage occurs, the blood vessel that has ruptured becomes thrombosed, and the area of the kidney that has previously been supplied by the vessel thereafter becomes totally ischemic and dies. Consequently, increasing proportions of the kidneys are lost, and, as will be noted later in the chapter, the loss of kidney function can result in even greater exacerbation of the hypertension. Approximately 10 per cent of all persons who die as a result of hypertension die because of kidney failure.

NEUROGENIC TYPES OF HYPERTENSION

Hypertension Produced by Cerebral Ischemia

Experimental Hypertension Caused by Generalized Cerebral Ischemia. Elevation of blood pressure in response to cerebral ischemia is an extremely powerful blood pressure regulation mechanism, as discussed in the previous chapter. Yet, to make the arterial pressure remain elevated for a prolonged period of time in an experimental animal, it is necessary to ligate all the major arteries to the brain, including even the anterior spinal artery. In other words, the ischemia must be extremely severe. There-

fore, it is doubtful that generalized cerebral ischemia is ever the cause of hypertension in the human being. However, localized ischemia in vital areas of the brain could easily result in hypertension.

Hypertension in Brain Tumor Patients. Development of any "space-occupying" lesion in the cranial vault, including both brain tumors and brain abscesses, can elevate the arterial blood pressure. Such lesions rarely increase the cerebrospinal fluid pressure above 45 mm. Hg, and this is not enough to compress the blood supply to the vasomotor centers. Consequently, brain tumors probably cause high blood pressure by directly pressing on vital areas of the brain, thereby causing these areas to become ischemic.

Sudden deterioration of blood pressure and rapid death in brain tumor patients. When ischemia of the vasomotor center becomes progressively greater, the blood pressure rises higher and higher to overcome the ischemia, but there is a limit beyond which the pressure cannot be elevated, for the heart usually cannot maintain a mean arterial pressure greater than approximately 210 mm. Hg. Therefore, if the ischemia becomes only slightly greater than the heart can overcome, the neuronal cells develop nutritional deficiency and begin to die. This causes decreasing numbers of impulses from the vasomotor center to the sympathetics so that the blood pressure falls, and then neurons die even more rapidly. Thus, once the process begins, a vicious cycle occurs, and the blood pressure can fall within less than a minute from a mean of 200 mm. Hg to the "spinal blood pressure level" of approximately 40 mm. Hg, the value observed after all impulses from the vasomotor center are abrogated.

When a brain tumor patient has a greatly elevated blood pressure, the slightest emotional strain or the slightest change in hemodynamics, as occurs, for instance, following intense sedation, can set off this vicious cycle of deterioration, and death will ensue before anything can be done. Not only does the blood pressure fall to the spinal level, but all other neuronal functions of the brain cease at the same time. This includes cessation of respiration and, of course, lapse into total coma.

Experimental Hypertension caused by Hypothalamic Lesions. On a few occasions lesions produced in the hypothalamus of dogs have caused experimental hypertension lasting many months. Such lesions probably cause the hypothalamus to excite the vasomotor center of the medulla, which in turn sends impulses through the sympathetics to the peripheral vessels, resulting in vasoconstriction and elevated blood pressure.

Experimental Hypertension Caused by Pressoreceptor Denervation

Normally, impulses from the pressoreceptors tonically inhibit the sympathetic centers of the medulla and thereby keep the arterial pressure continually depressed. Therefore, denervation of the pressoreceptors in an animal allows the sympathetic centers to become excessively active, thereby resulting in hypertension as illustrated in Figure 317. Note that denervation of one carotid sinus causes only slight elevation of the arterial pressure, but denervation of all the pressoreceptors causes an intense increase in pressure. This pressure usually falls back to normal within a few weeks but often later climbs back to a moderately high level and remains there indefinitely if all the pressoreceptors have been successfully denervated.

In the human being removal of the two carotid sinus nerves causes much greater elevation of arterial pressure than occurs in animals, but the pressure does not remain elevated for more than two to three weeks. Therefore, permanent hypertension in the human being has never been proved to result from diminished activity of the pressoreceptors, though there is yet no instance on record in which all the pressoreceptors, including those in the thorax, in human beings have been denervated.

HYPERTENSION CAUSED BY A PHEOCHROMOCYTOMA

A pheochromocytoma is a small, yellow tumor that develops usually in one of the adrenal medullae but occasionally in other chromaffin tissues of the sympatho-adrenal system of the abdomen. This tumor is composed of ganglion-like cells similar to the normal secreting cells of the adrenal medullae, and it is capable of secreting epinephrine and nor-epinephrine in response to sympathetic stimuli in the same manner that the normal adrenal medullae secrete these two hormones.

Because the secretion of the pheochromocytoma is controlled by sympathetic stimuli, the exact level of the arterial pressure can often vary from minute to minute, from hour to hour, and from day to day, as is illustrated in Figure 318. A clinical chart of blood pressure such as that shown in this figure is almost a certain sign of a pheochromocytoma. However, there are other ways of establishing the diagnosis of the pheochromocytoma type of hypertension, including the use of test doses of various drugs. First, injection of small amounts of either histamine or methacholine will stimulate the pheochromocytoma, causing it to secrete large quantities of nor-epinephrine and epinephrine and precipitating a very marked rise in arterial pressure. This is opposite to the effect usually observed when either histamine or methacholine is administered, both of which normally reduce the arterial pressure. A second type of drug that can be used to test for this type of tumor is the so-called sympatholytic drug, which prevents the action of epinephrine on the smooth muscle of the blood vessels. One of these drugs, Regitine, has been used often as a test for the disease, and it is also used for lowering the blood pressure prior to removal of the tumor.

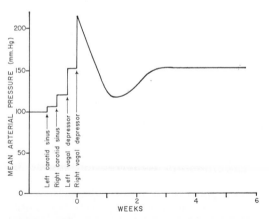

Figure 317. Moderate hypertension produced in a dog by total denervation of the arterial pressoreceptors.

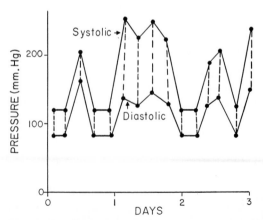

Figure 318. Clinical blood pressure chart of a patient with a pheochromocytoma.

Often a pheochromocytoma will secrete nor-epinephrine and epinephrine continually rather than only when the sympathetic nervous system stimulates it. In such cases the patient's blood pressure is maintained continuously at a high level, and it is difficult to differentiate this type of hypertension from other types. However, procedures have been worked out for actually measuring the quantities of nor-epinephrine and epinephrine in the blood and also the amounts secreted in the urine. The normal rate of urinary secretion is 15 to 40 micrograms per day, but this occasionally rises to as high as 600 to 2700 micrograms per day when a patient has a pheochromocytoma.

An especially interesting effect of continual secretion of nor-epinephrine and epinephrine by pheochromocytomas is a *decreased* blood volume, which is the opposite effect to that found in some other types of hypertension. Indeed, continuous injection of epinephrine into experimental animals can cause as much as 10 per cent decrease in blood volume during the first ten minutes of elevated blood pressure. This decrease in blood volume presumably results from constriction of the venous reservoirs, which causes abnormal elevation of capillary pressure and loss of fluid into the tissues.

EXPERIMENTAL HYPERTENSION INVOLVING THE KIDNEY

In general, anything that decreases the overall action of the kidney will cause hypertension. Consequently, hypertension has been produced in animals by many different types of experiments involving the kidneys. These include the following:

The "Goldblatt Animal." In the Goldblatt animal, a small clamp is placed around the renal artery of one kidney, and the other kidney is either totally removed or a similar clamp is placed around its artery. These clamps are constricted until the arterial lumina are almost totally occluded, thereby decreasing the flow of blood to the kidneys. The arterial pressure begins to rise, and over a period of several weeks the pressure in the renal arteries *beyond the clamp* returns almost to normal. It takes several weeks for the animal to develop full-blown hypertension following application of the Goldblatt clamp because the kidney mechanism for regulating pressure is slow to respond, as was pointed out in the preceding chapter.

A moderate degree of hypertension can also be induced in a dog by constricting only one renal artery while leaving the remaining kidney completely undisturbed. The arterial pressure rises slowly for a week or so and then falls essentially back to normal after another few weeks. In this preparation no measurable disturbance in overall renal function can be detected. It is believed by many physiologists that the ischemic kidney secretes a vasoconstrictor substance which in turn causes the elevated pressure. However, the pressure does not remain elevated, indicating that, even if a vasoconstrictor principle does exist, the kidney soon stops secreting it. This will be discussed in greater detail later in the chapter.

Removal of Kidney Tissue. Removing one kidney and then removing more and more of the second kidney causes progressive elevation of the arterial pressure, even though the remaining portion of the kidney continues to function normally. Usually, about one half of the second kidney must be removed before significant hypertension results.

Entire Removal of Both Kidneys—"Renoprival Hypertension." Animals kept in reasonably good condition by various means after both kidneys have been completely removed will develop hypertension. The means usually used for maintaining such an animal in satisfactory condition is to perform peritoneal dialysis. To do this, a large amount of fluid is injected into the peritoneal cavity of the animal once or twice daily; this allows those substances not needed by the body to diffuse from the blood into the dialysis fluid, and this fluid is then removed after several hours.

Experiments have shown that the amount of fluid and electrolytes, especially sodium, ion, that collect in the body of the arenal animal determines to great extent the height to which its arterial pressure will rise.

Enclosing the Kidney in a Cellophane Bag. In some small animals such as the rat, hypertension is very easily effected by placing around the kidney a cellophane bag or some other substance that will cause sclerosis of the perirenal tissues. This type of hypertension probably results from several factors. First, lymphatic drainage is reduced so that edema of the kidneys probably occurs, and second, the kidneys are probably constricted directly by the sclerotic process. In either instance it is easy to understand how kidney function could suffer.

Experimental Hypertension in Parabiotic Animals. It is possible to join two rats from the same litter of an inbred strain in "parabiosis." This is done by opening the abdominal cavities of both and then sewing the wound edges of one animal to the wound edges of the opposite animal, allowing common flow of serous fluid between the two peritoneal chambers. Ordinarily, parabiosis will not cause hypertension, but, if the kidneys of one of the animals are removed prior to parabiosis, the animal with the kidneys removed will be hypertensive and the other animal will be normotensive. The only means by which the hypertensive animal can rid itself of excretory substances is by dialysis into the second animal, which in turn excretes these substances into its urine. Therefore, the excretory function of the hypertensive animal is greatly impaired, which is presumably the cause of the hypertension.

Clinical Hypertension as a Result of Kidney Disease

Almost any kidney disease that causes destruction of a large proportion of the kidney will cause hypertension. For instance, patients who have severe arteriosclerotic disease with progressive occlusion of the arteries to the kidneys almost always have hypertension. The same is true of patients who have severe destruction of the kidneys resulting from pyelonephritis or polycystic kidney disease. Also, patients who have either acute or chronic glomerulonephritis in most instances have high blood pressure, though the extent of the disease determines whether or not hypertension will exist.

Any time the total mass of kidney tissue is reduced below about one-fourth normal, hypertension usually results, the degree of hypertension being proportional to the amount of kidney destruction beyond this point.

Theories of the Cause of "Renal" Hypertension. Even though it is not known why kidney failure causes the blood pressure to rise, this subject is of such extreme clinical importance that the following suggested theories deserve discussion:

The renin-angiotonin theory of blood pressure control. Figure 319 illustrates a schema of one theory for explaining the cause of renal hypertension. A kidney deprived of part of its blood supply produces an abnormal protein substance known as *renin.* Renin is a proteolytic enzyme that

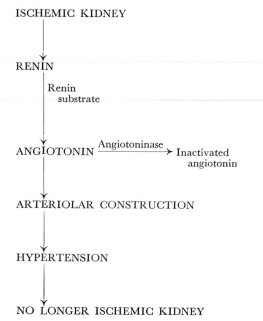

Figure 319. The renin-angiotonin mechanism of hypertension.

specifically hydrolyzes renin substrate (also known as "hypertensinogen"), one of the alpha$_2$-globulins of the plasma, and among the products of this hydrolysis is a protein derivative known as *angiotonin* (or "hypertensin").

Angiotonin acts directly on the arterioles to cause arteriolar constriction with resultant elevation of arterial pressure. However, angiotonin lasts in the blood only a few minutes because it is inactivated by other proteolytic enzymes of the plasma that are collectively called *angiotoninase* (or "hypertensinase"). Consequently, in order for the blood pressure to remain elevated as a result of this mechanism, it would be necessary for the ischemic kidney to produce renin continually and indefinitely.

There are several reasons why it is difficult to believe that the renin-angiotonin system is the cause of renal hypertension. First, except for the initial few days after a kidney has been made ischemic, essentially no renin or angiotonin is present in the circulating blood of the animal even though the blood pressure remains high. Second, the response of the arterioles to renin exhibits the phenomenon of "tachyphylaxis," which is illustrated in Figure 320: the first injection of renin or angiotonin causes a relatively high elevation of blood pressure lasting 10 to 15 minutes, but, even though the same dose is administered in subsequent injections, the blood pressure response becomes progressively less and less until almost no effect occurs.

Furthermore, in an animal that has renal hypertension caused by clamping the renal artery, repeated injections of renin to the point that the animal becomes totally nonresponsive to the renin does not reduce the arterial pressure in the least. Therefore, it is extremely doubtful that such a tachyphylactic substance as renin could possibly be the cause of sustained high arterial pressure.

Finally, there is no reason to believe that in any but a few instances of renal hypertension the kidney tissue is actually ischemic, which is a condition supposedly necessary for formation of large amounts of renin.

Fluid and electrolyte retention as a possible explanation of renal elevation of blood pressure. Because the blood volume increases only slightly during kidney failure, it is doubtful whether fluid retention could cause renal hypertension. Yet, a number of observations on renal hypertension can hardly be explained except by the possibility that some abnormality of fluid or electrolyte balance is the cause of elevated blood pressure in kidney disease. Principal among these have been the results obtained from animals with both kidneys completely removed, for the blood pressure rises in proportion to the amount of water and electrolytes, especially sodium ions, retained by the animals. Also, water and electrolytes are retained in great quantities when excess adrenocortical hormone is secreted by the adrenal glands, as will be discussed below, and the blood pressure rises simultaneously.

The elevated blood pressure related to fluid and electrolyte retention could possibly result from an abnormal ratio of electrolytes in the body fluids rather than an abnormal

quantity of fluids and electrolytes. It is well known that kidney disease causes greatly elevated levels of phosphate, potassium, and sodium under some circumstances. Although no one of these particular ions has been proved to be the cause of elevated blood pressure, many physiologists suspect that abnormal retention of sodium, or perhaps a combination of ionic abnormalities, might be the factor that causes high pressure in kidney dysfunction, particularly since sodium restriction in the diet of renal hypertensive patients causes the pressure to fall.

Hypertension caused by failure to excrete a pressor principle. Normal urine contains a vasoconstrictor polysaccharide, though only minute quantities of it can be isolated from very large amounts of urine. This material is probably formed in other parts of the body besides the kidney, perhaps in the liver, and it is normally excreted by the kidneys. It has been suggested that when the kidneys are nonfunctional, the substance cannot be excreted into the urine and it collects in the blood, possibly causing elevation of the blood pressure. Quantitatively, however, it is doubtful that a sufficient quantity of it is produced in the body to have any significant effect.

HYPERTENSION RESULTING FROM ADRENOCORTICAL TUMORS OR ADRENOCORTICAL HYPERPLASIA

The adrenal cortex frequently secretes excessive quantities of adrenocortical hormones either in response to excessive adrenocorticotropic hormone produced in the pituitary gland or as a result of a tumor in the adrenal cortex. Some of these hormones, *aldosterone* in particular, cause the kidneys to reabsorb far more sodium, chloride, and water than usual from the distal tubules. The extracellular fluid volume and blood volume increase sometimes as much as 15 to 20 per cent, the heart dilates, the cardiac output increases, and the blood pressure rises to as high as $260/170$.

The precise mechanism by which adrenocortical hormones increase the arterial pressure is not known. However, several possibilities are summarized in Figure 321 as follows: (1) The increased extracellular fluid and blood volumes possibly increase the venous return to the heart, thereby increasing the arterial pressure. (2) It has been suggested that the hormone directly

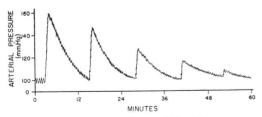

Figure 320. Tachyphylaxis exhibited by response of arterioles to successive injections of renin.

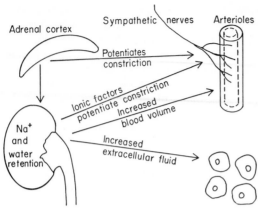

Figure 321. Possible mechanisms and causes of hypertension in adrenocortical hypersecretion.

potentiates the effect of nor-epinephrine on the blood vessels, thus increasing the vasoconstrictor effect of sympathetic impulses. (3) The hormone is known to cause excessive accumulation of sodium in the extracellular fluid, and it is possible that this in turn potentiates the vasoconstrictor effect of sympathetic impulses. (4) Finally, it has been suggested that increased sodium ions in the extracellular fluids cause the arteriolar walls to swell, thus increasing their resistance and in this way elevating the arterial pressure.

Toxemic Hypertension of Pregnancy.
Approximately one woman out of 20 develops hypertension during pregnancy, and coincident with this she almost always develops considerable extracellular fluid edema. The placenta secretes large quantities of steroid hormones into the mother's blood during pregnancy, and these steroid hormones, especially progesterone and to a lesser extent the estrogens, cause retention of sodium and water by the kidneys in exactly the same manner as aldosterone. Therefore, it is probable that the hypertension in "toxemic" patients has very much the same mechanism as that in patients who have excess adrenocortical hormone secretion. Thus, increased blood and extracellular fluid volume or direct vasoconstrictor effects of the hormones are both possible causes of the elevated blood pressure, or there might be still other factors yet undiscovered.

ESSENTIAL HYPERTENSION

Essential hypertension, which accounts for by far the largest proportion of hypertensive patients, is characterized by elevation of both systolic and diastolic pressures.

The pressure occasionally rises to $270/170$ with a mean pressure of 210. A person is generally considered to be hypertensive when his systolic blood pressure has risen above approximately 150 mm. Hg and his diastolic blood pressure above 90 mm. Hg, but these limits are quite arbitrary. Outward signs and symptoms in patients with essential hypertension may be nonexistent, for these patients often feel perfectly normal or even have a feeling of well-being. In more severe cases, there is a tendency for them to develop various cardiac ailments and also very severe headache. These developments are the result of pathologic changes that result from the prolonged high arterial pressure and therefore are not part of the original picture of essential hypertension.

Inheritance of Essential Hypertension.
By far the greater majority of patients with essential hypertension have histories of hypertension in one or more of their parents or grandparents, whereas the majority of persons with normal arterial pressures have no history of hypertension in their forebearers. Figure 322 illustrates the distribution of mean arterial pressures in the general population contrasted with the distribution in relatives of patients with known essential hypertension. This shows that a large group of persons have a general inheritable predisposition to higher levels of arterial pressures than the general population. Therefore, the disease is probably not a contracted disease but instead an inherited abnormality of the circulatory system itself, whether this

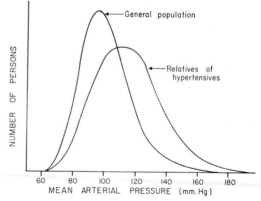

Figure 322. Distribution of mean arterial pressures in (a) the general population and (b) the relatives of known hypertensives.

abnormality be in the blood vessels, the heart, or the fluid regulatory system.

Malignant Hypertension. The term *malignant hypertension* usually applies to severe essential hypertension that is developing very rapidly. In malignant hypertension, the blood pressure often rises from normal to a mean pressure of 250/160 in only a few months, and ordinarily the disease runs its entire course in less than one to two years, resulting in death from coronary disease, kidney disease, or cerebral vascular accident.

Figure 323 illustrates an eyeground of a patient with malignant hypertension, showing that the circulation in the small blood vessels is greatly affected in this disease. Severe edema occurs at the optic disk where the retinal vessels enter and leave the eye, fluid and proteinaceous material exudes from the capillaries, and hemorrhages occur among the retinal fiber tracts. All these effects can combine to cause total blindness. Similar vascular effects occur throughout the body in very much the same manner as in the eye.

Arteriolar Constriction as the Possible Cause of Essential Hypertension. In patients with essential hypertension the total peripheral resistance is usually greatly increased, though the cardiac output is usually approximately normal. For these reasons most physiologists have argued that the *primary* cause of essential hypertension must be *increased arteriolar constriction*. This

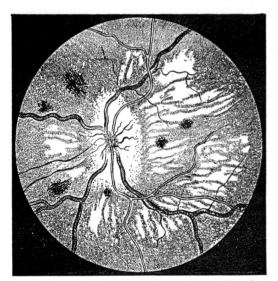

Figure 323. The retina of a patient with malignant hypertension, illustrating edema of the optic disk, spasm of the arterioles, dark areas of retinal hemorrhages, and light areas of protein exudate in the retina.

logic may well be correct, but *not necessarily so,* as will be explained in the following section.

Increased Force of Cardiac Pumping as the Possible Cause of Essential Hypertension. Any factor that increases the tendency for blood to return to the heart, such as increased blood volume, increased extracellular fluid volume, or decreased venous resistance (which will be discussed in Chapter 35), will increase the force of pumping by the heart in accordance with Starling's law of the heart, discussed in Chapter 25. Furthermore, the force of pumping can be increased by sympathetic stimulation of the cardiac musculature or by hypertrophy of the heart. It is theoretically possible for any of these factors to increase the cardiac output and thereby cause hypertension. Yet, measurements show that the cardiac output is not above the normal range in persons with essential hypertension. One must realize, though, that this state of events can come about as a secondary response, despite increased force of cardiac pumping, in the following way: In Chapter 28 it was pointed out that essentially all tissues of the body regulate their own blood flow in proportion to the metabolic needs of the tissues. If the heart should become more effective than usual as a pump and should increase the cardiac output, the blood flow to the tissues would be far greater than that needed. As a result, the local blood vessels in the tissues would automatically constrict, increasing the total peripheral resistance. This in turn would load the heart progressively more and more until the cardiac output would return to normal. Yet, *the final result would still be elevated arterial pressure and increased total peripheral resistance,* though the increased resistance would be entirely a secondary phenomenon.

Thus, the old argument that essential hypertension must be caused by some factor that directly affects the blood vessels is not necessarily true, for factors influencing fluid volumes and cardiac pumping effectiveness could lead to the same result.

Possible Causes of Essential Hypertension

The different types of hypertension of known cause fall into three general classes:

(1) neurogenic hypertension caused by excessive flow of vasoconstrictor nerve impulses from the vasomotor centers to the blood vessels, (2) hypertension resulting from kidney failure, caused by yet unknown causes, and (3) hypertension resulting from hormonal abnormalities.

At various times, all of these different mechanisms have been suggested as the possible or probable cause of essential hypertension, but none of them has been proved. A few especially prevalent theories of the cause of essential hypertension deserve special comment, as follows:

Kidney Disease. Because of the powerful effects of kidney disease on blood pressure control, it has been assumed by many physiologists that the kidneys are most likely responsible for elevated blood pressure in essential hypertension; this is the reason for the many experiments that have been performed in an attempt to clarify the mechanism of renal hypertension. Yet, *the kidneys of patients with newly developed essential hypertension do not show significant pathologic abnormalities,* although it is still possible that some physiologic derangement of the kidneys could cause essential hypertension.

Psychogenic Factors. Because emotions can cause greatly elevated blood pressures for short intervals of time, many psychiatrists claim that essential hypertension results from continual emotional disturbance, and some physicians believe that the strained existence of urban living is particularly prone to cause essential hypertension. However, studies made on colored races in Africa and colored inhabitants of some of our larger cities of America show the incidence of hypertension under most tribal conditions to be about the same as in our cities. Thus, doubt has been cast on stress as a cause of high blood pressure. Furthermore, essential hypertension follows a strong hereditary pattern from generation to generation, and as many as 13 children in the same family have all developed severe essential hypertension at an early age. Therefore, it is doubtful that environmental factors are the usual cause of essential hypertension, though it is possible that occasional cases can result from this cause.

Ischemic Lesions of the Brain. The blood pressure of many patients with essential hypertension can be lowered to normal or even sub-normal values by anesthetizing the sympathetic nerves in the spinal canal with a spinal anesthetic or by blocking the sympathetic impulses in any other way. Also, hypertension often occurs in patients following mild cerebral vascular accidents and in brain infections such as poliomyelitis. Both these facts indicate that ischemia or irritative lesions of some areas of the brain can cause hypertension. Ischemic lesions develop throughout the brain in later life as small blood vessels become plugged, and this could be a cause of essential hypertension.

Hormonal Abnormalities. In hypertension caused by adrenocortical or sex hormones, the blood and extracellular fluid volumes are increased, and the cardiac output is also increased. None of these effects is found in essential hypertension; for this reason it is believed that essential hypertension is probably not caused by hormonal factors.

On the other hand, essential hypertension can often be treated effectively by removal of sodium from the diet or by surgical removal of the adrenal glands. Indeed, even patients with malignant hypertension have attained normal blood pressures after removal of these glands, though the many other side effects of removing these glands are usually more dangerous than the hypertension. This fragile evidence makes many physiologists believe that essential hypertension is caused by some form of masked hormonal imbalance.

Inherited Abnormality of the Peripheral Blood Vessels as the Possible Cause of Hypertension. In the preceding chapter it was pointed out that an increased ratio of arterial resistance to venous resistance will cause elevated arterial pressure. Therefore, if an inherited factor should simply increase the thickness of the arteriolar walls of a person, this in itself could cause hypertension. Since no one of all the known causes of experimental hypertension has been proved to be the cause of essential hypertension, such a genetic abnormality in the peripheral vessels themselves must be considered as another possible cause.

Possibility of Many Different Causes of Essential Hypertension. It is obvious from the above discussion that evidence exists for

tion of the dye as it passes through one of the peripheral arteries, a curve such as one of those illustrated in Figure 333 will be obtained. In each of these instances 5 mg. of T-1824 dye was injected at zero time. In the top recording none of the dye passed into the arterial tree until approximately 3 seconds after the injection, but then the arterial concentration of the dye rose very rapidly to a maximum in approximately 6 to 7 seconds. After that, the concentration fell rapidly. However, before the concentration reached the zero point, some of the dye had already circulated all the way through some of the peripheral vessels and returned through the heart for a second time. Consequently, the dye concentration in the artery began to rise again. For the purpose of calculation, however, it is necessary to extrapolate the early downslope of the curve to the zero point, as shown by the dashed portion of the curve. In this way, the *time-concentration curve* of the dye in an artery can be measured in its first portion and estimated reasonably accurately in its latter portion.

Once the time-concentration curve has been determined, one can then calculate the mean concentration of dye in the arterial blood for the duration of the curve. In the above figure, this was done by measuring the area under the entire curve, and then spreading this area evenly over a total of 30 seconds; one can see from the upper curve of the figure that the average concentration of dye was approximately 0.1 mg./100 ml. blood, as illustrated by the shaded rectangular area. However, a total of 5 mg. of dye was injected at the beginning of the experiment. In order for blood carrying only 0.1 mg. of dye in each 100 ml. to carry the entire 5 mg. of dye through the heart and lungs, it would be necessary for a total of 50 100-ml. portions of blood to pass through the heart during the 30 second

period, and this would be the same as a cardiac output of 5 liters per 30 seconds, or 10 liters per minute.

In the bottom curve of Figure 333 the blood flow through the heart was considerably slower, and the dye did not appear in the arterial system until approximately 6 seconds after it had been injected. It reached a maximum height in 12 to 13 seconds and was extrapolated to 0 at approximately 30 seconds. Averaging the dye concentrations over the 30-second period one finds approximately 0.2 mg. of dye in each 100 ml. of blood for the 30-second time interval. To transport the total 5 mg. of dye, twenty-five 100-ml. portions of blood would have had to pass through the heart during the 30-second time interval. Therefore, the cardiac output was 2.5 liters per 30 seconds, or 5 liters per minute.

To summarize, the cardiac output can be determined from the following formula:

$$\text{Cardiac output} = \frac{\text{Mg. of dye injected}}{\substack{\text{Average \quad concentration \quad of} \\ \text{dye in each ml. of blood for} \\ \text{the duration of the curve}}}$$

This formula gives the cardiac output *for the duration of the curve*, and this can easily be converted to cardiac output per minute.

Different substances that can be injected for determining cardiac output by the dye dilution method. Almost any material that can be analyzed satisfactorily in the arterial blood can be injected when making use of the dye dilution method for determining cardiac output. Indeed, even saline solution, water, or plasma can be injected, for these will change the hematocrit of the arterial blood or the electrical conductivity in the same manner that injected dye will change the color of the blood. However, for optimum accuracy it is necessary that the injected substance not be lost into the lung tissues during their passage through the lungs. Saline and water are both lost to the extent of about 3 to 6 per cent, which causes the results to be slightly inaccurate. For best results, substances that combine with the plasma proteins or with the red blood cells are usually used. These are the same substances, in general, that can be used for measuring blood volume, and they include *T-1824, radioactive iodinated albumin,* and *radioactive red blood cells.* When radioactive substances are used, a Geiger or scintillation counter is employed to measure the concentration curves in the arterial tree.

Estimation of Cardiac Output by the Pulse Pressure Method. A fairly reliable estimation of cardiac output can usually be made from recordings of pressure pulse contours from the aorta. The basic theory of this method is the

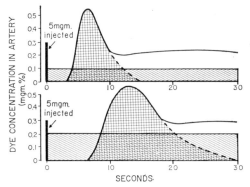

Figure 333. Dye concentration curves used to calculate cardiac output by the dye dilution method. (The rectangular areas are the calculated average concentrations of dye in the arterial blood over a period of 30 seconds.)

following: During diastole no blood flows into the arteries from the heart, but it does continue to flow from the central arteries through the peripheral circulatory system, thus allowing the pressure in the arterial tree to decline. Obviously, the greater the rate of blood flow, the greater also is the rate of blood pressure fall during diastole. By using empirical formulas, the cardiac output can be calculated from the downward slope of the pressure pulse contour and other characteristics of the curve.

The beauty of this method for estimating cardiac output is that continuous records can be made. Unfortunately, the characteristics of the pressure pulse curve depend on the distensibility of the arteries as well as on the rate of run-off of blood through the peripheral vessels, and the empirical formulas are based on the assumption that the arterial distensibility remains the same from one person or animal to another. This certainly is not true—especially in pathological conditions of the circulation—, thus making the method sometimes very seriously in error.

FACTORS THAT AFFECT PUMPING ABILITY OF THE HEART

Basically, cardiac output is a function of the heart itself, and any factor that changes the effectiveness of the heart as a pump also alters cardiac output. The pumping action of the heart was discussed in detail in Chapter 25, but this earlier discussion was concerned chiefly with the underlying principles of cardiac contraction and with the stroke volume output with each heart beat. We need now to see how the basic factors that affect the pumping action of the heart can affect the total cardiac output.

There are four major factors that affect the output of the normal heart. These are (1) the contractile strength of the heart, (2) the pressure against which the heart must pump, (3) the heart rate, and (4) the mean right atrial pressure. In pathological states additional factors can affect the pumping action of the heart; these factors include valvular destruction, abnormal shunts between the two sides of the heart, and damage to the myocardium itself. Also, changes in the pressure surrounding the heart resulting from opening the chest or from cardiac tamponade can greatly affect the heart's pumping effectiveness.

Effect of Contractile Strength and Cardiac Abnormalities on Cardiac Output. The strength of contraction of the heart can

be greatly increased or decreased under different normal or pathological conditions. For instance, stimulation of the cardiac muscle by the sympathetic nervous system can increase the strength of cardiac contraction by as much as two- to three-fold. Also, hypertrophy of the heart muscle increases the overall strength of cardiac contraction.

Many more conditions can decrease the strength of cardiac contraction, including (1) vagal stimulation, which inhibits atrial contractility, (2) diminished sympathetic stimulation of the heart, which reduces the contractility of the entire heart, and (3) damage to the cardiac musculature itself, which can result in any degree of cardiac weakening varying from very mild weakness to such great weakness that the heart will not contract at all.

Cardiac abnormalities, including valvular damage or shunts, also have almost exactly the same effect on the output of the heart as decreased contractile strength, for the presence of an abnormality requires a greater amount of contractile strength in the cardiac musculature to pump the same amount of blood as the normal heart.

Effect of Increased Systemic Pressure on the Output of the Heart. The greater the pressure against which the heart must pump blood, the less effective is the heart as a pump. In general, raising the systemic pressure does not diminish the output to a major extent until the pressure rises so high that it loads the heart beyond its contractile limit, but, when the systemic pressure does rise this high, the excess pressure can reduce the cardiac output tremendously. In the case of the heart with severe myocardial damage, even normal systemic arterial pressures may be sufficient to overload the heart.

Figure 334 illustrates the difference between the normal, unstimulated heart and the heart whose contractility is greatly enhanced by sympathetic stimulation, showing that the cardiac output falls drastically in the normal, unstimulated heart as the pressure rises much above normal, while the stimulated heart can continue to pump almost normal quantities of blood even when the arterial pressure rises to double normal.

Effect of Heart Rate on the Output of the Heart. If the normal heart is stimulated electrically so that its rate increases, the cardiac output rises a little, but only slightly so, for the following reasons: An increase in rate does not significantly increase the rate at which the blood flows into the heart. Therefore, despite the increase in rate, the stroke volume output decreases so greatly that this nullifies the advantage that might have been gained by the increased rate of the heart.

On the other hand, during exercise, the heart rate increases sometimes to as much as three times normal, but at the same time greatly increased amounts of blood also flow from the systemic vessels into the heart, thus keeping the heart well-filled with blood and allowing the rapidly beating heart to pump greatly increased amounts of blood. Therefore, in exercise, as well as in some other physiologic states, an increase in heart rate is an important factor in making the heart a more effective pump, but additional blood must also be provided for the heart to pump.

Effect of Right Atrial Pressure on the Output of the Heart. Within normal physiological limits, increasing the right atrial pressure increases the amount of blood that flows from the right atrium to the right ventricle and consequently also increases the amount of blood pumped by the heart. If the right atrial pressure falls to less than the intrathoracic pressure, no blood at all will flow into the right ventricle, and, however much contractile strength the heart might have, there will still be no cardiac output.

On the other hand, when the right atrial pressure rises to very high values, the right ventricle eventually becomes filled to its "physiological limit" during each diastolic filling period so that still further increase in right atrial pressure will not further enhance the output of the heart. Indeed, under some conditions further increase in right atrial pressure so overstretches the myocardium that the heart becomes weakened and the cardiac output decreases rather than increases. This overstretching effect does not occur in the normal heart within usual physiological ranges of right atrial pressure, but in the heart greatly weakened by myocardial damage it does very often occur.

Graph Depicting the Effects of the Above Factors on Cardiac Output—Family of Cardiac Output Curves

In the above discussion it was noted that sympathetic stimulation, cardiac hypertrophy, increased heart rate, and several other factors can all enhance the pumping capability of the heart, while myocardial damage, vagal stimulation, diminished sympathetic activity, and several other factors can all diminish the effectiveness of the heart as a pump. The effects of all these different factors on cardiac output can be expressed on the same graph as shown in Figure 335, the different curves representing (1) the normal unstimulated heart, (2) the strengthened heart, (3) the greatly strengthened heart, (4) the weakened heart, and (5) the greatly weakened heart. It can be seen from the figure that the output of the heart, whether the heart be normal, weakened, or strengthened, is still highly dependent on the right atrial pressure.

The curves of Figure 335 are called a *family of cardiac output curves.* To predict the cardiac output from these curves one selects the appropriate curve for the state of the heart—that is, normal, strengthened or weakened and how much so. Then he determines the right atrial pressure to ascertain the exact point on the curve at which the heart will momentarily be operating. For instance, if the heart is moderately weakened and the right atrial pressure is 6 mm. Hg, the cardiac output depicted by this curve at 6 mm. Hg right atrial pressure will be 6.7 liters per minute. As another ex-

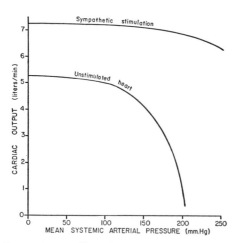

Figure 334. Effect of increasing the systemic arterial pressure on the cardiac output, both in the unstimulated heart and in the heart whose contractile power has been enhanced by sympathetic stimulation.

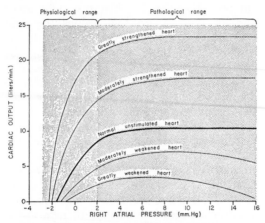

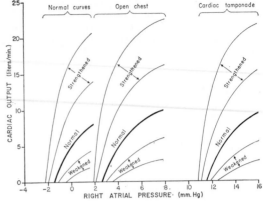

Figure 335. Effect of right atrial pressure on cardiac output in the normal heart and in hearts that have been strengthened or weakened. This graph illustrates a *family of cardiac output curves.*

Figure 336. Effect of opening the chest and of cardiac tamponade on the family of cardiac output curves, showing a shift of the curves to the right in proportion to the increase in pressure outside the heart.

ample, if the heart is greatly strengthened and the right atrial pressure is 2 mm. Hg, the cardiac output will be 20.6 liters per minute.

The different factors that can "strengthen" the heart (that is, can increase its pumping ability) are worth repeating: (1) sympathetic stimulation, (2) hypertrophy of the heart, (3) increased heart rate, (4) diminished vagal stimulation, (5) increased body temperature up to certain limits, as discussed in Chapter 21, and (6) various hormones or nutritive factors that might excite the cardiac musculature.

The factors that can decrease the pumping effectiveness of the heart are: (1) myocardial damage, (2) structural abnormalities of the heart, (3) vagal stimulation, (4) diminished sympathetic stimulation, (5) diminished nutritive factors to the heart, (6) diminished stimulatory hormones, and (7) increased load on the heart.

Effect of Opening the Chest or of Cardiac Tamponade on Cardiac Pumping. The normal intrathoracic pressure averages about −4 mm. Hg in relation to the atmospheric pressure. Therefore, opening the chest, which exposes the heart to the atmospheric pressure, immediately raises the pressure on the outside of the heart by 4 mm. Hg. For the heart to fill adequately now, the right atrial pressure must also rise approximately 4 mm. Hg. This effect is illustrated in Figure 336, which shows, first, the normal cardiac output curves for all degrees of cardiac capabilities and, second, a similar set of curves shifted to

the right for the person whose chest has been opened. The two sets of curves are identical except that the right atrial pressures must now be 4 mm. Hg greater in each instance.

Cardiac tamponade means increased pressures around the heart because of pericardial constriction or increased fluid in the pericardium. Figure 336 also shows a third set of curves that depict the effects of cardiac tamponade on cardiac output when the fluid pressure around the heart is approximately 9 mm. Hg—some 13 mm. Hg greater than the normal intrathoracic pressure. As a result, the right atrial pressure in each instance must be 13 mm. Hg greater than normal for maintenance of normal operation of the heart.

Unfortunately, either when the chest is opened or in the case of cardiac tamponade the right atrial pressures usually do not become enhanced sufficiently to maintain normal filling of the heart, and for this reason the heart fails to pump adequate quantities of blood—not because the capability of the heart as a pump has changed but because sufficient venous pressure is not available to overcome the pressures around the heart and therefore to fill the ventricles adequately.

VENOUS RETURN AND ITS RELATIONSHIP TO RIGHT ATRIAL PRESSURE

Venous return is the rate of blood flow into the right atrium from the systemic circulation. In the discussion above it was very evident that right atrial pressure is one of the most important of all of the factors that determine the pumping ability of the heart. If the venous return is very great, the right atrial pressure will tend to rise, and this in turn will cause the heart to pump greatly increased quantities of blood. On the other hand, if the venous return is very slight, the right atrial pressure will fall, causing the heart to pump diminished amounts of blood. Therefore, it is very important for us now to consider the different factors that affect venous return. The three most important are (1) right atrial pressure, (2) mean circulatory pressure, and (3) resistance to blood flow through the systemic vessels.

Effect of Right Atrial Pressure on Venous Return—the Normal Venous Return Curve. Though increased venous return can increase the right atrial pressure, it is equally true that increasing the right atrial pressure can act in the reverse direction to decrease venous return. This seems to be a paradox at first, but on second thought it is obvious that the higher the right atrial pressure the greater becomes the back pressure on the veins, which automatically opposes the flow of blood toward the heart and thereby decreases the venous return.

Figure 337 illustrates the effects of different right atrial pressures on venous return when the circulatory reflexes have been completely blocked. This figure shows that the normal right atrial pressure is approximately 0 mm. Hg in relation to the atmospheric pressure. At this level the venous return is 5 liters per minute under basal conditions. Then, as the right atrial pressure is progressively increased, the venous return progressively decreases until it reaches zero at a right atrial pressure of approximately 7 mm. Hg. On the other hand, when the right atrial pressure is decreased well below

normal, the venous return reaches a "plateau" and will not rise any further. The reason for this is that the atmospheric pressure pressing against the outside of the body can act through the tissues to compress the veins if ever the venous pressure falls to negative values. The resultant "collapse" of the veins prevents the negative pressures in the right atrium from "sucking" blood toward the heart. After the right atrial pressure falls beyond approximately —2 mm. Hg, any further decrease in right atrial pressure does not cause additional increase in venous return, which is also illustrated in Figure 337.

The complete curve of Figure 337 is called the *normal venous return curve*, which shows a progressive decrease in venous return as the right atrial pressure rises above —2 mm. Hg and a plateau in venous return at all negative values of right atrial pressure below approximately —2 mm. Hg. The significance of this curve is the following: If the heart becomes so weakened that it fails to pump adequate quantities of blood out of the right atrium and thereby allows the right atrial pressure to rise, then the venous return to the heart diminishes. On the other hand, if the heart is strengthened in any one of the ways discussed above, more and more blood will be pumped from the right atrium, the right atrial pressure will fall, and the venous return will increase. However, *the maximum limit to which the venous return can increase is the level of the plateau on the venous return curve.* This, therefore, often limits the amount of blood that the heart can pump.

Effect of Mean Circulatory Pressure on Venous Return. The *mean circulatory pressure*, which was discussed in Chapter 26, is the pressure in the entire circulatory system that would be measured if the heart could be stopped suddenly and all pressures everywhere could be brought instantaneously to equilibrium. The normal mean circulatory pressure of a dog is about 7 mm. Hg. Though this has never been measured in the human being, there is reason to believe that it is probably very nearly the same as in the dog.

Referring once more to Figure 337, it will be noted that *the venous return is directly proportional to the* difference *between the mean circulatory pressure and the right atrial pressure.* When the right atrial pressure rises

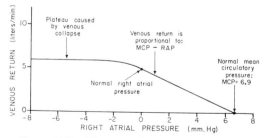

Figure 337. The normal venous return curve.

to equal the mean circulatory pressure—that is, when it has risen to 7 mm. Hg—venous return becomes zero because all the pressures everywhere in the circulatory system then will have become equal so that no pressure gradient is available to force blood from the systemic vessels back to the heart. However, when the right atrial pressure is reduced to 6 mm. Hg, which is 1 mm. less than the mean circulatory pressure, then the venous return will have risen to approximately 700 ml. per minute. When the right atrial pressure has fallen to 5 mm. Hg, 2 mm. Hg below the mean circulatory pressure, the return will be about 1400 ml. per minute, and finally when the right atrial pressure has fallen to its normal value of zero, which is about 7 mm. Hg less than the mean circulatory pressure, the return will be 5 liters per minute.

Effect of altering the mean circulatory pressure. Figure 338 illustrates the effect on the venous return curve of altering the mean circulatory pressure. Note that a fall of mean circulatory pressure reduces the venous return at each right atrial pressure level while an increase of mean circulatory pressure increases the venous return. Therefore, it is evident that the following relationship still holds true: Even when the mean circulatory pressure changes, *the venous return remains approximately proportional to the mean circulatory pressure minus the right atrial pressure.*

The mean circulatory pressure as the upper limit of right atrial pressure. Note especially in both Figure 337 and Figure 338 that, as the right atrial pressure rises, the venous return always decreases and becomes zero when the right atrial pressure equals the mean circulatory pressure. *Therefore, the upper limit to which the right atrial pressure can rise is equal to the mean circulatory pressure, for venous return cannot fall below zero.*

Factors that alter the mean circulatory pressure. The different factors that can increase the mean circulatory pressure were discussed in Chapter 26. The two most important of these are (1) an increase in *blood volume* and (2) an increase in *vasomotor tone.* Either of these can greatly affect venous return to the heart.

It is often stated that the degree of "venous tone" is one of the major factors affect-

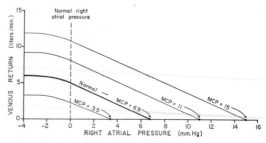

Figure 338. Effect on the venous return curve of altering the mean circulatory pressure.

ing venous return to the heart. To be more exact, all the blood vessels of the circulatory system should be considered in making this statement, and we should say that an increase in "vasomotor tone" increases venous return because an increase in tone in any segment of the circulation, whether it be the veins or the arteries, will tend to increase the pressure in that segment of the circulation and to force its blood that much more rapidly toward the right atrium. Yet, since about 19/20 of the alterations in mean circulatory pressure result from alterations in venous tone, it is reasonable to state that venous tone is one of the main determinants of venous return.

Effect of Vascular Resistance on Venous Return. Obviously, the greater the resistance in the systemic vessels the more difficult will it be for blood to flow from these vessels to the heart and consequently the less will be the venous return. Conversely, the less the resistance the greater will the venous return be.

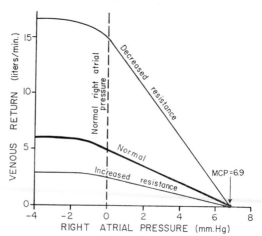

Figure 339. Effect on the venous return curve of altering the systemic resistance.

The three curves of Figure 339 illustrate the effects on the venous return curves of changing the systemic resistance. In all of these curves venous return still becomes zero when the right atrial pressure rises to equal the mean circulatory pressure, but at all other right atrial pressures the return is increased by decreased resistance and decreased by increased resistance.

Relative Effect of Venous Resistance versus Arterial Resistance on Venous Return. Since most of the blood attempting to return to the heart from the systemic circulation is in the veins rather than in the arteries, the resistance from the veins to the heart has much more effect on venous return than does arterial and capillary resistance. A more precise explanation of this effect is the following: When the outflow resistance of the major veins leading to the heart is increased, the blood becomes dammed up principally in the veins, which have a tremendous "capacitance." And, even though large amounts of blood collect in the veins, the venous pressure does not rise more than a few mm. Hg; this small increase in pressure can hardly overcome the increased resistance. On the other hand, when one increases the resistance from the arteries to the veins, the blood becomes dammed up in the arterial tree. The arteries, in contradistinction to the veins, have very little capacitance so that storage of blood in the arteries causes the arterial pressure to rise sometimes a hundred or more mm. Hg. Within physiological limits, this almost completely overcomes the extra applied resistance, allowing blood to flow almost normally on through the resistance and back to the right atrium. Experiments in our laboratory have shown that an increase in venous resistance reduces the venous return eight times as much as a similar increase in arteriolar resistance.

Mathematical Analysis of Venous Return

A very simple formula for venous return is the following:

$$\text{Venous return} = \frac{\text{Arterial pressure} - \text{Right atrial pressure}}{\text{Total peripheral resistance}}$$

(1)

Though this is the best known formula for venous return it is not of much value for predicting the effect of changing arterial pressure, right atrial pressure, or total peripheral resistance on venous return, because all the variables in the right side of the formula are "dependent variables." That is, when one of them changes, the other two are likely to change as well. Therefore, it is impossible to predict the effect on venous return of changing any one of the three factors.

In searching for a formula that could be used to predict the effect of right atrial pressure, blood volume, vasomotor tone, and vascular resistance on venous return we have found in our laboratory, both by mathematical analysis of the circulation and by experimentation, that the following simple relationship can be used with a high degree of accuracy:

$$\text{Venous return} \approx \frac{\text{Mean circulatory pressure} - \text{Right atrial pressure}}{8 \ (\text{Venous resistance}) + \text{Arterial resistance}}$$

(2)

In the numerator mean circulatory pressure minus right atrial pressure is called the *pressure gradient for venous return* while the denominator is called the *resistance to venous return*; that is:

$$\text{Venous return} \approx \frac{\text{Pressure gradient for venous return}}{\text{Resistance to venous return}}$$

(3)

This formula simply means that the rate of venous return is directly proportional to the difference between mean circulatory pressure and right atrial pressure and is inversely proportional to the resistances in the systemic circulation. Furthermore, the formula demonstrates that the outflow resistance from the veins is far more important in determining the venous return than is the resistance from the arteries to the veins. The real importance of Formula 2 lies in the fact that the factors in this formula that affect venous return are *independent variables*. That is, they do not affect each other significantly so that one can predict accurately the effect on venous return of changing any one of these. This is in contradistinction to Formula 1 (above).

Still another formula that has a great deal of usefulness in theoretical discussions of venous return is the following:

$$\text{Venous return} = \frac{\text{Mean capillary pressure} - \text{Right atrial pressure}}{\text{Venous resistance}}$$

(4)

Here again all the factors on the right hand side of the equation are relatively independent of each other. This formula shows that any factor that tends to increase capillary pressure, such as increased tissue pressure caused by edema in cardiac failure, will tend to increase the rate of venous return to the heart. It also shows that if the capillary pressure rises in cardiac failure concurrently with a rise in right atrial pressure, the two can nullify each other and thereby keep the venous return almost normal, which is a very common finding in cardiac failure. Even more important, this formula illustrates once again the extreme importance of venous resistance in regulating venous return in contradistinction to the almost insignificant effect of arterial resistance in most instances.

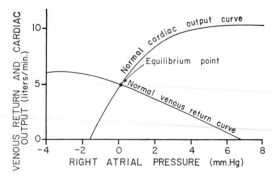

Figure 340.   Equilibration of venous return with cardiac output.

EQUALITY OF VENOUS RETURN AND CARDIAC OUTPUT

In the above sections we have discussed separately those factors that affect, first, the ability of the heart to pump blood, and, second, the tendency for blood to return to the heart. But we must return to the fact that, except for a few seconds at a time when blood is actually being accumulated or lost from the lungs or heart, venous return must equal cardiac output.

A *common factor* that affects both the pumping ability of the heart and the ability of the blood to return to the heart is the *right atrial pressure*. A rise in right atrial pressure causes increased quantities of blood to be pumped by the heart. But an increase in right atrial pressure also decreases the venous return. These effects can be seen readily in Figure 340, which shows the normal cardiac output curve contrasted with the normal venous return curve plotted on the same coordinates. If the right atrial pressure should suddenly rise very high, the cardiac output would be greater than the venous return. As a result, more blood would be pumped out of the right atrium than would be flowing in. Therefore, the right atrial pressure would fall until the cardiac output equals venous return. Experimental studies have shown that complete equilibrium occurs within about six beats of the heart, or in about 4 to 5 seconds. If the right atrial pressure falls low, then the venous return will become greater than the cardiac output, and blood will accumulate in the right

atrium until the right atrial pressure returns to a value at which cardiac output equals venous return once again. This also requires only a few beats of the heart.

Thus, one can see that venous return and cardiac output automatically adjust to equal each other. For a few seconds at a time, such as when the heart is suddenly stimulated by nerves or when a deep breath reduces the venous return to the heart, the two may be out of equilibrium, but this automatic adjustment goes on continuously, the right atrial pressure shifting up or down while maintaining equilibrium between cardiac output and venous return. This state of equilibrium is illustrated in Figure 340 by the "equilibrium point," which is the point at which the venous return curve crosses the cardiac output curve.

ANALYSIS OF CHANGES IN CARDIAC OUTPUT IN DIFFERENT PHYSIOLOGICAL STATES

Whenever one attempts to analyze the effect of some physiological or pathological change on cardiac output, he must consider the effect that the change will have both on the ability of the heart to pump and also on the venous return. Then, finally, he must evaluate these together to find out what the final effect will be on cardiac output. The succeeding sections of this chapter will analyze separately the effects of some common physiological and pathological conditions on cardiac output. Then, in the next two chapters the effects on cardiac output of the different stages of cardiac failure and shock will be analyzed.

Effect of Sympathetic Stimulation on Cardiac Output

Sympathetic stimulation strengthens the heart, thereby increasing its ability to pump blood. Also, sympathetic stimulation increases the tendency for venous return. The effects of moderate and maximum sympathetic stimulation on the pumping ability of the heart are depicted by the cardiac output curves of Figure 341, showing *great enhancement of the pumping ability of the heart* when it is stimulated by the sympathetics.

The effects of sympathetic stimulation on venous return is also illustrated in Figure 341. The principal effect is an *increase in mean circulatory pressure,* which causes an overall enhancement of venous return. However, sympathetic stimulation sometimes also slightly increases the "resistance to venous return" and, therefore, decreases the slope of the venous return curve a mild amount.

Now to analyze the effects of moderate and maximum sympathetic stimulation on cardiac output. Point A depicts the normal cardiac output and normal right atrial pressure, for this is the equilibrium point between the normal cardiac output curve and the normal venous return curve. Under moderate sympathetic stimulation the two new curves are both elevated, and their equilibrium point is point B, showing that the cardiac output will have increased a small amount and the right atrial pressure will have actually decreased. Finally, with maximum sympathetic stimulation both these curves are again elevated, and the cardiac output will have risen still more, while the right atrial pressure is now −1½ mm. Hg, rather than the normal 0 mm. Hg.

Effect of Exercise on Cardiac Output

Two factors in exercise have profound effects on cardiac output. First, during exercise *the sympathetic nervous system is greatly stimulated* so that all the same effects as those discussed in the above section also occur in exercise. Second, *the resistance to blood flow through the exercising muscles decreases greatly,* thereby markedly reducing the "resistance to venous return," and this greatly increases the slope of the venous return curve, as shown in Figure 342.

In analyzing the effect of exercise on cardiac output, we find that moderate exercise increases the cardiac output curve moderately, that it shifts the venous return curve to the right because of an increased mean circulatory pressure resulting from sympathetic stimulation, and that it causes the slope of the venous return curve to increase because of decreased "resistance to venous return." The net result is a change in cardiac output from point A to point B, about doubling the output, while the right atrial pressure remains approximately constant.

In severe exercise, the heart is stimulated

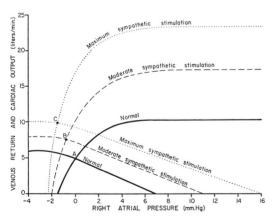

Figure 341. Effect of moderate and maximum sympathetic stimulation on cardiac output and right atrial pressure.

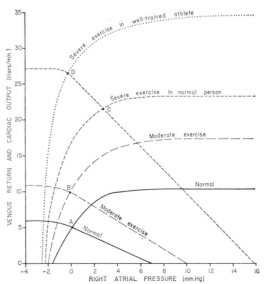

Figure 342. Effect of moderate and severe exercise on cardiac output and right atrial pressure, showing also the effect of athletic training.

by the sympathetics even more, the cardiac output curve rises to its maximum, and the venous return curve shifts still farther to the right because of an increased mean circulatory pressure while sloping upward rather markedly because of decreased resistance. The net result is a new equilibrium at point C with a cardiac output of slightly over 21 liters per minute and a right atrial pressure which has now risen to about 3 mm. Hg above normal. This is approximately the maximum effect that can be observed in the young but athletically untrained male adult.

Effect of Athletic Training on Adjustments in Cardiac Output

Athletic training strengthens the heart, thereby increasing its pumping capability. Part of this results from actual hypertrophy of the heart muscle itself and part from an increase in efficiency of the muscle because of deposition of increased amounts of glycogen, proteins, and other constituents. The dotted curve of Figure 342 illustrates this increased response of the heart in the well-trained athlete, showing the new equilibrium point D. Thus, in the well-trained athlete the cardiac output can sometimes rise to as high as 25 to 30 liters per minute with still a completely normal right atrial pressure.

Effect of Massive Transfusion on Cardiac Output

Figure 343 illustrates the immediate effect of transfusion of large quantities of blood into a person. The effect on the venous return curve is the following: First, because of the increased blood volume, the *mean circulatory pressure rises* to a very high value, shifting the entire curve to the right. Second, because of distention of the blood vessels, the *"resistance to venous return" decreases,* causing the slope of the venous return curve to become steeper than normal.

The effect on the cardiac output curve is to *reduce the strength of the heart* because of reflexes caused by excess pressures in the arteries and other central vessels of the chest.

The net result is a change in equilibrium from point A to point B with a considerably increased cardiac output and a rise in right atrial pressure to as high as 5 to 10 mm.

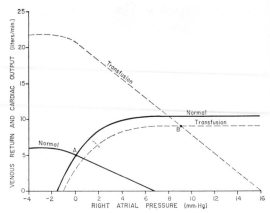

Figure 343.   Effect of massive transfusion on cardiac output.

Hg. However, this state does not last more than a few minutes because of (a) progressive "stress-relaxation" of the vascular system so that it can accommodate more blood than usual and (b) leakage of fluid from the blood vessels into the interstitial spaces, which was discussed in Chapter 34, Regulation of Blood Volume.

Effect of Fever on Cardiac Output

Figure 344 illustrates the effect of fever on cardiac output. First, the cardiac output curve may be enhanced or decreased, depending on the cause of the fever. If the cause is some disease that is not cardiotoxic, then the rise in temperature may actually increase the capability of the heart to pump blood, at least for temporary periods of time. On the other hand, if the fever is caused by some infectious disease, this more than likely will have a toxic effect on the heart to decrease its capability as a pump.

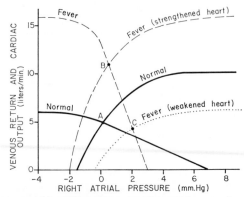

Figure 344.   Effect of non-cardiotoxic fever and cardiotoxic fever on cardiac output.

The principal effect of fever on venous return is to decrease vasomotor tone throughout the body, thus reducing the mean circulatory pressure and shifting the venous return curve to the left. However, the vasodilatation also reduces systemic vascular resistance and thereby increases the slope of the curve.

In the case of non-cardiotoxic fever the net result is a change in the equilibrium from point A to point B. Thus, the cardiac output may actually increase to as great as double normal while the right atrial pressure remains almost normal. In the case of the cardiotoxic fever the equilibrium point would shift from point A to point C with a decrease in cardiac output but an increase in right atrial pressure.

Effect of Opening the Chest and of Cardiac Tamponade on Cardiac Output

Figure 345 illustrates the effect of opening the chest on the cardiac output curve and the venous return curve. Immediately after opening the chest, the cardiac output curve shifts to the right, as shown by the dotted curve. This is caused by loss of the normal negative intrathoracic pressure around the heart, as discussed earlier in the chapter. On the other hand, there is no immediate effect on the venous return curve. Therefore, the equilibrium point shifts immediately from A to B, showing a rise in right atrial pressure of about 3 mm. Hg and a fall in cardiac output to about one half normal. However, within 15 to 30 seconds the sympathetic nervous system becomes active, increasing both the cardiac output curve and the venous return curve, so that the equilibrium shifts to point C with the

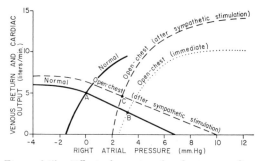

Figure 345. Effect of opening the chest on cardiac output and right atrial pressure.

cardiac output almost returned to normal but a right atrial pressure elevated to about 3 mm. Hg. Under deep anesthesia the sympathetic reflexes may be almost blocked. In this case, the secondary reaction does not occur appreciably, and, obviously, the cardiac output suffers greatly from the opened chest without the benefit of this reflex compensation.

In cardiac tamponade exactly the same effects result except that all levels of pressure on the outside of the heart can occur. Sometimes the pericardial pressure rises to as high as 20 mm. Hg. When this occurs suddenly, the venous return curve cannot increase rapidly enough to maintain life. However, if it occurs gradually, fluid and reflex readjustments in the circulation can increase the mean circulatory pressure to a value high enough that venous return can still be maintained and thereby keep the person alive. The maximum intrapericardial pressure that can be overcome, and this only for short periods of time, is about 20 to 30 mm. Hg.

Effect of Ateriovenous Fistula on Cardiac Output

The primary effect of an arteriovenous fistula is to greatly reduce the systemic vascular resistance. The sequence of events that occur following the opening of an A-V fistula is illustrated in Figure 346. Immediately upon opening a very large fistula, the decreased resistance causes the slope of the venous return curve to rise markedly. This causes the cardiac output to rise to about 9 liters per minute, as depicted by point B. However, since the A-V fistula is extremely large, even this increase in cardiac output is not sufficient to supply all the blood required to go through the fistula plus that required for the tissues and organs. Yet, the arterial pressure falls, eliciting cardiovascular reflexes. These reflexes cause the mean circulatory pressure to increase, shifting the venous return curve to the right; they also cause the strength of the heart to increase. These two changes result in a new equilibrium at point C with a cardiac output of about 14 liters. Even this is not sufficient to supply all the tissues with adequate blood flow. Renal retention of fluid and increased blood volume cause the mean circulatory

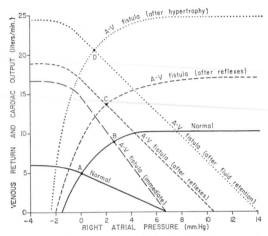

Figure 346. Effect of opening a very large arteriovenous fistula on cardiac output (a) immediately after opening, (b) after autonomic reflexes have occurred, and (c) several weeks later.

pressure to rise still more, shifting the venous return curve still farther to the right. The continual load on the heart causes the cardiac musculature to hypertrophy, shifting the cardiac output curve upward. A number of weeks after opening the fistula, therefore, the equilibrium point rises to point D with a greatly enhanced cardiac output, about three quarters of the blood flowing through the fistula and one quarter through the organs and tissues. Yet, the right atrial pressure is still well within normal limits.

Summary

This chapter has been written with one major concept in mind: The cardiac output is regulated by two separate groups of factors: first, those that affect the ability of the heart itself to pump blood and, second, those that affect the flow of blood from the systemic vessels to the heart. These factors can be separated from each other and expressed respectively in terms of cardiac output and venous return curves. Then the two curves can be graphically equated with each other to analyze the overall effect on cardiac output. Most important of all, the student must never make the error of thinking that he can predict changes in cardiac output on the basis of cardiac effects alone or on peripheral effects alone. Very rarely do conditions change in the heart without simultaneous changes occurring in the peripheral circu-

latory system, and, conversely, very rarely do changes occur in the peripheral circulation without changes in the pumping ability of the heart occurring at the same time.

REFERENCES

Asmussen, E., and Nielsen, M.: Cardiac output during muscular work and its regulation. *Physiol. Rev.,* 35:778, 1955.

Barcroft, H., and Starr, I.: Comparison of the actions of adrenaline and noradrenaline on the cardiac output in man. *Clin. Sc. (London),* 10:295, 1951.

Barger, A. C., Richards, V., Metcalfe, J., and Gunther, B.: Regulation of the circulation during exercise; cardiac output (direct Fick) and metabolic adjustments in the normal dog. *Am. J. Physiol.,* 184:613, 1956.

Braunstein, J. B.: The Ballistocardiogram. Springfield, Illinois, Charles C Thomas, 1953.

Brecher, G. A.: Cardiac variations in venous return studied with a new bristle flowmeter. *Am. J. Physiol.,* 176:423, 1954.

Brecher, G. A.: Venous Return. New York, Grune & Stratton, Inc., 1956.

Brecher, G. A., and Kissen, A. T.: Relation of negative intraventricular pressure to ventricular volume. *Circ. Res.,* 5:157, 1957.

Brecher, G. A., Mixter, G., Jr., and Share, L.: Dynamics of venous collapse in superior vena cava system. *Am. J. Physiol.,* 171:194, 1952.

Buckley, N. M., Ogden, E., and Linton, D. S., Jr.: The effects of work load and heart rate on filling of the isolated right ventricle of the dog heart. *Circ. Res.,* 3:434, 1955.

Buckley, N. M., Sidky, M., and Ogden, E.: Factors altering the filling of the isolated left ventricle of the dog heart; effects of epinephrine and norepinephrine. *Circ. Res.,* 4:148, 1956.

Dow, B.: Dimensional relationships in dye-dilution curves from humans and dogs, with an empirical formula for certain troublesome curves. *J. Appl. Physiol.,* 7:399, 1955.

Dow, B.: Estimations of cardiac output and central blood volume by dye dilution. *Physiol. Rev.,* 36:77, 1956.

Fell, S. C., McIntosh, H. D., Hornsby, A. T., Horton, C. E., Warren, J. V., and Pickrell, K.: The syndrome of the chronic leg ulcer; the phlebodynamics of the lower extremity; physiology of the venous valves. *Surgery,* 38:771, 1955.

Ferguson, T. B., Gregg, D. E., and Shadle, O. W.: Effect of blood and saline infusion on cardiac performance in normal dogs and dogs with arteriovenous fistulas. *Circ. Res.,* 2:565, 1954.

Gerst, P. H., Taylor, C., and Peterson, L. H.: Indicator recirculation as a limiting factor of indicator dilution techniques. *Am. J. Physiol.,* 189:191, 1957.

Guyton, A. C.: Determination of cardiac output by equating venous return curves with cardiac response curves *Physiol. Rev.,* 35:123, 1955.

Guyton, A. C.: Factors which determine the rate of venous return to the heart. World Trends in Cardiology. Paul B. Hoeber, New York, 1956, p. 32.

Guyton, A. C.: La circulation veineuse. Symposia

from the IIIrd World Congress of Cardiology, 1958, p. 109.

Guyton, A. C., Abernathy, B., Langston, J. B., Kaufmann, B. N., and Fairchild, H. M.: Relative importance of venous and arterial resistance in controlling venous return and cardiac output. *Am. J. Physiol.*, 196:1008, 1959.

Guyton, A. C., and Adkins, L.: Quantitative aspects of the collapse factor in relation to venous return. *Am. J. Physiol.*, 177:523, 1954.

Guyton, A. C., Farish, C. A., and Abernathy, J. B.: A continuous cardiac output recorder employing the Fick principle. *Circ. Res.*, 7:661, 1959.

Guyton, A. C., Farish, C. A., and Williams, J. W.: An improved arteriovenous oxygen difference recorder. *J. Appl. Physiol.*, 14:145, 1959.

Guyton, A. C., Lindsey, A. W., Abernathy, J. B., and Langston, J. B.: Mechanism of the increased venous return and cardiac output caused by epinephrine. *Am. J. Physiol.*, 192:126, 1958.

Guyton, A. C., Lindsey, A. W., Abernathy, J. B., and Richardson, T. Q.: Venous return at various right atrial pressures and the normal venous return curve. *Am. J. Physiol.*, 189:609, 1957.

Guyton, A. C., Lindsey, A. W., and Kaufmann, B. N.: Effect of mean circulatory filling pressure and other peripheral circulatory factors on cardiac output. *Am. J. Physiol.*, 180:463, 1955.

Guyton, A. C., Lindsey, A. W., Kaufmann, B. N., and Abernathy, J. B.: Effect of blood transfusion and hemorrhage on cardiac output and venous return. *Am. J. Physiol.*, 194:263, 1958.

Guyton, A. C., Nichols, R. J., and Farish, C. A.: An arteriovenous oxygen difference recorder. *J. Appl. Physiol.*, 10:158, 1957.

Guyton, A. C., Satterfield, J. H., and Harris, J. W.: Dynamics of central venous resistance with observations on static blood pressure, *Am. J. Physiol.*, 169:691, 1952.

Hamilton, W. F.: Cardiac output; in Glasser, O. (ed.): Medical Physics. Chicago, Year Book Publishers, 1944.

Howell, C. D., Horvath, S. M. and Farrand, E. A.: Evaluation of variability in the cardiac output of dogs. *Am. J. Physiol.*, 196:193, 1959.

Hubay, C. A., Waltz, R. C., Brecher, G. A., Praglin, J., and Hingson, R. A.: Circulatory dynamics of venous return during positive-negative pressure respiration. *Anesthesiology*, 15:445, 1954.

Kaufman, W. C., and Marbarger, J. P.: Pressure breathing: functional circulatory changes in the dog. *J. Appl. Physiol.*, 9:33, 1956.

Kilburn, K. H., and Sieker, H. O.: Hemodynamic effects of continuous positive and negative pressure breathing in normal man. *Circ. Res.*, 8:660, 1960.

Lawson, H. C., Shadle, O. W., Coleman, E. S., and Holtgrave, D. E.: A comparison of intracardiac and intravenous injections for the measurement of cardiac output by the dilution technic. *Circ. Res.*, 2:251, 1954.

Morgan, W. L., Jr., Binion, J. T., and Sarnoff, S. J.: Circulatory depression induced by high levels of positive pressure breathing counteracted by metaraminol (aramine). *J. Appl. Physiol.*, 10:26, 1957.

Nickerson, J. L., and Mathers, J. A.: A study of the physical properties of the ballistocardiograph. *Am. Heart J.*, 47:1, 1954.

Otis, A. B., Rahn, H., and Fenn, W. O.: Venous pressure changes associated with positive intrapulmonary pressures: their relationship to distensibility of lung. *Am. J. Physiol.*, 146:307, 1946.

Remington, J. W., Hamilton, W. F., Wheeler, N. C., and Hamilton, W. F., Jr.: Validity of pulse contour method for calculating cardiac output of dog, with notes on effect of various anesthetics. *Am. J. Physiol.*, 159:379, 1949.

Richardson, T. Q., and Guyton, A. C.: Effects of polycythemia and anemia on cardiac output and other circulatory factors. *Am. J. Physiol.*, 197:1167, 1959.

Sheppard, C. W., Jones, P., and Couch, B. L.: Effect of catheter sampling on the shape of indicator-dilution curves: mean concentration versus mean flux of outflowing dye. *Circ. Res.*, 7:895, 1959.

Sjöstrand, T.: Volume and distribution of blood and their significance in regulating circulation. *Physiol. Rev.*, 33:202, 1953.

Starr, I.: Role of the "static blood pressure" in abnormal increments of venous pressure especially in heart failure. II. Clinical and experimental studies. *Am. J. M. Sc.*, 199:40, 1940.

Starr, I., and Rawson, A. J.: Role of the "static blood pressure" in abdominal increments of venous pressure, especially in heart failure: I. Theoretical studies on improved circulation schema whose pumps obey Starling's law of the heart. *Am. J. M. Sc.*, 199:27, 1940.

Swan, H. J., and Wood, E. H.: A method for the continuous determination of total systemic blood flow in the dog by an indicator-dilution technique. *J. Physiol.*, 133:44P, 1956,

Weissler, A. M., Warren, J. V., Estes, E. H., Jr., McIntosh, H. D., and Leonard, J. J.: Vasodepressor syncope; factors influencing cardiac output. *Circulation*, 15:875, 1957.

Wiedeman, M. P.: Response of Subcutaneous Vessels to Venous Distention. *Circ. Res.*, 7:238, 1959.

Wood, E. H., Bowers, D., Shepherd, J. T., and Fox, I. J.: O_2 content of mixed venous blood in man during various phases of the respiratory and cardiac cycles in relation to possible errors in measurement of cardiac output by conventional application of the Fick method. *J. Appl. Physiol.*, 7:621, 1955.

Visscher, M. B., and Johnson, J. A.: The Fick principle: analysis of potential errors in its conventional application. *J. Appl. Physiol.*, 5:635, 1953.

See also Chapter 25, The heart as a pump; Chapter 28, Venous dynamics; Chapter 36, Cardiac failure; Chapter 37, Shock; Chapter 38, General bibliography for the cardiovascular system.

Cardiac Failure

Perhaps the most important ailment that must be treated by the physician is cardiac failure, which can result from any heart condition that reduces the capability of the heart to pump blood. Usually the cause is decreased contractility of the myocardium itself caused by coronary disease, but failure of the heart to pump adequate quantities of blood can also be caused by damage to the heart valves, external pressure around the heart, vitamin deficiency, or any other abnormality that makes the heart an ineffective pump.

Definition of Cardiac Failure. The term cardiac failure means simply failure of the heart to pump blood adequately. This does not mean that the cardiac output in all instances of failure is less than normal, for the output can be normal or sometimes above normal provided the tendency for venous return is high enough to offset the diminished strength of the heart. Therefore, cardiac failure may be manifest in either of two ways: (1) by a decrease in cardiac output or (2) by an increase in either left or right atrial pressure even though the cardiac output is normal or above normal.

A physiological definition of cardiac failure. Since the pumping ability of the heart can be expressed best by a cardiac output curve, perhaps the best physiological definition of cardiac failure is *diminished pumping ability of the heart as represented by a lowered cardiac output curve.* Figure 347 illustrates the normal cardiac output curve and two abnormal cardiac output curves, representing moderate and severe cardiac failure. Such curves will be used throughout this chapter to depict the failing heart.

Unilateral versus Bilateral Cardiac Failure. Most frequently, cardiac failure is caused by decreased pumping ability of both

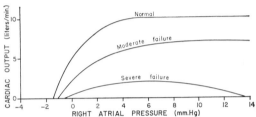

Figure 347. Cardiac output curves of the normal heart, the moderately failing heart, and the severely failing heart.

sides of the heart at the same time. However, since the left and right sides of the heart are actually two separate pumping systems, it is possible for one of these to fail independently of the other. For instance, unilateral failure can result from coronary thrombosis in one or the other of the ventricles. Because debilitating thrombosis occurs approximately 30 times as often in the left ventricle as in the right ventricle, there is a tendency among clinicians to view failure following myocardial infection as almost always primarily left-sided. Occasionally, however, right-sided failure does occur with no left-sided failure at all; this happens most frequently in patients with pulmonary stenosis or some other congenital disease affecting primarily the right heart.

Usually, though, when one side of the heart becomes weakened, this causes a sequence of events that makes the opposite side of the heart also fail. For instance, in left-sided failure the left atrial pressure increases greatly, resulting in considerable back pressure in the pulmonary system and a rise in pulmonary arterial pressure sometimes to two to three times normal. This loads the right ventricle, causing combined failure of both ventricles, even though the initiating cause was in the left side of heart only. On the other hand, primary damage to the right ventricle sometimes reduces the overall cardiac output, resulting in diminished coronary blood flow and at least a mild degree of left heart weakening.

In the first part of this chapter on cardiac failure we will consider the whole heart failing as a unit and then return to the specific features of unilateral left- and right-sided failure.

DYNAMICS OF THE CIRCULATION IN CARDIAC FAILURE

The dynamics of the circulation are not always the same in all types of cardiac failure nor in all stages of failure. Several reasons for this variability are (1) different degrees of damage to the heart itself, (2) autonomic reflexes that sometimes compensate for much of the failure, and (3) fluid retention by the kidneys which also may compensate to varying extents for the failure. In the following discussion we will consider the progressive changes in the circulation following acute cardiac failure, first, when the failure is moderately severe and, second, when it is almost lethal. (Note: *Before attempting to understand the analyses in this chapter, it is essential that the student become familiar with the graphical procedure presented in the previous chapter for equating venous return with cardiac output.*)

Dynamics of Moderate Cardiac Failure

Acute Effects. If a heart suddenly becomes severely damaged in any way, such as by myocardial infarction, the pumping ability of the heart is immediately depressed. As a result, two essential effects occur: (a) reduced cardiac output and (b) increased systemic venous pressure. These effects are shown graphically in Figure 348. This figure shows, first, a normal cardiac output curve and a normal venous return curve depicting the state of the circulation prior to the cardiac damage. The point at which these two curves cross, point A, represents the normal equilibrium state of the circulation, showing that the normal cardiac output under resting conditions is 5 liters per minute and the right atrial pressure essentially 0 mm. Hg.

Immediately after the heart becomes damaged, the cardiac output curve becomes greatly reduced, falling to the lower, dashed curve. Within the first few seconds after the damage nothing at all happens to the venous return curve, for the systemic circulation has not yet been altered. Therefore, within a few seconds after the acute heart attack, a new equilibrium is established at point B rather than point A, showing that the cardiac output has fallen to about two-fifths normal while the right atrial pressure has risen to 4 mm. Hg. This low cardiac output is still sufficient to sustain life, but it is certainly not sufficient to allow a person to stand or even to sit up without fainting. Fortunately, this acute stage lasts for only a few seconds because autonomic reflexes occur immediately that can compensate to a great extent for the damaged heart as follows:

Compensation for Acute Cardiac Failure by Autonomic Reflexes. When the cardiac output falls precariously low, many of the different circulatory reflexes discussed in Chapter 32 immediately become active. The best known of these reflexes is the pressoreceptor reflex, which is activated by diminished arterial pressure. It is probable that the CNS ischemic reflex and possibly even reflexes originating in the damaged heart itself might also become activated. Whatever all the reflexes might be, the sympathetics become strongly stimulated within a few seconds, and the parasympathetics become reciprocally inhibited at the same time.

Strong sympathetic stimulation has two major effects on the circulation, first, on the heart itself, and, second, on the peripheral vasculature. Even a damaged myocardium usually responds with increased force of contraction following sympathetic stimulation. If all the musculature is diffusely damaged, sympathetic stimulation will usually

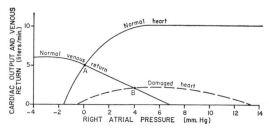

Figure 348. Immediate effect of acute myocardial damage on cardiac output and right atrial pressure.

strengthen this damaged musculature. Likewise, if part of the muscle is totally nonfunctional while part of it is still normal, the normal muscle is strongly stimulated by sympathetic stimulation, in this way compensating for the non-functional muscle. Thus, *the heart one way or another becomes a stronger pump, often as much as 100 per cent stronger, under the influence of the sympathetic impulses.*

Sympathetic stimulation also increases the tendency for venous return, for it increases the tone of most of the blood vessels of the circulation, *raising the mean circulatory pressure* to a very high value. As will be recalled from the discussion in the previous chapter, this greatly increases the tendency for blood to flow back to the heart. Therefore, the damaged heart becomes primed with more inflowing blood than usual, and, at least under certain circumstances, this increased priming helps the heart to pump larger quantities of blood.

The sympathetic reflexes become maximally developed in about 30 seconds to a minute, and the resulting increased ability of the heart and increased tendency for venous return add together to cause the cardiac output to become once again almost normal. As a result, the person who has a sudden moderate heart attack might experience nothing more than a few seconds of fainting. Shortly thereafter, with the aid of the autonomic compensation, his circulation may be completely adequate as long as he remains quiet.

Graphical representation of the effects of the autonomic reflexes. Two of the curves shown in Figure 348 are repeated in Figure 349, the normal venous return curve and the cardiac curve of the acutely damaged heart, these two curves crossing at the equilibrium point B. Within a minute, neither of these two curves any longer applies because sympathetic stimulation will have increased the cardiac output and venous return curves to the two dashed curves. These two new curves equilibrate at point C, showing that the cardiac output within a minute has risen back to approximately 4 liters a minute, which is four-fifths normal, while the right atrial pressure has risen to 5 mm. Hg, a rise of approximately another millimeter. The student should observe especially in this analysis that it is impossible to predict what will happen to cardiac output and right atrial pressure from the changes in the heart alone or in the systemic circulation alone.

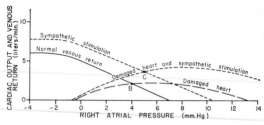

Figure 349. Effect of autonomic reflexes in helping to compensate for depressed cardiac output in acute failure.

The changes in both must be considered simultaneously; this graphical procedure provides a means for doing this.

The Chronic Stage of Failure—Compensation by Renal Retention of Fluid.

A low cardiac output has a profound effect on renal function, sometimes causing complete anuria when the cardiac output falls to as low as one-half to two-thirds normal. In general, the urinary output is less than normal as long as the cardiac output is less than normal, and it usually does not return to normal after an acute heart attack until the cardiac output rises either all the way back to normal or almost to normal. This relationship of renal function to cardiac output is one of the most important of all the factors affecting the dynamics of the circulation in chronic cardiac failure.

Causes of renal retention of fluid in cardiac failure. There are two known causes of the reduced renal output during cardiac failure, both of which are perhaps equally important.

First, a decrease in cardiac output has a tendency to reduce the arterial pressure, which in turn reduces the glomerular pressure in the kidneys. And, even more important, acute cardiac failure is always followed by intense sympathetic reflexes as discussed above; these cause *marked constriction of the afferent arterioles of the kidney,* which further reduces the glomerular pressure. As a consequence, the glomerular filtration rate becomes less than normal. When the cardiac output falls to about one-half normal, this factor alone can result in almost complete anuria.

The second factor that causes reduced renal output in cardiac failure is *an increase in aldosterone secretion* by the adrenal cortices. The aldosterone increases the rate of reabsorption of sodium by the renal tubules, and this in turn leads to a secondary increase in water reabsorption for two reasons: First, as the sodium is reabsorbed, it reduces the osmotic pressure in the tubules while increasing the osmotic pressure in the renal interstitial fluids; these changes promote osmosis of water into the blood. Second, the absorbed sodium increases the osmotic concentration of the extracellular fluid and elicits *antidiuretic hormone* secretion by the supraoptico-hypophyseal system, which is discussed in Chapter 9. The antidiuretic hormone then promotes increased tubular reabsorption of water.

The cause of the increased aldosterone secretion in cardiac failure has not yet been determined, though it might result partially from ischemia of the hypothalamic portions of the brain that control aldosterone secretion (see Chapter 74). Or it is possible that decreased cardiac output causes sufficient metabolic stress throughout the body to elicit the aldosterone response in some yet undisclosed manner. Yet, despite the fact that we do not know how reduced cardiac output promotes the increased aldosterone secretion, measurements in patients have shown aldosterone secretion to be sometimes doubled or even tripled.

In extremely severe cardiac failure, still a third factor causes increased renal retention of water—direct stimulation of the antidiuretic hormone mechanism by the ischemia resulting from low cardiac output. The mechanism of this effect, too, is not known, although, when the cardiac output falls to very low values, the supraoptico-hypophyseal system immediately begins secreting antidiuretic hormone, sometimes causing so much water reabsorption that the body fluids actually become considerably diluted.

Effect of fluid retention on cardiovascular dynamics. As best is known, fluid retention does not have any significant effect on the pumping ability of the heart itself, but it does have an extreme effect on the tendency for venous return. The fluid retained by the kidneys causes a progressive increase in extracellular fluid volume, and part of this increased fluid usually remains in the blood, causing an increase in blood volume as well. For two different reasons this increases the tendency for venous return to the heart: First, both the increased extracellular fluid

and blood volumes increase the mean circulatory pressure, which *increases the pressure gradient for flow of blood toward the heart.* Second, *reduced vascular resistances* caused by distention of the veins allows increased flow of blood toward the heart.

In moderate cardiac failure, retention of fluid helps to compensate for the failure by allowing more blood to flow into the heart and thereby priming the heart with increased quantities of blood. In severe cardiac failure, however, the amount of blood priming the heart often becomes so great that the cardiac muscle fibers are stretched beyond their normal physiological lengths, and this sometimes decreases the effectiveness of the heart as a pump. Thus, in the late stages, as will be discussed in subsequent sections of the chapter, it can be very detrimental.

Recovery of myocardial contractility in chronic failure. After a heart becomes suddenly damaged, the natural reparative processes of the body begin immediately to help restore normal cardiac function. For instance, after myocardial infarction a new collateral blood supply begins to penetrate the peripheral portions of the infarcted area, often completely restoring the muscle function. Also, the undamaged musculature hypertrophies, in this way offsetting the cardiac damage.

Obviously, the degree of recovery depends greatly on the type of cardiac damage and it varies from no recovery at all to almost complete recovery. Ordinarily, after myocardial infarction the heart will have reached its final state of recovery within two to six months.

Graphical analyses of the changes in circulatory dynamics during chronic failure. The two dashed curves of Figure 350 are the same as the dashed curves of Figure 349, illustrating

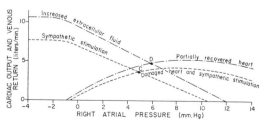

Figure 350. Effect of fluid retention by the kidneys and partial recovery of the heart on the compensation of the heart in chronic cardiac failure.

the dynamics of the circulation about 1 minute after an acute heart attack—that is, after the autonomic reflexes have partially compensated for the failure. During the ensuing few days to few weeks the retention of fluid causes the venous return curve to change gradually to the upper curve illustrated by the dots and dashes. Partial recovery of the heart, on the other hand, increases the cardiac output curve to the upper one shown in the figure. Thus, after these two compensations have taken place, the new point of equilibrium between cardiac output and venous return is point D, which is now at a cardiac output of 5 liters per minute, though the right atrial pressure is up to a level of 6 mm. Hg.

Since the cardiac output has now returned to normal, renal output also will have returned to normal and no further fluid retention will occur. Therefore, except for the high right atrial pressure represented by point D in the figure, the person now has essentially normal cardiovascular dynamics as long as he remains at rest.

It should be noted that if the heart itself recovers to a significant extent and if adequate fluid retention occurs, the sympathetic stimulation will gradually abate toward normal for the following reasons: The partial recovery of the heart can do the same thing for the cardiac output curve as sympathetic stimulation, and fluid retention in the circulatory system can do the same thing for venous return as sympathetic stimulation. Thus, as these two factors develop, the fast pulse rate, the cold skin, the sweating, and the pallor resulting from sympathetic stimulation in the acute stage of cardiac failure gradually disappear.

Summary of the Changes That Occur following Cardiac Failure— "Compensated Heart Failure"

To summarize the events discussed in the past few sections describing the dynamics of circulatory changes following an acute, moderate heart attack, we may divide the stages into (1) the instantaneous effect of the cardiac damage, (2) compensation by the autonomic nervous system, and (3) chronic compensations resulting from partial cardiac recovery and renal retention of fluid. All these changes are shown graphically in Figure 351, which is a composite of the preceding three figures. This figure shows the normal state of circulation (point A), the state a few seconds after the heart attack but before autonomic reflexes have occurred (point B), the rise in cardiac output toward normal caused by sympathetic stimulation

(point C), and final return of the cardiac output to normal following several days to several weeks of cardiac recovery and fluid retention (point D). This final state is called *compensated heart failure.*

Compensated Heart Failure. It should be especially noted from Figure 351 that the pumping ability of the heart in compensated heart failure, as depicted by the cardiac output curve, is still depressed to about one-half normal. This fact illustrates that compensations that increase the tendency for venous return can return the cardiac output to a normal level despite continued weakness of the heart itself. However, one of the results of chronic cardiac weakness is an increased right atrial pressure; in Figure 351 it is shown to be 6 mm. Hg. There are many persons, especially in old age, who have completely normal basal cardiac outputs but mildly to moderately elevated right atrial pressures because of compensated heart failure. These people may never have known that they have had cardiac damage because the damage more often than not occurs a little at a time and the compensation occurs concurrently with the progressive stages of damage.

A slight elevation of right atrial pressure has essentially no harmful effects on the circulatory system. Indeed, as was discussed in Chapter 28, the right atrial pressure usually must rise to as high as 4 to 6 mm. Hg before the rise in pressure is even transmitted to the peripheral veins. The reason for this is that most of the veins leading to the heart are compressed at some point by bones, organs, or other tissues and a moderate rise in right atrial pressure is necessary to fill out the veins before any of the rise can be transmitted back into the more peripheral areas of the circulatory system.

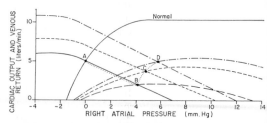

Figure 351. Diagram showing the progressive changes in cardiac output and right atrial pressure during different stages of cardiac failure. This figure is a composite of the three preceding figures.

Yet, the person with compensated heart failure certainly does not have a normal circulatory system, for should he try to exercise strongly or should any other stress be placed on his circulatory system, such as might occur in some disease condition, his heart would be unable to respond normally. The reason for this is that the compensatory mechanisms normally used to increase the cardiac output are already partially in use simply to provide a normal output. Therefore, the remaining compensation that can be invoked has been greatly reduced. To state this another way, the normal person has far greater *cardiac reserve* than the person with compensated heart disease. Cardiac reserve will be discussed at greater length later in the chapter.

Dynamics of Very Severe Cardiac Failure—Decompensated Heart Failure

If the heart becomes very severely damaged, then no amount of compensation, either by autonomic nervous reflexes or by fluid retention, can make this weakened heart pump a normal cardiac output. As a consequence, the cardiac output never rises to a high enough value to bring about return of normal renal function. Fluid will continue to be retained, the patient will develop progressively more and more edema, and this state of events will eventually lead to his death. This is called *decompensated heart failure*. The basis of decompensated heart failure is *failure of the heart to pump sufficient blood to make the kidneys function normally*.

Graphical Analysis of Decompensated Heart Disease.
Figure 352 illustrates by the two heavy lines (1) the normal venous return curve and (2) a cardiac output curve depicting the function of a heart that is extremely weakened. The equilibrium point of these two curves, point A, would not last more than a few seconds, for autonomic compensation will increase the venous return to the second venous return curve labeled "autonomic compensation." If we assume that the heart is so weakened that it still remains very weak even after autonomic compensation, the new point of equilibrium will be point B, illustrating that the cardiac output will have risen a slight amount as a result of the autonomic compensation, but at the same time the right atrial pressure will also have risen to approximately 5 mm. Hg. Since the cardiac output is still a liter per minute less than the critical cardiac output level for normal renal function, the output of the kidneys is still greatly depressed, and fluid continues to be retained. After a day of fluid retention the mean circulatory pressure rises 2 mm. Hg, shifting the venous return curve still farther to the right as shown by the curve labeled "second day." Here again, because the heart is still incapable of pumping the 5 liters cardiac output per minute required for normal renal function, fluid continues to be retained. By the fourth day the mean circulatory pressure will have increased another 2 mm. Hg and by the sixth another 2 mm. Hg so that the cardiac dynamics progress to point D and point E. By this time, the heart will have become so overstretched that the overstretching alone begins to reduce its capabilities as a pump. Therefore, further increase in the tendency for venous return can now only *reduce cardiac output*. By the eighth day, additional fluid retention shifts the venous return curve still farther to the right, and depresses cardiac output tremendously, down to point F. This represents the final stage of decompensation occurring shortly before death, for retention of only small quantities of fluid from this point on will cause rapid deterioration of cardiac pumping.

Thus, one can see from this graphical analysis that the failure of the cardiac output curve ever to rise to the critical cardiac output level required for normal renal function results in (a) progressive retention of fluid, which causes (b) progressive elevation of the mean circulatory pressure, then (c) progressive shift of the venous return curve to the right, and (d) progressive elevation of the right atrial pressure until finally the heart is so overstretched that it becomes unable to pump even moderate quantities of blood, and, therefore, fails completely. Clinically, one detects this serious condition of decompensation principally by the progressive edema associated with renal dysfunction. All clinicians know that failure to institute appropriate therapy when this state of events occurs leads to rapid death.

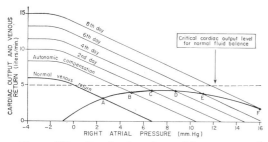

Figure 352. Graphical analysis of decompensated heart disease, showing progressive shift of the venous return curve to the right as a result of fluid retention.

Treatment of Decompensation. Basically, there are two ways in which the decompensation process can often be stopped. These are (1) to strengthen the heart in any one of several ways so that it can pump adequate quantities of blood to make the kidneys function normally again or (2) to administer diuretics and reduce water and salt intake, which brings about a balance between fluid intake and output despite the low cardiac output.

Both of these methods stop the decompensation process in the same way: that is, they reestablish normal fluid balance so that at least as much fluid leaves the body as enters it.

Treatment by strengthening the heart. A weakened heart can frequently be strengthened by administering digitalis or an allied cardiotonic drug. Recent experimental evidence indicates that these drugs strengthen the heart by increasing the rate of diffusion of calcium through the membrane to the interior of the muscle fibers; the calcium then promotes increased force of contraction by the actomyosin complex, as explained in Chapter 19. The chronically weakened heart can often be strengthened by as much as 20 to 50 per cent by these drugs.

Another means by which the heart often becomes strengthened is simply prolonged bed rest, for this protects the heart against excessive overloading and allows maximum recovery from any myocardial disease.

Figure 353 illustrates graphically the effect of strengthening the heart on the dynamics of the circulation. The two light curves of the figure represent (1) the cardiac output curve of Figure 352 and (2) the venous return curve of Figure 352 on the sixth day. Point E is the equilibrium point with a cardiac output of 4 liters per minute and a right atrial pressure of 11 mm. Hg. At this point the patient is in a state of serious decompensation and within a few more days would be dead. Within a few hours after administering digitalis, the strength of the heart might well be increased up to the dark cardiac output curve of the figure. The venous return curve does not change significantly at first because all the fluid that had been retained in the body will still be present. Therefore, a few hours after digitalization a new equlibrium will be established at point G with a cardiac output now of almost 6 liters per minute and a right atrial pressure of 9 mm. Hg. Thus, simply strengthening the heart reduces the

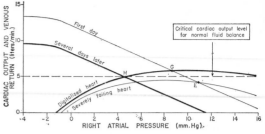

Figure 353. Treatment of decompensated heart disease, showing the effect of digitalis in elevating the cardiac output curve, this in turn causing progressive shift of the venous return to the left.

right atrial pressure a small amount and elevates the cardiac output greatly. Note especially that the cardiac output is now greater than the critical level for normal fluid balance, and the kidneys now begin to put out more urine than normally, causing a net loss of fluid from the body. Therefore, during the subsequent few days, with progressively more and more fluid loss, the venous return curve shifts to the left until it becomes the dark one of the figure; the new equilibrium point is now point H with a cardiac output of 5 liters per minute and a right atrial pressure of 4½ mm. Hg. The circulatory system is now in a stable state.

An especially interesting point is the extra flow of urine, or *diuresis*, that occurs after the administration of digitalis. Because of this, digitalis is frequently said to be a "diuretic." Actually, its diuretic properties probably result not from a direct action on the kidney but from the strengthening of the heart; this allows the heart to pump increased quantities of blood into the kidneys.

It is also interesting that the *circulatory dynamics become stable only when the venous return curve and cardiac output curve cross each other at the cardiac output level that provides normal renal function.* If these two curves cross above approximately the 5-liter level, then the renal output will be too great, causing fluid loss and shift of the venous return curve to the left until the cardiac output falls back to the 5-liter level. On the other hand, if the equilibrium point is below the 5-liter mark, then fluid will be retained until the cardiac output rises back to the 5-liter level.

Treatment of decompensation by fluid retention and administration of diuretics. The second means by which the process of decompensation can be stopped is to administer a diuretic that makes the kidneys put out far greater quantities of urine than normally or to restrict the patient's intake of salt and water. By these two measures the output of fluid can be increased to a greater value than the intake, thereby preventing further retention of fluid even though the cardiac output is considerably less than normal.

Often, it is possible to stop the process of decompensation simply by excluding salt from the diet of the patient, for, if this is done, the extracellular fluid tends to become slightly less concentrated than usual; this inhibits the osmoreceptor system, thereby allowing extra quantities of water to be lost into the urine. Thus, reduction of dietary salt alone in the earlier stages of cardiac failure is often sufficient to prevent or even to stop the process of decompensation though, in very severe cases, water retention may also be required.

Figure 354 shows graphically the recompensation of a patient by administering a diuretic and restriction of salt and water. After instituting these two procedures, fluid balance can then be maintained with a cardiac output down to as low as 3.5 liters per minute. The cardiac output curve and the venous return curve labeled "first day" are the same as the initial conditions of Figure 353. That is, the patient is at an equilibrium point E and within a few days would be dead from decompensation. The cardiac output at point E is 4 liters per minute, which is greater than the 3.5 liters required with this new therapy to maintain normal fluid balance. Because of this the output of fluid becomes slightly greater than the intake so that fluid is progressively lost from the circulation. The venous return curve over a period of several days shifts progressively to the left because of decreasing mean circulatory pressure. Finally, the new equilibrium point (I) is reached at which the venous return curve and cardiac output curve cross each other at the critical cardiac output level for maintenance of normal fluid balance. Thus, a stable situation has now been attained and the patient is "compensated" even though the cardiac output is considerably below normal. The ideal use of diuretics, obviously, is to

give just the amount required to compensate the patient, without giving enough to harm his circulation.

EDEMA IN CARDIAC FAILURE

Much of the preceding discussion has emphasized the elevated right atrial pressure in cardiac failure equally as much as the reduced cardiac output. Referring to Chapter 28, it will be recalled that any time the right atrial pressure rises the capillary pressure likewise is likely to rise; this causes transfer of fluid into the interstitial spaces. Thus, one of the most important problems in cardiac failure is the development of very severe *cardiac edema*.

Dynamics of Edema Formation in Cardiac Failure. On first thought it seems that cardiac edema is a very simple problem— that increased right atrial pressure causes increased capillary pressure, which causes the edema. Unfortunately, this is not true for reasons which can be explained best by Figure 355. When the heart progressively fails as a pump, the cardiac output falling from normal to one-half normal and then finally to zero, the right atrial pressure rises progressively while the systemic arterial pressure falls progressively. These approach each other at an equilibrium value of about 13 mm. Hg. It is quite obvious that capillary pressure must also fall from its normal value of 25 mm. Hg down to the equilibrium pressure of 13 mm. Hg. Thus, it is reasonable to

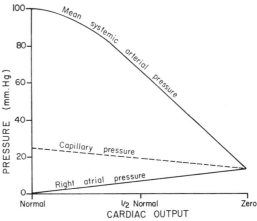

Figure 355. Progressive changes in mean systemic arterial pressure and right atrial pressure as the cardiac output falls from normal to zero. This figure also shows the probable effect of decreased cardiac output on capillary pressure.

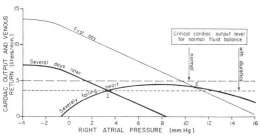

Figure 354. Treatment of cardiac decompensation by administering a diuretic, showing shift of the venous return curve to the left as a result of fluid loss through the kidneys.

believe that severe acute cardiac failure would actually cause a fall in capillary pressure rather than a rise, as is so often claimed. And animal experiments as well as experience in human beings shows that acute cardiac failure does not cause immediate development of peripheral edema.

Instead, the edema develops during the succeeding days *because of fluid retention by the kidneys,* as explained earlier in the chapter. The retention of fluid increases the mean circulatory pressure, resulting in increased tendency for blood to return to the heart. This now elevates the right atrial pressure to a higher value which, because of back pressure, elevates the capillary pressure. Finally, with sufficient retention of fluid, the capillary pressure does rise above 25 mm. Hg, the normal value, and edema results.

Edema of cardiac failure can occur either in the systemic circulation, or in the lungs, or in both, depending on which side or sides of the heart might be failing. Pulmonary edema will be further discussed below in relation to unilateral left heart failure.

CARDIAC SHOCK

Acute heart failure is frequently associated with temporarily greatly reduced cardiac output—sometimes to such low levels that the tissues throughout the body suffer from ischemia. This state of events is called *circulatory shock,* the effects of which will be explained in greater detail in the following chapter. When circulatory shock results from cardiac weakness, the condition is known as *cardiac shock.*

Vicious Cycle of Cardiac Deterioration in Cardiac Shock. The arterial pressure often falls very low in cardiac shock, resulting in greatly reduced coronary blood flow to the heart itself. This then weakens the heart still more, further reducing its pumping effectiveness. The coronary flow falls once more; the cycle repeats itself again and again, and the patient dies within a few minutes to a few hours. Thus, a vicious cycle of deterioration often develops in cardiac shock.

Experiments in our laboratory have indicated that reduction in mean arterial pressure to 35 to 50 mm. Hg can cause even the normal dog heart to fall into this vicious cycle of deterioration. In a heart that has

been damaged by a myocardial infarct, the critical pressure level at which the vicious cycle of deterioration begins might well be 80, 90, or even 100 mm. Hg, depending upon the severity of the heart attack.

Physiology of Treatment. Often a patient dies of cardiac shock before the various compensatory processes can return his cardiac output to a life-sustaining level. Therefore, treatment of this condition is one of the most important problems in the management of acute heart attacks. Immediate digitalization of the heart is often employed for strengthening the heart, but more frequently intravenous infusion of nor-epinephrine is used to sustain the arterial pressure. If this is done, the coronary blood flow can often be elevated to a high enough value to prevent the vicious cycle of deterioration noted above until appropriate compensatory mechanisms in the body have corrected the shock.

Occasionally, cardiologists treat cardiac shock by intravenous administration of blood, plasma, or other fluids. This is not practical when the patient has serious pulmonary edema because extra fluids can then actually drown the patient. However, in the absence of pulmonary edema the increased volume has often been found to be very beneficial in "priming" the heart to greater volumes, thereby promoting increased cardiac output.

UNILATERAL CARDIAC FAILURE

In all the discussions thus far in this chapter, we have considered failure of the heart as a whole. The principles discussed apply to almost all cases of cardiac failure because only rarely does one side of the heart fail without some degree of failure of the other side. Yet, in a large number of patients with early cardiac failure, left-sided failure predominates over right-sided failure, and in rare instances, especially in congenital heart disease, the right side may fail without significant failure of the left side. Therefore, we now need to discuss the special features of unilateral cardiac failure.

Unilateral Left Heart Failure

When the left side of the heart fails without concomitant failure of the right side, blood continues to be pumped into the lungs

agglutinate. The point of this experiment is this: In shock, blood flow through many tissues becomes extremely sluggish, but tissue metabolism continues so that large amounts of acid, either carbonic acid or lactic acid, continue to empty into the blood. Only a few minutes of very sluggish flow in some tissues can lower the capillary pH to the agglutinating level, and minute vascular plugs develop in the small vessels.

Failure of tissue use of oxygen. Another finding by Crowell that has helped to explain many of the phenomena observed in shock has been that the ability of the body tissues to utilize oxygen following prolonged periods of shock, even if excess oxygen is supplied, becomes greatly depressed. A preliminary suggestion of the cause of this depression is also based on the pH changes in the tissues in shock. It should be recalled that proteins precipitate and often change their chemical properties when the pH of the solution approaches the isoelectric point of the protein. The isoelectric points of most of the body proteins are below pH 7.0, and since the tissues develop a low pH when the blood flow becomes sluggish it is quite possible that this in turn could depress activity of the oxidative enzyme systems.

Irreversible Shock

After shock has progressed to a certain stage, transfusion or any other type of therapy becomes incapable of saving the life of the patient. Therefore, the patient is then said to be in the *irreversible stage of shock*. Paradoxically, therapy often returns the arterial pressure and even the cardiac output to normal, but after another 10 to 40 minutes the circulatory system will begin again to deteriorate and then continue on to death. Figure 368 illustrates this effect, showing

that transfusion during the irreversible stage can cause the cardiac output (as well as the arterial pressure) to return to normal. However, the circulation soon begins to fail again, and subsequent transfusions cause less and less effect. Thus, something changes in the overall function of the circulatory system during shock that does not affect the *immediate* ability of the heart to pump blood but over a long period of time does depress this ability and eventuates in death. Now the question remains: What is this factor or what are the factors that lead to the eventual deterioration of the circulation?

Association of Irreversibility with Failure of the Tissues to Use Oxygen. Though most attempts to discover the basic factor that makes shock irreversible have yielded fruitless results, the studies of Crowell quoted above offer at least a partial answer to this question as follows: First, referring once again to Figure 368 we find that the cardiac output can still be brought back to normal by means of transfusion in the early phase of irreversible shock. However, despite adequate transport of blood to the tissues, the tissues themselves are now incapable of using adequate quantities of oxygen. This represents a metabolic deficit that is possibly caused by inactivation of oxidative enzymes as discussed above. And the metabolic deficit then leads to still more and more deterioration of the circulation, thus leading to death.

Length of Time That an Animal Can Remain in Progressive Shock Prior to Development of Irreversibility—Relationship to Oxygen Deficit. Figure 369 shows that very severe shock results in irreversibility in about one-half hour, while moderate shock results in irreversibility in

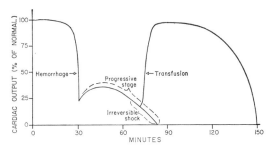

Figure 368.   Failure of transfusion to prevent death in irreversible shock.

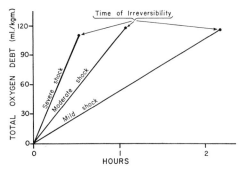

Figure 369.   Relationship of total oxygen deficit to the irreversibility of shock.

about an hour, and mild shock in two or more hours. Plotted also on the curve is the total oxygen deficit that develops in the body during the shock. This was calculated by subtracting the actual oxygen usage by the animal during shock from the basal amount used prior to shock. Note that the total oxygen deficit at the time of irreversibility is about the same in each instance, about 120 ml. per kilogram. This figure shows again that irreversibility is correlated with deficient oxygen usage by the body. The more rapidly the oxygen deficit develops, the shorter is the time required for the shock to become irreversible.

Other Causes of Hypovolemic Shock

Plasma Loss Shock. Loss of plasma from the circulatory system can sometimes be severe enough to reduce the total blood volume markedly, in this way causing typical hypovolemic shock similar in almost all details to that caused by hemorrhage. Severe plasma loss occurs in the following conditions:

(1) Severe *venous obstruction,* particularly when this occurs in the major veins leading to the heart, can sometimes cause the capillary pressure distal to the obstruction to rise so high that large quantities of fluid leak rapidly into the tissues, thereby reducing the total plasma volume.

(2) *Intestinal obstruction* is also often a cause of reduced plasma volume. The distention of the intestine in this condition causes fluid to leak from the intestinal capillaries into the intestinal walls and intestinal lumen. This increased loss of fluid might result from elevated capillary pressure caused by increased resistance in the stretched veins over the surface of the intestine, or it might be caused by direct damage to the capillaries themselves. Nevertheless, the lost fluid contains a very high content of protein, thereby reducing the total plasma protein as well as the plasma volume.

(3) In the *nephrotic syndrome* (see Chapthe 11) so much protein is often lost into the urine that normal plasma protein concentration cannot be maintained. This in turn can result in such low plasma colloid osmotic pressure that fluid is lost into the interstitial spaces throughout the body, thereby reducing the plasma volume.

(4) Likewise, *nutritional hypoproteinemia,* which occasionally occurs in war-torn and famine areas, can reduce the plasma protein concentration to such low values that shock finally ensues.

(5) Often, in patients who have very *severe burns* or other denuding conditions of the skin, so much plasma will be lost through the exposed areas that the plasma volume becomes markedly reduced.

The hypovolemic shock that results from plasma loss has almost the same characteristics as the shock caused by hemorrhage, except for one additional complicating factor—the blood viscosity increases very greatly as a result of plasma loss, and this further exacerbates the sluggishness of blood flow.

Shock Caused by Dehydration. Loss of fluid from all fluid compartments of the body is called *dehydration;* this, too, can also reduce the blood volume and cause hypovolemic shock very similar to that resulting from hemorrhage. Some of the causes of this type of shock are: (a) simple loss of too much sweat; (b) fluid loss in diarrhea or vomiting; (c) excess loss of fluid by nephrotic kidneys; (d) failure to supply adequate intake of fluid and electrolytes; (e) destruction of the adrenal cortices with consequent failure of the kidneys to reabsorb sodium, chloride, and water; and (f) loss of the secretion of antidiuretic hormone by the supraoptico-hypophyseal system.

NEUROGENIC SHOCK—INCREASED VASCULAR CAPACITY

Occasionally, shock results without any loss of blood volume whatsoever. Instead, the *vascular capacity* increases so much that even the normal amount of blood becomes incapable of adequately filling the circulatory system. One of the major causes of this is *loss of vasomotor tone* throughout the body, and the resulting condition is then known as *neurogenic shock.*

The relationship of the vascular capacity to blood volume was discussed in Chapter 34, where it was pointed out that either an increase in vascular capacity or a decrease in blood volume *reduces the mean circulatory pressure,* which in turn reduces the pressure gradient for venous return, and thereby reduces the tendency for venous return to the heart. This effect is often called "venous pooling" of blood.

Importance of Body Position in Neurogenic Shock. Ordinarily, sudden loss of vasomotor tone throughout the body will not cause shock at all if the person is lying in a slightly headdown position (Trendelenburg position), and, if he is lying in a completely horizontal position, only mild to moderate degrees of reduced cardiac output result. But, if the person is in the upright position, the vessels of the lower part of the body become so distended that the blood "pools" and fails to flow uphill in sufficient quantities to maintain cardiac output. As a result, all tissues suffer from lack of adequate nutrition.

Causes of Neurogenic Shock. Some of the different factors that can cause sudden loss of vasomotor tone include:

(1) *Deep general anesthesia* often depresses the vasomotor center deeply enough to cause vasomotor collapse, with resulting neurogenic shock.

(2) Likewise, *spinal anesthesia,* especially when this extends all the way up the spinal cord, blocks the sympathetic outflow from the nervous system and is a very common cause of neurogenic shock.

(3) *Brain damage* is often also a cause of vasomotor collapse. Many patients who have had brain concussion or contusion of the basal regions of the brain develop profound neurogenic shock. Also, even though short periods of medullary ischemia cause extreme vasomotor activity, prolonged ischemia can result in death of the vasomotor neurons and can cause development of severe neurogenic shock.

(4) In *fainting caused by diminished sympathetic activity,* the peripheral blood vessels become greatly dilated. As a result, blood pools, and the cardiac output falls drastically. If such a person is held in an upright position, he will go into the progressive stage of shock and can die as a result. Fortunately, on fainting, a person usually falls to a horizontal position so that almost normal cardiac output ordinarily reensues almost immediately.

Vaso-vagal Syncope—Emotional Fainting. The circulatory collapse that results from "emotional" fainting usually is not caused by vasomotor failure but instead by strong emotional excitation of the parasympathetic nerves to the heart and of the vasodilator nerves to the skin and skeletal muscles, thereby slowing the heart and reducing the arterial pressure. Therefore, the fainting that results from an emotional disturbance is called *vaso-vagal syncope* to differentiate it from the other types of fainting which result from diminished sympathetic activity throughout the body or from the causes of reduced cardiac output.

Other Types of Shock That Result from Increased Vascular Capacity

Occasionally, the vascular capacity is increased in other ways besides reduction in vasomotor tone. For instance, a patient who has had severe abdominal ascites often develops immediate shock if the ascitic fluid is removed rapidly. This results from loss of the pressure that the ascites had been exerting on all the blood vessels of the abdominal cavity and on the blood reservoirs —the liver and spleen. Suddenly, therefore, an increased amount of blood is needed to fill the circulatory system. Since this is not available, shock often ensues.

Likewise, shock often occurs after a very large abdominal tumor has been removed, and a *tendency* to shock even occurs when a mother gives birth to a baby because of suddenly increased vascular capacity, illustrating the importance of the extra blood volume that a mother accumulates prior to parturition (Chapter 80).

ANAPHYLACTIC SHOCK

"Anaphylaxis" is an allergic condition in which the cardiac output and arterial pressure often fall drastically. This was discussed in Chapter 14. It results primarily from an antigen-antibody reaction that takes place all through the body immediately after an antigen to which the person is sensitive has entered the circulatory system. Such a reaction detrimentally affects the circulatory system in several important ways, as illustrated in Figure 370. First, if the antigen-antibody reaction takes place in direct contact with the vascular walls or cardiac musculature, then damage to these tissues pre-

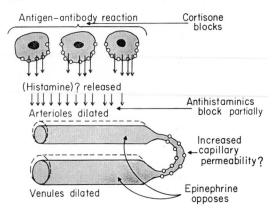

Figure 370.　Some of the factors that cause anaphylactic shock.

sumably can result directly. Second, cells damaged anywhere in the body by the antigen-antibody reaction release several highly toxic substances into the blood. Among these is histamine or a histamine-like substance that has a very strong vasodilator effect. The histamine in turn causes (1) an increase in vascular capacity because of venous dilatation and (2) dilatation of the arterioles with resultant greatly reduced arterial pressure. Unfortunately, all the precise relationships of the above factors in anaphylaxis have not yet been determined, but the sum total of the effects is a profound reduction in venous return and often such serious shock that the person dies in a matter of minutes.

It is interesting that intravenous injection of large amounts of histamine causes "histamine shock," which has characteristics almost identical with those of anaphylactic shock, though usually less profound.

TOXIC SHOCK

For many years various toxic substances have been believed to play a part in some types of shock. In fact, some physiologists have claimed that irreversible shock is caused by the development of a toxic substance in the circulating body fluids, this substance in turn causing cardiac depression and resulting in death. Yet, cross transfusion experiments have thus far failed to demonstrate such a toxic factor in most types of shock.

On the other hand, toxic factors are known to predispose to shock in the following conditions: (1) The histamine secreted in anaphylactic shock (and perhaps other toxic products resulting from the antigen-antibody reaction) certainly represents a toxin that helps to promote a type of shock. (2) Several hours following thrombosis of the intestinal arteries toxic substances formed by bacteria in the gangrenous intestine can cause profound shock and almost immediate death. (3) When tourniquets are applied tightly to all the limbs of an animal so that blood flow is completely blocked for 30 minutes or more, release of these tourniquets can cause a toxic factor to enter the circulation from the occluded limbs that promotes very profound shock. This phenomenon is called *tourniquet shock,* a condition that the clinician should specifically avoid when he uses tourniquets on patients. Here again the precise toxic substance is unknown. (4) In patients with severe burns toxic factors from the damaged tissues, including considerable amounts of histamine, can help to make the shock more profound. (5) Toxins secreted by certain bacteria during some types of infection, particularly several types of clostridial infections, dysentery, typhoid fever, tularemia, and anthrax infection, can cause severe circulatory damage with resultant shock.

TRAUMATIC SHOCK

One of the most common causes of circulatory shock is trauma to the body. Often the shock results simply from hemorrhage, but it can also occur even without hemorrhage, for contusion of the body can often damage the capillaries sufficiently to allow excessive loss of plasma into the tissues. This results in greatly reduced plasma volume with resultant hypovolemic shock. Thus, whether or not hemorrhage occurs when a person is severely traumatized, the blood volume can still be markedly reduced.

The *pain* associated with serious trauma can be an additional aggravating factor in traumatic shock, for pain sometimes strongly inhibits the vasomotor center, thereby increasing the vascular capacitance and reducing the tendency for venous return. Various attempts have also been made to implicate toxic factors released by the traumatized tissues as one of the causes of shock following trauma. However, cross-transfusion experiments have failed to show any such toxic element.

In summary, traumatic shock seems to result mainly from hypovolemia, though there may also be a moderate degree of concomitant neurogenic shock caused by the pain.

CARDIAC SHOCK

At the outset of this discussion on shock we pointed out that either peripheral factors that tend to reduce venous return or cardiac factors that reduce the ability of the heart to pump blood can result in shock. When the heart is the portion of the circulatory system that fails, the condition is called *cardiac shock.* The basic factors that can cause such weakness of the heart have already been discussed in Chapter 36, and this previous discussion now needs only to be related to the basic principles of shock caused in other ways.

When the heart becomes so weakened that the cardiac output falls to ischemic levels, all the tissues of the body begin to suffer, and the person can exhibit exactly the same symptoms as those listed earlier in the chapter for other types of shock—that is, mental haziness, muscular weakness, decreased skin temperature, and so forth. To help offset the weakness of the heart, circulatory reflexes become active throughout the body, often increasing the heart rate despite the weakness and also causing vasospasm in the skin and intense sweating.

In exactly the same manner that a critical cardiac output level exists below which the shock becomes progressive following hemorrhage, this is also true in cardiac shock, setting off a vicious cycle of circulatory deterioration and eventuating in death. Indeed, cardiac shock is usually even more likely to become progressive than is hemorrhagic shock because the heart is already damaged at the outset. Thus, in hemorrhagic shock progression of cardiac weakness does not usually begin until the coronary perfusion pressure falls to 40 to 60 mm. Hg, whereas in cardiac shock progression often begins when the coronary perfusion pressure falls as low as 80 to 90 mm. Hg.

We do not wish to underemphasize the importance of cardiac shock because probably as many patients die of cardiac shock as of all the other types of shock put together, but the student will now be referred to Chapter 36 for a complete discussion of the basis of low cardiac output and cardiac shock in cardiac failure.

TREATMENT OF SHOCK

Basically shock can be treated by any type of therapy that will increase the cardiac output. In general, the best therapy is to correct the condition that is causing the shock. Aside from the treatment of cardiac shock, which was discussed in Chapter 36, the two most common types of treatment of the different types of shock are (1) replacement therapy with whole blood or other fluids and (2) use of sympathomimetic drugs.

Replacement Therapy

Blood and Plasma Transfusion. If a person is in shock due to hemorrhage, the best possible therapy is usually transfusion of whole blood. If the shock is caused by plasma loss, the best therapy is administration of plasma; when dehydration is the cause, administration of the appropriate electrolytic solution can correct the shock.

The basic principles of blood typing and the use of whole blood and plasma for transfusion were discussed in Chapter 15. Unfortunately, properly matched whole blood is not always available, such as under battlefield conditions. However, plasma can usually substitute very adequately for whole blood because it will increase the blood volume and restore normal hemodynamics. Plasma will not restore a normal hematocrit, but the human being can usually stand a decrease in hematocrit to about one-third normal before serious consequences result. Therefore, in acute conditions it is perfectly reasonable to use plasma in place of whole blood for treatment of hemorrhagic and most other types of hypovolemic shock.

Sometimes plasma also is unavailable. For these instances, various *plasma substitutes* have been developed that will perform almost exactly the same hemodynamic functions as plasma. Some of these are the following:

Dextran solution as a plasma substitute. The principal requirement of a truly effective plasma substitute is that it remain in the circulatory system—that is, not filter through the capillary pores into the tissue spaces. But, in addition, the solution must be non-toxic and must contain appropriate electrolytes to prevent derangement of the extracellular fluid electrolytes on administration. To remain in the circulation the plasma substitute must contain some substance that exerts colloid osmotic pressure. One of the most satisfactory substances that have been developed thus far for this purpose is *dextran*, a large polysaccharide polymer of glucose. Certain bacteria secrete dextran as a byproduct of their growth, and commercial dextran is manufactured by a bacterial culture procedure. By varying the growth conditions of the bacteria the molecular weight of the dextran can be controlled to any desired value. Dextrans of appropriate molecular size will not pass through the capillary pores and can therefore replace plasma proteins as colloid osmotic agents.

Fortunately very few toxic reactions have been observed when using dextran to provide colloid osmotic pressure; therefore, solutions of this substance have proved to be a very satisfactory substitute for plasma in fluid replacement therapy.

Other plasma substitutes. Other substances besides dextran that have been employed in the past to provide colloid osmotic pressure have been gelatin, pectins, gum acacia, and bovine albumin. All these are quite capable of providing the colloid osmotic pressure, but, except in rare instances, they all have been discarded because of their toxic reactions. In the case of bovine albumin, for instance, the patient can actually develop immune bodies against the albumin and as a result can develop serum sickness as described in Chapter 14.

Maximum Allowable Rate of Transfusion. If the donor blood is perfectly "matched" with the recipient's blood, the blood can be administered *to a person who has hypovolemia* as rapidly as it can be injected. However, if the person already has a normal blood volume—such as a patient with anemia who simply needs an increased volume of cells—the transfusion must be given very slowly so that the excess plasma in the circulatory system will have time to filter out of the blood vessels. Otherwise, the circulatory volume will become so greatly increased that abnormally high pressures can cause serious internal hemorrhage. Such hemorrhage is very common in the gastrointestinal tract, and both hemorrhage into the lungs and pulmonary edema are especially likely to occur.

Unfortunately, one is never certain that donor blood is 100 per cent "compatible" with the recipient's blood. Therefore, except in very acute conditions it is advisable to administer blood slowly enough that the transfusion can be stopped at the first sign of any transfusion reaction. Furthermore, if the blood has been stored with an anticoagulant, the transfusion must be given slowly enough for the recipient's circulatory system to rid itself of the injected anticoagulant. For instance, citrate ion, which is the usual anticoagulant, is converted by the liver into glucose or is metabolized directly for energy. Yet, several minutes are usually required for this process to occur. Therefore, blood transfusions are usually given no more rapidly than 500 ml. every 30 minutes.

Treatment of Shock with Sympathomimetic Drugs or Other Therapy

Treatment of shock with sympathomimetic drugs is presented here principally to point out that these drugs are of little value in most types of shock except neurogenic and anaphylactic shock.

Sympathomimetic drugs have often been used in treating hemorrhagic and other types of hypovolemic shock—usually with very poor success. Since the vasomotor system of the body is usually almost maximally activated by the circulatory re-

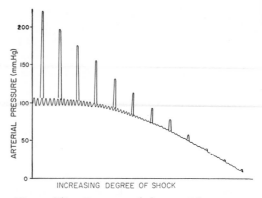

Figure 371. Response of the arterial pressure to standard injections of nor-epinephrine during different degrees of shock.

flexes in severe hypovolemic shock, administration of sympathomimetic drugs usually causes little additional increase in vasomotor tone. Figure 371 illustrates this fact, showing that as the arterial pressure falls in hemorrhagic shock, the ability of the circulatory system to respond to standard injections of nor-epinephrine decreases markedly, simply because the body's own sympathetic nervous system causes almost maximum vasoconstriction by its own secreted nor-epinephrine.

Treatment of Neurogenic Shock. In *neurogenic shock*, sympathomimetic drugs actually reverse the basic cause of the shock itself by increasing the vasomotor tone throughout the body, but even in this condition these drugs may not be required, for, as long as the patient is in the horizontal position, adequate venous return to the heart usually still occurs and maintains an adequate cardiac output to prevent progressive shock.

Treatment of Anaphylactic Shock. Unfortunately, *anaphylactic shock* occurs so rapidly that one often cannot institute any therapy before death ensues, but if therapy can be instituted the condition can often be ameliorated or almost completely reverted by rapid administration of nor-epinephrine or some other sympathomimetic drug. This does not correct the basic cause of the anaphylaxis, but it does cause vasoconstriction, which opposes the vasodilatation caused by histamine in anaphylaxis. Also, if one suspects that anaphylaxis might occur in a patient, its severity can usually be reduced by preliminary administration of *cortisone*, which attenuates the allergic reaction responsible for the anaphylaxis or preliminary administration of *antihistaminics*, which reduce the effects of the histamine released during anaphylaxis. However, in both these instances the therapy must be given before anaphylaxis takes place, for which reason they are usually of little value in therapy of anaphylaxis.

Pain-relieving Drugs in Traumatic Shock. The use of pain-relieving drugs such as morphine has been found clinically to reduce the severity of most traumatic shock, supposedly by removing the neurogenic element of the shock.

CIRCULATORY ARREST

A condition closely allied to circulatory shock is *circulatory arrest* in which all blood flow completely stops. This occurs most frequently on the surgical operating table as a result of *cardiac arrest* or of *ventricular fibrillation*. Ventricular fibrillation can usually be stopped by the following procedure: The heart is pumped by hand for 5 to 10 minutes to restore adequate coronary flow to the ventricular muscle. Then a strong electrical current is passed through the heart from two electrode plates pressing against the sides of the heart. This throws essentially all the heart into a state of refractoriness, and usually a normal cardiac rhythm is restored thereafter. The basic principles of this procedure were described in Chapter 21.

Cardiac arrest usually results from too little oxygen in the anesthetic gaseous mixture or from a depressant effect of the anesthesia itself. A normal cardiac rhythm can usually be restored simply by removing the anesthetic and then pumping the heart by hand for a few minutes while supplying the patient's lungs with adequate quantities of ventilatory oxygen.

Effect of Circulatory Arrest on the Brain

The real problem in circulatory arrest is usually not to restore cardiac function but instead to prevent detrimental effects in the brain as a result of the circulatory arrest. In general, 4 to 5 minutes circulatory arrest causes permanent brain damage in over half the patients, and circulatory arrest for as long as 10 minutes almost universally destroys most, if not all, of the mental powers. For many years it has been taught that these detrimental effects on the brain were caused by the cerebral anoxia that occurs during circulatory arrest. However, recent studies by Crowell have shown that dogs can almost universally stand 20 minutes of circulatory arrest without brain damage if they have been treated with appropriate anticoagulants prior to the arrest. On the basis of this study it is postulated that the circulatory arrest causes many minute vascular clots to develop throughout the brain and that these cause permanent or semipermanent ischemia of many brain areas. This accords very well with the results in human beings who have undergone long periods of circulatory arrest, for complete destruction of large areas in one side of the brain often occurs while corresponding areas in the opposite side of the brain, which should also be affected if anoxia were the cause of the damage, are not affected even in the slightest.

REFERENCES

Alexander, R. S.: Venomotor tone in hemorrhage and shock. *Circ. Res.*, 3:181, 1955.

Baratz, R. A., and Ingraham, R. C.: Capillary permeability during hemorrhagic shock in the rat. *Proc. Soc. Exp. Biol. and Med.*, 89:642, 1955.

Bing, R. J.: The role of coronary circulation in shock. *Ann. N. Y. Acad. Sc.*, 55:367, 1952.

Crowell, J. W., Bounds, S., and Johnson, W. W.: The effect of varying the hematocrit ratio on the susceptibility to hemorrhagic shock. *Am. J. Physiol.*, 192:171, 1958.

Crowell, J. W., Ford, R. G., and Lewis, V. M.: Oxygen transport in hemorrhagic shock as a function of the hematocrit ratio. *Am. J. Physiol.*, 190:1003, 1959.

Crowell, J. W., and Johnson, W. W.: The role of the hematocrit ratio in circulatory arrest. *Surgery*, 45:432, 1959.

Crowell, J. W., Lambright, R. L., and Sharpe, G. P.: Changes in coagulation time due to acute circulatory failure. *Am. J. Physiol.*, 179:268, 1954.

Crowell, J. W., Sharpe, G. P., and Lambright, R. L.: Prolonged massage of the fibrillating heart. *Surgery*, 42:701, 1957.

Crowell, J. W., Sharpe, G. P., Lambright, R. L., and Read, W. L.: The mechanism of death after resuscitation following acute circulatory failure. *Surgery*, 38:696, 1955.

Crowell, J. W., and Read, W. L.: *In vivo* coagulation —a probable cause of irreversible shock. *Am. J. Physiol.*, 183:565, 1955.

Crowell, J. W., and Smith, E. E.: The effect of fibrinolytic activation on survival and cerebral damage following various periods of circulatory arrest. *Am. J. Physiol.*, 186:283, 1956.

Cull, T. E., Soibetta, M. P., and Selkurt, E. E.: Arterial inflow into the mesenteric and hepatic vascular circuits during hemorrhagic shock. *Am. J. Physiol.*, 185:365, 1956.

Farrell, G. L., Rosnagle, R. S., and Rauschkolb, E. W.: Increased aldosterone secretion in response to blood loss. *Circ. Res.*, 4:606, 1956.

Fozzard, H. A., and Gilmore, J. P.: Use of levarterenol in treatment of irreversible hemorrhagic shock. *Am. J. Physiol.*, 196:1029, 1959.

Glaviano, V. V., Bass, N., and Hykiel, F.: Adrenal

medullary secretion of epinephrine and norepinephrine in dogs subjected to hemorrhagic hypotension. *Circ., Res.,* 8:564, 1960.

Green, H. D. (ed.): Shock and Circulation Hemostasis. New York, Josiah Macy, Jr., Foundation, 1957.

Greever, C. J., and Watts, D. T.: Epinephrine levels in the peripheral blood during irreversible hemorrhagic shock in dogs. *Circ. Res.,* 7:192, 1959.

Gronwall, A.: Dextran and Its Use in Colloidal Infusion Solutions. New York, Academic Press, 1957.

Guyton, A. C.: The venous system and its role in the circulation. *Mod. Concepts of Cardiovas. Dis.,* 27:483, 1958.

Guyton, A. C., Batson, H. M., and Smith, C. M.: Adjustments of the circulatory system following very rapid transfusion or hemorrhage. *Am. J. Physiol.,* 164:351, 1951.

Hampton, J. K., Jr., Friedman, J. J., and Mayerson, H. S.: Evaluation of role of ferritin (VDM) in traumatic shock. *Proc. Soc. Exp. Biol. & Med.,* 79:643, 1952.

Hatcher, J. D., Sunahara, F. A., Edholm, O. G., and Woolner, J. M.: The circulatory adjustments to posthemorrhagic anemia in dogs. *Circ. Res.,* 2:499, 1954.

Manning, J. W., Jr., and Hampton, J. K., Jr.: Utilization of oxygen by normal and trauma-resistant rats following trauma and exposure to hypoxia. *Am. J. Physiol.,* 188:99, 1957.

Meyers, F. H., Schoolar, J. C., and Overman, R. R.: Characteristics of shock following acute reduction of cardiac output in dogs. *Circ. Res.,* 2:304, 1954.

Morrison, K. A. E., Jr., Lundy, J. S., and Essex, H. E.: Evaluation of replacement fluids in laboratory animals following controlled hemorrhage. *Circulation,* 5:208, 1952.

Natof, H. E.: Cardiovascular Collapse in the Operating Room. Philadelphia, J. B. Lippincott Co., 1958.

Pirani, C. L., Juster, R., Froeb, H. F., Consolazio, C. F., and Ingraham, R. C.: Use of dextran in hemorrhagic shock. *J. Appl. Physiol.,* 8:193, 1955.

Rawson, R. A., Chien, S., Peng, M. T., and Dellen-back, R. J.: Determination of residual blood volume required for survival in rapidly hemorrhaged splenectomized dogs. *Am. J. Physiol.,* 196:179, 1959.

Remington, J. W.: An index to the bleeding volume of the dog. *Am. J. Physiol.,* 170:285, 1952.

Remington, J. W.: Role of vasoconstrcition in response of dog to hemorrhage. *Am. J. Physiol.,* 161:116, 1950.

Rothstein, D. A., Rosen, S., Markowitz, A., and Fuller, J. B.: Ferritin and antiferritin serum treatment of dogs in irreversible hemorrhagic shock. *Am. J. Physiol.,* 198:844, 1960.

Sapirstein, L. A., Buckley, N. M., and Ogden, E.: Splanchnic blood flow after hemorrhage. *Science,* 122:1138, 1955.

Selkurt, E. E.: Intestinal ischemic shock and the protective role of the liver. *Am. J. Physiol.,* 197:281, 1959.

Selkhurt, E. E., and Brecher, G. A.: Splanchnic hemodynamics and oxygen utilization during hemorrhagic shock in the dog. *Circ. Res.,* 4:693, 1956.

Smith, J. J., Roth, D. A., and Grace, R. A.: Oxygen saturation of hepatic blood during hemorrhagic shock in the dog. *Circ. Res.,* 3:311, 1955.

Squire, J. R., et al.: Dextran. Springfield, Illinois, Charles C Thomas, 1955.

Strait, R. O.: Evaluations of crystalloidal solutions in hemorrhaged dogs. *Am. J. Physiol.,* 170:351, 1952.

Walker, W. F., Zileli, M. S., Reutter, F. W., Shoemaker, W. C., Friend, D., and Moore, F. D.: Adrenal medullary secretion in hemorrhagic shock. *Am. J. Physiol.,* 197:773, 1959.

Weil, M. H., Maclean, L. D., Visscher, M. B., and Spink, W. W.: Studies on the circulatory changes in the dog produced by endotoxin from gram-negative microorganisms. *J. Clin. Invest.,* 35:1191, 1956.

Wiggers, C. J.: The Physiology of Shock. New York, Commonwealth Fund, 1950.

See also Chapter 35, Cardiac output; Chapter 36, Circulatory failure; Chapter 38, General bibliography for the cardiovascular system.

Auscultation; Dynamics of Valvular and Congenital Heart Defects

THE HEART SOUNDS

The function of the heart valves was discussed in Chapter 25, and it was pointed out that the valves make an audible sound when they close but ordinarily make no sound whatsoever when they open. The purpose of the present section will be to discuss the factors that cause the sounds in the heart, under both normal and abnormal conditions.

The Normal Heart Sounds

When one listens with a stethoscope to a normal heart, he hears a sound usually described as "lub, dub, lub, dub - - - -." The "lub" is caused by closure of the A-V valves, and the "dub" by closure of the semilunar valves. Clinically, the period between the "lub" and the "dub" is considered to be systole, while the period between the "dub" and the "lub" is diastole. The "lub" sound is called the *first heart sound,* and the "dub" the *second heart sound* because the normal cycle of the heart is considered to start with the beginning of systole and to end with the end of diastole.

Characteristics of the First and Second Heart Sounds. The duration of each of the heart sounds is slightly more than one tenth of a second; the first sound lasts about 0.14 second and the second about 0.11 second. And both of them are described as very low pitch sounds, the first lower than the second. Sound consists of vibrations of different frequencies. Figure 372 illustrates by the shaded area to the left the amplitude of the sounds of the different frequencies in the heart sounds and murmurs, illustrating that these are composed of frequencies ranging

all the way from 0 cycles per second up to more than 1000 cycles per second. However, also shown in the figure is another curve called the "threshold of audibility," which depicts the capability of the ear to hear sounds of different amplitudes. Note that in the very low frequency range the heart vibrations have a high degree of amplitude, but the threshold of audibility is so high that ordinarily the heart vibrations below approximately 30 to 50 cycles per second are not heard by the ears. Then above about 500 cycles per second, the heart sounds are so weak that despite a low threshold of audibility no frequencies in this range are heard. For practical purposes, then, we can consider that all the heart sounds lie in the range of approximately 40 to 500 cycles per second, though some of these will have their major frequencies in

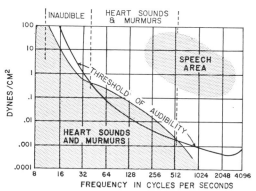

Figure 372. Amplitude of different frequency vibrations in the heart sounds and heart murmurs in relation to the threshold of audibility, showing that the range of sounds that can be heard is between about 40 and 500 cycles per second. (Modified from Butterworth, Chassin, and McGrath: Cardiac Auscultation. Grune and Stratton.)

the lower portion of this range, while others will have their major frequencies in the higher portion. Both the first and second heart sounds have a mixture of frequencies in the entire audible range of the heart sounds, though the first sound has slightly more low frequency sounds, while the second heart sound has more high frequency sounds.

Causes of the First and Second Heart Sounds.   Closure of the valves in any pump system usually causes a certain amount of noise because the valves slap together or because they close solidly and suddenly over some opening, setting up vibrations in the fluid or walls of the pump. However, in the heart, the valves are cushioned by blood, and it is difficult to understand why these valves can create as much sound as they do. Therefore, the exact cause of the heart sounds has never been determined though a number of suggestions have been made.

The simplest suggestion for the cause of the heart sounds is that slapping of the vanes of the valves together sets up vibrations. This probably causes very little if any of the sound because of the cushioning effect of the blood.

The more probable cause is vibration of the walls or fluid in the heart or major vessels around the heart. For instance, sudden contraction of the ventricles causes sudden pressure of blood against the A-V valves, causing the valves to bulge toward the atria. The elasticity of the valves then causes the onsurging pressure waves to bounce backward into each respective ventricle. The pressure waves travel rapidly to the opposite sides of the ventricles where they are reflected once again, thereafter reverberating back and forth between the valves and the walls of the ventricles. This is probably the cause of the major part of the first heart sound.

A third possible cause of the first heart sound is contraction of the heart muscle itself, for intrinsic rearrangement of muscular elements during contraction, even in skeletal muscles, causes sounds that can be heard through an overlying stethoscope. However, this contribution to heart sounds is probably extremely slight because the first and second heart sounds disappear when the valves are removed.

The second heart sound probably results from vibration in the pulmonary artery, in the aorta, and to a certain extent inside the ventricles themselves. When the semilunar valves first close, they are undoubtedly bulged backward toward the ventricles, and then the elastic stretch repulses the pressure waves back into the arteries, which causes a short period of reverberation back and forth between the walls of the arteries or between the walls of the arteries and the valves. Intracardiac phonocardiograms have demonstrated that most of the vibrations of the second heart sound occur in the great arteries and not in the chambers of the heart itself.

The reason the frequency of the first heart sound is lower than that of the second sound is probably that the elastic modulus of the A-V valves and of the walls of the ventricles is far less than the elastic modulus of the semilunar valves and the arteries, for it is well known that any mechanical vibrating system having a low elastic modulus oscillates at a slower rate than a system having a greater modulus. Furthermore, the volume of blood in the great vessels is less than that in the ventricles, which means that the inertia of the vibrating mass is less; this also would cause the second heart sound to have a higher frequency than the first.

The reason the second heart sound is shorter in duration than the first is possibly that the frequency of oscillation is higher, causing the sound to be "damped" out by the viscosity of the vascular and cardiac walls much more rapidly than occurs for the lower frequency first heart sound.

The Third Heart Sound.   Occasionally, a third heart sound is heard at the beginning of the middle third of diastole. The most logical explanation of this sound is vibration of blood back and fourth between the walls of the ventricles initiated by inrushing blood from the atria. This is analogous to running water from a faucet into a sack, the inrushing water reverberating back and forth between the walls of the sack to cause noise.

The third heart sound is an extremely weak rumble of such low frequency, 30 cycles per second, or less, that it usually cannot be heard with a stethoscope, but it can be recorded quite frequently in the phonocardiogram, as will be noted below. The very low frequency of this sound presumably results from the flaccid, inelastic condition of the heart during diastole; the reason the third heart sound does not occur until after the first third of diastole is presumably that in the early part of diastole the heart is not filled sufficiently to create even the small amount of elastic tension in the ventricles necessary for reverberation. The reason the third heart sound does not continue into the latter part of diastole is presumably that little blood flows into the ventricles during the latter part of diastole so that no initiating stimulus then exists for causing reverberation of blood.

The Atrial Heart Sound. An atrial heart sound can be recorded in many persons, but it can almost never be heard with a stethoscope because of its low frequency—usually 20 cycles per second or less. This sound occurs when the atria contract, and presumably it is caused by an inrush of blood into the ventricles, which initiates vibrations similar to those of the third heart sound.

Areas for Auscultation of Normal Heart Sounds. Figure 373 illustrates the areas of the chest wall from which the heart sounds from each valve are usually best heard. With the stethoscope placed in any one of the special valvular areas, the sounds from all the other valves can still be heard, though the sound from the special valve is then as loud, *relative to the other sounds,* as it ever will be. It is essential that the cardiologist learn to distinguish the sounds from the different valves. He usually does this by a process of elimination; that is, he moves the stethoscope from one area to another, noting the loudness of the sounds in different areas and gradually picking out the sound components from each valve.

The areas for listening to the different heart sounds are not directly over the valves themselves. The aortic area is upward along the aorta, the pulmonic area is upward along the pulmonary artery, the tricuspid area is over the right ventricle, and the mitral area is over the apex of the heart, the portion of the left ventricle nearest to the surface of the chest. In other words, the sounds caused by the A-V valves are transmitted to the chest wall through each respective ventricle, and the sounds from the semilunar valves are transmitted especially along the great vessels leading from the heart. This transmission of the sounds is in keeping with the theory that reverberating pressure waves are the probable cause of the heart sounds.

The Phonocardiogram. If a microphone specially designed to detect low-frequency sound waves is placed on the chest, the heart sounds can be amplified and recorded by a special high-speed recording apparatus such as an oscilloscope, a high-speed pen recorder, or a string galvanometer recorder, all of which are described in Chapter 17 or Chapter 22. The recording is called a phonocardiogram, and the heart sounds appear as vibrations, which are illustrated in Figure 374. Record A in Figure 374 illustrates a recording of normal heart sounds, showing the vibrations of the first heart sound, the second heart sound, the third heart sound, and even the atrial sound. It will be noted specifically that the vibrations of the second heart sound are of slightly higher frequency than the vibrations of the first heart sound, and the vibrations of the third and atrial heart sounds are each a very low rumble. The third heart sound can be recorded in only one third to one half of all persons, and the atrial heart sound can be recorded in perhaps one fourth of all persons. Even though these sounds are of such low frequency that they are normally below

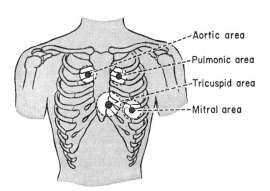

Figure 373. Chest areas from which each valve sound is best heard. (Redrawn from Adams: Physical Diagnosis. Williams & Wilkins Co.)

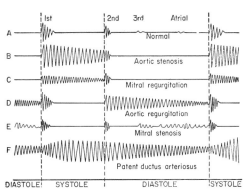

Figure 374. Phonocardiograms from normal and abnormal hearts.

the audible range of the human ear, a phonocardiograph designed to record extremely low frequencies can occasionally make records of them.

Abnormal Heart Sounds

Rheumatic Valvular Lesions. By far the greatest number of valvular lesions result from rheumatic fever. Rheumatic fever is believed to result from an immune reaction initiated by streptococcic toxin. The mechanism of this has been suggested to be the following: The entire sequence of events is almost always initiated by a preliminary streptococcic infection such as a sore throat, scarlet fever, middle ear infection, or so forth. The streptococci release a toxin that is highly hemolytic, and this breaks down the membranes of red blood cells and probably also of other cells throughout the body. The toxin then supposedly combines with protein from the destroyed cells, and this combination initiates an immune response so that specific immune bodies are released into the blood. It is a well-known principle of immunology that such immune bodies can then react with either of the two parties of the combination that initiated the response. Therefore, even after the streptococcic toxin has left the body, the immune bodies are still capable of reacting with the proteins of the cells, and this reaction can continue to take place as long as the immune bodies exist among the plasma globulins—six months or more. As a result of this continuing reaction, rheumatic fever causes damage in all parts of the body but especially in certain very susceptible areas such as the heart valves. The principles of immunity relating to this type of reaction were discussed in Chapter 14, and it was also noted in Chapter 11 that acute glomerular nephritis has a similar etiology.

Regardless of the actual cause of rheumatic fever, large hemorrhagic, bulbous lesions grow along the inflamed edges of the heart valves. Because the mitral valve receives more trauma during valvular action than do any of the other valves, this valve is the one most often affected, and the aortic valve is second most frequently involved. The tricuspid and pulmonary valves are very rarely involved because the stresses acting on these valves are slight compared to those in the left ventricle.

Scarring of the valves. The bulbous, hemorrhagic lesions of acute rheumatic fever frequently adhere to adjacent valve leaflets simultaneously so that the edges of the leaflets become stuck together. Then, in the late stages of rheumatic fever, the lesions become scar tissue, permanently fusing portions of the leaflets. Also, the free edges of the leaflets, which are normally filmy and free-flapping, become solid, scarred masses.

A valve in which the leaflets adhere to each other so extensively that blood cannot pass satisfactorily is said to be *stenosed.* On the other hand, when the valve edges are so destroyed by scar tissue that they cannot close together, *regurgitation* of blood occurs when the valve should be closed. Stenosis usually does not occur without coexistence of at least some degree of regurgitation, and vice versa. Therefore, when a patient is said to have stenosis or regurgitation, it is usually meant that one merely predominates over the other.

Other Causes of Valvular Lesions. Until the last few years, a prominent cause of aortic valvular destruction was vascular syphilis. However, with the advent of modern treatment, syphilis now very rarely proceeds to such a severe state. In syphilitic lesions aortic regurgitation almost always occurs without any stenosis of the valve, differing in this respect from regurgitation caused by rheumatic fever.

Occasionally, stenosis or lack of one or more leaflets of a valve occurs as a congenital defect. Complete lack of leaflets is very rare, though stenosis is quite common, as will be discussed later in this chapter.

Abnormal Heart Sounds Caused by Valvular Lesions. As illustrated by the phonocardiograms of Figure 374, many abnormal heart sounds, known as "murmurs," occur in abnormalities of the valves, as follows:

The murmur of aortic stenosis. In aortic stenosis blood is ejected from the left ventricle through only a small opening at the aortic valve. Because of the resistance to ejection, the pressure in the left ventricle rises sometimes to as high as 450 mm. Hg while the pressure in the aorta is still normal. Thus, a nozzle effect is created with blood jetting under tremendous force through the small opening of the valve. The blood impinging against the aortic walls causes very intense vibration in the aorta, and a loud

ductus arteriosus, interventricular septal defect, and interatrial septal defect will be discussed as examples of this type of congenital heart disease.

In all right-to-left shunts, much of the blood bypasses the lungs and therefore fails to become oxygenated. Consequently, large quantities of venous blood enter the arterial system directly, and the patient is usually cyanotic (blue) all of the time. By far the most common type of right-to-left shunt is the *Tetralogy of Fallot*, which will be described below; most other right-to-left shunts are some variation of this abnormality.

Causes of Congenital Anomalies. One of the most common causes of congenital heart defects is a virus infection of the mother during the first trimester of pregnancy when the chambers of the fetal heart are being formed. Defects are particularly prone to develop when the mother contracts German measles at this time—so often indeed that obstetricians advise termination of pregnancy if German measles occurs in the first trimester. However, some congenital defects of the heart are believed to be hereditary because the same defect has been known to occur in identical twins and also in succeeding generations. Congenital defects of the heart are frequently also associated with other congenital defects of the body.

Patent Ductus Arteriosus—A Left-to-Right Shunt

During fetal life the lungs are collapsed, and the elastic fibers that keep the alveoli collapsed also keep the blood vessels collapsed. Therefore, in the collapsed lung the resistance to blood flow is considerably greater than in the inflated lung. For this

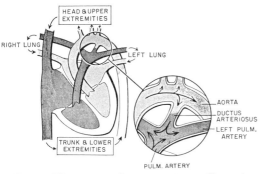

Figure 379. Patent ductus arteriosus, illustrating the degree of blood oxygenation in the different parts of the circulation.

reason, and because of the very low systemic resistance through the large vessels of the placenta, the pressure in the pulmonary artery is higher than in the aorta. As a result, almost all the pulmonary arterial blood flows through the ductus arteriosus into the aorta rather than through the lungs first. This allows immediate recirculation of the blood through the systemic arteries of the fetus. Obviously, this lack of blood flow through the lungs is of no detriment to the fetus because the blood is oxygenated by the placenta of the mother.

Closure of the Ductus. As soon as the baby is born he inflates his lungs, and not only do the alveoli fill, but the resistance to blood flow through the pulmonary vascular tree decreases tremendously. Simultaneously, the aortic pressure rises because of sudden cessation of blood flow through the placenta. Thus, the pressure in the pulmonary artery falls, while that in the aorta rises. As a result, forward blood flow through the ductus ceases soon after birth, and blood may even flow backward from the aorta to the pulmonary artery. This new state of blood flow causes the ductus arteriosus to become occluded within a few hours to a few days in most babies so that blood flow through the ductus does not persist. The possible causes of ductus closure will be discussed in Chapter 81. In many instances it takes several months for the ductus to close completely, and in about 1 out of every 4000 babies the ductus never closes, causing the condition known as *patent ductus arteriosus*, the dynamics of which are illustrated in Figure 379.

Dynamics of Persistent Patent Ductus. During the early months of an infant's life a patent ductus usually does not cause severely abnormal dynamics because the blood pressure of the aorta then is not much higher than the pressure in the pulmonary artery, and only a small amount of blood flows backwards into the pulmonary system. However, as the child grows older, the differential between the pressure in the aorta and that in the pulmonary artery progressively increases with corresponding increase in the backward flow of blood from the aorta to the pulmonary artery. Also, the diameter of the partially closed ductus increases with time, making the condition worse.

In the older child with a patent ductus, as much as one half to three fourths of the aortic blood flows into the pulmonary artery, then through the lungs, into the left atrium, and finally back into the left ventricle, passing through this circuit two or more times for every one time that it passes through the systemic circulation.

It should be noted particularly that these persons do not show cyanosis until the heart fails or until the lungs become congested. Indeed, the arterial blood is often better oxygenated than normally because of the extra passage of blood through the lungs. Furthermore, in the early stages of patent ductus arteriosus the quantity of blood flowing into the systemic aorta remains essentially normal because the quantity of blood returning to the heart from the peripheral circulatory system is normal. Yet, because of the tremendous accessory flow of blood around and around through the lungs and left side of the heart, the cardiac output of the left ventricle in patent ductus arteriosus is usually two to four times normal.

The major effect of patent ductus arteriosus on the patient is his low cardiac and respiratory reserve. His left ventricle is already pumping approximately two or more times the normal cardiac output, and the maximum that it can possibly pump is about four to six times normal. Therefore, during exercise the cardiac output can be increased much less than usual. Under basal conditions, the patient usually appears normal except for possible heaving of his chest with each beat of the heart, but just as soon as he tries to perform even moderately strenuous exercise he is very likely to become weak and occasionally even faint from momentary heart failure. Also, the high pressures in the pulmonary vessels soon lead to pulmonary congestion.

The entire heart usually hypertrophies greatly in patent ductus arteriosus. The left ventricle hypertrophies because of the excessive work load that it must perform in pumping a far greater than normal cardiac output, while the right ventricle hypertrophies because of increased pulmonary arterial pressure resulting from, first, increased flow of blood through the lungs caused by the extra blood from the patent ductus and, second, increased resistance to blood flow through the lungs caused by progressive sclerosing of the vessels as they are exposed year in and year out to excessive pulmonary blood flow.

As a result of the increased load on the heart and because of the pulmonary congestion, most patients with patent ductus die between the ages of 20 and 40 unless the defect is corrected by surgery.

The Machinery Murmur. In the infant with patent ductus arteriosus, occasionally no abnormal heart sounds will be heard because the quantity of reversed blood flow may be insignificant. As the baby grows older, reaching the age of 1 to 3 years, a harsh, blowing murmur begins to be heard in the pulmonic area of the chest. This sound is much more intense during systole when the aortic pressure is high and much less intense during diastole, so that it waxes and wanes with each beat of the heart, creating the so-called "machinery murmur."

Surgical Treatment of Patent Ductus. Surgical treatment of patent ductus arteriosus is extremely simple, for all one needs to do is to ligate the patent ductus. A ligature is very likely to cut directly through the patent ductus as a wire cuts through a cake of ice, and the two ends of the ductus often recannulate, causing recurrence of patency. Therefore, most surgeons actually divide the two ends of the ductus, suturing each end separately so that recannulation cannot occur.

Interventricular Septal Defect—a Left-to-Right Shunt

Because the systolic pressure in the left ventricle is normally about six times that in the right ventricle, a large amount of blood flows from the left to the right ventricle whenever an interventricular defect is present. As a result of elevated pressure in the right ventricle, the right ventricle hypertrophies, sometimes to such an extent that its muscular wall approximately equals that of the left ventricle.

Diagnosis of an interventricular septal defect is based (1) on the presence of a systolic blowing murmur heard over the anterior projection of the heart, (2) on high right ventricular systolic pressure recorded from a catheter, and (3) on the presence of oxygenated blood in a blood sample removed through the catheter from the right ventricle, this blood having leaked backward from the left ventricle.

Blood flowing from the left ventricle into the right ventricle passes one or more times through the lungs and then back to the left ventricle again before finally entering the peripheral circulatory system. This condition, therefore, is analogous to patent ductus arteriosus except that the flow of blood from the systemic circulation to the pulmonary circulation occurs only during systole rather than during both systole and diastole as in patent ductus.

Interatrial Septal Defects—a Left-to-Right Shunt

Closure of the Foramen Ovale.

During infant life much of the blood entering the right atrium fails to pass into the right ventricle but instead courses directly through the foramen ovale into the left atrium and thence out into the systemic circulation. This mechanism aids the ductus arteriosus in shunting blood around the lungs, thereby relieving the fetal heart from unnecessary load. Immediately after birth of the child, the pressure in the pulmonary artery decreases while that in the aorta increases, as discussed above. These changes decrease and increase respectively the loads on the right and left ventricles so that the right atrial pressure decreases and the left atrial pressure increases. As a result, blood then attempts to flow from the left atrium back into the right atrium. However, the foramen ovale is covered by a small valvelike vane, which closes over the foramen. In two thirds of all persons the foramen later becomes totally occluded by fibrous tissue, but in one third the foramen never becomes totally occluded. Yet, this non-occluded opening does not cause any physiologic abnormality in the heart because the left atrial pressure remains 3 to 4 mm. Hg higher than the right atrial pressure, keeping the valve permanently closed.

Dynamics of Interatrial Defects.

Occasionally, the valve does not cover the foramen ovale, and a hole persists permanently between the left atrium and the right atrium. If this hole is small, only a small amount of blood will pass from the left atrium back to the right atrium, but occasionally almost the entire wall between the two atria is missing. In this case a tremendous quantity of blood flows from the left atrium into the right atrium and circulates repeatedly through the lungs before finally passing into the systemic circulation. Therefore, even though a small opening between the atria does not make a great deal of difference in the function of the heart, large openings greatly reduce the cardiac reserve, and the patient dies an early death because of right ventricular failure and pulmonary congestion.

The diagnosis of an interatrial septal defect is difficult to make, for no murmurs can be heard, the patient's arterial blood is well oxygenated, and the usual x-ray studies are relatively non-specific. The means by which the diagnosis can be made accurately are (1) by angiocardiograms—that is, x-rays made after injecting a radiopaque dye into the heart, (2) by finding oxygenated blood in a catheter specimen from the right atrium, and (3) by applying the new diagnostic technique illustrated in Figure 380. This figure shows the concentration of dye in the arterial blood following injection of a single slug of the

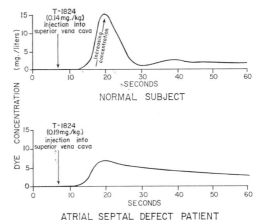

Figure 380. Technique for diagnosing an interatrial septal defect. (Modified from Keys, Swan, and Wood: *Proc. Staff Mayo Clinic.* 31:138, 1956.)

dye into the venous system. Note that in the normal person the dye appears in the arteries reasonably rapidly, and its peak falls off in only a few seconds. However, in interatrial septal defect the curve is much prolonged because large amounts of the dye recirculate again and again through the lungs before reaching the peripheral arterial tree. Obviously, this same type of curve could be recorded in almost any left-to-right shunt, but, in the absence of a heart murmur, as is true in patients with interatrial defects, one can use this technique to make a diagnosis of interatrial septal defect.

Tetralogy of Fallot—a Right-to-Left Shunt

Tetralogy of Fallot is illustrated in Figure 381, from which it will be noted that four different abnormalities of the heart occur simultaneously. First, the aorta originates from the right ventricle rather than the left, or it overrides the septum as shown in the figure. Second, the pulmonary artery is stenosed so that a much less than normal amount of blood passes from the right side of the heart into the lungs; instead the blood passes into the aorta. Third, blood from the left ventricle usually flows through a ventricular septal defect into the right ventricle and into the aorta or directly into the overriding aorta. Fourth, because the right side of the heart must pump large quantities of blood against the high pressure in the aorta, its musculature is very highly developed, causing an enlarged right ventricle. These four abnormalities exist together so frequently that this heart disease comprises a large percentage of the congenitally abnormal hearts.

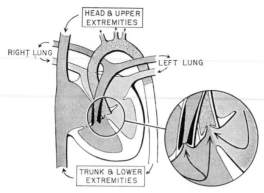

Figure 381. Tetralogy of Fallot, illustrating the degree of blood oxygenation in the different parts of the circulation.

Abnormal Dynamics. It is readily apparent that the major physiologic difficulty caused by tetralogy of Fallot is shunt of blood past the lungs without its becoming oxygenated. As much as 75 per cent of the venous blood returning to the heart may pass directly from the right ventricle into the aorta without becoming oxygenated. Tetralogy of Fallot is the major cause of cyanosis in babies ("blue babies").

A diagnosis of tetralogy of Fallot is usually based, first, on the fact that the baby is blue; second, on records of high systolic pressure in the right ventricle recorded through a catheter; third, on characteristic changes in the x-ray silhouette of the heart; and, fourth, on systolic murmurs resulting from abnormal blood flow through the interventricular septal defect and the pulmonary stenotic area, though these murmurs are not at all distinctive because similar murmurs can occur in many other abnormalities of the heart.

Surgical Treatment of Tetralogy of Fallot. In recent years tetralogy of Fallot has been treated relatively successfully by surgery. The treatment is to create an artificial ductus arteriosus, thereby correcting the cyanosis and increasing the life expectancy of the patient with tetralogy of Fallot from approximately 1 to 10 years to an age of perhaps 30 to 50 years.

This is performed in one of two ways. First, the right subclavian artery or some other chest artery can be sectioned and then sutured into a small opening made in the side of a pulmonary artery. Second, a small opening can be made in adjacent sides of both the aorta and left pulmonary artery and then these two openings sutured together so that a small fistula is developed. As a result of either of these operations, much of the aortic blood then flows through the lungs instead of passing into the systemic circulation so that the left ventricle then pumps blood through both the lungs and through the systemic circulation. If exactly the right size hole has been made between the aortic and pulmonary systems, the blood will become adequately oxygenated without excessively overloading the heart. Yet, the patient will still have a far greater than normal load on both ventricles of his heart, and there is still the possibility of an early death caused by cardiac failure; the operations have not yet been performed for enough years to give a definite prognosis.

Pulmonary Stenosis

Often a child is born with pulmonary stenosis but without other congenital abnormalities. Mild stenosis occurs in many persons, producing mild pulmonary stenotic murmurs. Such murmurs are called "functional murmurs" because the condition is innocuous. However, such severe pulmonary stenosis occasionally occurs that the right side of the heart is likely to fail at an early age because blood flow from the right ventricle into the lungs is greatly impeded, the right ventricular systolic pressure rising to 75 to 100 mm. Hg instead of the normal 22 mm. Hg. The right side of the heart dilates, and the muscle becomes greatly hypertrophied in order to withstand the load. Also, a very loud stenotic murmur is heard over the pulmonary valve area. In many cases of pulmonary stenosis, the stenotic area can be enlarged by surgical maneuvers so that the heart resumes normal function.

Use of Extracorporeal Circulation in Cardiac Surgery

It is almost impossible to repair intracardiac defects while the heart is still pumping. Therefore, many different types of artificial *heart-lung machines* have been developed to take the place of the heart and lungs during the course of operation. Such a system is called an *extracorporeal circulation*. The system consists principally of two parts: (1) a pump and (2) an oxygenating device. Almost any type of pump that does not cause hemolysis of the blood seems to be suitable, but many special problems have been encountered in developing an adequate oxygenator. The different principles that have been used for oxygenating blood are (1) bubbling oxygen through the blood and then removing the bubbles from the blood before passing it back into the patient, (2) dripping the blood downward over the surfaces of large areas of screen wire, (3) passing the blood over the surfaces of rotating discs, and (4) passing the blood between thin membranes that are porous to oxygen and carbon dioxide. The use of all these oxygenators has been fraught with one difficulty or another, including hemolysis of the blood, development of small clots in the blood, likelihood of small bubbles of oxygen or small emboli of antifoaming agent passing into the arteries of the patient, necessity for very large quantities of blood to prime the entire system, failure to exchange adequate quantities of oxygen, and the necessity to use heparin in the system to prevent blood coagulation, the heparin also preventing adequate hemostasis during the surgical procedure. From a physiologic point of view there is no reason to doubt eventual complete success of artificial heart-lung machines, and even now in the hands of experts few patients die as a result of the extracorporeal circulation itself during the surgical procedure.

HYPERTROPHY OF THE HEART IN VALVULAR AND CONGENITAL HEART DISEASE

Because the total work performed by each ventricle is a product of cardiac output times pressure output, one can easily calculate approximately how much hypertrophy will occur and in which chamber of the heart the hypertrophy will exist in the different types of valvular and congenital heart disease.

In *aortic stenosis* and *aortic regurgitation,* the left ventricular musculature hypertrophies tremendously, sometimes to as much as four to five times normal, so that the weight of the heart on occasion may be as great as 1000 grams instead of the normal 300 grams.

In mitral disease, the left atrium hypertrophies and dilates, but no left ventricular hypertrophy occurs in *mitral stenosis,* and only mild to moderate hypertrophy of the left ventricle occurs in *mitral regurgitation.* Some hypertrophy of the right ventricle may develop owing to back pressure effects through the lungs causing elevation of the pulmonary arterial pressure.

In *patent ductus arteriosus,* the work load of both ventricles is increased. The left ventricle must pump twice the quantity of blood that it normally pumps; therefore, it would be expected that the left ventricle would hypertrophy to approximately twice normal size. On the other hand, the right ventricle must pump its blood against a much higher than normal pulmonary arterial pressure because of the large quantity of blood refluxing from the aorta into the pulmonary artery. Consequently, the right ventricle also hypertrophies approximately in proportion to the left ventricular hypertrophy.

In *tetralogy of Fallot,* one of the cardinal signs is the marked right ventricular hypertrophy, for the right ventricle must pump against the pressure in the aorta. On the other hand the work load of the left ventricle is actually less than normal because of the reduced blood flow from the lungs into the left heart. Therefore, the right ventricle in tetralogy of Fallot is often larger than the normal left ventricle, while the left ventricle may be relatively small.

It should be pointed out once again that *the coronary blood flow does not increase to the same extent as the mass of muscle* when *cardiac hypertrophy occurs.* This means that relative ischemia develops as the muscle hypertrophies, and coronary insufficiency very easily ensues. Therefore, anginal pain is a very frequent accompaniment of many valvular and congenital heart diseases—especially in aortic stenosis and aortic regurgitation.

REFERENCES

Abbott, M. E.: Atlas of Congenital Cardiac Disease. New York, Am. Heart. A., 1936.

Allen, J. G., Moore, F. D., Morrow, A. G., and Swan, H., II.: Extracorporeal Circulation. Springfield, Illinois, Charles C Thomas, 1958.

Bahnson, H. T., and Otis, A. B.: Physiological consideration of cardiovascular surgery. *Physiol. Rev.,* 35:363, 1955.

Bing, R. J.: Catheterization of heart. *Adv. Int. Med.,* 5:59, 1952.

Bing, R. J.: The physiology of congenital heart disease; in Levy, R. L. (ed.): Disorders of the Heart and Circulation. New York, Thomas Nelson and Sons, 1951.

Bing, R. J., Lombardo, T. A., Bargerow, L. M., Taeschler, M., and Tuluy, S.: Congenital heart disease: a clinical and physiologic correlation. *Ann. Int. Med.,* 37:664, 1952.

Burchell, H. B.: Indicator substances in the diagnosis of congenital heart disease. World Trends in Cardiology. V. Instrumental Methods in Cardiac Diagnosis. New York, Paul B. Hoeber, 1956, p. 16.

Butterworth, J. S., Chassin, M. R., McGrath, R., and

Reppert, E. H.: Cardiac Auscultation—Including Audio-Visual Principles. 2nd ed., New York, Grune & Stratton, Inc., 1960.

Connolly, D. C., and Wood, E. H.: Hemodynamic data during rest and exercise in patients with mitral valve disease in relation to the differentiation of stenosis and insufficiency from the pulmonary artery wedge pressure pulse. *J. Lab. Clin. Med., 49:* 526, 1957.

Connolly, D. C., Thompkins, R. G., Lev, R., Kirklin, J. W., and Wood, E. H.: Pulmonary-artery wedge pressures in mitral valve disease; relationship to left atrial pressures. *Proc Staff Meet., Mayo Clin., 28:3*, 1953.

Cournand, A., Baldwin, J. S., and Himmelstein, A.: Cardiac Catheterization in Congenital Heart Disease. New York, Commonwealth Fund, 1949.

Cross, F. S., Berne, R. M., Hirose, Y., Jones, R. D., and Kay, E. B.: Evaluation of a rotating disc type reservoir-oxygenator. *Proc. Soc. Exp. Biol. and Med., 33:210*, 1956.

Dotter, C. F., and Steinberg, I.: Angiocardiography. New York, Paul B. Hoeber, 1953.

Edwards, J. E., Dry, T., Parker, R., Burchell, H. Wood, E., and Bulbulian, A.: An Atlas of Congenital Anomalies of the Heart and Great Vessels. 2nd ed., Springfield, Illinois, Charles C Thomas, 1954.

Gollan, F.: Physiology of Cardiac Surgery: Hypothermia, Extracorporeal Circulation and Extracorporeal Cooling. Springfield, Illinois, Charles C Thomas, 1959.

Henry Ford Hospital: Cardiovascular Surgery. Philadelphia, W. B. Saunders Co., 1955.

Holling, H. E.: Compensatory mechanisms for the anoxia of cyanotic congenital heart disease. *Clin. Sc., 11:283*, 1952.

Hufnagel, C. A., Harvey, W. P., Rabil, P. J., and McDermott, T. F.: Surgical correction of aortic insufficiency. *Surgery, 35:673*, 1954.

Keys, J. R., Swan, H. J., and Wood, E. H.: Dye-dilution curves from systemic arteries and left atrium of patients with valvular heart disease. *Proc. Staff Meet., Mayo Clin., 31:138*, 1956.

Kjellberg, S. R., Mannheimer, E., Rudhe, U., and Jonsson, B.: Diagnosis of Congenital Heart Disease. Chicago, Year Book Publishers, 1959.

Levine, S. A., and Harvey, W. P.: Clinical Auscultation of the Heart. 2nd ed., Philadelphia, W. B. Saunders Co., 1959.

McKusick, V. A.: Cardiovascular Sound in Health and Disease. Baltimore, Williams & Wilkins Co., 1958.

Nadas, A. S.: Pediatric Cardiology, Philadelphia, W. B. Saunders Co., 1957.

Oppenheimer, M. J., Durant, T. M., and Lynch, P.: Body position in relation to venous air embolism and the associated cardiovascular respiratory changes. *Am. J. M. Sc., 225:362*, 1953.

Patten, B. M.: Human Embryology. 2nd ed., New York, McGraw-Hill Book Co., Inc., 1953.

Ravin, A. R.: *Auscultation of the Heart,* Chicago, Year Book Publishers, 1958.

Rodriguez, J.: An Atlas of Cardiac Surgery, Philadelphia, W. B. Saunders Co., 1957.

Rushmer, R. F., Finlayson, B. L., and Nash, A. A.: Movements of the mitral valve. *Circ. Res., 4:337*, 1956.

Stewart, H. J., and Glenn, F.: Mitral Valvulotomy. Springfield, Illinois, Charles C Thomas, 1959.

Swan, H. J., Zapata-Diaz, J., Burchell, H. B., and Wood, E. H.: Pulmonary hypertension in congenital heart disease. *Am. J. Med., 16:12*, 1954.

Taussig, H. B.: Congenital malformations of the heart. New York, Commonwealth Fund, 1947.

Taussig, H. B. and Cain, A. S., Jr. (eds.): World Trends in Cardiology. II. Cardiovascular Surgery. New York, Paul B. Hoeber, 1956.

Warren, J. V.: Gallop rhythm. *Circulation, 15:321,* 1957.

West, J. W., Wendel, H., and Foltz, E. L.: Effects of aortic insufficiency on circulatory dynamics of the dog: with special reference to coronary blood flow and cardiac oxygen consumption. *Circ. Res., 7:685*, 1959.

Wood, E. H., Sutterer, W., Swan, H. J., and Helmholz, H. F., Jr.: The technic and special instrumentation problems associated with catheterization of the left side of the heart. *Proc. Staff Meet., Mayo Clin., 31:108*, 1956.

GENERAL BIBLIOGRAPHY FOR THE CARDIOVASCULAR SYSTEM

Allen, E. V.: Peripheral Vascular Diseases. Philadelphia, W. B. Saunders Co., 1955.

American Heart Association: World Trends in Cardiology. Vols. I, II, III, IV, and V, New York, Paul B. Hoeber, 1956.

Crismon, J. M.: Peripheral circulation. *Ann. Rev. of Physiol., 22:317*, 1960.

Friedberg, C. K.: Diseases of the Heart. 2nd ed., Philadelphia, W. B. Saunders Co., 1956.

Gordon, B. L.: Clinical Cardiopulmonary Physiology. 2nd ed., New York, Grune & Stratton, Inc., 1960.

Guyton, A. C.: Peripheral circulation. *Ann. Rev. Physiol., 21:239*, 1959.

Hardy, J. D.: Pathophysiology in Surgery. Baltimore, Williams & Wilkins Co., 1958.

Harris, A. S.: Heart. *Ann. Rev. of Physiol., 22:283,* 1960.

Levine, S. A.: Clinical Heart Disease. 5th ed., Philadelphia, W. B. Saunders Co., 1958.

Lorber, V.: Heart. *Ann. Rev. Physiol., 20:97*, 1958.

Luisada, A. A. (ed.): Cardiology: An Encyclopedia of the Cardiovascular System. New York, McGraw-Hill Book Co., Inc., 1959.

Martin, P. Lynn, R. B., Dible, J. H., and Aird, I.: Peripheral Vascular Disorders, London, Livingstone, 1956.

Rushmer, R. F.: Cardiovascular Dynamics. Philadelphia, W. B. Saunders Co., 1961.

Schaefer, H.: Heart. *Ann. Rev. Physiol., 18:195*, 1956.

Scher, A. M.: Heart. *Ann. Rev. Physiol., 21:211*, 1959.

Scherf, D., and Boyd, L. J.: Cardiovascular Diseases. 3rd ed., New York, Grune & Stratton, Inc., 1958.

Stroud, W. D., and Stroud, M. W., III: Cardiovascular Disease, Philadelphia, F. A. Davis Co., 1959.

Wood, P.: Diseases of the Heart and Circulation. 2nd ed., Philadelphia, J. B. Lippincott Co., 1956.

Visscher, M. B., and Stephens, G. J.: Heart. *Ann Rev. Physiol., 19:359*, 1957.

Part Seven

RESPIRATION

Chapter 39

Pulmonary Ventilation

and the Mechanics of Respiration

Respiration means the transport of oxygen from the atmosphere to the cells and, in turn, the transport of carbon dioxide from the cells back to the atmosphere. This process can be divided into four major stages: (1) pulmonary ventilation, which means the actual inflow and outflow of air between the atmosphere and the alveoli, (2) diffusion of oxygen and carbon dioxide between the alveoli and the blood, (3) transport of oxygen and carbon dioxide in the blood and body fluids to and from the cells, and (4) regulation of ventilation and other aspects of respiration. The present chapter and the following three will discuss, respectively, these four major aspects of respiration. In subsequent chapters various pulmonary disorders and special respiratory problems related to aviation medicine and deep sea diving physiology will be discussed to illustrate the basic principles of respiratory physiology.

THE PULMONARY VOLUMES AND CAPACITIES

Pulmonary ventilation is accomplished by expansion and contraction of the lungs. Figure 382 gives a graphical representation of changes in lung volume under different conditions of breathing. At the beginning of the record the lung volume is 2300 ml., and then it rises and falls approximately 550 ml. with each normal respiration. When the person inspires as deeply as he can, the maximum lung volume rises to 5800 ml. At another point, he expires as much as pos-

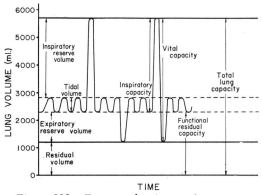

Figure 382. Diagram showing respiratory excursions during normal breathing and during maximal inspiration and maximal expiration.

sible, and the minimum lung volume falls to 1200 ml. For ease in describing the events of pulmonary ventilation, the air in the lungs has been subdivided into four different *volumes* and four different *capacities*, which will be described as follows:

The Pulmonary "Volumes"

To the left in Figure 382 are shown four different pulmonary lung "volumes" which, when added together, equal the maximum volume to which the lungs can be expanded. The significance of each of these volumes is the following:

(1) The *tidal volume* is the volume of air inspired and expired with each normal breath, and it amounts to about 500 ml. in the normal young male adult.

(2) The *inspiratory reserve volume* is the extra volume of air that can be inspired over

511

and beyond the normal tidal volume, and it is usually equal to approximately 3000 ml. in the young male adult.

(3) The *expiratory reserve volume* is the amount of air that can still be expired by forceful expiration after the end of a normal tidal expiration; this normally amounts to about 1100 ml. in the young male adult.

(4) The *residual volume* is the volume of air remaining in the lungs even after the most forceful expiration. This volume averages about 1200 ml. in the young male adult.

The Pulmonary "Capacities"

In describing events in the pulmonary cycle, it is sometimes desirable to consider two or more of the above volumes together. Such combinations are called *pulmonary capacities*. To the right in Figure 382 are shown the different pulmonary capacities, which can be described as follows:

(1) The *inspiratory capacity* equals *the tidal volume* plus *the inspiratory reserve volume*. This is the amount of air that a person can breathe beginning at the normal expiratory level and distending his lungs to the maximum amount (about 3500 ml.).

(2) The *functional residual capacity* equals *the expiratory reserve volume* plus *the residual volume*. This is the amount of air remaining in the lungs at the end of normal expiration (about 2300 ml.).

(3) The *vital capacity* equals *the inspiratory reserve volume* plus *the tidal volume* plus *the expiratory reserve volume*. This is the maximum amount of air that a person can expel from his lungs after first filling his lungs to their maximum extent and then expiring to the maximum extent (about 4600 ml.).

(4) The *total lung capacity* is equal to *the inspiratory reserve volume* plus *the tidal volume* plus *the expiratory reserve volume* plus *the residual volume*, or, in other words, this is the maximum volume to which the lungs can be expanded with the greatest possible inspiratory effort (about 5800 ml.).

All pulmonary volumes and capacities are about 20 to 25 per cent less in the female than in the male, and they obviously are greater in large and athletic persons than in small and asthenic persons.

Resting Expiratory Level. Normal pulmonary ventilation is accomplished almost entirely by the muscles of inspiration. On relaxation of the inspiratory muscles the elastic properties of the lungs and thorax cause the lungs to contract passively. Therefore, when all inspiratory muscles are completely relaxed the lungs return to a relaxed state, and the volume of air then in the lungs is called the *resting expiratory level*. This is equal to the functional residual capacity or about 2300 ml. in the young male adult.

Measurement of the Pulmonary Volumes and Capacities and Their Significance

Spirometry. A simple method by which most of the pulmonary volumes and capacities can be measured is that of *spirometry*. A typical spirometer is illustrated in Figure 383. This consists of a drum inverted over a chamber of water, the drum counterbalanced by a weight. In the drum is a breathing mixture of gases, usually air or oxygen, and a tube connects the mouth with this gas chamber. On breathing in and out of the chamber the drum rises and falls and an appropriate recording is made on another drum. When using this spirometer only a few breaths can be recorded because of the buildup of carbon dioxide and loss of oxygen from the gas chamber. However, a respirometer such as that illustrated in Figure 658 of Chapter 68 can be used for continual recording of the spirogram. This more elaborate apparatus chemically removes the carbon dioxide as it is formed.

Figure 382, which was discussed above, represents a typical spirogram recorded by use of the spirometer. From this figure it is

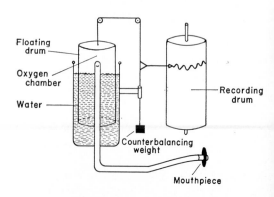

Figure 383. A spirometer.

obvious that the following lung volumes and capacities can be measured by simple spirometry: (1) the tidal volume, (2) inspiratory reserve volume, (3) the expiratory reserve volume, (4) the inspiratory capacity, and (5) the vital capacity. The volumes that cannot be measured are (a) the residual volume, (b) the functional residual capacity, and (c) the total lung capacity. Failure of the spirometer to measure these results from its inability to measure the residual volume still remaining in the lungs after a forceful expiration.

Determination of Residual Volume, Functional Residual Capacity, and Total Lung Capacity by the Nitrogen Washout Method. The functional residual capacity can be measured by the following indirect procedure:

At the end of a normal expiration the subject suddenly switches from breathing normal air to breathing pure oxygen, and he continues to breathe the pure oxygen for several minutes. During this period of time all the nitrogen in his lungs is "washed out" into the expired air. By collecting the expired air and analyzing the total amount of nitrogen that has been washed out of the lungs, one can calculate the amount of air in the lungs at the beginning of the test, which equals the functional residual capacity, by the following formula:

lumen endotracheal tube is passed into the trachea, with one of the lumens connecting to one of the major bronchi and the second lumen to the second major bronchus. Mixing of the air between the two lumens is prevented by inflated balloons on the endotracheal tube. Each of the two lumens of the endotracheal tube is then connected to separate bronchospirometers, and appropriate spirograms are recorded.

Bronchospirometry is also of value for studying the ability of the separate lungs to transfer gases between the alveoli and the pulmonary blood, which will be discussed further in the following chapter.

Significance of the Pulmonary Volumes and Capacities

In normal persons the volumes of air in the lungs depend primarily on the size of the person and his build. Furthermore, the different "volumes" and "capacities" change with the position of the body, most of them decreasing when the person lies down and increasing when he stands. This change with position is caused by two major factors: first, a tendency for the abdominal contents to press upward against the diaphragm in the lying position, and, second, increase in the pulmonary blood volume in the lying position, which correspondingly decreases the space available for pulmonary air.

Physiologically, the three most important of the volumes and capacities are the tidal

$$\text{Functional residual capacity} = \text{Volume of nitrogen washed out} \times \frac{100}{78}$$

This formula is based on the fact that 78 per cent of the gases in the lungs is nitrogen and 22 per cent is oxygen and water vapor. To be completely accurate in the measurement, additional minor corrections must be made for nitrogen diffusion out of the blood into the lungs.

Once the functional residual capacity has been determined, the residual volume can then be determined by subtracting the expiratory reserve volume from the functional residual capacity. Also, the total lung capacity can be determined by adding the inspiratory capacity to the functional residual capacity.

Bronchospirometry. At times it is desired to measure the pulmonary volumes and capacities of the two lungs separately. To do this a double

volume, the residual volume, and the vital capacity. The tidal volume is important because this represents the inflow and outflow of air with each breath and determines to a great extent the rate of exchange of new air with alveolar air. This problem will be discussed at much greater length later in the chapter.

Significance of the Residual Volume. The residual volume represents the air that cannot be removed from the lungs even by forceful expiration. This is important because it provides air in the alveoli to aerate the blood even between breaths. Were it not for the residual air, the amounts of oxygen and carbon dioxide in the blood would rise and fall very markedly with each respiration, which would certainly be disadvantageous to the respiratory process.

Significance of the Vital Capacity.
Other than the anatomical build of a person, the major factors which affect vital capacity are (1) the position of the person during the vital capacity measurement, (2) the strength of the respiratory muscles and (3) the distensibility of the lungs and chest cage, which is called "pulmonary compliance."

The average vital capacity in the young adult male is about 4.6 liters, and in the young adult female about 3.1 liters, though these values are much greater in some persons of the same weight than in others. A long thin person usually has a higher vital capacity than his more obese counterpart, and a well-developed athlete may have a vital capacity as great as 30 to 40 per cent above normal—that is, as much as 6 to 7 liters.

Vital capacity following paralysis of the respiratory muscles. Paralysis of the respiratory muscles, which occurs quite often following spinal cord injuries or poliomyelitis, can cause a tremendous decrease in vital capacity to as low as 500 to 1000 ml.—barely enough to maintain life.

Decreased vital capacity caused by diminished pulmonary compliance. Obviously, any factor that reduces the ability of the lungs to expand will also reduce the vital capacity. Thus, tuberculosis, emphysema, chronic asthma, carcinoma, chronic bronchitis, and fibrotic pleurisy can all reduce the expansibility of the lungs (the pulmonary compliance) and thereby decrease the vital capacity. For this reason vital capacity measurements are among the most important of all clinical respiratory measurements for assessing the progress of different types of pulmonary fibrotic diseases.

Changes in vital capacity resulting from pulmonary congestion. In left heart disease or any other disease that causes pulmonary vascular congestion, the vital capacity becomes reduced because excess fluid in the tissues of the lungs decreases pulmonary compliance.

Vital capacity measurements made periodically in left-sided heart disease are one of the best means for determining whether the disease is progressing or getting better, for these measurements can indicate the degree of pulmonary edema.

THE MINUTE RESPIRATORY VOLUME—RESPIRATORY RATE AND TIDAL VOLUME

The *minute respiratory volume* is the total amount of new air moved into the lungs each minute, and this is equal to *the tidal volume times the respiratory rate.* The normal tidal volume of a young male adult, as pointed out above, is 500 ml., and the normal respiratory rate is approximately 12 breaths per minute. Therefore, the *minute respiratory volume averages about 6 liters per minute.* A person can occasionally live with a minute respiratory volume as low as 1.5 liters per minute and with a respiratory rate as little as two to four breaths per minute. Obviously, a greatly increased tidal volume can compensate for a markedly reduced rate. It should also be emphasized that variations in tidal volume and respiratory rate are usually of significance to the respiratory process only in so far as they affect the total volume of new air entering the alveoli each minute.

Maximum Breathing Capacity. A young male adult forcing himself to breathe as much volume of air as possible can usually breathe from 125 to 170 liters per minute for a period of about 15 seconds. This is called the *maximum breathing capacity.* On the average, this same person can maintain for long periods of strenuous exercise a minute respiratory volume as high as 100 to 120 liters per minute. It is evident, then, that the respiratory system has a very marked reserve, being capable of increasing its minute respiratory volume as much as 25-fold for short periods of time and as much as 20-fold for prolonged periods of time. Yet, despite this tremendous reserve, pathological conditions of the lungs can often so decrease the breathing capacity that the person becomes a respiratory invalid. Some of these pathological conditions will be discussed in Chapter 43.

VENTILATION OF THE ALVEOLI

The truly important factor of the entire pulmonary ventilatory process is the rate at which the alveolar air is renewed each minute by atmospheric air; this is called *alveolar ventilation.* One can very readily understand that alveolar ventilation per minute is not equal to the minute respiratory volume because a large portion of the inspired air goes to fill the respiratory passageways, the membranes of which are not capable of significant gaseous exchange with the blood.

The Dead Space

The air that goes to fill the respiratory passages with each breath is called *dead space air*. It is this dead space air that causes the minute alveolar ventilation to be different from the minute respiratory volume. On inspiration, much of the new air must first fill the different dead space areas—the nasal passageways, the pharynx, the trachea, and the bronchi—before any reaches the alveoli. Then, on expiration, all the air in the dead space is expired first before any of the air from the alveoli reaches the atmosphere. *The volume of air that enters the alveoli with each breath, therefore, is equal to the tidal volume minus the dead space volume.*

Measurement of the Dead Space Volume. A simple method for measuring the dead space volume is illustrated by Figure 384. In making this measurement the subject first breathes normal air and then suddenly takes a deep inspiration of oxygen. This, obviously, fills his entire dead space with pure oxygen, and some of the oxygen also mixes with the alveolar air. Then he expires through a rapidly recording nitrogen meter, which makes the record shown in the figure. The first portion of the expired air contains only pure oxygen, and the per cent nitrogen is zero, but, toward the end of the expiration, as the alveolar air reaches the nitrogen meter, the nitrogen concentration rises, in this instance up to 60 per cent, and then levels off. The total volume of air expired in this instance was 500 ml., and it can readily be seen that the area covered by the dots represents the dead space portion of the expired air while the area covered by the diagonals represents the alveolar portion of the expired air. Thus, one can determine the amount of dead space air from the following equation:

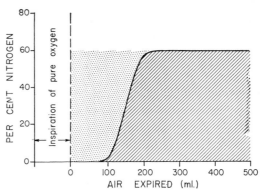

Figure 384. Continuous record of the changes in nitrogen concentration in the expired air following a previous inspiration of pure oxygen. This record can be used to calculate dead space as discussed in the text.

The normal dead space air in the young male adult is about 150 ml. This increases slightly with age, and it also changes greatly in different physiological states. For instance, it is reduced when the person lies down, and it is reduced in maximal expiration when the lungs are collapsed to their smallest possible size, for this causes the bronchi and trachea also to collapse to a certain extent. On the other hand, the dead space increases as much as 50 per cent when the lungs are excessively expanded. For instance, during the hyperventilation of exercise the *mean volume* of the lungs is usually considerably greater than normal, and the dead space is about 30 to 40 per cent greater than normal.

Anatomical versus Physiological Dead Space. The method described above for measuring the dead space measures the volume of all the spaces of the respiratory system besides the alveoli; this is called the *anatomical dead space*. On occasion, however, some of the alveoli themselves are not functional and, therefore, must be considered also to be dead space because there is no blood flow through the adjacent pulmonary vessels. Also, at other times the *ratio of pulmonary blood flow to alveolar ventilation* in certain alveoli is so low that these, too, can be considered to be partially dead space. When the alveolar dead space is included in the total measurement of dead

$$\text{Dead space air} = \frac{\text{Area of the dots} \; \times \; \text{Total air expired}}{\text{Area of the diagonals} \; + \; \text{Area of the dots}}$$

space this is then called *physiological dead space* in contradistinction to the anatomical dead space. In the normal person, the anatomical and the physiological dead space are essentially equal because all alveoli are functional, but in persons with non-functional alveoli or with abnormal ratios of blood flow to alveolar ventilation in some parts of the lungs, the physiological dead space is sometimes as much as 10 times the anatomical dead space or as much as 1 to 2 liters. These problems will be discussed further in Chapter 43 in relation to certain pulmonary diseases.

The Rate of Alveolar Ventilation

Alveolar ventilation per minute is the total volume of new air entering the alveoli each minute. It is equal to the respiratory rate times the amount of new air that enters the alveoli with each breath:

$$\text{Alveolar ventilation per minute} = \text{Respiratory rate} \times (\text{Tidal volume} - \text{Dead space volume})$$

Theoretically, when the tidal volume falls to equal the dead space volume, no new air at all will enter the alveoli with each breath, and the alveolar ventilation per minute will become zero however rapidly the person breathes. (This relationship is not entirely true because all the dead space air is never completely expired before some of the alveolar air begins to be expired, and the same is true for inspiration. Therefore, there can be a slight amount of alveolar ventilation even with tidal volumes as little as 60 to 75 ml.)

On the other hand, when the tidal volume is several liters, the effect of dead space volume on alveolar ventilation is almost insignificant, and under these conditions the alveolar ventilation per minute almost equals the minute respiratory volume. For instance, if the tidal volume is 4 liters and the dead space volume is 200 ml., then the alveolar ventilation per minute will be 95 per cent of the minute respiratory volume.

With a normal tidal volume of 500 ml., a normal dead space of 150 ml. and a respiratory rate of 12 times per minute, alveolar ventilation equals 12 (500 − 150) or 4200 ml. per minute.

Alveolar ventilation is one of the major factors determining the concentrations of oxygen and carbon dioxide in the alveoli.

Therefore, almost all discussions of gaseous exchange problems in the following chapters will emphasize alveolar ventilation. It should be pointed out once again that the respiratory rate, the tidal volume, and the minute respiratory volume are of importance only in so far as they affect alveolar ventilation.

THE MECHANICS OF RESPIRATION

Basic Mechanisms of Lung Expansion and Contraction

The lungs may be expanded by two methods: first, contraction of the diaphragm to increase the longitudinal length of the chest cavity and, second, elevation of the anterior portion of the chest cage so that the anteroposterior diameter of the chest cavity increases. Figure 385 illustrates these two methods. It is readily evident that contraction of the diaphragm pulls the lower border of the chest cavity downward and therefore increases its longitudinal length. On the other hand, upward movement of the diaphragm can be caused by active contraction of the different abdominal muscles to force the abdominal contents upward against the bottom of the diaphragm.

Elevation of the anterior portion of the chest cage causes the anteroposterior dimension of the chest cavity to increase by the following mechanism (which is also illustrated in Figure 385): During expiration the ribs extend in a downward direction

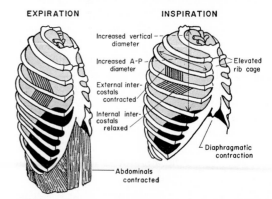

Figure 385. Expansion and contraction of the thoracic cage during expiration and inspiration, illustrating especially diaphragmatic contraction, elevation of the rib cage, and function of the intercostals.

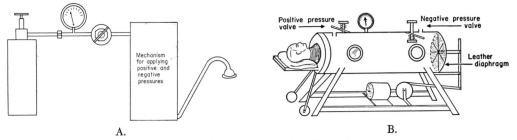

Figure 393. (A) The resuscitator, (B) the tank respirator.

The Tank Respirator. Figure 393 B illustrates the usual tank respirator with a patient's body inside the tank and his head protruding through a flexible but airtight diaphragm. At the end of the tank opposite to the patient's head is a motor driven leather diaphragm that moves back and forth with sufficient excursion to raise and lower the pressure inside the tank. As the diaphragm moves inward, positive pressure develops around the body and causes expiration, and as the leather diaphragm moves outward negative pressure causes inspiration. Check valves on the respirator control the positive and negative pressures. Ordinarily these pressures are adjusted so that the negative pressure that causes inspiration falls to −10 to −20 cm. of water and the positive pressure rises to 0 to +5 cm. of water.

Effect of the Resuscitator and the Tank Respirator on Venous Return. When air is forced into the lungs under positive pressure, or when the pressure around the patient's body is greatly reduced, as in the case of the tank respirator, so that the pressure in the lungs is greater than the pressure everywhere else in the body, the flow of blood into the lungs from the peripheral veins becomes impeded. The reason for this is the following: A high pressure in the alveoli also causes a high pressure in the intrapleural space, thus compressing the intrathoracic veins. In the case of the resuscitator, the peripheral veins are exposed to the atmospheric pressure around the body, while the intrathoracic veins are exposed to an elevated positive pressure caused by the resuscitator. In the case of the tank respirator, the peripheral veins are exposed to a negative pressure around the body while the lungs are exposed to atmospheric pressure. In either instance, the higher pressure in the thoracic veins holds the venous blood back, keeping it from entering the right heart. Therefore, use of excessive pressures with either the resuscitator or the tank respirator can reduce the cardiac output—sometimes to lethal levels. A person can usually survive with as much as 20 mm. Hg intrathoracic pressure, but prolonged exposure to greater than 30 mm. Hg will usually cause death.

The Electrophrenic Respirator

The electrophrenic respirator is an electrical stimulator used to excite intermittently one or both phrenic nerves. This is performed very simply with a geared motor driving a potentiometer connected to a nerve stimulator. The voltage of the stimuli increases and decreases, and the cycle repeats itself indefinitely.

Artificial respiration caused by the electrophrenic respirator, when used properly, is almost identical with normal respiration and does not have the drawback of diminished venous return as is true of the resuscitator and tank respirator. However, the obvious difficulty with electrophrenic respiration is application of the electrical stimuli to the phrenic nerve. A well-trained technician can hold the electrode directly over the phrenic nerve on the surface of the neck and cause adequate excitation, or an incision can be made to expose the phrenic nerve and the electrode placed around the nerve.

Unfortunately the electrophrenic respirator can be used only in patients who still have viable nerves to the diaphragm. For instance, in poliomyelitis this apparatus can be used very satisfactorily if the paralysis is caused by bulbar disease, but, if the paralysis is caused by damage to the anterior motoneurons in the spinal cord, the electrophrenic respirator can be used only for the first two to three days of the disease because the nerve fibers degenerate beyond that time.

THE ANESTHETIC MACHINE

The anesthetic machine, illustrated in Figure 394, is another respiratory apparatus based on interesting physiological principles. Before attempting to explain this machine it is first necessary to discuss the mechanism by which inhalation anesthetics work. These anesthetics include nitrous oxide, ethylene, cyclopropane, ether, chloroform, and others. In the early stages of anesthesia any one of these five different types of anesthetics is administered in relatively large concentration. The anesthetic is absorbed into the

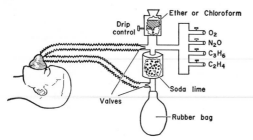

Figure 394.   The anesthetic machine.

blood stream, it passes to the brain, and there it causes a physical effect on the membranes of the neurons to block impulse conduction across the synapses. Once the patient's blood has become sufficiently saturated with one of the anesthetics, the anesthetist no longer needs to give the patient more anesthetic but merely to keep that anesthetic that has already been absorbed from leaving the body. To do this a small concentration of the anesthetic is maintained in the gases breathed by the patient so that the anesthetic absorbed into the blood exactly equals the anesthetic diffusing out of the blood into the lungs.

When using ether or chloroform, the anesthetic is introduced into the anesthetic circuit by means of a drip, which is illustrated in Figure 394, rather than in the form of a gas, because these two agents are liquid at normal atmospheric pressures and must vaporize in the anesthetic machine.

The anesthetic circuit consists of two large tubes leading to a mask over the patient's face, with a rubber bag somewhere in the circuit and a cannister filled with soda lime placed in the flow of the circuit to remove carbon dioxide. As the patient breathes, he breathes into and out of the rubber bag. During inspiration the anesthetic gases pass from the rubber bag, through one of the tubes, into the mask, and into the patient's lungs. Then when the patient breathes outward, he breathes through the opposite tube back into the rubber bag. Valves are appropriately arranged in these tubes to make certain that the air flows in the appropriate direction. The reason for this is that these tubes contain a large amount of instrumental dead space, and, if the patient should breathe back and forth through the same tube, he would breathe with each inspiration a large quantity of the air that he had just expired. As the expired air flows from the lungs to the rubber bag, the expired carbon dioxide reacts chemically with the soda lime and is thus removed from the anesthetic gases. Consequently, when the gases are reinspired from the bag, very little or no carbon dioxide remains. The anesthetic in the circuit is not lost except into the blood of the lungs. Once the patient's body fluids are saturated with the anesthetic, very little more

anesthetic is admitted to the circuit, and yet the quantity of anesthetic in the body remains nearly constant thereafter, for none of the already present anesthetic can leave the circuit. The only constituent that is then being removed to a major extent from the anesthetic circuit is oxygen. As the rubber bag gets smaller and smaller, the anesthetist simply allows oxygen to flow into it.

It can be seen, then, that by use of the anesthetic machine a patient may be anesthetized to a certain depth, and thereafter his level of anesthesia is maintained very easily without continuous administration of new anesthetic except for a very minute quantity to replace that destroyed in the body or lost by leaks around the mask.

REFERENCES

Altman, P. L., Gibson, J. F., and Wang, C. C.: Handbook of Respiration. Philadelphia, W. B. Saunders Co., 1958.

Bedell, G. N., Marshall, R., Dubois, A. B., and Comroe, J. H., Jr.: Plethysmographic determination of the volume of gas trapped in the lungs. *J. Clin. Invest.,* 35:664, 1956.

Bergan, F.: The Investigation of the Relative Function of the Right and Left Lung by Broncho-Spirometry—Technique, Physiology and Application. New York, Grune & Stratton, Inc., 1957.

Boyden, E. A.: Segmental anatomy of the lungs. New York, McGraw-Hill Book Co., Inc., 1955.

Bucher, K.: Pathophysiology and pharmacology of cough. *Pharmacol. Rev.,* 10:43, 1958.

Campbell, F. J. M.: The Respiratory Muscles. Chicago, Year Book Publishers, 1958.

Campbell, E. J. M.: The Respiratory Muscles and the Mechanics of Breathing. Chicago, Year Book Publishers, 1958.

Comroe, J. H., Forster, R. E., Dubois, A. B., Briscoe, W. A., and Carlsen, E.: The Lung. Chicago, Year Book Publishers, 1955.

Cullen, S. C.: Anesthesia. 5th ed., Chicago, Year Book Publishers, 1957.

Drinker, P., and Hatch, T.: Industrial Dust. 2nd ed., New York, McGraw-Hill Book Co., Inc., 1954.

Dubois, A. B., Botelho, S. Y., and Comroe, J. H., Jr.: A new method for measuring airway resistance in man using a body plethysmograph: values in normal subjects and in patients with respiratory disease. *J. Clin. Invest.,* 35:327, 1956.

Dubois, A. B., Botelho, S. Y., Bedell, G. N., Marshall, R., and Comroe, J. H., Jr.: A rapid plethysmographic method for measuring thoracic gas volume: a comparison with a nitrogen washout method for measuring functional residual capacity in normal subjects, *J. Clin. Invest.,* 35:322, 1956.

Dubois, A. B., Brody, A. W., Lewis, D. H., and Burgess, B. F., Jr.: Oscillation mechanics of lungs and chest in man. *J. Appl. Physiol.,* 8:587, 1956.

Du Brul, K. L.: Evolution of the Speech Apparatus. Springfield, Illinois, Charles C Thomas, 1958.

Folkow, B., and Pappenheimer, J. R.: Components of the respiratory dead space and their variation with pressure breathing and with bronchoactive drugs. *J. Appl. Physiol.,* 8:102, 1955.

Fowler, W. S.: Intrapulmonary distribution of inspired gas. *Physiol. Rev.*, 32:1, 1952.

Frank, N. R., Lyons, H. A., Siebens, A. A., and Storey, C. F.: Measurements of pulmonary compliance in seventy healthy young adults. *J. Appl. Physiol.*, 9:38, 1956.

Garland, T. O.: Artificial Respiration. New York, The Macmillan Co., 1955.

Goodheart, C. R., Haddy, F. J., Grodins, F., and Ebert, R. V.: Elastance and resistance of lungs-chest of dogs. *Am. J. Physiol.*, 196:525, 1959.

Gray, J. S., Grodins, F. S., and Carter, E. T.: Alveolar and total ventilation and the dead space problem. *J. Appl. Physiol.*, 9:307, 1956.

Greene, M.: The Voice and Its Disorders. New York, The Macmillan Co., 1957.

Guyton, A. C.: Analysis of respiratory patterns in laboratory animals. *Am. J. Physiol.*, 150:78, 1947.

Guyton, A. C.: Electronic counting and size determination of particles in aerosols. *J. Indust. Hyg. & Toxicol.*, 28:133, 1946.

Guyton, A. C.: Measurement of the respiratory volumes of laboratory animals. *Am. J. Physiol.*, 150: 70, 1947.

Heomstra, H.: Respiration. *Ann. Rev. Physiol.*, 18: 121, 1956.

Hemingway, A., Pocock, D., and Short, J. J.: Variation of basal respiration with age. *J. Chronic Dis.*, 3:201, 1956.

Hughes, R., May, A. J., and Widdicombe, J. G.: Stress relaxation in rabbits' lungs. *J. Physiol.*, 146: 85, 1959.

Mead, J., McIlroy, M. B., Selverstone, N. J., and Kriete, B. C.: Measurement of intraesophageal pressure. *J. Appl. Physiol.*, 7:491, 1955.

Mead, J., Whittenberger, J. L., and Radford, E. P., Jr.: Surface tension as a factor in pulmonary volume-pressure hysteresis. *J. Appl. Physiol.*, 10:191, 1957.

Negus, V.: Comparative Anatomy and Physiology of the Nose and Paranasal Sinuses. Baltimore, Williams & Wilkins Co., 1958.

Nims, R. G., Conner, E. H., and Comroe, J. H., Jr.: The compliance of the human thorax in anesthetized patients. *J. Clin. Invest.*, 34:744, 1955.

Otis, A. B.: Respiration. *Ann. Rev. Physiol.*, 20:159, 1958.

Otis, A. B., and Bembower, W. C.: Effect of gas density on resistance to respiratory gas flow in man. *J. Appl. Physiol.*, 2:300, 1949.

Otis, A. B., Fenn, W. O., and Rahn, H.: Mechanics of breathing in man. *J. Appl. Physiol.*, 2:592, 1950.

Otis, A. B., McKerrow, C. B., Bartlett, R. A., Mead, J., McIlroy, M. B., Selverstone, N. J., and Radford, E. P., Jr.: Mechanical factors in distribution of pulmonary ventilation. *J. Appl. Physiol.*, 8:427, 1956.

Otis, A. B., and Proctor, D. F.: Measurements of alveolar pressure in human subjects. *Am. J. Physiol.*, 152:106, 1948.

Pressman, J. J., and Kelemen, C.: Physiology of the larynx. *Physiol. Rev.*, 35:506, 1955.

Price, H. J.: General anesthesia and circulatory homeostasis. *Physiol. Rev.*, 40:187, 1960.

Rahn, H.: Respiration. *Ann. Rev. Physiol.*, 17:107, 1955.

Rossier, P. H., and Buhlmann, A.: The respiratory dead space, *Physiol. Rev.*, 35:860, 1955.

Sarnoff, S. J., Maloney, J. V., Jr., and Whittenberger, J. L.: Electrophrenic respiration; effect on circulation of electrophrenic respiration and positive pressure breathing during respiratory paralysis of high spinal anesthesia. *Ann. Surg.*, 132:921, 1950.

Shephard, R. J.: Pressure-volume relationships in the chest before and after death. *J. Physiol.*, 149:178, 1959.

Shephard, R. J.: The timed airway resistance. *J. Physiol.*, 145:459, 1959.

Taylor, A.: The contribution of the intercostal muscles to the effort of respiration in man. *J. Physiol.*, 151: 390, 1960.

Tenney, S. M., and Miller, R. M.: Dead space ventilation in old age. *J. Appl. Physiol.*, 9:321, 1956.

Whittenberger, J. L.: Artificial respiration. *Physiol. Rev.*, 35:611, 1955.

Whittenberger, J. L., Affeldt, J. E., Goodale, W. T., and Sarnoff, S. J.: Mechanics of breathing in relation to manual methods of artificial respiration. *J. Appl. Physiol.*, 4:476, 1951.

Whittenberger, J. L., and Maloney, J. V., Jr.: Respiratory system. *Ann. Rev. Physiol.*, 14:143, 1952.

Wylie, W. D.: A Practice of Anesthesia. Chicago, Year Book Publishers, 1960.

Young, A. C.: Dead space at rest and during exercise. *J. Appl. Physiol.*, 8:91, 1955.

Chapter 40

Physical Principles of Gaseous Exchange; Diffusion of Oxygen and Carbon Dioxide Through the Pulmonary Membrane

After the alveoli are ventilated with fresh air, the next step in the respiratory process is diffusion of oxygen from the alveoli into the pulmonary blood and diffusion of carbon dioxide in the opposite direction—from the pulmonary blood into the alveoli. The process of diffusion is really quite simple, involving merely random molecular motion of molecules, these intertwining their ways back and forth through the pulmonary membrane. However, in respiratory physiology we are not only concerned with the basic mechanism by which diffusion occurs but also with the *rate* at which it can occur, and this is a much more complicated problem, requiring a rather deep understanding of the physics of gases.

The two major problems to be discussed in this chapter, therefore, are, first, the physical factors that determine the alveolar concentrations of gases, particularly of oxygen, and carbon dioxide, and, second, the factors that affect the rate at which these gases can diffuse through the pulmonary membrane. Since the following discussions will entail many basic physical principles of gases, a brief review of this subject will be presented as a prelude to the main text of the chapter. The student who is already well versed in these basic principles should go directly to the discussion of the composition of alveolar air.

THE PHYSICS OF GASES

Relationship of Pressure to Volume—Boyle's Law. If the mass and temperature of a gas in a chamber remain constant but the pressure is increased or decreased, then the volume of the gas varies inversely with the pressure. That is

$$\text{Pressure} \times \text{Volume} = \text{Constant}$$

Figure 395 illustrates the physical principles of Boyle's law, showing that, as the pressure increases from 1 to 2 atmospheres (760 to 1520 mm. Hg), the volume of 1 gram-mol of gas at 0° C. decreases from 22.4 liters to 11.2 liters. On the other hand, if the pressure of this same gram-mol

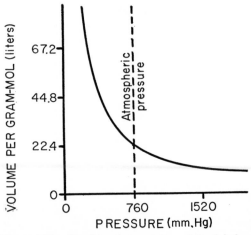

Figure 395. Graphic representation of Boyle's law.

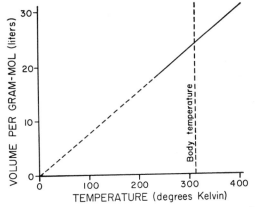

Figure 396. Graphic representation of Gay-Lussac's law.

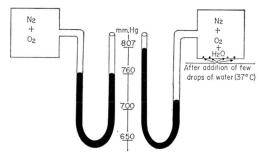

Figure 397. Demonstration of 47 mm. Hg vapor pressure in the chamber to the right.

of gas is decreased from 760 mm. Hg to 380 mm. Hg, then the total volume increases from 22.4 liters to 44.8 liters.

Relationship of Temperature to Volume —Gay-Lussac's Law (Charles's Law). If the pressure of a given quantity of gas remains constant but the temperature is varied, the volume of the gas increases directly in proportion to the increase in temperature. When the temperature is expressed in absolute (Kelvin) degrees, the following relationship holds:

$$\frac{\text{Volume}}{\text{Temperature (K)}} = \text{Constant}$$

Figure 396 illustrates this relationship when the pressure is kept constant, beginning at 0° K. for the so-called ideal gas. It is shown that one gram-mol of gas has a volume of 22.4 liters at 273° K., which is 0° C. At body temperature of 37° C. (310° K.) one gram-mol of gas has a volume of 25.4 liters.

The Gas Law. Combining Boyle's Law and Gay-Lussac's Law, the following gas law applies:

$$PV = nRT$$

in which P is pressure, V is volume, n is the quantity of gas, R is a constant depending on the units of measure used for the other factors in the formula, and T is temperature. When P is expressed in millimeters Hg, V in liters, n in gram-mols, and T in absolute degrees, the value of the constant R is 62.36.

The Vapor Pressure of Water

All gases in the body are in indirect contact with water. Therefore, all gaseous mixtures in the body are saturated with water vapor, and this must always be considered when the dynamics of gaseous exchange are discussed.

Figure 397 illustrates to the left a chamber containing normal dry air that has in it only nitrogen and oxygen. The pressure in this chamber is the normal atmospheric pressure of 760 mm. Hg, which is illustrated on the scale of the manometer. In the second chamber a few drops of water are added. Immediately, some of the water vaporizes, this vaporization increasing the mass of gas in the chamber; if the temperature in the chamber is body temperature (37°C.), the pressure increases 47 mm. Hg (the vapor pressure of water at 37°C.).

The vapor pressure of water depends entirely on the temperature of the water and gases. The greater the temperature, the greater is the activity of the molecules in the water, and the greater is the likelihood these molecules will escape from the surface of the water into the gaseous phase. On the other hand, the lower the temperature, the greater will be the condensation of water from the gaseous phase. When dry air is suddenly mixed with water, the water vapor pressure is 0 at first, but water molecules immediately begin escaping from the surface of the water into the air. As the air becomes progressively more and more humidified, an equilibrium vapor pressure is approached at which the rate of condensation of water becomes equal to the rate of water vaporization. Because the kinetic activity of molecules in water increases with increased temperature, the equilibrium pressure (the *water vapor pressure*) also increases with increased temperatures. The water vapor pressure at various temperatures from 0° to 100°C. is given in Table 15.

The Solution of Gases in Water

Figure 398 illustrates three chambers, with chamber A having oxygen in the top of the chamber at a pressure of 100 mm. Hg and pure water in the bottom of the chamber. Large numbers of oxygen molecules continually strike the surface of the water and some of them enter the water to become dissolved. However, the quantity of dis-

Table 15. Vapor Pressure of Water

Temp. (°C.)	Vapor pressure (mm.)	Temp. (°C.)	Vapor pressure (mm.)
0	4.6	39	52.0
5	6.5	40	54.9
10	9.1	41	57.9
14	11.9	42	61.0
16	13.5	43	64.3
18	15.3	44	67.8
20	17.4	46	75.1
22	19.6	48	83.2
24	22.2	50	92.0
26	25.0	55	117.5
28	28.1	60	148.9
30	31.5	65	187.1
31	33.4	70	233.3
32	35.3	75	288.8
33	37.4	80	354.9
34	39.5	85	433.2
35	41.8	90	525.5
36	44.2	95	633.7
37	46.6	100	760.0
38	49.3		

solved oxygen in chamber A is zero because the processs is just beginning. In chamber B a fairly large number of molecules of oxygen has already been dissolved in the water so that the number of molecules striking the surface of the water from below upwards and leaving the water to enter the gaseous phase is equal to approximately one-half the number of molecules striking the surface from above and entering the dissolved state. Therefore, a greater number of oxygen molecules are still entering the dissolved state than are leaving the dissolved state. In chamber C the amount of oxygen in the dissolved state has become great enough that the number of molecules leaving the surface of the water to enter the gaseous phase is equal to the number of molecules entering the water to become dissolved. Thus, at this point a state of equilibrium exists.

Two factors determine the quantity of a gas that will be dissolved in water or in any other

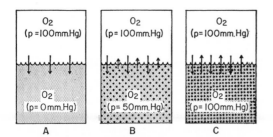

Figure 398. Solution of oxygen in water: (A) when the oxygen first comes in contact with pure water, (B) after the dissolved oxygen is half way to equilibrium with the gaseous oxygen, and (C) after equilibrium has been established.

fluid when the equilibrium state has been reached. These factors are (1) the pressure of the gas surrounding the water, and (2) the solubility coefficient of the gas in water at the temperature of the water. When the gas has reached the equilibrium state, as in Figure 398C, the total quantity of dissolved gas at any particular temperature may be expressed by the following formula:

$$\text{Volume} = \text{Pressure} \times \text{Solubility coefficient}$$

When volume is expressed in volumes of gas dissolved in each volume of water at 0° C. and pressure is expressed in atmospheres, the solubility coefficients for different gases at body temperature are the following:

Oxygen	0.024
Carbon dioxide	0.57
Nitrogen	0.012
Helium	0.008

Pressure of Dissolved Gases

If the oxygen should be removed suddenly from the chamber above the water in Figure 398A, no oxygen molecules would be striking the surface of the water from beneath and passing into the gaseous phase. Therefore, there would be no upward pressure against the surface of the water exerted by oxygen. In chamber B of Figure 398, half as many molecules of oxygen are pushing upward from the surface of the water as are striking the surface of the water from above. Because pressure is the force of impact of molecules against a surface, if half as many molecules are striking upward against the surface of the fluid as are striking downward against the surface of the fluid, the pressure exerted upward is equal to one-half the pressure exerted downward. In other words, in Figure 398B the pressure of the oxygen in the gaseous phase is 100 mm. Hg and in the dissolved phase 50 mm. Hg. In chamber C the total number of oxygen molecules striking upward against the surface is equal to the total number of molecules striking downward against the surface, which means that the pressure exerted upward by oxygen is equal to the pressure exerted downward by oxygen. At this point the pressure of the oxygen in the gaseous phase is in equilibrium with the pressure of the oxygen in the dissolved phase, and both are equal to 100 mm. Hg.

The pressure exerted by a gas as it attempts to pass outward from the surface of a liquid is generally written as P_{O_2}, P_{CO_2}, P_{N_2}, P_{He}, etc., for each of the gases dissolved in the liquid.

The pressure of a dissolved gas is proportional to the quantity of gas dissolved in the fluid divided by the solubility coefficient of the gas in that particular fluid. Molecules of gases that are **highly soluble are attracted by the fluid molecules** so that, as they strike the surface of the fluid, this attraction prevents many of these highly soluble molecules from leaving the surface. Consequently, the total number of molecules that must be dissolved to exert a given pressure is considerably greater for very soluble gases than for gases not so soluble.

Partial Pressures

An understanding of *partial pressures* is a very important preliminary to understanding gaseous diffusion from the alveoli to the pulmonary blood, for it is the partial pressure of a gas that determines the force it exerts in attempting to diffuse through the pulmonary membrane.

Figure 399 illustrates four separate chambers, each of which has a capacity of 100 volumes of gas and initially is completely empty of gas. The second chamber is divided by a partition, and 79 volumes of nitrogen at 760 mm. Hg pressure are placed above the partition and 21 volumes of oxygen at 760 mm. Hg below. Then all the nitrogen in the upper part of chamber 2 is moved to chamber 1, which has a total capacity of 100 volumes. In other words, 79 volumes of nitrogen are expanded to 100 volumes. As this nitrogen is expanded, it can be shown from Boyle's law that the pressure falls to 79/100 of 760 mm. Hg—that is, to 600 mm. Hg.

The 21 volumes of oxygen at 760 mm. Hg are moved from the second chamber to the third chamber. Here again it can be shown from Boyle's law that this expansion causes the pressure of the oxygen to fall to 21/100 of 760 mm. Hg—that is, to 160 mm. Hg.

Finally, the nitrogen in the first chamber and the oxygen in the third chamber are mixed together in the fourth chamber. The original pressure of the nitrogen is 600 mm. Hg, and the pressure of the oxygen is 160 mm. Hg, but the total pressure in chamber 4 after mixing is 760 mm. Hg. It is obvious that 600 mm. of this 760 mm. Hg is due to the presence of nitrogen in the chamber, and 160 mm. is due to the presence of oxygen in the chamber. The 600 mm. Hg pressure

exerted by nitrogen and the 160 mm. Hg pressure exerted by the oxygen are known, respectively, as the *partial pressures* of each of these two gases in the mixture, and the partial pressures of the gases in a mixture are designated by the same terms used to designate pressures in liquids, i.e., P_{O_2}, P_{CO_2}, P_{N_2}, P_{He}, etc.

From the kinetic theory of gases it will be recalled that pressure against any membrane or against any other surface is determined by the number of molecules striking the membrane at any given instant times the average kinetic energy of each of these molecules. Therefore, the partial pressure of a gas in a mixture is in reality the force of impact of all the molecules of that particular gas against the surface. In other words, in chamber 4 the total force of the nitrogen molecules striking against the chamber walls is sufficient to elevate the mercury in a manometer to a level of 600 mm. The total force exerted by the oxygen molecules striking against the walls of the chamber is sufficient to elevate the mercury in a manometer to a level of 160 mm. With both these gases exerting force against the walls of the chamber at the same time, the mercury is elevated to a total level of 760 mm. Hg.

Molecules in a mixture of gases are constantly striking each other and thereby imparting energy to each other. As a result, each molecule of the mixture, regardless of its molecular weight, has the same mean kinetic energy as the next molecule. Therefore, *the partial pressure of a gas in a mixture is also a direct measure of the number of molecules of that particular gas striking a surface in a given period of time.*

Pressures of Dissolved Gases in Equilibrium with a Mixture of Gases. Because each gas in a mixture exerts its own partial pressure in proportion to the concentration of its molecules, when the gases of a mixture dissolve in a liquid and come to equilibrium with the gaseous phase of the mixture, the pressure of each dissolved gas is equal to the partial pressure of the same gas in the gaseous mixture. In other words, *each gas is independent of the others in its ability to dissolve in a liquid;* obviously, this principle also applies to the solution of gases in blood. Thus, an increase in quantity of carbon dioxide dissolved in the blood fluids does not affect the quantity of oxygen that can be dissolved in the same fluids. (However, the various dissolved gases often do interfere with the chemical reactions of each other, as will be discussed in the following chapter in connection with the reactions of oxygen and carbon dioxide with hemoglobin.)

The Diffusion of Gases Through Liquids

Figure 400 illustrates a chamber filled with water. The water at one end of this chamber contains a relatively large amount of dissolved oxy-

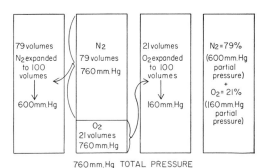

Figure 399. Relationship of partial pressures to gaseous percentages in mixtures of gases.

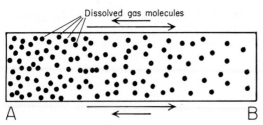

Figure 400. Net diffusion of oxygen from one end of a chamber to the other.

gen. Because of the kinetic energy of matter, the dissolved gaseous molecules are constantly undergoing molecular motion, bouncing among the molecules of the solvent. Thus, in Figure 400 the oxygen molecules are bouncing in all directions, and this process is called *diffusion*. More of them bounce from the area of high concentration toward the area of low concentration for the following reasons:

The Pressure Gradient for Diffusion. What physical factors determine how rapidly a gas will diffuse from an area of high pressure to an area of low pressure? The molecules in the area of high pressure, because of their greater number, have more statistical chance of bouncing into the area of low pressure than do molecules attempting to go in the other direction. However, some molecules do bounce from the area of low pressure toward the area of high pressure. Therefore, the net flow of gas from the area of high pressure to the area of low pressure is equal to the number of molecules bouncing in this direction minus the number bouncing in the opposite direction, and this in turn is proportional to the pressure difference between the two areas. The pressure in area A of Figure 400 minus the pressure in area B is known as the *pressure gradient* or *diffusion gradient*, and the rate of net gas diffusion from area A to area B is directly proportional to this gradient. This principle of diffusion from an area of high pressure to an area of low pressure holds true for diffusion of gases in a gaseous mixture, diffusion of dissolved gases in a solution, and even diffusion of gases from the gaseous phase into the dissolved state in liquids. That is, *gases always diffuse from areas of high pressure to areas of low pressure.*

As more and more gas diffuses in the chamber of Figure 400 and the pressure in area B approaches the pressure in area A, the net rate of gaseous diffusion becomes less and less. After a reasonable length of time, the gaseous pressures in both ends of the chamber become essentially equal, and, thereafter, no net diffusion of gas occurs from one end to the other end. This does not mean that no molecules of gas diffuse, but merely that as many molecules then diffuse backward as forward.

If at any time the gaseous pressure at one end of the chamber falls below that at the other end, gas immediately begins anew to diffuse from the high pressure area to the low pressure area until the two pressures again approach each other and eventually reach a state of equilibrium.

The Rate of Diffusion. In addition to the pressure gradient, several other factors affect the rate of gas diffusion in a fluid. These are (1) the solubility of the gas in the fluid, (2) the cross-sectional area of the fluid, (3) the distance through which the gas must diffuse, (4) the molecular weight of the gas, (5) the viscosity of the fluid, and (6) the temperature of the fluid. In the body, the last two of these factors remain reasonably constant and usually need not be considered.

Obviously, the greater the solubility of the gas, the greater will be the number of molecules available to diffuse for any given pressure gradient. Also, the greater the cross-sectional area of the chamber, the greater will be the total number of molecules to diffuse. On the other hand, the longer the distance that the molecules must diffuse, the longer it will take the molecules to diffuse the entire distance. Finally, the greater the velocity of kinetic movement of the molecules, which at any given temperature is inversely proportional to the square root of the molecular weight, the greater is the rate of diffusion of the gas. All of these factors may be expressed in a single formula, as follows:

$$DR \approx \frac{PG \times CA \times S}{D \times \sqrt{MW}}$$

in which DR is the diffusion rate, PG is the pressure gradient between the two ends of the chamber, CA is the cross-sectional area of the chamber, S is solubility of the gas, D is the distance of diffusion, and MW is the molecular weight of the gas.

It is obvious from the above formula that the characteristics of the gas itself determine two factors of the formula: solubility and molecular weight. Therefore, the *diffusion coefficient*—that is, the rate of diffusion—for any given gas is proportional to $S/\sqrt{MW}$. Considering the diffusion coefficient for oxygen to be 1, the diffusion coefficients for different gases of respiratory importance in the body fluids are:

Oxygen	1.0
Carbon dioxide	20.3
Nitrogen	0.53
Helium	0.95

The Diffusion of Gases Through Tissues

Diffusion through the tissues means mainly diffusion through the tissue fluids. Therefore, diffusion of gases through the tissues is almost equal

Table 16. **Partial Pressures of Respiratory Gases as They Enter and Leave the Lungs (at Sea Level)—Per Cent Concentrations Are Given in Parentheses**

	Atmospheric Air* (mm. Hg)		Humidified Air (mm. Hg)		Alveolar Air (mm. Hg)		Expired Air (mm. Hg)	
N_2	597.0	(78.62%)	563.4	(74.09%)	569.0	(74.9%)	566.0	(74.5%)
O_2	159.0	(20.84%)	149.3	(19.67%)	104.0	(13.6%)	120.0	(15.7%)
CO_2	0.3	(0.04%)	0.3	(0.04%)	40.0	(5.3%)	27.0	(3.6%)
H_2O	3.7	(0.5%)	47.0	(6.2%)	47.0	(6.2%)	47.0	(6.2%)
Total	760.0	(100.0%)	760.0	(100.0%)	760.0	(100.0%)	760.0	(100.0%)

* On an average cool, clear day.

to the diffusion of gases through water. Obviously, the cell membranes offer some resistance to passage of gases, but, as pointed out in Chapter 2, the membrane resistance to gases is probably not enough to affect the rate of diffusion of most gases significantly.

COMPOSITION OF ALVEOLAR AIR

Alveolar air does not have the same concentration of gases as atmospheric air by any means, which can readily be seen by comparing the alveolar air composition in Column 3 of Table 16 with the composition of atmospheric air in Column 1. There are several reasons for the differences. First, the alveolar air is only partially replaced by atmospheric air with each breath. Second, oxygen is constantly being absorbed from the alveolar air. Third, carbon dioxide is constantly diffusing from the pulmonary blood into the alveoli. And, fourth, dry atmospheric air which enters the alveoli is immediately humidified.

Humidification of the Air as It Enters the Respiratory Passages. Column 1 of Table 16 shows that atmospheric air is composed almost entirely of nitrogen and oxygen; it normally contains almost no carbon dioxide and very little water vapor. However, as soon as the atmospheric air enters the respiratory passages, it is immediately exposed to the fluids covering the respiratory surfaces. Even before the air enters the alveoli it becomes totally humidified, or certainly so within a fraction of a second after it enters the alveoli. The partial pressure of water vapor at normal body temperature of 37° C. is 47 mm. Hg, which, therefore, is the partial pressure of water in the alveolar air. Since the total pressure in the alveoli cannot rise to more than the atmospheric pressure, this water vapor sim-

ply expands the air and *dilutes* all the other gases in the inspired air. In Column 2 of Table 16 it can be seen that humidification of the air reduces the oxygen partial pressure at sea level from an average of 159 mm. Hg down to 149 mm. Hg, and it reduces the nitrogen partial pressure from 597 to 563 mm. Hg.

Rate at Which Alveolar Air Is Renewed by Atmospheric Air

In the previous chapter it was pointed out that the *functional residual capacity* of the lungs, which is the amount of air remaining in the lungs at the end of normal expiration, measures approximately 2300 ml. Furthermore, approximately only 350 ml. of new air are brought into the alveoli with each normal respiration. Therefore, the amount of alveolar air replaced by new atmospheric air with each breath is but one seventh of the total so that many breaths are required to exchange most of the alveolar air. Figure 401 illustrates the effect of this on the rate of renewal of the alveolar air. In the first alveolus of the figure is a highly concentrated foreign gas that has been placed momentarily in all the alveoli. The second al-

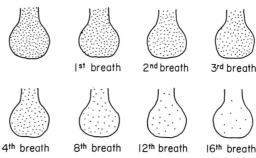

Figure 401. Expiration of a foreign gas from the alveoli with successive breaths.

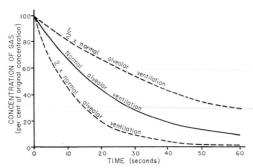

Figure 402. Rate of removal of a foreign gas from
the alveoli.

veolus shows slight dilution of this foreign
gas with the first breath; the next alveolus
shows still further dilution with the second
breath, and so forth for the third, fourth,
eighth, twelfth, and sixteenth breaths. Note
that even at the end of 16 breaths the foreign gas still has not been completely
removed from the alveoli. Figure 402 illustrates graphically the rate at which a foreign gas in the alveoli is normally removed,
showing that with normal alveolar ventilation approximately half the foreign gas will
be removed in 17 seconds. When a person's
rate of alveolar ventilation is only one-half
normal, half the gas will be removed in 34
seconds, and, when his rate of ventilation is
two times normal, half will be removed in
about 8 seconds.

**Value of the Slow Replacement of
Alveolar Air.** This slow replacement of
alveolar air is of particular importance in
preventing sudden changes in gaseous concentrations in the blood.

This makes the respiratory control mechanism much more stable than it would
otherwise be and helps to prevent the person
from having *Cheyne-Stokes breathing*, which
is characterized by overbreathing for a few
seconds, then underbreathing, then overbreathing, the cycle continuing indefinitely,
as will be described in Chapter 42.

Oxygen Concentration in the Alveoli

Oxygen is continually being absorbed into
the blood of the lungs, and new oxygen is
continually entering the alveoli from the
atmosphere. The more rapidly oxygen is
absorbed, the lower becomes its concentration in the alveoli; on the other hand, the
more rapidly new oxygen is brought into

the alveoli from the atmosphere, the higher
becomes its concentration. Therefore, oxygen concentration in the alveoli is controlled
by, first, the rate of absorption of oxygen
into the blood and, second, the rate of new
oxygen entry into the lungs.

Figure 403 illustrates both the effect of
ventilatory rate and the effect of rate of
oxygen absorption into the blood on the alveolar partial pressure of oxygen. The normal ventilatory rate is 4.2 liters per minute,
and the normal quantity of oxygen absorbed
into the blood during quiet, resting conditions is 250 ml. per minute. Therefore, the
normal operating point in Figure 403 is
point A; however, during exercise, the rate
of oxygen utilization is increased in proportion to the intensity of the exercise. From
Figure 403 it can be seen that, when 1000
ml. of oxygen are being absorbed each minute, the ventilatory rate must increase four-
fold to maintain the alveolar P_{O_2} at the normal value of 104 mm. Hg, and at still
higher rates of oxygen absorption, the ventilatory rate must rise proportionately to
maintain normal alveolar P_{O_2}.

Another effect well illustrated by Figure
403 is the effect of ventilatory rate on the
alveolar P_{O_2} when the rate of oxygen absorption does not change. An extremely marked
increase in ventilatory rate can never increase the alveolar P_{O_2} above 149 mm. Hg
as long as the subject is breathing normal
atmospheric air, for this is the maximum
content of oxygen in humidified air. However, if the subject breathes gases containing
concentrations of oxygen higher than 149
mm. Hg, then the alveolar P_{O_2} can approach
these higher concentrations when the ventilatory rate approaches maximum. On the

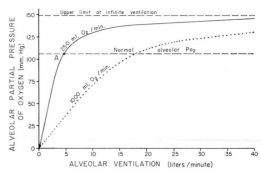

Figure 403. Effect of alveolar ventilation and rate
of oxygen absorption from the alveoli on the alveolar
P_{O_2}.

other hand, a greatly depressed ventilatory rate always decreases the alveolar P_{O_2} if the rate of oxygen absorption into the blood remains constant.

Carbon Dioxide Concentration in the Alveoli

Carbon dioxide is continually being formed in the body and then discharged into the alveoli, and it is continually being removed from the lungs by the process of ventilation. Therefore, the two factors that determine carbon dioxide partial pressure in the lungs are (1) the rate of excretion of carbon dioxide from the blood into the alveoli and (2) the rate at which carbon dioxide is removed from the alveoli by pulmonary ventilation. The greater the ventilatory rate, the lower becomes the alveolar P_{CO_2}; on the other hand, the greater the rate of carbon dioxide excretion into the alveoli, the greater becomes the alveolar P_{CO_2}.

Figure 404 illustrates the effects of both alveolar ventilation and the rate of carbon dioxide excretion on the alveolar P_{CO_2}. The normal rate of carbon dioxide excretion is 200 ml. per minute, and the normal rate of alveolar ventilation is 4.2 liters per minute. Therefore, under normal, quiet conditions, the operating point for alveolar P_{CO_2} is at point A in Figure 404—this is, 40 mm. Hg.

Two other facts are especially evident from Figure 404: First, *the alveolar P_{CO_2} increases directly in proportion to the rate of carbon dioxide excretion.* Second, *the alveolar P_{CO_2} decreases in inverse proportion to the ventilatory rate.* Therefore, the concentration of both oxygen and carbon dioxide in the alveoli is determined by the rate of absorption or excretion, respectively, of these two gases and also by the ventilatory rate.

Expired Air

Expired air is a combination of dead space air and alveolar air, and its overall composition is, therefore, determined by three factors: first, the proportion of the expired air that is dead space air and the proportion that is alveolar air, second, the concentrations of the gases in the dead space air, and, third, the concentrations of the gases in the alveolar air. Figure 405 shows the progressive changes in oxygen and carbon dioxide concentrations in the expired air during the course of expiration. The very first portion of this air, the dead space air, is typical humidified air as shown in Column 2 of Table 16. Then, progressively more and more alveolar air becomes mixed with the dead space air until all of the dead space air has finally been washed out and nothing but alveolar air remains. Thus, the oxygen concentration in the first portion of the expired air is 149 mm. Hg and of the latter portion approximately 104 mm. Hg, the value in normal alveolar air. On the other hand, the early portion of the expired air has essentially no carbon dioxide, but the final portion, the alveolar air portion, has a carbon dioxide pressure of 40 mm. Hg. Indeed, one of the means for collecting alveolar air for study is simply to collect a sample of the last portion of expired air.

Normal expired air, containing both dead space air and alveolar air, has gaseous concentrations approximately as shown in Column 4 of Table 16—that is, concentrations somewhere between

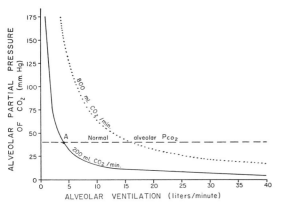

Figure 404. Effect of alveolar ventilation and rate of carbon dioxide excretion from the blood on the alveolar P_{CO_2}.

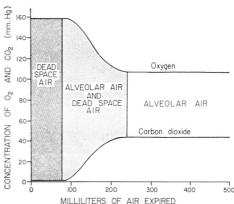

Figure 405. Oxygen and carbon dioxide concentrations in the various portions of expired air.

those of humidified atmospheric air and alveolar air.

DIFFUSION OF GASES THROUGH THE RESPIRATORY MEMBRANE

The Respiratory Membrane. Figure 406 illustrates the respiratory unit, which is comprised of a *respiratory bronchiole, alveolar ducts, atria,* and *alveolar sacs.* The epithelium of these structures is a very thin membrane, and the alveolar gases are in close proximity to the blood of the capillaries. Consequently, gaseous exchange between the alveolar air and the pulmonary blood occurs through the membranes of all these terminal portions of the lungs.

The respiratory membrane is between ½ and 4 microns in thickness, and it has three layers. One of these is the *endothelial cells of the capillary,* another is the *epithelial cells of the respiratory epithelium,* and between these is the *interstitial layer.* The capillaries are approximately 8 microns in diameter so that red blood cells must actually squeeze through their lumina. Therefore, the red blood cell membranes usually touch the walls of the capillaries, and oxygen need traverse little plasma before it enters the red blood cells. Obviously, this aids the rapidity of oxygen pickup by the cells.

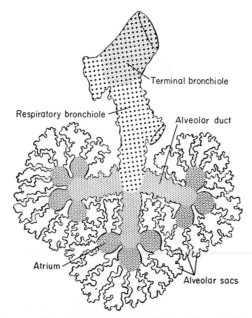

Figure 406. The respiratory lobule. (From Miller: The Lung. Charles C Thomas.)

From histologic studies it has been estimated that the total surface area of the respiratory membrane is approximately 50 to 70 square meters in the normal adult. This is equivalent to the floor area of a room approximately 30 feet long by 20 feet wide. The total quantity of blood in the capillaries of the lung at any given instant is about 60 to 100 ml. If this small amount of blood were spread over the entire surface of a 20 by 30 foot floor, one could very readily understand how respiratory exchange of gases occurs as rapidly as it does.

Factors Affecting Gaseous Diffusion Through the Pulmonary Membrane

Referring to the above discussion of diffusion through water, one can apply the same principles and same formula to diffusion of gases through the respiratory membrane. Thus, (1) the *thickness of the membrane,* (2) the *surface area* of the membrane, (3) the *diffusion coefficient* of the gas in the substance of the membrane, and (4) the *pressure gradient* between the two sides of the membrane, all combined, determine how rapidly a gas will pass through the membrane.

The *thickness of the respiratory membrane* occasionally increases markedly, usually as a result of the presence of edema fluid in the interstitial space of the membrane. Also, fluid may collect in the alveolar sacs so that the respiratory gases must diffuse not only through the membrane but also through this fluid. Finally, some pulmonary diseases cause fibrosis of the lungs, which can increase the thickness of some portions of the respiratory membrane. Because the rate of diffusion through the membrane is inversely proportional to the thickness of the membrane, any factor that increases the thickness more than two to three times above normal can interfere markedly with normal respiratory exchange of gases.

The *surface area of the respiratory membrane* may be greatly decreased by many different conditions. For instance, removal of an entire lung decreases the surface area to one half normal. Also, in the condition known as *emphysema* many of the alveoli coalesce with dissolution of the septa between the alveoli. Therefore, the new chambers are much larger than the original alveoli, but the total surface area of the respiratory membrane is considerably decreased because of loss of the alveolar septa. When the total surface area is decreased to approximately one-third to one-fourth normal, exchange of gases through the membrane is impeded to a significant degree even under resting conditions. And even the slightest decrease in surface area of the lungs can be a detriment to respiratory exchange of gases during heavy exercise. Obviously, many other destructive diseases, such as tuberculosis, cancer of the lungs, pneumonia, etc., can also decrease the total respiratory area.

The *diffusion coefficient* for the transfer of each gas through the respiratory membrane depends on its *solubility* in the membrane and on its *molecular weight*. The rate of diffusion in the respiratory membrane is almost exactly the same as that in water, indicating that the cellular membranes of the pulmonary epithelium offer no significant obstacle to the movement of the gaseous molecules. Therefore, carbon dioxide diffuses through the membrane about 20 times as rapidly as oxygen, and oxygen diffuses about two times as rapidly as nitrogen and at almost the same rate as helium. It is especially interesting to note the more rapid diffusion of oxygen than of nitrogen through the membrane since the molecular weights of these two gases are not far different from each other. This difference is caused by approximately two times as great solubility of oxygen as nitrogen in the body fluids.

The *pressure gradient* across the respiratory membrane is the difference between the partial pressure of the gas in the alveoli and the pressure of the gas in the blood. It has already been pointed out that partial pressure represents a measure of the total number of molecules of a particular gas striking the alveolar surface of the membrane, and the pressure of the same gas in the blood represents the number of molecules striking the membrane from the opposite side. Therefore, the differences between these two pressures, the pressure gradient, is a measure of the net tendency for any particular gas to pass through the membrane. Obviously, when the partial pressure of a gas in the alveoli is greater than the pressure of the gas in the blood, as is true of O_2, net diffusion from the alveoli into the blood

occurs, but, when the pressure of the gas in the blood is greater than the partial pressure in the alveoli, as is true of CO_2, net diffusion from the blood into the alveoli occurs.

Diffusing Capacity of the Respiratory Membrane

The overall ability of the respiratory membrane to exchange a gas between the alveoli and the pulmonary blood can be expressed in terms of the *diffusing capacity,* which is defined as the *volume of a gas that will diffuse through the membrane each minute for a pressure gradient of 1 mm. Hg.*

Obviously, all the factors discussed above that affect diffusion through the respiratory membrane can affect the diffusing capacity.

The Diffusing Capacity for Oxygen. In the average young male adult the diffusing capacity for oxygen under resting conditions averages 21 ml. per minute. Since the average oxygen pressure gradient across the respiratory membrane during quiet breathing averages 11 mm. Hg, this gives a total of about 250 ml. of oxygen diffusing through the pulmonary membrane each minute.

Change in oxygen-diffusing capacity during exercise. During strenuous exercise, or during other conditions which greatly increase pulmonary activity, the diffusing capacity for oxygen increases in young male adults to a maximum of about 65 ml. per minute, which is three times the diffusing capacity under resting conditions. This increase is caused by three different factors: (1) opening up of a number of previously dormant pulmonary capillaries, thereby increasing the surface area of the diffusing membrane, (2) dilatation of all the pulmonary capillaries that were already open, thereby increasing also the total surface area, and (3) possibly also opening up some previously atelectatic alveoli. Therefore, during exercise, the oxygenation of the blood is increased not only by increased alveolar ventilation but also by a greater capacity of the respiratory membrane for transmitting oxygen into the blood.

Diffusing Capacity for Carbon Dioxide. The diffusing capacity for carbon dioxide has never been measured because of the following technical difficulty: the carbon dioxide pressure in the pulmonary blood is not

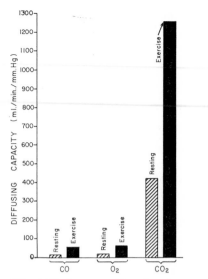

Figure 407. Diffusing capacities of carbon monoxide, oxygen, and carbon dioxide in the normal lungs.

far different from the carbon dioxide pressure in the alveoli, and with available techniques this difference is too small to be measured accurately.

Nevertheless, measurements of diffusion of other gases have shown that the diffusing capacity varies directly with the diffusion coefficient of the particular gas. Since the diffusion coefficient of carbon dioxide is 20 times that of oxygen, one would expect a diffusing capacity for carbon dioxide under resting conditions of about 400 to 450 ml. and during exercise of about 1200 to 1300 ml. per minute.

The importance of these very high diffusing capacities for carbon dioxide is this: When the lung becomes progressively damaged its capacity for transmitting oxygen into the blood is always impaired enough to cause death of the person long before any significant impairment of carbon dioxide diffusion occurs. The only time that a low diffusing capacity for carbon dioxide ever causes any significant difficulty is when lung damage is far beyond that which ordinarily causes death but the person's life is being maintained by intensive oxygen therapy which overcomes the reduction in oxygen-diffusing capacity.

Figure 407 illustrates the diffusing capacities of oxygen, carbon dioxide, and carbon monoxide both at rest and during exercise, showing the extreme diffusing capacity of carbon dioxide and also the effect of exercise on the diffusing capacities of all the gases.

Measurement of Diffusing Capacity. The oxygen-diffusing capacity can be estimated from measurements of (1) alveolar oxygen partial pressure, (2) oxygen pressure in the pulmonary capillary blood, and (3) the rate of oxygen utilization. To measure the oxygen pressure in the pulmonary blood is a very difficult procedure and is usually accomplished by measuring the P_{O_2} in the pulmonary arterial blood and the P_{O_2} in the aortic arterial blood and then mathematically obtaining a reasonable average for pulmonary capillary blood. This average must be a time-integrated average rather than a simple average because pulmonary arterial blood on entering the capillaries becomes rapidly oxygenated during the first fraction of its transit through the capillaries and then progressively more slowly during the latter stages of transit. Obviously, this procedure is quite complicated, and one is never sure exactly how accurate his results might be.

To obviate the difficulties encountered in measuring oxygen-diffusing capacity, pulmonary physiologists usually measure carbon monoxide–diffusing capacity instead, and calculate the oxygen-diffusing capacity from this. The principle of the carbon monoxide method is the following: A small amount of carbon monoxide is breathed into the alveoli and the partial pressure of the carbon monoxide in the alveoli is measured from appropriate alveolar air samples. Under most conditions it can be assumed that the carbon monoxide pressure in the blood is essentially zero because the hemoglobin absorbs this so rapidly that the pressure never has time to build up. Therefore, the diffusion gradient of carbon monoxide across the respiratory membrane is equal to the partial pressure in the alveoli. Then, by measuring the volume of carbon monoxide absorbed in a short period of time and dividing this by the pressure gradient, one can determine very accurately the carbon monoxide–diffusing gradient.

To convert carbon monoxide–diffusing capacity to oxygen-diffusing capacity the value is multiplied by a factor of 1.23 because the diffusion coefficient for oxygen is 1.23 times that for carbon monoxide. Thus, the average diffusing capacity for carbon monoxide in young male adults is 17 ml. per minute, and the diffusing capacity for oxygen is 1.23 times this, or 21 ml. per minute.

REFERENCES

Aksnes, E., and Rahn, H.: Measurement of total gas pressure in blood. *J. Appl. Physiol.*, 10:173, 1957.

Atwell, R. J., Ryan, J. M., Hull, H. B., and Tomashefski, J. F.: Factors influencing the alveolar-arterial oxygen pressure gradient; role of the left heart. *Am. J. Physiol.*, 183:451, 1955.

Atwell, R. J., Tomashefski, J. F., and Ryan, J. M.: Factors influencing alveolar-arterial oxygen pressure gradient: effect of ventilation and alveolar oxygen tension. *Am. J. Physiol.*, 186:501, 1956.

Barcroft, J.: The Respiratory Function of the Blood. The Diffusion of O_2 through Pulmonary Epithelium. Cambridge, Cambridge University Press, 1925.

Barratt-Boyes, B. G., and Wood, E. H.: The oxygen saturation of blood in the venae cavae, right-heart chambers, and pulmonary vessels of healthy subjects. *J. Lab. & Clin. Med.*, 50:93, 1957.

Briscoe, W. A., Forster, R. E., and Comroe, J. H., Jr.: Alveolar ventilation at very low tidal volume. *J. Appl. Physiol.*, 1:27, 1954.

Chinard, F. P., Enns, T., and Nolan, M. F.: Contributions of bicarbonate ion and of dissolved CO_2 to expired CO_2 in dogs. *Am. J. Physiol.*, 198:78, 1960.

DuBois, A. B., Britt, A. G., and Fenn, W. O.: Alveolar CO_2 during respiratory cycle. *J. Appl. Physiol.*, 4:535, 1952.

DuBois, A. B., Fowler, R. C., Soffer, A., and Fenn, W. O.: Alveolar CO_2 measured by expiration into rapid infrared gas analyzer. *J. Appl. Physiol.*, 4:526, 1952.

Farhi, L. E., and Rahn, H.: A theoretical analysis of the alveolar-arterial O_2 difference with special reference to the distribution effect. *J. Appl. Physiol.*, 7:699, 1955.

Farhi, L. E., and Rahn, H.: Gas stores of the body and the unsteady state. *J. Appl. Physiol.*, 7:472, 1955.

Fenn, W. O., Rahn, H., and Otis, A. B.: A theoretical study of the composition of the alveolar air at altitude. *Am. J. Physiol.*, 146:637, 1946.

Filley, G. F., MacIntosh, D. J., and Wright, G. W.: Carbon monoxide uptake and pulmonary diffusing capacity in normal subjects at rest and during exercise. *J. Clin. Invest.*, 33:530, 1954.

Fleisch, A.: New Methods of Studying Gaseous Exchange and Pulmonary Function. Springfield, Illinois, Charles C Thomas, 1960.

Forster, R. E.: Exchange of gases between alveolar air and pulmonary capillary blood; pulmonary diffusing capacity. *Physiol. Rev.*, 37:391, 1957.

Forster, R. E.: The absorption of CO by the lungs during breath holding. *J. Clin. Invest.*, 32:1135, 1954.

Fowler, W. S.: Intrapulmonary distribution of inspired gas. *Physiol. Rev.*, 32:1, 1952.

Fowler, W. S.: Uneven pulmonary ventilation. *J. Appl. Physiol.*, 2:283, 1949.

Fowler, W. S., Cornish, E. R., and Kety, S. S.: Analysis of alveolar ventilation by pulmonary N_2 clearance curves. *J. Clin. Invest.*, 31:40, 1952.

Guyton, A. C., Nichols, R. J., and Farish, C. A.: An arteriovenous oxygen difference recorded. *J. Appl. Physiol.*, 10:158, 1957.

Henderson, L. J.: Blood: A Study in General Physiology. New Haven, Yale University Press, 1928.

Kety, S. S.: Physiological and physical factors governing uptake of anesthetic gases by body. *Anesthesiology*, 11:517, 1950.

Kety, S. S.: Pulmonary diffusion coefficient. *Methods in Medical Research*, 2:234, 1950.

Lilienthal, J. L., Riley, R. L., Proemmel, D. D., and Franke, R. E.: An experimental analysis in man of the O_2 pressure gradient from alveolar air to arterial blood. *Am. J. Physiol.*, 147:199, 1946.

McGrath, M. W., and Thomson, M. L.: The effect of age, body size and lung volume change on alveolar-capillary permeability and diffusing capacity in man. *J. Physiol.*, 146:572, 1959.

Otis, A. B., Rahn, H., and Fenn, W. O.: Alveolar gas change during breath holding. *Am. J. Physiol.*, 152:674, 1948.

Perkins, J. F., Jr., Adams, W. E., and Flores, A.: Arterial oxygen saturation vs. alveolar oxygen tension as a measure of venous admixture and diffusion difficulty in the lung. *J. Appl. Physiol.*, 8:455, 1956.

Rahn, H.: A concept of mean alveolar air and the ventilation-blood flow relationships during pulmonary gas exchange. *Am. J. Physiol.*, 158:21, 1949.

Rahn, H., and Fenn, W. O.: A Graphical Analysis of the Respiratory Gas Exchange. Washington, D. C., Am. Physiol. Soc., 1955.

Rahn, H., Mohney, J., Otis, A. B., and Fenn, W. O.: Method for continuous analysis of alveolar air. *J. Aviat. Med.*, 17:173, 1946.

Rahn, H., and Otis, A. B.: Alveolar air during simulated flights to high altitudes. *Am. J. Physiol.*, 150:202, 1947.

Riley, R. L.: Pulmonary gas exchange. *Am. J. Med.*, 10:210, 1951.

Riley, R. L., and Cournand, A.: Analysis of factors affecting partial pressures of O_2 and CO_2 in gas and blood of lungs: theory. *J. Appl. Physiol.*, 4:77, 1951.

Riley, R. L., and Cournand, A.: Ideal alveolar air and the analysis of ventilation-perfusion relationships in the lungs. *J. Appl. Physiol.*, 1:825, 1949.

Riley, R. L., Cournand, A., and Donald, K. W.: Analysis of factors affecting partial pressures of O_2 and CO_2 in gas and blood of lungs: methods. *J. Appl. Physiol.*, 4:102, 1951.

Riley, R. L., Shepard, R. H., Cohn, J. E., Carrol, D. G., and Armstrong, B. W.: Maximal diffusing capacity of the lungs. *J. Appl. Physiol.*, 6:573, 1954.

Simmons, D. H., and Hemingway, A.: Functional residual capacity and respiratory nitrogen excretion of dogs. *J. Appl. Physiol.*, 8:95, 1955.

Chapter 41

Transport of Oxygen and Carbon Dioxide by the Blood and Body Fluids

Once oxygen has diffused from the alveoli into the pulmonary blood, it is transported principally in combination with hemoglobin to the tissue capillaries where it is released for use by the cells. The presence of hemoglobin in the red cells of the blood allows the blood to transport 30 to 100 times as much oxygen as could be transported simply in the form of dissolved oxygen in the water of the blood.

In the tissue cells oxygen reacts with various foodstuffs to form large quantities of carbon dioxide. This in turn enters the tissue capillaries and is transported by the blood back to the lungs. Carbon dioxide, like oxygen, also combines with chemical substances in the blood which increase the ease of carbon dioxide transport by about 20- to 30-fold.

The purpose of the present chapter, therefore, is to present both qualitatively and quantitatively the physical and chemical principles of oxygen and carbon dioxide transport in the blood and body fluids.

PRESSURE GRADIENTS OF OXYGEN AND CARBON DIOXIDE FROM THE LUNGS TO THE TISSUES

In the discussions of the previous chapter it was pointed out that gases move from one tissue area to another by the process of diffusion and that the cause of this movement is always a pressure gradient from one point to another. Thus, oxygen diffuses from the alveoli into the pulmonary capillary blood because of a pressure gradient. The oxygen pressure (P_{O_2}) in the alveoli averages 104 mm. Hg, while the P_{O_2} of oxygen in the venous blood entering the lungs from the systemic veins averages 40 mm. Hg. Therefore, immediately on entry of this blood into the pulmonary capillaries a very large pressure gradient, 64 mm. Hg, causes oxygen to diffuse rapidly into the pulmonary capillary blood. After passing through the lungs, the blood is transported by way of the arteries to the peripheral tissues. There the oxygen pressure is very low in the cells though high in the arterial blood entering the capillaries. Here again a large pressure gradient causes oxygen to diffuse out of the capillaries and through the interstitial spaces to the cells.

Conversely, when oxygen is metabolized with the foods in the cells to form carbon dioxide, the carbon dioxide pressure (P_{CO_2}) in the cells rises to a high value, which causes it then to diffuse into the tissue capillaries. Once in the blood the carbon dioxide is transported to the pulmonary capillaries where it diffuses out of the blood into the alveoli because the P_{CO_2} in the alveoli is lower than that in the pulmonary capillary blood.

Basically, then, the transport of oxygen and carbon dioxide by the blood depends both on the process of diffusion and on the movement of blood. We now need to consider quantitatively the factors responsible for these effects as well as their significance in the overall physiology of respiration.

Uptake of Oxygen by the Pulmonary Blood

Figure 408 illustrates a pulmonary alveolus adjacent to a pulmonary capillary,

bination with hemoglobin and then in the dissolved state.

The Reversible Combination of Oxygen with Hemoglobin

The chemistry of hemoglobin was presented in Chapter 12, where it was pointed out that the oxygen molecule combines very loosely and reversibly with the heme portion of the hemoglobin. When the P_{O_2} is high, oxygen binds with the hemoglobin, but, when the P_{O_2} is low, oxygen is released from the hemoglobin. This is the basis for oxygen transport from the lungs to the tissues, for the blood P_{O_2} rises to high values in the pulmonary capillary blood and falls to low values in the tissue capillaries.

The Oxygen-Hemoglobin Dissociation Curve. Figure 415 illustrates the *oxygen-hemoglobin dissociation curve* which shows the progressive increase in quantity of oxygen that is bound with hemoglobin as the pressure of oxygen increases. Since the blood leaving the lungs usually has a P_{O_2} in the range of 100 mm. Hg, one can see from the dissociation curve that the usual oxygen saturation of arterial blood is about 97 per cent. On the other hand, the P_{O_2} in normal venous blood is about 40 mm. Hg, and the per cent saturation of the hemoglobin is then about 70 per cent.

Maximum amount of oxygen that can combine with the hemoglobin of the blood. The blood of a normal person contains approximately 15 grams of hemoglobin in each 100 ml. of blood, and each gram of hemoglobin can bind with a maximum of about 1.3 ml. of oxygen. Therefore, on the average, the hemoglobin in 100 ml. of blood can combine with a total of about 19.5 ml. of oxygen. This is usually expressed as 19.5 *volumes per cent,* and in round figures it is usually considered to be 20 volumes per cent. The oxygen-hemoglobin dissociation curve for the normal person, therefore, can be expressed in terms of volume per cent of oxygen, as shown in Figure 416, rather than per cent saturation of hemoglobin.

Amount of Oxygen Released from the Hemoglobin in the Tissues. Note in Figure 416 that the total quantity of oxygen bound with hemoglobin in the normal arterial blood (P_{O_2} of 95 mm. Hg) is approximately 19.4 ml. On passing through the tissue capillaries, this amount is reduced to 14.4 ml. (P_{O_2} of 40 mm. Hg) or a total loss of about 5 ml. of oxygen from each 100 ml. of blood. Then, when the blood returns to the lungs, the same quantity of oxygen diffuses from the alveoli to the hemoglobin, and this too is carried to the tissues. Thus, *under normal conditions about 5 ml. of oxygen are transported by each 100 ml. of blood during each cycle through the tissues.*

Transport of Oxygen during Strenuous Exercise. In heavy exercise the muscle cells utilize oxygen at a very rapid rate, which causes the interstitial fluid P_{O_2} to fall as low as 15 mm. Hg. At this pressure only 4.4 ml. of oxygen binds with the hemoglobin in each 100 ml. of blood, as shown in Figure 416. Thus, 19.4 — 4.4, or 15 ml., is the total quantity of oxygen transported by each 100 ml. of blood in each cycle through the tissues. This, obviously, is three times as much

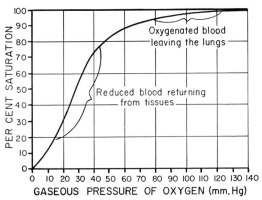

Figure 415. The oxygen-hemoglobin dissociation curve.

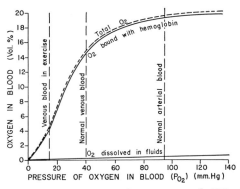

Figure 416. Quantity of oxygen in each 100 ml. of normal blood (a) bound with hemoglobin and (b) dissolved in the water of the blood; (c) total O_2 in both forms.

as that normally transported by the same amount of blood, illustrating that simply an increase in rate of oxygen utilization by the tissues causes an automatic increase in the rate of oxygen release from the hemoglobin.

The Utilization Coefficient. The fraction of the hemoglobin that gives up its oxygen as it passes through the tissue capillaries is called the *utilization coefficient.* Normally, this is approximately 27 per cent of the hemoglobin, or, in round figures, the normal utilization coefficient is approximately one fourth. During strenuous exercise, as high as 77 per cent of the hemoglobin can give up its oxygen, or, in round figures, the utilization coefficient is then approximately three quarters. This value, three quarters, is about the highest utilization coefficient that can be attained in the overall body even when the tissues are in extreme need of oxygen. However, in local tissue areas where the blood flow is very slow or the metabolic rate very high, utilization coefficients approaching 100 per cent have been recorded—that is, essentially all of the oxygen is removed.

The Total Rate of Oxygen Transport from the Lungs to the Tissues

If we consider that under resting conditions about 5 ml. of oxygen are transported by each 100 ml. of blood, and, if we consider the normal cardiac output to be approximately 5,000 ml. per minute, the calculated total quantity of oxygen delivered to the tissues each minute is about 250 ml. This is also the amount measured by a respirometer.

This rate of oxygen transport to the tissues can be increased in heavy exercise and in other instances of excessive need for oxygen up to about 15 times normal. It can be increased to three times normal simply by an increase in utilization coefficient, and it can be increased another five-fold as a result of increased cardiac output, thus accounting for the total 15-fold increase. Therefore, the maximum rate of oxygen transport to the tissues is about 15×250 ml., or 3750 ml., per minute in the normal young adult. Special adaptations in athletic training, such as an increase in total hemoglobin concentration, increase in maximum cardiac output, and so forth, can sometimes

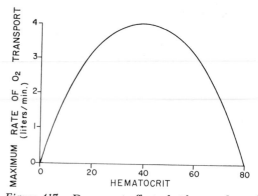

Figure 417. Depressant effect of either an elevated or a decreased hematocrit on oxygen transport.

increase this value to as high as 4½ to 5 liters per minute.

Effect of Hematocrit on Oxygen Transport to the Tissues. An increase in the blood hematocrit much above the normal level of 40 reduces the cardiac output because of increased blood viscosity, and the reduction in cardiac output is more than the increase in oxygen-carrying capacity of the blood. Since the total amount of oxygen that can be carried to the tissues each minute is the product of these two, then the rate of oxygen transport is actually reduced by an excessive rise in hematocrit.

On the other hand, in anemia the oxygen-carrying capacity of the blood is reduced in proportion to the decrease in hematocrit; there is some compensatory increase in cardiac output, but this is not so great as the decrease in oxygen-carrying capacity. Here again, there is an overall reduction in the rate of oxygen transport to the tissues. Figure 417 illustrates this effect, showing that *maximum oxygen transport occurs at a hematocrit of about 40 and that oxygen transport falls off at either high or low hematocrits.* Therefore, it is very fortunate that the normal hematocrit of 40 is approximately optimal for oxygen transport.

Though it has long been known that anemia will reduce oxygen transport, its reduction in polycythemia has only recently been discovered. It explains many of the harmful effects of polycythemia.

The Oxygen Buffer Function of Hemoglobin

Though hemoglobin is necessary for transport of oxygen to the tissues, it performs still another major function essential to life. This is the function of hemoglobin as an "oxygen buffer" system, for it is the hemoglobin in the blood which is mainly responsible for controlling the oxygen pressure in the tissues. Were it not for the hemoglobin oxygen buffer system, extreme variations in the P_{O_2} of the tissues would occur with exercise and with every change in metabolism, blood flow, and atmospheric oxygen concentrations.

Value of Hemoglobin for Maintaining Constant P_{O_2} in the Tissue Fluids. Even under basal conditions the tissues require about 5 ml. of oxygen from every 100 ml. of blood passing through the tissue capillaries. Referring back to the oxygen-hemoglobin dissociation curve in Figure 416, for 5 ml. of oxygen to be released from each 100 ml. of blood, the P_{O_2} must fall to about 40 mm. Hg. Therefore, tissue P_{O_2} ordinarily does not rise above approximately 40 mm. Hg, for if such should occur the oxygen needed by the tissues could not be released from the hemoglobin. In this way, the hemoglobin normally sets an upper limit on the gaseous pressure in the tissues at approximately 40 mm. Hg.

On the other hand, in very heavy exercise the oxygen pressure in the tissues falls, causing the hemoglobin to release extra quantities of oxygen to the tissues. This in turn helps to prevent the tissue P_{O_2} from falling below about 15 mm. Hg.

It can be seen, then, that hemoglobin automatically delivers oxygen to the tissues at a pressure between approximately 15 and 40 mm. Hg. This seems to be a very wide range of P_{O_2} in the interstitial fluid, but, when one considers how much the interstitial fluid oxygen pressure might possibly change during exercise and other types of stress, this range of 15 to 40 mm. Hg is relatively narrow.

This automatic regulation of oxygen pressure in the tissue fluids emphasizes once again the basic function of all the organs in the body to maintain more or less constant conditions in the interstitial fluids which bathe the individual cells of the body. By maintaining these constant conditions, the cells themselves, which are the ultimate living structures of the body, can continue to exist.

Value of Hemoglobin for Automatically Adjusting the Body to Different Concentrations of Atmospheric Oxygen. The normal partial pressure of oxygen in the alveoli is approximately 104 mm. Hg, but, as one ascends a mountain or goes high in an airplane, the partial pressure of oxygen falls considerably, or, when one enters areas of compressed air, such as deep below the sea or compressed air tunnels, the oxygen partial pressure may rise to very high values. It will be seen from the oxygen-hemoglobin dissociation curve of Figure 415 that, when the P_{O_2} is decreased to as low as 60 mm. Hg, the hemoglobin is still 89 per cent saturated. Consequently, whenever the alveolar partial pressure of oxygen is above 60 mm. Hg, the quantity of oxygen combined with the hemoglobin is never more than 10 per cent below the normal saturation of 97 per cent. Furthermore, the tissues still remove approximately 5 ml. of oxygen from every 100 ml. of blood passing through the tissues, and to remove this oxygen, the P_{O_2} of the venous blood falls to only slightly less than 40 mm. Hg.

On the other hand, when the alveolar partial pressure of oxygen rises far above the normal value of 104 mm. Hg, the maximum oxygen saturation of hemoglobin can never rise above 100 per cent. Therefore, even though the oxygen in the alveoli should rise to a partial pressure of 500 mm. Hg, or even more, the increase in the saturation of hemoglobin would be only 3 per cent because even at 104 mm. Hg oxygen pressure, 97 per cent of the hemoglobin is already combined with oxygen. Then, when the hemoglobin that has been subjected to high pressures of oxygen in the alveoli passes to the tissue capillaries, it still loses several milliliters of oxygen to the tissues, and this loss automatically reduces the P_{O_2} of the blood to a value only a few millimeters greater than the normal 40 mm. Hg.

Consequently, it can be seen that the atmospheric oxygen content may vary tremendously—from 60 to more than 500 mm. Hg partial pressure of oxygen—and still the P_{O_2} of the tissues does not vary more than a few millimeters from normal.

Transport of Oxygen in the Dissolved State

At the normal arterial P_{O_2} of 95 mm. Hg, approximately 0.29 ml. of oxygen is dissolved in every 100 ml. of water in the blood. When the

Po$_2$ of the blood falls to 40 mm. Hg in the tissue capillaries, 0.12 ml. of oxygen remain dissolved. In other words, 0.17 ml. of oxygen is transported to the tissues by each 100 ml. of blood water. This compares with about 5.0 ml. transported by the hemoglobin. Therefore, the amount of oxygen transported to the tissues in the dissolved state is normally very slight; only about 3 per cent of the total is transported as compared with the 97 per cent transported by the hemoglobin. During heavy exercise, when the utilization coefficient rises, the quantity transported in the dissolved state then falls to as little as 1.5 per cent. In Figure 416 the quantitative relationships of the amount of oxygen that can be transported in the dissolved state versus that bound with hemoglobin can be seen. This figure shows that the total oxygen in the blood under normal conditions is accounted for almost entirely by that bound with hemoglobin, while only a minute portion is dissolved in the fluids. Yet, under abnormal conditions the amount transported in the dissolved state can become tremendous as follows:

Effect of Extremely High Oxygen Partial Pressures on Oxygen Transport.
When the oxygen pressure in the blood rises much above 100 mm. Hg, this does not increase the amount of oxygen bound with hemoglobin significantly because the hemoglobin is already almost 100 per cent saturated, but it does continue to increase the amount of oxygen dissolved in the water of the blood. These effects are illustrated in Figure 418, which depicts the same data as Figure 416 except that the oxygen pressures in the lungs are now extended to over 3000 mm. Hg instead of 140 mm. Note that in the normal range of alveolar oxygen pressures almost none of the total oxygen in the blood is accounted for by dissolved oxygen, but, as the pressure rises progressively into the thousands of mm. Hg, a very significant portion of the total oxygen is dissolved rather than bound with hemoglobin.

Effect of High Pulmonary Po$_2$ on Tissue Po$_2$.
Let us assume that the oxygen partial pressure in the lungs is about 3000 mm, Hg (4 atmospheres pressure). Referring to Figure 418, this would represent a total oxygen content in each 100 ml. of blood of about 29 volumes per cent, as illustrated by point A in the figure. Now as this blood passes through the tissue capillaries and the tissues utilize their normal amount of oxygen, about 5 ml. from each 100 ml. of blood, then we find that the total quantity of oxygen still in the blood on leaving the tissue capillaries will be 24 volumes per cent, which is represented by point B in the figure. At this point, the oxygen pressure in the blood leaving the tissue capillaries is still about 1200 mm. Hg. From earlier discussions it will be recalled that the oxygen pressure of the venous blood leaving the tissue capillaries

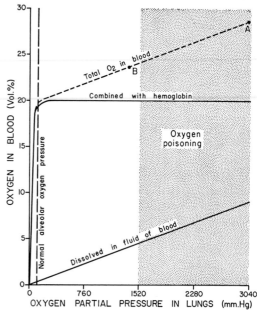

Figure 418. Quantity of oxygen dissolved in the water of the blood and in combination with hemoglobin at very high oxygen pressures.

is approximately equal to the oxygen pressure in the tissues themselves. Thus, very high partial pressures of oxygen breathed by the lungs can also cause very high tissue Po$_2$'s if these pressures are high enough for transport of excessive quantities of oxygen in the dissolved state.

Oxygen Poisoning.
When the oxygen pressure in the tissues rises too high, it has a tendency to change the rates of many of the chemical reactions within the cells, sometimes to such an extent that it actually "poisons" the tissues. The tissues most likely to be poisoned are the ones that have a high rate of metabolism, for it is in these cells that metabolism is most deranged. Among the most sensitive tissues of the body are those of the central nervous system; in its early stages oxygen poisoning causes severe convulsions and in late stages actual destructive lesions. Also, the pulmonary membranes often suffer severely because they are directly exposed to very high oxygen pressures in the lungs. This often results in serious pulmonary edema.

What is it that determines the upper limit of oxygen partial pressure that can be breathed before poisoning results? Referring once again to Figure 418 we can see that a person who picks up oxygen at point A on the curve and then delivers the oxygen to his tissues at point B never does release any oxygen from his hemoglobin but only from the dissolved fluids. Thus, all the oxygen carried to the tissues is transported in the dissolved state. In fact any time the Po$_2$ in the lungs is within the shaded area of the figure—

that is, above about 1500 mm. Hg—essentially no oxygen will be released from the hemoglobin as it passes through the tissues. On the other hand, if the oxygen pressure in the lungs is below 1500 mm. Hg, at least some of the oxygen bound with the hemoglobin will usually have to be released to supply the needs of the tissues. When this occurs the oxygen pressure in the tissues is once again regulated within a reasonably normal range by the *steep portion* of the oxygen-hemoglobin dissociation curve in the manner discussed earlier in the chapter. To express this another way, if all the oxygen needed by the tissues can be transported in the dissolved state, oxygen poisoning will almost always result because the *hemoglobin-oxygen buffer system* cannot function, but if at least part of the required oxygen must be released from the hemoglobin, the tissue oxygen pressure will be in a nearly normal range.

It is especially interesting that a person breathing oxygen above a partial pressure of about 1500 mm. Hg (2 atmospheres pressure) for several hours almost always develops convulsions, just as would be predicted from Figure 418. To be on the safe side it is recommended that a person never breathe oxygen for a prolonged period of time at a pressure above about 1000 mm. Hg.

Experimental Treatment of Anemia with Very High Concentrations of Oxygen in the Lungs. An obvious implication of this discussion is that a person with severe anemia whose blood could not carry sufficient quantities of oxygen to the tissues in combination with hemoglobin would be aided greatly by breathing pure oxygen or by being placed in a pressure chamber containing a high partial pressure of oxygen, for then a large quantity of oxygen could be carried to the tissues in the dissolved state rather than combined with hemoglobin. Indeed, in dogs treated in such pressure chambers, it has been possible to transport enough dissolved oxygen to supply more than two thirds of the quantity of oxygen needed by the tissues. Yet, whenever more oxygen than that used by the tissues is supplied in the dissolved state to the dog, then no oxygen is removed from the hemoglobin, and the oxygen buffer function of the hemoglobin is abrogated. In order for hemoglobin to control the level of oxygen in the tissues, at least several per cent of the hemoglobin must lose its oxygen. Then the oxygen-hemoglobin dissociation curve operates along the steep portion of the curve, thus buffering the P_{O_2} of the tissue fluids as explained above. Therefore, administration of oxygen under extreme pressure to an anemic animal may lead to death, not because of failure to transport oxygen but because of failure of the oxygen buffer function of hemoglobin.

Combination of Hemoglobin with Carbon Monoxide

Carbon monoxide combines with hemoglobin at the same point on the hemoglobin molecule as does oxygen. Furthermore, it binds with approximately 210 times as much tenacity as oxygen, which is illustrated by the carbon monoxide–hemoglobin dissociation curve in Figure 419. This curve is almost identical with the oxygen-hemoglobin dissociation curve except that the pressures of the carbon monoxide are at a level 210 times less than those in the oxygen-hemoglobin dissociation curve of Figure 415. Therefore, a carbon monoxide pressure of only 0.5 mm. Hg in the alveoli, 210 times less than that of the alveolar oxygen, will cause half the hemoglobin in the blood to become bound with carbon monoxide instead of with oxygen; a carbon monoxide pressure of 0.7 mm. Hg (a concentration of about 0.1 per cent) is lethal.

A patient severely poisoned with carbon monoxide can be very advantageously treated by administering pure oxygen, for oxygen at high alveolar pressures removes carbon monoxide from its combination with hemoglobin far more rapidly than can be achieved at the low pressure of atmospheric oxygen. That is, the pressure allows the oxygen actually to force its way into the hemoglobin molecule and thereby displace the carbon monoxide.

The patient can also be benefited by simultaneous administration of a few per cent carbon dioxide because this prevents the release of carbon dioxide from the blood; the carbon dioxide in turn strongly stimulates the respiratory center as will be

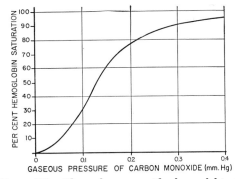

Figure 419. The carbon monoxide–hemoglobin dissociation curve.

discussed in the following chapter. The resulting increase in alveolar ventilation reduces the alveolar carbon monoxide concentration and thereby allows increased carbon monoxide release from the blood.

With intensive oxygen and carbon dioxide therapy, carbon monoxide can be removed from the blood 10 to 20 times as rapidly as without therapy.

TRANSPORT OF CARBON DIOXIDE IN THE BLOOD

Transport of carbon dioxide is not nearly so great a problem as transport of oxygen because even in the most abnormal conditions carbon dioxide can usually be transported by the blood in far greater quantities than can oxygen. However, the amount of carbon dioxide in the blood does have much to do with acid-base balance of the body fluids, which was discussed in detail in Chapter 10. Therefore, carbon dioxide transport is principally of importance because of its relationship to acid-base balance of the body fluids.

Chemical Forms in Which Carbon Dioxide Is Transported. Carbon dioxide is transported in four different chemical forms: (1) *dissolved carbon dioxide*, (2) carbon dioxide combined with water to form *carbonic acid*, (3) *bicarbonate ions* resulting from dissociation of the carbonic acid, and (4) *carbamino compounds* resulting mainly from combination of carbon dioxide with hemoglobin but to a slight extent with plasma protein as well.

To begin the process of carbon dioxide

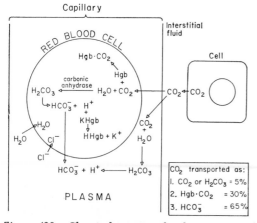

Figure 420. Chemical reactions for the transport of carbon dioxide.

transport, carbon dioxide diffuses out of the cells in the gaseous form but not to a significant extent in the bicarbonate form because the cell membrane is far less permeable to bicarbonate than to the dissolved gas. On entering the capillary, the chemical reactions illustrated in Figure 420 occur immediately; the quantitative aspects of these can be described as follows:

Transport of Carbon Dioxide in the Dissolved State

Some of the carbon dioxide remains in the blood fluids in the dissolved state and is transported in this form all the way to the lungs. It will be recalled that the P_{CO_2} of venous blood is 45 mm. Hg and that of arterial blood is 40 mm. Hg. Because of this slight differential, only about 0.2 ml. of CO_2 is transported by each 100 ml. of blood in the form of dissolved CO_2. This is about 4 per cent of all the carbon dioxide transported.

Transport of Carbon Dioxide in Combination with the Water of the Plasma

It is well known that carbon dioxide reacts with water to form carbonic acid. Almost all this acid dissociates immediately into bicarbonate ion and hydrogen ion, and these compounds react with the buffers of the plasma. Consequently, some carbon dioxide is transported in the plasma principally in the form of bicarbonate ion. However, the total quantity of carbon dioxide that combines with the water of the plasma is probably very small because the reaction of carbon dioxide with plasma water requires a number of seconds to occur to a significant degree. Yet, possibly 0.1 to 0.3 ml. of carbon dioxide might be transported in this manner in each 100 ml. of blood.

Transport of Carbon Dioxide in Combination with Hemoglobin and Plasma Proteins—Carbaminohemoglobin

When carbon dioxide enters the red blood cell, two reactions take place immediately. One of these is combination of carbon dioxide with hemoglobin, and the second is combination with the water of the red blood cell. The combination of carbon dioxide with hemoglobin is a reversible reaction that occurs with a very loose bondage. The reaction can take place in a fraction of a second, and carbon dioxide can be released once again from the hemoglobin in a fraction of a second in the lungs. The compound formed by the reaction is known as "carbamino-hemoglobin." A small amount of carbon dioxide reacts in this same way with the plasma proteins, but this is much less significant because of the four times less quantity of these proteins in the blood.

The total quantity of carbon dioxide carried from the tissues to the lungs in combination with hemoglobin and plasma proteins is approximately 30 per cent of the total quantity transported—that is, about 1.5 ml. of carbon dioxide in each 100 ml. of blood.

Carbon dioxide does not combine with hemoglobin at the same point on the hemoglobin molecule as oxygen; therefore, hemoglobin can combine with both oxygen and carbon dioxide at the same time. Yet, oxygen and carbon dioxide do interfere indirectly with the combination of hemoglobin with each other, as follows:

Mutual Interference between Oxygen and Carbon Dioxide Combination with Hemoglobin. Even though oxygen and carbon dioxide combine with hemoglobin at different points on the molecule, when carbon dioxide is bound with hemoglobin, slightly less oxygen can combine with the same hemoglobin solution for a given P_{O_2}. However, the change is small enough that the transport of oxygen from the lungs to the tissues is not significantly affected by this interference phenomenon.

On the other hand, when oxygen binds with hemoglobin this causes the hemoglobin to bind very poorly with carbon dioxide, which is of special physiologic importance as follows:

Figure 421 illustrates small portions of two car-bon dioxide dissociation curves in the same blood, the upper curve representing blood with a P_{O_2} of 40 mm. Hg (venous blood) and the lower curve representing blood with a P_{O_2} of 100 mm. Hg (arterial blood). The total quantity of carbon dioxide bound with 100 ml. of blood as it leaves the tissue capillaries is approximately 53 ml., as indicated by point A in the figure. Then, when blood passes through the lungs, the hemoglobin becomes saturated with oxygen. Therefore, the carbon dioxide dissociation curve with blood immediately becomes the lower one. Furthermore, because of carbon dioxide loss into the alveoli, the P_{CO_2} of the blood falls to 40 mm. Hg. At this level the quantity of carbon dioxide bound with the blood is represented by point B in the figure, illustrating that the total quantity of carbon dioxide bound with 100 ml. of blood leaving the pulmonary capillaries is 48 ml., approximately 5 ml. less than in the blood entering the capillaries. If oxygen had not helped to displace carbon dioxide from the blood by shifting the CO_2 dissociation curve, the P_{CO_2} would have fallen to 36 mm. Hg rather than 40 mm. Hg. This effect is represented by point C in Figure 421.

Thus, the release of oxygen in the tissues allows the blood to pick up extra quantities of carbon dioxide, and the oxygenation of blood in the lungs causes extra release of carbon dioxide.

Transport of Carbon Dioxide in the Form of Bicarbonate Ion Inside the Red Blood Cell

The second very rapid reaction of carbon dioxide inside the red blood cells is combination of carbon dioxide with water under the influence of the catalytic enzyme *carbonic anhydrase* to form carbonic acid; 99.9 per cent of this immediately dissociates into bicarbonate and hydrogen ions. As shown in Figure 420, the dissociative products of carbonic acid account for the transport of approximately 65 per cent of all the carbon dioxide carried from the tissues to the lungs. This means that normally about 3 ml. of carbon dioxide are transported in each 100 ml. of blood from the tissues to the lungs by this means.

An enzyme inside the red blood cells, *carbonic anhydrase,* accelerates the reaction of carbon dioxide with water 200 to 300 times; therefore, this reaction, instead of requiring 10 or more seconds for half the carbon dioxide to react as in the plasma, occurs in less than one-tenth second in the red blood cells. This is the reason that transport of

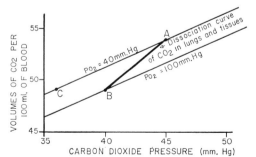

Figure 421. Effect of P_{CO_2} on the carbon dioxide content of the blood, illustrating increased affinity of the hemoglobin molecule for carbon dioxide in the tissue capillaries, where the P_{O_2} is low, and decreased affinity of hemoglobin for carbon dioxide in the lungs, where the P_{O_2} is high.

carbon dioxide in combination with water is extremely important inside the red blood cells though this same mechanism is relatively insignificant in the plasma.

The hydrogen ion formed when carbonic acid dissociates inside red blood cells reacts rapidly with the hemoglobin, which is a powerful acid-base buffer. Hemoglobin in the more alkaline state is combined with potassium, but, when an excess of hydrogen ions are present as a result of carbonic acid dissociation, the hydrogen combines with the hemoglobin, and the hemoglobin in turn releases ionic potassium.

The Bicarbonate Shift and the Chloride Shift.

As illustrated in Figure 420, when bicarbonate ion is formed from carbonic acid the concentration of bicarbonate ion increases in the red blood cells and becomes much higher than the bicarbonate concentration in the plasma. Therefore, bicarbonate ion diffuses through the red blood cell membrane into the plasma. However, potassium ion, which electrically balances the bicarbonate ion in the red blood cell, cannot pass through the cell membrane nearly as easily as the bicarbonate ion. As a result, when the bicarbonate ions diffuse out, other negative ions must diffuse inward to take the place of the bicarbonate. The negative ion in greatest abundance in the plasma—chloride—therefore enters the red blood cell at the same time that bicarbonate diffuses outward.

Consequently, as carbon dioxide leaves the tissues and enters the blood, bicarbonate ion shifts from the red blood cells into the plasma, and chloride ion shifts from the plasma into the red blood cells. As a result, the content of chloride in red blood cells of *venous* blood is slightly higher than the content of chloride in the *arterial* red blood cells.

The Water Shift.

Referring again to Figure 420, it will be noted that carbon dioxide diffuses directly from the tissues into the red blood cell, but nothing happens at first to the quantity of osmotic elements within the red blood cells because the carbon dioxide is freely diffusible and therefore is not an osmotically active substance. However, as the series of reactions takes place in the red blood cell, bicarbonate ion is formed, and potassium is liberated from its chemical combination with hemoglobin. Thus, the entry of carbon dioxide into the red blood cell in this manner increases the number of osmotically active elements within the cell. To maintain osmotic equilibrium between the red blood cells and the plasma, water from the plasma flows inward through the red blood cell membrane. As a result, the red blood cells of venous blood are slightly larger than the red blood cells of arterial blood.

The chloride shift and the water shift of red blood cells are not of great importance in themselves, but an understanding of these shifts aids greatly in an overall understanding of the reactions of the red blood cells for transporting carbon dioxide.

Change in Blood Acidity during Carbon Dioxide Transport

The carbonic acid formed when carbon dioxide enters the blood reacts with the buffers of the blood, thereby preventing the hydrogen ion concentration from rising greatly. Ordinarily, arterial blood has a pH of approximately 7.40, and, as the venous blood acquires carbon dioxide and carbonic acid is formed, the pH of the blood falls to approximately 7.36. In other words, a pH change of 0.04 unit takes place when carbon dioxide enters the blood from the tissues, and the reverse occurs when carbon dioxide is released from the blood in the lungs, the pH rising to the arterial value once again.

The Dissociation Curve of Carbon Dioxide with Blood

Figure 422 illustrates the relationship of the total quantity of carbon dioxide in all forms in each 100 ml. of blood to the P_{CO_2} of the blood. As the P_{CO_2} increases, the overall quantity of carbon dioxide progressively increases, and along the normal operating portion of this *carbon dioxide dissociation curve* there is neither a steep slope nor a plateau comparable to those of the oxygen-hemoglobin dissociation curve.

Release of Carbon Dioxide in the Lungs

In the lungs the P_{CO_2} in the alveoli is slightly less than that of the blood, which

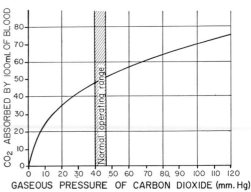

Figure 422.   Effect of P_{CO_2} on the total carbon dioxide content of the blood.

causes carbon dioxide to diffuse from the blood into the alveoli. This decreases the P_{CO_2} of the red blood cells so that carbaminohemoglobin releases carbon dioxide, and at the same time the carbonic acid of the cells, under the influence of carbonic anhydrase, changes back into water and carbon dioxide. In other words, exactly the reverse reactions occur in a split second in the lung capillaries as in the systemic capillaries, because all the reactions for transport of carbon dioxide are reversible.

REFERENCES

Allen, T. A., and Root, W. S.: Partition of carbon monoxide and oxygen between air and whole blood of rats, dogs and men as affected by plasma pH. *J. Appl. Physiol.*, 10:186, 1957.

Bigelow, W. G.: Oxygen transport and utilization in dogs at low body temperature. *Am. J. Physiol.*, 160:125, 1950.

Bjurstedt, H.: Respiratory system. *Ann. Rev. Physiol.*, 19:151, 1957.

Burchill, H. B., Taylor, B. E., Knutson, J. R. B., and Wood, E. H.: Circulatory adjustments to hypoxemia of congenital heart diseases of the cyanotic type. *Circulation*, 1:404, 1950.

Coxon, R. V., and Robinson, R. J.: The transport of radioactive carbon dioxide in the blood stream of the dog after administration of radioactive bicarbonate. *J. Physiol.*, 147:469, 1959.

Darling, R. C.: Blood gas transport. *Ann. Rev. Physiol.*, 12:265, 1950.

Davies, P. W., and Brink, F., Jr.: Microelectrodes for measuring local oxygen tension in animal tissues. *Rev. Scient. Instruments*, 13:524, 1942.

Dill, D. B., and Forbes, W. H.: Blood gas transport. *Ann. Rev. Physiol.*, 9:357, 1947.

Drury, D. R., Wick, A. N., and Almen, M. C.: Rate of elimination of labeled carbon dioxide from the body. *Am. J. Physiol.*, 186:361, 1956.

Ferris, B. G., Jr., Kriete, H. A., and Kriete, B. C.: Alveolar-arterial oxygen difference—comparison of two methods. *J. Appl. Physiol.*, 3:519, 1951.

Fowler, W. S., Blackburn, C. M., and Helmholz, H. F., Jr.: Determination of basal rate of oxygen consumption by open- and closed-circuit methods. *J. Clin. Endocr. Metab.*, 17:786, 1957.

Haldane, J. S., and Priestley, J. G.: Respiration. New Haven, Yale University Press, 1935.

Henderson, L. J.: Blood: A Study in General Physiology. New Haven, Yale University Press, 1928.

Kety, S. S., and Schmidt, C. F.: Effects of altered arterial tensions of carbon dioxide on oxygen consumption of normal young men. *J. Clin. Invest.*, 27:484, 1948.

Killick, E. M., and Marchant, J. V.: Resuscitation of dogs from severe acute carbon monoxide poisoning. *J. Physiol.*, 147:274, 1959.

Markus, G., and Baumberger, J. P.: Oxygen dissociation of whole blood studied polarographically. *J. Gen. Physiol.*, 36:255, 1952.

Nahas, C. G., Morgan, E. H., and Wood, E. H.: Oxygen dissociation curve of arterial blood in men breathing high concentrations of oxygen. *J. Appl. Physiol.*, 5:169, 1952.

Roughton, F. J. W.: Some recent work on the chemistry of carbon dioxide transport by the blood. *Harvey Lect.*, 39:96, 1943–44.

Roughton, F. J. W.: The average time spent by the blood in the human capillary and its relation to the rates of CO-uptake and elimination in man. *Am. J. Physiol.*, 143:621, 1945.

Roughton, F. J. W., and Kendrew, J. C.: Haemoglobin. New York, Interscience Publishers, Inc., 1949.

Stacy, R. W., and Hitchcock, F. A.: Dynamic effects of low oxygen tension of inspired air on alveolar gas tensions. *J. Appl. Physiol.*, 5:665, 1953.

Vallee, B. L., and Altschule, M. D.: Zinc in the mammalian organism with particular reference to carbonic anhydrase. *Physiol. Rev.*, 29:311, 1949.

Vannotti, A.: Iron Metabolism. New York, Grune & Stratton, Inc., 1949.

Wang, H. H., and Wang, S. C.: Respiration, *Ann. Rev. Physiol.*, 21:151, 1959.

Wood, E. H.: Blood gas transport. *Ann. Rev. Physiol.*, 14:235, 1952.

Chapter 42

Regulation of Respiration

During exercise and other physiological states that increase the metabolic activity of the body, the respiratory system is called upon to supply increased quantities of oxygen to the tissues and to remove increased quantities of carbon dioxide. The *respiratory center* in the brain stem adjusts the rate of alveolar ventilation almost exactly to the demands of the body so that, as a result, the blood P_{O_2} and P_{CO_2} are hardly altered even during the course of very strenuous exercise or other types of respiratory stress.

The present chapter will describe the operation of this neurogenic system for regulation of respiration.

THE RESPIRATORY CENTER AND RESPIRATORY RHYTHMICITY

Actually, there is no precise "center" in the central nervous system that controls all the respiratory functions. However, neurogenic mechanisms in the reticular substance of the medulla oblongata and pons can provide almost normal respiration even when the remainder of the central nervous system above the level of the pons has been destroyed. Therefore, this diffuse area is considered to be the *respiratory center.*

The Inspiratory and Expiratory Centers. Located in the ventral portion of the reticular substance at the lower end of the fourth ventricle, as shown in Figure 423, are bilateral *inspiratory centers,* which, when stimulated, cause the muscles of inspiration to contract. Lateral and dorsal to the inspiratory centers are bilateral *expiratory centers,* which excite the muscles of expiration. The inspiratory and expiratory centers overlap each other so that movement of an electrode gradually from one to the other causes

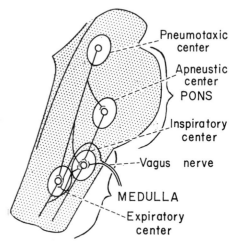

Figure 423. The respiratory center in the medulla and pons, illustrating the interrelationships between the inspiratory, expiratory, apneustic, and pneumotaxic centers.

a gradual change from inspiration to expiration, or vice versa. In general, these two centers operate reciprocally with each other. That is, when one is stimulated, the other becomes inhibited.

The Apneustic and Pneumotaxic Centers. In addition to the inspiratory and expiratory centers are two bilateral centers in the pons called respectively the *apneustic center* and the *pneumotaxic center;* they are located in the mid-pons and upper pons, as illustrated in Figure 423. Stimulation of the apneustic center causes *apneustic breathing,* which means forceful inspirations lasting 20 to 30 seconds but weak expirations lasting only 1 to 2 seconds. Stimulation of *the pneumotaxic center inhibits the apneustic type of breathing* and usually accelerates the rate of respiration.

Though the precise mechanism by which

all these areas of the "respiratory center" operate together to control the rate of alveolar ventilation is not known, the general plan of neurogenic control of respiration is presented in the following section.

THE BASIC RESPIRATORY RHYTHM

Oscillation in the Inspiratory and Expiratory Centers

A basic oscillation occurs continually in the medullary inspiratory and expiratory centers, causing rhythmic inspiratory and expiratory impulses to be transmitted to the muscles of respiration. When nerve impulses to these two centers from the apneustic center, the pneumotaxic center, and the vagi are all blocked, the depth of respiration becomes much less than normal and the rhythm quite irregular. Yet, the persistence of a basic respiratory rhythm in the medulla even under these adverse conditions shows the medulla to be the major area for coordinating respiratory control.

The medullary respiratory rhythmicity occurs principally in the inspiratory center, but also involves the expiratory center to some extent. The oscillatory mechanism has been postulated, though not proved, to be the following: It is believed that the inspiratory center is composed of neurons that, when not inhibited, transmit a continual stream of impulses to the inspiratory muscles and cause inspiration. However, when these inspiratory impulses are transmitted, others are transmitted through a *delay circuit* to the expiratory center, exciting this 2 to 3 seconds later. The expiratory center then excites the expiratory muscles and at the same time inhibits the inspiratory center, allowing the inspiratory muscles to relax. After another 2 to 3 seconds, the impulses in the expiratory center die out, and the inspiratory center again becomes active to initiate a new cycle of respiration.

Effect of the Apneustic and Pneumotaxic Centers on the Basic Respiratory Rhythmicity. When the connections from the apneustic center to the medulla are intact, the intensity of the signals transmitted from the inspiratory center to the inspiratory muscles is greatly enhanced, indicating that the apneustic center is necessary for truly forceful inspiration. If the pons is divided above the apneustic center but below the pneumotaxic center, apneustic breathing with prolonged inspirations occurs. But, if the pneumotaxic center is also operative, the apneustic type of breathing is inhibited and in its place is a normal respiratory rhythm with normal periods of expiration as well as inspiration. Thus, the pneumotaxic center seems to be more closely allied to expiration than to inspiration, whereas the apneustic center is more closely allied to inspiration.

Thus, when the pons and medulla are both intact, the respiratory rhythmicity is no longer of the primitive quality described above for the medullary centers alone. The rhythm is very regular, and the tidal volumes are completely adequate to promote normal alveolar ventilation. Therefore, it is presumed that even though the apneustic and pneumotaxic centers do not have a basic rhythmicity of their own they do nevertheless modify and control the activities of the medullary centers to provide a much more advantageous respiratory rhythm than can be achieved by the medullary centers alone.

Modification of the Respiratory Rhythm by the Hering-Breuer Reflex

The Hering-Breuer Reflex. In the lungs are many *stretch receptors,* located especially in the visceral pleura, that have a very profound effect on the rhythmicity of respiration. When the lungs become stretched, these receptors transmit impulses through the vagus nerves into the *tractus solitarius* of the brain stem and thence into the reticular substance. These impulses in turn inhibit inspiration. This effect is called the *Hering-Breuer reflex.* Inspiration excites stretch receptors that in turn inhibit inspiration. This prevents overdistention of the lungs, but at the same time it also has a very significant effect on respiratory rhythmicity.

The reflex operates in reverse during expiration: as the stretch receptors become unstretched the inhibition of the inspiratory center becomes reduced and inspiration begins anew.

The major effects of the Hering-Breuer reflex are (1) to decrease the tidal volume and (2) to cause a compensatory increase in respiratory rate. These effects result as follows: The inspiratory phase of respiration is cut off at an earlier point than would occur were it not for the reflex. Likewise, the period of expiration is also shortened as a consequence of the reverse Hering-Breuer reflex. Thus, each period of respiration is shortened with resultant increase in respiratory rate while the tidal volume decreases. As a result, alveolar ventilation is hardly changed by the *Hering-Breuer* reflex, though the rate of rhythm and depth of respiration are inversely altered.

Maintenance of Respiratory Rhythmicity by the Hering-Breuer Reflex. In addition to altering respiratory rhythmicity, the Hering-Breuer reflex also helps to maintain the respiratory rhythm. This is particularly true when the reticular substance of the brain stem has been damaged by some pathological condition and the basic rhythmicity within the reticular substance is very weak or even absent; transection of the vagus nerves under these conditions can actually cause respiration to stop because of loss of the Hering-Breuer reflex. Thus, the feedback that occurs through this reflex is quite important in the maintenance of respiratory rhythmicity. This operates in the following manner: When inspiration stretches the lungs the Hering-Breuer reflex, after a second or two, inhibits inspiration and initiates expiration. This allows the lungs to collapse, which initiates a reverse Hering-Breuer reflex that after another second or two inhibits expiration and excites inspiration. Then another cycle of respiration begins and is repeated again and again. Thus, the Hering-Breuer reflex constitutes an oscillating system all by itself that many times can maintain respiration even when the intrinsic rhythmicity of the respiratory centers is lacking. Under normal conditions, however, the intrinsic and extrinsic oscillatory mechanisms support each other, causing a faster rate of respiration than would occur if only one of the mechanisms were present.

CONTROL OF ALVEOLAR VENTILATION

In the previous section, we discussed the origin of the respiratory rhythmicity itself; now it is necessary to consider the mechanisms that in different physiological states modify this rhythmicity to control the rate and depth of respiration, thereby maintaining almost exactly constant P_{O_2} and P_{CO_2} in the body fluids. In general, the factors that control alveolar ventilation can be divided into (1) *chemical factors* and (2) *nervous factors*. The three most important chemical factors are the *arterial concentrations of* (a) *carbon dioxide,* (b) *hydrogen ions,* and (c) *oxygen.* The most important nervous factor affecting respiration is *nervous stimuli initiated during strenuous exercise.*

Carbon Dioxide—the Major Chemical Factor Regulating Alveolar Ventilation

Figure 424 illustrates the effect of arterial concentrations of carbon dioxide, hydrogen ion, and oxygen on alveolar ventilation, showing especially that carbon dioxide has far greater effect on respiration than either hydrogen ions or oxygen. This figure shows that an increase in P_{CO_2} from only 40 mm. Hg to 45 mm. Hg causes a three-fold in-

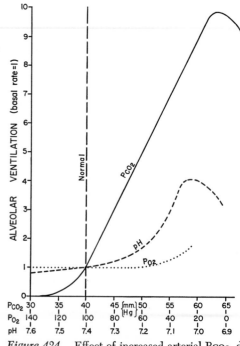

Figure 424. Effect of increased arterial P_{CO_2}, decreased arterial P_{O_2}, and decreased arterial pH on the rate of alveolar ventilation.

son's maximum breathing capacity. For instance, *spasm of the larynx, edema of the larynx, diphtheritic infection of the larynx or trachea, foreign objects in the respiratory passageway, mucus plugs in the smaller bronchi, infectious exudates in the bronchi,* and so forth, can all so greatly impede air flow to and from the alveoli that the respiratory muscles often simply cannot provide normal ventilation. The degree of incapacity is determined by the ratio of the airway resistance to the strength of the respiratory muscles.

Airway resistance is especially increased in two diseases that affect the bronchioles, *asthma* and *emphysema,* which will be discussed in further detail later in the chapter. Both of these impede air flow in the smaller bronchioles, causing far greater breathing effort during expiration than inspiration for the following reasons: When the muscles of respiration expand the lungs, they not only open the alveoli but also the small bronchioles. Consequently, air flows easily into the alveoli. On the other hand, during expiration the pressure of the thoracic cage against the lungs not only compresses the alveoli but also compresses the small bronchi, in this way reducing their diameters and thereby increasing the airway resistance. As a result, the airway resistance sometimes becomes several times as great during expiration as during inspiration, and the process of expiration is correspondingly prolonged. Also, because of this differential between expiratory and inspiratory resistance, the lungs become greatly distended, with a marked increase in functional residual capacity and residual volume.

Increased tissue resistance. Another factor that increases the work of respiration is often loss of normal pulmonary elasticity. In normal respiration, the inspiratory muscles stretch the lungs and thorax, and then the elastic recoil of the lungs and thorax causes the lungs to deflate during expiration. In this way, no effort is usually required for expiration. Many diseases of the lungs, particularly such destructive diseases as *emphysema, pulmonary fibrosis, tuberculosis, and various infections,* often destroy much of the elasticity of the lungs so that no recoil will occur. As a result, effort must then be expended by the respiratory muscles to deflate the lungs as well as to inflate them.

Decreased compliance of the lungs. The term "compliance" means the change in lung volume caused by a unit change in intra-alveolar pressure, as was explained in Chapter 39. Normally, a one centimeter of water rise in intra-alveolar pressure increases the lung volume 0.13 liter. But any disease that makes the tissues of the lungs less distensible than usual, such as *silicosis, sarcoidosis, tuberculosis, cancer,* and even *pneumonia,* all reduce the compliance and, therefore, increase the effort that must be expended by the respiratory muscles to expand the lungs. Also, any disease that decreases the total amount of functional lung tissue reduces the compliance and, therefore, increases the effort of respiration.

Diseases that Decrease Pulmonary Diffusing Capacity

Three different types of abnormalities can decrease the diffusing capacity of the lungs. These are: (1) decreased area of the pulmonary membrane, (2) increased thickness of the pulmonary membrane, called *alveolocapillary block,* and (3) abnormal ventilation-perfusion ratio in some parts of the lungs.

Decreased Area of the Pulmonary Membrane. Diseases or abnormalities that decrease the area of the pulmonary membrane include *removal of part or all of one lung, tuberculous destruction of the lung, cancerous destruction,* and *emphysema,* which causes gradual destruction of the alveolar septa.

Also, any acute condition that fills the alveoli with fluid or otherwise prevents air from coming in contact with the alveolar membrane, such as *pneumonia, pulmonary edema,* and *atelectasis,* can temporarily reduce the surface area of the pulmonary membrane.

Increased Thickness of the Pulmonary Membrane—Alveolocapillary Block. The most common acute cause of increased thickness of the pulmonary membrane is *pulmonary edema* resulting from left heart failure or pneumonia. However, *silicosis, tuberculosis,* and *many other fibrotic conditions* can cause progressive deposition of fibrous tissue in the interstitial spaces between the alveolar membrane and the pulmonary capillary membrane, thereby increasing the thickness of the pulmonary membrane. This is usually called *alveolo-capillary block,* or, occasionally, *interstitial fibrosis.* Since the rate of gaseous diffusion through the pulmonary membrane is inversely proportional to the distance that the gas must diffuse, it is readily understood how alveolo-capillary block can reduce the diffusing capacity of the lungs.

Abnormal Ventilation-Perfusion Ratio. Abnormal ventilation-perfusion ratio of the lungs is one of the most difficult to understand of all the abnormalities that can cause decreased pulmonary diffusing capacity, but it can be explained as follows: If the main bronchus of one lung is blocked so that all the pulmonary ventilation is going to the opposite lung though blood is still perfusing both lungs, the blood flowing through the ventilated lung will become almost totally saturated with oxygen while the other blood will pick up no oxygen at all. When the two bloods mix beyond the lungs, the resulting oxygenation of the blood is greatly depressed despite the fact that the ventilation of the lungs is far greater than that needed if the air could be distributed appropriately to both lungs.

Abnormal ventilation perfusion need not occur from one lung to the other, for exactly the same effect can occur from one alveolus to an adjacent one. Furthermore, it can occur in two different ways, (1) normal ventilation of the alveolus but reduced perfusion of the pulmonary membrane with blood or (2) hypoventilation of the alveolus but normal perfusion. To express this another way, an abnormal ventilation-perfusion ratio wastes a large amount of pulmonary ventilation in overventilating alveoli that cannot utilize the oxygen while at the same time not providing adequate oxygen to other alveoli.

Diseases that cause abnormal ventilation-perfusion ratios include *thrombosis of a pulmonary artery, arteriovenous shunts in the lungs, excessive airway resistance to some alveoli (emphysema), and reduced compliance of one lung without concomitant abnormality of the other lung.*

Abnormalities of Oxygen Transport from the Lungs to the Tissues

Different conditions that reduce oxygen transport from the lungs to the tissues include *anemia,* in which the total amount of hemoglobin available to transport the oxygen is reduced, *carbon monoxide poisoning,* in which a large proportion of the hemoglobin becomes unable to transport oxygen, and *decreased blood flow to the tissues* caused by either low cardiac output or localized tissue ischemia. All these have been discussed in Chapters 12, 41, and 35 respectively.

PHYSIOLOGIC PECULIARITIES OF SPECIFIC PULMONARY ABNORMALITIES

Pulmonary Fibrosis

Pulmonary fibrosis results from pulmonary disease in which large amounts of fibrous tissue grow into the substance of the lungs either diffusely or in localized areas. An interesting generalized type of pulmonary fibrosis is that caused by *silicosis,* which results from prolonged inhalation of very fine particles of silica dust, often occurring in anthracite coal miners, granite cutters, grinders in industrial plants, and so forth. The silicon dioxide causes a toxic reaction in the lung tissues with gradually increasing deposition of fibrous tissue. The earliest effect is *decreased pulmonary compliance,* as shown in Figure 433. This increases the muscular effort required for respiration, but it can usually be compensated by increased development of the respiratory muscles. In the late stages of silicosis, infectious processes develop in the diseased lungs, causing a multitude of other abnormalities besides the decreased compliance. For instance, *tuberculosis* is a very common result which can cause further fibrosis as well as much destruction of pulmonary substance.

However, the principal effect of pure pulmonary fibrosis is an increase in the work load of

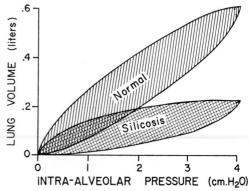

Figure 433. Compliance curves of normal and silicotic lungs.

the respiratory muscles. A late effect is alveolo-capillary block with reduced diffusing capacity of the lungs.

Other conditions besides silicosis that can cause pulmonary fibrosis are granulomatous *lesions of the lungs caused by mycotic infections, tuberculosis, prolonged chronic bronchitis,* and *emphysema.*

Tuberculosis

In tuberculosis the tubercle bacilli cause a peculiar tissue reaction in the lungs including, first, invasion of the infected region by macrophages and, second, walling off the lesion by fibrous tissue to form the so-called "tubercle." This walling-off process helps to limit further transmission of the tubercle bacilli in the lungs and, therefore, is part of the protective process against the infection. However, in approximately 3 per cent of all persons who contract tuberculosis (most people contract it some time or other), the walling-off process fails and the tubercle bacilli spread throughout the lungs, causing fibrotic tubercles in many areas. In late cases of tuberculosis, secondary infection by other bacteria causes extensive destruction of the lungs. Thus, tuberculosis results in many areas of fibrosis throughout the lungs, and, secondly, it reduces the total amount of functional lung tissue. These effects cause (1) increased effort on the part of the respiratory muscles to cause pulmonary ventilation and therefore *reduced vital capacity and maximum breathing* capacity, (2) *reduced total pulmonary membrane surface* and *increased thickness of the pulmonary membrane,* these causing progressively diminishing pulmonary diffusing capacity, and (3) *abnormal ventilation-perfusion ratio* in the lungs, further reducing the pulmonary diffusing capacity.

Pulmonary Edema

The circulatory aspects of pulmonary edema were discussed in detail in Chapter 29. Briefly, any abnormality that reduces the pumping capability of the left side of the heart will cause blood to dam up in the pulmonary circulation. And, if the pulmonary capillary pressure rises above approximately 28 mm. Hg, which is the amount of the colloid osmotic pressure of the plasma proteins, fluid immediately begins to transude out of the capillaries into the pulmonary interstitial spaces and even into the alveoli. This results in acute thickening of the pulmonary membrane, thereby reducing the diffusing capacity of the lungs. It also results in actual blockage of many of the alveoli as a result of total filling with fluid. This further reduces the diffusing capacity by reducing the total area of the pulmonary membrane. Finally, the presence of large quantities of fluid in the lungs increases the *tissue resistance* of the lungs so much that they cannot be expanded and contracted with ease; this factor increases the work load of the respiratory muscles, though it is not so detrimental an effect as the greatly reduced pulmonary diffusing capacity.

Pneumonia

The term pneumonia describes any lung condition in which the alveoli become filled with fluid and/or blood cells, as shown in Figure 436. Thus, the filling of the alveoli with fluid in very severe pulmonary edema is a type of pneumonia, but another even more common type of pneumonia is *bacterial pneumonia* caused most frequently by pneumococci. This disease begins with an infection in the alveoli of one part of the lungs; the alveolar membrane becomes edematous and highly porous so that fluid and often even red and white blood cells pass out of the blood into the alveoli. Thus, the infected alveoli become progressively filled with fluid and cells, and the infection spreads by extension of bacteria from alveolus to alveolus. Eventually, large areas of the lungs, sometimes whole lobes or even a whole lung, become "consolidated," which means that they are filled with fluids and cellular debris.

The pulmonary function of the lungs during pneumonia changes in different stages of the disease. In the early stages, the pneumonia process might well be localized in only one of the lungs, and alveolar ventilation may be reduced even though blood flow through the lung continues normally. This results in two major pulmonary abnormalities: (1) reduction in the total available surface area of the respiratory membrane, and (2) abnormal ventilation-perfusion ratio. Both these effects cause reduced diffusing capacity, which results in anoxemia. Figure 434 illustrates the effect of an abnormal ventilation-perfusion ratio in pneumonia, showing that the blood passing through the aerated lung becomes 97 per cent saturated while that passing through the unaerated lung remains only 60 per cent saturated, causing the mean saturation of the aortic blood to be about 78 per cent, which is far below normal.

In other stages of pneumonia the blood

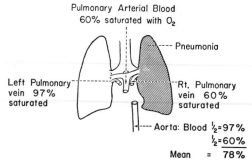

Figure 434.   Effect of pneumonia on arterial blood
oxygen saturation.

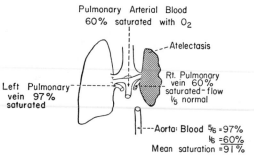

Figure 435.   Effect of atelectasis on arterial blood
oxygen saturation.

flow through the diseased areas decreases concurrently with the decrease in ventilation. This gives much less debility than that resulting from an abnormal ventilation-perfusion ratio.

Atelectasis

Atelectasis means collapse of the alveoli. It can occur in localized areas of the lungs, in an entire lobe of a lung, or in an entire lung. In the latter instance the condition is called *massive collapse* of a lung.

The pulmonary dynamics of atelectasis are illustrated in Figure 435. Collapse of the lung tissue in atelectasis causes the resistance to blood flow through the pulmonary vessels to increase as much as five-fold, presumably because of folding and kinking of the vessels as the volume of the lungs becomes compressed. As a result, the blood flow through the atelectatic lung is very slight while most of the blood passes through the ventilated lung and becomes well aerated. In the situation shown in Figure 435, five sixths of the blood passes through the aerated lung, and is saturated to 97 per cent. The remaining one sixth passes through the unaerated lung and is saturated to 60 per cent. The resultant aortic blood is 91 per cent saturated, which is not far from normal.

The usual cause of atelectasis is blockage of many small bronchi with mucus or obstruction of a major bronchus by either a large mucus plug or some solid object. The air beyond the block becomes entrapped, and the blood flowing in the adjacent capillaries gradually absorbs the air, pulling the walls of the alveoli together. The physics of air absorption in an entrapped cavity will be discussed in detail later in the chapter.

Bronchial Asthma

Bronchial asthma is usually caused by allergic hypersensitivity of the person to foreign substances in the air—especially to plant pollens. The allergic reaction causes localized edema in the walls of the terminal bronchioles as well as spasm of their smooth muscle walls. These effects greatly increase the airway resistance to the alveoli. For reasons discussed earlier in the chapter, the bronchiolar diameter becomes even further reduced during expiration and then opens up to a certain extent during inspiration. Therefore, the asthmatic person usually can inspire quite adequately but has great difficulty expiring. This results in dyspnea, or "air hunger," which will be discussed in detail later in the chapter.

The functional residual capacity and the residual volume of the lung become greatly increased during the asthmatic attack because of the difficulty in expiring air from the lungs. Over a long period of time the chest cage becomes permanently enlarged, causing a "barrel chest," and the functional residual capacity and residual volume also become permanently increased.

Chronic Obstructive Emphysema

The term *emphysema* actually means "blowing up of the lungs." The disease *chronic obstructive emphysema*, which is caused by prolonged subacute bronchial infection, is rapidly becoming one of the most prevalent of all respiratory diseases for two reasons: (1) chronic pulmonary infection followed by emphysema is very common among elderly persons, and the average age of our population is increasing year by year; (2) the growing prevalence of smoking has

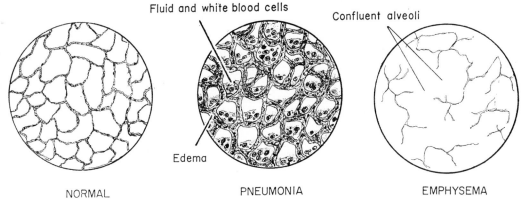

Figure 436. Pulmonary changes in pneumonia and emphysema.

resulted in an increase in secondary infections followed by emphysema.

The usual course of development of emphysema is, first, an infectious process in the terminal bronchioles which causes edema and mucus plugs that obstruct certain bronchioles. Second, irritation in the bronchioles causes a persistent cough. Third, the obstruction plus the cough, as well as intermittent infection in the alveoli themselves, causes gradual breaking down of many alveolar septa between adjacent terminal respiratory units, as shown in Figure 436. Fourth, some of the terminal bronchioles become permanently occluded by fibrosis, and air then passes into the occluded alveoli through ruptured alveolar membranes from the adjacent aerated alveoli. Thus, there are five basic abnormalities that result: (1) loss of many alveolar septa, which greatly reduces the pulmonary membrane surface area, (2) increased airway resistance due to the reduced number of bronchioles and the devious route by which the air flows to some of the alveoli, (3) abnormal ventilation-perfusion ratios because some alveoli are ventilated readily while others are ventilated very poorly, (4) fibrous replacement of the destroyed tissue in many areas, which causes some degree of alveolo-capillary block, and (5) elevated pulmonary arterial pressure, caused principally by destruction of many of the pulmonary vessels.

Because all these different abnormalities occur in chronic obstructive emphysema, a patient typically goes through three stages of pulmonary insufficiency: First, the increased airway resistance causes greatly increased work load on the respiratory muscles, leading to chronic increase in respiratory effort. Second, greatly reduced diffusing capacity of the lungs results from (a) reduced membrane area, (b) alveolo-capillary block, and (c) abnormal ventilation-perfusion ratios, and this necessitates still more increase in ventilation. This, combined with the increased work load even for normal ventilation, multiplies the effort of respiration to the point that the person develops severe dyspnea, or "air hunger." Third, the difficulty finally becomes so severe that the person develops hypoxia and hypercapnia in his body fluids, thus resulting in respiratory difficulties in the tissue cells themselves.

ANOXIA

The term *anoxia,* as usually used, means diminished availability of oxygen to the cells of the body. The term *anoxemia* means reduced oxygen in the body fluids, and refers especially to the oxygen in the arterial blood. Obviously, almost any of the conditions discussed in the past few sections of this chapter can cause serious degrees of anoxia. In some of these, oxygen therapy is of great value; in others it is of moderate value, while in still others it is of almost no value. Therefore, it is important to classify the different types of anoxia; then from this classification we can readily discuss the physiological principles of appropriate therapy. The following is a descriptive classification of the different types of anoxia:

1. Atmospheric anoxia
2. Hypoventilation anoxia
   a. Paralysis of the respiratory muscles

b. Increased airway resistance
c. Decreased pulmonary compliance
d. Increased pulmonary tissue resistance
3. Diffusion anoxia
a. Reduced active pulmonary membrane area
b. Thickened pulmonary membrane
4. Abnormal ventilation-perfusion ratio anoxia
a. Abnormal alveolar ventilation-perfusion ratios
b. Right-to-left shunts in the lungs or heart
5. Hypohemoglobinemic anoxia
a. Hemoglobin deficiency (usually caused by anemia)
b. Carbon monoxide poisoning
c. Methemoglobinemia
d. Other abnormalities of hemoglobin
6. Ischemic anoxia
a. Generalized decrease in cardiac output
b. Localized tissue ischemia
7. Tissue utilization anoxia
a. Poisoning of tissue oxidative enzymes
b. Tissue edema causing poor oxygen diffusion
c. Excessive tissue demand for oxygen

This classification of the different types of anoxia is mainly self-evident from the discussions earlier in the chapter of the different factors that can cause pulmonary insufficiency. Only two of the types of anoxia in the above classification need further elaboration; these are the anoxia caused by right-to-left shunts and tissue utilization anoxia.

Anoxia Caused by Right-to-Left Shunts. A right-to-left shunt means simply a direct pathway for blood to flow directly from the systemic veins to the systemic arteries without going through the lungs. The anoxia that results is identical with that caused by abnormal ventilation-perfusion ratios in the lungs. A little more than 1 per cent of the blood even in the normal person usually passes through several small right-to-left shunts, and, rarely, as much as 80 per cent of the blood can pass through very large pulmonary or cardiac shunts. This results in the condition found in the *blue baby*, which was discussed in Chapter 38 in relation to right-to-left cardiac shunts.

Tissue Utilization Anoxia. The most classical type of tissue utilization anoxia is that caused by cyanide poisoning in which certain ones of the oxidative enzymes are almost completely inactivated—to such an extent that the tissues simply cannot utilize the oxygen even though plenty is available. This type of anoxia is frequently also called *histotoxic anoxia*. Mild degrees of tissue utilization anoxia also occur frequently in some of the vitamin deficiency diseases because several of the vitamins, especially the B vitamins, are precursors of some of the oxidative enzymes.

A very common type of tissue anoxia occurs in tissue edema, which causes increased distances through which the oxygen must diffuse before it can be utilized by the cells. This type of anoxia can become so severe that the tissues in the edematous areas actually die, as is often illustrated by very serious ulcers in edematous skin areas.

Finally, tissues can become anoxic when the cells themselves demand more oxygen than can be made available to them by the normal respiratory and oxygen transport systems. For instance, in very strenuous exercise, one of the major limiting factors to the degree of exercise that can be performed is the tissue anoxia that develops.

Effects of Anoxia on the Body

Anoxia, if severe enough, can actually cause death of the cells, but in less severe degrees it results principally in (1) depressed mental activity, sometimes culminating in coma and (2) reduced work capacity of the muscles. These effects will be discussed in detail in the following chapter in relation to aviation medicine, and, therefore, are only mentioned here.

Cyanosis

The term *cyanosis* means blueness of the skin, and its cause is usually the presence of excessive amounts of deoxygenated blood in the skin capillaries. The presence or absence of cyanosis is one of the most common clinical signs used to assess different degrees of respiratory insufficiency, and for this reason it is important to understand the factors that determine the degree of cyanosis. These are the following:

1. The most important factor determining the degree of cyanosis is *the quantity of deoxygenated hemoglobin in the arterial blood,* for deoxygenated hemoglobin has a very intense dark blue color. It should be noted that it is not the percentage deoxygenation of the hemoglobin that causes the bluish hue to the skin, but, instead, it is principally the *concentration of deoxygenated hemoglobin* without regard to the concentration of oxygenated hemoglobin. The reason for this is that the red color of oxygenated blood is very weak in comparison with the very dark blue color of deoxygenated blood. Therefore, when the two are mixed together, the oxygenated blood has relatively little coloring effect in comparison with the deoxygenated blood.

In general, frank cyanosis will appear whenever the arterial blood contains more than 5 grams per cent of deoxygenated hemoglobin, and very mild cyanosis can frequently be discerned when as little as 3 to 4 grams per cent deoxygenated hemoglobin is present.

2. Another very important factor that affects the degree of cyanosis is the *rate of blood flow through the skin* for the following reasons: It is principally the blood in the capillaries that determines the color of the skin; the blueness of this blood is determined by two factors: (1) the concentration of deoxygenated hemoglobin in the arterial blood entering the capillaries and (2) the amount of deoxygenation that occurs as the blood passes through the capillaries. Ordinarily, the metabolism of the skin is relatively low so that little deoxygenation occurs as the blood passes through the skin capillaries. However, if the blood flow becomes extremely sluggish, even a small amount of metabolism can still cause marked desaturation of the blood as it passes through the capillaries and therefore can cause cyanosis. This explains the cyanosis that appears in very cold weather, particularly in children who have thin skins.

3. The *pigmentation in the skin* also affects the degree of cyanosis, for one simply cannot observe cyanosis in a darkly colored skin. In such an instance, however, cyanosis can still be observed in the mucous membranes of the mouth.

4. A final factor that affects the blueness of the skin is the *skin thickness.* For instance, in newborn babies, who have very thin skin, cyanosis occurs readily, particularly in highly vascular portions of the body such as the heels. Also, in adults (as well as babies) the lips and fingernails often appear cyanotic before the remainder of the body shows any blueness.

Cyanosis in Polycythemia. Polycythemia, which means an excess concentration of red cells in the blood, usually causes the skin over large areas of the body to remain mildly cyanotic all the time. There are three reasons for this: First, the quantity of hemoglobin in the blood is greatly increased so that for a given percentage of deoxygenation, the *concentration of deoxygenated hemoglobin* is greater than in the normal person. Second, the blood viscosity is very high, which causes sluggish blood flow through the skin. This results in further deoxygenation of the blood and, therefore, increased tendency for cyanosis. Third, all the blood vessels of the skin are usually greatly distended in polycythemia, which makes a larger quantity of reduced hemoglobin available to cause cyanosis than in the normal person.

Red Skin in Hyperemia. Excessive blood flow through the skin normally causes it to turn red. This occurs for two reasons: (1) The blood flowing rapidly through the skin hardly becomes deoxygenated at all. In the normal person, the arterial blood is 97 per cent saturated with oxygen, which gives the skin a very red hue rather than the blue hue of cyanosis. (2) Also, in hyperemia the blood vessels of the skin become dilated, making additional blood available to enhance further the redness.

Pale Skin in Anemia. In anemia, whether the blood is blue because of deoxygenated hemoglobin or red because of oxygenated hemoglobin, the skin nevertheless has a very pale hue, and this, too, is caused by two different effects: (1) Lack of hemoglobin in the vessels allows the whitish hue of the subcutaneous tissues to become the dominant color of the skin. (2) There is often a tendency to cutaneous vasoconstriction in anemia, and this further reduces the hemoglobin in the skin, thereby further enhancing the pale whitish color.

Dyspnea

Dyspnea means simply a desire for air, and a common synonym is "air hunger." In reality, dyspnea is a state of mind, for a person can feel a sensation of air hunger many times when he is not anoxic or hypercapnic at all. On the other hand, he might be severely anoxic and yet experience no dyspnea at all. For instance, an anoxic person who is asleep certainly has no sensation of dyspnea.

At least three different factors often enter into the development of the sensation of dyspnea. These are: (1) an actual abnormality of the respiratory gases in the body fluids, especially hypercapnia but to a much less extent anoxia, (2) the amount of work that must be performed by the respiratory muscles to provide adequate ventilation, and (3) the state of the mind itself. Thus, a person normally becomes very dyspneic when his muscles become paralyzed so that he simply cannot breathe adequately to obtain oxygen and blow off CO_2. This dyspnea undoubtedly results from excess buildup of CO_2 and reduction of oxygen in the body fluids.

At times, however, the levels of both carbon dioxide and oxygen in the body fluids are completely normal, but to attain this the person has to breathe extremely forcefully. In these instances, the forceful activity of the respiratory muscles themselves gives the patient a sensation of air hunger. Indeed, the dyspnea can be so intense, despite the normal gaseous concentrations in the body fluids, that clinicians often overemphasize this cause of dyspnea while forgetting that dyspnea can also result from abnormal gaseous concentrations.

Finally, the person's respiratory functions may be completely normal, and still he experiences dyspnea because of an abnormal state of mind. This is called *neurogenic dyspnea* or, sometimes, *emotional dyspnea*. For instance, almost anyone momentarily thinking about his act of breathing will suddenly find himself taking breaths a little more deeply than ordinarily because of a feeling of mild dyspnea. However, this feeling is greatly enhanced in persons who have a psychic fear of not being able to receive a sufficient quantity of air. For example, many persons on entering small or crowded rooms immediately experience emotional dyspnea, and patients with "cardiac neurosis," who have heard that dyspnea is associated with heart failure, frequently experience very se-

vere psychic dyspnea even though the blood gases are completely normal. Neurogenic dyspnea has been known to be so intense that the person over-respires himself into alkalotic tetany.

In summary, then, dyspnea can be caused by thoughts in the brain itself or by almost any abnormality of respiration that gives one the feeling that his respiratory system is not performing adequately. It is probably useless ever to try to find a single factor that causes dyspnea. Dyspnea, like the regulation of respiration, can undoubtedly be a product of multiple factors.

Clubbing of the Fingers

A very peculiar pathologic phenomenon, clubbing of the fingers, occurs in many patients with lung abscess, bronchiectasis, or almost any pulmonary disease that causes generalized anoxia. It occurs also in the cyanotic types of congenital heart diseases and occasionally in cirrhosis of the liver, certain gastrointestinal diseases, and other toxemic conditions.

Clubbing of the fingers means hypertrophy of the distal phalanx of each finger so that the fingers look like clubs. This is caused principally by soft tissue hypertrophy, but in very severe cases even the bone hypertrophies.

At present, the physiologic cause of clubbing is totally unknown, though its very common association with anoxic and ischemic conditions suggests that it results directly from diminished oxygen supply to the tissues. Yet, its presence in liver and intestinal diseases indicates that toxic factors of many types can cause the same result.

HYPERCAPNIA

Hypercapnia Associated with Hypoventilation Anoxia

Hypercapnia means excess carbon dioxide in the body fluids and especially refers to excess carbon dioxide at the cellular level.

One might suspect at first thought that any respiratory condition which causes anoxia will also cause hypercapnia. However, only *hypoventilation anoxia* is commonly associated with hypercapnia. The reasons for this are the following:

Obviously, *atmospheric anoxia, hypohemoglobinemic anoxia, and anoxia caused by poisoning of the oxidative enzymes* have to do only with the availability of oxygen or use of oxygen by the tissues. Therefore, it is readily understandable that hypercapnia is *not* a concomitant of these types of anoxia.

Also, in anoxia resulting from poor diffusion through the pulmonary membrane or through the tissues, hypercapnia usually does not occur because carbon dioxide diffuses 20 times as rapidly as oxygen. Therefore, even though oxygen diffusion may become very greatly depressed, carbon dioxide diffusion will usually be still many times as great as that needed for adequate carbon dioxide transfer. Therefore, persons who have lost large portions of their lungs as a result of tuberculosis, surgical removal of a lung, atelectasis, and so forth, rarely have significant hypercapnia.

However, in *hypoventilation anoxia*, carbon dioxide transfer between the alveoli and the atmosphere is affected as much as is oxygen transfer. Therefore, hypercapnia results equally as much as the anoxia.

In short, then, the only respiratory conditions that usually cause serious tissue hypercapnia are the different conditions that cause pulmonary hypoventilation. These include: (a) *paralysis of the respiratory muscles*, (b) *obstruction of the respiratory passageways*, (c) *increased tissue resistance of the lungs*, and (d) *decreased compliance of the lungs*.

Effects of Hypercapnia on the Body

The strong stimulatory effect of hypercapnia on the respiratory system was discussed in detail in the previous chapter on respiratory regulation. When the alveolar P_{CO_2} rises above approximately 60 to 65 mm. Hg, dyspnea becomes intolerable, and, as it rises into the range of 70 to 80 mm. Hg, the person becomes lethargic and sometimes even semi-comatose. Total anesthesia and death result when the P_{CO_2} rises to 100 to 150 mm. Hg.

OXYGEN THERAPY IN THE DIFFERENT TYPES OF ANOXIA

Oxygen therapy can be administered (1) by placing the patient's head in a "tent" which contains air fortified with oxygen, (2) by allowing the patient to breathe either pure oxygen or high concentrations of oxygen from a mask, or (3) by administering oxygen through an intranasal tube.

Oxygen therapy is of tremendous value in certain types of anoxia but of almost no value at all in other types. However, if one will simply recall the basic physiologic principles of the different types of anoxia, he can readily decide when oxygen therapy will be of value and, if so, how valuable. For instance:

In *atmospheric anoxia*, oxygen therapy can obviously completely correct the depressed oxygen level in the inspired gases and, therefore, provide 100 per cent effective therapy.

In *hypoventilation anoxia*, a person breathing 100 per cent oxygen can move five times as much oxygen into the alveoli with each breath as he can when breathing normal air. Therefore, here again oxygen therapy can be extremely beneficial, increasing the available oxygen to as much as 400 per cent above normal.

In *diffusion anoxia*, essentially the same result occurs as in hypoventilation anoxia, for oxygen therapy can increase the oxygen partial pressure in the lungs from a value of about 100 mm. Hg to as high as 600 mm. Hg. This causes a greatly increased diffusion gradient between the alveoli and the blood, the gradient rising from a normal value of 60 mm. Hg to as high as 560 mm. Hg, or an increase of over 800 per cent. This highly beneficial effect of oxygen therapy in diffusion anoxia is illustrated in Figure 437, which shows that the pulmonary blood in a patient wtih pulmonary edema picks up oxygen up to eight times as rapidly as it would with no therapy.

In *hypohemoglobinemic anoxia*, which re-

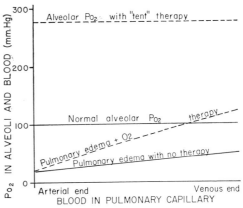

Figure 437. Absorption of oxygen into the pulmonary capillary blood in pulmonary edema with and without oxygen therapy.

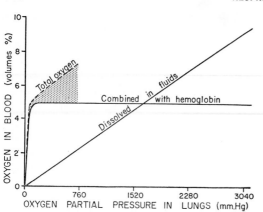

Figure 438. Effects of oxygen therapy in hypohemoglobinemic anoxia.

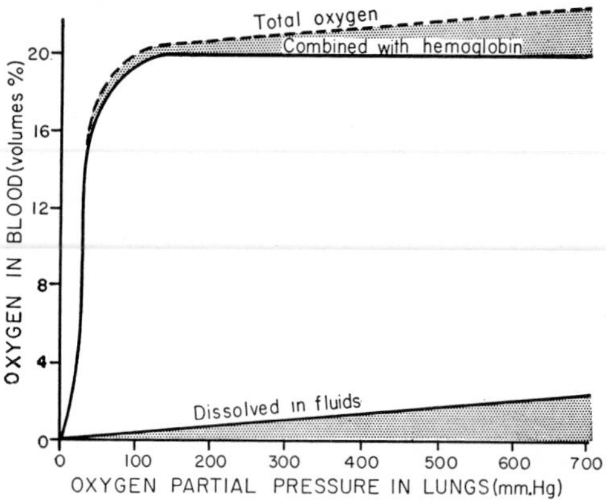

Figure 439. Effects of oxygen therapy in ischemic
anoxia.

sults from *anemia, carbon monoxide poisoning,* or *any other abnormality of hemoglobin
transport,* oxygen therapy is of moderate
value because the amount of oxygen transported in the dissolved form in the fluids of
the blood can be greatly increased above
normal even though that transported by the
hemoglobin is hardly altered. This is illustrated in Figure 438, which shows that an
increase in alveolar oxygen pressure from a
normal value of 100 mm. Hg up to 600 mm.
Hg increases the total oxygen in the blood
from 5 volumes per cent up to 6½ volumes
per cent. This represents a 30 per cent increase in the amount of oxygen transported
to the tissues, and 30 per cent is often the
difference between life and death.

In *ischemic anoxia* the value of oxygen
therapy is still less than in hypohemoglobinemic anoxia, because the problem here is
sluggish flow of blood and not insufficient
oxygen. Figure 439, however, illustrates that
even normal blood can carry a small amount
of extra oxygen to the tissues (about 10 per
cent extra) when the alveoli oxygen concentration is increased to 600 mm. Hg. Here
again, this 10 per cent difference may mean
saving the life of the patient, as, for example, following an acute heart attack which
causes the cardiac output to fall very low.

In the different types of *tissue utilization
anoxia* there is no abnormality of oxygen
pickup by the lungs nor of transport to the
tissues. Instead, the tissues simply need more
oxygen than can reach them or than the
enzymes can utilize. Therefore, oxygen therapy is usually of very little benefit, though
perhaps in a few instances high pressure

oxygen therapy will increase the P_{O_2} in the
tissues sufficiently to increase oxygen utilization by as much as 1 to 5 per cent.

Danger of Hypercapnia during Oxygen Therapy

In *hypoventilation anoxia,* much of the
stimulus that helps to maintain the ventilation results from anoxic stimulation of the
aortic and carotid chemoreceptors. In the
previous chapter it was noted that in chronic
anoxia oxygen lack becomes far more powerful as a stimulus of respiration than usual,
sometimes increasing the ventilation as
much as five- to seven-fold. Therefore, in
treating hypoventilation anoxia, relief of the
anoxia occasionally causes pulmonary ventilation to decrease so low that lethal levels
of hypercapnia develop. For this reason, oxygen therapy in hypoventilation anoxia is
sometimes contraindicated.

It was also noted above that oxygen therapy can provide as much as 800 per cent
increase in oxygen availability to the tissues
in *diffusion anoxia,* sometimes completely
relieving the anoxia. And, as the patient's
condition further deteriorates, serious anoxia
can still be prevented by oxygen therapy
long after the patient would otherwise have
died. However, the pulmonary membrane
finally becomes so impaired that even carbon
dioxide diffusion becomes inadequate, and
serious hypercapnia ensues. This obviously
could not occur if the anoxia were not corrected by oxygen therapy, for the patient
would die long before any significant degree
of hypercapnia could develop.

per second, etc. However, as his rate of fall increases, the air resistance tending to slow his fall through the atmosphere also increases. Finally, the air resistance is equal to the acceleratory force of gravity so that by the time he has fallen for approximately 12 seconds and a distance of approximately 1400 feet, he will be falling at a "terminal velocity" of 109 to 119 miles per hour (175 feet per second). This is illustrated by the curve in Figure 448. However, if the pilot jumps from a very high altitude, where the atmosphere offers little resistance, the terminal velocity will be much greater than 175 feet per second, but it will slow to 175 feet per second as the body reaches the higher density atmosphere close to earth.

If the parachutist has already reached the terminal velocity of fall before he opens his parachute, an "opening shock load" of approximately 1200 pounds occurs on the parachute strands. Even in rarified atmospheres where the terminal velocity is great, the shock load is still only 1200 pounds because the rarefied atmosphere exerts less restraining force on the parachute.

The usual size parachute slows the fall of the parachutist to approximately one-ninth of the terminal velocity. In other words, the speed of landing is approximately 20 feet per second, and the force of impact against the earth is approximately 1/81 of the force of impact without a parachute. Even so, the force of impact is still great enough to cause considerable damage to the body unless the parachutist is properly trained in landing, for it is not evident as one descends how rapidly the earth is approaching. Actually, the force of impact with the earth is approximately the same as that which would be experienced from jumping from a height of about 7 feet. If the parachutist is not careful, his senses will allow

him to strike the earth with his legs still extended, and this will result in tremendous deceleratory forces along the skeletal axis of his body with fracture of the pelvis, a vertebra, or a leg. Consequently, the trained parachutist strikes the earth with knees bent to cushion the shock of landing.

PERCEPTIONS IN AVIATION

Depth Perception

When a person is standing completely still, his ability to perceive depth, particularly of objects close to him, as will be discussed in Chapter 52, depends to a great extent on *stereoscopic vision*, and this in turn depends on the two eyes' seeing the same objects at the same time. One eye sees the object at a slightly different angle from the other eye, and the brain interprets the difference in the two images as distance. As the object is moved farther and farther away from the eyes, the two images more and more duplicate each other until at far distances the phenomenon of stereoscopic vision is almost totally valueless. Indeed, stereoscopic vision is not very satisfactory for depth perception more than 10 to 50 feet away.

Therefore, other methods for depth perception are probably of more importance to the aviator who is several hundred feet from the ground; one of these is *memory of the sizes of familiar objects*. The farther away a person is from an object, the smaller is the size of its image on the retina, and, if the aviator knows the approximate size of the object—such as how far apart furrows are plowed, etc.—then automatically his mind tells him the approximate distance.

During landing or take-off the aviator uses to a great extent still another depth perception mechanism, the phenomenon of *moving parallax depth perception*. This will be described in detail in Chapter 52; simply it means that objects close to a person in motion appear to move across the fields of his vision much more rapidly than objects far away from him. By judging the speeds of movement of the images across the retina, the relative distances of the objects can be estimated.

It can be seen from the above discussion that only to a slight extent are both eyes needed to perceive distances in aviation. Consequently, extreme emphasis on binocular vision in pilot selection probably is not justified. There have been and are one-eyed aviators who are capable of flying airplanes as well as persons with normal binocular vision.

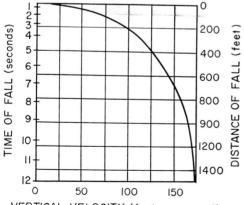

Figure 448. Velocity of fall of a human body from a high altitude, showing the attainment of a "terminal velocity." (From Armstrong: Principles and Practice of Aviation Medicine. Williams & Wilkins.)

Perceptions of Balance in Blind Flying

The various sensations of equilibrium will be discussed in detail in Chapter 50, but, in essence, any time the position of the head is not along the vertical axis of forces applied to the body, the otoliths in the utricles of the labyrinths apprise the psyche of this lack of equilibrium. However, the degree of proficiency of equilibrium perceptions has certain limits. For instance, the body must lean forward as much as 5 to 10 degrees before the utricles perceive this forward leaning. When the aviator is not flying blind, he can perceive forward leaning of the airplane by observing the ground, but, when he is flying blind, it is necessary that appropriate instruments be available to indicate the rate of descent. Also, the utricle may fail to apprise the pilot of ascent up to an error as much as 24 degrees. Obviously, then, blind flying often results in stall of the airplane unless appropriate instruments are available.

Perhaps the least effective of the perceptive organs in blind flying are those for angular acceleration, because the organs that perceive angular acceleration, the semicircular canals, are excited only for the first few seconds after angular acceleration begins and only for the first few seconds after angular acceleration ends. Consequently, an airplane may gradually go into a turn and the aviator might perceive going into the turn, but once in it he usually loses all perception of continuing to turn. Furthermore, if he goes into the turn very slowly—at a rate less than 2 degrees per second—he may not even perceive the fact that he enters the turn. Consequently, of especial importance among the instruments for blind flying are those that appraise the direction of travel of the airplane and the rate of turn.

PROBLEMS OF TEMPERATURE AND ELECTROMAGNETIC RADIATION IN AVIATION

The cold temperature of the upper atmosphere involves essentially the same physiologic problems as cold temperatures on the surface of the earth; these problems will be discussed in Chapter 71. Therefore, for the present it shall only be pointed out how the temperatures change as one ascends to higher and higher elevations. If the temperature at the earth's surface is approximately 20° C., the temperatures at different altitudes are approximately the following:

0 ft. and above	20°	C.
10,000 ft. and above	0°	C.
20,000 ft. and above	−22°	C.
30,000 ft. and above	−44°	C.
40,000 ft. and above	−55°	C.

It is obvious from these values that special clothing or special heating apparatus must be designed for flying at high altitudes.

The electromagnetic radiations at high altitudes also involve essentially the same problems in aviation medicine as in other types of medicine, and these will be considered in relation to radiation other than light in Chapter 82, and in relation to light in Chapters 52 to 54 in connection with the physiology of vision. The electromagnetic radiations change considerably between the surface of the earth and in higher altitudes because the atmosphere filters some of these radiations out of the spectrum before they reach the earth's surface. Ordinarily most of the ultraviolet light is absorbed before it reaches the earth's surface. Consequently, a person exposed to the sun in the upper atmosphere is many times as likely to develop sunburn as on the earth's surface.

Approximately 18 per cent of the visible light is filtered out of the sun's rays before they strike the surface of the earth even on a perfectly clear day. Therefore, the brightness of the sun is 1.2 times as great in the upper atmosphere as on earth. This makes the earth less distinct to the aviator than otherwise for two reasons: first, he is looking from an area of greater brightness toward an area of lesser brightness, and, second, light is reflected from the atmosphere into his eyes. This reflected light especially blocks his vision of the horizon.

In aviation there is no significant hazard from gamma and x-rays, but this does become a problem in space physiology, as will be discussed later in the chapter.

SPACE PHYSIOLOGY

The problems of space physiology are not greatly different from those of aviation physiology, except that in some instances the problems are multiplied—especially in relation to gamma and x-ray radiation hazards and linear acceleration problems. Other factors that must be considered in space physiology are: weightlessness, survival in a sealed cabin, and the temperature in space.

Weightlessness in Space. A person in an orbiting satellite or in any non-propelled space ship will experience a feeling of weightlessness. That is, he will not be drawn toward the bottom, the sides, or the top of the space ship, but will simply float inside its chambers. The cause of this is not the failure of gravity to pull on the body, because gravity from any nearby heavenly body will certainly be active. However, the gravity will act on both the space ship and the person at the same time, and, since there is no resistance to movement in space, both will be pulled in the same direction to the same extent. For this reason, the person simply will not be attracted toward any wall of the space ship.

Weightlessness has been artificially created in airplane experiments designed to produce zero g, and it has not proved to be a physiological problem but an engineering problem in regard to providing adequate hand holds, foot holds, and stability of the person in the space ship so that he can adequately control the operation of the ship.

Acceleratory Forces in Space Travel. In contrast with aviation physiology, the space ship will not make rapid turns; therefore, angular acceleration will be of little importance. On the other hand, take-off acceleration and landing deceleration might be tremendous; both of these are types of linear acceleration.

Figure 449 illustrates a typical profile of the acceleration expected to occur during take-off in a three-stage space ship, showing that the first stage booster will cause acceleration as high as 9 g and the second stage booster as high as 8 g. In the standing position the human body could not withstand this much acceleration, but in a lying or semi-reclining position *transverse to the axis of acceleration,* this amount of acceleration can be withstood with ease despite the fact that the acceleratory forces will continue for as long as 5 minutes at a time. Therefore, we see that another of the problems of space travel is not insurmountable.

Problems also occur during deceleration when the space ship reenters the atmosphere. A person traveling at Mach 1 (the speed of sound and of very fast airplanes) can be safely decelerated in a distance of approximately 0.12 mile, while a person traveling at a speed of Mach 100, a speed possible in space travel, requires a distance

of about 10,000 miles for safe deceleration. The principal reason for this difference is that the total amount of energy that must be dispelled during deceleration is proportional to the *square* of the velocity, which alone will increase the distance 10,000-fold. But, in addition to this, a human being can stand far less deceleration if it lasts for a long period of time than he can stand for short periods of time. Therefore, deceleration must be accomplished much more slowly than is necessary at the slower initial velocities.

Thus, here is another important engineering problem—gradual deceleration over a long distance rather than abrupt deceleration—which must be handled properly for safe space travel.

Radiation Hazards in Space Physiology. Much has been speculated about the possibility of radiation hazards in space travel, and, true enough, measurements indicate that there is far greater gamma and x-ray radiation at certain altitudes in space than on the surface of the earth. Figure 450 shows the increase in gamma radiation caused by cosmic rays as one ascends to approximately 20 miles above the earth; yet, despite this seemingly great increase in radiation, the amount of cosmic radiation on the surface of the earth is so small that even this very great multiplication of its value still does not make it a significant hazard up to an altitude of 300 to 600 miles.

Unfortunately, though, two belts of high energy radiation have been discovered at

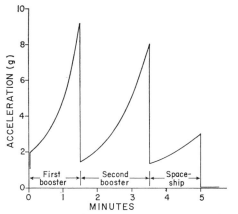

Figure 449. Acceleratory forces during the take-off of a space ship.

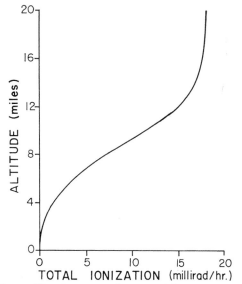

Figure 450. Ionizing radiation at different altitudes.

(1) a level of about 600 to 3000 miles high and (2) a level many thousand miles high. These radiations can be withstood (particularly the lower one) for only a few minutes at a time without serious radiation damage. For interplanetary travel, it will be possible for the space ships to travel through these belts in a short enough time to prevent damage. But the radiation does limit the use of space stations at certain altitudes.

Temperature in Space. As pointed out earlier in relation to aviation physiology, the temperature falls to about −55° C. several miles above the earth. But, in the ionosphere several hundred miles above the earth, the kinetic energy of the atmospheric molecules, atoms, and ions is extreme. The reason for this is that any particles that can escape this far away from the gravitational pull of the earth must have a very great velocity of movement. As a result, by the time the space ship has reached an altitude of about 350 miles, the temperature of the surrounding particles is about 3000 degrees centigrade. Yet, strangely enough, this has almost no effect on the temperature of the space ship because of the *sparsity* of these particles— they are far too few to impart any significant amount of heat to the space ship. Instead, the temperature of the space ship will be determined by the relative absorption of radiant energy from the sun versus the re-radiation of energy away from the space ship into the far reaches of the universe. Different coatings for the space ship have different absorptive and radiation characteristics so that with appropriate engineering design the surface of the space ship can be so constructed as to make the temperature inside almost exactly the desired value. For instance, bright metallic surfaces absorb heat easily but radiate heat very poorly. Such a surface would give the space ship an extremely high temperature. On the other hand, white surfaces absorb reasonable amounts of heat and also radiate reasonably well and, therefore, can be used to provide a temperature in a more nearly normal range.

Survival in a Sealed Cabin. The ability of a person to survive in a sealed cabin depends principally on appropriate engineering design. Space travel from one part of the earth to another part will require only minutes, in which case all the oxygen and other essentials for survival can be carried along on the trip. On the other hand, in an orbiting satellite or in travel through outer space, the time will be measured in weeks, months, or years, and it will be impossible to carry along an adequate store of oxygen and food. For this reason "recycling techniques" have already been developed and are daily being improved for use over and over again of the same oxygen and food. Basically, these techniques involve (1) a method for removing oxygen from carbon dioxide, (2) a method for removing water from the human excreta, and (3) use of the human excreta for resynthesizing or regrowing an adequate food supply. Large amounts of energy are required for these processes, and the real problem at present is to derive enough energy from the sun's radiation to energize the necessary chemical reactions. Some of the recycling processes depend on purely physical procedures such as distillation, electrolysis of water, capture of the sun's energy by solar batteries, and so forth, while others depend upon biologic methods such as the use of algae, with its large store of chlorophyll, to generate foodstuffs by the process of photosynthesis. Unfortunately, a completely practical system for recycling is yet to be achieved.

Much has been written about the possibility of psychic problems among space men in sealed cabins. Experiments thus far have failed to show that such problems will be any more severe than those associated with any other type of confinement such as putting a patient in a body cast, enclosing a person in a submarine, or placing a person in jail.

REFERENCES

Anthony, A., Ackerman, E., and Strother, G. K.: Effects of altitude acclimatization on rat myoglobin. Changes in myoglobin content of skeletal and cardiac muscle. *Am. J. Physiol., 196:*512, 1959.

Armstrong, H.: Aviation Medicine. Philadelphia, W. B. Saunders Co., 1954.

Armstrong, H. G.: Principles and Practices of Aviation Medicine. 3rd ed., Baltimore, Williams & Wilkins Co., 1952.

Aviation medicine on the threshold of space: a symposium. *J. Aviat. Med., 29:*485–539, 1958.

Becker, E. L., Schilling, J. A., and Harvey, R. B.: Renal function in man acclimatized to high altitude. *J. Appl. Physiol., 10:*79, 1957.

Bergin, K. G.: Aviation Medicine: Its Theory and Application. Baltimore, Williams & Wilkins Co., 1949.

Bibliography of Space Medicine. National Library of Medicine, Reference Division, Washington, 1958, and *U. S. Armed Forces Med. J.,* 10:172, 1959.

Bloom, A., and Michel, E. L.: Problems of oxygen mask development. *J. Aviat. Med.,* 28:180, 1957.

Bondurant, S., Blanchard, W. G., Clarke, N. P., and Moore, F.: Effect of water immersion on human tolerance to forward and backward acceleration. *J. Aviat. Med.,* 29:872, 1958.

Brand, E. D., Britton, S. W., and French, C. R.: Gravitational shock in different animal species and various factors affecting resistance. *Am. J. Physiol.,* 165:539, 1951.

Dill, D. B., and Penrod, K. E.: Man's ceiling as determined in altitude chamber. *J. Appl. Physiol.,* 1:409, 1948.

Dorman, P. J., and Lawton, R. W.: Effect on g tolerance of partial supination combined with the anti-g suit. *J. Aviat. Med.,* 27:490, 1956.

Fenn, W. O., Rahn, H., and Otis, A. B.: Theoretical study of composition of alveolar air at altitude. *Am. J. Physiol.,* 146:637, 1946.

Fulton, J. F.: Aviation Medicine in Its Preventive Aspect. New York, Oxford University Press, 1949.

Gell, C. F., Hall, W. M., and Mostofi, F. K.: Pathologic evaluation of explosive decompression to 65,000 feet. *J. Aviat. Med.,* 29:15, 1958.

Hall, F. G.: Regulation of breathing in man at altitude. *Proc. Soc. Exper. Biol. & Med.,* 78:580, 1951.

Hendler, E.: Linear acceleration as a survivable hazard in aviation. *J. Aviat. Med.,* 26:495, 1955.

Henry, J. P., Gauer, O. H., Kety, S. S., and Kramer, K.: Factors maintaining cerebral circulation during gravitational stress. *J. Clin. Invest.,* 30:292, 1951.

Hess, J. L., and Lombard, C. F.: Theoretical investigations of dynamic response of man to high vertical accelerations. *J. Aviat. Med.,* 29:66, 1958.

Hitchcock, F. A.: Physiological and pathological effects of explosive decompression. *J. Aviat. Med.,* 25:578, 1954.

Hitchcock, F. A., and Kemph, J.: The boiling of body liquids at extremely high altitudes. *J. Aviat. Med.,* 26:289, 1955.

Husson, G., and Otis, A. B.: Adaptive value of respiratory adjustments to shunt hypoxia and to altitude hypoxia. *J. Clin. Invest.,* 36:270, 1957.

Kemph, J. P., and Hitchcock, F. A.: Changes in blood and circulation of dogs following explosive decompression to low barometric pressures. *Am. J. Physiol.,* 168:592, 1952.

Kemph, J. P., and Hitchcock, F. A.: Respiratory effects of high intrapulmonic pressure at a simulated altitude of 72,000 feet. *J. Aviat. Med.,* 24:5, 1953.

Knight, L. A.: An approach to the physiologic simulation of the null-gravity state. *J. Aviat. Med.,* 29:283, 1958.

Korner, P. I.: Circulatory Adaptations in Hypoxia. *Physiol. Rev.,* 39:687, 1959.

Kydd, G. H., and Stoll, A. M.: G tolerance in primates. I. Unconsciousness end point. *J. Aviat. Med.,* 29:413, 1958.

Lawton, R. W., Greene, L. C., Kydd, G. H., Peterson, L. H., and Crosbie, R. J.: Arterial blood pressure responses to G forces in the monkey. I. Sinusoidal positive G. *J. Aviat. Med.,* 29:97, 1958.

Lewis, D. H.: Analysis of some current methods of G-protection. *J. Aviat. Med.,* 26:479, 1955.

Luft, V. C., Claman, H. G., and Opitz, E.: The latency of hypoxia on exposure to altitude above 50,000 feet. *J. Aviat. Med.,* 22:112, 1951.

Marbarger, J. P. (ed.): Space Medicine; the Human Factor in Flights beyond the Earth, Urbana, University of Illinois Press, 1951.

Marbarger, J. P., Kemp, W. E., Kadetz, W., and Hansen, J.: Studies in aeroembolism. *J. Aviat. Med.,* 29:291, 1958.

Margaria, R., Gualtierotti, T., and Spinell, D.: Protection against acceleration forces in animals by immersion in water. *J. Aviat. Med.,* 29:433, 1958.

Monge, C.: Chronic mountain sickness. *Physiol. Rev.,* 23:166, 1943.

Nims, L. F.: Anoxia in aviation. *Ann. Rev. Physiol.,* 10:305, 1948.

Ower, E.: High-Speed Flights. New York, Philosophical Library, 1957.

Poppen, J. R.: Support of upper body against accelerative forces in aircraft. *J. Aviat. Med.* 29:76, 1958.

Roxburgh, H. L., and Erasting, J.: The physiology of pressure suits. *J. Aviat. Med.* 28:260, 1957.

Rushmer, R. F., Beckman, E. L., and Lee, D.: Protection of the cerebral circulation by the cerebrospinal fluid under the influence of radial acceleration. *Am. J. Physiol.,* 151:355, 1947.

Schilling, J. A., Harvey, R. B., Becker, E. L., Velasquez, T., Wells, G., and Balke, B.: Work performance at altitude after adaptation in a man and dog. *J. Appl. Physiol.,* 8:381, 1956.

Space travel: a symposium. *J. Aviat. Med.,* 28:479, 1957.

Stapp, J. P.: Human tolerance to deceleration. *J. Aviat. Med.,* 22:42, 1951.

Stickney, J. C., and Van Liere, E. J.: Acclimatization to low oxygen tension. *Physiol. Rev.,* 33:13, 1953.

Stoll, A. M., and Mosely, J. D.: Physiologic and pathologic effects in chimpanzees during prolonged exposure to 40 transverse G. *J. Aviat. Med.,* 29:575, 1958.

Symposium on life in space. *Fed. Proc.,* 18:1241, 1959.

Taylor, E. R.: Physical and Physiological Data for Bioastronautics. U. S. Air Force School of Aviation Medicine, Randolph Air Force Base, Texas, 1958.

Ullrick, W. C., Whitehorn, W. V., Brennan, B. B., and Krone, J. G.: Tissue respiration of rats acclimatized to low barometric pressure. *J. Appl. Physiol.,* 9:49, 1956.

Webster, A. P.: High velocity flying with reference to the human factors—open shock of parachute descents. *J. Aviat. Med.,* 24:189, 1953.

White, C. S. (ed.): Physics and Medicine of the Upper Atmosphere. Albuquerque, University of New Mexico Press, 1952.

White, C. S., Lovelace, W. R., II, and Hirsch, F. G. (ed.): Aviation Medicine. New York, Pergamon Press, 1958.

Whitehorn, W. V., Lein, A., and Hitchcock, F. A.: Effect of explosive decompression on occurrence of intravascular bubbles. *J. Aviat. Med.,* 18:392, 1947.

See also Chapter 40, Physics of gases; Chapter 41, Transport of gases in the blood.

Chapter 45

Physiology of Deep Sea Diving and Other High Pressure Operations

When a person descends beneath the sea, the pressure around him increases tremendously. To keep his lungs from collapsing, air must be supplied to him also under very high pressure, which exposes the blood in his lungs to extremely high alveolar gaseous pressures. Beyond certain limits these high pressures can cause tremendous alterations in the physiology of the body, which explains the necessity for the present discussion.

Other persons often exposed to very high atmospheric pressures are Caisson workers who, in digging tunnels beneath rivers or elsewhere, often must work in a pressurized area to keep the tunnel from caving in. Here again, the same problems of excessively high gaseous pressures in the alveoli occur.

Before making an attempt to explain the effects of very high alveolar gaseous pressures on the body, it is first necessary to review some of the physical principles of pressure and volume changes at different depths beneath the sea.

Relationship of Sea Depth to Pressure. A column of fresh water 33 feet high (sea water, 32 feet) exerts the same pressure at its bottom as all the atmosphere above the earth. Therefore, a person 33 feet beneath

Sea level—1 atmosphere
33 feet deep—2 atmospheres
66 feet deep—3 atmospheres
100 feet deep—4 atmospheres
133 feet deep—5 atmospheres
166 feet deep—6 atmospheres
200 feet deep—7 atmospheres
300 feet deep—10 atmospheres
400 feet deep—13 atmospheres
500 feet deep—16 atmospheres

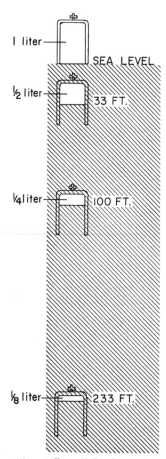

Figure 451. Effect of depth on gas volumes.

the water surface will be exposed to a pressure of two atmospheres, one atmosphere of pressure caused by the air above the water and the other by the weight of the water itself. At 66 feet the pressure will be three atmospheres, and so forth, approximately in accordance with the table in the opposite column.

Effect of Depth on the Volume of Gases. Another important effect of depth is the compression of gases to smaller and smaller volumes. Figure 451 illustrates a bell jar at sea level containing 1 liter of air. At 33 feet beneath the sea where the pressure is two atmospheres, the volume has been compressed to only one-half liter. At 100 feet, where the pressure is 4 atmospheres, the volume has been compressed to one-fourth liter, and at 8 atmospheres (233 feet depth) the volume has been compressed to one-eighth liter. This is an extremely important effect in diving because it can cause the air chambers of the diver's body, including the lungs, to become so small in some instances that serious damage results, as will be discussed later in the chapter.

Many times in the discussion of this chapter it will be necessary to refer to *actual volume* versus *sea level volume*. For instance, we might speak of an actual volume of 1 liter at 300 feet depth; this is the same quantity of air as a sea level volume of 10 liters. Therefore, these two terms must be kept in mind while studying this chapter.

EFFECT OF HIGH PARTIAL PRESSURES OF GASES ON THE BODY

The three gases to which a diver breathing air is normally exposed are nitrogen, oxygen, and carbon dioxide. However, helium is often substituted for nitrogen in the diving mixture; therefore, the effects of this gas under high pressure must also be considered.

Nitrogen Narcosis at High Nitrogen Pressures. Approximately four fifths of the air is nitrogen. At sea level pressure this has no known effect on the function of the body, but at very high pressures it can cause varying degrees of narcosis. When the diver is breathing air, the depth at which the first symptoms of mild narcosis appear is approximately 130 to 150 feet, at which level he may feel sleepy and may develop a lethargy for work. At 200 to 250 feet his strength wanes considerably, and he often becomes unable to direct his efforts to perform the work required of him. Beyond 300 feet depth (10 atmospheres of pressure) the diver usually becomes almost useless as a result of nitrogen narcosis, and he may become completely anesthetized at 350 to 400 feet. It

should be noted, however, that *an hour or more of the high pressure is usually required* before enough nitrogen will dissolve in the body to cause these effects.

Nitrogen narcosis has characteristics very similar to those of alcohol intoxication, and for this reason it has frequently been called "raptures of the depths."

The mechanism of the narcotic effect is believed to be the same as that of essentially all the gas anesthesias. That is, nitrogen dissolves very freely in the fats of the body, and it is presumed that it, like the other anesthetic gases, dissolves in the membranes of the neurons and thereby reduces their excitability.

Oxygen Toxicity at High Pressures. The basic principles of oxygen toxicity at high oxygen pressures were discussed in Chapters 41 and 43. Therefore, at the present time, it is sufficient to say that breathing oxygen under very high partial pressures can cause especially detrimental effects on the central nervous system, sometimes resulting in convulsions of the epileptic type followed by coma. In an extensive study of persons who have developed oxygen toxicity, the following frequencies of different symptoms were encountered:

Nausea—40 per cent
Muscular twitchings—21 per cent
Dizziness—17 per cent
Disturbances of vision—6 per cent
Restlessness and irritability—6 per cent
Numbness and pins-and-needles sensations—6 per cent
Convulsive seizures and coma—4 per cent

It should be noted especially that exercise greatly reduces the diver's tolerance for oxygen at high pressures, causing symptoms to appear much earlier and with far greater severity than in the resting person. Figure 452 gives the so-called *oxygen tolerance curve* for persons performing moderate amounts of work at different depths under the sea while breathing 100 per cent oxygen. This shows that a person performing work at a depth of only 40 feet is safe for not more than 23 minutes. At a depth of 30 feet, he is safe for about 45 minutes and at 20 feet for about 1½ hours. It must be emphasized, however, that there is tremendous variability in the tolerance of different persons for oxygen, and this curve has been

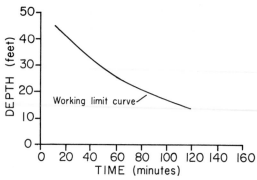

Figure 452. The "oxygen tolerance" curve, showing the length of time that a person can remain without danger at different depths when breathing pure oxygen. (Modified from Submarine Medicine Practice. U. S. Navy Bureau of Medicine and Surgery.)

worked out on the basis of fewer than 100 tests. Therefore, since a convulsion underneath the sea might be lethal, even this tolerance curve is probably far too liberal for absolute safety.

Problems of Carbon Dioxide Toxicity at Great Depths. If the diving gear is properly designed and is functioning properly, the diver will develop no problem from carbon dioxide toxicity, for depth alone does not increase the carbon dioxide partial pressure in the alveoli. This is true because carbon dioxide is a manufactured gas in the body, and, as long as the diver continues to breathe a normal tidal volume, he will continue to expire the carbon dioxide as it is formed, maintaining his alveolar carbon dioxide concentration at a normal value.

Unfortunately, though, in certain types of diving gear such as the diving helmet and the different types of rebreathing apparatuses, carbon dioxide can frequently build up in the air breathed by the diver. Up to an air concentration of 10 per cent carbon dioxide, the diver tolerates this buildup, his minute respiratory volume increasing up to a maximum of about 10-fold to compensate for the increased CO_2. However, beyond the 10 per cent level the situation becomes intolerable, and the respiratory center begins to be depressed rather than excited; the diver's respiration then actually begins to fail rather than to compensate. As a result, he develops varying degrees of lethargy, narcosis, and, finally, anesthesia, as was discussed in Chapter 42.

Effects of Helium under High Pressures. In very deep dives, helium is used to re-

place the nitrogen because it has no narcotic effect at least down to a depth of about 500 feet. Furthermore, it has three other properties which make it desirable under some conditions in the diving gas mixture: (1) Because of its small molecular weight, its density is very slight, which reduces the airway resistance of the diver. At great depths the density of air is often great enough to impede breathing in some divers. Under these conditions, helium in the breathing mixture is obviously of value. (2) Also because of its low molecular weight, helium diffuses through the tissues much more rapidly than nitrogen, which allows more rapid removal of helium from the body fluids under some conditions. (3) Helium is less soluble in the body fluids than nitrogen, which reduces the quantity of bubbles that can form in his tissues when the diver is decompressed after a prolonged dive. Yet, there are other problems in the use of helium that make it undesirable under some conditions, as will be discussed below in relation to decompression.

Effects of Carbon Monoxide under High Pressure. Rarely, when compressed air cylinders are being filled, a small amount of carbon monoxide from the exhaust of the gasoline driven pump may be compressed along with the air. It should be remembered that the toxicity of carbon monoxide is dependent on its partial pressure. At great depths beneath the sea, the partial pressures of all the gases in the breathing mixture are increased in proportion to the sea pressure. Therefore, insignificant surface problems with carbon monoxide will be multiplied many fold at great sea depths. For this reason, divers have on more than one occasion been poisoned with carbon monoxide when breathing gaseous mixtures which are completely innocuous at sea level.

Decompression of the Diver after Exposure to High Pressures

When a person breathes air under high pressure for a long period of time, the amount of nitrogen dissolved in his body fluids becomes very great. The reason for this is the following: The blood flowing through the pulmonary capillaries becomes saturated with nitrogen to the same pressure as that in the breathing mixture. Over a period of several hours, nitrogen is carried to all the tissues of the body to saturate them also with dissolved nitrogen. And, since nitrogen is not metabolized by the body, it remains dissolved until the nitrogen pressure in the lungs decreases and the nitrogen can then be removed by the respiratory process.

Volume of Nitrogen Dissolved in the Body Fluids at Different Depths. At sea level almost exactly 1 liter of nitrogen is dissolved in the entire body. A little less than half of this is dissolved in the water of the body, and a little more than half is dissolved in the fat of the body. This is true despite the fact that fat constitutes only 15 per cent of the normal body, and it is explained by the fact that nitrogen is five times as soluble in fat as in water.

After the diver has become totally saturated with nitrogen the *sea level volume of nitrogen* dissolved in his body fluids at the different depths will be:

  33 feet— 2 liters
  100 feet— 4 liters
  200 feet— 7 liters
  300 feet—10 liters

However, several hours are required for the gaseous pressures of nitrogen in all the body tissues to come to equilibrium with the gaseous pressure of nitrogen in the alveoli simply because the blood does not flow rapidly enough nor the nitrogen diffuse rapidly enough to cause an instantaneous effect. The nitrogen dissolved in the water of the body comes almost to complete equilibrium in about one hour, but the fat, requiring much more nitrogen for saturation and also having a relatively poor blood supply, reaches saturation only after several hours. For this reason, a person who remains at deep levels for only a few minutes will not dissolve great amounts of nitrogen in his fluids and tissues, while one who remains at a deep level for several hours will reach almost complete saturation.

Decompression Sickness (Synonyms: Compressed Air Sickness, Bends, Caisson Disease, Diver's Paralysis, Dysbarism). If a diver has been beneath the sea long enough to dissolve large amounts of nitrogen in his body and then suddenly comes back to the surface of the sea, significant quantities of nitrogen bubbles can develop in his body fluids either intracellularly or extra-

cellularly, and these can cause minor or very serious damage in almost any area of the body, depending on the amount of bubbles formed. The principles underlying this effect are shown in Figure 453. To the left, the diver's tissues have become equilibrated to a very high nitrogen pressure. However, as long as the diver remains deep beneath the sea, the pressure against the outside of his body compresses all the body tissues sufficiently to keep the gases in solution. Then, after the diver suddenly rises to sea level, the pressure on the outside of his body becomes only one atmosphere (760 mm. Hg), while the pressure inside the body fluids is the sum of the water vapor pressure, the carbon dioxide pressure, the oxygen pressure, and the nitrogen pressure—or a total of 4045 mm. Hg, which is far greater than the pressure on the outside of the body. Therefore, the gases can now escape from the dissolved state and form actual bubbles inside the tissues.

Exercise hastens the formation of bubbles during decompression because of increased agitation of the tissues and fluids. Exercising has an effect analogous to that of shaking an opened bottle of soda pop to release the bubbles.

Fortunately, the phenomenon of "supersaturation" normally allows nitrogen to remain dissolved and not form significant quantities of bubbles if the nitrogen pressure in the body fluids does not rise too much above the pressure on the outside of the body. Ordinarily, significant amounts of bubbles will not form until the nitrogen pressure inside the body rises to 3.0 times the pressure outside the body. Therefore, a diver can theoretically be brought immedi-

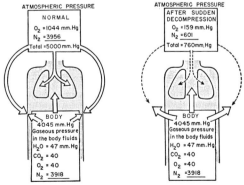

Figure 453. Gaseous pressures responsible for bubble formation in the body tissues.

ately from a depth of 66 feet beneath the sea (3 atmospheres pressure) to sea level (1 atmosphere pressure) without significant bubble formation and without developing decompression sickness, even though on arrival at sea level the gas pressure in his body fluids will be almost three times the pressure on the outside of his body. Yet, for safety's sake the diver is rarely allowed to push this theoretical limit in his ascent from beneath the sea.

Symptoms of decompression sickness. In those persons who have developed decompression sickness, symptoms have occurred with the following frequencies:

Local pain in the legs or arms—89 per cent

Dizziness—5.3 per cent

Paralysis—2.3 per cent

Shortness of breath ("the chokes")—1.6 per cent

Extreme fatigue and pain—1.3 per cent

Collapse with unconsciousness—0.5 per cent

From the above list of symptoms of decompression sickness it can be seen that the most serious problems are usually related to bubble formation in the central nervous system. Pathologically, bubbles have actually been shown to disrupt important pathways in the brain or spinal cord, and bubbles in the peripheral nerves can cause very serious pain. Unfortunately, formation of very large bubbles in the central nervous system can lead to permanent paralysis or permanent mental disturbances.

But the nervous system is not the only locus of damage during decompression sickness, for bubbles can also form in the blood and become caught in the capillaries of the lungs; these bubbles block pulmonary blood flow and cause the "chokes," characterized by serious shortness of breath. This is often followed by severe pulmonary edema, which further aggravates the condition and can cause death.

The symptoms of decompression sickness usually appear within a few minutes to an hour after sudden decompression. However, an occasional instance of decompression sickness develops as long as 6 or more hours after decompression.

Rate of Nitrogen Elimination from the Body. Decompression Tables. Fortunately, if a diver is brought to the surface

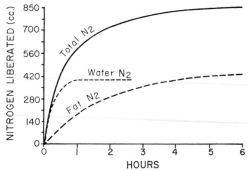

Figure 454. Rate of nitrogen liberation from the body when a person has come to sea level from prolonged exposure to compressed air at 33 feet depth, showing separately the rate of nitrogen release from the whole body, from the water of the body, and from the fat. (From Armstrong: Principles and Practice of Aviation Medicine. Williams and Wilkins.)

very slowly, he can eliminate the dissolved nitrogen through his lungs rapidly enough to prevent decompression sickness. Figure 454 illustrates the rate at which nitrogen will be liberated from the water of the body, from the fat of the body, and from both of these sources combined when a person is first saturated to a depth of 33 feet and then brought suddenly to sea level. Approximately two thirds of the total nitrogen is liberated in 1 hour and about 90 per cent in 6 hours. However, some of the excess nitrogen is still present in the body fluids for still many more hours, and the diver is not completely safe for as long as 9 to 12 hours. Therefore, a diver must be decompressed sometimes for many hours if he has been deep beneath the sea for long periods of time.

The rate at which a diver can be brought to the surface depends on two factors: first, *the depth* to which he has descended and, second, *the amount of time* he has been there. If he remains at deep levels for only a short period of time, the body fluids will not become saturated, and, therefore, the decompression time can be accordingly reduced. Table 19 gives a typical decompression table used by the U. S. Navy when the diver breathes compressed air. Note that only 20 minutes at a depth of 300 feet requires over 2½ hours decompression time, and 45 minutes at 300 feet requires over 5 hours. On the other hand, a person can remain at 50 feet for as long as three hours

Table 19. Navy Standard Decompression Table (using compressed air) (From Submarine Medicine Practice. U. S. Navy Bureau of Medicine and Surgery.)

1	2	3 Stops (feet and minutes)									4
Depth of dive (feet)	Optimal time on bottom (minutes)	Feet 90	Feet 80	Feet 70	Feet 60	Feet 50	Feet 40	Feet 30	Feet 20	Feet 10	Approximate total decompression time (minutes)
40	240									4	6
50	190									9	12
60	150								5	15	24
70	120								13	16	33
80	115								22	26	53
90	95							2	27	21	56
100	85							6	28	21	61
110	75							14	27	37	84
120	65							13	28	32	80
130	60							13	28	28	76
140	55							15	28	32	82
150	50							16	28	32	84
160	45							17	28	43	96
170	40							19	28	46	102
185	35							19	28	46	102
200	35							22	28	46	106
210	30						5	16	28	40	100
225	27						22	26	35	48	143
250	25					2	23	26	35	51	150
300	20					9	23	26	35	51	159

and yet be decompressed in only 12 minutes.

The "optimal time on the bottom," as given in Table 19, represents the optimum exposure time at each depth for the best balance between length of work period and amount of useful work the average diver can perform. Note how short these times are at great depths; this is caused principally by the nitrogen narcosis effect and to a less extent by the labored breathing that results from increased density of gases in the lungs.

Oxygen administration for more rapid decompression. If oxygen is pumped to the diver in higher than normal concentrations as he ascends closer to the surface of the sea, the nitrogen partial pressure in his alveoli will be considerably reduced, and, as a consequence, the rate of nitrogen removal from his body fluids is correspondingly increased. Therefore, a diver can be brought to the surface far more rapidly when oxygen is pumped to him once he has come close enough to the surface to tolerate the necessary oxygen partial pressures. Different decompression tables are used when oxygen is so supplied.

Decompression in a Tank and Treatment of Decompression Sickness. Another procedure for decompression, used especially in heavily polluted waters and when climatic situations require it, involves bringing the diver immediately to the surface and then placing him in a decompression tank within 5 minutes after arriving at the surface. Pressure is reapplied, and an appropriate decompression table that will prevent bubble formation is used.

A person who begins to develop symptoms of decompression sickness can also be treated by placing him in such a decompression tank for long periods of time, several times as long as the usual decompression times, and allowing the nitrogen to be released from his body very slowly.

Use of Helium-Oxygen Mixtures in Very Deep Dives. In very deep dives helium has advantages over nitrogen, including (1) decreased decompression time, (2) lack of narcotic effect, and (3) decreased airway resistance in the lungs. The decreased decompression time results from two of its properties: (a) Only 40 per cent as much helium dissolves in the body as does nitrogen. (b) Because of its small molecular size it diffuses through the tissues at a velocity about 2½ times that of nitrogen.

However, helium has not proved to be as advantageous as was once thought because of another property of helium that is different from nitrogen: bubbles begin to form when the pressure of helium in the body fluids is only 1.7 times the pressure on the outside of the body. This compares with 3.0 for nitrogen. Therefore, a diver cannot be brought up as far at a time with helium as with nitrogen. And still another factor makes nitrogen better than helium for shallow dives: the rapid diffusion of helium allows far more helium than nitrogen to become dissolved in the body fluids in a short period of time. Therefore, for short dives at moderate depths, nitrogen is still preferable.

If one calculates the relative advantages of helium versus nitrogen, he finds that long, deep dives favor the use of helium while short, shallow dives favor the use of nitrogen. Figure 455 illustrates the dividing line for most effective use of the two types of gaseous mixtures. For instance, point A illustrates a dive of 150 feet for a period of 120 minutes. This is a long dive at a deep depth, and in this instance helium is far more satisfactory than nitrogen. On the other hand, point B shows a dive of 10 minutes at 200 feet depth, and here the person can be decompressed for a shorter period of time when using nitrogen than helium. Beyond 300 feet, nitrogen cannot be used at all because of nitrogen narcosis, which can develop extremely rapidly.

SOME PHYSICAL PROBLEMS OF DIVING

Aside from the effects of high gaseous pressures on the body, there are still other physical factors that place limitations on diving. These are based principally on changes in gas volumes from sea level to greater depths and include the following:

Volume of Air That Must Be Pumped to the Diver—Relationship to Rate of CO_2 Elimination. To blow off CO_2 from the lungs, the tidal volume of air flowing in and out of the lungs with each breath must remain the same regardless of the depth of the dive. A tidal volume of ½ liter at 300 feet depth (ten atmospheres pressure) would be a sea level volume of 5 liters. Therefore, a compressor operating at sea level must pump 5 liters of air to the diver at 300 feet depth for each breath that the diver takes in order to wash the CO_2 out of his lungs. Stating this another way, the amount of air that must be pumped to the diver to keep his alveolar carbon dioxide normal is directly proportional to the pressure under which he is operating. At sea level the working diver requires about 1.5 cubic feet of air per minute for adequate CO_2 washout from his diving helmet. Therefore, the sea level volumes of air that must be pumped each minute for different depths of operation are the following:

Sea level— 1.5 cubic feet
33 feet— 3 cubic feet
66 feet— 4.5 cubic feet
100 feet— 6 cubic feet
200 feet—10.5 cubic feet
300 feet—15 cubic feet

Effect of Rapid Descent—the "Squeeze." On rapid descent, the volumes of all gases in the body become greatly reduced because of increasing pressure applied to the outside of the body. If additional quantities of air are supplied to the gas cavities during descent—including especially the lungs—no harm will be done, but, if the person continues to descend without addition of gas to his cavities, the volume becomes greatly reduced, and serious physical damage results; this is called the "squeeze." The most dam-

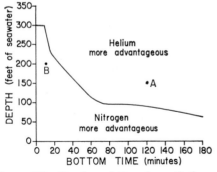

Figure 455. Depths and times beneath the sea at which it is more advantageous to use helium versus the depths and times at which it is more advantageous to use nitrogen. (Modified from Submarine Medicine Practice. U. S. Navy Bureau of Medicine and Surgery.)

aging effects of the squeeze occur in the lungs, for the smallest volume that the lungs can normally achieve is approximately 1.5 liters. Even if the diver inspires a maximal breath prior to descending, he can go down no farther than 100 feet before his chest begins to be caved in. Therefore, to prevent lung squeeze, the diver must inspire additional air as he descends.

When air becomes entrapped in the middle ear during descent, the squeeze can cause a ruptured ear drum, and when air is entrapped in one of the nasal sinuses very intense pain results. Occasionally, also, when a diver loses air pressure to his helmet his body is literally squeezed upward into the helmet, and, when air volume is lost from the mask of a free diving apparatus, the eyes can actually pop out into the mask and the face can become greatly distorted to fill the mask.

It is especially interesting that descending the first 33 feet beneath the surface of the water can cause much more squeeze than descending 33 feet once the diver is deep beneath the sea. The reason for this is the following: When a person descends from sea level to 33 feet below, the pressure increases a total of two-fold, and the volume is reduced to one-half its original value. When a person descends from 300 to 333 feet, the pressure increases from 10 atmospheres to 11 atmospheres, causing only a ten per cent reduction in volume of the gases. Thus, a fall from sea level to 33 feet depth can cause serious damage, while a similar fall in deep water usually causes no significant effect.

Over-expansion of the Lungs on Rapid Ascent. Exactly the opposite pulmonary effects occur on rapid ascent if the person fails to expel air from his lungs on the way up. Unfortunately, panic can frequently cause a person to close his glottis spastically and, therefore, result in serious damage to the lungs. When the lungs become expanded to their limit the pressure continues to rise, and above an alveolar pressure of 80 to 100 mm. Hg, air is forced into the pulmonary capillaries, causing air embolism in the circulation and often resulting in death. Also, increased pressure in the lungs frequently blows out large blebs on the surfaces of the lungs or ruptures the lungs to cause pneumothorax.

In rare instances, in a diver who has been deep below the sea for a long period of time and has formed large amounts of gas in his abdomen, rapid ascent can also cause very serious trauma in the gastrointestinal tract.

Rapid ascent can be especially serious when a person is attempting to escape from a submarine and must rise to the suface rapidly without appropriate diving gear. It also occurs frequently when the diver loses control of his diving gear and his suit balloons up so greatly that he "blows up" to the surface.

SCUBA DIVING (SELF-CONTAINED UNDERWATER BREATHING APPARATUS)

In recent years a diving apparatus which does not require connections with the surface has been perfected and is probably best known under the trade name "Aqualung." There are two basic types of *self-contained underwater breathing apparatuses* from which various modifications have been made. These are (1) the open circuit demand system and (2) the closed circuit system.

The Open Circuit Demand System. Figure 456 illustrates an open circuit demand

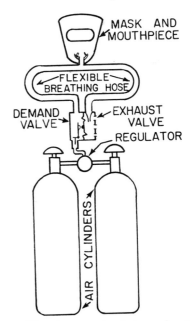

Figure 456. An open circuit demand system type of self-contained underwater breathing apparatus. (Modified from Submarine Medicine Practice. U. S. Navy Bureau of Medicine and Surgery.)

type of underwater breathing apparatus showing the following components: (1) tanks of compressed air or other breathing mixture, (2) a regulator valve for reducing the pressure from the tanks, (3) a "demand" valve which allows air to be pulled into the mask with very slight negative pressure in the system, (4) a mask and tube system with small "dead space," and (5) an exhalation valve located in close contiguity with the demand valve.

Basically, the demand system operates as follows: With each inspiration slight negative pressure in the mask pulls the diaphragm of the demand valve inward, and this automatically releases air from the compressed air containers into the mask. In this way only the amount of air needed for inhalation enters the system. Then, on expiration, the air cannot go back into the tank but instead is expired through the expiration valve.

Several problems exist in relation to the open circuit demand system. First, the demand valve itself must be located as closely as possible to the level of the person's lungs. Otherwise, the hydrostatic pressure of the water pressing against the diaphragm of the demand valve would either cause too much air to flow into the mask (if the demand valve should be located deeper in the sea than the lungs) or make it difficult to inspire (if the demand valve should be located at a shallower level than the lungs). Second, it is essential that the expiration valve be located in close contiguity with the demand valve because the difference between the level of the expiration valve and the level of the demand valve determines the least pressure difference that will be required to activate the demand valve. Third, the most important problem in use of the self-contained underwater breathing apparatus is the time limitation that one can remain beneath the surface; only a few minutes are allowed at great depths, as will be discussed below.

Closed Circuit Systems. The simplest type of closed circuit system is one in which a person breathes pure oxygen. This system contains the following elements: (1) a tank of pure oxygen, (2) a rubber bellows into which the diver can breathe back and forth, (3) a valve system for allowing oxygen to

flow from the oxygen tank into the bellows as needed to keep it moderately filled, (4) a canister containing soda lime through which the rebreathed gas passes to absorb the carbon dioxide, and (5) an appropriate mask system with valves to keep the gaseous mixture flowing through the canister for carbon dioxide removal. Thus, the closed circuit system is very similar to a standard anesthetic machine in which oxygen is continually rebreathed—except that no anesthetic is used.

The most important problem in use of the closed circuit system is limitation in depth that a person can remain beneath the sea because of poor oxygen tolerance. Figure 452 gives these tolerances for depth and time. A safe working rule is no more than 30 minutes at 30 feet depth.

Instead of using pure oxygen, various combinations of helium or nitrogen along with the oxygen have been used in closed circuit systems. However, appropriate methods have not yet been worked out to keep the oxygen partial pressure within a safe range. If such could be worked out, then only one liter of compressed oxygen would be capable of supplying a person with sufficient breathing mixture to remain at any depth for about 2½ hours. Ordinarily, the breathing gases are used up principally to keep carbon dioxide washed out of the lungs and not to supply oxygen. For instance, a diver using the open circuit demand system at 150 feet depth makes use of only 1 per cent of the total volume of gases to supply him with oxygen. The remaining 99 per cent is wastage. When appropriate apparatus is developed for rebreathing, without danger of oxygen toxicity, SCUBA diving will be removed from many of its present limitations.

"Zero Decompression Limits" for Air Breathing in SCUBA Diving

One of the most important problems in SCUBA diving is that the diver often must be decompressed before coming to the surface. To be completely on the safe side the diver needs to know how long he can remain beneath the sea at each depth before sufficient nitrogen will be dissolved in his body fluids to cause danger of decompression sickness. Figure 457 gives the "zero decompression limits" for compressed air diving, show-

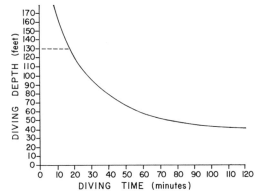

Figure 457. "Zero decompression" limits for compressed air diving. (From Submarine Medicine Practice. U. S. Navy Bureau of Medicine and Surgery.)

ing that, theoretically, a person can remain at a depth of 160 feet for about 10 minutes without needing any decompression whatsoever. At the other extreme, he can remain 40 feet deep for 2 hours without any decompression. The dashed line in the figure shows the recommended depth limit for SCUBA diving to be 130 feet because it is too difficult to keep accurate time for only a few minutes, and a person can very easily overstay his limit and require decompression for longer periods of time than his available air supply can last. Indeed, an absolute depth limit of 60 feet for not over 1 hour is usually recommended.

The zero decompression limits can be extended about 40 per cent when a person breathes a 60 per cent nitrogen–40 per cent oxygen mixture rather than air. The reason for this is that the nitrogen in the lungs is proportionately reduced while the oxygen is increased. Down to the safe depth limits, this amount of oxygen still does not reach the usual toxicity stage.

Decompression when using the self-contained underwater breathing apparatus. Occasionally, it is necessary to go beyond the zero decompression limits. If this is done the person must know by memory the appropriate decompression stages for ascent back to sea level. Furthermore, he must also know the time that the amount of gases in his tanks will allow him to remain beneath the sea. Otherwise, he might readily dissolve more nitrogen in his body fluids than can be decompressed within the time that his apparatus allows. Thus diving under these conditions becomes very much of a scientific maneuver.

SPECIAL PHYSIOLOGICAL PROBLEMS OF SUBMARINES

Escape from Submarines. Essentially the same problems of deep sea diving are often met in relation to submarines, especially when it is necessary to escape from a submerged submarine. Escape is usually possible from as deep as 300 feet even without using any special type of apparatus. However, a rebreathing device is usually provided. Beyond this point the difficulty of nitrogen toxicity limits the practicality of escape with most presently available apparatus. Proper use of helium could allow escape from depths of 600 feet or perhaps even more.

The main problems of escape are (1) being able to hold one's breath long enough to get to the surface and (2) prevention of air embolism. As the person ascends the gases expand in his lungs, and he must exhale continually a certain proportion of these— especially as he nears the surface.

Health Problems in the Submarine Internal Environment. Except for escape, submarine medicine generally centers around several engineering problems to keep hazards out of the internal environment of the submarine. In atomic submarines there exists the problem of radiation hazards, but, with appropriate shielding, the amount of radiation received by the crew submerged beneath the sea has actually been less than the normal radiation received above the surface of the sea from cosmic rays. Therefore, no essential hazard results from this unless some failure in the apparatus causes unexpected release of radioactive materials.

Second, poisonous gases on occasion escape into the atmosphere of the submarine and must be controlled very exactly. For instance, during several weeks' submergence, cigarette smoking by the crew can liberate sufficient amounts of carbon monoxide, if it is not removed from the air, to cause carbon monoxide poisoning, and on occasion even Freon gas has been found to diffuse through the walls of the tubes in refrigeration systems in sufficient quantity to cause dangerous toxicity. Finally, the fact that chlorine and other poisonous gases are released when salt water comes in contact with the batteries in the old type submarines is well known.

A highly publicized factor of submarine medicine has been the possibility of psychological problems caused by prolonged submergence. Fortunately, this has turned out to be more a figment of the public's imagination than truth, for the problems here are the same as those relating (1) to any other confinement or (2) to any other type of danger. Psychological screening has been used to great advantage to keep such problems almost to zero even in month-long submergence.

REFERENCES

Bean, J.: Reserpine, chlorpromazine, and the hypothalamus in reactions to oxygen at high pressure. *Am. J. Physiol., 187:*389, 1956.

Bean, J. W.: Tensional changes of alveolar gas in reactions to rapid compression and decompression and question of nitrogen narcosis. *Am. J. Physiol., 161:*417, 1950.

Behnke, A. R.: Decompression sickness incident to deep sea diving and high altitude ascent. *Medicine, 24:*381, 1945.

Blair, H. A., Dern, R. J., and Smith, V. G.: Intestinal gas in simulated flight to high altitude. *J. Aviat. Med., 18:*352, 1947.

Catchpole, H. R., and Gersh, I.: Pathogenic factors and pathological consequences of decompression sickness. *Physiol. Rev., 27:*360, 1947.

Chapin, J. L.: Anticonvulsant threshold of CO_2 in oxygen under high pressure. *Proc. Soc. Exp. Biol. and Med., 90:*663, 1955.

Fulton, J. F.: Decompression Sickness. Philadelphia, W. B. Saunders Co., 1951.

Gerschman, R., Gilbert, D. L., Nye, S. W., Nadig, P. W., and Fenn, W. O.: Role of adrenalectomy and adrenal-cortical hormones in oxygen poisoning. *Am. J. Physiol., 178:*346, 1954.

Gerschman, R., Gilbert, D. L., Nye, S. W., Price, W. E., Jr., and Fenn, W. O.: Effects of autonomic drugs and of adrenal glands on oxygen poisoning. *Proc. Soc. Exp. Biol. and Med., 88:*617, 1955.

Goff, L., and Bartlett, R., Jr.: Elevated end-tidal CO_2 in trained underwater swimmers. *J. Appl. Physiol., 10:*203, 1957.

Goff, L., Brubach, H., and Specht, H.: Measurements of respiratory responses and work efficiency of underwater swimmers utilizing improved instrumentation. *J. Appl. Physiol., 10:*197, 1957.

Goff, L., Frassetto, R., and Specht, H.: Oxygen requirements in underwater swimming. *J. Appl. Physiol., 9:*219, 1956.

Harvey, E. N.: Decompression sickness and bubble formation in blood and tissues. *Harvey Lect., 40:* 41, 1944–1945.

Johnson, P., and Bean, J.: Effect of sympathetic blocking agents on the toxic action of O_2 at high pressure. *Am. J. Physiol., 188:*593, 1957.

Kaufman, W. C., and Marbarger, J. P.: Pressure breathing: Functional circulatory changes in the dog. *J. Appl. Physiol., 9:*33, 1956.

Love, A., Roddie, R., Rosensweig, J., and Shanks, R.: The effect of pressure changes in the respired air on the renal excretion of water and electrolytes. *Clin. Sc., 16:*281, 1957.

Marbarger, J. P., Kadetz, W., Variakojis, D., and Hansen, J.: The occurrence of depression sickness following denitrogenation at ground level and altitude. *J. Aviat. Med., 28:*127, 1957.

Marshall, R., Lanphier, E. H., and Dubois, A. B.: Resistance to breathing in normal subjects during simulated dives. *J. Appl. Physiol., 9:*5, 1956.

National Research Council: Decompression Sickness. Philadelphia, W. B. Saunders Co., 1951.

Penrod, K.: Effect of intermittent nitrogen exposures on tolerance to oxygen at high pressures. *Am. J. Physiol., 186:*149, 1956.

Penrod, K.: Nature of pulmonary damage produced by high oxygen pressures. *J. Appl. Physiol., 9:*1, 1956.

Specht, H., Goff, L., Brubach, H., and Bartlett, R., Jr.: Work efficiency and respiratory response of trained underwater swimmers using a modified self-contained underwater breathing apparatus. *J. Appl. Physiol., 10:*376, 1957.

Submarine Medicine Practice, Department of the Navy. Washington, U. S. Gov't. Printing Office, 1956.

Taylor, H. J.: Underwater swimming and diving. *Nature, 180:*883, 1957.

U. S. Navy Diving Manual. Washington, U. S. Gov't. Printing Office, 1958.

Part Nine

CENTRAL NERVOUS SYSTEM

AND SPECIAL SENSES

Chapter 46

Design of the Nervous System; Basic Functions of Receptors and Effectors

The nervous system, along with the endocrine system, provides the control functions for the body. In general, the nervous system controls the rapid activities of the body such as muscular contractions, rapidly changing visceral events, and even the rates of secretion of some endocrine glands. The endocrine system regulates principally the metabolic functions of the body.

The nervous system is unique in the vast complexity of the control reactions that it can perform. It can receive literally thousands of bits of information from the different sensory organs and then integrate all these to determine the response made by the body. It is the purpose of this chapter to present a general outline of the basic mechanisms by which the nervous system performs such functions and then, in the succeeding chapters, to analyze in detail the functions of the individual parts of the nervous system. Before beginning this discussion, however, the student is referred to Chapters 17 and 18, which have already presented the basic principles of membrane potentials and transmission of impulses in nerves.

THE REFLEX FUNCTIONS OF THE NERVOUS SYSTEM

The nervous system functions principally by means of vast numbers of *reflexes*. Sensory information enters the nervous system from the sensory organs and then is transmitted through appropriate pathways to cause reflex responses in many different parts of the body. To understand the succession of reflexes that control our daily activities, we must now consider the mechanisms by which reflexes originate, are transmitted, and cause actions.

The Basic Essentials of the Reflex Arc

There are three basic essentials of the reflex arc: (1) a receptor, (2) a conducting system, and (3) an effector.

The *receptor* may be any of the sense organs that are capable of detecting some change in the surroundings. For instance, light shining in the eyes can elicit nerve impulses in the retinae, a pin pricking the skin can excite the pain endings of the skin, and movement of a limb can excite the kinesthetic end-organs of the joint capsules, and any one of these can provide the initial nerve impulses required to elicit the reflex.

The *conducting system* is the system through which impulses are conducted from the receptor to the effector. In the case of the nervous system the conducting system is the nerves, while in the case of the endocrine system the conducting system is the hormones that are transported from the receptor site to the effector site. The conducting pathway of a nervous reflex can be very simple or very complex, depending on the extent of the nervous system through which the reflex signal must be conducted before it finally reaches the effector organ.

The *effector* is the organ that responds to the impulses initiated by the reflex. The different types of effector organs include the *skeletal muscles,* the *smooth muscles of the viscera,* and *glandular cells* that are controlled by nerve impulses.

Levels of Reflex Activity

The Simple Reflex. Shown to the left in Figure 458 is one of the simplest of all the nervous reflexes. This is called the *stretch,* or *myotatic, reflex.* It originates in a muscle spindle which initiates impulses when the muscle is stretched. These impulses are transmitted into the spinal cord and are then reflexly returned to the motor end-plates of the same muscle, causing the muscle to contract automatically whenever it becomes suddenly stretched. This is a "simple" reflex because it involves only two neurons in the reflex arc and because it always responds very much the same way—that is, by increased contraction of the muscle—when the muscle becomes stretched. This is quite different from many of the more complex reflexes in which the response may sometimes be negative, sometimes positive, or sometimes multiphasic, depending on other sensory impulses that are entering the central nervous system at the time of the reflex.

This simple stretch reflex will be discussed in much more detail in Chapter 56; it is used here only to illustrate the simplicity of some of the nervous reflexes that help to control bodily function.

Reflexes of Intermediate Complexity. To the right in Figure 458 is illustrated a reflex of intermediate complexity called the *withdrawal reflex.* This shows pain endings of the hand being stimulated, followed by reflex contraction of the biceps muscle to remove the hand from the painful object. This reflex is more complicated than the stretch reflex in the following ways: First, many neurons, instead of only two, are involved in the reflex arc. Second, the response caused by the reflex is much more frequently modified than is the stretch reflex by impulses that originate in other parts of the brain or in other peripheral sense organs. For instance, if a person steps on a sharp rock, this withdrawal reflex obviously would tend to withdraw the foot from the rock.

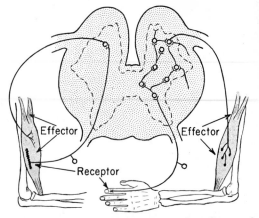

Figure 458. The simple stretch reflex, illustrated to the left, and a withdrawal reflex, illustrated to the right.

But, if movement at that moment should be dangerous or otherwise inconvenient, impulses from the cerebrum could completely block the reflex. Thus, whether or not this reflex response will occur depends on far more factors than simply the initiation of impulses in the pain receptors.

Finally, other major differences between the withdrawal reflex and the simpler stretch reflex are: (a) a tendency for this reflex to last for a second or more after the sensory impulses are over and (b) a tendency for the reflex to spread to adjacent muscles innervated by adjoining areas of the spinal cord.

We might rapidly list some of the progressively more and more complex reflexes that illustrate the general organization of the nervous system:

1. Associated with the withdrawal reflex is a *crossed extensor reflex* that extends the limbs on the opposite side of the body; it pushes the whole body away from any painful object that initiates the withdrawal reflex.

2. Reflexes initiated by pressure on the bottom of the foot cause automatic stiffening of the limb so that it will support the body against gravity.

3. Pressure on the side of the foot pad will initiate a spinal reflex that causes the foot to be pushed in the direction of the pressure; this helps the animal to maintain equilibrium.

4. Backward movement of a limb often causes automatic forward movement of the

limb a fraction of a second later; in turn the forward movement causes automatic backward movement. This repetitive motion can be recognized as the basic movement of walking.

5. Forward and backward movement of the right hindlimb of an animal will usually cause opposite movement of the left hindlimb. Also, movements of the hindlimbs are usually automatically coordinated with movements of the forelimbs so that when one hindlimb moves backwards the corresponding forelimb moves forward. These are additional elements of the walking process, and they all involve nothing more than spinal reflexes.

6. Reflexes originating in the vestibular apparatuses and involving only the brain stem, cerebellum, and spinal cord cause appropriate contraction of the different postural muscles to maintain equilibrium and thus prevent the person from falling to the earth.

7. Other reflexes from the vestibular apparatuses actually "anticipate" that the person will lose his balance in the next fraction of a second if he suddenly turns; these reflexes make corrections in the postural muscle contractions to prevent loss of equilibrium even before it occurs.

The Complex Reflexes. All the reflexes mentioned thus far have involved only the spinal cord and basal areas of the brain. These reflexes alone can perform many of the inbred, automatic functions of the nervous system. But now we must move to the truly complex reflexes that involve the thought processes, the storage of information (memory), analyses of different qualities of sensation, and initiation of "patterns" of motor functions. These functions are characteristic of the cerebrum. Furthermore, reflexes which involve the cerebrum might well be initiated by sensory signals that enter the brain many months or even years before the final reactions occur.

Many persons would like to believe that the cerebrum is not part of the overall reflex mechanism of the nervous system but instead that it is something set aside for the abstract processes of the brain alone. However, even abstract thoughts enter into the reflex pattern of organization, for they begin with information that enters the brain by way of the sensory organs, and they con-

tinually modify the motor responses of the body.

The detailed complexities of cerebral action are more than we can possibly discuss at this time, but the student himself can well characterize many different complicated reflexes that begin with information from the sensory organs and then, after a period of cerebration, cause some bodily reaction. The general patterns of cerebral action will be discussed in detail in Chapters 57 through 60.

The Sensory and Motor Pathways

The somatic sensory pathways from the peripheral parts of the body to essentially all portions of the brain are illustrated in Figure 459. From this figure it is readily

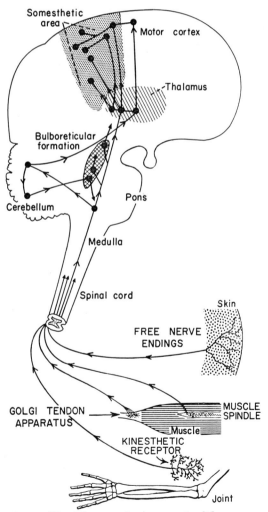

Figure 459. The somatic sensory axis of the nervous system.

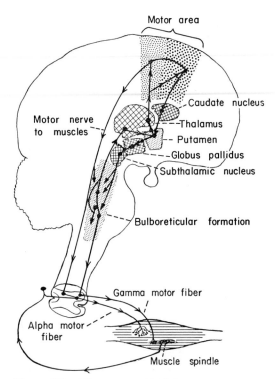

Figure 460. The motor axis of the nervous system.

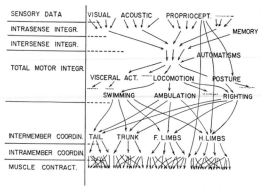

Figure 461. The coordinating and integrating functions of the nervous system, illustrating the sensory input and the motor output. (From Weiss in Bard: Patterns of Organization in the Central Nervous System. Williams and Wilkins Co.)

evident that the spinal cord, the brain stem, the cerebellum, the thalamus, and the cerebral cortex all constantly receive information from the sensory end-organs located everywhere in the body. And reference to Figures 520, 561, 572, and 575 in later chapters will show the sensory pathways for sight, hearing, taste, and smell. Obviously, impulses in this *sensory axis* can provoke simple reflexes that involve only one segment of the spinal cord, intermediate reflexes that involve both the cord and brain stem, and complex reflexes that involve the entire nervous system.

The basic motor pathways are illustrated in Figure 460, showing that impulses originating in different parts of the cerebrum, in the brain stem, and in different segments of the spinal cord can all cause muscular activities everywhere in the body. Not shown in this figure but also constituting part of the motor axis are (a) the motor pathways into the autonomic nervous system and (b) pathways from the hypothalamus to the hypophysis, both of which are very important in controlling many of the functions.

Figure 461 illustrates the complexities of the reflex organization of the nervous system

as well as the involvement of the sensory and motor axes. Note particularly the many different sensory input circuits and the funneling of most of the signals through the same central channels of the nervous system, but note also the passage of some signals directly from the sensory receptors to the motor output. Essentially this same pattern of organization is found in all animals, though the human being has added an excessive abundance of the complex types of reflexes, such as those associated with planning, consciousness, awareness, ambition, conscience, and intelligence.

THE RECEPTORS AND THEIR BASIC MECHANISMS OF ACTION

Types of Receptors and the Sensations They Detect

Basically there are four different types of receptors: (1) mechanoreceptors, (2) chemoreceptors, (3) thermoreceptors, and (4) receptors for electromagnetic radiations.

Mechanoreceptors. The mechanoreceptors respond to physical stimuli that cause mechanical displacement of one or more of the tissues. Such stimuli include touch, movements of the limbs, pressure against the body, sound waves striking the ear, tension in the muscles, tension in the tendons, acceleration of the body, and stretch of the arterial walls by high arterial pressure. The different mechanoreceptors can also be classified in accordance with their functions as follows:

1. The *touch* and *pressure receptors* in-

clude (1) *free nerve endings* that are present in all tissues of the body, (2) *Meissner's corpuscles,* which lie beneath the surface of the skin, (3) *Pacinian corpuscles,* which lie deep in the skin, (4) *hair end-organs,* (5) Merkel's corpuscles, which lie beneath the skin in special areas of the body, and (6) probably several other specialized types of end-organs. Some of these are illustrated in Figure 462, and others will be discussed in Chapter 48 in relation to the somatic sensory system.

2. The mechanoreceptors called *kinesthetic receptors,* which detect movements at the joints and thereby detect positions of the different parts of the body, are the same as several of the touch and pressure receptors except that they are located principally in the joint capsules.

3. The mechanoreceptors in the ear that respond to sound are in the *cochlea,* and are composed of (a) a membrane that vibrates with the sound waves and (b) "hair cells" on the surface of the membrane that stimulate the endings of the cochlear nerve fibers. The functions of these will be discussed in Chapter 51.

4. The mechanoreceptors that respond to acceleration and changes in equilibrium are the *hair cells in the maculae* and *semicircular canals* of the *vestibular apparatuses.* The hair cells in the maculae detect "static" equilibrium sensations and linear acceleration, while those of the semicircular canals detect angular acceleration (Chapter 50).

5. The mechanoreceptors that detect stretch of the muscles are the *muscle spindles,* and those that detect stretch of the tendons are the *Golgi tendon apparatuses* (Chapter 50).

The *pressoreceptors* and the *stretch receptors* in the lungs and heart are also mechanoreceptors. These detect changes in pressure, stretch of the lungs, and stretch of the heart muscle (Chapter 32).

Thermoreceptors. The thermoreceptors can be divided into two types, the *cold receptors* and the *warm receptors.* Some of these are special types of free nerve endings and some are probably more complicated sensory end-organs. The functions of these receptors will be discussed in Chapter 48.

Chemoreceptors. The chemoreceptors are (1) the *taste buds* of the mouth, which respond to different chemicals in the food, (2) the *olfactory cells* of the nose, which detect chemical substances in the air, and (3) the cells of the *carotid* and *aortic bodies,* which detect oxygen concentration in the blood. The functions of these are discussed in Chapters 42 and 55.

Electromagnetic Receptors. The electromagnetic receptors are the rods and cones of the eyes which respond to light, a type of electromagnetic radiation. The functions of these will be presented in Chapter 53.

Mechanism by which the Receptors Stimulate Sensory Nerve Fibers—the "Receptor Potential"

A nerve fiber can be stimulated by crushing it, pricking it, heating it, or in any other way altering the fiber membrane sufficiently to elicit an action potential. However, in these instances of artificial stimulation, the fiber is usually stimulated one time only and not repetitively. On the contrary, stimulation of a fiber by a sensory receptor ordinarily causes repetitive impulses as long as the receptor itself remains excited. Therefore, the receptors obviously stimulate the nerve

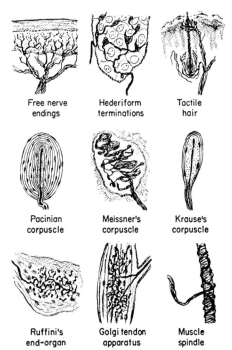

Free nerve endings

Hederiform terminations

Tactile hair

Pacinian corpuscle

Meissner's corpuscle

Krause's corpuscle

Ruffini's end-organ

Golgi tendon apparatus

Muscle spindle

Figure 462. Several types of somatic sensory nerve endings. (Modified from Ramon y Cajal: Histology. William Wood and Co.)

fibers in a different way from the stimulation that occurs following artificial stimulation.

Excitation of all receptors that have been studied causes all of them to generate electrical potentials called *receptor potentials.* We might consider, as an example, the mechanism by which the Pacinian corpuscle generates a receptor potential. Note in Figure 462 that the nerve fiber extends through a "central core" of the Pacinian corpuscle. This central core fiber is non-medullated, and compression on the outside of the corpuscle tends to elongate or shorten the fiber momentarily, depending on how the compression is applied, thus deforming the fiber membrane. During the deformation, a small amount of electrical current is generated by the fiber. The current from the central core fiber spreads to the outer layers of the corpuscle, there exciting the *myelinated* sensory fiber that leads away from the Pacinian corpuscle. Furthermore, the sensory fiber continues to be stimulated as long as the receptor potential continues to be generated by the central core fiber.

Precisely the same effects occur in the muscle spindle; stretching the muscle spindle causes immediate development of a receptor potential in the local vicinity. Such a potential is illustrated in Figure 463, showing that a 5-gram load applied to a frog's muscle causes an initial increase in receptor potential which lasts only a second or more; thereafter the receptor potential settles down to a lower, continuous value. Upon removing the load, the receptor potential falls immediately to a very low value, but after another second or so returns to its original resting value.

Relationship of the Frequency of Stimulation to the Receptor Potential. The frequency of stimulation of the sensory nerve leading from either the muscle spindle

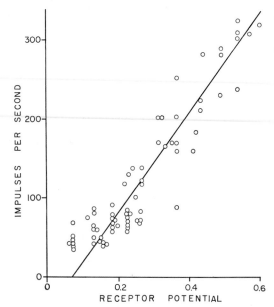

Figure 464. Relationship between the receptor potential of a muscle spindle and the frequency of sensory impulses transmitted from the spindle. (From Katz: *J. Physiol., 111:*161, 1950.)

or the Pacinian corpuscle is approximately proportional to the receptor potential. This relationship is illustrated in Figure 464, which shows the voltage of the receptor potential recorded from the muscle spindle and the frequency of impulses discharged in the nerve fiber. This figure illustrates an almost exact proportional relationship between the receptor potential and the impulses transmitted per minute.

Voltage of the Receptor Potential. Receptor potentials have never been recorded from inside the receptors themselves because of the almost impossible task of placing electrodes in the receptors without destroying their function. However, potentials recorded from the fluids surrounding the receptors, which undoubtedly are far less than the actual voltages in the receptors themselves, indicate that the receptor potentials can range up to about 100 millivolts. That is, a receptor potential can have almost equally as much voltage as an action potential.

Increased Permeability of the Membrane as the Cause of the Receptor Potential. In the case of the Pacinian corpuscle, the basic cause of the receptor potential is almost certainly increased permeability of the fiber membrane in the central core of the corpuscle when it be-

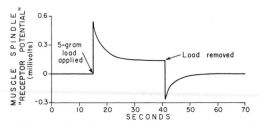

Figure 463. Changes in the receptor potential recorded from a frog muscle spindle when a 5-gram load was applied to the muscle and later removed.

comes deformed, which allows sodium ions to diffuse to the interior of the membrane, thereby causing electropositivity inside the membrane and electronegativity outside the membrane. If the deformation should be great enough to make the membrane completely permeable to sodium ions, the voltage of the receptor potential would theoretically equal that of an action potential.

Presumably, other receptors function in a similar manner, the exciting stimulus causing the receptor membrane permeability to increase and the resultant receptor potential to elicit action potentials in the sensory nerve fiber.

Adaptation of Receptors. Referring once again to Figure 463, we see that sudden stretch of a muscle spindle causes the receptor potential to rise considerably at first and then to fall off to a lower but sustained value. This causes a rapid rate of impulses from the spindle at first and then a progressively slower rate. The decrease in rate is called *adaptation.*

Some of the sensory receptors adapt to a far greater extent than others, and the rate of adaptation is related to the function to be performed by the particular receptor. Figure 465 shows the adaptation of different types of receptors. Note that the receptors of the joint capsules adapt very little. Similarly, the muscle spindle adapts very little except during the initial few seconds. On the other hand, light touch receptors usually adapt to "extinction" within a second or more, while the Pacinian corpuscles adapt to extinction in only a small fraction of a second after a stimulus is applied.

Function of the poorly adapting receptors. The poorly adapting receptors keep the

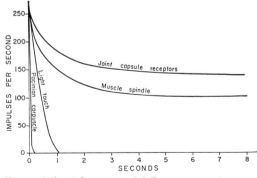

Figure 465. Adaptation of different types of sensory receptors.

brain constantly apprised of the physical status of the body or of its relations to its surroundings. For instance, the impulses from the joint capsule receptors allow the person to know the positions of the different parts of his body at all times, while the impulses from the muscle spindles and Golgi tendon apparatuses allow the central nervous system to know the status of muscle contraction and muscle load at each instant.

Other types of poorly adapting receptors include the receptors of the maculae in the vestibular apparatus, the receptors of the ear, the pain receptors, the pressoreceptors of the arterial tree, and the chemoreceptors of the carotid and aortic bodies.

Function of the rapidly adapting receptors. The rapidly adapting receptors detect *changes* in the physical surroundings rather than their "static" state. For instance, Pacinian corpuscles, which normally adapt to extinction within a small fraction of a second, obviously cannot detect prolonged alterations in the physical status of the body. But, on the other hand, they react very strongly *while a change is actually taking place.* Therefore, Pacinian corpuscles that lie deep in the skin perform the very important function of apprising the nervous system of the *rate at which pressure is applied* to the skin. And Pacinian corpuscles around the joints apprise the nervous system of the *rate of movement* of the joints, which is equally as important as the information about the momentary positions of the joints.

Also important is the very rapid adaptation of most of the light touch receptors of the skin, including the hair end-organs and other specialized mechanoreceptors immediately beneath the skin. These adapt to extinction within a second or more. The importance of this is that, when the physical contacts of a person's body change, he becomes immediately aware of the change, but his brain does not continue to be bombarded with impulses except for the first few seconds after the change. Indeed, if all the tactile receptors should keep on transmitting impulses from all the parts of the body that touch the clothes, the seat of the chair, the shoes, and so forth, the brain would be kept in a continual state of confusion. Therefore, it is very important that the brain be apprised very strongly and forcefully of *changes* in the physical contacts of the body but, nevertheless, not be continually overloaded with unnecessary information from this source.

Slowly adapting receptors. Still other receptors adapt tremendously but do so over a period of many minutes instead of seconds —e.g., the rods and cones of the eyes. These adapt as much as 100,000- to 500,000-fold on exposure to very bright light, but as long as several hours may be required for full adaptation.

The adapation of the eye is quite different from that of the Pacinian corpuscles and the light touch receptors, for these latter two types of receptors adapt all the way to complete extinction rather than only a certain proportion of the way, as is true of the rods and cones. Other types of slowly adapting sensory organs are those of taste, smell, and temperature detection.

Mechanism by which the receptors adapt. Adaptation of the receptors seems to be an individual property of each one of the separate types of receptors. Furthermore, the different receptors do not necessarily adapt in the same manner. In the case of the Pacinian corpuscles, for instance, within a fraction of a second after pressure on the corpuscle deforms the central core fiber, despite continual pressure, the central core fiber returns to its natural state. Thus, adaptation in the case of the Pacinian corpuscle seems to be simply mechanical readjustment of forces within the receptor.

In the case of the retina, on the other hand, adaptation results from a decrease in concentration of light sensitive chemicals. Before the eye is exposed to bright light, large quantities of rhodopsin are present in the rods, but, on exposure, the rhodopsin decomposes and the sensitivity of the rod becomes correspondingly reduced; a similar mechanism exists for the cones, as will be discussed in detail in Chapter 53.

Therefore, again we will point out that the mechanism of adaptation, as well as the degree and the rate of adaptation, is an individual property of each of the different types of receptors.

Logarithmic Responses of Receptors— the "Weber-Fechner Law." The number of impulses generated in a sensory nerve usually is not proportional to the intensity of the initiating stimulus, but, instead, is more nearly proportional to the *logarithm*

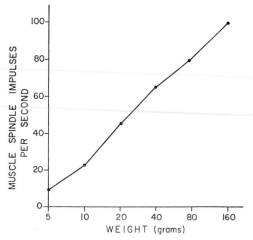

Figure 466. Demonstration of the logarithmic response of the muscle spindle when increasing loads are applied to a cat's muscle. (Drawn from data from Matthews: *J. Physiol.,* 78:1, 1933.)

of the stimulus intensity. This effect, which is known as the *Weber-Fechner Law,* is illustrated in Figure 466, which shows the frequency of impulse transmission from a muscle spindle when increasing loads are applied to the muscle. Note that the abscissa is a logarithmic scale and that when this scale is used the relationship between load and the number of impulses is approximately linear.

This same type of logarithmic response occurs for almost all sensory receptors in at least part of their ranges. For instance, the ear detects changes in sound intensity in proportion to the logarithm of the sound intensity and not directly in proportion to the intensity itself. Likewise the eye detects light intensities in proportion to the logarithm of the intensities rather than in proportion to the actual intensities.

One can express this logarithmic response of receptors in still another way. If a 5 per cent increase in stimulus strength will be barely perceptible when the stimulus is very weak, then approximately a 5 per cent increase in intensity will also be necessary to cause a barely perceptible change when the stimulus is very strong. In other words, most receptors detect *percentage changes* in intensity rather than actual changes in intensity.

Mechanism of the logarithmic response of receptors. The logarithmic response of receptors is an inherent property of the receptors themselves, for the intensity of the receptor potential as well as the rate of impulses changes approximately in proportion to the logarithm of the stimulus intensity. Thus, in the case of the muscle spindle, an increase in load on a muscle from 10 grams to 11 grams causes approximately the same voltage increase in the receptor potential as an increase in load from 100 grams to 110 grams. Yet, in the first instance, the actual increase is only 1 gram in comparison with 10-grams increase in the second instance.

Importance of the logarithmic response of receptors. The logarithmic response of receptors allows them to have an extreme range of responsivity. As an example, the ear can respond to very weak sounds only one ten-billionth as strong as the strongest sounds that it can also detect with accuracy. And the eyes can see very acutely in very bright light or in light that has an intensity as small as 1/100,000 that of the very bright light. For example, the intensity of sunlight is approximately 30,000 times that of moonlight, and yet the eye can see at least moderately well in both these lights.

Were it not for the logarithmic response of the receptors, the changes in stimulus strength that could be detected accurately would never be more than several hundredfold, because one or more impulses per second usually must be transmitted along a sensory fiber for even the weakest sensation to be perceived, while, on the other hand, the maximum rate of impulse transmission in most instances is only several hundred impulses per second. Yet, by using the logarithmic method of responsiveness the receptors have extended their range of perceptivity up to millions to one and in some instances even to billions to one.

Centrifugal Control of the Receptors

The responsiveness of a few of the sensory receptors can be altered by *centrifugal impulses* that pass through *efferent* nerve fibers from the central nervous system to the receptors. Such efferent fibers are known to control the sensitivity of the retinae of the eyes, the olfactory receptors, the cochlea, and the muscle spindles in the skeletal muscles. The functions of the *gamma efferent* system that controls the responsiveness of

the muscle spindles have been studied especially. Stimulation of this system increases the degree of reactivity of the spindles, thus increasing the intensity of the reflexes that arise in these receptors. This is such an important method for control of muscular function that it will be discussed in detail in Chapter 56.

Though the responsiveness of only some of the sensory receptors is controlled by efferent fibers, the sensory effects of all the other receptors can also be regulated by changes in reactivity of central nuclei into which they lead, which will be discussed in Chapter 58. Thus, in two different ways, the central nervous system can regulate its own degree of responsiveness to almost any type of external stimulus.

THE EFFECTORS AND THEIR MECHANISMS OF ACTION

The parts of the body that can be controlled by the nervous system are the effectors, and, since essentially all cells are controlled at least to some extent by the central nervous system, we can probably consider every portion of the body to be part of the effector system. Yet, certain parts of the body stand out as effectors, reacting rapidly and intensely to nerve stimuli. These include the *skeletal muscles, cardiac muscle,* the *smooth muscle organs,* some of the *endocrine glands,* and certain ones of the *exocrine glands.*

Skeletal muscle contraction can occur very weakly, very strongly, or with all gradations of strength between the two extremes. Maximal strength of skeletal muscle contraction usually occurs when the rate of stimulation reaches 100 to 250 nerve impulses per second. For further analysis of skeletal muscle function and its control, the student is referred to Chapter 19, which discusses the function of skeletal muscles themselves, and to Chapter 18, which discusses the transmission of impulses from motor nerves into the muscle.

Cardiac muscle is innervated by the sympathetic and parasympathetic nervous systems. However, the heart can continue to beat without any stimulation from these two sources. Parasympathetic stimulation decreases the rate of heart beat and reduces the strength of contraction of the atria. On the other hand, sympathetic stimulation greatly increases the strength of contraction of both the atria and the ventricles and sometimes doubles or triples the heart rate. Chapter 21 gives a detailed analysis of these effects.

The *smooth muscle organs* are also innervated by sympathetic nerves, or parasympathetic nerves, or both. Some of these organs are excited by sympathetic stimulation while others are inhibited, and usually the parasympathetics cause exactly the opposite effects. The precise responses of the different organs to autonomic stimulation are different for each individual organ and were discussed in detail in Chapter 20.

The *endocrine glands* controlled by the central nervous system include especially the adrenal medulla, the neurohypophysis, and the adenohypophysis. Sympathetic impulses directly stimulate the adrenal medulla to cause nor-epinephrine and epinephrine secretion. In turn, the nor-epinephrine and epinephrine are transmitted in the blood to all cells of the body. Both of these, but epinephrine especially, increase the metabolic rate of all the cells of the body, sometimes causing as much as two-fold increase in the overall basal metabolic rate. Therefore, in this instance, all the cells of the body are actually effector organs.

The secretion of oxytocin and vasopressin by the neurohypophysis is directly regulated by nervous impulses generated in the hypothalamus. The oxytocin acts principally on the uterus to cause uterine contraction and on the breasts to cause "milk ejection," while vasopressin (also called *antidiuretic hormone*) acts on the renal tubules to cause increased reabsorption of water.

Finally, stimulation of certain areas of the hypothalamus causes neurosecretory substances to flow by way of the hypophyseal portal system to the adenohypophysis and there to stimulate secretion of most, if not all, of the adenohypophyseal hormones. These hormones in turn regulate the greater majority of the metabolic functions of the body, including growth and secretion of hormones by the thyroid gland, the sex glands, and the adrenal cortex. Thus, in a sense, the adenohypophysis and the other endocrine glands that it controls are all effector organs of the nervous system.

Almost all the *exocrine glands* are stimulated by the nervous system, including especially the sweat glands and the glands of the upper alimentary tract. For instance, the salivary and most of the esophageal glands are controlled almost entirely by nerve reflexes. About two thirds of the secretion in the stomach is controlled by the nervous system and about one third by local hormonal mechanisms in the stomach itself; pancreatic secretion is controlled to a moderate extent by the nervous system. On the other hand, glands elsewhere in the gastrointestinal tract, though controlled mainly by local mechanisms, can be modified at least to some extent by autonomic excitation or inhibition. Therefore, essentially all the exocrine glands of the body can be considered to be nervous effector organs.

COMPARISON OF THE NERVOUS SYSTEM WITH AN ELECTRONIC COMPUTER

When electronic computers were first designed in many different laboratories of the world by as many different engineers, it soon became apparent that all these machines had many common features. First, they all had input circuits which were comparable to the receptors of the nervous system and output circuits which were comparable to the effector organs of the nervous system. In the conducting pathway between the inputs and the outputs were the mechanisms for performing the different types of computations.

In simple computers, the output signals were controlled directly by the input signals, operating in a manner similar to that of the simple reflexes of the nervous system. But, in the more complex computers, the output was determined both by the input signals and by information that had already been stored in the computer, which is analogous to the more complex reflex mechanisms of our nervous system. Furthermore, as the computers became even more complex it became necessary to add still another unit, called the *programming unit*, which determines the sequence of computational operations. This unit is analogous to the mechanism in our brain that allows us to direct our attention first to one thought, then to another, and so forth, until very complex sequences of thought take place.

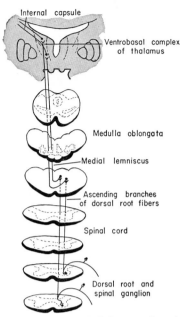

Figure 485. The medial lemniscal pathway for transmitting the critical types of mechanoreceptive sensations. (Modified from Ranson and Clark: Anatomy of the Nervous System.)

from the *main sensory nucleus of the trigeminal nerve*, these fibers subserving the same sensory functions for the head that the dorsal column fibers subserve for the body.

From the ventrobasal complex, *third order neurons* project, as shown in Figure 486, to the *postcentral gyrus* of the *cerebral cortex*. But, in addition still other fibers project to closely associated regions of the cortex behind, in front of, and lateral to the postcentral gyrus.

Collateral Fibers from the Medial Lemniscal Pathway to Centers in the Cord, Brain Stem, and Thalamus. Collateral fibers deviate from the medial lemniscal system to several distinct areas: First, a large number of collaterals spread from the dorsal column fibers to the gray matter of the spinal cord in the segments where the dorsal roots enter. Second, collateral fibers pass from the nuclei gracilis and cuneatus to the anterior cerebellum. Third, a few collateral fibers pass to the brain stem nuclei, particularly to those in the tegmentum of the mesencephalon. And, fourth, still many more collaterals project to additional nuclei in the thalamus besides those of the ventrobasal complex. These collateral fibers subserve the functions of (a) localized segmental reflexes in the cord, (b) cerebellar reflexes that help to coordinate motor movements in the body, and (c) tegmental and thalamic responses that are probably at least partially responsible for the conscious perception of sensations.

It is particularly notable that the lower portions

of the brain stem do not receive great numbers of collaterals from the medial lemniscal system. But, as will be pointed out later, very large numbers of collaterals do enter this area from the spinothalamic system.

Spatial Orientation of the Nerve Fibers in the Medial Lemniscal Pathway. All the way from the origin of the dorsal columns to the cerebral cortex, a distinct spatial orientation of the fibers from individual parts of the body is maintained. The fibers from the lower parts of the body lie toward the center of the dorsal columns, while those that enter the dorsal columns at progressively higher and higher levels form successive layers to the lateral sides of the dorsal columns.

In the thalamus, a distinct spatial orientation is still maintained, with the tail end of the body represented by the most lateral portions of the ventrobasal complex and the head and face represented in the medial component of the complex. However, it should be noted that because of the crossing of the medial lemnisci in the medulla the left side of the body is represented in the right side of the thalamus and the right side of the body is represented in the left side. In a similar manner the fibers passing to the cerebral cortex also are very accurately spatially oriented so that a single part of

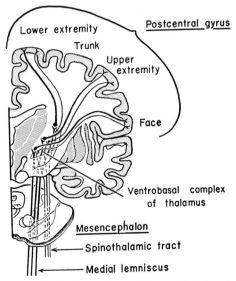

Figure 486. Projection of the medial lemniscal system from the thalamus to the somesthetic cortex. (Modified from Brodal: Neurological Anatomy in Relation to Clinical Medicine. Oxford University Press.)

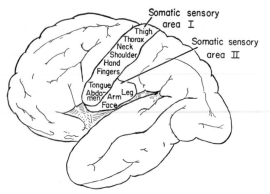

Figure 487. The two somesthetic cortical areas, somatic sensory area I and somatic sensory area II.

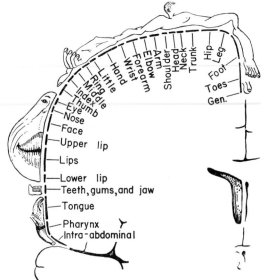

Figure 488. Representation of the different areas of the body in the somatic sensory area I of the cortex. (From Penfield and Rasmussen: The Cerebral Cortex in Man. The Macmillan Co.)

the somatic cortex receives signals from a discrete area of the body, as will be described below.

The Somesthetic Cortex

The area of the cerebral cortex to which the primary sensory impulses are projected is called the *somesthetic cortex.* In the human being, this area lies mainly in the anterior portions of the parietal lobes. Two distinct and separate areas are known to receive direct afferent nerve fibers from the relay nuclei of the thalamus; these are called respectively *somatic sensory area I* and *somatic sensory area II,* and they are illustrated in Figure 487.

Though the term "somesthetic cortex" actually means all the areas of the cerebral cortex that receive sensory information from the body, the presence of somatic sensory area I in the cortex has been known so much longer than that of somatic sensory area II that in popular usage the term somesthetic cortex is almost always used to designate area I exclusive of area II. Therefore to keep these two areas separated, we will henceforth refer to them separately as somatic sensory area I and somatic sensory area II.

Projection of the Body in Somatic Sensory Area I. Somatic sensory area I lies in the postcentral gyrus of the human cerebral cortex. A very distinct spatial orientation exists in this area for reception of nerve fibers from the different areas of the body. Figure 488 illustrates a cross-section through the brain at the level of the postcentral gyrus, showing the representations of the different parts of the body in separate parts

of somatic area I. Note especially that each side of the cortex receives sensory information from the opposite side of the body.

Some areas of the body are represented by very large areas in the somatic cortex—the lips by far the greatest area of all, followed by the face and thumb—while the entire trunk and lower part of the body are represented by relatively small areas. It should be noted especially that the sizes of these areas are directly proportional to the numbers of specialized nerve endings in each one of the respective peripheral areas of the body. For instance, a tremendous number of specialized nerve endings are found in the lips and thumb, while only very few are present in the skin or deeper tissues of the entire trunk.

Note also that the head is represented in the lower or lateral portion of the postcentral gyrus, while the lower end of the body is represented in the medial or upper portion of the postcentral gyrus.

Somatic Sensory Area II. The second cortical area to which somatic afferent fibers project, the somatic sensory area II, lies posterior and inferior to the lower end of the postcentral gyrus and on the upper surface of the lateral fissure. The degree of localization of the different parts of the body is less acute in this area than in somatic area I.

The face is represented anteriorly, the arms centrally, and the legs posteriorly.

A special difference between somatic areas I and II seems to be that somatic area I receives afferent fibers principally from the medial lemniscal system and, to a less extent, from the spinothalamic system, while there is reason to believe that somatic area II might receive the major proportion of its fibers from the spinothalamic pathway rather than from the medial lemniscal pathway.

Functions of the Somesthetic Cortex. The functional capabilities of different areas of the somesthetic cortex have been determined by selective excision of the different portions. Widespread excision of both the somatic sensory areas destroys one's ability to judge critically the different types of sensory information that are derived from the body. The following types of sensory judgment are missing:

1. The person is unable to localize very discretely the different sensations in the different parts of the body. However, he can localize these sensations crudely, which indicates that the thalamus or parts of the cerebral cortex not normally considered to be concerned with somesthetic sensations can perform some degree of localization.

2. He is unable to judge critical changes in forces pressing against his body. For instance, he is unable to judge very exactly the weights of objects causing pressure against his skin.

3. He is unable to judge shapes or forms of objects. This is called *astereognosis.*

4. He is unable to judge texture of materials, for this type of judgment depends on highly critical sensations caused by movement of the skin over the surface to be judged.

5. He is unable to judge fine gradations in temperature.

6. He is unable to recognize the relative orientation of the different parts of his body with respect to each other.

Difference in functions of somatic areas I and II. So little is known about the function of somatic area II and so little disturbance is caused by removing this area that its precise function is almost totally unknown. On the other hand, if somatic area I is removed, the person's critical somatic sensibilities are at first almost completely lost, which demonstrates that this area, the postcentral gyrus, is the major sensory area for perception of the critical sensibilities. However, some months later these sensibilities recover to a great extent, and it is possible that somatic area II takes over many of these functions.

Also, stimulation of somatic area II in some instances will cause complex motor responses throughout the body, for which reason it possibly is particularly valuable for sensory control of motor functions. Also, in the following chapter we will note that this area might be especially responsive to pain sensations.

In summary, we generally associate most of the functions of the somesthetic cortex with somatic area I rather than with somatic area II, but this may be because of our present lack of knowledge about somatic area II.

Characteristics of Transmission in the Medial Lemniscal Pathway

The most important functional characteristic of the medial lemniscal pathway is its *faithfulness* of transmission. That is, each time a point in the periphery is stimulated, a signal ordinarily is transmitted all the way up to the somesthetic cortex. Also, if this peripheral stimulus increases in intensity, the intensity of the signal at the cerebral cortex increases. And, finally, when a discrete area of the body is stimulated, the signal from this area is transmitted to a highly discrete area of the cerebral cortex. Thus, the medial lemniscus is very adequately organized for transmission of accurate information from the periphery to the sensorium. Furthermore, the responsiveness of this system can be altered only moderately by stimuli from other areas of the nervous system, and it cannot be depressed to a significant extent by extraneous agents such as moderate degrees of anesthesia.

Basic Neuronal Circuit and Discharge Pattern in the Medial Lemniscal System. The lower part of Figure 489 illustrates the basic organization of the neuronal circuit of the medial lemniscal system, showing that at each synaptic stage a moderate degree of divergence occurs. However, the upper part of Figure 489 shows that a single receptor stimulus on the skin does not cause all the cortical neurons with which that receptor

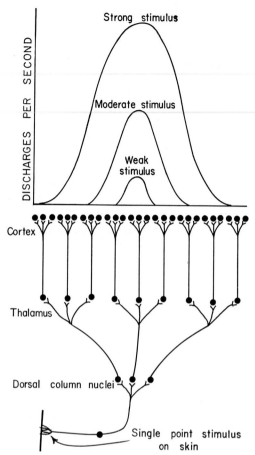

Figure 489. Basic circuit of the medial lemniscal system, showing also the transmission of impulses to the cortex when a receptor is weakly, moderately, or strongly stimulated.

connects to discharge at the same rate. Instead, the cortical neurons that discharge to the greatest extent are those in the centermost spot of the cortical "field" for each respective receptor. Thus, referring to Figure 489 once again, a weak stimulus will cause only a few of the centralmost neurons to fire, while a moderate stimulus will cause still more neurons to fire but with those in the very center still discharging at a considerably more rapid rate than those farther away from the center. Finally, a strong stimulus causes widespread discharge in the cortex, but again very rapid discharge of the central neurons in comparison with peripheral neurons.

Transmission of Signals of Different Intensities from the Periphery to the Cortex. From the above description of the basic circuit of the medial lemniscal pathway, it is quite obvious that signals of dif-

ferent intensities are transmitted to the cortex by two means: (a) transmission of impulses to greater or less numbers of cortical neurons, which is a type of *spatial summation,* and (b) transmission of greater or less number of impulses to all stimulated neurons, which is a type of *temporal summation.*

Spatial summation occurs by "recruiting" additional neurons peripheral to the central stimulus as the stimulus becomes stronger and stronger. That is, only the centralmost part of the pathway has sufficient presynaptic terminals on the successive neurons to cause stimulation when a weak signal originates in the periphery. However, when a strong signal originates, far greater numbers of neurons to the sides of the central point are *recruited* into the pattern of discharge.

Temporal summation results partly from increased numbers of impulses transmitted from the sensory receptors as the stimulus becomes stronger and partly from a very distinct mechanism in the medial lemniscal system which causes the successive orders of neurons to fire at faster and faster rates as the input signal increases. For instance, a single strong volley of impulses from several contiguous dorsal column fibers arriving in the nucleus cuneatus does not cause only a single discharge from this nucleus but, instead, causes repetitive discharge in the second order neurons of two to seven rapidly successive impulses. In other words, this nucleus detects the fact that many neurons are involved in the original signal even though there is only one impulse in each of the involved neurons, and the nucleus responds by transmitting a train of impulses, thus converting the spatially summated signal into a temporally summated signal.

Point-to-Point Transmission in the Medial Lemniscal Pathway. Referring once again to Figure 489, it is evident that, when a single receptor is stimulated in the skin, a particular point in the somesthetic cortex is also excited more intensively than are all the surrounding areas. This does not mean that adjacent areas of the somesthetic cortex are not also stimulated. However, these adjacent areas are stimulated less intensively than the centralmost point in the cortical field of the stimulated receptor. Thus, by this means, the sensory cortex is always capable of detecting the precise localization of signals from the skin despite the spread of the excitation in the cortex.

Two-point discrimination. A method frequently used to test a person's tactile capabilities is to determine his so-called "two-point discriminatory ability." To perform this test two needles are pressed against the skin, and the subject determines whether he feels two points of stimulus or one point. Over the tips of the fingers a person can distinguish two separate points even when the needles are as close together as 1 millimeter. However, on his back the needles must usually be as far as 8 to 10 millimeters apart before he can detect two separate points. The reason for this is that there are many specialized tactile receptors in the tips of the fingers in comparison with a very small number in the back. Referring back to Figure 488, we can see also that the portions of the body that have a high degree of two-point discrimination have a correspondingly large cortical representation in somatic sensory area I.

Figure 490 illustrates the mechanism by which the medial lemniscal pathway transmits two-point discriminatory information. This shows two adjacent points on the skin that are strongly stimulated, and it shows the small area of the somesthetic cortex (greatly enlarged) that is stimulated by the signals from the two points in the skin. The two dashed curves show the individually excited cortical fields, and the solid curve shows the resultant cortical excitation when both the skin points are stimulated simultaneously. Note that the resultant zone of excitation has two separate humps, which is the mechanism by which the sensory cortex detects the presence of two stimulatory points rather than a single stimulatory point.

Inhibition of the somesthetic cortex by peripheral stimuli. Some of the impulses transmitted from the periphery to the somesthetic cortex cause inhibition rather than excitation. Furthermore, stimulation of a single receptor can excite a very small and discrete area of the cortex while inhibiting the immediately adjacent areas. It is believed that this inhibition might be a means by which an extremely high degree of point-to-point transmission in the medial lemniscal system can be achieved. That is, the signal to the cortex might excite the neurons in the very center of its cortical field while at the same time sending collateral inhibitory impulses to the sides, thus preventing too much spread of the signal in the cortex.

Transmission of Rapidly Changing and Repetitive Sensations. The medial lemniscal system is of particular value for apprising the sensorium of rapidly changing peripheral conditions. Since most of the tactile impulses are elicited by rapidly changing conditions, one readily understands the importance of rapid transmission of the resultant signals. This allows us to direct our attention immediately to any point of contact, which, in turn, allows us to make necessary corrections before damage can be done.

Vibratory sensation. Vibratory sensation is not a modality of sensation itself but instead is caused by rapidly repetitive impulses from tactile or pressure receptors. Because of the necessity for transmitting rapidly repetitive signals, vibratory sensations can be transmitted only in the medial lemniscal system and not at all in the slowly transmitting spinothalamic system. For this reason, application of vibration with a tuning fork to different peripheral parts of the body is a very important tool used by the neurologist for testing the functional integrity of the medial lemniscal system.

TRANSMISSION IN THE SPINOTHALAMIC SYSTEM

It was pointed out earlier in the chapter that the spinothalamic tract transmits sensa-

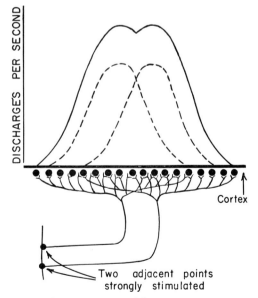

Figure 490. Response of the cortex to strong stimulation of two adjacent points on the surface of the skin. The dashed curves show the response of the cortex to stimulation of each of the two points individually.

tions that do not require rapid transmission nor highly discrete localization in the body. These include pain, heat, cold, crude touch, crude pressure, and sexual sensations. In the following chapter, we will discuss pain specifically, but in the present chapter we are concerned principally with transmission of crude touch, crude pressure, heat, and cold sensations in the spinothalamic system.

The Spinothalamic Pathway

Figure 491 illustrates the spinothalamic pathway, which begins in the lateral division of the dorsal sensory roots of the spinal cord. These fibers travel upward in the *tract of Lissauer* for one to six segments and then terminate on *second order neurons* in the gray matter of the dorsal horns. The fibers from these then form the spinothalamic tract that passes all the way to the thalamus. Almost all the fibers of the spinothalamic tract cross through the anterior commissure of the cord gray matter immediately after their origin and pass to the opposite anterolateral columns of the spinal cord.

The spinothalamic tract is divided into an anterior division called the *ventral spinothalamic tract*, which lies ventral to the anterior horn of the cord, and into a *lateral spinothalamic tract*, which lies lateral to the anterior horn. The ventral tract transmits crude touch, crude pressure, and sexual sensations, while the lateral tract transmits pain and thermal sensations.

Both the ventral and lateral spinothalamic tracts terminate in the posterior portion of the thalamus in close association with the medial lemniscal pathway. Indeed, many of the fibers pass directly to the *ventrobasal complex*, the major terminus of the medial lemniscus, but anatomical studies show that many of the fibers also end in a small region of the thalamus that lies between the ventrobasal complex and the medial geniculate body. In their passage through the brain stem these tracts are joined by the *bulbothalamic tract*, which arises in the *spinal nucleus of the fifth nerve* and transmits sensations from the head comparable to those transmitted from the body by the spinothalamic tracts.

Third order neurons project from the thalamus to both the somatic sensory areas of the cortex. Some of these project from the ventrobasal complex of the thalamus to *somatic sensory area I* along the fibers of the medial lemniscal pathway, but it is believed that a very large portion of the third order neurons from the nuclei near the medial geniculate body project to *somatic sensory area II*. If this should prove to be true, it would be reasonable to suppose that somatic area I is principally concerned with sensations transmitted

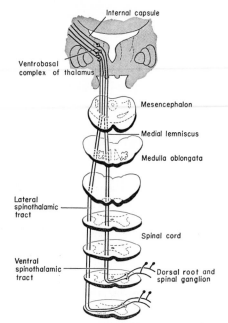

Figure 491. The spinothalamic system for transmission of pain, thermal, crude touch, crude pressure, and sexual sensations. (Modified from Ranson and Clark: Anatomy of the Nervous System.)

in the medial lemniscal system while somatic area II is principally concerned with impulses transmitted in the spinothalamic system.

Spatial Orientation in the Spinothalamic Tract. The same type of spatial orientation, though less discrete, occurs in the spinothalamic tract as in the medial lemniscal system. The spinothalamic tract is very small in comparison with the medial lemniscal system, but the fibers are also much smaller so that it is still possible to have a reasonably high degree of spatial representation of the body in this tract despite its small size. Little is known about the spatial orientation of the terminals of the spinothalamic tract in the thalamus or cerebral cortex, but it is assumed to be at least to some extent the same as that for the medial lemniscal system.

Collaterals from the Spinothalamic Pathway to the Spinal Cord, Brain Stem, and Thalamus. A special feature of the spinothalamic pathway is the vast numbers of collateral fibers that leave this pathway before it reaches the cortex; this organization is distinctly different from that of the medial lemniscal system, which gives off very few collaterals. Many collaterals leave the tracts in the original segment of the cord and probably also at many points along the spinal cord. Extreme numbers then pass into the reticular areas of the brain stem. Indeed, the spinothalamic tract itself becomes much thinner as it progresses through the brain stem toward the thalamus, illustrating that this tract is probably equally as much concerned with transmission of information into the brain stem as to the higher areas. Finally, still many more collateral fibers spread to thalamic areas adjacent to the primary relay nuclei in the ventrobasal complex.

Characteristics of Transmission in the Spinothalamic Tract. The precise nature of transmission in the spinothalamic tract is not nearly so well known as in the medial lemniscal system. In general, the same principles apply to transmission in this tract as in the medial lemniscal system except for the following differences: (a) the velocity of transmission is several times less in the spinothalamic tract than in the medial lemniscal system, (b) the spatial localization of signals transmitted in the spinothalamic tract is far less acute than in the medial lemniscal system, (c) the gradations of intensities are also far less acute than in the medial lemniscal system, most of the sensations being recognized in ten to twenty gradations of strength rather than the hundred or more gradations in the medial lemniscal system, and (d) the ability to transmit rapidly repetitive sensations is almost nil in the spinothalamic system.

Thus, it is evident that the spinothalamic tract represents a cruder type of transmission system by far than the medial lemniscal system. However, it must be realized that certain types of sensations are, nevertheless, transmitted only by the spinothalamic tract, including pain, thermal sensations, and sexual sensations. Only the mechanoreceptive sensations are transmitted by both of the systems, the medial lemniscal system having to do with the critical types of mechanoreceptive sensations, and the spinothalamic tract having to do with the cruder type of mechanoreceptive sensations.

THERMAL SENSATIONS

Thermal Receptors and Their Excitation

The human being can perceive different gradations of cold and heat, progressing from *cold* to *cool* to *indifferent* to *warm to hot;* some persons perceive even freezing cold and burning hot.

The different thermal gradations in the body are discriminated by at least three different types of sensory end-organs, the *cold endings,* the *warm endings,* and the *pain endings.* The pain endings are stimulated only by extreme degrees of heat or cold and therefore will not be considered as thermal receptors but merely as pain receptors that become stimulated when either heat or cold becomes sufficiently severe to cause damage.

Both heat and cold can be perceived from areas of the body that contain only free nerve endings, such as the cornea. Therefore, it is known that free nerve endings can subserve these sensory functions. However, it has also been suggested that certain special types of specialized nerve endings can also detect heat and cold. In certain areas of the body, the number of "warm spots" at which distinct sensations of warmth can be perceived has been found to be approximately equal to the number of *Ruffini's sensory endings.* Therefore, it has long been believed that Ruffini's nerve endings might well be specialized warmth receptors, though more recent studies make this doubtful. Likewise the number of cold spots in certain tissues have been closely correlated with the number of Krause's end-organs, for which reason this type of end-organ has also been postulated to be a specialized thermal receptor, but, in this situation, perceiving cold rather than warmth. This, too, is still much in doubt.

Stimulation of Thermal Receptors— Sensations of Cold, Warmth, and Hot. Figure 492 illustrates the responses to different skin temperatures of three different types of nerve fibers; (1) a cold fiber, (2) a warm fiber, and (3) a pain fiber. Note

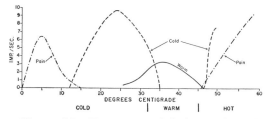

Figure 492. Frequencies of discharge of a cold receptor, a warm receptor, and a pain nerve fiber at different temperatures. (The responses of the cold and warm receptors are modified from Zotterman: *Ann. Rev. Physiol.,* 15:357, 1953.)

especially that all these fibers respond differently at different levels of temperature. For instance, in the *very* cold region only the pain fibers are stimulated (if the skin becomes even colder so that it nearly freezes or actually does freeze, then even these fibers cannot be stimulated). As the temperature rises, pain impulses cease but the cold receptors begin to be stimulated. Then, above about 25° C. the warm end-organs become stimulated while the cold end-organs fade out of the picture. Finally, at around 45° C. the warm endings become nonresponsive once more, but the cold endings begin to respond again and the pain endings also begin to be stimulated.

One can understand from Figure 492, therefore, that a person determines the different gradations of thermal sensations by the relative degrees of stimulation of the different types of endings. For instance, at 20° C. only cold endings are stimulated, whereas at 40° C. only warm endings are stimulated; at 33° C. both cold and warm endings are stimulated, and at 50° C. both cold and pain endings are stimulated. One can understand also from this figure why extreme degrees of cold and extreme degrees of heat can be painful and why both these sensations, when intense enough, may give almost exactly the same quality of sensations —freezing cold and burning hot sensations feel almost alike to the person.

It is particularly interesting that a few areas of the body, such as the tip of the penis, do not contain any warmth receptors; but these areas can experience the sensations of cold with ease and of "hot," which depends on stimulating cold and pain endings, but never the sensation of warmth.

Stimulatory Effects of Rising and Falling Temperature—Adaptation of Thermal Receptors. When a cold receptor is suddenly subjected to an abrupt fall in temperature, it becomes strongly stimulated at first, but this stimulation fades rapidly during the first minute and progressively more slowly during the next half hour or more. In other words, the receptor adapts to a great extent; this is illustrated in Figure 493, which shows that the frequency of discharge of a cold receptor rose approximately four-fold when the temperature fell suddenly from 32° C. to 30° C., but in less than a minute the frequency fell about five sixths of the

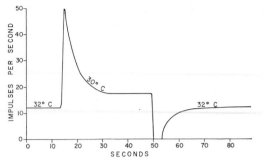

Figure 493. Response of a nerve fiber from a cold receptor following, first, instantaneous change in skin temperature from 32° C. to 30° C. and, second, instantaneous change back to 32° C. Note the adaptation of the receptor and also the higher steady state level of discharge at 30° than at 32°.

way back to the original control value. Later, the temperature was suddenly raised from 30° C. to 32° C. At this point the cold receptor stopped firing entirely for a short period of time, but after adaptation returned to its original control level. Precisely the same type of response occurs in warm receptors.

Thus, it is evident that thermal receptors respond markedly to *changes in temperature* in addition to being able to respond to steady states of temperature, as was depicted in Figure 492. This means, therefore, that when the temperature of the skin is actively falling, a person will feel much colder than he will when the temperature is at exactly the same level but is not at the moment falling. Conversely, if the temperature is actively rising the person will feel much warmer than he would at the same temperature if it were constant.

The response to changes in temperature explains the extreme degree of heat that one feels when he first enters a hot tub of water and the extreme degree of cold he feels when he goes from a heated room to the out-of-doors on a cold day. The adaptation of the thermal receptors explains the ability of the person to become gradually accustomed to his new temperature environment.

However, since the thermal receptors do not adapt all the way to extinction, they still remain stimulated to some extent at the different steady states of temperature. Therefore, even after prolonged exposure to different temperatures, the person can still perceive cold and warmth even though the perceived intensity will not be nearly so great as it is on first exposure.

Mechanism of Stimulation of the Thermal Receptors. Thermal receptors are directly responsive to (1) the temperature of the receptor itself and (2) changes in temperature. On the other hand, they do not respond, as has been claimed in the past, to temperature gradients either between different depths or different areas of the skin. Therefore, we can summarize the excitation of thermal receptors by saying that they are stimulated by the actual temperature of the receptor itself but that the receptor can adapt to a very great extent and, therefore, is responsive to thermal changes as well as to thermal steady states.

It is believed, though not proved, that the thermal receptors are stimulated by changes in their metabolic rates, these changes resulting from the fact that temperature alters the rates of intracellular chemical reactions about 2.3 times for each $10°$ C. change. In other words, thermal detection probably results not from direct physical stimulation but instead from chemical stimulation of the endings as modified by the temperature.

Transmission of Thermal Impulses in the Nervous System

Thermal impulses are transmitted by the smallest myelinated fibers of the peripheral nerves, the delta group with diameters of only 2 to 3 microns. It is also possible that some thermal sensations might be transmitted by type C fibers.

On entering the central nervous system, the thermal fibers travel in the lateral spinothalamic tract. The exact point in the thalamus at which the impulses synapse is not known, but since essentially all other peripheral sensory tracts terminate at least partially in the ventrobasal complex of the thalamus, it is believed that the thermal tracts do too. Then, third order neurons transmit impulses to the cerebral cortex, but, here again, the portion of the cerebral cortex to which the major share of thermal fibers radiate is also unknown. Occasionally, a neuron in the somatic sensory area I has been found by microelectrode studies to be directly responsive to either cold or warm stimuli in specific areas of the skin. Furthermore, it is known that removal of the postcentral gyrus in the human being reduces his ability to distinguish different gradations of temperature. Therefore, it is believed that somatic area I is at least one of the major areas of the cortex concerned with thermal sensations. In the following chapter, it will be noted that there is some reason to believe that somatic area II is more concerned with pain than is somatic area I. Since thermal sensations travel the same pathway with pain sensations up to at least as far as the thalamus, it is also possible that somatic sensory area II might be of considerable importance in temperature perception, though this is yet unexplored.

SOME SPECIAL ASPECTS OF SENSORY FUNCTION

Function of the Thalamus in Somatic Sensations. The major function of the thalamus in tactile and thermal sensations is probably to relay information to the cortex. However, since a person with his somesthetic cortex removed still has a high degree of crude tactile and thermal sensibility, it must be assumed that the thalamus can do much more than simply relay the information. As will be pointed out in the following chapter, the thalamus seems to be even more important in pain sensation.

Cortical Control of Sensory Sensitivity. Almost all the sensory information that enters the cerebrum is relayed through one or another of the thalamic nuclei, including sensory information from the eyes, the ears, the taste receptors, and all the somatic receptors. Furthermore, we must keep in mind that the conscious brain is capable of directing its attention to different segments of the sensory system. This function is believed to be partly achieved through facilitation or inhibition of the relay stations in the thalamus.

But, in addition, "centrifugal" impulses are also transmitted from the cortex to the lower relay stations in the sensory pathways to facilitate or inhibit transmission. For instance, centrifugal pathways that control the sensitivity of the first synapses of both the medial lemniscal and spinothalamic systems have definitely been demonstrated, and similar systems are already known for the visual, auditory, and olfactory systems, which will be elaborated in later chapters. One can readily see that this mechanism also allows the brain to focus its attention on specific

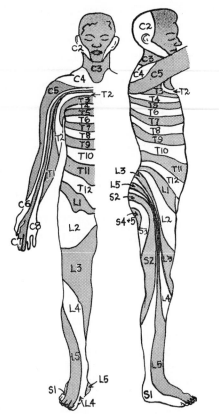

Figure 494. The dermatomes. (Modified from Grinker and Bucy: Neurology. Charles C Thomas.)

types of information, a very important and necessary quality of cerebration.

Segmental Fields of Sensation—The Dermatomes. Each spinal nerve innervates a "segmental field" of the skin called a dermatome. The different dermatomes are illustrated in Figure 494. However, these are shown as if there were a distinct border between the adjacent dermatomes, which is far from true because much overlap exists from segment to segment. Indeed, because of the great overlap, the posterior roots from an entire segment of the spinal cord can frequently be destroyed without causing significant loss of sensation in the skin.

Figure 494 shows that the anal region of the body lies in the dermatome of the most distal cord segment. In the embryo, this is the tail region and is the most distal portion of the body. The legs develop from the lumbar and upper sacral segments rather than from the distal sacral segments, which is evident from the dermatomal map. Obviously, one can use a dermatomal map such as that illustrated in Figure 494 to determine the level in the spinal cord at which various cord injuries may have occurred.

REFERENCES

Adey, W. R.: Somatic aspects of the nervous system. *Ann. Rev. Physiol.*, 19:489, 1957.

Adrian, E. D.: The Physical Background of Perception. Oxford, Clarendon Press, 1947.

Amassian, V. E., Patton, H. D., Woodbury, J. W., Towe, A., and Schlag, J. E.: An interpretation of the surface response in somatosensory cortex to peripheral and interaneal afferent stimulation. *Electroencephalography*, 7:480, 1955.

Autrum, H.: Nonphotic receptors in lower forms. *Handbook of Physiology*, 1:369, 1959.

Benjamin, R. M., and Welker, W. I.: Somatic receiving areas of cerebral cortex of squirrel monkey. *J. Neurophysiol.*, 20:286, 1957.

Bernhard, C. G.: Somatic functions of the nervous system. *Ann. Rev. Physiol.*, 21:325, 1959.

Bishop, G. H.: Neural mechanisms of cutaneous sense. *Physiol. Rev.*, 26:78, 1946.

Chang, H.: The evoked potentials. *Handbook of Physiology*, 1:299, 1959.

Chang, H. T., and Ruch, T. C.: Organization of dorsal columns of spinal cord and their nuclei in spider monkey. *J. Anat.*, 81:140, 1947.

Dell, P., and Bonvallet, M.: Somatic functions of the nervous system. *Ann. Rev., Physiol.*, 18:309, 1956.

Dusser de Barenne, J. G., Carol, H. W., and McCulloch, W. S.: Functional organization of sensory and adjacent cortex of the monkey. *J. Neurophysiol.*, 4:324, 1941.

Frank, K.: Identification and analysis of single unit activity in the central nervous system. *Handbook of Physiology*, 1:261, 1959.

Granit, R.: Receptors and Sensory Perception. New Haven, Yale University Press, 1955.

Hamuy, T. P., Bromiley, R. B., and Woolsey, C. N.: Somatic afferent areas I and II of dog's cerebral cortex. *J. Neurophysiol.*, 19:485, 1956.

Hensel, H., and Witt, I.: Spatial temperature gradient and thermoreceptor stimulation. *J. Physiol.*, 148:180, 1959.

Hunt, C. C.: Relation of function to diameter in afferent fibers of muscle nerves. *J. Gen. Physiol.*, 38: 117, 1954.

Li, C., Cullen, C., and Jasper, H. H.: Laminar microelectrode studies of specific somatosensory cortical potentials. *J. Neurophysiol.*, 19:111, 1956.

Long, R. G.: Modification of sensory mechanisms by subcortical structures. *J. Neurophysiol.*, 22:412, 1959.

Mountcastle, V. B.: Modality and topographic properties of single neurons of cat's somatic sensory cortex. *J. Neurophysiol.*, 20:408, 1957.

Mountcastle, V. B.: Somatic functions of the nervous system. *Ann. Rev. Physiol.*, 20:471, 1958.

Mountcastle, V. B., Davies, P. W., and Berman, A. L.: Response properties of neurons of cat's somatic sensory cortex to peripheral stimuli. *J. Neurophysiol.*, 20:374, 1957.

Orbach, J., and Chow, K. L.: Differential effects of

resections of somatic areas I and II in monkeys. *J. Neurophysiol.*, 22:195, 1959.

Perl, E. R., and Whitlock, D. G.: Potentials evoked in cerebral somatosensory region. *J. Neurophysiol.*, 18:486, 1955.

Pieron, H.: The Sensations: Their Functions, Processes, and Mechanisms. London, Frederick Muller, Ltd., 1952.

Rose, J. E., and Mountcastle, V. B.: Touch and kinesthesis. *Handbook of Physiology*, 1:387, 1959.

Spivy, D. F. and Metcalf, J. S.: Differential effect of medial and lateral dorsal root sections upon subcortical evoked potentials. *J. Neurophysiol.*, 22: 367, 1959.

Towe, A. L., and Amassian, V. E.: Patterns of activity in single cortical units following stimulation of the digits in monkeys. *J. Neurophysiol.*, 21:292, 1958.

Zotterman, Y.: Special senses: thermal receptors. *Ann. Rev. Physiol.*, 15:357, 1953.

Zotterman, Y.: Thermal sensations. *Handbook of Physiology*, 1:431, 1959.

Chapter 49

Pain—Referred Pain, Visceral Pain, and Headache

Many if not most ailments of the body cause pain, and this is the symptom that brings most patients to the doctor. Furthermore, one's ability to diagnose different ailments depends to a great extent upon a knowledge of the different qualities of pain, a knowledge of how pain can be referred from one part of the body to another, how pain can spread in all directions from the painful site, and, finally, what the different causes of pain are. For these reasons, the present chapter is devoted to pain and to the physiologic basis of some of the associated clinical phenomena.

The Purpose of Pain. Pain is a protective mechanism for the body, for it occurs whenever any tissues are being damaged, and it causes the individual to react reflexly to remove the pain stimulus. Even such simple activities as sitting for a long time on the ischia can cause intense damage because blood flow to the skin over weight-bearing points is cut off by the weight of the body. When the skin becomes painful as a result of prolonged ischemia, the person shifts his weight unconsciously. However, a person who has lost his pain sensation entirely, such as after spinal cord injury, fails to feel the pain and therefore fails to shift his weight. This eventually results in ulceration at the areas of pressure unless special measures are taken to protect these areas and to move the patient from time to time.

Qualities of Pain

Pain has been classified into three different types: (1) pricking pain, (2) burning pain, and (3) aching pain.

Pricking pain is felt when a needle is stuck into the skin or when the skin is cut with a knife. It is also often felt when a widespread area of the skin is diffusely but strongly irritated.

Burning pain has many of the characteristics of pricking pain except that the "prickly" points throughout the pained area are not felt. As the term indicates, burning pain feels like a burn.

Aching pain ordinarily is not felt on the surface of the body, but, instead, is a deep pain with varying degrees of annoyance. Aching pain of low intensity in widespread areas of the body can summate into a very disagreeable sensation.

It is not necessary to describe these different qualities of pain in great detail because they are well known to all persons. The real problem—what causes the differences in quality—is yet unsolved. It is possible that pricking pain results from stimulation of tactile nerve endings in the skin as well as of pain endings, and it is possible that it is caused by very intense stimulation of some pain endings without stimulation of others. On the other hand, burning pain seems to result from very diffuse stimulation of all pain endings in a given area. Aching pain, which may be highly localized or very diffuse, is characteristic of certain types of tissues, such as bones, joints, and muscles, in contradistinction to pricking and burning pains, which are more often felt in the skin. Thus, the different qualities of pain are believed to be caused either by different patterns of stimulation of pain nerve endings or by different locations in the body.

to become much more sensitive to sensory stimuli than normally.

It is interesting that pain referred from one part of the body to another usually causes referred hyperesthesia rather than specifically hyperalgesia. In other words, collateral branches apparently spread from pain fibers to pathways that transmit all modalities of sensation. Therefore, when pain impulses referred from an internal organ to a skin area are too weak to cause actual referred pain, the particular skin area is likely to be very sensitive to touch, heat, cold, and pressure, as well as to pain.

Spread of Pain as Intensity Increases

If a sharp needle is placed very lightly against the skin, the pain is localized almost exactly at the point of the needle, but, if the pin is thrust more heavily into the skin, the pain spreads over a larger area, the degree of spread depending on the intensity of the pain stimulus. Indeed, with extreme intensity of stimulus, the pain may spread many centimeters horizontally, or several segments up or down the body, and even to the opposite side of the body. This spread of the pain obviously apprises the individual of greater and greater degrees of tissue damage, but it also makes the localization of pain less exact.

The mechanism by which pain spreads is probably the same as the mechanism of referred pain, for pain fibers on entering the spinal cord branch considerably and spread to many adjacent neurons. When the pain stimulus is extremely strong, then the few presynaptic terminals that branch off from the main pathway and terminate on adjacent neurons are stimulated sufficiently to excite these neurons. This gives the subject the sensation of pain coming not only from the discrete area stimulated but also from the closely associated areas, and the more intense the pain, the more extensive is the spread of pain away from the precise area of stimulus.

Referred Pain Due to Reflex Muscular Spasm

Some types of referred pain are probably caused secondarily by reflex muscular spasm. For instance, pain in a ureter can cause reflex spasm of the lumbar muscles. Indeed, the pain from the ureter itself is sometimes hardly felt at all, but instead almost all the pain results from spasm of the lumbar muscles.

Many back pains and some types of headache also appear to be caused by muscular spasms, the spasm originating reflexly from pain impulses originating elsewhere in the body.

Spasm of a muscle probably causes pain in the following way: Spastic contraction of a muscle causes the muscle to utilize extremely large amounts of nutrient substances, and at the same time such contraction decreases the flow of blood through the muscle because of compression of the vessels. Therefore, muscle ischemia with resultant damage to the muscle is presumably the factor that causes the pain.

VISCERAL PAIN

In clinical diagnosis, pain from the different viscera of the abdomen and chest is one of the few criteria that can be used for diagnosing visceral inflammation, disease, and other ailments. In general, the viscera do not have any sensory receptors for other modalities of sensation besides pain, and visceral pain differs from surface pain in many important aspects. From some viscera almost no pain impulses are ever transmitted. In other viscera, stimuli that cause extensive tissue contusion are painless, but stretching or ischemia is very painful. For instance, crushing or burning the gut is usually entirely painless, but distending the gut or causing spasm of the gut may cause severe pain. The main types of stimuli that can promote visceral pain are *chemical stimuli* such as acids, *ischemia, distention of a hollow viscus, spasm of a hollow viscus,* and *stretching of the ligaments.*

The parietal peritoneum of the abdomen, the parietal pericardium, and the parietal pleura of the thorax are unlike the internal viscera in their responses to pain because these structures respond to pain almost in the same manner as the skin. Crushing, tearing, cutting, burning, or damaging the parietal peritoneum, the parietal pericardium or pleura by any other means initiates extreme burning and pricking pain exactly like the sensations from the surface of the body.

It is probable that some visceral pain sensations can be transmitted to the brain without causing referred pain, but these are usually interpreted as nausea or as deep aches that have no strict localization. Indeed, unless one has been told so, he does not even know that a stomach, a liver, a kidney, etc., exists inside his body. Therefore, the sensorium usually cannot actually localize visceral pain in the organ itself but instead localizes it as referred pain in some specific surface area of the body.

Causes of Visceral Pain

Chemical Stimuli and Ischemia. Leakage of acidic stomach contents or of other digestive enzymes into the abdominal cavity, or even strong acid in the crater of a gastric or duodenal ulcer, can cause intense burning pain. Such pain is probably caused by the direct action of the noxious agents on the free nerve endings.

Ischemia is a type of chemical stimulus that often causes visceral pain. Most physiologists believe that ischemic pain is caused by the large quantities of lactic acid, pyruvic acid, and perhaps a number of phosphoric acid compounds that are released into the tissues during anaerobic tissue metabolism. Regardless of the exact mechanism by which the pain fibers are stimulated, perhaps the most intense abdominal pain ever felt is the ischemic pain resulting from thrombosis of one of the major arteries supplying the gastrointestinal tract.

Ischemic pain is not limited to the viscera, for ischemia of the muscles, the skin, the bones, and almost any other tissue of the body causes typical aching or burning pain.

Distention and Spasm—Cramps. One of the most common causes of pain in the various abdominal organs is distention of a hollow viscus. Distention of a hollow viscus presumably excites the pain endings by overstretching the tissues and damaging them in this way. It is also quite possible that stretching the wall of a hollow viscus collapses the encircling blood vessels so that ischemic pain occurs; or possibly both of these mechanisms occur under different circumstances.

Spasm of the gut also causes pain. This pain probably results from increased metabolism and compressed blood vessels, as probably also occur in spastic skeletal muscles.

The pain resulting from distention and spasm usually causes aching *cramps,* but it can also have a burning quality. The reason for the cramps is that every time a rhythmic contraction of the viscus occurs the pain is exacerbated. The cramps associated with gastroenteritis, constipation, menstruation, parturition, gallbladder disease, ureteral obstruction, etc., are all examples of this type of pain.

Insensitive Viscera

A few visceral areas are almost entirely insentitive to pain of any type. These include the internal structures of the liver and the alveoli of the lungs. Yet, the liver capsule is extremely sensitive both to direct trauma and to stretch, and the bile ducts are sensitive to pain. In the lungs, even though the alveoli are insensitive, the bronchi and the parietal pleura are both very sensitive to pain.

Localization of Visceral Pain

Pain from the different viscera is notably difficult to analyze and to localize for a number of reasons. First, the brain does not know that the different organs exist, and, therefore, any pain that is localized internally can be localized only generally. Second, sensations from the abdomen and thorax are transmitted by two separate pathways to the central nervous system—the *visceral pathway* and the *parietal pathway.* Visceral senations are transmitted via devious routes through the autonomic nervous system, and the sensations are *referred* to surface areas of the body often far from the painful organ. On the other hand, parietal sensations are conducted *directly* from the parietal peritoneum and parietal pleura, and sensations are *localized directly over the painful area.*

The Visceral Pathway for Transmission of Pain. Most of the internal organs of the body are supplied by pain fibers that pass along the visceral sympathetic nerves into the spinal cord and thence up the lateral spinothalamic tract along with the pain fibers from the body's surface. A few visceral pain fibers—those from the distal portions of the colon, from the rectum, and from the bladder—enter the spinal cord through the sacral parasympathetic nerves, and some enter the central nervous system through various cranial nerves. These include fibers in the glossopharyngeal and vagus nerves, which transmit pain from the pharynx, trachea, and upper esophagus; fibers in the fifth, seventh, and ninth nerves, which carry pain from the ear; and fibers in the fifth cranial and second cervical nerves, which transmit pain from inside the cranial vault.

Localization of referred pain transmitted by the visceral pathways. The position in the cord to which visceral afferent fibers pass from each organ depends upon the segment of the body in which the organ developed embryologically. For instance, the heart originated in the neck and upper thorax. Consequently, the heart's visceral pain fibers enter the gray matter of the cord all the way from C-3 down to T-5. The stomach had its origin approximately from the seventh to the ninth thoracic segments of the embryo, and consequently the visceral afferents from the stomach enter the spinal cord between these levels. The gallbladder had its origin almost entirely in the ninth thoracic segment, so that the visceral afferents from the gallbladder enter the spinal cord at T-9.

Because the visceral afferent pain fibers are responsible for transmitting referred pain from the viscera, the location of the referred pain on the surface of the body is in the dermatome of the segment from which the visceral organ was originally derived in the embryo. Some of the areas of referred pain on the surface of the body are shown in Figure 500.

The Parietal Pathway for Transmission of Abdominal and Thoracic Pain. Where skeletal nerves overlie the abdomen or thorax, pain fibers penetrate inward to innervate the parietal peritoneum, parietal pleura, and parietal pericardium. Also, retroperitoneal visceral organs and perhaps por-

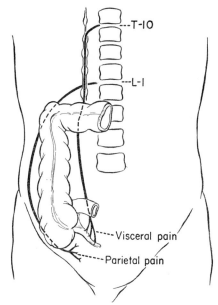

Figure 501. Visceral and parietal transmission of pain from the appendix.

tions of the mesentery are innervated to some extent by parietal pain fibers. The kidney, for instance, is supplied by both visceral and parietal fibers.

Pain from the viscera will frequently be localized in two surface areas of the body because of the dual pathways for transmission of pain. Figure 501 illustrates dual transmission of pain from an inflamed appendix. Impulses pass from the appendix through the sympathetic visceral pain fibers into the sympathetic chain and then into the spinal cord at approximately T-11 or T-12; this pain is referred to an area around the umbilicus. On the other hand, pain impulses also often originate in the parietal peritoneum where the inflamed appendix touches the abdominal wall, and these impulses pass directly through the skeletal nerves into the spinal cord at a level of approximately L-1 or L-2. This pain is localized directly over the irritated peritoneum in the right lower quadrant of the abdomen.

Visceral Pain from Various Organs

Cardiac Pain. Because the heart is insensitive to direct traumatic stimuli, almost all the pain that originates in the heart results from ischemia and is referred mainly to the base of the neck, over the shoulders, over the pectoral muscles, and down the arms. Most frequently, the referred

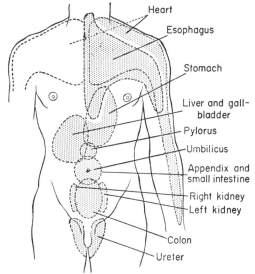

Figure 500. Surface areas of referred pain from different visceral organs.

pain is on the left side rather than on the right—probably because the left side of the heart is much more frequently involved in cardiac disease than is the right side—but occasionally mild referred pains occur on the right side of the body as well as on the left.

The pain impulses are conducted through nerves passing to the middle cervical ganglia, to the stellate ganglia, and to the first four or five thoracic ganglia of the sympathetic chains. Then the impulses pass into the spinal cord through the second, third, fourth, and fifth white rami and respective posterior roots of the skeletal nerves.

Ischemic pain in the heart. Ischemic pain in the heart may result from either physical narrowing of the coronary vessels or temporary spasm of these vessels. In *coronary sclerosis* the coronaries are permanently narrowed, and heart pain may persist continually. Likewise, immediately after a *coronary thrombosis* ischemia of the muscle is almost always great enough to cause persistent and severe pain in the heart.

In the syndrome of *angina pectoris* pain from the heart lasts for only a few minutes, and it seems to occur as a result of coronary spasm during times of overexcitement or other types of stress. Usually, this pain can be relieved by administration of coronary dilator drugs such as amyl nitrite or nitroglycerin.

Angina pectoris also occurs in patients with coronary sclerosis who overexercise and, therefore, overload the heart in relation to its blood supply. This pain cannot be relieved by coronary dilators, but reduced cardiac activity does relieve it.

Direct parietal pain from the heart. When coronary ischemia is extremely severe, such as immediately after a coronary thrombosis, very intense cardiac pain sometimes occurs directly underneath the sternum simultaneously with pain referred to other areas. This direct pain from underneath the sternum is difficult to explain on the basis of the visceral nerve connections. Therefore, it is highly probable that skeletal nerve endings in the parietal pericardium or passing from the heart through the pericardial reflections around the great vessels conduct these direct pains.

In addition to pains from the heart, other sensations may accompany coronary thrombosis. One of these is a tight, oppressive sensation beneath the sternum. The exact cause of this is unknown, but a possible cause of such a feeling is reflex spasm of blood vessels, bronchioles, or muscles in the chest region.

Relief of referred cardiac pain by sympathectomy. To interrupt pain impulses from the heart one can either cut the sympathetic nerves that pass from the heart to the sympathetic chains or, as is usually performed, cut the nerve fibers as they pass through the sympathetic chains into the spinal cord. Relief of cardiac pain can frequently be accomplished simply by removing the sympathetic chain from T-2 through T-5 on only the left side, but sometimes it is necessary to remove the fibers on both sides in order to obtain satisfactory results.

Esophageal Pains. Pain from the esophagus is usually referred to the pharynx, to the lower neck, to the arms, or to midline chest regions beginning at the upper portion of the sternum and ending approximately at the lower level of the heart. Irritation of the gastric end of the esophagus may cause pain directly over the heart, though the pain has nothing whatsoever to do with the heart. Such pain may be caused by cardiospasm with consequent excessive dilatation of the lower esophagus, or it may result from chemical, bacterial, or other types of inflammatory irritations.

Gastric Pain. Pain arising in the fundus of the stomach—usually caused by gastritis—is referred to the anterior surface of the chest either directly above the heart or slightly below the heart. These pains are frequently characterized as burning pains, and they cause the condition known as "heart burn."

Most peptic ulcers are located within one to two inches on either side of the pylorus, in the stomach or in the duodenum, and pain from such ulcers is usually referred to a surface point approximately midway between the umbilicus and the xyphoid process. The origin of ulcer pain is almost undoubtedly chemical, because when the acid juices of the stomach are not allowed to reach the pain fibers in the ulcer crater the pain does not exist. This pain is characteristically intensely burning and the surface area to which it is referred is very small. Because of the quality of this pain and the discreteness of localization, it is possible that the ulcer pain is transmitted by parietal pain fibers rather than by visceral fibers.

Biliary and Gallbladder Pain. Pain from the bile ducts and gallbladder is localized in the midepigastrium almost coincident with pains caused by peptic ulcers. Also, biliary and gallbladder pain is often burning, like that from ulcers, though cramps often occur too. It is possible that that part of the biliary pain referred to the anterior surface of the abdomen is conducted through parietal rather than sympathetic visceral afferent pain fibers.

Biliary disease, in addition to causing pain on the abdominal surface, frequently refers pain to a small area at the tip of the right scapula. This pain is transmitted through sympathetic afferent fibers that enter the ninth thoracic segment of the spinal cord.

Pancreatic Pain. Lesions of the pancreas, such as in acute or chronic pancreatitis in which the pancreatic enzymes eat away the pancreas and surrounding structures, promote intense pain felt in areas both anterior to and behind the pancreas. It should be remembered that many skeletal nerve fibers enter the parietal peritoneum and that the pancreas is located beneath this peritoneum. Therefore, the pain is frequently localized directly behind the pancreas in the back and is very severe and burning in character.

Renal Pain. The kidney, kidney pelvis, and ureters, all being retroperitoneal structures, receive most of their pain fibers directly from skeletal nerves, and, therefore, pain is usually felt directly behind the ailing structure. However, pain occasionally is referred via visceral afferents to the anterior abdominal wall below and about two inches to the side of the umbilicus.

Pain from the bladder is felt directly over the bladder, presumably because the bladder is well innervated by parietal pain fibers. However, pain is also frequently referred into the groin and testicles because the parietal nerve fibers supplying the bladder apparently synapse in the cord in association with fibers from the genital areas.

Uterine Pain. Both parietal and visceral afferent pain may be transmitted from the uterus. The low abdominal cramping pains of dysmenorrhea are always mediated through the sympathetics, and an operation to cut the hypogastric nerves between the hypogastric plexus and the uterus will in almost all instances relieve the pains of true dysmenorrhea. On the other hand, lesions of the uterus that spread into the adnexa around the uterus, or lesions of the fallopian tubes and broad ligaments, usually cause pain in the abdominal wall over the lesion, or the pain is referred to the lower back. This type of pain is conducted over parietal nerve fibers and is usually quite aching or burning in nature rather than resembling the cramping pain of true dysmenorrhea.

SOME CLINICAL ABNORMALITIES OF PAIN AND OTHER SENSATIONS

Paresthesias and Hyperesthesias

Sometimes a sensory nerve tract becomes irritated by a lesion in a peripheral nerve or in the central nervous system. Spontaneous impulses are then transmitted from the irritated nerve fiber all the way to the brain, and a sensation is localized in a peripheral area of the body. Obviously, the irritative lesion can cause any one of the different somesthetic modalities of sensation, depending upon which type of fiber is involved. Such sensations are known as *paresthesias* because they occur spontaneously without any stimulation of the peripheral receptors.

Occasionally the irritative process stimulates the sensory tract only to a mild degree, and this only *facilitates* the higher order neurons without stimulating them. In this instance the central excitatory state of these neurons is raised, and even weak stimuli from the peripheral receptors will elicit a response; the excessively excitable surface area that results is said to be *hyperesthetic*.

Tabes Dorsalis

One of the common lesions caused by syphilis is fibrosis around the dorsal nerve rootlets as they enter the spinal cord. This fibrosis progressively constricts the rootlets, destroying some of the nerve fibers therein. The large myelinated nerve fibers that enter the dorsal columns are easily destroyed by pressure, but the small myelinated fibers and the unmyelinated type C fibers are not so easily destroyed. Therefore, the syphilitic process usually destroys proprioception, localization, two-point discrimination, and vibratory sensations. Most of the sensation of light touch is also lost, through some crude touch sensations transmitted through the ventral spinothalamic tracts sometimes still persist. One of the major effects of the loss of the dorsal columns in tabes dorsalis is *ataxia* because the individual loses all concept of the position of his feet with respect to the rest of his body. Therefore, he walks down the street slapping the soles of his shoes on the ground so that he can hear when his feet have touched. Another major effect in tabes is often severe lancinating pains in different parts of the body—particularly the abdomen—these presumably resulting from fibrous constriction around the sensory rootlets.

Herpes Zoster

Occasionally a virus similar to (and possibly identical with) that of chickenpox infects a dorsal root ganglion, irritating and stimulating the dorsal root neurons and causing a disease known as herpes zoster. Impulses spread into the central nervous system and cause severe paresthetic pain, other types of paresthesias, or hyperesthesias. Usually, only one dorsal root ganglion is infected at a time. Therefore, the paresthesias and hyperesthesias are localized in the entire dermatome subserved by the infected dorsal root ganglion and are not present even to the slightest extent in neighboring dermatomes or on the opposite side of the body.

The impulses that radiate peripherally from the infected ganglion cause several effects at the sensory nerve endings in the dermatome subserved by the dorsal root ganglion. First, vasodilatation may occur, and second, vesicles can appear. The exact cause of these is not known, but impulses spreading peripherally along a sensory nerve fiber probably liberate a humoral substance at the endings that in turn causes the vasodilatation and exudation. Among the possible humoral substance that have been suggested are adenosine phosphate compounds, histamine, and acetylcholine.

The Brown-Séquard Syndrome

Obviously, if the spinal cord is transected entirely, all sensations and motor functions distal to the segment of transection are blocked, but if only one side of the spinal cord is transected, the so-called Brown-Séquard syndrome occurs. The following effects of a unilateral transection could be predicted from a knowledge of the fiber tracts as illustrated in Figure 502: All motor functions are blocked on the side of the transection in all segments below the level of the transection, while only some of the modalities of sensation are lost on the transected side, and others are lost on the opposite side. The sensations of pain, heat, and cold are lost on the opposite side of the body in all dermatomes two to six segments below the level of the transection. The sensations that are transmitted only in the dorsal columns—kinesthetic sensation, vibration sensation—discrete localization, and two-point discrimination—are lost entirely on the side of the transection in all dermatomes below the level of the transection. Touch is impaired on the side of the transection because the principal pathway for transmission of light touch, the dorsal columns, is transected. Yet, "crude touch" still persists because of transmission in the opposite ventral spinothalamic tract.

The Thalamic Syndrome

Occasionally a small branch of the middle cerebral artery supplying the posterior and ventral portions of the thalamus becomes blocked by thrombosis or otherwise. The nuclei of the posterior and ventral portions of the thalamus degenerate, but many of the medial and anterior nuclei

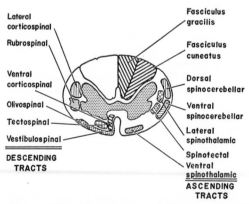

Lateral corticospinal
Rubrospinal
Ventral corticospinal
Olivospinal
Tectospinal
Vestibulospinal

DESCENDING TRACTS

Fasciculus gracilis
Fasciculus cuneatus
Dorsal spinocerebellar
Ventral spinocerebellar
Lateral spinothalamic
Spinotectal
Ventral spinothalamic

ASCENDING TRACTS

Figure 502. Cross-section of the spinal cord, showing principal ascending tracts on the right and principal decending tracts on the left.

of the thalamus remain intact. The patient suffers a series of abnormalities, as follows: First, transmission of almost all sensations from the opposite side of the body occurs because of transient ischemia or destruction of the relay nuclei. Second, transient paralysis of the muscles on the opposite side of the body occurs because of transient ischemia of the pyramidal tract in the posterior limb of the internal capsule, which is partly supplied by the same artery. Third, after the paralysis is over, ataxia may still be evident because of loss of kinesthetic impulses normally relayed through the thalamus to the motor cortex. Fourth, after a few weeks to a few months some sensory perception in the opposite side of the body returns, but strong stimuli are necessary to elicit sensations. The sensations elicited are almost always very painful, sometimes "lancinating," regardless of the type of stimulus applied to the body. Fifth, the individual is likely to perceive many affective sensations of extreme unpleasantness or, occasionally, extreme pleasantness, and these are associated with emotional tirades.

It is especially difficult to explain the emotional and affective phenomena that occur in the thalamic syndrome, but the medial nuclei of the thalamus are not destroyed by thrombosis of the small artery, and it is possible that these nuclei become facilitated and give rise to the affective sensations.

Tic Douloureux

Lancinating pains occur in some persons over one side of the face in part of the sensory distribution area of the fifth or ninth nerves; this phenomenon is called *tic douloureux*. The pains feel like sudden electric shocks, and they may appear for only a few seconds at a time or they may be almost continuous. Often, they are set off by exceedingly sensitive "trigger areas" on the surface of the head, in the mouth, or in the nose. For instance, when the patient swallows a bolus of food, as the food touches a tonsil it might set off a severe lancinating pain in the mandibular portion of the fifth nerve.

The pain of tic douloureux can usually be blocked by cutting the peripheral nerve from the hypersensitive area. The fifth nerve is usually sectioned immediately inside the cranium, where the motor and sensory roots of the fifth nerve can be separated so that the motor portions, which are responsible for many of the jaw movements, are spared while the sensory elements are destroyed. Obviously, this operation leaves the side of the face anesthetic, which in itself may be annoying. Therefore, still another operation is often performed in the medulla for relief of this pain, as follows: The sensory nuclei of the fifth nerve divide into the main sensory nucleus, which is located in the pons, and the spinal sensory nucleus, which descends into the upper part of the spinal cord. It is the spinal nucleus that subserves the function of pain. Therefore, the spinal tract of the fifth nerve can be cut in the medulla as it passes to the spinal nucleus. This blocks pain sensations from the side of the face but does not block the sensations of touch and pressure.

A few patients have tic douloureux in the distribution of the ninth nerve; the sensory fibers in the ninth nerve can also be sectioned for relief of pain.

HEADACHE

Headaches are one of the most baffling problems in the field of clinical medicine because the precise causes of only a few of the different types of headaches are known. Yet, attempts have been made to classify the possible types of headaches and to determine what types of stimuli can be responsible for headache. Headaches are actually referred pain to the surface of the head from the deep structures, and most headaches probably result from pain stimuli arising inside the cranium, but at least some are known to result from pain arising outside the cranium, as will be pointed out below.

Headache of Intracranial Origin

Pain-sensitive Areas in the Cranial Vault. The brain itself is almost totally insensitive to pain. Even cutting or electrically stimulating the somesthetic centers of the cortex usually does not cause pain but causes mild tactile paresthesias on the area of the body represented by the portion of the somesthetic cortex stimulated. Therefore, it is obvious from the outset that much or most of the pain of headache probably is not caused by damage within the brain itself.

On the other hand, *tugging on the venous sinuses, damaging the tentorium,* or *stretching the dura at the base of the brain* can all cause intense pain that is recognized as headache. Also, almost any type of traumatizing, crushing, or stretching stimulus to the *blood vessels of the dura* can cause headache. One of the most sensitive structures of the entire cranial vault is the middle meningeal artery, and neurosurgeons are careful to remain clear of this artery as much as possible when performing brain operations under local anesthesia.

Areas of the Head to Which Intracranial Headache Is Referred. Stimula-

tion of pain receptors in the intracranial vault above the tentorium, including the upper surface of the tentorium itself, initiates impulses in the fifth nerve and, therefore, causes referred headache on the outside of the head in the area supplied by the fifth cranial nerve. This area includes the upper part of the head anterior to the ear, as illustrated by the shaded area of Figure 503. Thus, pain arising above the tentorium causes what is called "frontal headache."

On the other hand, pain impulses from beneath the tentorium enter the central nervous system through the second cervical nerve, which also supplies the scalp behind the ear. Therefore, subtentorial pain stimuli cause "occipital headache" referred to the area shown in Figure 503.

Types of Intracranial Headache. *Headache of meningitis.* One of the most severe headaches of all is that resulting from meningitis, which causes inflammation of all the meninges, including the sensitive areas of the dura and the sensitive areas around the venous sinuses. Such intense damage as this can cause extreme pain stimuli referred over the entire head as headache.

Headache resulting from meningeal trauma. Following a brain operation one ordinarily has very intense headache for several days to several weeks. Though part of this headache may result from the trauma of the brain itself, experiments indicate that most of it is due to meningeal irritation.

Another type of meningeal trauma that almost invariably causes headache is the

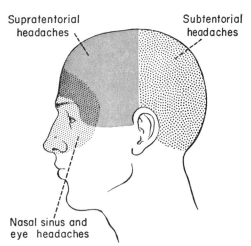

Figure 503. Areas of headache resulting from different causes.

meningeal irritation resulting from brain tumor. Usually, tumor headache is referred to a localized area of the head, the exact area depending on the portion of the meninges affected by the tumor. If it is remembered that any tumor above the tentorium refers its pain to the frontal areas and any tumor below the tentorium refers its pain to the occipital region of the skull, the general location of an intracranial tumor can be predicted from the area of the headache.

Headache due to low cerebrospinal fluid pressure. Removing as little as 20 ml. of fluid from the spinal canal, particularly if the individual remains in the upright position, can cause intense intracranial headache. Removing this quantity of fluid causes the pressure in the cranial vault to fall to a negative value of about —200 mm. of water. This presumably stretches the various dural surfaces and thereby elicits the pain which causes the headache. Also, it is quite possible that the decreased fluid in the cranial vault allows the brain to rub excessively against the vault, thereby causing undue stretch or irritation of the meninges.

On the other hand, increased cerebrospinal fluid pressure in various controlled experiments has not caused headache. Therefore, the headache of meningitis, brain tumor, and other conditions that increase the cerebrospinal fluid pressure is presumably not caused by the high pressure but instead by meningeal irritation.

Migraine headache. Migraine headache is a special type of headache that is generally conceded to result from abnormal vascular phenomena, though the exact mechanism is unknown.

Migraine headaches often begin with various prodromal sensations such as nausea, loss of vision in part of the fields of vision, visual aura, or other types of sensory hallucinations. Ordinarily, the prodromal symptoms begin half an hour to an hour prior to the beginning of the headache itself. Therefore, any theory that explains migraine headache must also explain these prodromal symptoms.

One of the theories of the cause of migraine headaches is that prolonged emotion or tension causes reflex vasospasm of some of the arteries of the head, including arteries that supply the brain itself. The vasospasm theoretically produces ischemia of portions of the brain, and this is responsible for the prodromal symptoms. Then, as a result of the intense ischemia, something happens to the vascular wall to allow it to become flaccid and incapable of maintaining vascular tone for 24 to 48 hours. The blood pressure in the vessels causes them to dilate and pulsate intensely, and it is supposedly the excessive stretching of the walls of the arteries that causes the actual pain of migraine headaches. However, it is possible that diffuse after-effects of ischemia in the brain itself are responsible for this type of headache.

Treatment of the migraine syndrome in the prodromal stage with ergotamine tartrate can in many if not most instances prevent subsequent development of a severe migraine headache. One theory explaining this effect is that ergotamine tartrate dilates the spastic arteries during the prodromal phase of the migraine syndrome. This presumably prevents the ischemia and thereby prevents the damage that leads to secondary vascular dilatation or other pain-producing after-effects; if the ischemia is thus prevented, the 24 to 48 hour period of headache supposedly does not ensue.

Headache due to hypertension. Many people with hypertension have headache, and some persons who have labile blood pressures have headaches when the blood pressure is high but have no headaches when the blood pressure is low. It is possible that the headache resulting from high blood pressure is caused by spasm or rupture of the small vessels or by exudation into the tissue spaces, all of which are known to occur in the retinae of the eyes in hypertension.

Histamine headache. An experimental type of headache that has been produced many times is the so-called "histamine headache." After injection of histamine, rather intense vasodilatation of the large arteries occurs both inside and outside the cranial vault. At the same time the blood pressure of the individual falls at first but rises again in a few minutes. After this sequence of events the arteries of the head—especially the temporal arteries—remain considerably distended and pulsate strongly. Because arterial stretch is one of the causes of pain in the head, it has been surmised that histamine headache is caused by the intense stretch of the vessels.

Alcoholic headache. As many people have experienced, a headache usually follows an alcoholic binge. It is quite possible that alcohol, because it is toxic to tissues, directly irritates the meninges and causes the cerebral pain. Also, it is possible that alcohol causes prolonged vasodilatation of the arteries of the head and that this in turn causes the pain.

Drinking a relatively large quantity of salt water following an alcoholic binge can ameliorate somewhat the headache that usually follows. Therefore, it is quite often assumed that the headache of alcoholism is due to the diuretic effect of alcohol on the kidney, which results in loss of fluid from the extracellular fluid spaces and from the spinal fluid system. This could cause headache in the same manner that removal of fluid by spinal puncture does. However, a similar degree of dehydration resulting from other causes does not usually cause headache. Therefore, if dehydration is one of the causes of headache in alcoholism, it almost certainly is not the only cause. It is possible that many different factors, including direct irritation of the meninges, vascular dilatation, dehydration, and perhaps even edema of the brain, might enter into the headache of alcoholism.

Headache due to constipation. Constipation causes headache in many persons. Because it has been shown that constipation headache can occur in individuals whose spinal cords have been cut, we know that this headache is not caused by nervous impulses from the colon. Therefore, it possibly results from absorbed toxic products or from changes in the circulatory system. Indeed, constipation sometimes does cause temporary loss of plasma into the wall of the gut, and a resulting poor flow of blood to the head could be the cause of the headache.

Extracranial Types of Headache

Extracranial Headache Resulting from Distention of Blood Vessels. In many different types of headache, including histamine headache, toxic headache, and migraine headache, the extracranial arteries may be distended at the same time that the intracranial arteries are distended. On other occasions, distention of extracranial vessels alone occurs without distention of intracranial vessels, and yet headache still results. In these instances occlusive pressure at the base of the distended artery often relieves the headache as the distention of the vessel disappears. The cause of such abnormal vascular distention is unknown, though there is a clinical tendency to implicate histamine or histamine-like substances formed in various parts of the body as the initiating stimulus for the vasodilatation.

Headache Resulting from Muscular Spasm. Emotional tension often causes many of the muscles of the head, including especially those muscles attached to the scalp and also the neck muscles attached to the occiput, to become moderately spastic, and this causes headache.

The pain of the spastic head muscles is referred to the overlying areas of the head, and it gives one almost exactly the same type of headache as do intracranial lesions.

Headache Caused by Irritation of the Nasal and Accessory Nasal Structures. The mucous membranes of the nose and also of all the nasal sinuses are sensitive to pain, but not intensely so. Nevertheless, infection or other irritative processes in widespread areas of the nasal structures usually cause headache that is referred behind the eyes or, in the case of frontal sinus infection, to the frontal surfaces of the scalp, as illustrated in Figure 503. Also, pain from the lower sinuses—such as the maxillary sinuses—can be felt in the face.

Headache Caused by Eye Disorders. Difficulty in focusing one's eyes clearly may cause excessive contraction of the ciliary muscles in an attempt to gain clear vision. Even though these muscles are extremely small, tonic contraction of them can be the cause of the retro-orbital headache that occurs as a result of "eye-strain." Also, excessive attempts to focus the eyes can result in reflex spasm in the various facial muscles and in the extraocular muscles. Tonic spasm in these muscles is also a possible cause of headache.

Occasionally, another cause of headache probably is imbalance of the extraocular muscles. If the tension of the extraocular muscles of the two eyes is not balanced, one or more of the extraocular muscles must work continually and excessively to keep the images of the two eyes fused. furthermore, because of the imbalance of the two eyes, it is presumed that the neural mechanisms for fusion remain in a mild state of confusion most of the time and that this causes all the extraocular muscles to be contracted to a greater extent than would otherwise be necessary. Consequently, tonic contraction of these muscles could result in headache.

A third type of headache originating in the eyes is that which occurs when the eyes are exposed to excessive irradiation by ultraviolet and visible light rays. Watching the sun or the arc of an arc-welder for even a few seconds may result in a headache that lasts from 24 to 48 hours. The headache probably results mainly from "actinic" irritation of the conjunctivae, and the pain is referred to the surface of the head or retro-orbitally. However, focusing very intense light from an arc or the sun on the retina can actually burn the retina, and this could result in headache.

REFERENCES

Bonica, J. J.: Management of Pain. Philadelphia, Lea & Febiger, 1953.

Chapman, W. P., Herrera, R., and Jones, C. M.: A comparison of pain produced experimentally in lower esophagus, common bile duct, and upper small intestine with pain experienced by patients with diseases of biliary tract and pancreas. *Surg., Gynec. & Obst.,* 89:573, 1949.

Cope, Z.: The Early Diagnosis of the Acute Abdomen. New York, Oxford University Press, 1928.

Friedman, A. P. (ed.), and Merritt, H. H.: Headache: Diagnosis & Treatment. Philadelphia, F. A. Davis Co., 1959.

Gerard, R. W.: Physiology of pain: abnormal neuron states in causalgia and related phenomena. *Anesthesiology,* 12:1, 1951.

Guyton, A. C., and Reeder, R. C.: Pain and contracture in poliomyelitis. *Arch. Neurol. & Psychiat.,* 63:954, 1950.

Hardy, J. D.: The nature of pain. *J. Chronic Dis.,* 4:22, 1956.

Hardy, J. D.: Wolff, H. G., and Goodell, H.: Pain Sensations and Reactions. Baltimore, Williams & Wilkins Co., 1952.

Judovich, B., and Bates, W.: Pain Syndromes. 4th ed., Philadelphia, F. A. Davis Co., 1954.

Lewis, T.: Pain. New York, The Macmillan Co., 1942.

Leyton, N.: Migraine and Periodic Headache. 2nd ed., Springfield, Illinois. Charles C Thomas, 1955.

Lipkin, M., Bailey, O., and Hardy, J. D.: Effect of ultraviolet irradiation upon the cutaneous pain threshold. *J. Appl. Physiol.,* 7:683, 1955.

Melzack, R., Stotler, W. A., and Livingston, W. K.: Effects of discrete brainstem lesions in cats on perception of noxious stimulation. *J. Neurophysiol.,* 21:353, 1958.

Moench, L. G.: Headache. 2nd ed., Chicago, Year Book Publishers, 1951.

Nakao, H., and Koella, W. P.: Influence of nociceptive stimuli on evoked subcortical and cortical potentials in cat. *J. Neurophysiol.,* 19:187, 1956.

Pottenger, F. M.: Symptoms of Visceral Disease. 7th ed., St. Louis, C. V. Mosby Co., 1953.

Rinzler, S. H.: Cardiac Pain. Springfield, Illinois, Charles C Thomas, 1951.

Ryan, R. E.: Headache, 2nd ed., St. Louis, C. V. Mosby Co., 1957.

Sweet, W. H.: Pain. *Handbook of Physiology,* 1:459, 1959.

White, J. C., and Sweet, W. H.: Pain: Its Mechanisms and Neurosurgical Control. Springfield, Illinois, Charles C Thomas, 1955.

Wolff, H. G.: Headache and Other Pain. New York, Oxford University Press, 1950.

Wolff, H. G.: Pain. 2nd ed., Springfield, Illinois, Charles C Thomas, 1958.

Wolff, H. G., and Hardy, J. D.: On the nature of pain. *Physiol. Rev.,* 27:167, 1947.

Zoll, P. M., Wessler, C., and Blubgart, H. L.: Angina pectoris. *Am. J. Med.,* 11:331, 1951.

Chapter 50

The Proprioceptor Sensations:

Kinesthesia, Muscle Sense, and Equilibrium

The proprioceptor sensory organs apprise the nervous system of physical states, including (1) the movement of joints, (2) the positions of joints, (3) the tensions of muscles, (4) the tensions of tendons, and (5) the orientation of the body with respect to the pull of gravity or other acceleratory forces. The sensations from the joints, muscles, and tendons are all somatic sensations and have certain characteristics in common with the other peripheral sensations which have been considered in the last two chapters. The vestibular sensations, which detect the pull of gravity and the forces of acceleration, originate in the vestibular apparatuses which transmit impulses into the vestibular portions of the eighth nerves and are closely associated with the inner ears. These sensations are considered in this chapter because their central representations are not greatly different from those of many of the peripheral sensations and because they operate in very close association with the somatic proprioceptor sensations to regulate skeletal muscle tone and equilibrium of the body.

KINESTHETIC SENSATIONS

The term *kinesthesia* means conscious recognition of the orientation of the different parts of the body with respect to each other as well as of the rates of movement of the different parts of the body. These functions are subserved principally by extensive sensory endings in the joint capsules and ligaments.

The Kinesthetic Receptors. Three major types of nerve endings have been described in the joint capsules and ligaments about the joints. (1) By far the most abundant of these is a spray type of ending similar to *Ruffini's end-organ,* which was illustrated in Figure 462 of Chapter 46. These endings are stimulated strongly when the joint is suddenly moved; they adapt slightly at first but hardly at all thereafter. (2) A second type of ending resembling the Golgi tendon stretch receptor is found particularly in the ligaments about the joints. Though far less numerous than the Ruffini type end-organs, they have almost exactly the same response properties. (3) End-organs similar to but slightly different from the usual Pacinian corpuscles are also found in the tissues around joints. These adapt rapidly and presumably detect the *rate of movement* at the joint.

Stimulation of the joint receptors. A different set of joint receptors is stimulated by different degrees of angulation of the joint. For instance, if the forearm is flexed, one set of receptors will be stimulated, whereas another set will be stimulated when the forearm is fully extended. At intermediate points between these two extremes, still additional sets of receptors are stimulated. Figure 504 illustrates the excitation of seven different nerve fibers leading from separate joint receptors in the capsule of a cat's knee joint. Note that at 180 degrees angulation one of the receptors is being stimulated; then at 150 degrees still another is stimulated; at 140 degrees two are stimulated,

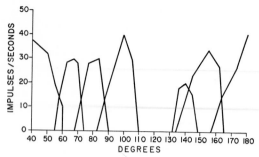

Figure 504. Responses of seven different nerve fibers from knee joint receptors in a cat. (Modified from Skogland: *Acta Physiol. Scandinav.* Suppl. 124, 36:1, 1956.)

and so forth. The information from these joint receptors continually apprises the central nervous system of the momentary position of the joint. These same receptors are stimulated to a still greater extent during actual movement at the joint, and the modified Pacinian receptors are also stimulated during movement. Thus, the necessary kinesthetic information for detection of joint movement is also transmitted into the central nervous system.

Transmission of the Kinesthetic Sensations in the Peripheral and Central Nervous System. Kinesthetic information is transmitted in the beta, gamma, and delta type A fibers. The beta fibers innervate the modified Pacinian corpuscles around the joints and therefore probably transmit information of *movement* in the joints, which obviously requires very rapid transmission when rapid movements are occurring. On the other hand, the gamma and delta fibers probably transmit information concerning the steady state conditions of the joint and, therefore, are perhaps more concerned with the momentary angulation of the joints than with movement.

In the central nervous system, the kinesthetic sensations are transmitted in the medial lemniscal system along with tactile sensations—that is, by first order neurons up the dorsal columns of the cord to the cuneate and gracile nuclei, then by second order neurons to the ventrobasal complex of the thalamus, and by third order neurons to somatic area I in the postcentral gyrus of the cerebral cortex. The somesthetic cortex is responsible for continually monitoring the positions of all parts of the body. Widespread damage to this area greatly dimin-

ishes one's awareness of the orientation of the different parts of his body.

MUSCLE AND TENDON SENSATIONS

The muscle and tendon sensations, sometimes called *muscle sense,* are concerned with (a) the degrees of contraction of the muscles, (b) the degrees of stretch of the muscles, and (c) the amounts of tension on the tendons. These sensations function either entirely or almost entirely subconsciously, for electrophysiological studies have failed to demonstrate transmission of any signals from the muscle proprioceptors to the conscious areas of the brain. Yet, tremendous amounts of information are transmitted from the muscles and tendons to (a) the spinal cord and (b) the cerebellum to cause reflexes associated with equilibrium, posture, and "damping" of movements. The two types of sensory organs responsible for muscle and tendon sensations are the *muscle spindle* and the *Golgi tendon apparatus.*

The Muscle Spindle and Its Excitation

The physiologic organization of the muscle spindle is illustrated in Figure 505. Each spindle is built around three to ten very small *intrafusal muscle fibers* that are pointed at their ends and attach to the surrounding skeletal muscle fibers. Midway between the ends of the intrafusal fibers is a heavily nucleated area that has lost all cross striations and cannot contract, but instead becomes stretched whenever the entire spindle is stretched. Entwined around the central area is a nerve ending called the *annulospiral ending,* and from this a large type A nerve fiber, averaging 16 microns in diameter, passes into the sensory roots of the spinal cord. On each side of the nucleated area of the muscle spindle is usually found

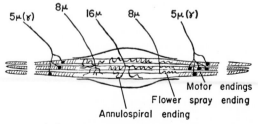

Figure 505. Functional anatomy of the muscle spindle.

another ending called the *flower-spray ending*, and this excites another sensory nerve fiber much smaller than that excited by the annulospiral ending, averaging approximately 8 microns in diameter. Stretch of the spindle also excites this nerve ending, though far more stretch is required.

The intrafusal muscle fibers of the spindle are innervated by small *gamma* motor nerve fibers which are distinct from the large alpha motor fibers to the extrafusal skeletal muscle fibers. It should be noted particularly that the intrafusal fibers cannot contract in their middle portion where the annulospiral and flower spray nerve endings attach but instead contract only in their two end portions. In fact, contraction of these end portions actually stretches the central portion of the spindle.

Stimulation of the Muscle Spindle. The muscle spindle can be stimulated in either of the following two ways: (1) It can be stimulated by stretch of the entire muscle belly, which also stretches the muscle spindle. (2) It can be stimulated by contraction of the intrafusal fibers of the spindle, which contracts the two ends of the spindle but stretches the middle. In other words, the stimulus that normally excites the muscle spindle is the stretch of its middle portion whether this be caused by stretching of the entire muscle or by stimulation of the intrafusal fibers.

Very minute intensities of stretch will excite the annulospiral ending, but considerable additional stretch is required to excite the flower-spray ending. This difference is very important because stretch of the annulospiral ending causes reflex excitation of the homonymous muscle, while excitation of the flower-spray ending, which occurs only at high degrees of stretch, reflexly inhibits the muscle.

Function of the Muscle Spindle. The principal functions of the muscle spindle are to initiate spinal cord and cerebellar reflexes, which will be discussed in detail in Chapters 56 and 58. However, the *receptor* functions of the muscle spindle will be presented here very briefly.

Detection of muscle length and rate of change in muscle length. Very rapid stretching of the muscle will cause marked stimulation of the annulospiral endings of the muscle spindle. However, this excessive stimulation lasts for only a few seconds before it settles down to a much lower steady state. The steady state impulses transmit information to the central nervous system, depicting the *steady length* of the muscle, while the intense instantaneous excitation transmits information depicting the *rate of change* of this length. To express this another way, the muscle spindle responds instantaneously to *phasic* changes in muscle length, but it adapts within a few seconds, and its degree of stimulation thereafter is determined by the *static* length of the muscle.

Transmission of information to the cerebellum. When muscles are stretched, information is immediately transmitted from the muscle spindles directly to the cerebellum. This information is used to help control the damping mechanism of the cerebellum that prevents "overshoot" of muscular contractions and keeps the different muscular contractions throughout the body coordinated. However, these functions of the muscle spindles in relation to the cerebellum yet represent a poorly explored field, as will be discussed in Chapter 58.

Control of Muscle Spindle Excitability by the Gamma Efferent Fibers. It was pointed out above that stimulation of the gamma efferent fibers to the muscles causes contraction of the ends of the intrafusal fibers of the muscle spindles and that this in turn stretches the central portions of the spindles where the sensory nerve receptors attach. Because of this, gamma efferent stimulation increases the number of impulses transmitted from the muscle spindle. Conversely, reduction in the degree of gamma efferent excitation reduces the excitability of the muscle spindle.

This gamma efferent control of the muscle spindle provides a means by which the central nervous system can regulate the response of the muscle spindle under different conditions. For instance, stimulation of the reticular substance in the mesencephalon and diencephalon increases the activity of the gamma efferent fibers and thereby increases the excitability of the muscle spindles. This in turn reflexly increases the tone of the respective muscles, as will be explained in Chapter 56. Conversely, stimulation of certain areas in the cerebellum and reticular substance of the pons and medulla reduces the degree of stimulation of the afferent fibers and thereby reduces the activity of the muscle spindles, thus decreasing the tone of the muscles.

The Golgi Tendon Apparatus and Its Excitation

The Golgi tendon apparatus, which is illustrated in Figure 506, lies between the fibers of the muscle tendons and is stimulated in only one way, by tension on the tendon. The major difference between the function of the Golgi tendon apparatus and of the muscle spindle is that the spindle detects changes in muscle *length*, while the Golgi tendon apparatus detects muscle *load*.

However, there is also a difference between the sensitivity of the muscle spindle and of the Golgi tendon apparatus. The annulospiral ending of the muscle spindle responds to very minute changes in muscle stretch while the Golgi tendon apparatus (and flower-spray ending of the muscle spindle) are far less responsive, and extreme loads on the tendons can occur before the Golgi tendon apparatus becomes maximally stimulated.

The Golgi tendon apparatus is like the flower-spray ending in still another aspect: both these endings initiate inhibitory reflexes in the muscle. These reflexes normally are very weak, but, if the tension on the tendon becomes great enough that it might actually cause damage to the muscle, then the inhibitory reflex originating in the Golgi tendon apparatus (and possibly to some extent that originating in the flower-spray endings) relaxes the muscle and prevents the excessive overload from causing muscular damage.

Transmission of Impulses from the Muscle Spindle and Golgi Tendon Apparatus

Impulses are transmitted from the annulospiral receptor of the muscle spindle and

from the Golgi tendon apparatus in the largest known sensory nerve fibers, averaging approximately 16 microns in diameter. However, the fibers that transmit the impulses from the flower-spray endings are considerably smaller, averaging about 8 microns.

In the spinal cord, impulses from the muscle spindles pass directly to the anterior motor neurons of the cord to cause excitatory reflexes. But, in the case of the Golgi tendon apparatus, at least a single inhibitory neuron is believed to be intercalated between the input neuron and the anterior motor neuron so that this circuit can cause an inhibitory reflex to the muscle instead of an excitatory reflex.

Fibers from the muscle spindles and Golgi tendon apparatuses also pass to *Clarke's cells* in the dorsal horns of the spinal cord, as shown in Figure 507, and from here impulses pass upward in second order neurons through the *dorsal* and *ventral spinocerebellar tracts* to the anterior cerebellum. The impulses from the muscle spindles are transmitted in the dorsal spinocerebellar tracts and from the Golgi tendon apparatuses in the ventral spinocerebellar tracts. It is especially important that the nerve fibers in these tracts are the largest in the spinal cord and that velocities of impulses in them have been

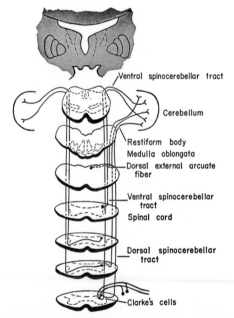

Figure 507. Transmission of muscle spindle and Golgi tendon impulses in the central nervous system.

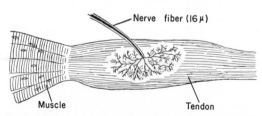

Figure 506. Anatomy of a Golgi tendon apparatus.

measured as great as 130 meters per second. This high velocity of transmission is in keeping with the general functions of the cerebellum to help coordinate rapid movements of the different parts of the body. Obviously, if the cerebellum is to do this it must continually obtain proprioceptive information directly from the peripheral parts of the body without any significant delay.

Lack of Transmission of Information from the Muscle Spindles and Golgi Tendon Apparatuses to the Somesthetic Cortex. Thus far microelectrode recordings from the somesthetic cortex or from the relay nuclei in the thalamus have revealed no excitation following stimulation of either the muscle spindles or the Golgi tendon apparatuses. Therefore, it is believed that these two types of receptors are strictly concerned with subconscious reflex activities of the muscles that subserve principally posture, equilibrium, and "damping" of muscular contractions.

However, this raises the question, how does our conscious nervous system perceive differences in weights of objects if tension on the muscles cannot be detected? Perhaps this is accomplished in other ways such as (a) from information transmitted by pressure receptors in the peripheral parts of the body or (b) from the amount of motor energy that must be expended by the motor areas of the brain to lift or to move a particular weight.

Pain Nerve Fibers in Muscles

Before leaving the different muscle sensations, we must note that many free nerve endings are also present in muscles. Since it is known that ischemia and certain other types of stimuli can cause pain in muscles, it is assumed that these free endings are mainly if not entirely pain endings. It is also possible that they can detect muscle fatigue as well. Impulses from these endings are transmitted in type C fibers to the spinal cord and are presumably then transmitted upward in the spinothalamic tracts along with pain fibers from other sources.

VESTIBULAR SENSATIONS AND THE MAINTENANCE OF EQUILIBRIUM

Equilibrium is controlled especially by the vestibular apparatuses, though other mechanisms, including vision and proprioceptive impulses from the limbs, aid in this control. Equilibrium is maintained by automatic shift of tone in the muscles from one side of the body to the other side or forward and backward in accordance with various signals arriving from the vestibular apparatus, the eyes, and the proprioceptors. These signals apprise the central nervous system of the position of the body with respect to gravity and with respect to other forces. It is quite appropriate that the vestibular apparatus, which is the most important organ of equilibrium, is located in close approximation with the reticular nuclei of the brain stem, because the vestibular apparatus performs its function of maintaining equilibrium by controlling the interplay between respective portions of these nuclei.

The Vestibular Apparatus

The top of Figure 508 illustrates the membranous labyrinth, which is composed mainly

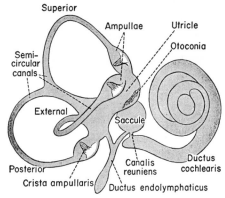

MEMBRANOUS LABYRINTH

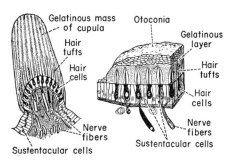

CRISTA AMPULLARIS AND MACULA

Figure 508. The membranous labyrinth, and organization of the crista ampullaris and the macula. (From Goss: Gray's Anatomy of the Human Body. Lea & Febiger; and modified from Kolmer by Buchanan: Functional Neuroanatomy. Lea & Febiger.)

of the cochlear duct, the three semicircular canals, and two large chambers known as the utricle and the saccule. The cochlear duct is concerned with hearing and has nothing to do with the function of equilibrium; the saccule is concerned with hearing in some lower animals but probably is non-functional in the human being. However, the *utricle* and the *semicircular canals* are especially important for maintaining equilibrium and are collectively called the *vestibular apparatus.*

The Utricle. Located in the utricle is the *macula,* which is covered by a gelatinous layer in which many small bony masses known as *otoconia* are embedded. Also in the macula are many *hair cells,* which project hair tufts up into the gelatinous layer. Around these hair cells are entwined sensory axons of the vestibular nerve so that bending the hair tufts to one side transmits impulses to apprise the central nervous system of the relative position of the otoconia in the gelatinous mass over the macula. Therefore, it is the weight of the otoconia compressing the hair tufts that provides signals from the utricle, and these signals in turn are transmitted by appropriate nerve tracts to the brain, thence controlling equilibrium.

The Semicircular Canals. In the *ampullae* of the semicircular canals, as illustrated in Figure 508, are small crests, each called a *crista ampullaris,* and on top of the crest is another gelatinous mass known as the *cupula.* Into the cupula are projected hair tufts from hair cells in the ampullary crest, and these hair cells in turn are connected to sensory nerve fibers that pass into the vestibular nerve. Bending the cupula to one side or the other stimulates the hair cells and sends appropriate signals through the vestibular nerve to apprise the central nervous system of fluid movement in the respective canal.

The three semicircular canals in each vestibular apparatus, known respectively as the superior, the posterior, and the external semicircular canals, are arranged at right angles to each other so that they represent all three planes in space. When the head is bent forward at approximately 30 degrees, the two external semicircular canals are located approximately horizontal with respect to the surface of the earth. The superior

canals are then located in vertical planes that project *forward and 45 degrees outward,* and the posterior canals are also in vertical planes but project *backward and 45 degrees outward.* Thus, the superior canal on each side of the head is in a plane parallel to that of the posterior canal on the opposite side of the head, whereas the two external canals on the two sides are located in approximately the same plane.

Neuronal Connections of the Vestibular Apparatus with the Central Nervous System. Figure 509 illustrates the central connections of the vestibular nerve. Most of the vestibular nerve fibers end in the vestibular nuclei, which are located approximately at the junction of the medulla and the pons, but some of the fibers pass through the vestibular nuclei without synapsing, ending in the flocculonodular lobes of the cerebellum and to a lesser extent in other regions of the cerebellum and brain stem. The fibers that end in the vestibular nuclei synapse with ganglia that in turn send fibers into the flocculonodular lobe of the cerebellum, the cortex of other portions of the cerebellum, the vestibulospinal tract, the medial longitudinal fasciculus, and to other areas of the brain stem.

The primary pathway for the reflexes of equilibrium begins in the *vestibular nerves,* passes next to the *vestibular nuclei,* and then to the *reticular nuclei* of the brain stem. The reticular nuclei in turn control the interplay between facilitation and inhibition of the extensor muscles, thus automatically controlling equilibrium.

However, it should be noted that destruction of the *flocculonodular lobes* of the cerebellum causes essentially the same effects on equilibrium as loss of the semicircular canals. Therefore, equilibrium

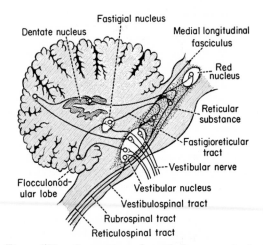

Figure 509. Connections of vestibular nerves in the central nervous system.

reflexes initiated in the semicircular canals undoubtedly require function of the flocculonodular lobes of the cerebellum as well as of the reticular nuclei of the brain stem. This is in keeping with the usual function of the cerebellum to coordinate very rapid body movements, for the semicircular canals are also concerned with equilibrium during *rapid changes in direction of* motion and not with equilibrium under static conditions, as will be pointed out in the subsequent sections.

Function of the Utricle in the Maintenance of Static Equilibrium

Gravitational pull on the *otoconia* causes them to press continually on the *macular hair tufts* in the utricles, and this constantly apprises the central nervous system of the position of the head with respect to the direction of gravitational pull. The density of the otoconia is almost three times that of the surrounding fluid and tissues, and because of this they bend the hair tufts forward when the head leans forward. Likewise, leaning the head to one side bends the hair tufts in that same direction.

It is especially important that the different hair cells are orientated in several different directions in the maculae so that at different positions of the head, different ones of the hair cells become stimulated. The "patterns" of stimulation of the different hair cells apprise the nervous system of the position of the head with respect to the pull of gravity. In turn, the reticular nuclei reflexly excite the appropriate muscles to attain proper equilibrium.

Very little is known about the actual mechanism by which the hair cells are stimulated except that bending the hair in the proper direction causes the cell to transmit a continual series of impulses. If the hair is bent in one direction, the rate of impulses increases, whereas, if the hair is bent in the opposite direction, the rate of impulses decreases.

Detection of Linear Acceleration by the Utricle. When the body is suddenly thrust forward, the otoconia, which have greater inertia than the surrounding fluids, fall backward on the hair tufts, and information of mal-equilibrium is sent into the nervous centers, causing the individual to feel as if he were falling backward. This automatically causes him to lean his body forward; the forward lean then shifts the otoconia an-

teriorly. Thus, the body automatically leans farther and farther forward until the anterior shift of the otoconia exactly equals the tendency for the otoconia to fall backward because of the linear acceleration. At this point, the nervous system detects a sense of equilibrium and therefore shifts the body no farther forward. As long as the degree of linear acceleration remains constant and the body is maintained in this forward leaning position, the person will fall neither forward nor backward. Thus, the otoconia operate to maintain equilibrium during linear acceleration in exactly the same manner as they operate in static equilibrium.

It should be pointed out that the otoconia do not operate for the detection of linear *motion.* When a runner first begins to run, he must lean very far forward to keep from falling over backward, but once he has achieved running speed, he would not have to lean forward at all if he were running in a vacuum. When running in air he leans forward to manitain equilibrium only because of the air resistance against his body, and in this instance it is not the otoconia that make him lean but the pressure of the air acting on pressure end-organs in the skin, which initiate the appropriate equilibrium adjustments to prevent falling.

Detection of Centrifugal Force by the Utricle. If a person in an airplane goes around and around in a deep bank, centrifugal force will push him against the seat of the plane. This force, like gravity, also presses the otoconia downward against the hair tufts in the utricles. Therefore, the centrifugal force is perceived in exactly the same manner as either gravitational or linear acceleratory forces, and, if the person were standing up in the airplane, it would still be the utricles that would control the necessary equilibrium adjustments of his postural muscles.

The Semicircular Canals and Their Detection of Angular Acceleration

When the head suddenly begins to rotate in any direction, the endolymph in the membranous semicircular canals, because of its inertia, tends to remain stationary while the semicircular canals themselves turn. This causes relative fluid flow in the canals in a direction opposite to the rotation of the head. Figure 510 illustrates an *ampulla* of one of the semicircular canals, showing the

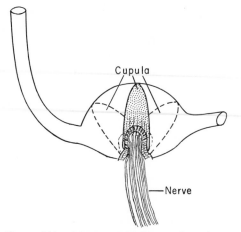

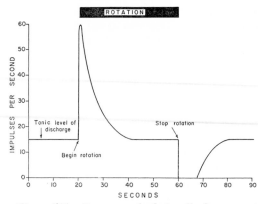

Figure 511. Response of a hair cell when a semicircular canal is stimulated first by rotation and then by stopping rotation.

Figure 510. Movement of the cupula and its embedded hairs during rotation first in one direction and then in the opposite direction.

cupula and its embedded hairs bending in the direction of fluid movement. And Figure 511 illustrates the discharge from a single hair cell in the crista ampularis when an animal is rotated for 40 seconds, showing that (1) even when the cupula is in its resting position the hair cell emits a tonic discharge of approximately 15 impulses per second; (2) when the animal is rotated, the hairs bend to one side and the rate of discharge increases very greatly; and (3) with continued rotation, the discharge of the hair cell gradually subsides over a period of about 20 seconds. The reason for this adaptation of the receptor is that within a second or more of rotation friction in the semicircular canal causes the endolymph to rotate as rapidly as the semicircular canal itself; then in an additional 15 to 20 seconds the cupula slowly returns to its resting position in the middle of the ampulla. Then, when the rotation suddenly stops exactly the opposite effects take place: the endolymph continues to rotate while the semicircular canal stops. This time the cupula is bent in the opposite direction, causing the hair cell to stop discharging entirely. After another few seconds, the endolymph stops moving, and the cupula returns gradually to its resting position in about 20 seconds, thus allowing the discharge of the hair cells to return to its normal tonic level as shown to the right in Figure 511.

It is immediately evident, therefore, that the semicircular canals are stimulated for about 20 seconds after the head begins to rotate in one direction or another. Furthermore, this receptor will respond to rotation in any plane—horizontal, sagittal, or coronal —for in each plane the fluid movement in one or more pairs of semicircular canals will always lag behind. However, once a steady state of rotation has been achieved, within another few seconds the semicircular canals will no longer emit any impulses. In summary, then, the semicircular canals detect the *rate of change* of rotation, which is called *angular acceleration*.

Angular Acceleration Required to Stimulate the Semicircular Canals. The angular acceleration required to stimulate the semicircular canals in the human being varies from 0.2 degrees per second per second up to as high as 2 degrees per second per second, or an average of about 1 degree per second per second. In other words, when one begins to rotate, his velocity of rotation must be as much as 1 degree per second by the end of the first second, 2 degrees per second by the end of the second second, 3 degrees per second by the end of the third second, and so forth, in order for him barely to detect that he is beginning to rotate.

The "Predictive" Function of the Semicircular Canals in the Maintenance of Equilibrium. Since the semicircular canals do not detect that the body is off balance in the forward direction, in the side direction, or in the backward direction, one might at first ask, what is the function of the semicircular canals in the maintenance of equilibrium? All they detect is that the person's head is beginning to rotate or to stop rotating in one direction or another. The function of the semicircular canals therefore could not possibly be to maintain static equilibrium nor to maintain equilibrium during linear acceleration or when the person is exposed to steady centrifugal forces. Yet, it is well known that loss of function of the semicircular canals causes a person to have very poor equilibrium, especially when he is performing rapid and intricate body movements. We can perhaps explain the function of the semicircular canals best by the following illustration. If a person is running forward very rapidly and then suddenly begins to turn to one side, he will fall off balance a second or so later unless appropriate corrections are made ahead of time. But, unfortunately, the utricle will not detect that he is off balance until *after* this has occurred. On the other hand, the semicircular canals will have already detected that the person is beginning to turn, and this information can easily apprise the central nervous system of the fact that the person *will* fall off balance within the next second or so unless some correction is made. In other words, the semicircular canals *predict ahead of time* that mal-equilibrium is going to occur even before it occurs and thereby cause the equilibrium centers to make appropriate adjustments. In this way, the person need not fall off balance before he begins to correct the situation.

Removal of the flocculonodular lobes of the cerebellum prevents normal function of the semicircular canals but does not prevent normal function of the macular receptors. It is especially interesting in this connection that the cerebellum serves as a "predictive" organ for most of the other rapid movements of the body as well as those having to do with equilibrium. These other functions of the cerebellum will be discussed in Chapter 58.

Other Factors Concerned with Equilibrium

Neck Proprioceptors. The vestibular apparatus detects the orientation and movements only of the head. Therefore, it is essential that the nervous centers also receive appropriate information depicting the orientation of the head with respect to the body and the orientation of the different parts of the body with respect to each other. This information is transmitted from the proprioceptors of the neck and body either directly into the reticular nuclei of the brain stem or by way of the cerebellum and thence into the reticular nuclei.

By far the most important proprioceptive information needed for the maintenance of equilibrium is that derived from the neck proprioceptors, for this apprises the nervous system of the orientation of the head with respect to the body. Indeed, experiments have shown that when the head is bent in one direction or the other, impulses from the neck proprioceptors keep the vestibular apparatuses from giving the person a sense of mal-equilibrium by exactly opposing the impulses transmitted from the vestibular apparatuses. However, *when the entire body* is angulated to a new position with respect to gravity, the impulses from the vestibular apparatuses *are not opposed* by the neck proprioceptors; therefore, the person in this instance does perceive a change in his state of equilibrium.

Proprioceptive and Exteroceptive Information from Other Parts of the Body. Proprioceptive information from other parts of the body besides the neck is also necessary for the maintenance of equilibrium because appropriate equilibrium adjustments must be made whenever the body is angulated in the chest or abdomen or elsewhere. Presumably, all this information is algebraically added in the reticular substance of the brain stem, thus causing appropriate adjustments to be made in the postural muscles.

Also important in the maintenance of equilibrium are several types of exteroceptive sensations. For instance, pressure sensations from the foot pads can tell one (a) whether his weight is distributed equally between his two feet and (b) whether his weight is more forward or backward on his feet. Obviously, this information can also help to correct states of mal-equilibrium.

Another instance in which exteroceptive information is necessary for maintenance of equilibrium occurs when a person is running very fast. The air pressure against the front of his body signals that an opposing force is acting against the body in a direction different from that caused by gravitational pull; as a result, the person leans forward to oppose this.

Importance of Visual Information in the Maintenance of Equilibrium. After complete destruction of the vestibular apparatuses, and even after loss of most proprioceptive information from the body, a person can still use his visual mechanisms to a high degree of efficiency for maintaining equilibrium. Visual images help the person maintain equilibrium simply by visual detection of the upright stance. Also, very slight linear or angular movement of the body instantaneously shifts the visual images on the retina, and this information is relayed to the equilibrium centers. In this respect the optic information is similar to that from the semicircular canals and can help the equilibrium centers predict that the person will fall off balance before this actually occurs if appropriate adjustments are not immediately made. Many persons with complete destruction of the vestibular apparatus will have almost normal equilibrium as long as their eyes are open and as long as they perform all motions very slowly. But, either in the case of very rapid movements or closure of the eyes, equilibrium is immediately lost.

Conscious Perception of Equilibrium. A cortical center for conscious perception of the state of equilibrium has been found in man to lie in the upper portion of the temporal lobe in close association with the primary cortical area for hearing. The sensations from the vestibular apparatuses, from the neck proprioceptors, and from most of the other proprioceptors are undoubtedly first integrated in the equilibrium centers of the brain stem before being transmitted to the cerebral cortex. And, it is well known that other factors besides impulses from the vestibular apparatus and from the proprioceptors can enter into a person's conscious perception of equilibrium. For instance, loud noises and rapidly moving objects in the field of vision can greatly effect the sense of balance. Also, various pathologic processes in the vestibular apparatuses or in the vestibular neuronal circuits often affect the equilibrium sensations. Thus, loss of one or both flocculonodular lobes or one or both fastigial nuclei of the cerebellum gives the person a sensation of constant mal-equilibrium; this probably results because impulses from these cerebellar areas are normally integrated into the subconscious sense of

equilibrium by the reticular nuclei even before equilibrium information is sent to the cerebral cortex.

Nystagmus Caused by Stimulation of the Semicircular Canals

When one rotates his head, his eyes must rotate in the opposite direction if they are to remain "fixed" on any one object long enough to gain a clear image. After they have rotated far to one side, they jump suddenly in the direction of rotation of the head to "fix" on a new object and then rotate slowly backward again. This sudden jumping motion forward and then slow backward motion is known as *nystagmus*. The jumping motion is called the *fast component* of the nystagmus, and the slow movement is called the *slow component.*

Nystagmus always occurs automatically when the semicircular canals are stimulated. For instance, if a person's head begins to rotate to the right, backward movement of fluid in the left horizontal canal and forward movement in the right horizontal canal cause the eyes to move slowly to the left; thus, the slow component of nystagmus is controlled entirely by the vestibular apparatuses and the vestibular nuclei. But, when the eyes have moved as far to the left as they reasonably can, centers located in the brain stem in close approximation with the nuclei of the abducens nerves cause the eyes to jump suddenly to the right; then the vestibular apparatuses take over once more to move the eyes again slowly to the left.

The precise pathways that transmit nystagmus information from the vestibular apparatus to the ocular nuclei are not known. A probable pathway is through the *medial longitudinal fasciculus,* which connects the vestibular nuclei directly with these nuclei. However, complete transection of this fasciculus does not prevent vestibular nystagmus, which indicates that other pathways are undoubtedly involved as well.

Clinical Tests for Integrity of Vestibular Function

Balancing Test. One of the simplest clinical tests for integrity of the equilibrium mechanism is simply to have the individual stand perfectly still with his eyes closed. If he no longer has a functioning static equilibrium system of the utricles, he will waver to one side or the other and possibly even fall. However, as noted above, some of the proprioceptive mechanisms of equilibrium are occasionally sufficiently well developed to maintain balance even with the eyes closed.

Barany Test. A second test that is frequently performed determines the integrity of the semicircular canals. In this instance the individual is placed in a "Barany chair" and rotated very rapidly while he places his head respectively in various planes—first forward, then angulated to one side or the other. By such positioning each pair of semicircular canals is successively placed in the horizontal plane of rotation. When the chair is stopped suddenly the endolymph, because of its momentum, continues to rotate around and around in the pair of semicircular canals that has last been placed in the horizontal plane, this flow of endolymph causing the cupula to bend in the direction of rotation. As a result, nystagmus occurs, with the slow component in the direction of rotation and the fast component in the opposite direction. Also, as long as the nystagmus lasts (about 10 to 20 seconds) the individual has the sensation that he is rotating in the direction opposite to that in which he was actually rotated in the chair. Obviously, this test checks the semicircular canals on both sides of the head at the same time.

Ice Water Test. A clinical test for testing one vestibular apparatus separately from the other depends upon placing ice water in one ear. The semicircular canals, especially the external canal, are in close contact with the ear, and cooling the ear can transfer a sufficient amount of heat from the semicircular canals to cool the endolymph. This increases the density of the endolymph, thereby causing it to sink downward and resulting in slight movement of fluid around the semicircular canal. This stimulates the canal, giving the individual a sensation of rotating and also initiating nystagmus. From these two findings one can determine whether the respective semicircular canals are functioning properly. When the semicircular canals are normal, the utricles are usually normal also, for disease usually destroys the function of both at the same time.

REFERENCES

Anderson, S., and Gernandt, B. E.: Ventral root discharge in response to vestibular and proprioceptive stimulation. *J. Neurophysiol., 19:*524, 1956.

Camis, M.: The Physiology of the Vestibular Apparatus, translated by R. S. Creed. London, Oxford University Press, 1930.

Carpenter, M. B., Fabrega, H., and Glinsmann, W.: Physiological deficits occurring with lesions of labyrinth and fastigial nuclei. *J. Neurophysiol., 22:* 222, 1959.

Cohen, L. A.: Activity of knee joint proprioceptors recorded from the posterior articular nerve. *Yale J. Biol., 28:*225, 1955.

Cohen, L. A.: Analysis of position sense in human shoulder. *J. Neurophysiol., 21:*550, 1958.

Cohen, L. A.: Contributions of tactile, musculo-tendinous and joint mechanisms to position sense in human shoulder. *J. Neurophysiol., 21:*563, 1958.

Cohen, L. A., and Cohen, M. L.: Arthrokinetic reflex of the knee. *Am. J. Physiol., 184:*433, 1956.

Deweese, D. D.: Dizziness. Springfield, Illinois, Charles C Thomas, 1954.

Dusser de Barenne, J. G.: The Labyrinthine and Postural Mechanisms. Worcester, Massachusetts, Clark University Press, 1934.

Fischer, J.: The Labyrinth: Physiology and Functional Tests. New York, Grune & Stratton, Inc., 1956.

Gerathewohl, S. J., and Stallings, H. D.: The labyrinthine posture reflex (righting reflex) in the cat during weightlessness. *J. Aviat. Med., 28:*345, 1957.

Gernandt, B. E.: Vestibular mechanisms. *Handbook of Physiology, 1:*549, 1959.

Gernandt, B. E., Katsuki, Y., and Livingston, R. B.: Functional organization of descending vestibular influences. *J. Neurophysiol., 20:*453, 1957.

Hellebrandt, F. A., and Franseen, E. B.: Physiological study of the vertical stance of man. *Physiol. Rev., 23:*220, 1943.

Langworthy, O. R.: The control of posture by the central nervous system. *Physiol. Rev., 8:*151, 1928.

Lorente de No, R.: Researches on labyrinth reflexes. *Trans. Am. Otol. Soc., 22:*287, 1932.

Pike, F. H.: The function of the vestibular apparatus. *Physiol. Rev., 3:*209, 1923.

Sherrington, C. S.: Decerebrate rigidity and reflex coordination of movements. *J. Physiol., 22:*319, 1898.

Tyler, D. B., and Bard, P.: Motion sickness. *Physiol. Rev., 29:*311, 1949.

Wang, S. C., and Chinn, H. I.: Experimental motion sickness in dogs; functional importance of chemoceptive emetic trigger zone. *Am. J. Physiol., 178:* 111, 1954.

Chapter 51

The Sense of Hearing and Its Abnormalities

In this chapter we begin the discussion of the so-called *special senses*, hearing, sight, taste, and smell. Hearing, like most of the somatic senses, is a mechanoceptive sense, for the ear responds to mechanical vibration of the sound waves in the air. The purpose of the present chapter will be to describe and explain the mechanism by which the ear receives sound waves, discriminates their frequencies, and finally transmits auditory information into the central nervous system.

The acoustical system can be divided into (a) the ear itself and (b) the auditory nervous pathways from the ear into the nervous system. And the ear can then be subdivided into the *external ear*, the *middle ear*, and the *inner ear*. The inner ear is also known as the *cochlea*.

Function of the External Ear

The external ear in the human being performs only the function of transmitting sound waves to the tympanic membrane. However, in lower animals the *auricle* of the external ear is highly mobile and can be directed to the sound source. In man, the ears are directed toward the sound by rotation of the head rather than by movement of the auricle.

It should be noted that the two ears are also located advantageously to prevent feedback of sound from the person's own voice. Furthermore, the location on the two sides of the head can cause differences in the qualities of the sounds received by the two ears as well as slight time delays between the sounds, thereby allowing the person to detect the direction from which the sound emanates.

THE TYMPANIC MEMBRANE AND THE OSSICULAR SYSTEM

Transmission of Sound from the Tympanic Membrane to the Cochlea

Figure 512 illustrates the *tympanic membrane,* or *ear drum,* and the *ossicular system.* The tympanic membrane is cone shaped, with its concavity facing downward toward the auditory canal. The superior position of the tympanic membrane in the canal prevents solid objects from falling against it. Attached to the very center of the tympanic membrane is the *handle* of the *malleus,* and the malleus is tightly bound at its other end with the *incus* so that whenever the malleus moves, the incus generally moves in unison with it. The opposite end of the incus is articulated with the stem of the *stapes,* and the *faceplate* of the stapes lies in the opening of the oval window where sound waves are transmitted into the cochlea.

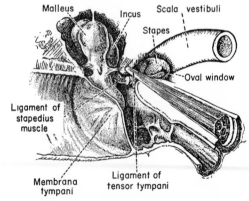

Figure 512. The tympanic membrane and the ossicular system of the ear.

The ossicles of the middle ear are suspended by ligaments in such a way that the combined malleus and incus act as a single lever having its fulcrum approximately at the border of the tympanic membrane. The large *head* of the malleus, which is on the opposite side of the fulcrum from the handle, almost exactly balances the other end of the lever so that changes in position of the body will not increase nor decrease the tension on the tympanic membrane.

The articulation of the incus with the stapes causes the stapes to rock in a backwards direction every time the handle of the malleus moves inward and to rock in a forward direction every time the malleus moves outward, which promotes inward and outward motion of the faceplate at the oval window.

The handle of the malleus is constantly being pulled inward both by ligaments and by the tensor tympani muscle, which keeps the tympanic membrane tensed all the time. This allows sound vibrations on *any* portion of the tympanic membrane to be transmitted to the malleus, which would not be true if the membrane were lax.

Impedance Matching by the Ossicular System. The amplitude of movement of the stapes faceplate with each sound vibration is almost exactly the same as the amplitude of the handle of the malleus. Therefore, the ossicular lever system does not amplify the movement of the stapes, as is commonly believed. However, the surface area of the tympanic membrane is approximately 70 square millimeters while the surface area of the stapes averages 3.2 square millimeters. This is a 22-fold difference, and it allows all the energy of a sound wave impinging on the tympanic membrane to be applied to the very small faceplate of the stapes, causing approximately 22 times as much pressure on the fluid of the cochlea as is exerted by the sound wave against the tympanic membrane. Since fluid has far greater inertia than air, it is easily understood that increased amounts of pressure are needed to cause the same degree of vibration in the fluid as in the air. Therefore, the tympanic membrane and ossicular system provide *impedance matching* between the sound waves in air and the sound vibrations in the fluid of the cochlea. Indeed, the impedance matching is almost perfect for sound frequencies above 500 cycles per second, which allows full utilization of the energy in the incoming sound waves and prevents reflection of sound from the tympanic membrane back into the air.

Transmission Characteristics of the Ossicular System. Every vibrating system that has inertia and that has an elastic component also has a natural frequency at which it can vibrate back and forth most easily. This is called its *resonant frequency*. Since the ossicular system does have inertia and since it is suspended by elastic ligaments, it has a distinct natural resonating frequency which is about 1700 cycles per second. However, the ligaments and other structures attached to the ossicles are also viscous in nature, which prevents excessive resonance; this is called *damping of the vibrations*. Because of the slight amount of resonance that does occur, sound waves of approximately 1700 cycles per second can be transmitted through the ossicular system with greater ease than can sound waves of other frequencies.

The external auditory canal because of its dimensions acts as an air column resonator and has a natural resonating frequency of about 4,000 cycles per second. But, here again, the degree of resonance is very slight and potentiates the 4,000 cycle sound only a minute amount.

Combining the resonant effects of the ossicular system and of the auditory canal, transmission of sound from the air to the cochlea is excellent between the limits of 800 and 6000 cycles per second but fades both above and below these limits.

Attenuation of Sound by Contraction of the Stapedius and Tensor Tympani Muscles. When very loud sounds are transmitted through the ossicular system into the central nervous system, a reflex occurs after a latent period of only 10 milliseconds to cause contraction of both the stapedius and tensor tympani muscles. The tensor tympani muscle pulls the handle of the malleus inward while the stapedius muscle pulls the stapes outward. These two forces oppose each other and thereby cause the entire ossicular system to develop a high degree of rigidity, thus greatly reducing the transmission of sound to the cochlea.

This *attenuation reflex* can reduce the intensity of sound transmission by as much as 30 decibels, which is about the same difference as that between a whisper and the sound emitted by a radio speaker. The function of this mechanism is partly to allow adaptation of the ear to sounds of different intensities and partly to protect the cochlea from damaging vibrations caused by excessively loud sounds.

Transmission of Sound through the Bone

Because the cochlea is embedded in a bony cavity in the temporal bone, vibrations of the entire skull can cause fluid vibrations in the cochlea itself. Fortunately, though, the cochlea is designed to minimize the detection of sound transmitted in this manner. As will become evident later when we discuss the transmission of sound vibrations in the scala vestibuli and the scala tympani, if the same amount of sound vibration occurs in each of these two scalae the receptor mechanism for sound is not stimulated. Yet, if the vibrations are intense enough, they may not be 100 per cent balanced in the two scalae and, therefore, can cause sound perception. For this reason a tuning fork or an electronic vibrator placed on any bony protuberance of the skull will cause the person to hear the sound if it is intense enough.

THE COCHLEA

Functional Anatomy of the Cochlea

The cochlea is a system of coiled tubes, as shown in Figure 513, with three different tubes coiled side by side, the *scala vestibuli,* the *scala media,* and the *scala tympani.* The scala vestibuli and scala media are separated from each other by the *vestibular*

membrane while the scala tympani and scala media are separated from each other by the *basilar membrane.* On the surface of the basilar membrane lies a structure, the *organ of Corti,* which contains a series of mechanically sensitive cells, the *hair cells.* These are the receptive end-organs that generate nerve impulses in response to sound vibrations.

Figure 514 illustrates the functional parts of the cochlea for transmission of sound vibrations. First, it should be noted that the vestibular membrane is missing from the figure. This membrane is so thin and so easily moved that it does not obstruct the passage of sound vibrations from the scala vestibuli into the scala media at all. Therefore, so far as the transmission of sound is concerned the scala vestibuli and scala media are considered to be a single chamber. The only known importance of the vestibular membrane is to maintain a special fluid in the scala media that is required for normal function of the sound receptive hair cells, which will be discussed later in the chapter.

Sound vibrations enter the scala vestibuli from the faceplate of the stapes at the oval window. The faceplate covers this window and is connected with its edges by a relatively loose annular ligament so that it can rock inward and outward. Inward movement causes the fluid to move into the scala vestibuli and scala media, which immediately increases the pressure in the entire cochlea and causes the round window to bulge outwards.

It will be noted from Figure 514 that the distal end of the scala vestibuli and scala tympani are continuous with each other by way of the *helicotrema.* If the stapes moves inward *very slowly,* fluid from the scala vestibuli will be pushed through the heli-

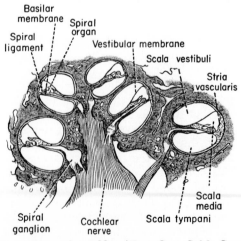

Figure 513. The cochlea. (From Goss, C. M.: Gray's Anatomy of the Human Body. Lea & Febiger.)

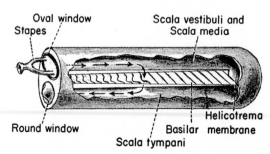

Figure 514. Movement of fluid in the cochlea following forward thrust of the stapes.

cotrema into the scala tympani, and this causes the round window to bulge outward. However, if the stapes vibrates inward and outward very rapidly, the fluid wave simply does not have time to pass all the way to the helicotrema, to the round window, and back again between each two successive vibrations. Instead, the fluid wave takes a short-cut through the basilar membrane, causing it to bulge back and forth with each sound vibration. We shall see below that each frequency of sound causes a different "pattern" of vibration in the basilar membrane and that this is one of the important means by which the sound frequencies are discriminated from each other.

The Basilar Membrane and Its Resonating Qualities. The basilar membrane is composed of some 20,000 or more *basilar fibers* that project from the bony center of the cochlea, the *modiolus,* to the outer wall. These fibers are stiff elastic structures that are relatively free to vibrate like reeds of a harmonica.

The lengths of the basilar fibers progressively increase from the base of the cochlea to the helicotrema, from approximately 0.04 millimeters at the base to 0.5 millimeters at the helicotrema, a 12-fold change in length. This change in length obviously allows the shorter fibers near the base of the cochlea to vibrate at a very high resonant frequency, while those near the helicotrema vibrate at a very low resonant frequency.

In addition to the differences in length of the basilar fibers, they are also differently "loaded" by the fluid of the cochlea. That is, when a fiber vibrates back and forth, all the fluid between the vibrating fiber and the oval and round windows must also vibrate back and forth at the same time. For a fiber vibrating near the base of the cochlea, the total mass of the fluid is slight in comparison with that for a fiber vibrating near the helicotrema, and this difference, too, favors high frequency vibration near the windows and low frequency vibration near the tip of the cochlea.

Thus, there are two causes of high frequency resonance of the fibers near the base and low frequency resonance near the apex: (1) difference in lengths of the fibers and (2) difference in "loading." The product of these two factors multiplied together is called the *volume elasticity* of the fibers. The volume elasticity of the fibers near the helicotrema is at least 100 times as great as that of the fibers near the stapes, which corresponds to a difference in resonating frequency between the two extremes of the cochlea of about 7 octaves.

Transmission of Sound Waves in the Cochlea—the "Traveling Wave"

If the foot of the stapes moves inward instantaneously the round window must also bulge outward instantaneously. Since the fluid wave will not have time to move all the way up to the helicotrema and back to the round window, the initial effect is to cause the basilar membrane at the very base of the cochlea to bulge in the direction of the round window. However, the elastic tension that is built up in the basilar fibers as they bend toward the round window initiates a wave that "travels" downward along the basilar membrane, as illustrated in Figure 515. Figure 515A shows movement of a high frequency wave down the basilar membrane, Figure 515B a medium frequency wave, and Figure 515C a very low frequency wave. Movement of the wave along the basilar membrane is comparable to the movement of a pressure wave along the arterial walls, which was discussed in Chapter 27, or it is also comparable to the wave that travels along a water hose when the end is moved up and down very rapidly.

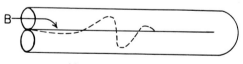

High frequency

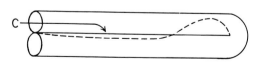

Medium frequency

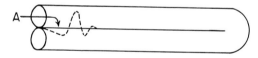

Low frequency

Figure 515. Diagrammatic representation of "traveling waves" along the basilar membrane for high, medium, and low frequency sounds.

Pattern of Vibration of the Basilar Membrane for Different Sound Frequencies. It is particularly important to note in Figure 515 the different patterns of transmission of sound waves of different frequencies along the basilar membrane. Note that each wave is relatively weak at the outset but becomes very strong when it reaches that portion of the basilar membrane that has a natural resonant frequency equal to the sound frequency. At this point the basilar membrane can vibrate back and forth with such great ease that the energy in the wave is completely dissipated. Consequently, the wave ceases at this point and fails to travel the remaining distance along the basilar membrane. Thus, a high frequency sound wave travels only a short distance along the basilar membrane before it dies out; a medium frequency sound wave travels about half way and then dies out; and, finally, a very low frequency sound wave travels the entire distance along the membrane before it dies.

Another feature of the traveling wave is that it travels very fast along the initial portion of the basilar membrane but progressively more slowly as it goes farther and farther into the cochlea. The cause of this is the high coefficient of elasticity of the basilar fibers near the stapes but a progressively decreasing coefficient farther along the membrane. This rapid initial transmission of the wave allows the high frequency sounds to travel far enough into the cochlea to spread out and separate from each other on the basilar membrane. Without this spread, all the high frequency waves would be bunched together within the first millimeter or so of the basilar membrane, and their frequencies could not be discriminated one from the other, as will be evident later in the chapter.

Amplitude pattern of vibration of the basilar membrane. The diagrams of Figure 515 illustrate the displacement of the basilar membrane at a single instant during the transmission of a sound wave. Figure 516 A, on the other hand, shows the position of the sound wave on the membrane (a) when the stapes is all the way inward, (b) when the stapes has moved back to the neutral point, (c) when the stapes is all the way outward, and (d) when the stapes has moved back again to the neutral point

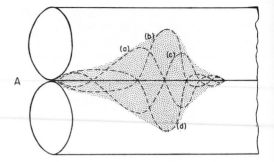

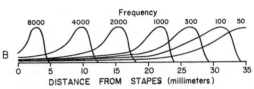

Figure 516. (A) Amplitude pattern of vibration of the basilar membrane for a medium frequency sound. (B) Amplitude patterns for sounds of all frequencies between 50 and 8000 per second, showing the points of maximum amplitude (the resonance points) on the basilar membrane for the different frequencies.

but is traveling inward. The shaded area around these different waves shows the maximum extent of vibration of the basilar membrane during a complete vibratory cycle. This is the *amplitude pattern of vibration* of the basilar membrane for this particular sound frequency.

Figure 516 B shows the amplitude pattern of vibration for different frequencies, showing that the maximum amplitude for 8,000 cycles occurs near the base of the cochlea, while that for frequencies of 50 to 100 cycles per second occurs near the helicotrema.

Another point that must be noted about the amplitude patterns of vibration in Figure 516 is that the basal end of the basilar membrane vibrates at least weakly for all frequencies. However, beyond the resonant area for each given frequency, the vibration of the basilar membrane cuts off very sharply. One of the methods by which sound frequencies are discriminated is based on the pattern of stimulation of the nerve fibers from the basilar membrane, as will be discussed below.

Function of the Organ of Corti

The *organ of Corti,* illustrated in Figure 517, is the receptor organ that generates nerve impulses in response to vibration of

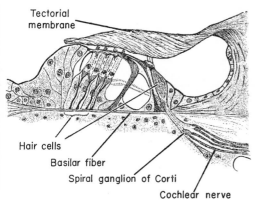

Tectorial
membrane

Hair cells

Basilar fiber

Spiral ganglion of Corti

Cochlear nerve

Figure 517. The organ of Corti, showing especially the hair cells and the tectorial membrane pressing against the projecting hairs.

the basilar membrane. Note that the organ of Corti lies on the surface of the basilar fibers and that the actual sensory receptors in the organ of Corti are two types of *hair cells,* a single row of *internal hair cells,* numbering about 3,500 and measuring about 12 microns in diameter, and three to four rows of *external hair cells,* numbering about 20,-000 and having diameters of only about 8 microns. The bases of the hair cells are enmeshed by a network of cochlear nerve endings. These lead to the *spiral ganglion of Corti,* which lies in the modiolus of the cochlea. The spiral ganglion in turn sends axons into the *cochlear nerve* and thence into the central nervous system at the level of the upper medulla. The relationship of the organ of Corti to the spiral ganglion is illustrated in Figure 513.

Excitation of the Hair Cells. Note in Figure 517 that minute hairs project upward from the hair cells and that these touch the *tectorial membrane* which lies above in the scala media. These hair cells are almost identical with the hair cells found in the macula and cristae ampullaris of the vestibular apparatus, which were discussed in the previous chapter. Bending of the hairs excites the hair cells, and this in turn excites the nerve fibers enmeshing their bases.

Figure 518 illustrates the mechanism by which vibration of the basilar membrane excites the hair endings. This shows that the upper ends of the hair cells are fixed tightly in a structure called the *reticular lamina.* Furthermore, the reticular lamina is continuous with a strong triangular structure called the *rods of Corti.* Upward movement of the

basilar membrane moves the rods of Corti and the reticular lamina in an upward and *inward* direction. Then, when the basilar membrane moves downward, the reticular lamina moves downward and *outward.* The inward and outward motion causes the hairs to rub back and forth against the tectorial membrane, thus exciting the cochlear nerve fibers whenever the basilar membrane vibrates.

The basilar membrane also vibrates to a slight extent in the longitudinal direction, as well as from side to side, because the "leading edge" of the traveling wave causes a distinct longitudinal motion. This, too, can bend the hairs and excite the auditory nerve fibers.

Mechanism by which the Hair Cells Excite the Nerve Fibers—Microphonic Potentials. Back-and-forth bending of the hairs causes alternate changes in the electrical potential across the hair surface of the hair cells, and this in turn generates alternating potentials, called *microphonic potentials,* between the fluid of the scala media and of the scala tympani. It is believed that these alternating electrical potentials either directly or through some hormonal mechanism stimulate the nerve filaments of the network surrounding the bases of the hair cells.

The endocochlear potential. To describe the electrical potentials generated by the hair cells, we need, first, to explain still another electrical phenomenon called the *endocochlear potential:* The scala media is filled with a fluid called *endolymph* in contradistinction to the *perilymph* present in the scala vestibuli and scala tympani. The scala vestibuli and scala tympani are connected with the subarachnoid space

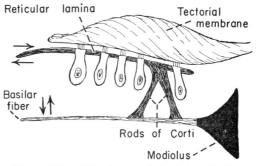

Reticular lamina

Tectorial
membrane

Basilar
fiber

Rods of Corti

Modiolus

Figure 518. Stimulation of the hair cells by to-and-fro movement of the hairs against the tectorial membrane.

around the brain; therefore, the perilymph is almost identical with cerebrospinal fluid and is only slightly different from the interstitial fluids. On the other hand, the endolymph that fills the scala media is an entirely different fluid secreted by the *stria vascularis*, a highly vascular area on the outer wall of the scala media. Endolymph contains a very high concentration of potassium and a very low concentration of sodium, which is exactly opposite to the perilymph.

Another factor of importance in relation to endolymph is that an electrical potential of approximately 80 millivolts exists all the time between the endolymph and the perilymph, with positivity inside the scala media and negativity outside. This is called the *endocochlear potential* and is generated by continual secretion of positive potassium ions into the scala media by the stria vascularis.

The importance of the endocochlear potential lies in the fact that the tops of the hair cells project through the reticular lamina into the endolymph of the scala media while perilymph bathes the lower bodies of the hair cells. Furthermore, the hair cells have a negative intracellular potential of minus 70 millivolts with respect to the perilymph, which means that the upper border of the hair cells has a total membrane potential between the endolymph and the intracellular fluids of 150 millivolts (70 + 80). It is believed that this very high electrical potential at the hair border of the cell greatly sensitizes the cell, thereby increasing its ability to respond to slight movement of the hairs.

Summating potentials. Vibration of the basilar membrane in some areas causes a prolonged change in the endocochlear potential, lasting far longer than the individual vibratory cycles, and sometimes making the potential more *positive* and sometimes more *negative* than normal. These changes are called respectively *positive* and *negative summating potentials*, and they probably result from stimulation of certain hair cells that respond with unidirectional potential changes rather than bidirectional potential changes. It has been postulated that these summating potentials also help to stimulate certain hair cells and that they might be important in frequency discrimination since positive summating potentials occur at one end of the basilar membrane and negative summating potentials at the other end.

Response of the Cochlear Nerve Fibers to Sounds of Different Frequencies. The cochlear nerve fibers are relatively small, only 2.5 to 4 microns in diameter, but they can transmit impulses at frequencies greater than 1000 cycles per second. When the basilar membrane vibrates at low frequencies, at least some of the fibers will fire during each cycle of vibration, and electrical recordings from the whole cochlear nerve will give a pattern of discharges that faithfully represents the sound frequencies entering the ear. Indeed, even at a frequency as high as 4000 cycles per second a faithful response can still be attained. In such a case, however, no single fiber will fire more than once every three to four vibrations, but the different fibers will alternate with each other in such a way that at least one or more fibers fire for each vibration. Above 4,000 impulses per second this is not true, and the discharges then transmitted through the cochlear nerve are not at all synchronous with the sound vibrations in the basilar membrane.

Determination of Pitch

In the above discussions we noted that sound waves of different frequencies cause different patterns of vibration in the basilar membrane, and we have also noted that, at least in the low frequency range, sound vibrations cause nerve discharges at the same frequencies as those of the sound. These two effects have given rise to two different theories for the determination of pitch by the auditory system. One of these is the *place theory*, which postulates that the frequency is determined by the position of the basilar membrane maximally excited by the sound wave. The other theory assumes that frequency determination does not occur in the cochlea at all but that the nerve impulses transmitted to the brain in synchrony with the sound waves allow the central nervous system to discriminate between the different frequencies. This is called the *frequency theory*. However, it is now known that both these theories are partially correct and neither is completely correct. They are combined together in the "duplex theory."

The Duplex Theory of Pitch Discrimination. This theory of pitch discrimination is based on the following two facts: (1) Destruction of the organ of Corti near the stapes destroys one's ability to discriminate high frequency sounds. (2) Destruction of the apical portions of the cochlea *does not* destroy one's ability to discriminate low frequency sounds but does reduce the loudness of these sounds.

In other words, the basal portions of the organ of Corti are definitely necessary for discrimination of high frequency sound, and, since this is the region of the basilar membrane at which high frequency sounds resonate, it is evident that the place theory provides an adequate explanation for this effect. On the other hand, since destruction of the apical portions of the basilar membrane does not prevent discrimination of low frequency sounds, and, since it is the apical portions of the basilar membrane at which low frequency sounds resonate, it is equally evident that the place theory cannot fully explain the discrimination of low frequency sounds. Therefore, the frequency theory must be invoked to explain this; that is, the central nervous system discriminates these frequencies after the auditory nerve impulses have reached the cochlear nuclei.

Determination of Loudness

Loudness is determined by the auditory system in at least three different ways: First, as the sound becomes louder, the amplitude of vibration of the basilar membrane and hair cells also becomes greater so that the hair cells now excite the nerve endings at faster rates. Second, as the amplitude of vibration increases, it causes more and more of the hair cells on the fringes of the vibrating portion of the basilar membrane to become stimulated, thus causing *spatial summation* of impulses—that is, transmission through many nerve fibers rather than through a few. Third, certain hair cells do not become stimulated until the vibration of the basilar membrane reaches a relatively high intensity, and it is believed that stimulation of these cells in some way apprises the nervous system that the sound is then very loud.

Detection of Changes in Loudness—the "Power Law" and the "Decibel." The ear, like essentially all other sensory organs, detects differences in sound intensity approximately in proportion to the logarithms of the actual differences in intensity. This is called the *power law* because the logarithm is proportional to the "power" of the intensity; it is also called the *Weber-Fechner law.*

Because of this ability of the ear to detect intensity changes in proportion to the logarithm of the intensity, sound intensities are usually also expressed in terms of the logarithm of its intensity. An increase in intensity of 10-fold is called *1 bel,* and one-tenth bel is called *1 decibel.* One decibel represents an actual increase in intensity of 1.26 times.

One of the principal reasons for using the decibel system in expressing changes in loudness is that the ears can usually detect approximately a 1 decibel change. That is, if the sound intensity increases by a factor of 1.26 times, the ears can barely perceive this increase. The maximum difference between the weakest and the loudest sounds that the ear can discriminate is about 120 decibels, which is an actual difference in intensity of *approximately 1 trillion times.*

The Threshold of Hearing for Sounds of Different Frequencies. The intensity of sound is measured by the amount of energy that the sound dissipates when it is absorbed at a surface, and sound engineers arbitrarily consider *1 microwatt of sound energy per square centimeter of surface area to have "unit" intensity, which is zero decibels when converted to the decibel scale because the logarithm of unity is zero.* If the intensity of a sound is plus 10 decibels intensity, then the actual intensity will be 10 microwatts/cm.^{2}; plus 30 decibels will be 1000 microwatts/cm.^{2}; and, conversely, minus 30 decibels will be 1/1000 microwatt/cm.^{2}.

Figure 519 shows the energy threshold at which sounds of different frequencies can be heard by

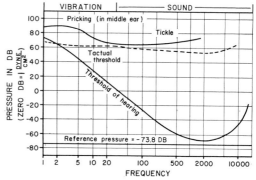

Figure 519. Relationship of the threshold of hearing and the threshold of somesthetic perception to the sound energy level at each sound frequency. (Modified from Stevens and Davis: Hearing. John Wiley & Sons.)

the ear. This figure illustrates that a 2000 cycle per second sound can be heard even when its intensity is as low as —70 decibels, which is one ten-millionth microwatt/cm.[2]. On the other hand, a 100 cycle per second sound can be detected only if its intensity is 10,000 times as great as this—that is, an intensity of —30 decibels.

Frequency range of hearing. The frequencies of sound that a young person can hear, before any aging has occurred in the ears, is generally stated to be between 30 and 20,000 cycles per second. However, if we will refer again to Figure 519 we can see that the sound range depends to a great extent on intensity. If the intensity is only —60 decibels, the sound range will be from 500 to 5,000 cycles per second, but, if the sound intensity is —20 decibels, the frequency range will be from about 70 to 15,000 cycles per second, and only with very intense sounds can the complete range of 30 to 20,000 cycles be achieved. In old age, as will be discussed more fully later in the chapter, the frequency range falls to 50 to 8,000 cycles per second or less.

CENTRAL AUDITORY MECHANISMS

The Auditory Pathway

Figure 520 illustrates the major auditory pathways. It shows that nerve fibers from the *spiral ganglion of Corti* enter the *dorsal* and *ventral cochlear nuclei* located in the upper part of the medulla. At this point, all the fibers synapse, and second order neurons pass mainly to the opposite side of the brain stem through the *trapezoid body* to end in the *superior olivary nucleus*. However, some of the second order fibers pass ipsilaterally to the superior olivary nucleus on the same side. Most of the fibers terminate in the superior olivary nucleus, but some of them pass on through this nucleus. From the superior olivary nucleus the auditory pathway then passes upward through the *lateral lemniscus*, and most of the fibers end in the *inferior colliculus*, but some pass on through this nucleus, too. A moderate number of fibers crosses from the lateral lemniscus through the *commissure of Probst* to the contralateral inferior colliculus. From the inferior colliculus, the pathway then passes through the *brachium of the inferior colliculus* to the *medial geniculate body*, where all the fibers synapse. From here, the auditory tract spreads by way of the *auditory radiation* to the *auditory cortex* located mainly in the superior temporal gyrus.

Several points of importance in relation to the auditory pathway should be noted. First, impulses from either ear are transmitted through the auditory pathways of both sides

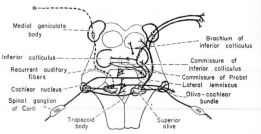

Figure 520. The auditory pathways. (Modified from Ades: *Handbook of Physiology,* 1:588, 1959.)

of the brain stem with only very slight preponderance of transmission in the contralateral pathway. There are at least three different places in the brain stem where crossing-over occurs between the two pathways: (a) in the trapezoid body, (b) in the commissure of Probst immediately beneath the inferior colliculi, and (c) in the commissure connecting the two inferior colliculi to each other.

Second, many collateral fibers from the auditory tracts pass directly into the reticular activating system of the brain stem. This system projects diffusely upward into the cerebral cortex and downward into the spinal cord.

Third, the pathway for transmission of sound impulses from the cochlea to the cortex consists of at least four neurons and sometimes as many as six. Neurons *may* or *may not* synapse in the superior olivary nuclei, in the nuclei of the lateral lemniscus, and in the inferior colliculi. Therefore, some of the tracts are more direct than others, which means that some impulses arrive at the cortex well ahead of others even though they might have originated at exactly the same time.

Fourth, several important pathways also exist from the auditory system into the cerebellum: (a) directly from the cochlear nuclei, (b) from the inferior colliculi, (c) from the reticular substance of the brain stem, and (d) from the cerebral cortex itself. These instantaneously activate the *cerebellar vermis* when a sudden noise enters the ear.

Integration of Auditory Information in the Relay Nuclei. Very little is known about the function of the different nuclei in the auditory pathway. However, a lower animal can still hear and can even respond almost normally to many auditory signals when the cerebral cortex is bilaterally removed, which indicates that the nuclei in the brain stem and thalamus can perform auditory functions even without the cerebral cortex.

One of the important features of auditory transmission through the relay nuclei is the spatial orientation of the pathways for sounds of different frequencies. For instance, in the dorsal cochlear nucleus, high frequencies are represented along the medial edge while low frequencies are represented along the lateral edge, and a similar type of spatial orientation occurs throughout the auditory pathway as it travels upward to the cortex.

Function of the Cerebral Cortex in Hearing

The projection of the auditory pathway to the cerebral cortex is illustrated in Figure 521, which shows that the auditory cortex lies principally on the *supratemporal plane of the superior temporal gyrus* but also extends widely over the *lateral border of the temporal lobe*, over much of the *insular cortex*, and even into the most lateral portion of the *parietal operculum*. Two areas are specified in Figure 521, a *short latency area* and a *long latency area*. The short latency area is directly excited by projections from

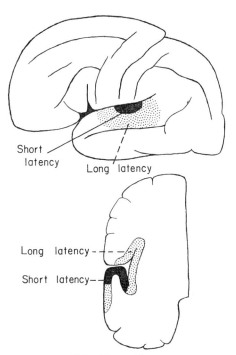

Figure 521. The auditory cortex.

the medial geniculate body, while the long latency area is usually excited secondarily by impulses from the short latency area but to some extent also by projections directly from the medial geniculate body. The short latency area is frequently also called the *primary auditory cortex* and the long latency area the *secondary auditory cortex.*

Frequency Patterns in the Auditory Cortex. Certain parts of the auditory cortex are known to respond to high frequencies and other parts to low frequencies. In monkeys, the posterior part of the supratemporal plane responds to high frequencies while the anterior part responds to low frequencies. It is also interesting that the frequency responsiveness of the cortex is arranged in concentric octaves. Unfortunately, the frequency localization in the human cortex is yet unknown.

The frequency range to which each individual neuron in the auditory cortex responds is much narrower than is true in the cochlear and brain stem relay nuclei. If we will refer back to Figure 516 B, we will note that the nerve fibers near the base of the cochlea can be stimulated by all frequency sounds, and in the cochlear nuclei this same breadth of sound representation is found, but by the time the excitation has reached the cerebral cortex, each neuron responds to only a narrow range of frequencies rather than to a broad range. Therefore, somewhere along the pathway integrative mechanisms in some unknown way "sharpen" the frequency response.

Some of the neurons in the auditory cortex do not respond at all to sounds in the ear. It is believed that these neurons "associate" different sound frequencies with each other or associate sound information with information from other sensory areas of the cortex. Indeed, the parietal portion of the auditory cortex partly overlaps the somatic sensory area II, which could provide very easy opportunity for association of auditory information with somatic sensory information.

It should be noted also that most of those neurons in the auditory cortex that respond to sound are not frequency selective but instead respond to sounds of any frequency. Thus, only a small fraction of the neurons in the auditory cortex discriminate sound frequencies while the other neurons presumably perform other functions such as detection of noise, sound quality, sound intensity, and so forth.

Discrimination of Sound Patterns by the Auditory Cortex. Complete bilateral removal of the auditory cortex does not prevent an animal from detecting sounds nor from reacting in a reasonably intelligent manner to the sounds. However, it does greatly reduce or sometimes even abolish his ability to discriminate different *patterns of sound.* For instance, an animal that had previously been trained to recognize a sequence of tones, one following the other in a particular pattern, will lose this ability when the cerebral cortex is destroyed, and, furthermore, he cannot relearn this type of response. Therefore, the cerebral cortex is important in the discrimination of *tonal patterns.*

In the human being stimulation in the short latency area of the auditory cortex will cause the person to hear (a) a tingling sound, (b) a loud roar, or (c) some other single discrete type of sound, whereas stimulation low down on the side of the temporal lobe will occasionally cause the person to perceive intelligible sounds that even include whole sentences. Thus, it would be possible to divide the auditory cortex into a short latency *receptive area* and a long latency *interpretive area.*

Perception of Direction from Which Sound Emanates

A person determines the direction from which sound emanates by at least two different mechanisms: (1) by the time lag between the entry of sound into one ear and the opposite ear and (2) by the difference between the intensities of the sounds in the two ears. The first of these two mechanisms functions much more exactly than the second, for it does not depend on extraneous factors but only on an exact interval of time between two acoustical signals. If a person is looking straight ahead, the sound will reach both ears at exactly the same instant while, if the right ear is closer to the sound than the left ear, the sound impulses from the right ear will be perceived ahead of those from the left ear. To distinguish sound from the front from sound from behind still a third mechanism must be invoked, *difference*

in quality of the sound. This difference results from the orientation of the auricles.

Detection of the direction of a sound is not dependent on the cerebral cortex, for a decorticated animal can still perceive direction very accurately. Therefore, the nuclei of the brain stem almost certainly perform this integrative function.

Retrograde Conduction of Impulses from the Central Nervous System to the Cochlea

Retrograde pathways have been demonstrated at each level of the central nervous system all the way from the auditory cortex to the cochlea. The final pathway is from the olivary nucleus to the organ of Corti.

These retrograde fibers are believed to be mainly inhibitory, signals from the cerebral cortex selectively depressing the sensitivity of different portions of the organ of Corti. Indeed, direct stimulation of discrete points in the olivary nucleus have been shown to inhibit specific areas of the organ of Corti. One can readily understand how this could allow a person to direct his attention to sounds of particular qualities while rejecting sounds of other qualities. This is readily demonstrated when one listens to a single instrument in a symphony orchestra.

HEARING ABNORMALITIES

Types of Deafness

Clinical deafness is usually divided into two types: first, that due to impairment of the cochlea or of the auditory nerve, which is usually classed under the heading "nerve deafness," and second, that due to impairment of the middle ear mechanisms for transmitting sound into the cochlea, which is usually called "conduction deafness." Obviously, if either the cochlea or the auditory nerve is completely destroyed the person will be irretrievably deaf. However, if the cochlea and nerve are still intact but the ossicular system has been destroyed or ankylosed, sound waves can still be conducted into the cochlea by means of bone conduction.

Tuning Fork Tests for Differentiation between Nerve Deafness and Conduction Deafness. Because the cochlea and also the neurogenic portions of the hearing mechanism are still intact in conduction deafness but one or the other of these portions of the hearing mechanism is not intact in nerve deafness, the two types of deafness can be differentiated by determining whether the deaf person can still hear by bone conduction. If his bone conduction as well as his air conduction is depressed, the disability is due to nerve deafness rather than to conduction deafness. Two tuning fork methods for distinguishing the type of deafness are the following:

The Rinne test. To test an ear for bone conduction with a tuning fork, a vibrating fork is placed in front of the ear and the subject listens to the tone of the fork until he can no longer hear it. Then the butt of the still weakly vibrating fork is immediately placed against the mastoid process. If his bone conduction is better than his air conduction, he will again hear the sound of the tuning fork. If this occurs, his deafness may be considered to be conduction deafness. However, if on placing the butt of the fork against the mastoid process he cannot hear the sound of the tuning fork, his bone conduction is probably decreased as much as his air conduction, and any deafness that exists in the ear is presumably due to damage in the cochlea or in the nervous system rather than in the ossicular system—that is, it is nerve deafness.

The Weber test. If a vibrating tuning fork is placed on the forehead of a normal person, he hears the sound of the fork in both ears approximately equally, but a person with conduction deafness in one ear hears the sound of the tuning fork more loudly in the deaf ear than in the normal ear. The reason for this apparently is that "fixation" of the ossicular system prevents as much movement of the oval window as of the round window, thus causing increased basilar membrane movement. Therefore, the deaf ear becomes more acutely attuned to sound waves conducted through bone than is the normal ear.

On the other hand, in applying the Weber test to a patient with nerve deafness in one ear, the sound appears to the patient to be more intense in the normal ear than in the abnormal ear, because hearing even by bone conduction is depressed in the abnormal ear.

The Audiometer. To determine the nature of hearing disabilities more exactly than can be accomplished by the above methods, the "audiometer" has been devised. This is simply an earphone connected to an electronic oscillator capable of emitting pure tones ranging from very low frequencies to very high frequencies. Based on previous studies of normal persons, the instrument is calibrated so that the 0 intensity level of sound at each frequency is the loudness of the sound that can barely be heard by the normal person. However, the calibrated volume control can be changed to increase or decrease the loudness of each tone above or below the zero level. If the loudness of a tone must be increased to 30 decibels above normal before the subject can hear the

tone, the subject is said to have a *hearing loss* of 30 decibels for that particular tone.

In performing a hearing test with an audiometer, approximately 8 to 10 tones covering the auditory spectrum are tested one at a time, and the hearing loss is determined for each of these tones. Then the so-called "audiogram" is plotted as shown in Figures 522 and 523, depicting the hearing loss for each of the tones in the auditory spectrum.

The audiometer, in addition to being equipped with an earphone for testing air conduction by the ear, is also equipped with an electronic vibrator for testing bone conduction from the mastoid process into the cochlea at each sound frequency. The bone conduction vibrator is excited by the electronic portion of the audiometer in the same manner as the earphone, and the audiometer is appropriately calibrated so that the zero intensity level of sound at each frequency is the loudness of bone-conducted sound that can barely be heard by the normal person.

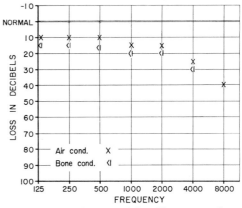

Figure 522. Audiogram of the old age type of nerve deafness.

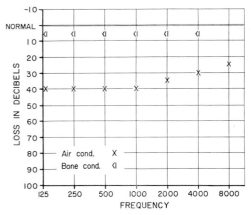

Figure 523. Audiogram of deafness resulting from middle ear sclerosis.

The audiogram in nerve deafness. If a person has nerve deafness—this term including damage to the cochlea, to the auditory nerve, or to the central nervous system circuits from the ear —he loses the ability to hear sound as tested by both the air conduction apparatus and the bone conduction apparatus. An audiogram depicting nerve deafness is illustrated in Figure 522. In this particular figure the deafness is mainly for high frequency sound. Such deafness could be caused by damage to the base of the cochlea.

Nerve deafness, in which mainly the high frequencies are lost, occurs to some extent in almost all older persons and to a major extent in some of them. The reason for this is the following: the high frequency areas of the basilar membrane are represented by so few nerve fibers that incipient degeneration of the auditory nerve almost always knocks out the high frequencies first.

The audiogram in conduction deafness. A second and frequent type of deafness is that due to fibrosis of the middle ear following infection in the middle ear. In this instance the sound waves cannot be transmitted easily to the oval window. Figure 523 illustrates an audiogram from a person with "middle ear deafness" of this type. In this case the bone conduction is essentially normal, but air conduction is greatly depressed at all frequencies, though more so at the low frequencies.

Occasionally, one becomes almost deaf to air conduction because of ankylosis of the stapes at the oval window, which means fibrous fixation or even bony growth of the faceplate of the stapes to the edges of the window. This ankylosis blocks the passage of all sound vibrations through the middle ear into the cochlea. However, sound transmission to the cochlea by bone conduction is still perfectly feasible, for, as was noted previously, when the oval window is not allowed to bulge back and forth, all the vibrations entering the cochlea must bulge at the round window. This means that any vibration entering the scala vestibuli will cause excessive bulging of the basilar membrane toward the scala tympani. Consequently, bone conduction into the cochlea in the presence of ankylosis of the stapes to the oval window causes an audiogram such as that illustrated in Figure 524, which shows that bone conduction in this instance is even better than normal.

REFERENCES

Ades, H. W.: Central auditory mechanisms. *Handbook of Physiology*, 1:585, 1959.

Ades, H. W.: Hearing. *Ann. Rev. Physiol.*, 16:391, 1954.

Butler, R. A., Diamond, I. T., and Neff, W. D.: Role of auditory cortex in discrimination of changes in frequency. *J. Neurophysiol.*, 20:108, 1957.

Davies, P. W., Erulkar, S. D., and Rose, J. E.: Single-unit activity in the auditory cortex of the cat. *J. Physiol.*, 126:25P, 1954.

Davis, H.: Biophysics and physiology of the inner ear. *Physiol. Rev.*, 37:1, 1957.

Davis, H.: Excitation of auditory receptors. *Handbook of Physiology*, 1:565, 1959.

Diamond, I. T., and Neff, W. D.: Ablation of temporal cortex and discrimination of auditory patterns. *J. Neurophysiol.*, 20:300, 1957.

Erulkar, S. D., Rose, J. E., and Davies, P. W.: Single unit activity in the auditory cortex of the cat. *Bull. Johns Hopkins Hosp.*, 99:55, 1956.

Fletcher, H.: Speech and Hearing in Communication. 2nd ed., New York, D. Van Nostrand Co., 1953.

Galambos, R.: Neural mechanisms of audition. *Physiol. Rev.*, 34:497, 1954.

Galambos, R.: Suppression of auditory nerve activity by stimulation of efferent fibers to cochlea. *J. Neurophysiol.*, 19:424, 1956.

Granit, R.: Receptors and Sensory Perception. New Haven, Yale University Press, 1955.

Harvard University Psycho-acoustic Laboratory: Bibliography on Hearing. Cambridge, Harvard University Press, 1955.

Hirsh, I. J.: The Measurement of Hearing. New York, The McGraw-Hill Book Co., Inc., 1952.

Irwin, R. B.: Speech and Hearing Therapy. New York, Prentice-Hall, Inc., 1953.

Jackson, C., and Jackson, C. L.: Diseases of the Nose, Throat and Ear. 2nd ed., Philadelphia, W. B. Saunders Co., 1958.

Katsuki, Y., Sumi, T., Uchiyama, H., and Watanabe, T.: Electric responses of auditory neurons in cat to sound stimulation. *J. Neurophysiol.*, 21:569, 1958.

Katsuki, Y., Watanabe, T., and Maruyama, N.: Activity of auditory neurons in upper levels of brain of cat. *J. Neurophysiol.*, 22:343, 1959.

Katsuki, Y., Watanabe, T., and Suga, N.: Interaction of auditory neurons in response to two sound stimuli in cat. *J. Neurophysiol.*, 22:603, 1959.

Mandl, M.: Hearing Aids. New York, The Macmillan Co., 1953.

Neff, W. D., Fisher, J. F., Diamond, I. T., and Yela, M.: Role of auditory cortex in discrimination requiring localization of sound in space. *J. Neurophysiol.*, 19:500, 1956.

Perl, E. R., and Casby, J. U.: Localization of cerebral

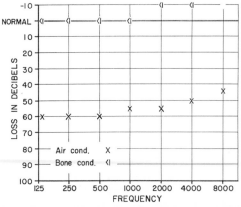

Figure 524. Audiogram of deafness caused by ankylosis of the stapes.

electrical activity, the acoustic cortex of cat. *J. Neurophysiol., 17:*429, 1954.

Riss, W.: Effect of bilateral temporal cortical ablation on discrimination of sound direction. *J. Neurophysiol., 22:*374, 1959.

Rosenzweig, M. R., and Sutton, D.: Binaural interaction in lateral lemniscus of cat. *J. Neurophysiol., 21:*17, 1958.

Simmons, F. B., Galambos, R., and Rupert, A.: Conditioned response of middle ear muscles. *Am. J. Physiol., 197:*537, 1959.

Tasaki, I.: Hearing. *Ann. Rev. Physiol., 19:*417, 1957.

Tasaki, I., and Spyropoulos, C. S.: Stria vascularis as source of endocochlear potential. *J. Neurophysiol., 22:*149, 1959.

Thompson, R. F.: Function of auditory cortex of cat in frequency discrimination. *J. Neurophysiol., 23:* 321, 1960.

Thompson, R. F., and Sindberg, R. M.: Auditory response fields in association and motor cortex of cat. *J. Neurophysiol., 23:*87, 1960.

Wever, E. G., and Lawrence, M.: Physiological Acoustics. Princeton, Princeton University Press, 1954.

Chapter 52

The Eye: Optics of Vision

PHYSICAL PRINCIPLES OF OPTICS

Before it is possible to understand the optical systems of the eye, it is essential that the student be thoroughly familiar with the basic physical principles of optics, including the physics of refraction, and that he should have a knowledge of focusing, depth of focus, etc. Therefore, in the present study of the optics of the eye, a brief review of these physical principles is first presented, and then the optics of the eye are discussed.

Refraction of Light

The Refractive Index of a Transparent Substance. Light rays travel through a vacuum at a speed of approximately 300,000 kilometers per second and practically as fast through air and other gaseous media but much slower through solids and liquids. The *refractive index* of a transparent substance is inversely proportional to the speed at which light travels through the substance, and the refractive index of air or a vacuum is arbitrarily considered to be 1.00. Therefore, if light travels through a particular type of glass at a speed of 200,000 kilometers per second, the refractive index of this glass is 300,000 divided by 200,000, or 1.50. In essence, then, the refractive index is an inverse measure of the speed of transmission of light waves through a transparent medium.

Refraction of Light Rays at an Interface between Two Media with Different Refractive Indices. When light waves traveling forward in a beam, as shown in the upper part of Figure 525, strike an interface that is perpendicular to the beam of light rays, the waves enter the second refractive medium without deviating in their course. The only effect that occurs is decreased speed of transmission. On the other hand, if, as illustrated in the lower part of Figure 525, the light waves strike an angulated interface, the light rays bend if the refractive indices of the two

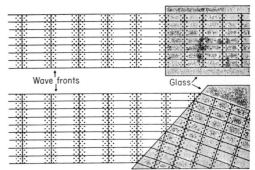

Figure 525. Wave fronts entering (top) a glass surface perpendicular to the light rays and (bottom) a glass surface angulated to the light rays. This figure illustrates that the distance between waves after it enters the glass is shortened to approximately two thirds that in air. It also illustrates that light rays striking an angulated glass surface are refracted.

media are different from each other. In this particular figure the light waves are leaving air, which has a refractive index of 1.00, and are entering a block of glass having a refractive index of 1.50. When the beam first strikes the angulated interface, the lower portion of the beam enters the glass ahead of the upper portion. Therefore, the wave front in the upper portion of the beam continues to travel at a speed of 300,000 kilometers per second while that which has entered the glass travels at a speed of 200,000 kilometers per second. This causes the wave front of each successive light wave in the upper portion of the light beam to move ahead of the wave front in the lower portion so that the wave front is no longer vertical but is angulated to the right. Because the direction in which light travels is always perpendicular to the wave front, the light beam now bends downward.

The bending of light rays at an angulated interface is known as *refraction* of the light rays. It is to be noted particularly that the degree of refraction increases as a function of (1) the difference between the two refractive indices of the two transparent media and (2) the degree of angulation between the interface and the wave front of the beam.

Application of Refractive Principles to Lenses

The Convex Lens. Figure 526 shows parallel light rays entering a convex lens. The light rays striking the center of the lens are exactly perpendicular to the surfaces of the lens and therefore pass through the lens without being refracted at all. Toward either edge of the lens, however, the light rays strike an interface that becomes progressively more angulated. Therefore, the rays progressively toward the edge of the lens bend more and more toward the center.

Then, when the rays have passed through the glass, the outer rays bend still more toward the center. Thus, parallel light rays entering an appropriately formed convex lens come to a single point focus at some distance beyond the lens.

The Concave Lens. Figure 527 shows the effect of a concave lens on parallel light rays. With the concave lens as well as with the convex lens, the rays that enter the very center of the lens strike an interface that is absolutely perpendicular to the beam and, therefore, do not refract at all. The rays closer to the edge of the concave lens enter the lens ahead of the rays toward the center. This is opposite to the effect in the convex

lens, and it causes the peripheral light rays to *diverge* away from the light rays that pass through the center of the lens.

Thus, the concave lens *diverges* light rays, whereas the convex lens *converges* light rays.

Spherical versus Cylindrical Lenses. Figure 528 illustrates a *convex spherical lens* and a *convex cylindrical lens*. It will be noted from this figure that the convex cylindrical lens bends the light rays from the two sides of the lens but not from either the top or the bottom of the lens. Therefore, parallel light rays are bent to a focal *line* rather than to a point focus. On the other hand, the light rays that pass through the spherical lens are refracted at all edges of the lens toward the central ray, and all the rays come to a focal *point*.

It is very difficult to describe the difference between cylindrical and spherical lenses, but a thorough study of Figure 528 should make the difference evident. The cylindrical lens is well illustrated by a test tube full of water. If the test tube is placed in a beam of light and a piece of paper is brought progressively closer and closer to the tube, a certain distance will be found at which the light rays come to a focal line. On the

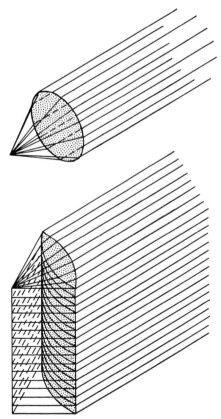

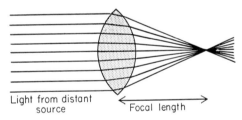

Figure 526. Bending of light rays at each surface of a convex spherical lens, showing that parallel light rays are focused to a point focus.

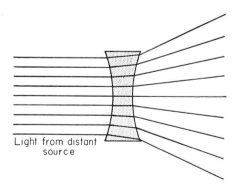

Figure 527. Bending of light rays at each surface of a concave spherical lens, illustrating that parallel light rays are diverged by a concave lens.

Figure 528. *Top:* point focus of parallel light rays by a spherical convex lens. *Bottom:* line focus of parallel light rays by a cylindrical convex lens.

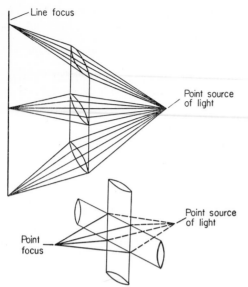

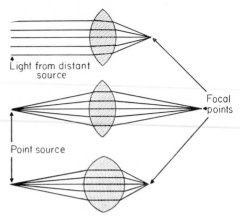

Figure 529. Two cylindrical convex lenses at right angles to each other, illustrating that one lens converges light rays in one plane and the other lens converges light rays in the plane at right angles. The two lenses combined give the same point focus as that obtained with a spherical convex lens.

Figure 530. The upper two lenses of this figure have the same strength, but the light rays entering the top lens are parallel, while those entering the second lens are diverging; the effect of parallel versus diverging rays on the focal distance is illustrated. The bottom lens has far more refractive power than either of the other two lenses, illustrating that the stronger the lens the nearer to the lens will be the point focus.

other hand, the spherical lens is illustrated by an ordinary magnifying glass. If such a lens is placed in a beam of sunlight and a piece of paper is brought progressively closer to the lens, the light rays will impinge on a common focal point at an appropriate distance.

Concave cylindrical lenses diverge light rays in only one plane in the same manner that convex cylindrical lenses converge light rays in one plane.

Figure 529 shows two convex cylindrical lenses at right angles to each other. The second cylindrical lens does not cause additional inward bending of the light rays that pass through the two sides of the first cylindrical lens. However, the light rays that strike the upper and lower portions of the first cylindrical lens now are bent down and up, respectively, by the second cylindrical lens. Therefore, the light rays diverging upward or downward are brought to meet each other by the horizontal cylindrical lens, and the light rays diverging to either side are brought to meet each other by the vertical cylindrical lens. Thus, all the light rays diverging in all directions come to a single point focus. In other words, *two cylindrical lenses crossed at right angles to each other perform the same function as one spherical lens of the same refractive power.*

Focusing by Convex Lenses

The distance from a convex lens at which parallel light rays converge to a common focal

point is the *focal length* of the lens. The diagram at the top of Figure 530 illustrates again this focusing of parallel light rays. In the middle diagram of Figure 530, the light rays that enter the convex lens are not parallel but are diverging because the origin of the light is a point source not far away from the lens itself. The rays striking the center of the lens are perpendicular to the lens surface and pass through the lens without any refraction. In the discussion above it was shown that the degree of bending of light rays is a function of (a) the change in index of refraction at the interface and (b) the angle of incidence of the light rays. Therefore, the edges of the convex lens bend the diverging rays approximately the same amount as they do parallel rays because the greater refraction at one interface is approximately balanced by less refraction at the other interface. However, because these rays are already diverging, even though they are bent the same extent as parallel rays, it can be seen from the middle diagram of Figure 530 that they do not come to a point focus at the same distance away from the lens as do the parallel rays. In other words, when rays of light that are already diverging enter a convex lens, the distance of focus on the other side of the lens is farther from the lens than is the case when the entering rays are parallel to each other.

In the lower portion of Figure 530 are shown light rays that also are diverging toward a convex lens from a point source not far from the lens. However, in this case the lens has greater curvature than that of the upper two lenses of the figure. Consequently, in this diagram the distance from the lens at which the light rays come to a focus is exactly the same as the focal distance from the lens in the first diagram, in which the lens was convex but the light rays entering it were parallel. This illustrates that both parallel rays and diverging rays can be focused at the same distance behind a lens provided that the lens changes its convexity. It is obvious that the nearer the point source of light to the lens, the greater is the divergence of the light rays and the greater must be the curvature of the lens.

The relationship of focal length of the lens, distance of the point source of light, and distance of the focal point is expressed by the following formula:

$$\frac{1}{f} = \frac{1}{a} + \frac{1}{b}$$

in which f is the focal length of the lens, a the distance of the point source of light from the lens, and b the distance of the focal point from the lens.

Formation of an Image by a Convex Lens

The upper drawing of Figure 531 illustrates a convex lens with two point sources of light to the left. Because light rays from any point source of light pass through the center of a convex lens without being refracted in either direction, the light rays from both point sources of light are shown to pass straight through the center of the lens. Furthermore, the other light rays from each point source of light, whether they pass through the upper edge of the lens, the center of the lens, or the lower edge, all come to the same point focus behind the lens *directly in line with the point source of light and the center of the lens.*

Any object in front of the lens is in reality a mosaic of point sources of light. Some of these points are very bright, some are very weak, and they vary in color. The light rays from each point source of light that enter the very center of the convex lens pass directly through this lens without any of the rays bending. Furthermore, the light rays that enter the edges of the lens finally come to a focal point behind the lens in line with the rays that pass through the center of the lens. Therefore, every point source of light on the object comes to a separate focal point on the opposite side of the lens. If all portions of the object are the same distance in front of the lens, all the focal points behind the lens will fall in a common plane a certain distance behind the lens. If a white piece of paper is placed at this distance, one can see an image of the object, as is illustrated in the lower portion of Figure 531. However, this image is upside down with respect to the original object, and the two lateral sides of the image are reversed with respect to the original object. This is the method by which the lens of a camera focuses light rays on the camera film.

Measurement of the Refractive Power of a Lens—The Diopter

The more a lens bends light rays, the greater is its "refractive power." This refractive power is measured in terms of *diopters*. By convention, a convex lens is said to have a refractive power of +1 diopter when it is capable of converging parallel light rays to a focal point 1 meter beyond the lens, as illustrated in Figure 532. If the lens is capable of bending parallel light rays twice as much as a lens with a power of +1 diopter, it is said to have a strength of +2 diopters, and, obviously, the light rays come to a focal point one half meter beyond the lens. A lens which is capable of converging parallel light rays to a focal point only 10 centimeters beyond the lens has a refractive power of +10 diopters.

The refractive power of concave lenses cannot be stated in terms of the focal distance beyond the lens because the light rays do not focus to a point. Therefore, the power of a concave lens is stated in terms of its ability to diverge light rays

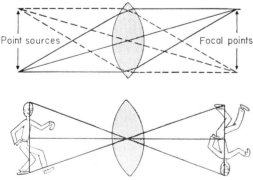

Figure 531. The top drawing illustrates two point sources of light focused at two separate points on the opposite side of the lens. The lower drawing illustrates formation of an image by a convex spherical lens.

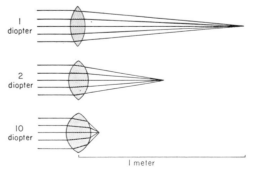

Figure 532. Effect of lens strength on the focal distance.

in comparison with the ability of convex lenses to converge light rays. That is, if a concave lens diverges light rays the same amount that a 1 diopter convex lens converges them, the concave lens is said to have a dioptric strength of −1. Likewise, if the concave lens diverges the light rays as much as a +10 diopter lens converges them, then it is said to have a strength of −10 diopters.

It should be noted particularly that concave lenses can "neutralize" the refractive power of convex lenses. Thus, placing a 1 diopter concave lens immediately in front of a 1 diopter convex lens results in a lens system with essentially zero refractive power.

It is to be noted in the above discussion that the strengths of converging lenses are stated to be *plus*, and the strengths of diverging lenses are stated to be *minus*.

The strengths of cylindrical lenses are computed in the same manner as the strengths of spherical lenses. If a cylindrical lens focuses parallel light rays to a line focus 1 meter beyond the lens, it has a strength of +1 diopter. On the other hand, if a cylindrical lens of a concave type *diverges* light rays as much as a +1 diopter cylindrical lens *converges* them, it has a strength of −1 diopter.

THE OPTICS OF THE EYE

The Eye as a Camera

The eye, as illustrated in Figure 533, is optically equivalent to the usual photographic camera, for it has a lens system, a variable aperture system, and a retina which corresponds to the film. The lens system of the eye is composed of (1) the interface between air and the anterior surface of the cornea, (2) the interface between the posterior surface of the cornea and the aqueous humor, (3) the interface between the aqueous humor and the anterior surface of the lens, and (4) the interface between the posterior surface of the lens and the vitreous humor. The refractive index of air is 1; the cornea, 1.38; the aqueous humor, 1.33; the lens (on the average), 1.40; and the vitreous humor, 1.34.

The total refractive power of both surfaces of the eye lens when it is surrounded by fluid on each side is only about 25 diopters; whereas, if this lens were removed from the eye and then surrounded by air, its refractive power would be about 150 diopters. Thus, it can be seen that the lens

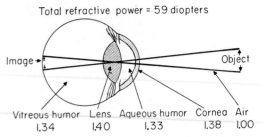

Figure 533. The eye as a camera. The numbers are the refractive indices.

inside the eye is not nearly so powerful as it is outside the eye. The reason for this is that the fluids surrounding the lens have refractive indices not much different from the refractive index of the lens itself, and the smallness of the differences greatly decreases the amount of light refraction at the lens interfaces.

The curvature of the anterior surface of the cornea is reasonably great, but more important than this is the fact that the refractive index of the cornea is markedly different from that of air. Therefore, this interface accounts for about 39 diopters of the refractive power of the eye.

The posterior surface of the cornea is concave and actually acts as a concave lens, but, because the difference in refractive index of the cornea and the aqueous humor is slight, this posterior surface of the cornea has a refractive power of only about −5 diopters, which neutralizes part of the refractive power of the other refractive surfaces of the eye.

The reduced eye. If all the refractive surfaces of the eye are algebraically added together and then considered to be one single lens, the optics of the normal eye may be simplified and represented schematically as a "reduced eye." This is very useful in simple calculations. In the reduced eye a single lens is considered to exist 17 mm. in front of the retina with a total refractive power of approximately 59 diopters.

Formation of an Image on the Retina. In exactly the same manner that a glass lens can focus an image on a sheet of paper, the lens system of the eye can also focus an image on the retina, and the image is inverted and reversed with respect to the object. However, the mind perceives objects in the upright position despite the upside down orientation on the retina because the brain is trained to consider an inverted image as the normal.

The Mechanism of Accommodation

The refractive power of the crystalline lens of the eye can be voluntarily increased from 25 diopters up to approximately 42 diopters in young children; this is a total "accommodation" of 17 diopters. To do this, the shape of the lens is changed from that of a moderately convex lens to that of a very convex lens. The mechanism of this is the following:

Normally, the lens is composed of a strong elastic capsule filled with viscous, protein-aceous but transparent fibers. When the lens is in a relaxed state, with no tension on its capsule, it assumes a spherical shape due entirely to the elasticity of the lens capsule. However, as illustrated in Figure 534, approximately 70 ligaments attach radially around the lens, pulling the lens edges toward the ciliary body. These ligaments are constantly tensed by the elastic pull of their attachments at the ciliary body, and the tension on these ligaments causes the lens to remain normally relatively flat. At the insertions of the tendons in the ciliary body is the ciliary muscle, which has two sets of smooth muscle fibers, the *meridional fibers* and the *circular fibers*. The meridional fibers extend from the corneoscleral junction to the insertions of the ligaments in the ciliary body approximately 2 to 3 mm. behind the corneoscleral junction. When these muscle fibers

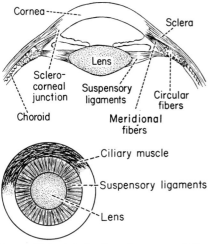

Figure 534. Mechanism of accommodation.

contract, the insertions of the ligaments are pulled forward, thereby releasing a certain amount of tension on the crystalline lens. The circular fibers are arranged circularly all the way around the eye so that when they contract a sphincter action occurs in the ciliary body, relaxing the tension on the ligaments still more and allowing the ligaments to pull less on the lens capsule.

Thus, contraction of both sets of smooth muscle fibers in the ciliary muscle relaxes the ligaments to the lens capsule, and the lens assumes a more spherical shape, like a balloon, because of its elasticity. When the ciliary muscle is completely relaxed, the lens is as flat as possible, and the dioptric strength of the lens is as weak as it can become. On the other hand, when the ciliary muscle contracts as strongly as possible, the dioptric strength of the lens becomes maximal.

Parasympathetic Control of Accommodation. The ciliary muscle is controlled mainly by the parasympathetic nervous system. Stimulation of the parasympathetic fibers to the eye contracts the ciliary muscle, which in turn relaxes the ligaments of the lens and increases its refractive power. With an increased refractive power, the eye is more capable of focusing on objects that are nearer to it than is an eye with less refractive power. Consequently, as a far-away object moves toward the eye, the number of parasympathetic impulses impinging on the ciliary muscle must be progressively increased for the eye to keep the object constantly in focus.

Presbyopia. As a person grows older, his eye lens loses its elastic nature and becomes a relatively solid mass, probably because of progressive denaturation of the proteins. Therefore, the ability of the lens to assume a spherical shape progressively decreases, and the power of accommodation decreases from approximately 17 diopters shortly after birth to approximately 2 diopters at the age of 45 to 50. Thereafter, the lens of the eye may be considered to be almost a totally non-accommodating lens, which condition is known as "presbyopia." Once a person has reached the state of presbyopia, each of his eyes remains focused permanently at an almost constant distance; this distance depends on the physical characteristics of each individual's eyes. Obviously, the eyes can no longer accommodate for both near vision and far vision. Therefore, for an older person to see clearly both in the distance and nearby, he must wear glasses for far-seeing or near-seeing—for one or the other or for both.

The Pupillary Aperture

A major function of the iris is to increase the amount of light that enters the eye during darkness and to decrease the light that enters the eye in bright light. The reflexes for controlling this mechanism will be considered in the discussion of the neurology of the eye in Chapter 54. The amount of light that enters the eye through the pupil is proportional to the area of the pupil or to the square of the diameter of the pupil. The pupil of the human eye can become as small as approximately 1.5 mm. and can become almost as large as 8 mm. in diameter. Therefore, the quantity of light entering the eye may vary approximately 30 times as a result of changes in pupillary aperture size.

Depth of Focus of the Lens System of the Eye. Figure 535 illustrates two separate eyes that are exactly alike except that the diameters of the pupillary apertures are different. In the upper eye the pupillary aperture is very small, and in the lower eye the aperture is very large. In front of each of these two eyes are two small point sources of light, and light from each passes through the pupillary apertures and focuses on the retina. Consequently, in both eyes the retina sees two spots of light in perfect focus. It is evident from the diagrams, however, that if

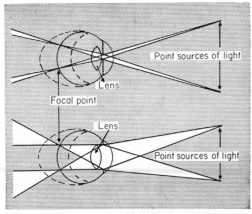

Figure 535. Effect of small and large pupillary apertures on the depth of focus.

the retina is moved forward or backward, the size of each spot will not change much on the retina of the upper eye, but on the retina of the lower eye the size of the spot increases greatly and becomes a "blur circle" when the retina is moved either in front of or behind the focal point of the lens system. In other words, the upper lens system has far greater *depth of focus* than the bottom lens system. When a lens system has great depth of focus, the retina can be considerably displaced from the focal point and still discern the various points of an image rather distinctly; whereas, when a lens system has shallow depth of focus, having the retina only slightly away from the focal plane causes extreme blurring of the image.

The greatest possible depth of focus occurs when the pupil is extremely small. The reason for this is that with a very small aperture the eye acts more or less as a pinhole camera. It will be recalled from the study of physics that light rays coming from an object and passing through a pinhole will be in focus on any surface at all distances beyond the pinhole. In other words, the depth of focus of a pinhole camera is infinite.

"Normal" Aberrations of Vision

Spherical Aberration. The crystalline lens of the eye is not nearly so regularly formed as are lenses made by good opticians. Indeed, the light rays passing through the peripheral edges of the eye lens are never brought to a really sharp focus with the other light rays; light rays passing through the outer edge of a lens may come to a focal point either behind or in front of the focal point of the other rays. This inability of all rays to come to exactly the same focal point, as illustrated in Figure 536, is known as "spherical aberration," and the lens system of the human eye is quite subject to such an error. Therefore, increasing the aperture of

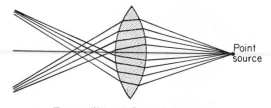

Figure 536. Spherical aberration.

the pupil progressively decreases the sharpness of focus. This partially explains why visual acuity is decreased at low illumination levels.

Chromatic Aberration. The lens of the eye is also subject to "chromatic aberration," which is illustrated in Figure 537. This means that the refractive power of the lens is different for the different colors, and these focus at different distances behind the lens. Furthermore, the greater the aperture of the lens the greater are the errors of chromatic aberration, and the smaller the aperture the fewer are the errors, for those light rays passing through the center of the lens are much less affected than are the rays passing through the periphery of the lens.

Diffractive Errors of the Eye. Still another error in the optical system of all eyes is "diffraction" of light rays. Diffraction means bending of light rays when they pass over sharp edges. Diffractive errors occur especially when the pupil becomes very small, because "interference" patterns then appear on the retina resulting from the passage of light rays over the sharp edges of the pupil. A thorough consideration of diffraction at this point is impossible, and this phenomenon is simply noted to explain that, as the pupil becomes almost pin-point in size, the sharpness of vision becomes less than it is when the pupil is approximately 2 mm. in size.

Cataracts. *Cataracts* in one or both of the eye lenses are an especially important eye abnormality. They are observed principally in old people. A cataract is a cloudy or opaque area in the cortex of the lens. In the early stage of cataract formation the proteins in the lens fibers immediately beneath the capsule become denatured. Later, these same proteins coagulate to form opaque areas in place of the normal transparent protein fibers of the lens. Finally, in still later stages, a considerable amount of calcium is deposited in the coagulated proteins, thus further increasing the opacity.

When a cataract has obscured light transmission so greatly that it seriously impairs vision, the condition can be corrected by surgical removal of the entire lens. When this is done, however, the eye loses a large portion of its refractive power, which must be replaced by a very powerful convex lens in front of the eye, as will be explained in the following sections.

Errors of Refraction

Emmetropia. As shown in Figure 538, the eye is considered to be normal or "emmetropic" if, when the ciliary muscle is completely relaxed, parallel light rays from distant objects are in sharp focus on the retina. This means that the emmetropic eye can, with its ciliary muscle completely relaxed, see all distant objects clearly, but to focus objects at close range it must contract its ciliary muscle and thereby provide various degrees of accommodation.

Hypermetropia (Also Called Hyperopia). Hypermetropia, which is also known as "far-sightedness," is due either to an eye-

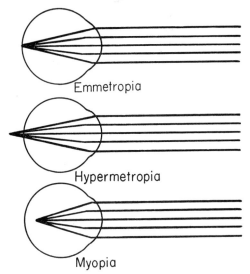

Figure 538. Emmetropia, illustrating parallel light rays focusing on the retina; hypermetropia, illustrating parallel light rays focusing behind the retina; and myopia, illustrating parallel light rays focusing in front of the retina.

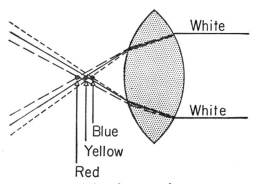

Figure 537. Chromatic aberration.

ball that is too short or to a lens system that is too weak when the ciliary muscle is completely relaxed. In this condition, parallel light rays are not bent sufficiently by the lens system to come to a focus by the time they reach the retina. In order to overcome this abnormality, the ciliary muscle may contract to increase the strength of the lens. Therefore, the far-sighted person is capable, by using his mechanism of accommodation, of focusing distant objects on his retina. If he has used only a small amount of strength in his ciliary muscle to accommodate for the distant objects, then he still has much accommodative power left, and objects closer and closer to the eye can also be focused sharply until the ciliary muscle has contracted to its limit. The distance of the object away from the eye at this point is known as the "near point" of vision.

In old age, when the lens becomes presbyopic, the far-sighted person often is not able to accommodate his lens sufficiently to focus even distant objects, much less to focus near objects.

Myopia. In the abnormality known as myopia, or "near-sightedness," even when the ciliary muscle is completely relaxed, the strength of the lens is still so great that light rays coming from distant objects are focused in front of the retina. This may be due either to too long an eyeball or to too much power of the lens system of the eye.

No mechanism exists by which the eye can decrease the strength of its lens beyond that which exists when the ciliary muscle is completely relaxed. Therefore, the myopic person has no mechanism by which he can ever focus distant objects sharply on his retina. However, as an object comes nearer and nearer to his eye it finally comes near enough that its image is focused on the retina. Then, when the object comes still closer to the eye, the person can use his mechanism of accommodation to keep the image focused clearly. Therefore, a myopic person has a very definite limiting "far point" for acute vision as well as a "near point"; when an object comes inside the "far point," he can use his mechanism of accommodation to keep the object in focus, but any object beyond the "far point" is always out of focus.

Correction of Myopia and Hypermetropia by Use of Lenses. It will be recalled that light rays passing through a concave lens

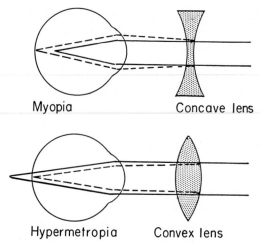

Figure 539. Correction of myopia with a concave lens and correction of hypermetropia with a convex lens

diverge. Therefore, if the refractive surfaces of the eye have too much refractive power, as in myopia, some of this excessive refractive power can be neutralized by placing in front of the eye a concave spherical lens, which will diverge the rays. On the other hand, in a person who has hypermetropia—that is, one who has too weak a lens for the distance of the retina away from the lens—the abnormal vision can be corrected by adding refractive power with a convex spherical lens in front of the eye. These corrections are illustrated in Figure 539. One usually determines the strength of the concave or convex lens needed for clear vision by "trial and error"—that is, by trying first a strong lens and then a stronger or weaker lens until the right one is found.

Astigmatism. Astigmatism is a refractive error of the lens system of the eye caused usually by an oblong shape of the cornea or, rarely, by an oblong shape of the lens. A lens surface like the side of a football lying edgewise to the incoming light, for instance, would be an example of an astigmatic lens. The degree of curvature in a plane through the long axis of the football is not nearly so great as the degree of curvature in a plane through the short axis. The same is true of an astigmatic lens. Because the curvature of the astigmatic lens along one plane is less than the curvature along the other plane, light rays striking the peripheral portions of the lens in one plane are not bent nearly so much as are light rays striking the peripheral portions of the other plane. This is illustrated in Figure 540, which shows what happens to rays of light emanating from a point source and passing through an astigmatic lens. The light rays in the vertical plane, which is indicated by plane BD, are refracted greatly by the astigmatic lens because of the greater curvature up and down this lens than around the lens. However, the light rays in the horizontal plane, which is indicated by plane AC, are not bent nearly so much as the light rays in the vertical plane. It is obvious, therefore, that the light rays passing through an astigmatic lens do not all come to a common focal point because the light rays passing through one plane of the lens focus far in front of those passing through the other plane.

Placing an appropriate *spherical* lens in front of an astigmatic eye can bring the light rays that pass through *one plane* of the lens into focus on the retina, but spherical lenses can never bring *all* the light rays into complete focus at the same time. This is the reason why astigmatism is a very undesirable refractive error of the eyes. Furthermore, the accommodative powers of the eyes cannot compensate for astigmatism for the same reasons that spherical lenses placed in front of the eyes cannot correct the condition.

Correction of astigmatism with a cylindrical lens. In correcting astigmatism with lenses it must always be remembered that two cylindrical lenses of equal strength may be crossed at right angles to give the same refractive effects as a spherical lens. How-

ever, if one of the crossed cylindrical lenses has a different strength from that of the second lens, the light rays in one plane may not be brought to a common focal point with the light rays in the opposite plane. This is exactly the situation that one finds in the astigmatic eye. In other words, one may consider an astigmatic eye as having a lens system made up of two cylindrical lenses of slightly different strengths. Another way of looking upon the astigmatic lens system of the eye is that this system is a spherical lens with a superimposed cylindrical lens.

To correct the focusing of an astigmatic lens system, it is necessary to determine both the *strength* of the cylindrical lens needed to neutralize the excess cylindrical power of the lens in the eye and the *axis* of this abnormal cylindrical lens.

There are several methods for determining the axis of the abnormal cylindrical component of the lens system of an eye. One of these methods is based on the use of parallel black bars, as shown in Figure 541. Some of these parallel bars are vertical, some horizontal, and some at various angles to the vertical and horizontal planes. After placing by trial and error various spherical lenses in front of the astigmatic eye, one set of these parallel bars finally will be brought into sharp focus on the retina of the astigmatic eye. If there is no accompanying myopia or hypermetropia, the spherical lenses may not be necessary. It can be shown from the

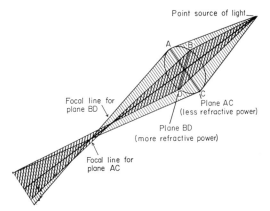

Figure 540. Astigmatism, illustrating that light rays focus at one focal distance in one plane and at another focal distance in the opposite plane.

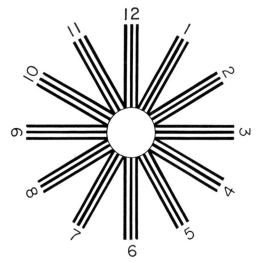

Figure 541. Chart composed of parallel black bars for determining the axis (meridian) of astigmatism.

physical principles of optics discussed earlier in this chapter that the axis of the out-of-focus cylindrical component of the optical system is at right angles to the black bars that are seen clearly. Once this axis is found, the examiner leaves the spherical lens in front of the eye and progressively tries stronger and weaker positive and negative cylindrical lenses placed at right angles to the clear bars until the patient sees all the crossed bars with equal clarity. When this has been accomplished, the examiner writes a prescription for the astigmatic eye so that the optician can grind a special lens having both the spherical correction plus the cylindrical correction at the appropriate axis. The lens supplied by the optician must always be oriented to the appropriate axis in front of the astigmatic eye for appropriate correction of the astigmatism to occur.

Keratoconus. In this condition the fibers of the cornea are weaker than normal as a result of some hereditary or developmental factor, so that the pressure in the eyeball causes the cornea to bulge outward. The refractive power of the normal corneal surface is about 39 diopters, but, if the cornea bulges outward as shown in Figure 542 into a pointed shape, the refractive power becomes as much as 60 or even 100 diopters at its very center, while the outer edges of the bulge may have almost normal refractive power. Furthermore, the surface is usually very irregular so that intense degrees of astigmatism result. This, obviously, completely destroys the ability of the eye to focus an image on the retina. Furthermore, it is almost impossible to correct this optical abnormality with glass lenses placed in front of the eyes, principally because of the very irregular shape of the cornea.

Correction of keratoconus with a contact lens. Contact lenses are ground on their posterior surfaces approximately to fit the cornea, and the anterior surface is ground to have appropriate refractive power for correction of eye ab-

normalities. The lenses are held to the eyeball by fluid adhesion. They may be worn by most persons for only a few hours at a time because of eye irritation, but others wear them almost constantly. The best method found thus far to correct keratoconus is to use a contact lens that fits over the cornea as shown in Figure 542. Because the fluid between the contact lens and the cornea has a refractive index not too different from that of the cornea, the interface between the fluid and the cornea has little refractive power. Therefore, by grinding the front surface of the contact lens to the shape of an almost normal cornea the refractive power of the eye is returned to essentially normal.

Size of the Image on the Retina and Visual Acuity

If the distance from an object to the lens is 17 meters and the distance from the lens to the image is 17 millimeters, the ratio of the object size to image size is 1000 to 1. Therefore, an object 17 meters in front of the eye and 1 meter in size will produce an image on the retina 1 millimeter in size.

The optical system of the normal eye, despite the errors noted above, is quite good—so good, in fact, that one of the major limiting factors that determine the acuity of vision is the distance between the cones in the fovea of the eye.

Theoretically, a point of light from a distant point source, when focused on the retina, should be infinitely small. However, since the lens system of the eye is not absolutely perfect, such a retinal spot ordinarily has a diameter of about 11 microns even with maximum visual acuity. It is brightest in its very center and shades off gradually toward the edges.

The average diameter of cones in the fovea of the retina is approximately 2 to 3 microns, which is only one-fourth the diameter of the spot of light. Nevertheless, since the spot of light has a bright center point and shaded edges, a person can distinguish two separate points if their centers lie approximately 2 microns apart on the retina, which is slightly less than the width of a retinal cone. Thus, the acuity of vision of an optically perfect eye is limited at least to some extent by the size of the retinal cones themselves.

The maximum visual acuity of the human eye for point sources of light is 26 seconds.

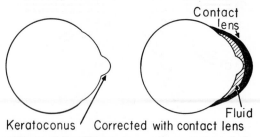

Keratoconus   Corrected with contact lens

Figure 542. Keratoconus and correction of abnormal corneal refractive power by use of a contact lens

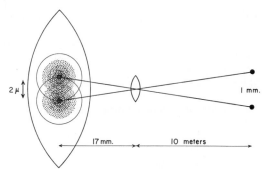

Figure 543. Maximal visual acuity for two point sources of light.

That is, when light rays from two separate points strike the eye with an angle of about 26 seconds between them, they can be recognized as two points instead of one. This means that a person with maximal acuity looking at two bright pin-point spots of light 10 meters away can barely distinguish the two spots as separate entities when they are 1 millimeter apart. This is illustrated in Figure 543.

Clinical Method for Stating Visual Acuity. Usually the test chart for testing eyes is placed 20 feet away from the patient, and, if the patient can see the letters of the size that he should be able to see at 20 feet, he is said to have 20/20 vision. If he can see only letters that he should be able to see at 200 feet, he is said to have 20/200 vision. On the other hand, if he can see at 20 feet letters that he should be able to see only at 15 feet, then he is said to have 20/15 vision. In other words, the clinical method of expressing vision is actually a mathematical fraction that expresses the ratio of two distances, but this is also approximately the ratio of one's visual acuity in comparison with that of the normal person.

Determination of Distance of an Object from the Eye—Depth Perception

There are three major means by which the visual apparatus normally perceives distance, a phenomenon that is known as *depth perception*. These are (1) relative sizes of objects, (2) moving parallax, and (3) stereopsis.

Determination of Distance by Relative Sizes. If a person knows that a man is six feet tall and then he sees this man even with

only one eye, he can determine how far away the man is simply by the size of the man's image on his retina. He does not consciously think about the size of this image, but his brain has learned to determine automatically from the image sizes the distance of objects from the eye when the dimensions of these objects are already known. The greater the distance, the smaller is the image, and the less the distance the larger is the image.

Determination of Distance by Moving Parallax. Another important means by which the eyes determine distance is that of moving parallax. If a person looks off into the distance with his eyes completely still, he perceives no moving parallax, but, when he moves his head to one side or the other, the images of objects close to him move rapidly across his retinae while the images of distant objects remain rather stationary. For instance, if he moves his head one inch and an object is only one inch in front of his eye, the image will move almost all the way across his retinae, whereas the image of an object 200 feet away from his eyes will not move perceptibly. Thus, by this mechanism of moving parallax, one can tell the *relative distances* of different objects even though only one eye is used.

Determination of distance by stereopsis. Another method by which one perceives parallax is that of binocular vision. Because one eye is a little more than two inches to one side of the other eye, the images on the two retinae are different one from the other—that is, an object that is one inch in front of the bridge of the nose will form an image on the temporal portion of the retina of each eye, whereas a small object 20 feet

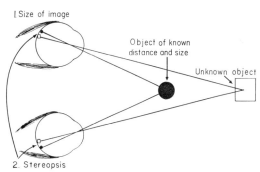

Figure 544. Perception of distance (1) by the size of the image on the retina and (2) as a result of stereopsis.

in front of the nose will have its image at closely corresponding points in the middle of the eye. This type of parallax is illustrated in Figure 544, which shows the images of a black spot and a square actually reversed on the retinae because they are at different distances in front of the eyes. This gives a type of parallax that is present all the time when both eyes are being used. It is almost entirely this binocular parallax (or stereopsis) that gives a person with two eyes far greater ability to judge relative distances *when objects are nearby* than a person who has only one eye. However, stereopsis is virtually useless for depth perception at distances beyond 20 feet.

OPTICAL INSTRUMENTS

The Ophthalmoscope

The ophthalmoscope is an instrument designed so that an observer can look through it into a patient's eye and see the retina with clarity. Though the ophthalmoscope appears to be a relatively complicated instrument, its principles are very simple. The basic portions of such an instrument are illustrated in Figure 545 and may be explained as follows:

If a very bright spot of light exists on the retina of an emmetropic eye, light rays from the spot diverge toward the lens system of the eye, and, after they pass through the lens system, they are parallel with each other because the retina is at the focal distance of the lens. When these parallel rays pass into an emmetropic eye of another person, they then are focused to a point on the retina of the second person. Therefore, any spot of light on the retina of the observed eye comes to a focal spot on the retina of the observing eye. Likewise, when the bright spot of light is moved to different portions of the observed retina, the focal spot on the retina of the observer will also move. Thus,

if the retina of one person is made to emit light, the image of this retina will be focused on the retina of the observer provided that the observer simply stands very close to the observed eye with the two eyes peering into each other. these principles, of course, apply only to completely emmetropic eyes with relaxed ciliary muscles.

To make an ophthalmoscope, one need only devise a means for illuminating the retina to be examined. Then, the reflected light from that retina can be seen by the observer simply by putting the two eyes close to each other. To illuminate the retina of the observed eye, an angulated mirror or a segment of a prism is placed in front of the observed eye in such a manner that light from a bulb may be reflected into the observed eye. Thus, the retina is lighted through the pupil, and the observer can also see into the subject's pupil by looking over the edge of the mirror or prism.

It was noted above that these principles apply only to persons with completely emmetropic eyes. If the refractive power of either of the eyes is abnormal, it is necessary to correct these refractive powers in order for the observer to see a sharp image of the observed retina. Therefore, the usual ophthalmoscope has a series of about 20 lenses mounted on a turret so that the turret may be rotated from one lens to another, and the correction for abnormal refractive powers of either or both of the eyes can be made at the same time by selecting a single lens of appropriate strength. In normal young persons, when the two eyes come close together, a natural accommodative reflex occurs that causes approximately +2 diopters increase in the strength of the lens of each eye. To correct for this +2 diopters in each eye, it is necessary that the lens turret of the ophthalmoscope, even though both eyes are normal, be rotated to approximately −4 diopters correction.

The Retinoscope

The retinoscope, which is illustrated in Figure 546, is an instrument that can be used to determine the refractive power of eyes even though the subject cannot converse with the observer.

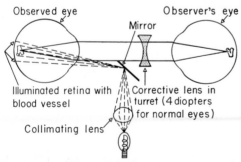

Figure 545. The optical system of the ophthalmoscope.

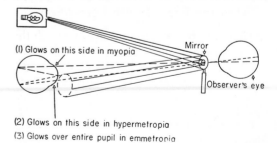

(1) Glows on this side in myopia
(2) Glows on this side in hypermetropia
(3) Glows over entire pupil in emmetropia

Figure 546. The optical system of the retinoscope.

Such a procedure is quite valuable for fitting glasses to an infant.

To use the retinoscope a bright spot of light is placed behind and to one side of the observed eye, and the observer stands approximately 1 meter away from the observed eye, looking through a hole in the middle of a mirror. The observer then rotates this mirror from side to side, casting a reflected beam of light into the pupil of the observed eye while the subject keeps his gaze intently on the observer's eye. If the observed eye is normal, when this beam of light first hits the edge of the pupil, the entire pupil will suddenly glow red to the observer. If the eye has abnormal refractive powers, the red glow appears either on the side of the pupil into which the light shines or on the opposite side of the pupil. *In hypermetropia the first glow appears on the side of the pupil from which the light beam is being moved across the pupil. In myopia the first glow appears on the opposite side of the pupil.*

A discussion of the complicated optics of the retinoscope is impossible at this point, and it is almost safe to say that all *simple* explanations of the retinoscope in physiology texts have been wrong. Therefore, reference is made to textbooks of ophthalmology.

One can fit glasses to a patient by placing selected lenses in front of the observed eye one at a time until the glow suddenly covers the pupil over its entire extent rather than spreading from one side of the pupil to the other. However, it should be noted that in retinoscopy one tests an eye that is focused on the observer's eye at 1 meter's distance. This must be taken into consideration in prescribing glasses.

REFERENCES

Adler, F. H.: Gifford's Textbook of Ophthalmology. 6th ed., Philadelphia, W. B. Saunders Co., 1957.

Adler, F. H.: Physiology of the Eye; Clinical Approach. St. Louis, C. V. Mosby Co., 1953.

Armstrong, G. G.: A model eye for the student laboratory. *J. M. Education, 33*:845, 1958.

Borish, I. M.: Clinical Refraction. 2nd ed., Chicago, Professional Press, 1954.

Brecher, G. A.: New method for measuring aniseikonia. *Am. J. Ophth., 34*:1016, 1951.

Brecher, G. A.: Quantitative studies on binocular fusion. *Am. J. Ophth., 28*:134, 1954.

Chang, H. T.: Physiology of vision. *Ann. Rev. Physiol., 15*:373, 1953.

Chapanis, A.: Vision. *Ann. Rev. Physiol., 10*:133, 1948.

Clark, G.: Factors contributing to the successful treatment of retinal detachments. *New York State J. Med., 56*:3298, 1956.

Crescitelli, F.: Physiology of vision. *Ann. Rev. Physiol., 22*:525, 1960.

Duke-Elder, S.: Textbook of Ophthalmology. Vols. I–VII. St. Louis, C. V. Mosby Co., 1932, 1938, 1941, 1949, 1952, 1954.

Duke-Elder, S.: The Cornea. Springfield, Illinois, Charles C Thomas, 1960.

Duke-Elder, S.: The Practice of Refraction. 5th ed., St. Louis, C. V. Mosby Co., 1949.

Fry, G. A.: The image-forming mechanism of the eye. *Handbook of Physiology, 1*:647, 1959.

Granit, R.: Physiology of vision. *Ann. Rev. Physiol., 12*:485, 1950.

Hartline, H. K.: Vision—introduction. *Handbook of Physiology, 1*:615, 1959.

Hartridge, H.: Recent Advances in the Physiology of Vision. Philadelphia, The Blakiston Co., 1950.

Hill, J. C., and Heggeness, F. W.: Electrolyte composition of experimental galactose cataracts. *Am. J. Physiol., 197*:85, 1959.

Hirsch, M. J., and Weymouth, F. W.: Distance discrimination; theoretic considerations. *Arch. Ophth., 39*:210, 1948.

Linksz, A.: Physiology of the Eye. Vol. I. Optics. New York, Grune & Stratton, Inc., 1950.

Mann, I. C.: The Development of the Human Eye. New York, Grune & Stratton, Inc., 1950.

Polyak, S.: The Vertebrate Visual System. Chicago, University of Chicago Press, 1957.

Rosen, E.: Atopic Cataract. Springfield, Illinois, Charles C Thomas, 1959.

Talbot, S. A.: Vision. *Ann. Rev. Physiol., 11*:245, 1949.

Thomas, C. I.: The Cornea. Springfield, Illinois, Charles C Thomas, 1956.

Veirs, E. R.: The Lacrimal System—Clinical Application. New York, Grune & Stratton, Inc., 1955.

Willmer, E. N.: Physiology of vision. *Ann. Rev. Physiol., 17*:339, 1955.

Wolff, E.: Anatomy of the Eye and Orbit. 4th ed., New York, Blakiston Co., 1954.

Wulff, V. J.: Physiology of the compound eye. *Physiol. Rev., 36*:145, 1956.

See also Chapter 53, Retinal mechanisms; Chapter 54, Neurology of vision.

The Eye:

The Receptor Function of the Retina

The retina is the light-sensitive portion of the eye, containing the cones, which detect specific colors, and the rods, which detect light of any color besides deep red. When the rods and cones are excited, nerve impulses are then transmitted through successive neurons in the retina itself and finally into the optic nerve fibers and cerebral cortex. The purpose of the present chapter is to explain specifically the mechanisms by which the rods and cones detect both white and colored light.

ANATOMY AND FUNCTION OF THE STRUCTURAL ELEMENTS OF THE RETINA

The Layers of the Retina. Figure 547 shows the functional components of the retina arranged in layers from the outside to the inside as follows: (1) pigment layer, (2) layer of rods and cones projecting into the pigment, (3) outer limiting membrane, (4) outer nuclear layer, (5) outer plexiform layer, (6) inner nuclear layer, (7) inner plexiform layer, (8) ganglionic layer, (9) layer of optic nerve fibers, and (10) inner limiting membrane.

Since the rods and cones are the light-sensitive portion of the retina, light must pass through all the other layers besides the pigment layer before reaching the excitable cells, and this obviously decreases the visual acuity. However, in the central region of the retina, as will be discussed more fully shortly, the inner layers are pulled aside to prevent this loss of acuity.

The Rods and Cones. The nuclei of the rods and cones are located in the outer nuclear layer while the light-sensitive portions of both these receptors project into the pigment layer of the retina. The rods are relatively slender, having a diameter of about 2 microns in the more central portions of the retina and 4 to 5 microns in

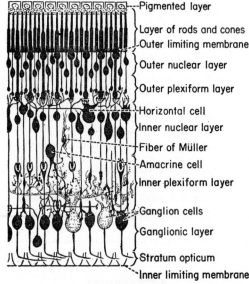

Figure 547. Plan of the retinal neurons. (From Polyak: The Retina. University of Chicago Press.)

the more peripheral portions. The cones on the other hand, have a diameter of 2 to 3 microns in the *fovea*, the centralmost portion of the retina, and some 5 to 8 microns in the periphery.

The sensitive portions of both the rods and cones contain light-sensitive chemicals which partially decompose on exposure to even the minutest quantities of light. The decomposition products in turn stimulate the cell membranes of the rods and cones, eliciting nerve impulses that are then transmitted into the nervous system. Indeed, the rods and cones themselves are modified neurons and can actually be considered to be part of the nervous system.

The Foveal Region of the Retina and Its Importance in Acute Vision. A very minute area in the center of the retina called the *macula* and occupying a total area of not over 1

710

square millimeter is especially capable of very acute and detailed vision. This area is composed entirely of cones, but the cones are very much elongated and have a diameter of only 2 to 3 microns in contradistinction to the very large cones located farther peripherally in the retina. The central portion of the macula is called the *fovea;* in this region the blood vessels, the ganglion cells, the inner nuclear layer of cells, and the plexiform layers are all displaced to one side rather than resting directly on top of the cones. This allows light to pass unimpeded to the cones rather than through several layers of retina, which aids greatly in the acuity of visual perception by this region of the retina.

Neural Connections of the Rods and Cones. As illustrated in Figure 548, the rods and cones in the peripheral portion of the retina converge on common bipolar cells in the inner nuclear layer, and these in turn converge on common optic nerve fibers. The retina contains a total of approximately 125 million rods and 5.5 million cones; yet, only 900,000 optic nerve fibers lead from the eye to the brain. Therefore, an average of about 140 rods and 6 cones converge on each optic nerve fiber.

There is a major difference between the peripheral retina and the central retina, for, as one approaches the fovea, fewer and fewer rods and cones converge on each single optic nerve fiber. Also, the rods and cones both become slenderer. These two effects obviously progressively increase the acuity of vision toward the central retina. Then, finally, in the very central portion, in the fovea, there are no rods at all, and the number of optic nerve fibers innervating the foveal cones is almost the same as the number of cones in the fovea, which is shown to the right in Figure 548. This partially explains the high degree of visual acuity in the central portion of the retina in comparison with the very poor visual acuity in the peripheral portions.

The Optic Disc. Located approximately 15 degrees medial to the fovea is the *optic disc,* where the optic nerve fibers and the central retinal blood vessels pass into the eyeball. The optic disc is structurally the weakest portion of the eyeball because of the many spaces in the sclera through which the optic nerve fibers pass. Therefore, whenever the fluid pressure in the eyeball becomes too high, the optic disc becomes punched outward, stretching or compressing the nerve fibers where they pass over the rim of the disc. In this manner, the optic nerve fibers are often destroyed with resultant blindness. This sequence of events occurs in *glaucoma,* which was discussed in Chapter 7 in connection with the fluids of the eye.

It should be noted, too, that no rods or cones are located directly over the optic disc. This causes a blind spot approximately 15 degrees temporally in the field of vision of each eye.

The Pigment Layer of the Retina. The pigment layer of the retina performs two functions. First, it provides *melanin,* which is the black pigment of this layer, and, second, it provides much of the nutrition for the rods and cones.

The melanin pigment prevents light reflection throughout the globe of the eyeball, which is extremely important for acute vision. This pigment performs the same function in the eye as the black paint inside the bellows of a camera. Without it, light rays would be reflected in all directions within the eyeball and would cause diffuse lighting of the retina rather than the contrasts between dark and light spots required for the formation of precise images. The importance of melanin in the pigment layer is particularly well illustrated by its lack in *albinos,* who are people hereditarily lacking in melanin pigment in all parts of their bodies. When an albino enters a bright area, light that impinges on the retina is reflected in all directions by the white surface of the choroid so that a single discrete spot of light that would normally excite only a few rods or cones is reflected everywhere and excites many of the receptors. Thus, the lack of melanin causes the vision of albinos, even with the best of optical correction, to be rarely better than 20/100 to 20/200.

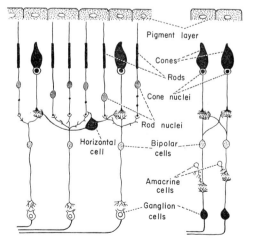

Figure 548. Basic neural connections of the rods and cones.

The rods and cones receive at least part of their nutrition by diffusion of fluids and nutrients from the choroid first into the pigment layer and thence into the rods and cones. For instance, vitamin A, which is necessary for formation of the photosensitive chemicals in both these receptors, is normally stored in the pigment layer in large amounts and can be called upon on demand by the rods and cones.

Relationship of the Retina to the Choroid. The normal retina is loosely adherent to the choroid, which is a highly vascular layer of the eye lying immediately between the pigment layer of the retina and the sclera. The nutrient blood supply to the inside layers of the retina is derived from the central retinal artery, which enters the inside of the eye along with the optic nerve and then divides to supply the entire inner retinal surface. The venous return from the retina, in turn, accompanies the arterial system back through the optic nerve. Thus, to a great extent the retina has its own blood supply independent of the underlying vascular choroid. However, as pointed out above, the outer layers of the retina, including especially the rods and cones themselves, are at least partially dependent on diffusion of nutrients from the choroid. This dependence for nutrients is especially apparent when the retina becomes detached from the choroid and remains detached for long periods of time, as will be discussed below.

Retinal detachment. The retina occasionally detaches from its loose connections with the choroid. In a few instances the cause of such detachment is an injury to the eyeball that allows fluid or blood to collect between the retina and the choroid, but more often it is caused by contracture of the very fine collagenous fibrils in the vitreous humor, which pull the retina unevenly toward the interior of the globe.

Fortunately, because of the independent blood supply to the retina through the retinal artery, the retina can resist degeneration for many days to weeks and can become functional once again if surgically replaced in its normal relationship with the choroid. But, if not replaced soon, the retina will finally degenerate and then will be unable to function even after surgical repair.

THE PHOTOCHEMISTRY OF VISION

Both the rods and cones contain chemicals that decompose on exposure to light. The chemical in the *rods* has been isolated and is called *rhodopsin.* Unfortunately, the light-sensitive chemical in the *cones* of human beings has not yet been isolated. However, in some of the lower animals these chemicals have been isolated and in all instances have been found to have the same chemical compositions as rhodopsin except for slight differences in the protein portions of the substances. These protein portions are called *opsins.*

In the present section we will discuss principally the photochemistry of rhodopsin, but it should be recognized that precisely the same principles apply to the photochemistry of the cones except that the protein opsins are slightly different.

The Rhodopsin-Retinene Visual Cycle of the Rods

Figure 549 illustrates the chemical changes that occur in the rods when light energy impinges on the retina. The segment of the rod that projects into the pigment layer contains about 40 per cent *rhodopsin,* which is also called *visual purple.* Immediately upon receipt of light energy in the rods, some of the rhodopsin changes into *lumi-rhodopsin,* which is a very unstable compound having a half-life of only a small fraction of a second. This substance, therefore, decays rapidly into *meta-rhodopsin,* which still is unstable and splits into two compounds, *retinene,* or *visual yellow,* and a protein opsin called *scotopsin.*

Retinene and scotopsin then react slowly with each other to reform rhodopsin because these compounds contain considerable quantities of free energy and therefore are highly reactive. Thus, the rhodopsin originally destroyed by the light energy is automatically reformed. Though the reaction for reformation of rhodopsin is not nearly so rapid as its original destruction, its half-time is still only a few minutes.

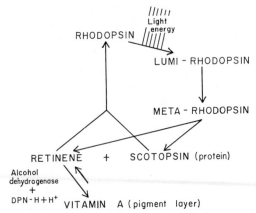

Figure 549. Photochemistry of the rhodopsin-retinene visual cycle.

In summary, light energy changes rhodopsin into an unstable compound, and this in turn changes automatically through several progressive stages until it becomes rhodopsin once again.

Relationship of the Rhodopsin-Retinene Cycle to Vitamin A. Retinene is a dehydrogenated product of vitamin A formed in accordance with the following reaction:

$$C_{19}H_{27}CH_2OH + DPN^+ \xleftarrow{\text{Alcohol dehydrogenase}} C_{19}H_{27}CHO + DPNH + H^+$$

Vitamin A   Retinene

Excitation of the Rods. Exactly how the above chemical changes elicit nerve impulses in the rods is unknown. However, it is believed that during the initial stage of rhodopsin breakdown the scotopsin becomes momentarily ionized when the prosthetic group breaks away, and these ions then attack the membrane directly to elicit nerve impulses. These excitatory effects all occur in a very short period of time, the total duration of excitation lasting only about one tenth second after an instantaneous flash of light.

It should be noted, too, that a flash of light lasting only 1 millionth of a second gives the person a sensation of seeing the light for about one tenth second, for the decomposition products of rhodopsin, once formed in the rod, continue exciting the rod as long as they remain.

Logarithmic sensitivity of the rod to light. The number of impulses emitted by a rod is not directly proportional to the intensity of the light but instead is proportional to the *logarithm* of the intensity. This is another example of the *Weber-Fechner Law,* which was explained in Chapter 46. This logarithmic response obviously allows the retina to respond differentially to lights of tremendously varying intensities.

The eye can detect an increase in light intensity whenever the increase is more than 2 to 5 per cent. Thus, if the intensity of light were an arbitrary value of 100 and were then increased up to 102, the person might barely perceive an increase in intensity. But, if the same eye were subjected initially to a light intensity of 1,000, the intensity would still have to increase by at least 2 per cent for the person to perceive a change—that is, up to an intensity of 1020. The actual increase in this instance is 10 times that in the first instance but the logarithm of the increase is still the same.

Furthermore, the equilibrium of the above equation is strongly in favor of vitamin A; therefore, a large amount of vitamin A must be present to synthesize only a minute amount of retinene. Ordinarily, when the retina is exposed to darkness, only minute quantities of retinene are present in the retina because it is rapidly changed into rhodopsin. Therefore, under these conditions, vitamin A automatically tends to form additional retinene until maximal amounts of rhodopsin have been achieved in the rod.

Conversely, when the eye is exposed to extremely bright light, almost all the rhodopsin becomes converted into retinene, and this immediately reverses the reaction from retinene to vitamin A, causing slow conversion of the retinene back into vitamin A. Therefore, the total quantity of rhodopsin and retinene in the retina becomes slowly depleted.

Thus, there are two means by which the amount of rhodopsin in the retina is reduced when an eye is exposed to bright light: (1) simple degradation of the rhodopsin into retinene and scotopsin and (2) conversion of retinene into vitamin A. The first of these two processes occurs very rapidly on exposure to light while the second occurs very slowly, requiring perhaps 30 minutes for halfway completion of the reaction and many hours to approach equilibrium.

Night blindness. Night blindness is associated with vitamin A deficiency, for, when the total quantity of vitamin A in the blood becomes greatly reduced, the quantities of vitamin A, retinene, and rhodopsin in the rods, as well as the color photosensitive chemicals in the cones, are all depressed, thus decreasing the sensitivities of the rods and cones. This condition is called *night blindness* because at night the amount of available light is far too little to permit adequate vision, whereas, in daylight, sufficient light is available to excite the rods and cones despite their reduction in photochemical substances.

For night blindness to occur, a person must usually remain on a vitamin A deficient diet for weeks or months because large quantities of vitamin A are normally stored in the liver and are made available to the rest of the body in times of need. However, once night blindness does develop it can often be completely cured in a half hour or more by intravenous injection of vitamin A. This results from the very ready conversion of vitamin A into retinene and thence into rhodopsin.

Several different chemical substances are classified as vitamin A. Some types of vitamin A will not form rhodopsin and, therefore, are not satisfactory for treatment of night blindness. However, the vitamin A of fish liver oils, the *cis* form, can be used to synthesize rhodopsin.

Photochemistry of Color Vision by the Cones

It was pointed out at the outset of this discussion that the photochemicals in the cones have the same chemical compositions as the rhodopsin in the rods except that the protein portions, the opsins, of the photochemicals are different from the scotopsin of the rods; these protein portions of the photochemicals are called *photopsins*. The color sensitive pigments of the cones, therefore, are combinations of retinene and photopsins. In the discussion of color vision later in the chapter it will become evident that at least three different types of pigments are present in different cones, thus making these cones selectively light sensitive to different colors. In other words, there is no essential difference between the photochemistry of rod and cone vision except that the light-sensitive chemicals of different cones respond differently to the various colors.

Iodopsin. The pigment *iodopsin*, which is chemically similar to rhodopsin, has been isolated from the cones of the chicken retina. Iodopsin is a combination of *retinene* and a *photopsin* that is synthesized in these cones. A light-sensitive chemical very similar to iodopsin is believed to be one of the three major light-sensitive pigments in the cones of human eyes. Iodopsin absorbs light maximally at a wavelength of 562 millimicrons, which

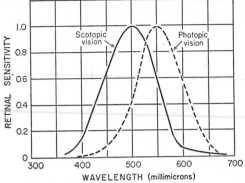

Figure 550. Spectral sensitivity curves for scotopic and photopic vision.

is in the yellow range, in comparison with rhodopsin which absorbs light maximally at a wavelength of 505 millimicrons, which is in the green range. One can readily understand, then, how light-sensitive pigments, responding to lights of different wavelengths, can easily provide color vision.

Photopic versus Scotopic Vision. The term *photopic vision* means color vision while *scotopic vision* means black and white vision. Furthermore, it is known that the cones are responsible for photopic vision while the rods are principally concerned in scotopic vision.

The cones are capable of resynthesizing their visual pigments much more rapidly after breakdown in light than are the rods. On the other hand, the rods are far more sensitive to light if they are given time to restore completely their complement of rhodopsin. Because of these differences, the rods are 1000 or more times as sensitive as the cones in areas of almost no illumination. On the other hand, when the illumination is intense, the failure of the rods to resynthesize rhodopsin rapidly makes them less sensitive than the cones. Therefore, a person has mainly scotopic vision in poor illumination and photopic vision in bright illumination.

Figure 550 illustrates the overall sensitivity of the retina at different wavelengths in both scotopic vision and photopic vision. Note especially that the eye is maximally sensitive to light of 505 millimicrons wavelength in scotopic vision and to light of 550 millimicrons wavelength in photopic vision. These curves illustrate a basic difference in the response to light of the photochemicals in the rods and cones.

Automatic Regulation of Retinal Sensitivity—Dark and Light Adaptation

Relationship of Sensitivity to Pigment Concentration. The concentrations of light-sensitive pigments in the rods and cones can change markedly under different physiological conditions, and the sensitivities of the rods and cones depend very greatly on these concentrations. In the case of the cones, relatively little is yet known about the quantitative relationship between sensitivity and pigment concentration, but, in the case of the rods, the sensitivity is approximately proportional to the antilogarithm of the rhodopsin concentration, which means that a very minute decrease in the rhodopsin reduces the sensitivity tremendously. For instance, the sensitivity of a rod is reduced about 8.5 times when the concentration of rhodopsin is reduced from maximum by only 0.006 per cent, and the sensitivity decreases over 3,000 times when the rhodopsin concentration is reduced 0.6 per cent. This antilog effect is believed to result from the fact that the first rhodopsin to be decomposed on exposure to light lies near the surface of the rod. After this portion has decomposed, far greater decomposition of the deeper layers of rhodopsin is required to excite the rods.

In summary, the sensitivity of the rods and cones can be altered up or down tremendously by only very slight changes in concentrations of the photosensitive chemicals.

Light and Dark Adaptation. If a person has been in bright light for a long period of time, very large proportions of the photochemicals in both the rods and the cones will have been reduced to retinene and opsins. Furthermore, much of the retinene will have been converted into vitamin A. Because of these two effects, the concentrations of the photochemicals will be considerably reduced, and the sensitivity of the eye to light will be even more reduced. This is called *light adaptation.*

On the other hand, if the person remains in the darkness for a long period of time, essentially all the retinene and opsins in the rods and cones become converted into light-sensitive pigments. Furthermore, large amounts of vitamin A are converted into retinene, which is then changed into additional light-sensitive pigments. Because of these two effects, the visual receptors gradually become very sensitive so that even the minutest amount of light causes excitation. This is called *dark adaptation.*

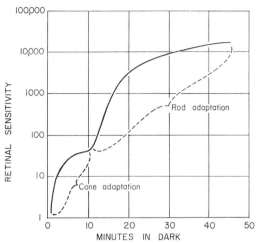

Figure 551. Dark adaptation, illustrating the relationship of cone adaptation to rod adaptation.

Figure 551 illustrates the course of dark adaptation after a person had been previously exposed to bright light for several hours. Note that immediately upon entering the darkness there was very low retinal sensitivity, but within one minute the sensitivity had increased 10-fold—that is, it could then respond to light of 10 times less intensity. At the end of 20 minutes it had become about 6000 times as sensitive as before, and at the end of 40 minutes it had become about 25,000 times as sensitive. This is called the *dark adaptation curve.* Note, however, the two inflections in the curve. The early portion of the curve is caused by adaptation of the cones, for these adapt much more rapidly than the rods because of the basic difference in the rate at which they resynthesize their photosensitive pigments. On the other hand, the cones can never achieve anywhere near the same degree of sensitivity as can the rods. Therefore, despite rapid adaptation by the cones, they cease adapting after only a few minutes while the slowly adapting rods continue to adapt for many minutes or even hours, their sensitivity increasing tremendously.

Figure 552 illustrates dark adaptation again, but in this figure it is shown that the rate of dark adaption differs following exposure of the retina to different amounts of light. Curve number 1 shows the rate of dark adaptation after the person has been in bright light for approximately twenty minutes, curve number 2 shows the rate after a person has been in bright light for only a few

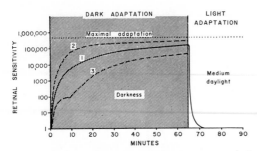

Figure 552. Dark and light adaptation. (The retina is considered to have a sensitivity of one when maximally light adapted.)

minutes, and curve number 3 after a person has been in bright light for many hours. Note that the eye exposed to bright light for a long period of time adapts very slowly in comparison with the eye that has been in bright light for only a few minutes. The cause of this difference is the slowness of the reaction between vitamin A and retinene. The eye that has remained in bright light for only a few minutes has not converted significant quantities of its retinene into vitamin A. Therefore, this eye can resynthesize its photosensitive pigments in a very short period of time. Conversely, the eye that has been exposed to prolonged bright light will have had time to convert most of its retinene into vitamin A, and since the reconversion from vitamin A back to retinene is very slow, dark adaption of the eye also is very slow.

To the right in Figure 552 is shown a typical light adaptation curve, illustrating that light adaptation occurs much more rapidly than dark adaptation. Also, the slow component caused by retinene-vitamin A interconversion does not play as prominent a role in light adaptation as in dark adaptation. Therefore, a person exposed to extremely bright light after having been in prolonged darkness will become adjusted to the new light conditions in only a few minutes. This is in contrast to dark adaptation, which requires 10 to 20 minutes for moderate adaptation and 10 to 18 hours for maximal adaptation.

Value of Light and Dark Adaptation in Vision. Between the limits of maximal dark adaptation and maximal light adaptation, the retina of the eye can change its sensitivity to light by as much as 100,000 to 500,000 times, the sensitivity automatically adjusting to changes in illumination.

Since the registration of images by the retina requires detection of both dark and light spots in the image, it is essential that the sensitivity of the retina always be adjusted so that the receptors will respond to the lighter areas and not to the darker areas. An example of maladjustment of the retina occurs when a person leaves the movie house and enters the bright sunlight, for even the dark spots in the images then seem exceedingly bright, and, as a consequence, the entire visual image is bleached, having little contrast between its different parts. Obviously, this is poor vision, and it remains poor until the retina has adapted sufficiently that the dark spots of the image no longer stimulate the receptors. Conversely, when a person enters darkness, the sensitivity of the retina is usually so slight that even the light spots in the image cannot excite the retina. But, after dark adaptation, the light spots begin to register. As an example of the extremes of light and dark adaptation, the light intensity of the sun is approximately 30,000 times that of the moon; yet, the eye can function quite well both in bright sunlight and in bright moonlight.

Negative After-images. If one looks very steadily at a scene for awhile, the bright portions of the image will cause light adaptation of the retina while the dark portions of the image will cause dark adaptation. In other words those areas of the retina that have been stimulated by light will become less sensitive while those areas that have been exposed only to darkness will gain in sensitivity. If the person then moves his eyes away from the scene and looks at a bright smooth surface he sees exactly the same scene that he had been viewing, but the light areas of the scene now appear dark, and the dark areas appear light. This is known as the *negative after-image,* and it is a natural consequence of light adaptation. That is, the portions of the retina that had been exposed to the dark areas of the image now become far more excited than the other portions of the retina that had been exposed to light portions of the image.

The negative after-image persists as long as any degree of light and dark adaptation remains in the respective portions of the retina. Referring back to Figure 552, one can see from the dark adaptation curves that a negative after-image could possibly persist as long as an hour under very favorable conditions.

Fusion of Flickering Lights by the Retina

A flickering light is one whose intensity alternately increases and decreases very rapidly. It was pointed out above that a flash of light excites the visual receptors for as long as a tenth of a second or more. Because of this persistence of excitation, rapidly successive flashes of light become *fused* together and give the appearance of being continuous. This effect is well known when one observes motion pictures or television. The images on the motion picture screen are flashed at a rate of 24 frames per second, while those of the television screen are flashed at a rate of 60 half-frames per second. As a result, the images fuse together, and continuous motion can be observed.

Figure 553 illustrates that the critical frequency at which flicker fusion occurs varies with the light intensity. At a very low intensity, fusion can result even when the rate of flicker is as low as 5 or 6 per second. However, in very bright illumination, the critical frequency for fusion rises to as great as 60 flashes per second. This difference results at least partly from the fact that the cones, which operate mainly at high levels of illumination, can detect much more rapid alterations in illumination than can the rods, which are the important receptors in very dim light.

COLOR VISION

In the above sections, we have already pointed out that the cones contain light sensitive pigments that are different from the rhodopsin in the rods and also that different cones are sensitive to different colors of light. In the present section we will explore further the mechanisms by which the retina detects all the different gradations of color in the visual spectrum.

The Tri-color Theory of Color Vision

Many different theories have been proposed to explain the phenomenon of color vision, and they are all based on the observation that the human eye can detect almost all gradations of colors when red, green, and blue monochromatic lights are appropriately mixed in different combinations. For instance, as illustrated in Figure 554, when a sheet of white paper is placed at the midpoint between lights of these three colors and then rotated so that, first, only red falls on the paper, the subject will perceive the sensation of red. As he rotates the paper farther toward the green, both red and green colors fall on the paper at the same time, and when the intensity of the red light is greater than that of the green, the person perceives orange. Then, when the intensities of the red and green lights become equal, he perceives yellow. However, as the paper turns still farther toward the green light, the color passes through all the transitional colors from yellow to green, and, again, as the paper rotates beyond the green so that both green and blue light fall on it, the person sees progressively all the green-

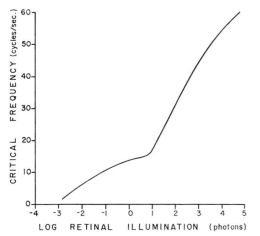

Figure 553. Relationship of intensity of illumination to the critical frequency for fusion.

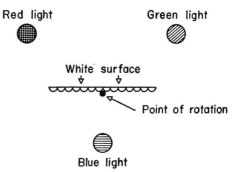

Figure 554. Psychological technique for demonstrating most colors of the spectrum with only three monochromatic lights.

ish-blue hues until finally he sees only blue. Then, when the paper turns to face both red and blue, he perceives the sensation of purple, which is almost the same sensation as that caused by violet light impinging on the eye.

The first important theory of color vision was that of Young, which was later expanded and given more experimental basis by Helmholtz. Therefore, the theory is known as the Young-Helmholtz theory. This theory assumes that there are three different types of cones, each of which responds maximally to different colors, one group of cones responding maximally to red, another to green, and another to blue.

As time has gone by, the Young-Helmholtz theory has been expanded and more details have been worked out, but even today the precise color responsiveness of each of the different types of cones in the human eye is still unknown. However, the following analysis of color vision seems to be one of the most reasonable at the present time.

Spectral Sensitivities of the Three Types of Cones. Even in experimental animals it has not yet been possible to determine the precise sensitivities of the individual cones to different colors of light. However, on the basis of psychological tests, the spectral sensitivities of three different types of cones have been determined as shown in Figure 555, and these could readily explain almost all the observed phenomena of color vision. The curves of this figure were adopted by the International Commission on Illumination as standards for the three primary types of colors detected by the retina. It should be recognized, however, that moderate differences between the actual spectral sensitivities of the three types of cones in the retinae and those in this diagram would not affect the theory to any significant extent.

Interpretation of Color in the Nervous System. Referring again to Figure 555, a red monochromatic light with a wavelength of 650 millimicrons stimulates the red cones to a stimulus value of approximately 0.4 while it stimulates the green cones to a stimulus value of approximately 0.1 and the blue cones not at all. Thus, the ratios of stimulation of the three different types of cones in this instance are 4:1:0. The nervous system interprets this set of ratios as the sensation of red. On the other hand, a mono-

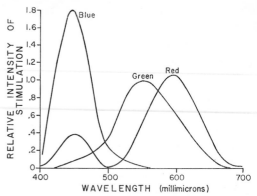

Figure 555. Spectral sensitivity curves of three different types of cones as postulated from psychological tests.

chromatic blue color with a wavelength of 450 millimicrons stimulates the red cones to a stimulus value of 0.4, the green cones to a value of 0.1 and the blue cones to a value of 1.8. This set of ratios—4:1:18—is interpreted by the nervous system as blue. Likewise, ratios of 1:1:0 are interpreted as orange-yellow and 2:8:1 as green.

This scheme also shows how it is possible for a person to perceive a sensation of yellow when a red light and a green light are shone into the eye at the same time for this will stimulate the red and green cones approximately equally, which will give a sensation of yellow even though no yellow is present.

Perception of white light. Approximately equal stimulation of all the red, green, and blue cones gives one the sensation of seeing white. Yet, there is no such color as white; instead white is a combination of all the colors of the spectrum. Furthermore, the sensation of white can be achieved by stimulating the retina with a proper combination of only three chosen colors that stimulate the respective types of cones in the retina.

Integration of Color Sensations by the Retina and the Cerebral Cortex. From psychological studies, we know that the interpretation of color is performed partly by the retina and partly by the cerebral cortex. For instance, if a person places a monochromatic green filter in front of his left eye and a monochromatic red filter in front of his right eye and then observes a white object, the object will appear yellow. This integration of color sensations obviously could not be occurring in the retina because one retina is allowed to respond only to green light and the other only to red light. However, the sensations perceived in this way are not precisely equivalent to those perceived when the two monochromatic lights are mixed in the same retina. Therefore, at least some degree of the interpretation of color occurs in the retina itself even before the light information is transmitted into the brain.

Transmission of Impulses from the Color Receptors by Optic Nerve Fibers. Though the spectral sensitivities of individual cones have never been measured directly from the cones themselves, the responses of single optic nerve fibers when the eyes are illuminated with different colors of the spectrum have shown that certain ones of the fibers are excited maximally by colors of one spectral range while others are excited maximally by colors of other spectral ranges. In every animal species that can perceive colors, at least two or more different spectral sensitivities have been found for the different optic nerve fibers. In the mammal, the spectral sensitivity curves fall into four categories, three of these responding to separate and narrow wavelength bands, as shown in Figure 556, and one responding to all colors and having a spectral response curve almost identical with that of the photopic spectral sensitivity curve illustrated in Figure 550. Note particularly that the bandwidths of the spectral sensitivity curves in Figure 556 are somewhat narrower than the bandwidths of the curves postulated above from psychological tests. Furthermore, the bandwidths are much narrower than have been postulated on the basis of light absorption by the different photosensitive pigments isolated from cones. Therefore, it is be-

lieved that the signals transmitted in the optic nerve fibers have already been partially integrated by the neuronal layers of the retina even before leaving the eye.

The spectral sensitivity curve of those optic nerve fibers that respond to all light wavelengths is called the *dominator curve;* this probably transmits the major portion of the "light" sensation to the nervous system but does not contribute to the distinguishing of colors. The narrow band curves are called *modulator curves* and are believed to transmit the color sensations.

Color Blindness

Red-Green Color Blindness. When a single group of color receptive cones is missing from the eye, the person will be unable to distinguish some colors from others. As can be observed from Figure 555, if the red cones are missing, light of 500 to 650 millimicrons wavelength can stimulate only the green sensitive cones. Therefore, the *ratio* of stimulation of the different cones does not change as the color changes from green all the way through the red spectrum. Therefore, within this wavelength range, all colors appear to be the same to this "color blind" person.

On the other hand, if the green-sensitive cones are missing, the colors in the range from green to red can stimulate only the red sensitive cones, and the person also perceives only one color within these limits. Therefore, when a person lacks either the red or the green types of cones, he is said to be "red-green" color blind.

The person with loss of red cones is called a *protanope;* his overall visual spectrum is noticeably shortened at the long wavelength end because of lack of the red cones. The color blind person who lacks green cones is called a *deuteranope;* this person has a perfectly normal visual spectral width because the green cones operate in the middle of the spectrum.

Blue Weakness. Occasionally, a person will have "blue weakness," which results from diminished or absent blue receptors. If we observe Figure 555 once again, we can see that the blue cones are sensitive to a spectral range almost entirely different from that of both the red and green cones. Therefore, if the blue receptors are completely absent, then the person will have a greater

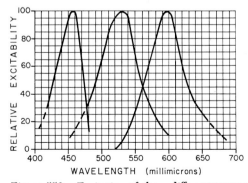

Figure 556. Excitation of three different types of optic nerve fibers in the cat by the different colors of the spectrum. (Modified from Granit: *J. Neurophysiol.,* 8:195, 1945.)

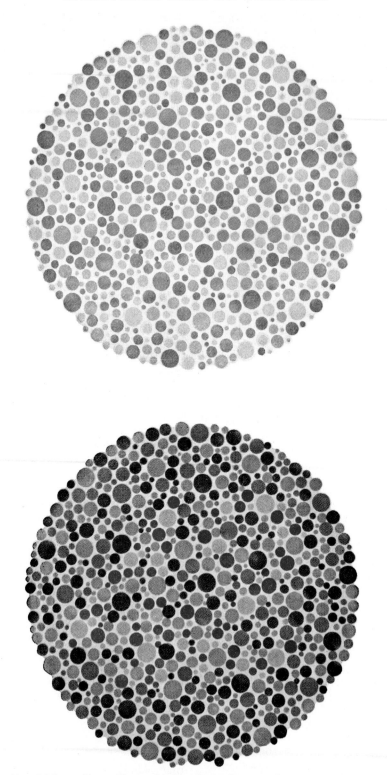

Figure 557. Two Ishihara charts: *Upper:* In this chart, the normal person reads "74," while the red-green color blind person reads "21." *Lower:* In this chart, the red-blind person (protanope) reads "2," while the green-blind person (deuteranope) reads "4." The normal person reads "42." (From Ishihara. Tests for Colour-Blindness. Kanehara and Company, Tokyo.)

preponderance of green, yellow, orange, and red in his visual spectrum than blue, thus giving this rarely observed type of color blindness.

Tests for Color Blindness. Tests for color blindness depend simply on the subject's ability to distinguish various colors from each other and also on his ability to judge correctly the degree of contrast between colors. For instance, to determine whether or not a person is red-green color blind, he may be given many small tufts of wool whose colors encompass the entire visual spectrum. He is then asked to place those tufts that have the same colors in the same piles. If he is not color blind he will recognize immediately that all the tufts have slightly different colors; however, if he is red-green color blind, he will place the red, orange, yellow, and yellow-green colors all together as having essentially the same color.

Stilling and Ishihara test charts. A very rapid method for determining color blindness is based on the use of spot-charts such as those illustrated in Figure 557. These charts are arranged with a confusion of spots of several different colors. In the top chart, the normal person reads "74," while the red-green color blind person reads "21." In the bottom chart, the normal person reads "42," while the red blind protanope reads "2," and the green blind deuteranope reads "4."

If one will study these charts while at the same time observing the spectral sensitivity curves of the different cones in Figure 555, he can readily understand how excessive emphasis can be placed on spots of certain colors by color blind persons in comparison with normal persons.

Genetics of Color Blindness. Color blindness is sex-linked and probably results from absence of appropriate color genes in the "X" chromosomes. This lack of color genes is a recessive trait, and, therefore, color blindness will not appear as long as another "X" chromosome carries the genes necessary for development of the respective color-receptive cones.

Because the male human being has only one X chromosome, all three color genes must be present in this single chromosome if he is not to be color blind. In approximately one out of every 50 times, the "X" chromosome lacks the red gene; in approximately one out of every 50 it lacks the green gene; and very rarely it lacks the blue gene. This means, therefore, that 2 per cent of all men are red color blind (protanopes) and 2 per cent are green color blind (deuteranopes) and that a total of approximately 4 per cent of all men are red-green color blind. Because a woman has two "X" chromosomes, only one woman out of every 2500 is red blind and only one out of every 2500 is green blind. Therefore, red-green color blindness is a very rare abnormality in the female, occurring in only one out of every 1250 women.

REFERENCES

Adler, F. H.: Physiology of the Eye: Clinical Application. 2nd ed., St. Louis, C. V. Mosby Co., 1953.

American Optical Company: Pseudo-isochromatic Plates for Testing Color Perception. Southbridge, Massachusetts, American Optical Co., 1940.

Auerbach, E., and Wald, G.: Identification of a violet receptor in human color vision. *Science, 120*:401, 1954.

Auerbach, E., and Wald, G.: The participation of different types of cones in human light and dark adaptation. *Am. J. Ophth., 39*:24, 1955.

Brindley, G. S.: *Physiology of the Retina and Visual Pathways.* Baltimore, Williams & Wilkins Co., 1959.

Brindley, G. S.: Physiology of vision. *Ann. Rev. Physiol., 20*:559, 1958.

Brindley, G. S.: The discrimination of after-images. *J. Physiol., 147*:204, 1959.

Brozek, J., and Simonson, E.: Visual performance and fatigue under conditions of varied illumination. *Am. J. Ophth., 35*:33, 1952.

Cohn, R.: A contribution to the study of color vision in cat. *J. Neurophysiol., 19*:416, 1956.

Dartnall, H. J. A.: On the question of the "narrow-band" pigment of the frog's retina. *J. Physiol., 145*:630, 1959.

Granit, R.: Receptors and Sensory Perception. New Haven, Yale University Press, 1955.

Granit, R.: Sensory Mechanisms of the Retina. New York, Oxford University Press, 1947.

Granit, R.: The colour receptors of the mammalian retina. *J. Neurophysiol., 8*:195, 1945.

Hartridge, H.: Recent Advances in the Physiology of Vision. Philadelphia, Blakiston, 1950.

Hurvich, L. M., and Jameson, D.: The binocular fusion of yellow in relation to color theories. *Science, 114*:199, 1951.

Jayle, G. E., and Ourgaud, A. G.: Night Vision. Springfield, Illinois, Charles C Thomas, 1959.

Landis, C.: Determinants of the critical-fusion threshold. *Physiol. Rev., 34*:256, 1954.

Linksz, A.: Physiology of the Eye. Vol. II. Vision. New York, Grune & Stratton, 1952.

Milne, L. J., and Milne, M.: Photosensitivity in invertebrates. *Handbook of Physiology, 1*:621, 1959.

Pickford, R. W.: Individual Differences in Colour Vision. New York, The Macmillan Co., 1952.

Pirie, A., and Van Heyningen, R.: The Biochemistry of the Eye. Springfield, Illinois, Charles C Thomas, 1956.

Polyak, S.: The Retina. Chicago, University of Chicago Press, 1941.

Simonson, E., and Brozek, J.: Flicker fusion frequency: background and applications. *Physiol. Rev.*, 32:349, 1952.

Szekeres, G.: A new determination of the Young-Helmholtz primaries. J. Optic. Soc. America, *38:* 350, 1948.

Talbot, S. A.: Green vision and binocular fusion of yellow. *Science, 115:*220, 1952.

Tansley, K.: Physiology of vision; bibiography of British books and periodicals. Brit. M. Bull., *9:*75, 1953.

Wagman, I. H., Waldman, J., Naidoff, D., Feinschil, L. G., and Cahan, R.: The recording of the electroretinogram in humans and in animals; investigation of retinal sensitivity following brief flashes of light. *Am. J. Ophth.*, 38:60, 1954.

Wald, G.: The chemical evolution of vision. *Harvey Lect., 41:*117, 1945–1946.

Wald, G.: The chemistry of visual excitation. *Bibl. Ophth., 47:*173, 1957.

Wald, G.: The molecular basis of visual excitation. *Science Progr.*, Series 9:133, 1955.

Wald, G.: The photoreceptor process in vision. *Handbook of Physiology, 1:*671, 1959.

Wald, G., and Brown, P. K.: Synthesis and bleaching of rhodopsin. *Nature, 177:*174, 1956.

Wald, G., Brown, P. K., and Smith, P. H.: Iodopsin. *J. Gen. Physiol., 38:*623, 1955.

Weale, R. A.: The absolute threshold of vision. *Physiol. Rev., 35:*233, 1955.

Willmer, E. N.: Retinal Structure and Colour Vision. New York, Cambridge University Press, 1946.

Wright, W. D.: Researches on Normal and Defective Colour Vision. London, Henry Kimpton, 1946.

Chapter 54

The Eye: Neurophysiology of Vision

NEURONAL FUNCTIONS IN THE RETINA

The retina is much more than simply an accumulation of light receptors, for, as was illustrated in Figure 547 of the preceding chapter, two discrete layers of neuronal cells for relaying visual information also are present in addition to the rods and cones. Furthermore, special neurons, the *horizontal* and *amacrine cells,* which lie, respectively, in the outer and inner plexiform layers of the retina, coordinate activity between the separate sections of the retina. To express this another way, the retina itself is a highly organized neuronal structure that performs many integrative functions even before the visual information is transmitted to the brain.

Organization of the Retina for Maximum Visual Acuity. In the preceding chapter, it was pointed out that the cones of the fovea connect with almost as many optic nerve fibers as there are cones, while in the rest of the retina there is a tremendous amount of convergence from the rods and cones to the optic nerve fibers. As would be expected, therefore, the acuity of vision in the foveal region is far greater than elsewhere in the retina. As one progresses away from the fovea, the number of cones becomes fewer and fewer while the number of rods becomes greater and greater. Furthermore, the degree of convergence becomes progressively greater so that, on the average, approximately 400 rods and several cones converge on each optic nerve fiber in the peripheral portions of the retina, with a corresponding decrease in visual acuity.

Coding of Information by the Retina Before Transmission to the Central Nervous System. The earlier theories of vision supposed that each rod and cone of the retina transmitted visual signals directly to the visual cortex, impressing upon the cortex a mosaic of excited and unexcited areas representative of the light and dark portions of the retinal image. However, it has become evident that the function of the retina is far more complicated than this, for it is now known that even when no light is impinging on the retina a moderate number of impulses are still transmitted over at least some of the optic nerve fibers. Furthermore, when a particular area of the retina becomes suddenly exposed to light, one optic nerve fiber from this area may become strongly excited while another from an adjacent area may become inhibited. Also, as will become evident in the discussions below, the retina transmits impulses for *changes in intensity of retinal illumination,* whether these changes be increases or decreases in illumination.

Figure 558 shows recordings of action potential spikes from three different types of optic nerve fibers, illustrating the so-called (1) "on" system, (2) "off" system, and (3) "on-off" system. In the "on" system, the resting discharge of the optic nerve fiber increases markedly when the light is turned on, but the system adapts within a fraction

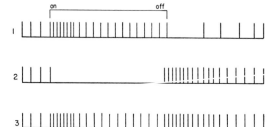

Figure 558. Response characteristics of three different types of optic nerve fibers when illumination to the eye is turned on and off. (From Granit: Receptors and Sensory Perception. Yale University Press.)

of a second, and the rate of impulses thereafter becomes only slightly greater than during the resting state. In the "off" system, turning on the light partially or totally abrogates the resting discharge. In the "on-off" system increased numbers of impulses are transmitted when the light is turned either on or off.

Thus, the retinal neuronal system "codes" the information from the visual receptors even before it is transmitted to the visual cortex. This coding allows two particular types of information to be transmitted: (a) the actual degree of illumination on each portion of the retina and (b) the rate of change of the illumination. Of these two, the second is actually more responsive than the first so that the retina detects *changes* in the visual image much more acutely than it does the actual bright and dark spots of the image itself.

Retinal Mechanism To Promote Contrast. One of the functions of the horizontal connections between adjacent portions of the retina is to promote contrast in the visual signals transmitted to the central nervous system. One can recognize the importance of this when he realizes that the visual system detects images only by virtue of the many *contrasts* between the light and dark areas.

When a bright spot of light is shown on the retina, the adjacent portions of the retina become inhibited, as illustrated in Figure 559, thus exacerbating the contrast between the lighted area and its surroundings. It is particularly interesting, also, that optic nerve fibers leading from the lighted area transmit an "on" signal to the visual cortex, fibers from the transitional zone transmit an "on-off" signal, and fibers from the inhibited area transmit an "off" signal.

Retinal Mechanisms for Detection of Movement. From the above discussion of the extreme ability of the retina to respond to *changes* in visual images, it is readily apparent that the retina is particularly sensitive to movement within the visual field. Because the number of impulses transmitted by the optic nerve fibers greatly increases for an instant after a change in the retinal image, the person's attention is immediately called to almost any minute movement. But unchanging conditions in the field of vision ordinarily do not need immediate attention

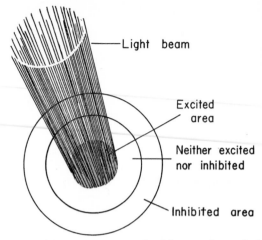

Figure 559. Excitation and inhibition of a retinal area caused by a small beam of light.

and also do not overly excite the visual apparatus.

Retinal Potential and the Retinogram. If an electrode is placed on the cornea of an eye and another on the back of the eyeball (or even to the back of the head), a potential difference of approximately 1 millivolt will be recorded; indeed, this occurs even when the eye is not stimulated by light. This potential is called the *retinal potential*. If a light is then suddenly shone into the eye, a series of changes occurs in the retinal potential; a record of these changes is called the *retinogram*, an example of which is shown in Figure 560. Both the retinal potential and the retinogram result from potentials generated in (a) the rods and cones and (b) the neurons of the inner nuclear layer of the retina but do not depend on activity of the ganglion cells of the retina. Furthermore, total destruction of the retina eliminates both the resting retinal potential and the retinogram that occurs in response to light; for this reason the retinogram has proved to be of some use clinically in diagnosing the presence or absence of retinal degeneration.

Regulation of Retinal Function by the Central Nervous System. Not only does

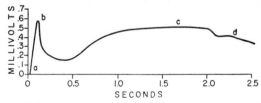

Figure 560. A retinogram recorded from an eye when illuminated by a light. The a, b, and c waves are caused by retinal action in response to light stimulation, and the d wave is caused by removal of the light.

the retina transmit visual information to the central nervous system, but, in turn, the sensitivity of the retina itself can be at least partially controlled by the central nervous system. Centrifugal fibers from the brain to the retina, passing in a retrograde direction in the optic nerve, synapse in the retina with the amacrine cells and perhaps also with the ganglion cells. Stimulation of specific areas in the brain stem have been shown to excite in some instances and inhibit in other instances the degree of sensitivity of specific areas of the retina. It is supposed that this represents a mechanism by which the central nervous system can direct one's attention to the important aspects of the visual field.

TRANSMISSION OF VISUAL INFORMATION INTO THE CENTRAL NERVOUS SYSTEM

The Visual Pathway and the Visual Cortex

Figure 561 illustrates the visual pathway from the two retinae back to the *visual cortex*. After impulses leave the retinae they pass backward through the *optic nerves*. At the *optic chiasm* all the fibers from the nasal halves of the two retinae cross to the opposite *optic tracts*, the nasal fibers from the left retina combining with the temporal fibers from the right retina to form the right optic tract, and, conversely, the fibers from the other halves of the retinae

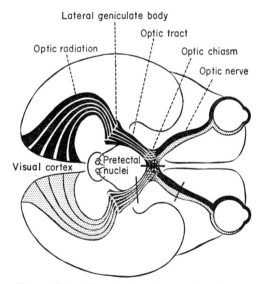

Figure 561. The visual pathways from the eyes to the visual cortex. (Modified from Polyak: The Retina. University of Chicago Press.)

combining to form the left optic tract. The fibers of each optic tract synapse in the *lateral geniculate body* from which *geniculocalcarine fibers* pass through the *optic radiation* or *geniculocalcarine tract* to the *optic* or *visual cortex* in the calcarine area of the occipital lobe.

Note also in Figure 561 that fibers pass directly from the optic tracts into the pretectal nuclei; other fibers not shown in the figure pass directly to the superior colliculi. Second order neurons pass from the lateral geniculate body to the lateral thalamus.

Function of the Lateral Geniculate Body. It is believed that the lateral geniculate body functions mainly to relay information from the retina to the visual cortex. However, the lateral geniculate body is not without some discrete functions of its own. First, it is known that the input impulses must rise to a certain threshold value before output impulses will be transmitted to the visual cortex. Second, many impulses are deviated from the lateral geniculate body into the lateral thalamus and probably to some extent into still other adjacent areas of the diencephalon.

The lateral geniculate body is composed of six separate layers of neurons. Layer I receives optic fibers from the retina of one of the eyes, while layer II receives optic fibers from the opposite eye, and a similar organization is true for the remaining four layers. It has been postulated that the different layers might subserve the functions of color vision in accordance with the tricolor theory of color vision. Or it is possible that the superimposition of alternate images from the two eyes might aid in the process of fusion of the eyes; this will be discussed later in the chapter.

Representation of the Retinal Fields in the Visual Cortex. Figure 562 illustrates the visual cortex and also shows the points to which the different parts of the retina connect. Note that the macula is represented at the occipital pole of the visual cortex and that the peripheral regions of the retina are represented in concentric circles farther and farther forward from the occipital pole. The upper portion of the retina is represented superiorly in the visual cortex, and the lower portion inferiorly. Stimulation of discrete points in the retina by minute spots of light

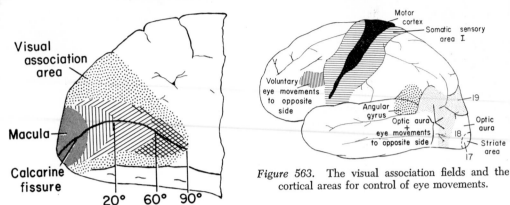

Figure 562. Representation of the different areas of the retina in the visual cortex.

Figure 563. The visual association fields and the cortical areas for control of eye movements.

will cause corresponding discrete activity in the respective portions of the visual cortex. However, the type of activity that occurs even here may be of the "on" type, the "off" type, or the "on-off" type. Furthermore, the visual cortex receives information both about the relative degrees of illumination of the different areas of the retina and about *changes* in the degrees of illumination of the respective receptors, the stimulus being considerably larger for changes than for constant degrees of illumination.

Electrical stimulation of discrete points in the visual cortex will cause a person to see bright flashes of light, colors, and occasionally simple forms such as stars, discs, triangles, and so forth. However, stimulation in this region will not cause a person to see any complex images.

Transmission of Visual Information into Other Regions of the Cerebral Cortex. Even when a single spot of light is applied to the retina, impulses appear within a few milliseconds in widespread areas of the cerebral cortex adjacent to the visual cortex. These are in addition to the point-to-point transmission of impulses to a discrete point in the visual cortex. Therefore, it is evident that the retina transmits a great deal of information into the cerebrum in addition to the mosaic pattern of the image.

For purposes of orientation, Figure 563 shows the areas on the lateral surface of the cortex that are concerned in vision. Area 17 is the visual cortex, which lies almost entirely on the medial aspect of the cerebral hemisphere but extends out of the longi-tudinal fissure onto the outer surface of the occipital pole. Area 17 is also called the *striate area* because of its striped appearance to the naked eye. Area 18 lies immediately above and lateral to the visual cortex, and area 19 lies still farther above and lateral to area 18.

Electrical stimulation in either area 18 or 19 causes a person to have optic auras similar to those which occur when the visual cortex is stimulated—that is, flashes of light, colors, or simple forms such as stars, discs, triangles, and so forth—but he does not see complicated forms. Stimulation in area 19 also causes eye movements to the opposite side of the body.

Stimulation of the *temporal cortex,* on the other hand, often elicits very complicated visual perceptions, sometimes causing the person to "see" a scene that he had known many years before.

Widespread destruction of areas 18 and 19 decreases one's ability to interpret the shapes of objects, their sizes, or their meanings, and can cause particularly an abnormality known as *alexia,* or *word blindness,* which means that the person can see words perfectly well but cannot identify their meanings. Destruction of the cerebral cortex in the angular gyrus region where the temporal, parietal, and occipital lobes all come together usually makes it difficult for a person to correlate visual images with the motor functions. For instance, he will be able to see his plate of food perfectly well but will be unable to utilize the visual information to direct his fork toward the food. Yet, if he feels the plate with his other hand, he can use stereotaxic information from his somesthetic cortex to direct the fork very accurately. Other aspects of visual interpretation in relation to overall function of the cerebral cortex will be discussed in Chapter 59, and later in this chapter we will return to the cortical control of eye movements.

Organization of the Visual Pathway

Figure 564 gives a greatly abbreviated organizational plan of the fiber pathways from the cones in the foveal region of the retina to the visual cortex. Not illustrated in this figure is the fact that a high degree of *divergence*, approximately 100 to 1, occurs in this pathway. However, the figure does show that a spot of light impinging on a single cone in the retina spreads to a much broader area of representation by the time it reaches the cortex. This results from the interconnections between the adjacent pathways at each one of the synaptic areas. The spreading tendency fortunately is opposed by the horizontal suppression discussed earlier in the chapter that occurs in the retina to inhibit the pathways adjacent to the primarily excited pathway. Furthermore, even if the cortical representation of two spots does overlap, the cortex can still interpret this as two separate spots because the *central points of maximum excitation* are separated from each other as shown in Figure 564.

The Fields of Vision; Perimetry

The *field of vision* is the entire expanse of space available at a given instant without moving the eye. The area seen to the nasal side is called the *nasal field of vision*, and the area seen to the lateral side is called the *temporal field of vision*.

To diagnose blindness in specific areas of the eyes, one charts the field of vision for each of the eyes by a process known as *perimetry*. This is done by having the subject look with one eye toward a central spot directly in front of the eye. Then a small dot of light or a small object is moved back and forth in all areas of the field of vision, both laterally and nasally and upward and downward, and the patient indicates when he can see the spot of light or object and when he cannot see it. At the same time a chart, (see Figure 565) is made for the eye, showing the areas in which the subject can see the spot and in which he cannot see it. Thus, the field of vision, with both its blind and normal areas, is plotted.

In all perimetry charts, a blind spot caused by the optic disc is found approximately 15 degrees lateral to the central point of vision, as illustrated in the figure.

Abnormalities in the Fields of Vision. Occasionally blind spots are found in other portions of the field of vision besides the optic disc area. Such blind spots are called *scotomata;* they frequently result from allergic reactions in the retina or from toxic conditions such as lead poisoning or even excessive use of tobacco.

Still another condition that can be diagnosed by perimetry is *retinitis pigmentosa*. In this disease, portions of the retina degenerate and excessive melanin pigment deposits in the degenerated areas. Retinitis pigmentosa generally causes blindness in the peripheral field of vision first and then gradually encroaches on the central areas.

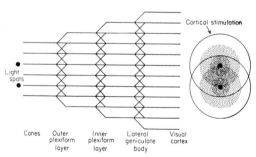

Figure 564. Organization of the visual pathway for conduction of impulses from the foveal region of the retina to the cortex, showing spread of excitation by the time the impulses reach the cortex, but also showing the greatest intensities of the signals in the centralmost portions of the excited cortical fields.

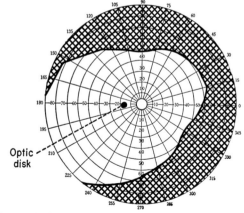

Figure 565. A perimetry chart, showing the field of vision for the left eye.

Effect of lesions in the optic pathway on the fields of vision. Perhaps the most important use of perimetry is in localization of lesions in the brain. Lesions in the optic nerve, in the optic chiasm, in the optic tract, and in the geniculocalcarine tract all cause blind areas in the visual fields, and the "patterns" of these blind areas indicate the location of the lesion in the optic pathway.

Destruction of an entire *optic nerve* obviously causes blindness of the respective eye. Destruction of the *optic chiasm,* as shown by the line across the chiasm in Figure 561, prevents the passage of impulses from the nasal halves of the two retinae to the opposite optic tracts. Therefore, the nasal halves are both blinded, which means that the patient is blind in both temporal fields of vision; this condition is called *bitemporal hemianopsia.* Such lesions frequently result from tumors of the adenohypophysis pressing upward on the optic chiasm.

Interruption of an *optic tract,* which is also shown by a line in Figure 561, denervates the corresponding half of each retina on the same side as the lesion, and, as a result, neither eye can see objects to the opposite side. This condition is known as *homonymous hemianopsia.* Destruction of the *optic radiation* or the *visual cortex* of one side also causes homonymous hemianopsia. A common condition that destroys the visual cortex is thrombosis of the posterior cerebral artery which infarcts most of the occipital cortex.

One can differentiate a lesion in the optic tract from a lesion in the geniculocalcarine tract or visual cortex by determining whether impulses can still be transmitted into the pretectal nuclei to initiate a pupillary light reflex. To do this, light is shown onto the blinded half of one of the retinae, and, if a pupillary light reflex can still occur, it is known that the lesion is beyond the lateral geniculate body, that is, in the geniculocalcarine tract or visual cortex. However, if the light reflex is also lost, then the lesion is in the optic tract itself.

EYE MOVEMENTS AND THEIR CONTROL

In primitive animals the peripheral portions of the retina have visual acuities equal to that of the central portion. Therefore, it is unimportant for the animal to direct its

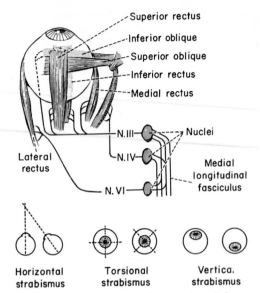

Figure 566. The extraocular muscles of the eye, their innervation, and the three basic types of strabismus.

eyes discretely toward each particular object that is to be seen. In the case of the human being, however, the central portion of the retina, the fovea, has developed an extremely high acuity of vision as well as accurate detection of color, detection of very fine intensity gradations, and so forth. However, to make use of these important abilities, it has been almost equally as important to develop a cerebral control system for directing the eyes toward the object to be viewed as to interpret the visual signals from the eyes.

Muscular Control of the Eye Movements. The eye movements are controlled, as shown in Figure 566, by three separate pairs of muscles: (1) the medial and lateral recti, (2) the superior and inferior recti, and (3) the superior and inferior obliques. The medial and lateral recti contract reciprocally to move the eyes from side to side. The superior and inferior recti contract reciprocally to move the eyes upward or downward. And the oblique muscles function mainly to rotate the eyeballs to keep the visual fields in the upright position.

Neuronal Pathways for Control of Eye Movements. Figure 566 also illustrates the control of the ocular muscles by the nuclei of the third, fourth, and sixth cranial nerves, and Figure 567 illustrates some of the interconnections between these nuclei and their control by the cerebrum.

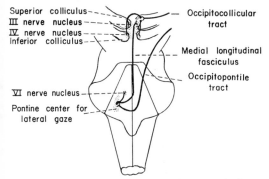

Superior colliculus
III nerve nucleus
IV nerve nucleus
Inferior colliculus

Occipitocollicular tract

Medial longitudinal fasciculus

Occipitopontile tract

VI nerve nucleus
Pontine center for lateral gaze

Figure 567. Postulated pathways for control of vertical and lateral conjugate movements of the eyes.

Each of the three sets of muscles to each eye is reciprocally innervated so that one muscle of the pair relaxes while the other contracts.

Simultaneous movement of both eyes in the same direction is called *conjugate movement* of the eyes. The two important conjugate movements are *vertical conjugate movements* and *lateral conjugate movements*. Though the precise brain centers that control conjugate movements are still unknown, it has been claimed that lateral conjugate movements are controlled by nuclei located in the pons which are called collectively the *pontile center for lateral gaze*. This supposedly transmits impulses both to the nuclei of the third and sixth nerves to cause the eyes to turn to one side or the other. In turn, the bilateral pontile centers for lateral gaze are controlled by impulses from the cerebral cortex by way of the *occipitopontile tract*. On the other hand, it has been claimed that the *superior colliculi* control vertical conjugate movements and that the superior colliculi in turn are controlled by impulses transmitted from the occipital cortex through the *occipitocollicular tracts*.

It must be pointed out, however, that bilateral destruction of the superior colliculi or of the pontile centers for lateral gaze does not prevent all vertical and lateral conjugate movements. Therefore, other centers of the brain stem are perhaps equally as important, or even more important, in the control of conjugate movements.

Fixation Movements of the Eyes

Perhaps the most important movements of the eyes are those that cause the eyes to "fix" on a discrete portion of the field of vision.

Fixation movements are controlled by two entirely different neuronal mechanisms. The first of these allows the person to move his eyes to find the object upon which he wishes to fix his vision; this is called the *voluntary fixation mechanism*. The second is an involuntary mechanism that holds the eyes very firmly on the object once it has been found; this is called the *involuntary fixation mechanism*.

The voluntary fixation movements are controlled by a small cortical field located bilaterally in the premotor cortical regions of the frontal lobes, as illustrated in Figure 563. Bilateral dysfunction or destruction of these areas makes it difficult or almost impossible for the person to "unlock" his eyes from one point of fixation and then move them to another point. It is usually necessary for him to blink his eyes or put his hand over his eyes for a short period of time, which then allows him to move the eyes.

On the other hand, the involuntary fixation mechanism that causes the eyes to "lock" on the object of attention is controlled by the *eye fields of the occipital cortex*—particularly area 19—which are also illustrated in Figure 563. When area 19 is destroyed bilaterally, the person becomes completely unable to keep his eyes directed toward a given fixation point.

To summarize, the posterior eye fields automatically "lock" the eyes on a given field of vision and thereby prevent movement of the image across the retina. To unlock this visual fixation, voluntary impulses must be transmitted from the "voluntary" eye fields located in the frontal areas.

Mechanism of Fixation. Visual fixation results from a negative feedback mechanism that prevents the object of attention from leaving the foveal portion of the retina. The eyes even normally have three types of continuous but almost imperceptible movements: (1) a *continuous tremor* at a rate of 30 to 50 cycles per second caused by successive contractions of the motor units in the ocular muscles, (2) a *slow drift* of the eyeballs in one direction or another, and (3) sudden *flicking movements* which are controlled by the involuntary fixation mechanism. When a spot of light has become fixed on the foveal region of the retina, the tremorous and drifting movements of the eyes cause the spot (a) to move back and forth at a rapid rate across the cones and (b) to drift slowly across the cones. However, each time the spot of light approaches the edge of the fovea, a sudden flick will occur away from this edge back toward the center, which is an automatic response to move the image back toward the central portion of the fovea. These drifting and flicking motions are illustrated in Figure 568, showing by the dashed lines the slow drifts across the retina and by the solid lines the flicks that keep the image from leaving the foveal region.

Fixation on Moving Objects—"Pursuit Movements." The eyes can also remain fixed on a moving object, which is called *pursuit movement*. A highly developed cortical mechanism automatically detects the course of movement of an object and then gradually develops a similar course of movement of the eyes. For instance, if an object is moving up and down in a wavelike form at a rate of several times per second, the eyes at first may be completely unable to fixate on it. However, after a second or so the eyes begin to jump coarsely in approximately the same pattern of movement as that of the object. Then after a few more seconds, the eyes develop progressively smoother and smoother movements and finally follow the course of movement almost exactly. This represents a high degree of calculating ability by the cerebral cortex.

Nystagmus. Optikokinetic nystagmus. A particularly important type of pursuit movement is that called *nystagmus*, which allows the eyes to fixate on successive points in a continuously moving scene. For instance, if a person is looking out the window of a train, his eyes fix on successive points in the visual scene. To do this, the eyes fixate on some object and move slowly backwards as the object also moves backwards. When the eyes have moved far to the side, they automatically jump forward to fix on a new object, which is followed again by slow movement in the backward direction. This type of movement is called *optikokinetic nystagmus*, and the slow movement in one direction is called the *slow component* of the nystagmus, while the rapid movement in the other direction is called the *fast component*.

Optikokinetic nystagmus obviously is a type of pursuit movement. That is, after an initial second or so of orientation, the visual system automatically calculates the course and rate of movement of the visual scene, then follows this exactly

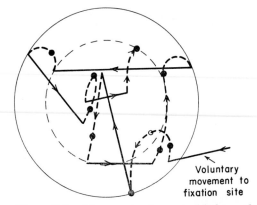

Figure 568. Movements of a spot of light on the fovea, showing sudden "flicking" movements to move the spot back toward the center of the fovea whenever its drifts to the foveal edge. (The dashed lines represent slow drifting movements, and the solid lines represent sudden flicking movements.) (Modified from: Whitteridge: *Handbook of Physiology,* 2: 1089, 1960.)

until the eyes reach a lateral limit, at which time they jump to a new point in the scene.

Vestibular control of eye movements. Another type of eye movement is elicited by stimulation of the vestibular apparatus. The vestibular nuclei are connected directly with the brain stem nuclei that control ocular movements, and, anytime the head is accelerated in a vertical, longitudinal, lateral, or angular direction, an immediate compensatory motion of the eyes occurs in the opposite direction. This allows the eyes to remain fixed on an object of attention despite rapid movements of the body or head. Vestibular control of the eyes is especially valuable when a person is subjected to jerky motions of his body. For instance, when a person with bilateral destruction of his vestibular apparatuses rides over rough roads, he has extreme difficulty fixing his eyes on the road or on any horizontal scene. The optikokinetic type of pursuit movement is not capable of keeping the eyes fixed under such conditions because this has a latent period of about one-fifth second before the direction of movement can be detected and followed by the eyes. Obviously, the movements of the body caused by bumps in a road occur much more rapidly than one-fifth second. On the other hand, the vestibular type of eye movement has a very short latent period, measured in hundredths of a second rather than one-fifth second.

When a person begins to rotate, his vestibular apparatus causes a vestibular type of nystagmus. That is, the eyes lag behind the rotating head, then jump forward, then lag behind again, jump again, and so forth. This type of nystagmus was discussed in Chapter 50.

Pathological Types of Nystagmus. Occasionally, abnormalities occur in the control system for eye movements that cause continuous nystagmus despite the fact that neither the visual scene nor the body is moving. This is very likely to occur when one of the vestibular apparatuses is damaged or when severe damage is sustained in the deep nuclei of the cerebellum. This will be discussed further in Chapter 58.

Another pathological type of eye movement that is sometimes called nystagmus occurs when the foveal regions of the two eyes have been destroyed or when the vision in these areas is greatly weakened. In such a condition the eyes continually search for a central visual point that can be seen with a high degree of acuity. The eyes attempt to fix the object of attention on the foveae but always overshoot the mark because of foveal insensitivity. Therefore, they oscillate back and forth but never achieve foveal fixation. Even though this condition is known clinically as a type of nystagmus, physiologically it is completely different from the nystagmus that keeps the eyes fixed on a moving scene.

Fusion of the Visual Images

To make the visual perceptions more meaningful and also to aid in depth perception by the mechanism of stereopsis, which was discussed in Chapter 52, the visual images in the two eyes normally *fuse* with each other on "corresponding points" of the two retinae. Furthermore, three different types of fusion are required: (1) lateral fusion, (2) vertical fusion, and (3) torsional fusion (same rotation of the two eyes).

Fusion of the images of the two eyes probably results from two mechanisms in the visual system. First, crude fusion is already inherent in the newborn child because of inherited conjugate movements of the eyes. Second, as the visual system becomes more and more developed, the ability of the two eyes to fixate on the same object of attention causes even greater accuracy of fusion. Then, as the visual system develops its pursuit abilities, the pathways for controlling the conjugate movements of the two eyes normally develop equally. And the more the two eyes are moved in unison with each other the more "set" become the patterns of movement for the eyes, and, consequently, the more exact becomes the degree of fusion that can be maintained regardless of the position or rapidity of movement of the eyes.

Strabismus. *Strabismus*, which is also called *squint* and *cross-eyedness*, means lack of fusion of the eyes in one or more of the coordinates described above. Three basic types of strabismus are illustrated in Figure 566: *horizontal strabismus*, *vertical strabismus*, and *torsional strabismus*. However, combinations of two or even of all three of the different types of strabismus often occur.

Strabismus is believed to be caused by an abnormal "set" of the fusion mechanism of the visual system. That is, in the early efforts of the child to fix the two eyes on the same object one of the eyes fixes satisfactorily while the other fails to fix, or they both fix satisfactorily but never simultaneously. Soon, the patterns of conjugate movements of the eyes become abnormally "set" so that the eyes never fuse.

Frequently, some abnormality of the eyes contributes to the failure of the two eyes to fixate on the same point. For instance, if at birth one eye is very weak in comparison with the other, the good eye will tend to fix on the object of attention while the poor eye might never learn to do so. Also, in hyperopic infants, intense impulses must be transmitted to the ciliary muscles to focus the eyes, and some of these impulses naturally overflow into the oculomotor nuclei to cause simultaneous convergence of the eyes. As a result, the child's fusion mechanism becomes "set" for continual inward deviation of the eyes.

Suppression of visual images from a repressed eye. In most patients with strabismus the eyes alternate in fixing on the object of attention. However, in some patients, one eye alone is used all of the time while the other eye becomes repressed and is never used for vision. The vision in the repressed eye develops only very slightly, usually remaining 20/400 or less. If the dominant eye then becomes blinded, vision in the repressed eye can develop slowly in the adult and far more rapidly in children. This illustrates that visual acuity is highly dependent on the proper development of the central synaptic connections from the eyes.

AUTONOMIC CONTROL OF ACCOMMODATION AND PUPILLARY APERTURE

The Autonomic Nerves to the Eyes. The eye is innervated by both parasympathetic and sympathetic fibers. The parasympathetic fibers arise in the *Edinger-Westphal nucleus* and then pass in the *third nerve* to the *ciliary ganglion,* which lies about a centimeter behind the eye. Here the fibers synapse with postganglionic parasympathetic neurons that pass through the *ciliary nerves* into the eyeball. These nerves excite the ciliary muscle and the sphincter of the iris.

The sympathetic innervation of the eye originates in the *intermediolateral horn cells* of the first thoracic segment of the spinal cord. From here, sympathetic fibers enter the sympathetic chain and pass upward to the *superior cervical ganglion* where they synapse with postganglionic neurons. Fibers from these spread along the carotid artery and successively smaller arteries to the eyeball. There the sympathetic fibers innervate the radial fibers of the iris as well as several extraocular structures around the eye, which will be discussed shortly in relation to Horner's syndrome.

Control of Accommodation

The accommodation mechanism—that is, the mechanism which focuses the lens system of the eye—is essential to a high degree of visual acuity. Accommodation results from contraction or relaxation of the ciliary muscle, contraction causing increased strength of the lens system, as explained in Chapter 52, and relaxation causing decreased strength. The question that must be answered now is, how does one adjust his accommodation to keep his eyes in focus all of the time?

Accommodation of the lens is regulated by a negative feedback mechanism that automatically adjusts the focal power of the lens for the highest degree of visual acuity. Though the precise mechanism by which this negative feedback operates is not known, there seem to be two specific processes involved:

First, if a visual image is not in focus, the ciliary muscle automatically begins to contract or relax. If the focus improves, the accommodation continues to change in the same direction, but, if it worsens, the accommodation automatically turns around to the other direction and changes until the proper focus is attained. Thus, the accommodation mechanism continually searches back and forth on the two sides of appropriate focus, thereby keeping the focus always near the point of maximal visual acuity.

Second, and perhaps even more important than the above mechanism is one that results from the fact that the center of the fovea is depressed in relation to the remainder of the retina. Because of this, an image might well be in better focus in the center of the fovea than along the edges. If this is true, the visual system theoretically could detect that the focal plane of the lens system lies too far posteriorly. On the other hand, if the focus on the edges of the fovea is better than in the very center, then it could be detected that the focal plane lies too far anteriorly. From this information, appropriate integrative impulses presumably adjust the degree of accommodation to maintain a continual state of precise focus halfway between the depth and the sides of the fovea.

It is presumed that the cerebral areas that control accommodation closely parallel those that control fixation movements of the eyes. Certainly the visual cortex is involved in the accommodative process, for, without this, detection of visual acuity, which is necessary for initiating the accommodation reaction, could not possibly occur.

Association of Accommodation and Convergence. When the eyes fixate on a distant object and then on another object nearby, the degree of accommodation of the lens must change to maintain proper focus. Fortunately, when the eyes converge while fixating on closer objects, an automatic association between convergence and accommodation causes increased accommodation of the lens at the same time. Conversely, accommodation of the lens for near vision automatically causes convergence.

Control of the Pupillary Aperture

Stimulation of the parasympathetic nerves excites the pupillary sphincter, thereby decreasing the pupillary aperture; this is called *miosis*. On the other hand, stimulation of the sympathetic nerves excites the radial fibers of the iris and causes pupillary dilatation, which is called *mydriasis*.

The Pupillary Light Reflex. When light is shone into the eyes the pupils constrict, a reaction which is called the *pupillary light reflex*. The neuronal pathway for this reflex is illustrated in Figure 569. When light impinges on the retina, the resulting impulses pass through the optic nerves and optic tracts to the pretectal nuclei. From here, impulses pass to the *Edinger-Westphal nucleus* and finally back through the *parasympathetic nerves* to the sphincter of the iris.

The function of the light reflex is to help

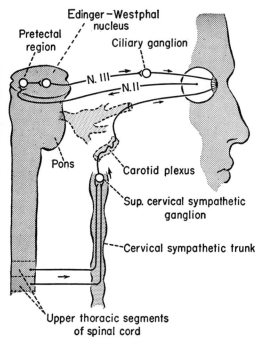

Pretectal region
Edinger–Westphal nucleus
Ciliary ganglion
N. III
N. II
Pons
Carotid plexus
Sup. cervical sympathetic ganglion
Cervical sympathetic trunk
Upper thoracic segments of spinal cord

Figure 569. Autonomic innervation of the eye, showing also the reflex arc of the light reflex. (Modified from Ranson and Clark: Anatomy of the Nervous System.)

the eye adapt to appropriate light conditions, the importance of which was explained in relation to retinal adaptation in the previous chapter. The limits of pupillary diameter are about 1.5 millimeters on the small side and 7 to 8 millimeters on the large side. Therefore, the range of light adaptation that can be effected by the pupillary reflex is about 25 to 1.

Association between Accommodation and Pupillary Constriction. In almost the same way that accommodation and convergence are associated, which was discussed above, the pupil of the eye also constricts when the eye accommodates for near vision. This effect presumably results from a spillover of impulses from the accommodative system into the pupillary control system. There is no known purposive value in this association, but it is used clinically to determine whether the parasympathetic nerves to the eye are intact.

Pupillary Reflexes in Syphilis. Central nervous system syphilis almost always eventually blocks the light reflex pathway between the retina and the Edinger-Westphal nucleus. It is believed that this block most likely occurs in the pretectal region of the brain stem, though it could result from destruction of small afferent fibers in the optic

nerves. One of the distinguishing features of the loss of the light reflex in syphilis is that the pupillary constriction associated with accommodation is not lost at the same time because the parasympathetic pathways to the eyes are not involved in syphilis.

When the impulses to the Edinger-Westphal nuclei are blocked by syphilis, these nuclei are also released from inhibitory impulses arriving from some outside source. As a result, the nuclei become tonically active, causing the pupils thereafter to remain constricted, in addition to their failure to respond to light. Such a pupil that fails to respond to light and also is very small in size (an *Argyll Robertson pupil*) is an important diagnostic sign of central nervous system syphilis. However, a few other conditions, including central nervous system damage from alcoholism, encephalitis, and so forth, can occasionally also cause an Argyll Robertson pupil.

The Ciliospinal Reflex. A relatively weak reflex known as the ciliospinal reflex is sometimes tested by clinicians to determine whether the sympathetics to the eyes are blocked. This reflex occurs as follows: Pinching the skin of the neck ordinarily causes the pupil on the pinched side to dilate. This reflex is mediated from the skin through the skeletal sensory nerves into the spinal cord, then from the spinal cord directly into the sympathetic chain, and finally upward to the eyes where sympathetic discharge causes the pupil to dilate. Unfortunately, this reflex is so weak that failure to elicit it cannot be used as definite evidence of lack of sympathetic innervation to an eye unless other signs corroborate the same fact.

Horner's Syndrome. The sympathetic nerves to the eye are occasionally interrupted, usually somewhere in the cervical chain. This results in *Horner's syndrome*, which consists of the following effects: First, because of interruption of fibers to the pupillary dilator muscle, the pupil remains persistently constricted to a smaller diameter than that of the pupil of the opposite eye. Second, the superior eyelid droops because this eyelid is normally maintained in an open position during the waking hours by a *smooth muscle levator* innervated by the sympathetics. Therefore, destruction of the sympathetics makes it impossible to open the superior eyelid nearly as widely as normally. Third, the blood vessels on the corresponding side of the face and head become persistently dilated. And, fourth, sweating cannot occur on the side of the face and head affected by Horner's syndrome.

REFERENCES

Bartley, S. H.: Central mechanisms of vision. *Handbook of Physiology,* 1:713, 1959.
Bishop, P. O., and Davis, R.: The recovery of respon-

siveness of the sensory synapses in the lateral geniculate nucleus. *J. Physiol., 150:*214, 1960.

Campbell, F. W., and Westheimer, G.: Dynamics of accommodation responses of the human eye. *J. Physiol., 151:*285, 1960.

Cogan, D. G.: Neurology of the Ocular Muscles. 2nd ed., Springfield, Illinois, Charles C Thomas, 1956.

Ditchburn, R. W., Fender, D. H., and Mayne, S.: Vision with controlled movements of the retinal image. *J. Physiol., 145:*98, 1959.

Doty, R. W.: Potentials evoked in cat cerebral cortex by diffuse and by punctiform photic stimuli. *J. Neurophysiol., 21:*437, 1958.

Faulkner, R. F., and Hyde, J. E.: Coordinated eye and body movements evoked by brainstem stimulation in decerebrated cats. *J. Neurophysiol., 21:* 171, 1958.

Granit, R.: Centrifugal and antidromic effects on ganglion cells of retina. *J. Neurophysiol., 18:*388, 1955.

Granit, R.: Neural activity in the retina. *Handbook of Physiology, 1:*693, 1959.

Granit, R.: Possibilities and limitations of electro-retinography. *Bibl. Ophth., 48:*38, 1957.

Guyton, J. S., and Kirkman, N.: Ocular movement: I. Mechanics, pathogenesis, and surgical treatment of alternating hypertropia (dissociated vertical divergence, double hypertropia) and some related phenomena. *Am. J. Ophth., 41:*438, 1956.

Harrington, D. O.: The Visual Fields. London, Henry Kimpton, 1956.

Hubel, D. H., and Wiesel, T. N.: Receptive fields of single neurones in the cat's striate cortex. *J. Physiol., 148:*574, 1959.

Hughes, B.: The Visual Fields. Springfield, Illinois, Charles C Thomas, 1955.

Hyde, J. E., and Davis, L. M.: Extraocular proprioception in electrically induced eye movements. *Am. J. Physiol., 198:*945, 1960.

Hyde, J. E., and Eason, R. G.: Characteristics of ocular movements evoked by stimulation of brainstem of cat. *J. Neurophysiol., 22:*666, 1959.

Ingvar, D. H., and Hunter, J.: Influence of visual cortex on light impulses in the brain stem of the un-

anesthetized cat. *Acta Physiol. Scand., 33:*194, 1955.

Krieger, H. P., Wagman, I. H., and Bender, M. B.: Eye movements obtained from the subcortex of the occipital lobe. *Tr. Am. Neur. Assn.,* 80th Meeting: 209, 1955.

Lyle, D. J.: Neuro-Ophthalmology. 2nd ed., Springfield, Illinois, Charles C Thomas, 1954.

Malis, L. I., and Kruger, L.: Multiple response and excitability of cat's visual cortex. *J. Neurophysiol., 19:*172, 1956.

Ogle, K.: Research in Binocular Vision. Philadelphia, W. B. Saunders Co., 1950.

Pasik, P., Pasik, T., and Krieger, H. P.: Effects of cerebral lesions upon optokinetic nystagmus in monkeys. *J. Neurophysiol., 22:*297, 1959.

Pribram, K. H.: Lesions of "frontal eye fields" and delayed response of baboons. *J. Neurophysiol., 18:* 105, 1955.

Pribram, K. H., and Mishkin, M.: Simultaneous and successive visual discrimination by monkeys with inferotemporal lesions. *J. Comp. Physiol. Psychol., 48:*198, 1955.

Rushton, W. A. H.: Excitation pools in the frog's retina. *J. Physiol., 149:*327, 1959.

Stark, L., and Sherman, P. M.: A servoanalytic study of the consensual pupil reflex to light. *J. Neurophysiol., 20:*17, 1957.

Tuckerman, J.: Perimetry. Philadelphia, J. B. Lippincott Co., 1954.

Wagman, I. H., and Battersby, W. S.: Neural limitations of visual excitability: II. Retrochiasmal interaction. *Am. J. Physiol., 197:*1237, 1959.

Wagman, I. H., Werman, R., Feldman, D. S., Sugarman, L., and Krieger, H. P.: The oculomotor effects of cortical and subcortical stimulation in the monkey. *J. Neuropath., 16:*269, 1957.

Walls, G. L.: Lateral Geniculate Nucleus and Visual Histophysiology. Berkeley, University of California Press, 1953.

Walsh, F. B.: Clinical Neuro-Ophthalmology. 2nd ed., Baltimore, Williams & Wilkins Co., 1957.

Whitterridge, D.: Central control of eye movements. *Handbook of Physiology, 2:*1089, 1960.

Chapter 55

The Chemical Senses

The chemical senses include *taste* and *smell;* however, some physiologists consider that the body also has a general *chemical sense,* which allows at least certain areas of the body, such as the intestines, the mouth, and perhaps even areas of the skin, to respond specifically to chemical irritation. This response is probably nothing more than excitation of pain nerve endings, for which reason the present chapter will consider only the chemical senses of taste and smell.

THE SENSE OF TASTE

Taste is a function of the *taste buds* in the mouth, and its importance lies in the fact it allows the person to select his food in accordance with his desires and also in accordance with the needs of the tissues for nutrition.

There are at least four *primary* sensations of taste: *sour, salty, sweet,* and *bitter.* Yet we know that a person can perceive literally hundreds of different tastes. These are all combinations of the four primary sensations in the same manner that all the colors of the spectrum are combinations of three primary color sensations as described in Chapter 53.

The Primary Sensations of Taste

Psychological studies have shown that different taste buds respond to different types of taste stimuli; four general classes of taste buds are recognized, corresponding to the four primary sensations of taste—sour, salty, sweet, and bitter.

The Sour Taste. The sour taste is caused by acids, and the intensity of the taste sensation is approximately proportional to the *hydrogen ion concentration.* That is, the

more acidic the acid the stronger becomes the sensation. However, weakly dissociated acids are likely to be slightly more sour for a given pH than a strong acid such as hydrochloric acid. The reason for this is probably that the *total quantity* of acid for a given pH is greater for a weak acid than for a strong acid, and, as hydrogen ions are used to stimulate the taste bud, still more hydrogen ions can dissociate from the undissociated portion of the weak acid but would be unavailable in the case of the already totally dissociated strong acids. Thus, the two factors that determine the degree of sourness are, first, the hydrogen ion concentration and, second, the total amount of hydrogen ions that is available to be released from the remaining undissociated acid.

The threshold concentration of hydrochloric acid for stimulation of the taste buds is 0.0009 N, and the threshold for stimulation by other acids may range from half this much to three times as much.

The Salty Taste. The salty taste is elicited by ionized salts. The quality of the taste varies somewhat from one salt to another because the salts also stimulate some of the other taste buds to varying extents. The cations of the salts are mainly responsible for the salty taste, but the anions also contribute at least to some extent to taste.

The threshold for stimulation of the salty taste buds is 0.01 M sodium chloride, but this threshold can vary up to as high as 0.03 M for some of the other salts.

The Sweet Taste. The sweet taste is not caused by any single class of chemicals. A list of some of the types of chemicals that cause this taste includes: (a) sugars, (b) glycols, (c) alcohols, (d) aldehydes, (e) ketones, (f) amides, (g) esters, (h) amino

Table 21. Relative Taste Indices of Different Substances

Sour Substances	Index	Bitter Substances	Index	Sweet Substances	Index	Salty Substances	Index
Hydrochloric acid	1	Quinine	1	Sucrose	1	NaCl	1
Formic acid	1.1	Brucine	11	1-propoxy-2-amino-		NaF	2
Chloracetic acid	0.9	Strychnine	3.1	4-nitrobenzene	5000	CaCl$_2$	1
Acetyllactic acid	0.85	Nicotine	1.3	Saccharin	675	NaBr	0.4
Lactic acid	0.85	Phenylthiourea	0.9	Chloroform	40	NaI	0.35
Tartaric acid	0.7	Caffeine	0.4	Fructose	1.7	LiCl	0.4
Malic acid	0.6	Veratrine	0.2	Alanine	1.3	NH$_4$Cl	2.5
Potassium H tartrate	0.58	Pilocarpine	0.16	Glucose	0.8	KCl	0.6
Acetic acid	0.55	Atropine	0.13	Maltose	0.45		
Citric acid	0.46	Cocaine	0.02	Galactose	0.32		
Carbonic acid	0.06	Morphine	0.02	Lactose	0.3		

From Derma: *Proc. Oklahoma Acad. Sc.*, 27:9, 1947, and Pfaffman: *Handbook of Physiology*, 1:507, 1959.

acids, (i) sulfonic acids, (j) halogenated acids, and (k) inorganic salts of lead and beryllium.

Table 21 shows the relative intensities of taste of certain substances that cause the sweet taste. *Sucrose,* which is common table sugar, is considered to have an index of 1. Note that one of the substances has a sweet index 5000 times as great as that of sucrose. However, this extremely sweet substance, known as *P-4000,* is unfortunately extremely toxic and therefore cannot be used as a sweetening agent. *Saccharin,* on the other hand, is also more than 600 times as sweet as common table sugar, and since it is not toxic it can be used with impunity as a sweetening agent. It should be noted specifically that almost all the substances that cause a sweet taste are organic chemicals; the only inorganic substances that elicit the sweet taste at all are certain salts of lead and beryllium.

The Bitter Taste. The bitter taste, like the sweet taste, is not caused by any single type of chemical agent, but, here again, the substances that give the bitter taste are almost entirely organic substances. Two particular classes of substances are especially likely to cause bitter taste sensations, the very long chain organic substances and the alkaloids. The alkaloids include many of the drugs used in medicines, such as quinine, caffeine, strychnine, and nicotine.

It is especially interesting that some substances that at first taste sweet will have a bitter after-taste. This is true of saccharin, which makes this substance objectionable to some people. Some substances have a sweet taste on the front of the tongue, where the sweet taste buds are principally located, and a bitter taste on the back of the tongue, where the bitter taste buds are principally located.

The bitter taste, when it occurs in high intensity, usually causes the person or animal to reject the food. This is undoubtedly an important purposive function of the bitter taste sensation because many of the deadly toxins found in poisonous plants are alkaloids, and these all cause an intensely bitter taste.

Threshold for Taste. The threshold for stimulation of the sour taste by hydrochloric acid averages 0.0009 N, for stimulation of the salty taste by sodium chloride: 0.01 M; for the sweet taste by sucrose: 0.01 M; and for the bitter taste by quinine: 0.000008 M. Note, especially, how much more sensitive is the bitter taste sense to stimuli than all the others, which would be expected since this sensation provides a very important protective function.

Table 21 gives the relative taste indices (the reciprocals of the taste thresholds) of different substances. In this table, the intensities of the four different primary sensations of taste are referred, respectively, to the intensities of taste of hydrochloric acid, quinine, sucrose, and sodium chloride, each of which is considered to have a taste index of 1.

Taste blindness. Many persons are taste blind for certain substances, especially for different types of thiourea compounds. A substance used very frequently by psychologists for demonstrating taste blindness is *phenylthiocarbamide,* for which approximately 15 to 30 per cent of all people exhibit taste blindness, the exact percentage depending on the method of testing.

The Taste Buds and Their Function

Figure 570 illustrates a taste bud, which has a diameter of about 1/20 millimeter and a length of about 1/10 millimeter. The taste bud itself is composed of modified epithelial cells, some of which are supporting cells, the *sustentacular cells*, and others of which are the actual *taste cells*. The taste cells have small hairs that project from their ends into a minute cavity, the *taste pore*, at the oral margin of the bud. Interweaving among the taste and sustentacular cells is a branching *network of nerve fibers* that transmits impulses into two or three *taste nerve fibers*.

An interesting feature of the taste buds is that they completely degenerate when the taste nerve fibers are destroyed. Then, if the taste fibers regrow to the epithelial surface of the mouth, the local epithelial cells regroup themselves to form new taste buds. This illustrates beautifully the important principle of "trophic" function of nerve fibers in certain parts of the body.

Location of the Taste Buds. The taste buds are found on three out of four of the different types of papillae of the tongue as follows: (1) A very large number of taste buds are on the circumvallate papillae which form a V line toward the posterior of the tongue. (2) Moderate numbers of taste buds are on the fungiform papillae all over the surface of the tongue. (3) Moderate numbers are on the foliate papillae located in folds along the posterolateral surfaces of the tongue. Additional taste buds are located on the tonsillar pillars and at other points around the nasopharynx, including even a few on the posterior pharyngeal wall itself. Adults have approximately 10,000 taste buds, and children a few more. Beyond the age of 45 many of the taste buds begin to degenerate, causing the taste sensation to become progressively less critical.

Especially important in relation to taste is the tendency for taste buds subserving particular primary sensations of taste to be localized in special areas. The *sweet taste buds* are localized *principally* on the anterior surface of the tongue, the sour taste buds on the two lateral sides of the tongue, and the bitter taste buds on the circumvallate papillae on the posterior surface of the tongue. The salty buds are present over the entire tongue.

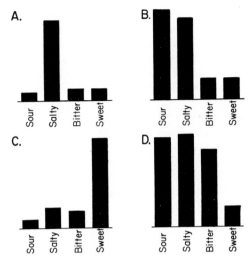

Figure 571. Specific responsiveness of four different types of taste buds, showing multiple stimulation by the different primary sensations of taste in the case of each of the taste buds.

Specificity of Taste Buds for the Primary Taste Stimuli. In the above paragraphs we have discussed taste buds as if each one of them responded to a particular type of taste stimulus and not to other taste stimuli. In a statistical sense this is true, but, so far as any single taste bud is concerned, it is not true, for most of the taste buds are responsive at least to varying extents to three and sometimes to all four of the primary taste stimuli. Figure 571 illustrates the responsiveness of four different taste buds to the different primary tastes. Figures 571 A illustrates a bud responsive to all four types of taste stimuli, but especially to saltiness. Figure 571 B illustrates a taste bud strongly responsive to sourness and saltiness but also responsive to a moderate degree to both bitterness and sweetness. Likewise, Figures 571 C and 571 D illustrate response characteristics of two other types of taste buds. Despite this overlap of taste sensibility in each taste bud, if one averages the taste sensations of hundreds of taste buds, he finds that they fall into statistical categories representing the four primary sensations of taste. The impor-

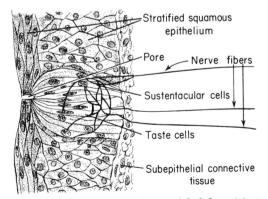

Figure 570. The taste bud. (Modified from Maximow and Bloom: A Textbook of Histology.)

tance of this mixed-up type of responsiveness of the taste buds is probably that it allows the taste sensations to differentiate between closely associated substances such as the different types of salts; as a matter of fact, no two salts are known to give the same taste sensation.

Mechanism of Stimulation of the Taste Buds. The basic mechanism by which the different taste stimuli excite the taste buds is not known, but experiments have demonstrated definitely that the degree of stimulation of the taste buds is almost directly proportional to that which would be expected from the mass law of chemical reactions. That is, the greater the quantity of the stimulating chemical, the greater becomes the degree of stimulation. Therefore, it is believed by most physiologists that the chemical substance to be tasted combines with a substance or substances in the hairs or surface of a taste cell. This chemical reaction supposedly alters the permeability of the receptor cells and in some way initiates impulses in the network of nerve fibers that surround the taste bud.

Other physiologists believe that excitation of the taste bud results not from a chemical reaction at the surface of the cell but instead from a physical change that occurs in the hair or cell membrane when the chemical to be tasted is adsorbed to or absorbed by these structures. But, whatever the mechanism might be, taste stimuli can occur in as little as $\frac{1}{20}$ of a second after the stimulating chemical is put into the mouth, and maximum intensity of taste is reached in less than 5 to 8 seconds.

Transmission of Taste Sensations into the Central Nervous System

Figure 572 illustrates the neuronal pathways for transmission of taste sensations from the tongue and pharyngeal region into the central nervous system. Taste impulses from the anterior two thirds of the tongue pass first into the *fifth nerve* and then through the *chorda tympani* into the *seventh nerve,* thence into the *tractus solitarius* in the brain stem. Taste sensations from the circumvallate papillae on the back of the tongue and from other posterior regions of the mouth are transmitted through the *ninth nerve* also into the *tractus solitarius* but at

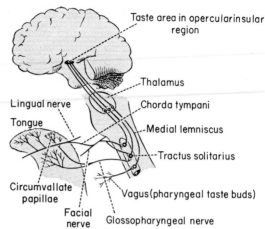

Figure 572. Transmission of taste impulses into the central nervous system.

a slightly lower level. Finally, a few taste impulses are transmitted into the *tractus solitarius* from the pharyngeal region by way of the *vagus nerve.* All taste fibers synapse in the nuclei of the tractus solitarius and send second order neurons to the *arcuate nuclei of the thalamus,* an area that constitutes part of the facial regions of the medial lemniscal system. From the thalamus third order neurons are transmitted to the *parietal opercular-insular area* of the cerebral cortex. This lies at the very lateral margin of the postcentral gyrus in close association with and overlapping the facial areas of somatic sensory area I.

From this description of the taste pathways it immediately becomes evident that they parallel almost exactly the somatic pathways from the face and mouth. Therefore, taste sensations are almost certainly an adapted form of somesthetic sensation. Presumably, higher order integration of the taste sensations is also achieved by the same cerebral areas that subserve the somatic sensory system, but about this we still have almost no factual information.

Taste Reflexes. From the tractus solitarius a large number of impulses are transmitted directly into the *superior* and *inferior salivatory nuclei,* and these in turn transmit impulses to the submaxillary and parotid glands to help control the secretion of saliva during the ingestion of food.

Adaptation of Taste. Everyone is familiar with the fact that taste sensations adapt very rapidly, sometimes within a few seconds and certainly within a minute or

cle fibers will stretch the muscle spindle and automatically excite the annulospiral endings of the spindle. However, there is also another means by which the spindle can be excited, for excitation of the intra-fusal muscle of the muscle spindle by the gamma efferent nerve fibers will shorten the ends of the muscle spindle and thereby stretch the middle portion, thus also exciting the annulospiral ending. In other words, either stretch of the surrounding skeletal muscle fibers or contraction of the muscle spindle itself will stimulate the muscle spindle. The basic organization and the more complete function of the spindle as a sensory receptor are discussed in Chapter 50.

Function of the Muscle Spindles for the Maintenance of Muscular Tone. One of the important functions of the muscle spindles is to help maintain muscle tone—especially in the postural muscles. This is accomplished by continuous discharge of impulses from the spindles even when the muscles are at rest. These impulses facilitate the anterior motoneurons and thereby provide a continual state of muscle tone.

Control of Muscle Tone by the Gamma Efferent Fibers. The intensity of excitation of the muscle spindles is controlled by the degree of contraction of the intrafusal fibers in the muscle spindles, and this in turn is controlled by impulses transmitted through the gamma efferent motor fibers to the muscles. And, since an increase in spindle activity increases muscle tone, any factor in the central nervous system that excites the gamma efferent system indirectly excites the muscles themselves. This provides a secondary means by which the central nervous system can control muscle contraction throughout the body.

The gamma efferent system is excited to a very extensive degree by the bulboreticular facilitatory region of the brain stem and secondarily by impulses transmitted into the bulboreticular facilitatory area from (a) the cerebellum, (b) the basal ganglia, and (c) even the cerebral cortex. Therefore, much of the tonic contraction of the muscles is provided through the gamma efferent system. This is particularly true for the postural contractions necessary to maintain the weight of the body against gravity, which will be discussed further later in the chapter.

An interesting relationship between the gamma and alpha motor fibers to the muscles is that almost all reflexes that require muscles to contract for purposeful movements stimulate both the gamma and alpha efferent fibers simultaneously. For instance, stimulation of the motor cortex in the cerebrum not only causes contraction of the large skeletal muscle fibers but also causes simultaneous contraction of the intrafusal fibers of the muscle spindle. This combined contraction of both intrafusal and large skeletal muscle fibers at the same time allows the muscle to contract without initiating an inverse stretch reflex. Otherwise, the stretch inverse reflex would oppose even the purposeful movements of the body.

To emphasize the importance of gamma control of muscles, it is particularly interesting that 31 per cent of the motor fibers to the muscles are gamma efferents rather than alpha efferents.

The Basic Stretch Reflex. The basic stretch reflex occurs any time the muscle is stretched. This causes impulses to be transmitted from the annulospiral endings directly to the anterior motoneurons which reflexly excite the stretched muscle, thus opposing the stretch. The net effect of the reflex, therefore, is *to oppose a change in length of the muscle.*

Simultaneous inhibition of the antagonistic muscle. At the same time that impulses are transmitted by the stretch reflex to excite the stretched muscle, inhibitory impulses are transmitted to the motoneurons of the antagonist muscles, thus inhibiting these muscles and allowing the reflex contraction of the stretched muscle to be more effective.

It is believed that the inhibitory signals transmitted to the antagonist muscles are transmitted through an internuncial *inhibitory neuron* and that this secretes an inhibitory hormone at its synapse with the anterior motoneuron. However, this inhibitory signal is transmitted with so little delay

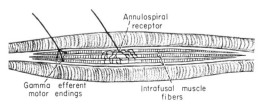

Figure 578. Arrangement of the muscle spindle with respect to the surrounding skeletal muscle fibers.

in the circuit that some neurophysiologists doubt that an extra synapse could be present. If this is true then some new mechanism must be postulated to explain inhibition besides the presently believed mechanism of inhibitory neurons.

Static versus Phasic Stretch Reflexes.

If we will refer back to the discussion of muscle spindle excitation in Chapter 50, we will see that the spindle can be stimulated many times as strongly by sudden increase in the degree of stretch as it can by continuous stretch. Therefore, as would be expected, the intensity of the reflex caused by a sudden increase in stretch is extremely powerful in comparison with the reflex caused by very slow increase in stretch. The relatively weak reflex caused by continuous stretch is called the *static stretch reflex*, while the very strong reflex that occurs following sudden increase in stretch is called the *phasic stretch reflex*.

The Negative Stretch Reflex.

When a muscle is shortened, the number of impulses transmitted by its muscle spindles becomes reduced, particularly so when the muscle is shortened very rapidly. This decrease in impulses immediately inhibits muscle tone in the shortened muscle and automatically excites the antagonist muscles. Obviously, therefore, this *negative stretch reflex* opposes the shortening of the muscle length, particularly if the shortening occurs rapidly.

The Shortening Reaction.

If a muscle is *suddenly* shortened, the stretch reflex will immediately attempt to prevent the shortening by relaxing all tone in the muscle as described above. However, within 5 to 10 seconds, the muscle spindle adapts to its shorter length, and most of the tone returns. This effect is called the *shortening reaction*. To express this reaction another way, upon passive shortening of a muscle at a rapid rate, the muscle becomes completely flaccid because of the negative stretch reflex, but after a few seconds of adaptation the muscle spindle becomes excitable again and the tone of the muscle returns.

Lengthening Reactions.

One type of *lengthening reaction* is the reverse of the shortening reaction. If a muscle is suddenly stretched to a new length, an immediate muscle contraction caused by the stretch reflex opposes the lengthening of the muscle. However, after a few seconds, the muscle spindle adapts to the new length, allowing the intense degree of contraction that had occurred to subside, and the tone of the muscle returns almost to its original level.

The Golgi tendon reflex and the clasp knife effect.

A second type of lengthening reaction involves much more than simply the muscle spindle reflex: If the muscle is stretched very strongly—that is, to such an extent that the Golgi tendon apparatuses also become stimulated—then a strong inhibitory reflex immediately sets in to block the stretch reflex, automatically nullifying the contractile resistance of the muscle that had been opposing the stretch and allowing the muscle suddenly to become entirely flaccid. This effect can cause a taut leg to give way completely when too much load is applied, and the leg folds up like a "clasp knife." After the muscle has been stretched to its new length, however, the muscle tone returns in a few seconds because of loss of the intense stretch that had originally initiated the inhibitory Golgi tendon apparatus reflex.

The Knee Jerk and Other Muscle Jerks.

Clinically, a method used to determine the functional integrity of the stretch reflexes is to elicit the knee jerk and other muscle jerks. The knee jerk can be elicited by simply striking the patellar tendon with a reflex hammer; this stretches the quadriceps muscle and initiates a phasic stretch reflex to cause the lower leg to jerk forward. The upper part of Figure 579 illustrates the myogram from the quadriceps muscle recorded during a knee jerk.

Similar reflexes can be obtained from almost any muscle of the body either by striking the tendon of the muscle or by striking the belly of the muscle itself. In other words, sudden stretch of muscle spindles is all that is required to elicit a stretch reflex.

The muscle jerks are used by neurologists to assess the degree of facilitation of spinal cord centers. When large numbers of facilitatory impulses are being transmitted from

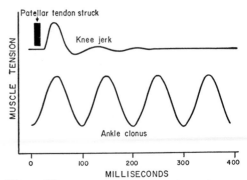

Figure 579. Myograms recorded from the quadriceps muscle during elicitation of the knee jerk and from the gastrocnemius muscle during ankle clonus.

the upper regions of the central nervous system into the cord, the muscle jerks will be greatly exacerbated. On the other hand, if the facilitatory impulses are depressed or abrogated, then the muscle jerks will be considerably weakened or completely absent. These reflexes are used most frequently to determine the presence or absence of muscle spasticity following lesions in the motor areas of the brain. Ordinarily, diffuse lesions in the contralateral motor areas of the cerebral cortex will cause greatly exacerbated muscle jerks.

Clonus. Under appropriate conditions, the muscle stretch reflex can oscillate, a phenomenon called *clonus* (see lower myogram, Fig. 579). Oscillation can be explained particularly well in relation to ankle clonus as follows. If a person is standing on his tiptoes and he suddenly drops his body downward to stretch one of his gastrocnemius muscles, impulses will be transmitted from the muscle spindles into the spinal cord. These reflexly excite the stretched muscle which lifts the body back up again. After a fraction of a second, the reflex contraction of the muscle dies out and the body falls again, thus stretching the spindles a second time. Again a phasic stretch reflex lifts the body, but this too dies out after a fraction of a second, and the body falls once more to elicit still a new cycle. In this way the stretch reflex of the gastrocnemius muscle continues to oscillate—often for long period of time; this is clonus.

Clonus ordinarily will occur only if the stretch reflex is highly sensitized by facilitatory impulses from the cerebrum. For instance, in the decerebrate animal, in which the stretch reflexes are highly facilitated, clonus develops very readily. Therefore, to determine the degree of facilitation of the spinal cord, neurologists test patients for clonus by suddenly stretching a muscle and then keeping a steady force applied to the muscle. If clonus occurs, the degree of facilitation is certain to be very high.

Damping Function of the Stretch Reflex. In the above discussion of the different manifestations of the stretch reflex, such as the shortening reaction and the lengthening reaction, it has been obvious that one of the primary functions of the stretch reflex is *to oppose changes in muscle length*—especially sudden changes in length. This has a very important function to "damp" muscle contractions, which removes jerkiness in the contractions. For instance, when impulses are transmitted down the corticospinal tract to the anterior motoneurons, these often arrive in fairly irregular packets, and in animals whose posterior roots to a respective muscle have been sectioned and the stretch reflex thereby knocked out, the muscle contraction is jerky rather than smooth. However, with the phasic stretch reflexes intact, the movements are so smooth that no jerkiness is perceptible.

Though neurophysiologists have not greatly emphasized the damping function of the stretch reflex, the basic theory of control systems indicates that this might be the most important or one of the most important of all the functions of the stretch reflex—perhaps as important as the control of postural tone by the stretch reflex. We must remember that the movements performed by the body are all pendular, and pendular movements cause the limbs, fingers, and other parts of the body to build up momentum and therefore to overshoot their marks unless some type of damping system is available to prevent the overshoot. Indeed, limbs with their posterior roots sectioned do overshoot their marks, which is called *hypermetria*, and this causes the animal to be unsure of his motions. This effect probably occurs partly because of loss of the stretch reflexes and partly because of loss of proprioceptor impulses to the cerebellum, which itself is a very important damping organ that functions in close harmony with the stretch reflexes, as will be discussed in Chapter 58.

Because of the jerkiness of movement and hypermetria that result from loss of the stretch reflex, we can assume that the highly intricate functions of our fingers and hands could not possibly be performed without adequate stretch reflexes to provide the necessary damping.

Furthermore, we might postulate that the gamma efferent system has a special function to increase or decrease the degree of damping of muscle functions. For instance, when a person performs some very delicate task, the motions of his fingers and hands must be highly damped to provide smooth and discretely controlled actions. Stimulation of the gamma efferents could provide this increased damping and therefore allow far more delicate control. At other times a person would not want such intense damping because damping unfortunately slows up movements as well as making them highly critical, and movements sometimes need to be very rapid and forceful rather than highly damped. Thus, the gamma efferent system could readily provide the critical damping that would be required for fine movements, and reduced gamma efferent stimulation could provide the lack of damping required for rapidity and forcefulness of movement. In support of this argument is the fact that the tone of the muscles in an area such as the hand greatly increases when delicate movements are to be performed.

Though this possible function of the gamma efferent system has not yet been proved, it is now being studied in our laboratory, and preliminary considerations indicate that it might be equally as important a function of the gamma efferent system and muscle stretch reflex as the postural tone function described above.

The Flexor Reflex

In the spinal or decerebrate animal, a very slight stimulus to a limb is likely to cause the flexor muscles of the limb to contract very strongly, thereby withdrawing the limb from the stimulus. This is called the *flexor reflex.*

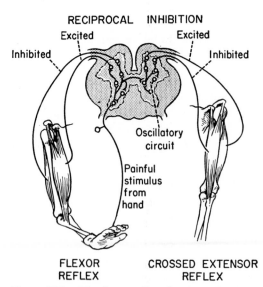

Figure 580. The flexor reflex, the crossed extensor reflex, and reciprocal inhibition.

In its classical form the flexor reflex is elicited most frequently by stimulation of pain endings, for which reason it is frequently called a *nociceptive reflex.* And, if some other part of the body besides one of the limbs is stimulated, this part also will be withdrawn from the stimulus, but the reflex may not be confined entirely to flexor muscles even though it is basically the same reflex. Therefore, the reflex is frequently called a *withdrawal reflex,* too.

The Neural Mechanism of the Flexor Reflex. The left-hand portion of Figure 580 illustrates the neuronal pathways for the flexor reflex. In this instance, a painful stimulus is applied to the hand; as a result, the flexor muscles of the upper arm become reflexly excited, thus withdrawing the arm from the painful stimulus.

The pathways for eliciting the flexor reflex do not pass directly to the anterior motoneurons but, instead, pass first into the internuncial pool of neurons and then to the motoneurons. Therefore, the shortest possible circuit for eliciting a flexor reflex is a three-neuron arc; however, most of the signals of the reflex traverse many more neurons than this and involve the following basic types of circuits: (1) diverging circuits to spread the reflex to the necessary muscles for withdrawal, (2) circuits to inhibit the antagonist muscles, called *reciprocal inhibition circuits,* and (3) circuits to cause an after-discharge even after the stimulus is over.

Figure 581 illustrates a typical myogram from a flexor muscle during a flexor reflex. Within a few milliseconds after a pain nerve is stimulated the flexor response occurs. Then, in the next few seconds the reflex *fatigues,* which is characteristic of essentially all integrative reflexes of the spinal cord.

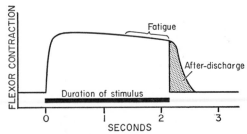

Figure 581. Myogram of a flexor reflex, showing rapid onset of the reflex and an interval of after-discharge after the stimulus is over.

Then, immediately after the stimulus is over, the contraction of the muscle begins to return toward the base line, but, because of after-discharge, will not return all the way for many milliseconds to as long as 4 to 5 seconds. The duration of the after-discharge depends on the intensity of the sensory stimulus that had elicited the reflex; a weak stimulus causes almost no after-discharge, in contrast to a prolonged after-discharge following a very strong stimulus. Furthermore, a flexor reflex initiated by non-painful stimuli and transmitted through the large sensory fibers causes essentially no after-discharge, whereas nociceptive impulses transmitted through the small type A fibers and type C fibers cause very prolonged after-discharge.

The after-discharge that occurs in the flexor reflex almost certainly results from both types of after-discharge circuits that were discussed in Chapter 47. Electrophysiological studies show that the immediate after-discharge, lasting for about 6 to 8 milliseconds, results from the parallel type of circuit, with impulses being transmitted from one interneuron to another to another and all of these in turn transmitting their signals successively to the anterior motoneuron. However, the very prolonged after-discharge that occurs following strong pain stimuli almost certainly involves reverberating circuits in the interneurons, these transmitting impulses to the anterior motoneurons sometimes for several seconds after the incoming sensory signal is completely over.

Thus, the flexor reflex is appropriately organized to withdraw a pained or otherwise irritated part of the body away from the stimulus. Furthermore, because of the after-discharge it will hold the irritated portion of the body away from the stimulus sometimes for 2 to 5 seconds even after the irritation is over. During this period of time, other reflexes and other actions of the central nervous system can move the entire body away from the painful stimulus.

The Pattern of Withdrawal. The pattern of withdrawal that results when the flexor (or withdrawal) reflex is elicited depends upon the sensory nerve that is stimulated. Thus, a painful stimulus on the inside of the arm will not only elicit a flexor reflex in the arm but will also contract the abductor muscles to pull the arm outward. In other words, the integrative centers of the cord cause those muscles to contract that can most effectively remove the pained part of the body from the object that causes the pain. This same principle applies to any part of the body but especially to the limbs for they have highly developed flexor reflexes.

The Principles of "Local Sign" and "Final Position" in Relation to the Flexor Reflex. The position to which a limb will be withdrawn following a painful stimulus is determined entirely by the point on the skin that is stimulated, and, if another point only a few centimeters away is stimulated, the withdrawal position will be correspondingly different. This is called the phenomenon of *local sign*. That is, the response depends on the locus of the stimulus.

Another extremely important principle in relation to the flexor reflex and to many other motor responses of the spinal cord is that the original position of the limb has nothing to do with the final position of the limb following the stimulus. For instance, a limb that is already flexed will be withdrawn to exactly the same position following stimulation of a particular pain nerve as it would if the original position of the limb had been full extension. This is called the *principle of final position*. It results from the organization of the interneurons between the incoming sensory nerve and the outgoing motor nerves. Thus, each incoming sensory nerve is connected to a particular complex of interneurons to give a different final position from that of any other incoming sensory nerve.

The Stretch Flexor Reflex. Another type of stretch reflex is that which results from stimulation of the flower-spray endings of the muscle spindles. These endings are not normally stimulated by minute degrees of stretch of the muscles but are stimulated by more intense stretch. They result in a flexor pattern of withdrawal of the entire limb regardless of whether the stretched muscle is a flexor muscle or an extensor muscle. The precise function of this type of flexor reflex is yet unknown, though it is believed to operate to some extent in the oscillating feedback circuits associated with walking, which will be discussed later in the chapter.

The Crossed Extensor Reflex

After a stimulus elicits a flexor reflex in one limb, approximately a quarter to a half second later the opposite limb begins to extend. This reflex is called the *crossed ex-*

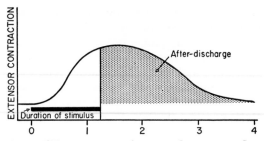

Figure 582. Myogram of a crossed extensor reflex, showing slow onset but prolonged after-discharge.

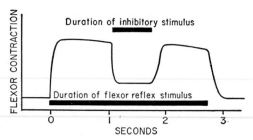

Figure 583. Myogram of a flexor reflex, illustrating crossed inhibition caused by a stronger flexor reflex in the opposite limb.

tensor reflex. Extension of the opposite limb obviously can push the whole body away from the object causing the painful stimulus.

The Neuronal Mechanism of the Crossed Extensor Reflex. The right hand portion of Figure 580 illustrates the neuronal circuit responsible for the crossed extensor reflex. Because the crossed extensor reflex usually does not begin until 200 to 500 milliseconds following the initial pain stimulus, it is certain that many internuncial neurons are in the circuit between the incoming sensory neuron and the motoneurons of the opposite side of the cord responsible for the crossed extension. Furthermore, after the painful stimulus is removed, the crossed extensor reflex continues for an even longer period of after-discharge than that for the flexor reflex. Therefore, again, it is almost certain that this prolonged after-discharge results from reverberatory circuits among the internuncial cells.

Figure 582 illustrates a myogram recorded from a muscle involved in a crossed extensor reflex. This shows the relatively long latency before the reflex begins and also the very long after-discharge following the end of the stimulus. The prolonged after-discharge obviously would be of benefit in holding the entire body away from the painful object until other neurogenic reactions should cause the body to move away.

The Principle of "Final Position" in the Crossed Extensor Reflex. In exactly the same way that a sensory stimulus from a given local area of the body causes a certain "final position of withdrawal," it also causes a "final position of extension" on the opposite side of the body.

Reciprocal Innervation

In the above paragraphs we have pointed out several times that excitation of one group of muscles is often associated with inhibition of another group of muscles. For instance, when a stretch reflex excites one muscle, it simultaneously inhibits the antagonist muscles. This is the phenomenon of *reciprocal inhibition,* and the neuronal mechanism that causes this reciprocal relationship is called *reciprocal innervation.* Likewise, reciprocal relationships exist between the flexor and extensor reflexes as described above.

We will see below that the principle of reciprocal innervation is also very important in most of the cord reflexes that subserve locomotion, for it helps to cause forward movement of one limb while causing backward movement of the opposite limb.

Figure 583 illustrates a typical example of reciprocal inhibition. In this instance, a moderate but prolonged flexor reflex is elicited from one limb of the body, and while this reflex is still being elicited a still stronger flexor reflex is elicited from the opposite limb, causing reciprocal inhibition of the first limb as long as the strong flexor reflex is sustained. Then removal of the strong flexor reflex allows the original reflex to reassume its moderate intensity.

Fatigue of Reflexes; Rebound

Figure 581 illustrated that the flexor reflex begins to *fatigue* within a few seconds after its initiation. This is a common effect in most of the cord reflexes as well as many other reflexes of the central nervous system, and it presumably results from progressive diminishment of excitability of some of the neurons in the reflex circuits.

Another effect closely allied to fatigue is *rebound.* This means that, immediately after a reflex is over, a second reflex of the same type is much more difficult to elicit for a given period of time thereafter. However, because of reciprocal innervation, reflexes of the antagonist muscles become even more easily elicited. For instance, if a flexor reflex occurs in a left limb, a second flexor reflex will be more difficult to establish for a few seconds thereafter, but a crossed-extensor reflex in this same limb will be greatly exacerbated. Rebound is probably one of the important mechanisms by which the rhythmical to-and-fro movements required in locomotion are effected, which will be described in more detail later in the chapter.

REFLEXES OF POSTURE AND LOCOMOTION

The *stretch reflex* which was discussed above has often been described as the basic reflex of posture, partly because facilitation of the anterior motoneurons by impulses from the muscle spindles is necessary to provide tonic contraction of the muscles. But, in addition to this, the sensitivity of the stretch reflex can be altered greatly by activation or deactivation of the gamma efferent system, in this way increasing or decreasing the tonic contraction of the muscles. Since posture requires continual tonic contraction, this mechanism for controlling muscle tone is well adapted to the control of postural contraction. In most instances, the postural contraction for support of the body against gravity does, indeed, result primarily from activation of the gamma efferent system rather than from *direct* activation of the anterior motoneurons. And superimposed on this basic background of the stretch reflex are many special reflexes that have to do both with posture and locomotion as follows:

Postural and Locomotive Reflexes of the Cord

The Positive Supportive Reaction. Pressure on the footpad of a decerebrate animal causes the limb to extend against the pressure that is being applied to the foot. Indeed, this reflex is so strong that a decerebrate animal can be placed on its feet, and the pressure on the footpads will reflexly stiffen the limbs sufficiently that they can support the weight of the body—and the animal will stand in a rigid position, sometimes for hours at a time. This reflex is called the *positive supportive reaction.*

The positive supportive reaction involves a complex circuit in the internuncial cells similar to those responsible for the flexor reflexes or the crossed-extensor reflexes. Furthermore, the principle of "final position" applies to this reflex equally as much as it applies to the flexor and crossed extensor reflex. That is, pressure on the pad of the foot causes a definite final position to which the limb is extended.

The magnet reaction. If the pressure is applied on one side of the foot, then the foot will move in that direction, or, if the pressure is moved forward, the foot will move forward, or, if it is moved backward, the foot will also move backward. In this way, the bottom of the foot remains continuously extended against the pressure that is being applied. This is called the *magnet reaction*, and it obviously would help in the maintenance of equilibrium, for, if an animal should tend to fall to one side, that side of the footpad would be stimulated, and the limb would automatically extend toward the falling side to push the body of the animal in the opposite direction.

Extensor Thrust Reflex. Another reflex closely allied to the positive supportive reaction is the *extensor thrust reflex*. This results from stretch of the skin to the sides of and beneath the toes. On pressing upward on the toes, a sudden contraction of the hip muscles occurs, thrusting the foot downwards and backwards. This reflex is undoubtedly important in such functions as jumping forward, galloping, or hopping. The extensor thrust reflex is more a phasic reflex than a static reflex, occurring rapidly and suddenly rather than continually as occurs in the case of the positive supportive reaction.

Cord "Righting" Reflexes. When a spinal cat or even a well-recovered spinal dog is laid on his side, he will make incoordinate attempts to rise to the standing position. This is called a *cord righting reflex,* and it illustrates that relatively complicated reflexes associated with posture are at least partially integrated in the spinal cord. Indeed, a puppy with a well-healed transected thoracic cord can completely right himself from the lying position and can even walk on his hindlimbs. And, in the case of the opossum with a similar transection of the thoracic cord, the walking movements of the hindlimbs are hardly different from

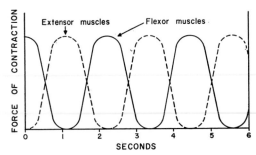

Figure 584. Alternate contraction of the extensor and flexor muscles in the limb of a spinal animal when a stepping reflex was elicited.

those in the normal opossum—except that the hindlimbs will move out of phase with the forelimbs rather than in phase as is usually the case.

Rhythmic Stepping Reflex of the Single Limb. Rhythmic stepping movements are frequently observed in the limbs of spinal animals. Indeed, even when the lumbar portion of the spinal cord is separated from the remainder of the cord and a longitudinal section is made down the center of the cord to block neuronal connections between the two limbs, each of the hind limbs can still perform stepping functions. Forward flexion of the limb is followed a second or so later by backward extension. Then flexion occurs again, and the cycle is repeated over and over. This oscillation back and forth between the flexor and extensor muscles seems to result mainly from reciprocal inhibition and rebound. That is, the forward flexion of the limb causes reciprocal inhibition of extensor muscles, but shortly thereafter the flexion begins to die out; as it does so, *rebound* excitation of the extensors causes the leg to move downwards and backwards. After extension has continued for a period of time, it, too, begins to die and is followed by rebound excitation of the flexor muscles. Another reflex that might enter into the rhythmical stepping pattern of the single limb is the stretch flexor reflex initiated as noted earlier in the chapter by stretch of the flower-spray endings in the muscle spindles. Downward extension of the limb can elicit such a reflex and cause the limb to lift again. Thus, several different neuronal circuits are available in the cord to cause continual oscillation of a limb in a stepping pattern.

Figure 584 shows myograms of alternate extensor and flexor contractions in a limb during the course of stepping movements.

Reciprocal Stepping of Opposite Limbs. If the lumbar spinal cord is not sectioned down its center as noted above, every time stepping occurs in the forward direction in one of the limbs, the opposite limb ordinarily steps in a backward direction. This effect results from reciprocal innervation between the two limbs.

Diagonal Stepping of All Four Limbs— The "Mark Time" Reflex. If a decerebrate animal is held up from the table and his legs are allowed to fall downward as illustrated in Figure 585, the stretch on the limbs often elicits stepping reflexes that involve all four limbs. In general, stepping occurs diagonally between the fore- and hindlimbs. That is, the right hindlimb and the left forelimb move backward together while the right forelimb and left hindlimb move forward. This diagonal response is another manifestation of reciprocal innervation, this time occurring the entire distance up and down the cord between the forelimbs and the hindlimbs. Such a walking pattern is often called a *mark time reflex*.

Galloping Reflex. Another type of reflex that occasionally develops in the spinal animal is the galloping reflex, in which both forelimbs move backward in unison while both hindlimbs move forward. If stretch or pressure stimuli are applied almost exactly equally to opposite limbs at the same time, a galloping reflex will likely result, whereas unequal stimulation of one side versus the other will elicit the diagonal walking reflex. This is in keeping with the normal

Walking movement

Figure 585. Diagonal stepping movements exhibited by a spinal animal.

patterns of walking and of galloping, for, in walking, only one limb at a time is stimulated, and this would predispose to continued walking. Conversely, when the animal strikes the ground during galloping, the limbs on both sides are stimulated approximately equally; this obviously would predispose to further galloping and, therefore, would continue this pattern of motion in contradistinction to the walking pattern.

Brain Stem Influences on Locomotion

From the above discussion, it is quite evident that essentially all the basic patterns for walking or even galloping are quite well integrated in the spinal cord itself. However, these are not sufficient in themselves to allow continued or purposive locomotion. For instance, a spinal animal, though capable of actually standing on its limbs because of the positive supportive reaction, usually fatigues within a few minutes and then falls to the ground. In the decerebrate animal, however, prepared by transection of the brain stem between the superior and inferior colliculus, the animal can stand for hours at a time. The difference results from a large number of facilitatory impulses transmitted by the brain stem into the cord to facilitate the cord centers. In addition special brain stem reflexes provide for effective equilibrium, as will be described below.

Function of the Vestibular and Reticular Nuclei in the Maintenance of Postural Tone. In the same manner that impulses from the muscle spindles cause continual facilitation of the anterior motoneurons, the vestibular and upper reticular nuclei of the brain stem also transmit tonic facilitatory impulses to the anterior motoneurons. Without these, sufficient tone ordinarily cannot develop in the postural muscles to allow the animal to stand indefinitely. Therefore, one of the most important functions of the brain stem in posture and locomotion is to provide at least part of the nervous energy required to keep the limbs rigid, thus opposing the tendency of gravity to collapse the animal to the ground.

The Vestibular "Righting" Reflex and Equilibrium. Earlier in this chapter it was pointed out that the crude motions required to move an animal from a lying to a standing position have their patterns of integration already present in the spinal cord. However, these cord-righting reflexes cannot perform the full function of righting an animal without impulses from the brain stem. The static equilibrium organ of the vestibular apparatus, the macula of the utricle, transmits impulses into the brain stem to apprise the nervous system of the status of the animal with respect to the pull of gravity, and, if the animal is in a lying position, these can elicit appropriate reflexes from the vestibular and reticular nuclei to cause the animal to climb to his feet. This is called the *vestibular righting reflex.*

If the standing decerebrate animal begins to fall to one side, the legs on that side will become automatically extended, or, if he begins to fall to the opposite side, the legs on that side will become extended. These effects, like the righting reflex, result also from the vestibular equilibrium reflexes described in Chapter 50 in relation to the functions of the vestibular apparatuses. These vestibular reflexes require neuronal integration in all parts of the brain stem up to as high as the mesencephalon.

Vestibular Phasic Reflexes. Sudden changes in the orientation of the animal in space will also elicit reflexes that help to maintain equilibrium and posture. For instance, if an animal is suddenly pushed to the right, even before he can fall more than a few degrees his right legs will become instantaneously extended. In other words this mechanism actually anticipates that the animal will be far off balance in a few seconds and makes appropriate adjustment to prevent this. These reflexes, also, were discussed in detail in Chapter 50.

Another type of vestibular phasic reflex occurs when the animal's head suddenly falls downward. When this occurs, the forepaws extend forward, the extensor muscles tighten, and the muscles in the back of the neck stiffen to prevent the animal's head from striking the ground. This reflex is probably also of importance in locomotion, for, in the case of the galloping horse, the downward thrust of the head could automatically provide reflex thrust of the forelimbs to move the animal forward for the next gallop.

Neck Reflexes. In an animal whose vestibular apparatuses have been destroyed, bending the neck will cause immediate muscular reflexes called *neck* reflexes especially in the forelimbs. For instance, bending the head forward will cause both forelimbs to relax. However, it should be noted that, when the vestibular apparatuses are intact, this effect does not occur because the vestibular reflexes function almost exactly oppositely to the neck reflexes. Thus, if the head is flexed downward, the vestibular reflex will tend to extend the forelimbs while the neck reflexes will tend to relax them. Since it is the equilibrium of the entire body and not of the head alone that must be maintained, it is quite easy to understand that the vestibular and neck reflexes must function oppositely. Otherwise, each time the neck should bend, the animal would immediately fall off balance.

Function of Higher Centers in Posture and Locomotion

Function of the Subthalamic Areas— Forward Progression. Much less is known about the function of higher centers in posture and locomotion than of the lower centers, principally because of the complexity of neuronal connections in the cerebral cortex, thalamus, basal ganglia, and other centers. However, it is known that stimulation of centers in or around the subthalamic nuclei can cause definite forward walking reflexes. This does not mean that the individual muscles of walking are necessarily controlled from this region but simply that excitation of this region excites the appropriate patterns of reaction in the brain stem and cord to cause the walking movements.

A cat with its brain transected beneath the thalamus can walk in an almost completely normal fashion—so much so that the observer cannot tell the difference. However, when the animal comes to an obstruction he simply butts his head against it and tries to keep on walking. Thus, he lacks purposefulness of locomotion.

The function of the subthalamic region in walking is frequently described as that of controlling *forward progression.* From our discussions above we have already noted that a decerebrate animal can stand perfectly well and that he can right himself from the lying position to the standing position. Unfortunately, though, the decerebrate animal does not have the capability of forcing himself to move forward in a normal walking pattern. This seems to be the function of areas either in or somewhere close to the subthalamic nuclei.

Function of the Cerebral Cortex in Posture and Locomotion — Cortical "Righting" Reflexes. The principal function of the cerebral cortex in locomotion is to add purposefulness to the locomotion, as illustrated above by the case of the cat that would not go around the obstruction. Such an effect obviously would not have occurred in an animal with a cerebral cortex. However, in addition to the purposefulness added by cortical function several postural and righting reflexes are also integrated in the cortex. These include the *visual righting reflex,* certain aspects of *exteroceptive righting reflexes,* and the *placing reaction.*

The visual and exteroceptive righting reflexes. The visual righting reflexes depend on function of the visual cortex, and, for full expression of these reflexes, the somesthetic sensory and motor areas of the cortex are also needed. That is, an animal can tell by images from the periphery whether his body is in the appropriate position with respect to its surroundings. From this information, he can raise himself from the lying position to the standing position even in the absence of the vestibular righting reflexes.

Similarly, the animal's sensory and motor cortex provides for righting in response to exteroceptive information that is transmitted into the cerebrum. It has been pointed out that sensations from the skin can cause crude righting responses even in the spinal animal and even much better responses in the decerebrate animal. However, for full expression of the exteroceptive righting reflexes, the cerebral cortex is also required.

The placing reaction. A blindfolded animal held in the air and then brought in contact with a surface so that almost any part of his body makes contact with the surface will immediately bring his paws toward the point of contact, thus placing his feet in an advantageous position to gain support. This is called the *placing reaction.* Though some expression of the placing reaction can occur even in animals without the cerebral cortex, here again the complete reaction can occur only when the cortex is available to provide stereognostic orientation of the different parts of the body in relation to each other, thus allowing the animal to know where his feet need to be moved in order to make appropriate contact.

The hopping reaction. The hopping reaction is another reaction that requires the cerebral cortex for full attainment. This reaction probably results mainly from direct transmission of proprioceptive and vestibular information to the somesthetic area in the postcentral gyrus, where direct connections are made with the motor cor-

deficit at all. However, if the ablated area is large, and particularly if the motor area, the "premotor" area, and the underlying caudate nucleus are removed at the same time, the paralysis is permanent. If the caudate nucleus is left intact, gross postural and limb "fixation" movements can still be performed, but discrete movements of the distal segments of the limbs are lost.

Ablation of the Premotor Cortex. If the premotor cortex is removed without destroying any of the adjacent motor cortex, the affected region of the body becomes quite spastic, but control of the discrete movements from the area is not affected. On the other hand, skilled movements which had previously been performed by the involved muscles can no longer be performed in a coordinate manner.

The forced grasping reflex. Removal of the hand region of the premotor cortex usually causes a *forced grasping reflex.* That is, a tactile stimulus in the palm of the hand causes it instantly to grasp very tightly, which is analogous to the forced grasping reflex that occurs in monkeys to allow them to hang for long periods of time by the hands.

The Babinski Sign. Destruction of the foot region of the motor cortex causes a peculiar response of the foot called the *Babinski sign,* which is demonstrated when a firm tactile stimulus is applied along the inner border of the sole—the great toe extends and the smaller toes fan out. This is in contradistinction to the normal effect in which all the toes bend downward. The Babinski sign is even more intense when the foot portion of the premotor cortex is destroyed along with the motor cortex. And a Babinski sign is often observed, also, following damage to the corticospinal tract. For all of these reasons, therefore, the Babinski sign is very often used clinically to detect abnormalities in the motor control system. Yet, even so, the physiologic cause of the Babinski sign is not known.

Effect of Hemidecortication. In rare instances it has been necessary to remove the cortex of an entire hemisphere. When this is done in a child and the basal ganglia and thalamus are left intact, the child usually learns to walk quite adequately and to perform postural and other crude subconscious movements. However, he can never learn to perform discrete movements with his hand on the contralateral side of his body or to perform complicated "voluntary" movements involving any of his contralateral muscles.

If the surgical incision involves significant portions of the caudate nuclei or of the thalamus, the person never learns to walk or to perform any satisfactory purposeful movements on the contralateral side of his body. This illustrates very forcefully the importance of the diencephalic nuclei and basal ganglia in the control of motor functions.

Effects of Pyramidal Transection

Since transection of a pyramid in the medulla destroys all or almost all of the corticospinal fibers from one cerebral hemisphere, such a procedure in an experimental animal discloses much information about the overall function of the corticospinal tract as distinguished from the extracorticospinal tracts.

Transection of a pyramid on one side of the medulla causes loss of all the discrete movements on the opposite side of the body, which illustrates that the corticospinal tract, and not the extracorticospinal tracts, controls the fine movements—especially in the hands, fingers, feet, and toes.

A second effect of pyramidal transection is *hypotonia* throughout the body; this results from loss of the normal facilitation of the corticospinal tract on the spinal motor centers. Associated with the hypotonia is gradual atrophy of the muscles everywhere in the body, especially the distal musculature of the limbs.

Two other effects of transecting the pyramidal tracts are *forced grasping* and the *Babinski sign.* This illustrates that these two phenomena are actually functions of the extracorticospinal pathways which are still intact and that destruction of the corticospinal tract removes a restraining influence, thus allowing forced grasping and the Babinski sign to occur.

Finally, pyramidal transection removes much of the cortical control over certain autonomic functions, which illustrates that not all autonomic influences are transmitted through the hypothalamus and extrapyramidal tracts. For instance, (1) the skin temperature over the entire body decreases, (2) stimulation of areas of the cortex which formerly had caused elevation of the arterial pressure often can no longer cause this effect, and (3) even cortical control over some of the gastrointestinal activities is decreased or lost after pyramidal transection.

Functions of the Extracorticospinal Pathways That Are Retained After Pyramidal Transection. After pyramidal transection, the motor functions not lost are mainly the postural contractions and other gross movements of the body. For instance, the different movements required for equilibrium and support of the body against gravity are still completely intact. Furthermore, stimulation of motor and premotor cortical regions will still cause gross movements of the trunk and upper portions of the limbs. These movements are sometimes called "fixation movements," and their function is the following: when a discrete motor function is to be performed by a hand, for instance, the trunk and upper arm must be "fixed" in appropriate positions before the hand can perform its required function. These fixation movements still occur even after complete transection of the pyramidal tract. In other words, the extracorticospinal pathways are responsible for almost all the postural and fixation movements, while the corticospinal tracts are responsible mainly for the superimposed discrete movements, especially those of the distal portions of the limbs.

FUNCTION OF THE INTERNUNCIAL SYSTEM OF THE SPINAL CORD

Only a very few of the corticospinal and extracorticospinal fibers end directly on the anterior motoneurons of the spinal cord; almost all of them end on internuncial cells. The internuncial system of the corticospinal pathway has been reasonably well worked out and is illustrated in Figure 593. On the other hand, much less is known about the internuncial systems of the reticulospinal, tectospinal, vestibulospinal, and rubrospinal pathways. But Figure 594 illustrates the supposed organization of these internuncial systems as well.

Referring again to Figure 593, we see that almost all the corticospinal fibers end directly on small *internuncial cells of the external basilar region of the dorsal horns*.

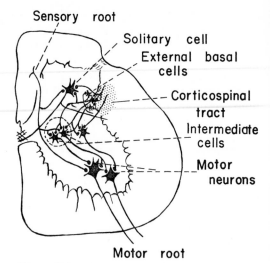

Figure 593. Connections of the corticospinal tract with the internuncial cells and anterior motoneurons of the spinal cord. (Modified from Lloyd: Handbook of Physiology, 2:929, 1960.)

From these, impulses are transmitted mainly through *intermediate internuncial cells* to the anterior motoneurons, but some impulses are also transmitted through so-called *solitary cells* that lie more posteriorly in the dorsal horns. Thus, at least two internuncial cells usually must relay the signals from the corticospinal tract to the anterior motoneurons, and sometimes three or even more. On the other hand, a very few corticospinal fibers end directly on the anterior motoneurons.

Functions of the Internuncial Cells in the Motor Transmission System

In the previous chapter we noted that the internuncial cells are the loci of "patterns of movement" in the spinal cord. These can be either fixed movements with "final positions," or they can be rhythmical movements such as stepping movements. scratching movements, and so forth. Therefore, we must presume that these same patterns of movement can be activated by impulses from the corticospinal and extracorticospinal tracts. In addition, still other "patterns of movement" not normally found in the spinal animal can almost certainly be elicited by impulses from the brain. It might be supposed that stimulation of successive points in the motor cortex causes a sequence of "patterns of movement," each one of which is actually an intrinsic function of the internuncial sys-

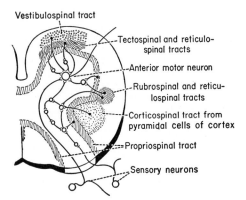

Figure 594. Convergence of all the different motor pathways on the anterior motoneurons.

tem. In this way, the impulses from the motor cortex would not be stimulating the individual muscles directly but instead would be stimulating successively different complexes of internuncial cells of the spinal cord. Thus, *a spreading excitation across a very minute area of the motor cortex could reasonably be expected to cause a sequential movement of a limb, perhaps involving a hundred or more successive cord integrated patterns of movement.*

Convergence of Signals in the Internuncial System. Another important function of the internuncial system is convergence of motor stimulatory signals from many different sources. For instance, sensory stimuli from the peripheral nerves can cause certain specific patterns of movement as described in relation to the cord reflexes in the previous chapter. Then the motor cortex can elicit its patterns of movement, and stimulation of other cortical motor areas as well as areas of the basal ganglia and the brain stem elicits still other patterns of movement mainly concerned with posture, equilibrium, and fixation of limbs. Since all these different types of patterns of movement might be elicited simultaneously, the internuncial cells and anterior motoneurons must algebraically add all the different stimuli and come out with the net result. Therefore, the internuncial system, along with the motoneurons themselves, constitutes a final level for integration of motor signals from all sources.

Stimulation of the Anterior Motoneuron and Its Output to the Periphery

We need to say very little about stimulation of the anterior motoneuron because this has already been discussed in great detail in relation to synaptic functions of neurons in Chapter 47. We can summarize the stimulation of the anterior motoneurons by pointing out that both excitatory and inhibitory impulses impinge on its dendrites and soma. The impulses from the corticospinal pathway, from the vestibulospinal pathway, and from parts of the reticulospinal tracts are all excitatory while impulses from another major portion of the reticulospinal tract are mainly inhibitory. Also, many of the internuncial cells that help to form the different patterns of movement transmit inhibitory impulses.

Though most of the impulses to the anterior motoneurons are routed through the internuncial cells, a few pass directly to the anterior motoneurons. These presumably perform much less complicated functions than do those that pass through the internuncial system, including such functions as exciting highly discrete muscular contractions instead of patterns of movement, or providing general facilitation or general inhibition.

Transmission of Impulses in the Motor Nerves. The anterior motoneurons give rise to large type A alpha fibers that leave the spinal cord through the ventral roots. These branch many times before finally innervating the skeletal muscle fibers, the initial branching beginning shortly before entry into the muscle belly and continuing extensively after entry into the muscle. All the muscle fibers excited by a single motor neuron are collectively called a *motor unit* because all these fibers contract in unison. As few as 5 to 10 muscle fibers may be present in a motor unit, such as in the ocular muscles, or as many as 4000 to 5000 fibers may be in a motor unit, as occurs in some of the postural muscles; the average is approximately 1600. The function of the motor unit was discussed in Chapter 19, and transmission of impulses through the neuromuscular junction was described in Chapter 18.

Function of the Renshaw Cells. Immediately after the motor axons originate from the motoneurons, small collateral fibers pass medially from these to the *Renshaw cells* that lie in the medial portion of the anterior horns. These in turn send axons to adjacent motoneurons to inhibit their activity. The importance of this system seems to be the following: Stimuli from the internuncial cells to a particular motoneuron tend to radiate also to adjacent motoneurons. However, it might not be desirable that these adjacent motoneurons be excited at the same time, for this would cause diffuse rather than discrete muscular movements. The Renshaw system provides inhibitory impulses that nullify the tendency for the signal to spread too widely, thus preventing this interference in the performance of discrete motor activities.

Another very important consideration in relation to the Renshaw cells is that they are excited by collaterals from the motor axons that are known to secrete acetylcholine in the skeletal muscles. Therefore, it is assumed that the Renshaw cells are excited also by the secretion of acetylcholine at their presynaptic terminals. This bit of evidence indicates more than any other that acetylcholine is either *the*, or at least *one of the*, excitatory hormones released at the synapses in the central nervous system.

REFERENCES

Brookhart, J. M.: Single pyramidal fiber response to electrical stimulation. *Proc. Soc. Exp. Biol. & Med.*, 82:341, 1953.

Brookhart, J. M.: Study of cortico-spinal activation of motor neurones. *A. Res. Nerv. & Ment. Dis. Proc.*, 30:157, 1952.

Bucy, P. C.: The Precentral Motor Cortex. 2nd ed., Urbana, Illinois, University of Illinois Press, 1959.

Eccles, R. M., and Lundberg, A.: Supraspinal control of interneurones mediating spinal reflexes. *J. Physiol.*, 147:565, 1959.

Fatt, P.: Sequence of events in synaptic activation of a motoneurone. *J. Neurophysiol.*, 20:61, 1957.

Gelfan, S., and Tarlov, I. M.: Interneurones and rigidity of spinal origin. *J. Physiol.*, 146:594, 1959.

Granit, R.: Descending effects of the reticular system with special reference to the gamma fibers. *Progr. Neurobiol.*, 2:295, 1956.

Granit, R.: Reflex rebound by post-tetanic potentiation; temporal summation spasticity. *J. Physiol.*, 131:32, 1956.

Granit, R., Henatsch, H. D., and Steg, G.: Tonic and phasic ventral horn cells differentiated by post-tetanic potentiation in cat extensors. *Acta Physiol. Scand.*, 37:114, 1956.

Guyton, A. C.: Reaction of the body to poliomyelitis and the recovery process. *Arch. Int. Med.*, 83:27, 1949.

Guyton, A. C.: Relation of symptoms to the pathological physiology in poliomyelitis. *J. Tennessee M. A.*, 41:254, 1948.

Hunt, C. C., and Kuno, M.: Background discharge and evoked responses of spinal interneurones. *J. Physiol.*, 147:364, 1959.

Hunt, C. C., and Kuno, M.: Properties of spinal interneurones. *J. Physiol.*, 147:346, 1959.

Kuffler, S. W., and Gerard, R. W.: Small-nerve motor system to skeletal muscle. *J. Neurophysiol.*, 10:383, 1947.

Lassek, A. M., and Evans, J. P.: The human pyramidal tract. XII. The effect of hemispherectomy on fiber components of the pyramids. *J. Comp. Neurol.*, 83:113, 1945.

Lassek, A. M.: The Pyramidal Tract: Its Status in Medicine. Springfield, Illinois, Charles C Thomas, 1955.

Li, C.: Some properties of pyramidal neurones in motor cortex with particular reference to sensory stimulation. *J. Neurophysiol.*, 22:385, 1959.

Liddell, E. G. T., and Phillips, C. G.: Striatal and pyramidal lesions in the cat. *Brain*, 69:264, 1946.

Martin, A. R., and Branch, C. L.: Spontaneous activity of Betz cells in cats with midbrain lesions. *J. Neurophysiol.*, 21:368, 1958.

Patton, H. D., and Amassian, V. E.: Single- and multiple-unit analysis of cortical stage of pyramidal tract activation. *J. Neurophysiol.*, 17:345, 1954.

Patton, H. D., and Amassian, V. E.: The pyramidal tract: its excitation and functions. *Handbook of Physiology*, 2:837, 1960.

Penfield, W., and Rasmussen, T.: The Cerebral Cortex of Man. New York, The Macmillan Co., 1950.

Segundo, J. P., and Galeano, C.: Somatic functions of the nervous system. *Ann. Rev. Physiol.*, 22:433, 1960.

Teasdall, R. D., and Stavraky, G. W.: Responses of deafferented spinal neurones to corticospinal impulses. *J. Neurophysiol.*, 16:367, 1953.

Terzuolo, C. A., and Adey, W. R.: Sensorimotor cortical activities. *Handbook of Physiology*, 2:797, 1960.

Van Harreveld, A., and Stamm, J. S.: Spreading cortical convulsions and depressions. *J. Neurophysiol.*, 16:352, 1953.

Welker, W. I., Benjamin, R. M., and Miles, R. C.: Motor effects of stimulation of cerebral cortex of squirrel monkey (Saimiri sciureus). *J. Neurophysiol.*, 20:347, 1957.

See also Chapter 58, The extrapyramidal tract.

Motor Functions of the Reticular Formation, the Basal Ganglia, and the Cerebellum

In the previous two chapters we have considered, first, the control of motor movements by the spinal cord, and, second, their control by the cerebral cortex. To complete the picture we need now to discuss the motor functions of the reticular formation, the basal ganglia, and the cerebellum, which are integral parts of the extracorticospinal motor system. These structures, in general, function coordinately with the spinal cord and the cerebral cortex in the control of motor activities, which will become evident as we proceed in this chapter.

THE RETICULAR FORMATION

Physiologic Anatomy of the Reticular Formation. The reticular formation represents essentially all the gray matter besides the special sensory and motor nuclei in the medulla, pons, mesencephalon, and even portions of the diencephalon. Actually, most extracorticospinal motor functions feed through the reticular formation, the input impulses to this area arriving from the cortex, the basal ganglia, the cerebellum, and various ones of the special nuclei in the brain stem. In turn, motor impulses are transmitted from the reticular substance into the spinal cord by way of the *reticulospinal tract*, the *tectospinal tract*, the *rubrospinal tract*, and the *vestibulospinal tract*.

Figure 595 illustrates the extent of the reticular formation, showing that it begins at

the upper end of the spinal cord and extends into the posterior part of the hypothalamus, to the sides of the thalamus, and upward through the central portion of the thalamus. The lower end of the reticular formation is continuous with the internuncial cells of the spinal cord. Therefore, the reticular formation of the brain stem is very much analogous

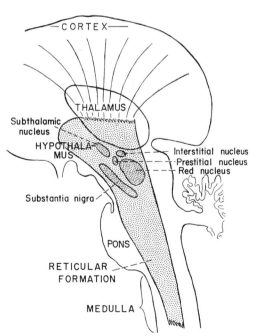

Figure 595. The reticular formation and its relationship to adjacent structures of the brain stem and cerebrum.

to the internuncial system of the cord. Several special nuclei illustrated in Figure 595, including the *red nucleus,* the *substantia nigra,* the *subthalamic nucleus,* the *interstitial nucleus,* and the *prestitial nucleus,* are aggregates of cells that can be considered to be special parts of the reticular formation, for they operate along with the other portions of the reticular formation as a functional unit. Likewise, the vestibular nuclei, located in the medulla, can also be considered from a functional point of view to be part of the reticular formation.

Excitatory and Inhibitory Functions of the Reticular Formation

The upper part of the reticular formation is mainly excitatory. Stimulation in this region will cause either large portions of musculature or sometimes discrete groups of muscles to contract, the effect depending on the site of stimulation.

On the other hand, a small portion of the reticular formation, located principally in the *ventro-medial portion of the medulla,* has mainly inhibitory functions; stimulation in this area causes greatly decreased tone of the musculature throughout the body.

It should be noted, however, that there is actually no distinct separation between the excitatory and inhibitory areas of the reticular formation, for some discrete areas in the upper so-called "facilitatory area" can cause inhibition, while some discrete areas in the lower so-called "inhibitory area" can cause excitation. Furthermore, stimulation of some points in the reticular formation can cause excitation of one group of muscles while inhibiting the antagonistic muscles.

Therefore, there are actually two different types of motor functions that can occur on stimulation of different parts of the reticular formation: (1) generalized facilitation or generalized inhibition of large segments of the musculature throughout the body or (2) discrete movements of distinct parts of the body with excitation of agonist and inhibition of antagonist.

Decerebrate Rigidity. In Chapter 56 it was pointed out that transection of the brain stem immediately beneath the superior colliculus ordinarily causes markedly increased muscular tone throughout the body. This results from removal of inhibitory influences normally trans-

mitted from above. Since the greater portion of the reticular formation is facilitatory rather than inhibitory, the normal effect is to facilitate all the muscles throughout the body, causing a general increase in muscular tone. However, if the transection occurs below the vestibular nuclei, the result is inhibition of muscular tone rather than facilitation, because the portion of the reticular formation below this area is mainly inhibitory.

A major part of the increased postural tone in decerebrate rigidity results from stimulation of the *gamma activating system of the muscle spindles* and not from direct activation of the alpha motor neurons. After decerebration, the upper portion of the reticular formation, partly under the influence of tonic impulses from the cerebellum, transmits a continual discharge of impulses through the gamma activating system. This, in turn, increases the responsiveness of the muscle spindles, and feedback from the muscle spindles markedly enhances the activity of the anterior motoneurons.

Support of the Body against Gravity and Control of Equilibrium. The function of the reticular formation in control of postural tone and support of the body against gravity was discussed in Chapter 56, and in Chapter 50 the role of the reticular formation along with the vestibular and cerebellar nuclei for control of equilibrium was presented. Briefly, impulses from the vestibular nuclei and from the reticular formation are transmitted continually to the postural muscles to support the body against gravity. In addition, the vestibular apparatuses continually modify the tone in the different antigravity muscles so that, if a person begins to fall off equilibrium, the extensor muscles to the falling side will be contracted while those on the opposite side will be relaxed.

Functions of the Reticular Formation in Controlling Subconscious, Stereotyped Movements

Rarely, a child is born without brain structures above the mesencephalic region, and at least one of these has been kept alive for many months. This child was able to perform essentially all the functions of feeding such as sucking, extrusion of unpleasant food from the mouth, and moving his hands to his mouth to suck his fingers. In addition, he could yawn and stretch and could cry and follow objects with his eyes and with movements of his head. Also, placing pressure on the upper anterior parts of his legs would cause him to pull to the sitting position.

Therefore, it is obvious that many of the

stereotyped motor functions of the human being are integrated in the reticular formation of the brain stem. Unfortunately, the loci of most of the different motor control systems in the reticular formation have not yet been found except for the following:

Stereotyped Body Movements Most of the movements of the trunk and head can be classified into several simple movements, such as forward flexion, extension, rotation, and turning movements of the entire body. These types of movements are controlled by special nuclei located mainly in the mesencephalic and lower diencephalic region. For instance, *rotational movements* of the head and eyes are controlled by the *interstitial nucleus*, which is illustrated in Figure 595. This nucleus lies in close approximation with the *medial longitudinal fasciculus*, through which it transmits a major portion of its control impulses. The *raising movements* of the head and body are controlled by the *prestitial nucleus*, which is located approximately at the juncture of the diencephalon and mesencephalon. On the other hand, the *flexing movements* of the head and body are controlled by the *nucleus precommissuralis* located at the level of the posterior commissure. Finally, the *turning movements*, which are very much more complicated, involve both the pontile and mesencephalic reticular formation. However, for full expression of the turning movements, the caudate nucleus and the cingulate gyrus of the cerebral cortex are also required. The turning movements can cause an animal or person to continue circling around and around in one direction or the other.

Control of Respiration and Autonomic Functions by the Reticular Formation. The regulation of respiration was discussed in Chapter 42 and the regulation of the vasomotor system was discussed in Chapter 32. From these discussions it will be recalled that both respiration and arterial pressure are controlled mainly by centers located in the medullary and pontile regions of the reticular formation. In the case of respiration, a natural oscillating system is present in the medullary reticular formation, and the intensity of the oscillation, as well as its frequency, increases or decreases in response to the needs of the body for pulmonary ventilation. Likewise, parasympathetic and sympathetic impulses for control of the heart and vascular system are also transmitted from this same general region. In addition, it contains a center for control of micturition (Chapter 11) as well as relay centers from the hypothalamus for control of body temperature and metabolic functions of the autonomic nervous system.

Finally, it should be noted that most of the hypothalamus itself is actually an upward exten-

sion of the reticular formation from the brain stem. Therefore, the many autonomic functions of this region can also be considered to be part of the overall functional picture of the reticular formation.

Activation of the Cerebrum by the Reticular Formation—the Reticular Activating System

Before leaving the reticular formation, we must point out that it has a very powerful ability to activate essentially all parts of the cerebrum in addition to its ability to cause motor functions by transmission of impulses downward. Excitation of the upper reticular formation transmits impulses upward through the medial portion of the thalamus to essentially all parts of the cortex and basal ganglia, causing general facilitation of the entire cerebrum. On the other hand, the cerebrum lapses instantly into sleep when major areas of the upper reticular formation are destroyed. Therefore, the reticular formation and the associated nuclei and pathways of the thalamus are called the *reticular activating system*. This system will be discussed in more detail in Chapter 60 in relation to the behavioral functions of the central nervous system.

THE BASAL GANGLIA

Physiologic Anatomy of the Basal Ganglia. The anatomy of the basal ganglia is so complex and is so poorly known in its details that it would be pointless to attempt a complete description at this time. However, Figure 596 illustrates the principal structures of the basal ganglia and their neural connections with other parts of the nervous system. Anatomically, the basal ganglia are the *caudate nucleus,* the *putamen,* the *globus pallidus,* the *amygdaloid nucleus,* and the *claustrum.* However, the amygdaloid nucleus, which will be discussed in Chapter 60, and the claustrum are not intimately concerned with the motor functions of the central nervous system and will not be considered in the present discussion. On the other hand, the *thalamus,* the *subthalamus,* the *substantia nigra,* and the *red nucleus* all operate in close association with the caudate nucleus, putamen, and globus pallidus and therefore must be considered to be part of the basal ganglia system for motor control.

Some of the important features of the different pathways illustrated in Figure 596 are the following:

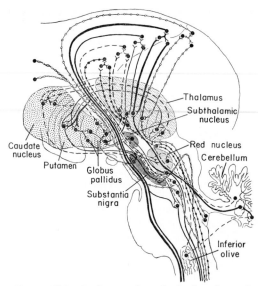

Figure 596. Pathways through the basal ganglia and related structures of brain stem, the thalamus, and cerebral cortex. (From Jung and Hassler: Handbook of Physiology, Vol. II. American Physiol. Society.)

1. Almost all parts of the cerebral cortex are connected by both afferent and efferent fiber pathways with the thalamus. Because of these connections, specific activity in a given part of the thalamus elicits activity also in a specific and corresponding area of the cerebral cortex. In turn, impulses from the cortex will cause corresponding activity in respective areas of the thalamus. Thus, the cerebral cortex and the thalamus are connected with each other in such a way that thalamic and cortical activities always occur in unison with each other.

2. From the *motor cortex* many impulses pass into the *putamen.* From the *anterior edge of the motor cortex* impulses pass into the *caudate nucleus.* From the *premotor cortex* impulses pass into the *putamen* and *substantia nigra.* From the *postcentral gyrus* impulses are transmitted directly to the *reticular formation* of the brain stem. And from all these different pathways, many additional short collaterals diffuse throughout the lower diencephalon, the mesencephalon, the pons, and the medulla.

3. Special pathways exist from both the *cerebral cortex* and *caudate nuclei* to the *cerebellum.* From the corticospinal tract almost as many collaterals are given off to the cerebellum through the *pontocerebellar pathway* as there are fibers passing downward through the corticospinal tracts. Another pathway to the cerebellum originates in the caudate nucleus, then passes to (a) the putamen, (b) the upper portion of the reticular formation, (c) the inferior olive, and (d) through the *olivocerebellar tracts* into the cere-

bellum. In turn, feedback impulses from the cerebellum pass upward through the thalamus back to the cerebral cortex, the caudate nucleus, and the putamen.

To summarize the physiologic anatomy of the basal ganglia—a very intimate association exists between the reticular formation, the basal ganglia, the thalamus, and the cerebral cortex. One notes particularly the many possibilities for feedback circuits operating (1) back and forth between the thalamus and the cortex, (2) between the cortex, the basal ganglia, the thalamus, and then the cortex again, and (3) from the cortex or basal ganglia to the cerebellum, then back to the thalamus and returning once again to the cortex or basal ganglia.

One of the most important deficits in our knowledge of the anatomy of the basal ganglia system concerns the pathways by which control impulses pass from the basal ganglia downward into the reticular formation, for only a few such fiber pathways have thus far been traced—mainly through the subthalamus, the substantia nigra, and the red nuclei—and these are insufficient to explain all the many known motor control functions of the basal ganglia. Therefore, it is presumed that impulses from the basal ganglia might be transmitted mainly by means of *multiple short pathways* into the reticular formation and then by way of the *reticulospinal, tectospinal, rubrospinal* and *vestibulospinal tracts* into the spinal cord.

Functions of the Different Basal Ganglia

Before attempting to discuss the functions of the basal ganglia in man, we should speak briefly of the better known functions of these ganglia in lower animals. In birds, for instance, the cerebral cortex is very poorly developed, whereas the basal ganglia are highly developed. Therefore, the basal ganglia, along with the thalamus, perform essentially all the sensory and motor functions, even controlling the voluntary movements in much the same manner that the motor cortex of the human being controls voluntary movements. Furthermore, in the cat, and to a less extent in the dog, decortication removes only the discrete types of motor functions and does not interfere with its ability to walk, to eat perfectly well, to fight, to de-

flocculonodular lobes are required for proper integration of the equilibratory impulses. Removal of the *nodulus* in particular will cause almost complete loss of equilibrium, and removal of the *flocculus* will cause temporary loss. The symptoms of mal-equilibrium are essentially the same as those which result from destruction of the semicircular canals. This indicates that these areas of the cerebellum are particularly important for integration of *changes in direction of motion* as detected by the semicircular canals, but not so important for integrating static impulses of equilibrium as detected by the maculae in the utricles. This is in keeping with the other functions of the cerebellum; that is, the semicircular canals allow the central nervous system to predict ahead of time that rotational movements of the body are going to cause mal-equilibrium, and this predictive function causes appropriate muscles to contract to prevent the person from losing equilibrium even before this state develops. This is very much the same as the predictive function of the cerebellum for coordination of rapid voluntary movements. For further discussion of the equilibrium mechanism, the student is now referred to Chapter 50.

Electrical Activity in the Cerebellum

The cerebellar cortex is continually active, rhythmical discharges occurring throughout the cortex at rates of 150 to 250 cycles per second—about 20 times as rapidly as the intrinsic discharge rate of the cerebral cortex. Feedback impulses through the cerebellum "modulate" the intrinsic activity of the cerebellum, sometimes increasing and at other times decreasing the activity.

The continual rhythmical impulses in the cerebellum facilitate the motor cortex. Enhanced activity of a particular region in the cerebellar cortex will enhance the degree of facilitation of a corresponding point in the motor cortex. Conversely, decreased activity in a given point of the cerebellum will cause corresponding decrease in activity of its representative area in the motor cortex.

Clinical Abnormalities of the Cerebellum

Destruction of small portions of the cerebellar cortex will cause no detectable abnormality in motor function. In fact, several months after as much as one half of the cerebellar cortex has been removed, the motor functions will again be almost entirely normal. Thus, the remaining areas of the cerebellum compensate tremendously for loss of part of the cerebellum.

To cause serious dysfunction of the cerebellum, the cerebellar lesion must usually involve the deep cerebellar nuclei—the *dentate, emboliform, globose,* and *fastigial nuclei*—as well as the cerebellar cortex.

Dysmetria and Ataxia. Two of the most important symptoms of cerebellar disease are *dysmetria* and *ataxia.* It was pointed out above that in the absence of the cerebellum a person cannot predict ahead of time how far his movements will go. Therefore, the movements ordinarily overshoot their intended mark, though at times they undershoot. This effect is called *dysmetria,* and it results in incoordinate movements which are called *ataxia.*

Dysmetria and ataxia can also result from lesions in the spinocerebellar tracts, for the feedback information from the moving parts of the body is essential for accurate control of the muscular movements.

Past pointing. Past pointing means that in the absence of the cerebellum a person will ordinarily move his hand or some other moving part of his body considerably beyond the point of intention. This probably results from the following effect: the motor cortex normally transmits more impulses to the muscles to perform a given motor function than are actually needed. The cerebellum automatically corrects this by inhibiting the movement after it has begun. However, if the cerebellum is not available to cause this inhibition, the movement ordinarily goes far beyond the intended point. Therefore, past pointing is actually a manifestation of dysmetria.

Failure of Progression. Dysdiadochokinesia. It was pointed out earlier in the chapter that when the motor control system fails to predict ahead of time where the different parts of the body will be at a given time, it temporarily "loses" the parts during rapid motor movements. As a result, the next succeeding movement may begin much too early or much too late so that no orderly "progression of movement" can occur. One can demonstrate this very readily in a patient with cerebellar damage by having him turn one of his hands upward and downward at a rapid rate. He very rapidly "loses" his hand and does not know its position during any portion of the movements. As a result, a series of jumbled movements occurs instead of the normal coordinate upward and downward motions. This is called *dysdiadochokinesia.*

Dysarthria. Another instance in which failure of progression occurs is in talking, for the formation of words depends on very rapid and orderly succession of individual muscular movements in the larynx. Lack of coordination between these and inability to predict either the intensity of the sound or the duration of each successive sound cause jumbled vocalization, with some syllables very loud, some very weak, some held long, some held for a short interval, and resultant speech that is almost completely unintelligible. This is called *dysarthria*.

Intention Tremor. When a person who has lost his cerebellum performs a voluntary act, his muscular movements are jerky; this reaction is called an *intention tremor* or an *action tremor*, and it results from failure of the cerebellar system to damp the motor movements. Tremor is particularly evident when the dentate nuclei or the brachium conjuctivum is destroyed, but it is not present when the spinocerebellar tracts from the periphery to the cerebellum are destroyed. This indicates that the feedback pathway from the cerebellum to the motor cortex is the principal pathway for damping of muscular movements.

Cerebellar nystagmus. Cerebellar nystagmus is a tremor of the eyeballs that occurs usually when a person attempts to fixate his eyes on a scene to the side of his head. This off-center type of fixation results in rapid tremorous movements of the eyes rather than a steady fixation, and it is probably another manifestation of the failure of damping by the cerebellum. However, it also occurs when the flocculonodular lobes are damaged, but in this condition it is associated with loss of equilibrium. The nystagmus in this instance might be the result of dysfunction of the pathways through the cerebellum from the semicircular canals. Nystagmus resulting from damage to the semicircular canals was discussed in Chapter 50.

Rebound. If a person with cerebellar disease is asked to contract his arm very tightly while the physician holds it back at first and then lets go, the arm will fly back until it strikes the face instead of being automatically stopped. This is called *rebound*, and it results from loss of the cerebellar component of the stretch reflex. That is, the normal cerebellum ordinarily instantaneously and very powerfully sensitizes the spinal cord stretch reflex mechanism whenever a portion of the body begins to move unexpectedly in an unwilled direction. But, without the cerebellum, this activation of the antagonist muscle fails to occur, thus allowing over-movement of the limb.

Hypotonia. Loss of the cerebellar hemispheres causes moderate decrease in tone of the peripheral musculature, though after several months the motor cortex usually compensates for this by an increase in its intrinsic activity. The hypotonia results from loss of facilitation of the motor cortex by the cerebellocortical pathways.

Loss of equilibrium. Destruction of the flocculonodular portion of the cerebellum causes loss of equilibrium, particularly when the person attempts to perform very rapid movements. This loss of equilibrium is similar to that which occurs when the semicircular canals are destroyed, as was discussed in Chapter 50.

REFERENCES

Alred, E., and Snider, R. S.: Cerebro-cerebellar relations in monkey. *J. Neurophysiol.*, 15:27, 1952.

Amassian, V. E., and Devito, R. V.: Unit activity in reticular formation and nearby structures. *J. Neurophysiol.*, 17:575, 1954.

Branch, C. L., and Martin, A. R.: Inhibition of Betz cell activity by thalamic and cortical stimulation. *J. Neurophysiol.*, 21:380, 1958.

Brookhart, J. M.: The cerebellum. *Handbook of Physiology*, 2:1245, 1960.

Bucy, P. C.: The Precentral Motor Cortex. 2nd ed., Urbana, Illinois, University of Illinois Press, 1949.

Calma, I., and Kidd, G. J.: The action of the anterior lobe of the cerebellum on α motoneurones. *J. Physiol.*, 149:626, 1959.

Carpenter, M. B., and Brittin, G. M.: Subthalamic hyperkinesia in rhesus monkey. Effects of secondary lesions in red nucleus and brachium conjunctivum. *J. Neurophysiol.*, 21:400, 1958.

Carpenter, M. B., Correll, J. W., and Hinman, A.: Spinal tracts mediating subthalamic hyperkinesia. Physiological effects of selective partial cordotomies upon dyskinesia in rhesus monkey. *J. Neurophysiol.*, 23:288, 1960.

Combs, C. M.: Bulbar regions related to localized cerebellar afferent impulses. *J. Neurophysiol.*, 19: 285, 1956.

Cooper, I. S.: The Neurosurgical Alleviation of Parkinsonism. Springfield, Illinois, Charles C Thomas, 1956.

Cranmer, J. I., Brann, A. W., and Bach, L. M. N.: An adrenergic basis for bulbar inhibition. *Am. J. Physiol.*, 197:835, 1959.

DeVito, R. V., Brusa, A., and Arduini, A.: Cerebellar and vestibular influences on Deitersian units. *J. Neurophysiol.*, 19:241, 1956.

Dow, R. S., and Moruzzi, G.: The Physiology and Pathology of the Cerebellum. Minneapolis, Univ. of Minnesota Press, 1958.

Forman, D., and Ward, J. W.: Responses of electrical stimulation of caudate nucleus in cats in chronic experiments. *J. Neurophysiol.*, 20:230, 1957.

French, J. D.: The reticular formation. *Handbook of Physiology*, 2:1281, 1960.

Gauthier, C., Mollica, S., and Moruzzi, G.: Physiological evidence of localized cerebellar projections to bulbar reticular formation. *J. Neurophysiol.*, 19: 468, 1956.

Gernandt, B. F., and Thulin, C. A.: Reciprocal effects upon spinal motoneurons from stimulation of bulbar reticular formation. *J. Neurophysiol.*, 18:118, 1955.

Gernandt, B. E., and Thulin, C. A.: Vestibular mechanisms of facilitation and inhibition of cord reflexes. *Amer. J. Physiol.*, 172:653, 1953.

Granit, R., and Phillips, C. G.: Effects on Purkinje

cells of surface stimulation of the cerebellum. *J. Physiol.*, 135:73, 1957.

Granit, R., and Phillips, C. G.: Excitatory and inhibitory process acting upon individual Purkinje cells of the cerebellum in cats. *J. Physiol.*, 133:520, 1956.

Granit, R., and Phillips, C. G.: Two types of inhibition of cerebellar Purkinje cells. *J. Physiol.*, 132: 58p, 1956.

Granit, R., Holmgren, B., and Merton, P. A.: The two routes for excitation of muscle and their subservience to the cerebellum. *J. Physiol.*, 130:213, 1955.

Grossman, R. G.: Effects of stimulation of non-specific thalamic system on locomotor movements in cat. *J. Neurophysiol.*, 21:85, 1958.

Jung, R., and Hassler, R.: The extrapyramidal motor system. *Handbook of Physiology*, 2:863, 1960.

Koella, W. P.: Influence of position in space on cerebellar inhibition and facilitation in cats. *Am. J. Physiol.*, 173:443, 1953.

Lamarche, G., and Morin, F.: Latencies and pathways for cutaneous projections to posterior cerebellar lobe. *J. Neurophysiol.*, 20:275, 1957.

Laporte, Y., Lundberg, A., and Oscarrson, O.: Functional organization of the dorsal-spino-cerebellar tract in the cat. I. Recording of mass discharge in dissected Flechsig's fasciculus. *Acta Physiol. Scand.*, 36:175, 1956.

Lippold, O. C. J., Redfearn, J. W. T., and Vuco, J.: The influence of afferent and descending pathways on the rhythmical and arrhythmical components of muscular activity in man and the anaesthetized cat. *J. Physiol.*, 146:1, 1959.

Magoun, H. W., and Rhines, R.: Inhibitory mechanism in bulbar reticular formation. *J. Neurophysiol.*, 6:165, 1946.

Magoun, H. W., and Rhines, R.: Spasticity: The Stretch Reflex and Extrapyramidal Systems. Springfield, Illinois, Charles C Thomas, 1948.

Moruzzi, G.: Problems in Cerebellar Physiology. Springfield, Illinois, Charles C Thomas, 1950.

Oberholzer, R. J. H., and Tofani, W. O.: The neural control of respiration. *Handbook of Physiology*, 2: 1111, 1960.

Olszewski, J.: Cytoarchitecture of the Human Brain Stem. Philadelphia, J. B. Lippincott, 1954.

Preston, J. B., and Whitlock, D. G.: Precentral facilitation and inhibition of spinal motoneurons. *J. Neurophysiol.*, 23:154, 1960.

Rhines, R., and Magoun, H. W.: Brain stem facilitation of cortical motor response. *J. Neurophysiol.*, 9:219, 1946.

Ruch, T. C.: Central control of the bladder, *Handbook of Physiology*, 2:1207, 1960.

Schoolman, A., and Delgado, J. M. R.: Cerebro-cerebellar relations in the awake cat. *J. Neurophysiol.*, 21:1, 1958.

Segundo, J. P., Migliaro, E. F., and Roig, J. A.: Effect of striatal and claustral stimulation upon spinal reflex and strychnine activity. *J. Neurophysiol.*, 21: 391, 1958.

Snider, R. S.: Facilitation produced by cerebellar stimulation. *J. Neurophysiol.*, 12:335, 1949.

Sprague, J. M., and Chambers, W. W.: Control of posture by reticular formation and cerebellum in the intact, anesthetized and unanesthetized and in the decerebrate cat. *Amer. J. Physiol.*, 176:52, 1954.

Uvnäs, B.: Central cardiovascular control. *Handbook of Physiology*, 2:1131, 1960.

Ward, A. A., Jr.: Decerebrate rigidity. *J. Neurophysiol.*, 10:89, 1947.

Chapter 59

Integrative Functions

of the Cerebral Cortex

It is ironic that we know least about the mechanisms of the cerebral cortex as compared with other parts of the brain, even though it is by far the largest portion of the entire nervous system. Yet, we do know the effects of destruction or specific stimulation of various portions of the cortex, and still more information has been gained from electrical recordings from the cortex or from the surface of the scalp. In the present chapter we will discuss, first, the known facts about cortical functions, and then we will present briefly some of the basic theories of the neuronal mechanisms involved in thought processes, memory, analysis of sensory information, and so forth.

Physiologic Anatomy of the Cerebral Cortex

Perhaps the most significant feature of the cerebral cortex is its homogeneity. It is made up mainly of a very thin layer of neurons 1.5 to 4 millimeters in thickness, covering the surface of all the convolutions of the cerebrum and having a total area of 2300 square centimeters. In the cerebral cortex is a total of approximately 9.3 billion neurons. Figure 602 illustrates the typical structure of the cerebral cortex, showing successive layers of different types of cells. Most of the cells are either *granule cells* or *pyramidal cells,* which have a characteristic pyramidal shape. To the right in Figure 602 is illustrated the typical organization of nerve fibers within the different layers of the cortex. Note particularly the very large number of horizontal fibers extending be-

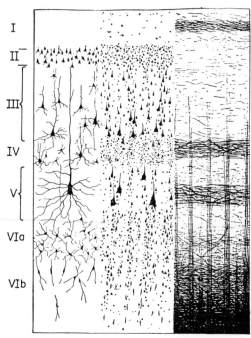

Figure 602. Structure of the cerebral cortex, illustrating: (I) molecular layer, (II) external granular layer, (III) layer of pyramidal cells, (IV) internal granular layer, (V) ganglionic layer, (VI) layer of fusiform or polymorphic cells. (From Ranson and Clark (after Brodmann): Anatomy of the Nervous System.)

tween adjacent areas of the cortex, but note also the vertical fibers that extend to and from the cortex to lower areas of the brain stem or to distant regions of the cerebral cortex itself through long association fibers.

Neurohistologists have divided the cerebral cortex into almost 100 different areas which have very slightly different archi-

the texture of a rug, and other individual characteristics that enter into the overall awareness of a particular instant.

The Basis of Memory

If we accept the above approximation of what constitutes a thought, then we can see immediately that the mechanism of memory must be equally as complex as the mechanism of a thought, for, to provide memory, the nervous system must be capable of recreating the same spatial and temporal pattern of stimulation in the central nervous system at some future date. Though we cannot explain in detail what a memory is, we do know some of the basic neuronal processes that probably lead to the process of memory.

Temporary Memory. There is much reason to believe that there are two types of memory, one which is only temporary and depends upon *prolonged excitation of the involved neurons* and another which lasts indefinitely and probably depends upon *physical alteration of the synapses*. The temporary type of memory is based on the following physiological observations: When an electrical stimulus is applied directly to the surface of the cerebral cortex and then removed after a second or more, the local area excited by this stimulus continues to emit rhythmical action potentials for minutes or, under very favorable conditions, for as long as an hour or more. This effect has been shown to result from local reverberating circuits, the impulses passing around and around a multiconnected chain of neurons in the local area of the cortex itself.

It is presumed that sensory signals reaching the cerebral cortex can set up similar reverberatory cycles that continue to oscillate for many minutes or even an hour or more. Then, gradually, as the reverberating circuits fatigue and the oscillation ceases, the temporary memory fades away.

Function of the lower centers in temporary memory. Though almost nothing is known about reverberating circuits in the lower brain centers, it is known that sufficiently powerful electrical stimuli applied to the cerebral cortex will initiate low frequency reverberations between the cortex and the thalamus, thus eliciting a prolonged after-discharge involving at the same time both the cerebral cortex and the thalamus. Therefore, it could be postulated that a given thought pattern initiates prolonged excitation of the thalamus at the same time that the cortex is excited. Such excitation of the thalamus could be responsible for the thalamic portion of the temporary memory, and similar mechanisms might also be operative in the other lower centers involved in memory.

Prolonged Memory—Alteration of the Synapses. Prolonged memory means recall of thoughts by the nervous system long after the initial excitation is over. We know that prolonged memory does not depend upon continued activity of the nervous system, because the brain can be totally inactivated by cooling, by general anesthesia, by hypoxia, by ischemia, or by any other method so that all functional activity temporarily ceases, and yet the memories that have been stored prior to such an event will still be retained when activity is restored. Therefore, it is assumed that prolonged memory must result from actual alteration of the synapses. In earlier years it was believed that use of the synapses for thought patterns caused new terminal fibrils and new presynaptic endings to form, thus increasing the excitability of the involved synapses. This theory was based on the fact that tremendous growth of fibrils and presynaptic terminals is observed in growing children, during the period of life when the greatest number of memories are being established. However, it is now known that the number of such endings is determined by other factors besides the storage of memories. It is now believed that thought patterns cause permanent changes in the size, shape, chemical enzyme systems, or some other characteristics of the presynaptic terminals. Indeed, electron micrographs do demonstrate that different states of synaptic activity change the anatomical characteristics of the presynaptic terminals.

Post-tetanic potentiation. Aside from the anatomical speculation and anatomical evidence for alteration of synapses in prolonged memory, we also know from physiological experiments that previous stimulatory experience of synapses can lead to facilitation of the synapse. For instance, if an anterior motoneuron is stimulated for a few seconds by very strong incoming sensory signals, *subsequent passage of individual test stimuli through the synapse occurs far more easily than before* for the next few seconds to few minutes. This is called *post-tetanic potentiation*, and it obviously is a type of "memory" that depends on a change in the excitability of the involved neuron. It is presumed that similar effects can occur in all areas of the central nervous system—indeed, probably far more so in the cerebral cortex than in the anterior horn cells.

The time factor in the establishment of memory. A prolonged memory is not established in the central nervous system during the first few minutes after a sensory experience. Instead, an hour or more is required to "fixate" the memory in the neuronal circuits. For instance, if a very strong sensory impression is made on the brain but is then followed by strong electrical stimulation all through the cortex, the sensory experience will not be remembered at all. However, if the same stimulus is impressed on the brain and the strong electrical shock is delayed for as long as an hour, then the memory "engram" is established. If we hold to the reverberation theory of temporary memory, one could explain these differences in the following way: If the reverberation is disrupted soon after it begins by strong electrical stimulation, significant post-tetanic potentiation will not occur to develop a prolonged memory. But, if the thought pattern is not disrupted, then sufficient reverberation could take place to establish a deeply trodden memory pathway.

Similarly, if many strong sensory experiences, one occurring immediately after another, are impressed on the brain, it usually will not be possible to remember any of them well, presumably because each successive experience disrupts the previous reverberating circuit before an engram of the memory can be established.

Locus of Memory. We need hardly discuss the subject of locus of memory, for as explained earlier in this discussion, memory involves both basal and cortical areas of the brain, and memory is a function of the entire nervous system and not of individual parts. Yet, it is true that different degrees of temporary and prolonged memory can probably occur in different portions of the central nervous system. For instance, electrical stimulation of the prefrontal lobes rarely if ever calls forth any previous sensory experience of a person. Furthermore, from psychological studies we believe that the prefrontal lobes are of special importance for organizing and correlating many temporary facts. Therefore, it is possible that the prefrontal lobes are more capable of the temporary type of memory and less capable of the prolonged type of memory. On the other hand, electrical stimulation of the temporal cortex often calls forth highly patterned memories dug from the distant past, which certainly would be associated with the prolonged type of memory.

It is reasonable to believe, too, that certain portions of the central nervous system can store memories far more easily than others. For instance, the storage of memories in the spinal cord is probably almost non-existent. Yet, it has been claimed on more than one occasion that, with extreme degrees of psychological training, memory patterns for conditioned reflex responses have been established even in the cord.

In neurophysiological studies of lower animals it has been shown that strongly engrained conditioned reflexes can still occur in an altered form even after the cerebral cortex is removed; the gross aspects of the reflex, such as gross body movements, will still take place when the detailed aspects of the reflex have been lost. Therefore, we know quite well that memory can be established in the thalamic and brain stem portions of the nervous system probably equally or almost equally as well as in the cerebral cortex.

Relationship of Conditioned Reflexes to Learning

Since the time of Pavlov, it has often been taught that learning depends entirely or almost entirely on alteration of the *natural, or unconditioned, reflexes*. The unconditioned reflexes result from inherent properties of the nervous system that are present at the time of birth, and they include such reflexes as the sucking act in response to oral stimuli, salivation in response to the smell of food, jerk of the arms in response to loud sounds or flashes of light, crying reflexes, reflexes that cause walking motions, flexion, extension, and so forth.

A *conditioned reflex* can be established by associating a new sensory stimulus with a natural stimulus that elicits an unconditioned reflex. For instance, in one of Pavlov's classical experiments, food given to an animal caused the unconditioned reflex of salivation. A bell was rung each time before food was offered to the animal. After this had been done a number of times, the bell was rung but food was not offered. Nevertheless, the dog still salivated a short interval after the bell had been rung. This reaction is called a conditioned reflex.

A *secondary* conditioned reflex can then be built onto the primary conditioned reflex. For instance, a flash of light followed by ringing of the bell and then the reflex salivation response, if the sequence is repeated again and again, will eventually establish a secondary conditioned reflex; then flashing the light alone will be followed by salivation.

One can easily see that, theoretically, many multitudes of successive reflexes can be built one on top of the other until finally the central nervous system can perform myriad reflex functions.

Learning by Association. Conditioned reflexes by themselves, however, are not sufficient to explain most learning that occurs in the brain, for many chance happenings can lead to learning—for instance, chance movement of the head to a position that provides a particularly interesting scene can elicit a memory that will cause the person to move his head to that same position again and again to see the same scene. Therefore, chance happenings that provide motor and sensory associations are undoubtedly another mechanism of learning—and perhaps an even more extensively used mechanism—in addition to that of conditioned reflexes. Even here, though, one might say that the original chance movement of the head was an unconditioned reflex, but this is a rather far-fetched application of the principle of conditioning.

In short, it seems that learning occurs principally by association, new sensory stimuli becoming associated with memory patterns that have already been established. Indeed, we are all aware of our ability to learn new facts that are similar to facts already stored in our brain. And we are also familiar with the extreme difficulty of learning new information that is completely foreign to anything that we have ever experienced previously.

INTELLECTUAL OPERATIONS OF THE BRAIN

Thus far, we have considered the approximate nature of thoughts and possible mechanisms by which memory and learning can occur. Now we need to consider the mechanisms by which the brain performs complex intellectual operations such as the analysis of sensory information and the establishment of abstract thoughts. About these mechanisms we know almost nothing, but experiments along these lines have established, first, that the brain can focus its attention on specific types of information and, second, that there are definite patterns of operation by which the brain goes about analyzing sensory information.

Direction of Attention. In the previous chapter it was pointed out that stimulation of the reticular activating system can stimulate widespread areas of the cerebral cortex; this will be discussed in detail in the following chapter. We know also from stimulatory experiments in lower animals that stimuli in specific portions of the reticular activating system, particularly in the thalamic portion of this system, can activate certain areas of the cerebral cortex one at a time. Also, stimulation of specific portions of the reticular activating system can selectively inhibit sensory transmission from (a) the somatic areas of the body, (b) the retina, (c) the cochlea, and (d) the olfactory receptors. In this way, only that portion of the sensory information desired can be allowed to pass.

These mechanisms, therefore, probably constitute the method by which we focus our attention to specific thoughts, by which we call forth memories, or evoke specific motor responses. But, unfortunately, we do not know how the reticular activating system itself is controlled to direct the attention in different directions. In the following chapter we will see that the reticular activating system itself can be excited either by sensory input signals or by impulses feeding into it from the cortex. We could suppose, then, that the attention is directed by reflex responses of the reticular activating system to summated signals coming from many different sources.

Analysis of Sensory Information. In analyzing sensory information, the cerebral cortex depends to a great extent upon "patterns" of stimulation of the sensory areas. For instance, a square seen by the eyes will be detected as a square regardless of its position in the visual field. Likewise, a series of parallel bars will be detected as parallel bars regardless of their orientation, or a fly will be detected as a fly whether it is seen in the peripheral field of vision or in the central field of vision. We can extend the same logic to the somatic sensory areas, for a person can detect a square simply by feeling it whether it be in an upright position, a horizontal, or an angulated position. Also, it can be detected even by the feet even though they may have never felt a square before.

It is believed that one of the major methods for analyzing sensory information is to dissect it into its component patterns. For instance, repetitive auditory sensations and visual sensations of parallel bars have at least one characteristic in common: both have the pattern of repetitiveness. Yet, we cannot say how patterns of sensations are detected. One theory holds that their detection results from traveling waves passing over the cortex. As these cross the brain they might cause a signal to be transmitted every time they interact with an excited point of the cortex. For instance, if a traveling wave were passing over a visual cortex that is being excited by a regular series of lights, every time this wave comes in contact with an activated point, a signal is transmitted away from the cortex to some *analyser portion* of the brain. Therefore, the analyser would receive a train of rhythmical impulses, each impulse denoting a separate light, and this train of impulses could then theoretically give the person the sensation of repetitiveness. Likewise, repetitive sounds entering the ears could transmit a train of impulses to the same analyser which would also give a sensation of repetitiveness, or movement of the hand over a corrugated surface could give the analyser the same sensation of repetitiveness.

If we use our imaginations, we can see that only a few different types of analytical patterns can go a long way toward explaining almost all types of sensory impressions. However, the analytical functions of the central nervous system are still very much matters for speculation.

Non-specific Locus of Analytical Functions in the Cerebral Cortex of Lower Animals. In a psychological test in which a rat has been trained to run through a specific maze, successive destruction of the non-sensory and non-motor portions of the brain shows that learning and memory depends in no detectable way on any specific portion of the cerebral cortex. However, as a greater and greater *quantity* of the non-specific cerebral cortex is removed, the learning and memory abilities fall off progressively

until the animal finally fails to run the maze at all. Thus, when the prefrontal lobes are intact but all other nonspecific areas are destroyed, this ability is still present; conversely, when the prefrontal lobes are destroyed but the other areas are intact, the ability also remains; but when both are destroyed, the rat fails to run the course.

Therefore, except for the specific functions of the sensory and motor areas, it seems that most of the cerebral cortex in lower animals has equal potential for most cerebral functions and that both memories and learning can utilize any or all portions of this cortex with approximately equal facility.

Yet, we possibly cannot apply these results from lower animals to the human being, for certainly in electrical stimulatory and ablation studies in the human being we do find variations in the abilities of different portions of the cortex. Thus, the angular gyrus region, which might be classified as a non-specific area in a lower animal, certainly has specific functions in the cerebral cortex of man. And the disruption of normal speech caused by destruction of the angular gyrus, of the supramarginal gyrus of the parietal lobe, or of Broca's area in the frontal cortex very forcefully belies some of the conclusions that have been drawn from lower animals. Therefore, for the present, we must believe that at least certain regions of the human cerebral cortex have highly specific functions, while perhaps still other large areas can be utilized interchangeably for many different types of intellectual functions.

REFERENCES

Alford, L. B.: Cerebral Localization. Baltimore, Williams & Wilkins Co., 1948.

Birren, J. E., Imus, H. A., and Windle, W. F. (eds.): The Process of Aging in the Nervous System. Springfield, Illinois, Charles C Thomas, 1959.

Brookhart, J. M., Arduini, A., Mancia, M., and Moruzzi, G.: Thalamocortical relations as revealed by induced slow potential changes. *J. Neurophysiol.*, 21:499, 1958.

Burns, B. D.: The electrophysiological approach to the problem of learning. *Canad. J. Biochem. Physiol.*, 34:380, 1956.

Burns, B. D.: The Mammalian Cerebral Cortex. Baltimore, Williams & Wilkins Co., 1958.

Burns, B. D., Grafstein, B., and Olszewski, J.: Identification of neurones giving burst response in isolated cerebral cortex. *J. Neurophysiol.*, 20:200, 1957.

Cajal, S. R.: Studies on the Cerebral Cortex. Chicago, Year Book Publishers, 1955.

Campbell, B., and Sutin, J.: Organization of cerebral cortex. IV. Post-tetanic potentiation of hippocampal pyramids. *Am. J. Physiol.*, 196:330, 1959.

Campbell, J.: Functional organization of the central nervous system with respect to orientation in time. *Neurology*, 4:295, 1953.

Chow, K. L., Dement, W. C., and John, E. R.: Conditioned electrocorticographic potentials and behavioral avoidance response in cat. *J. Neurophysiol.*, 20:482, 1957.

Ciba Foundation Symposium: Neurological Basis of Behavior. Boston, Little, Brown and Co., 1958.

Critchley, M.: Parietal Lobes. Baltimore, Williams & Wilkins Co., 1953.

Doty, R. W.: Potentials evoked in cat cerebral cortex by diffuse and by punctiform photic stimuli. *J. Neurophysiol.*, 21:437, 1958.

Doty, R. W., and Rutledge, L. T.: "Generalization" between cortically and peripherally applied stimuli eliciting conditioned reflexes. *J. Neurophysiol.*, 22:428, 1959.

Doty, R. W., Rutledge, L. T., Jr., and Larsen, R. M.: Conditioned reflexes established to electrical stimulation of cat cerebral cortex. *J. Neurophysiol.*, 19: 401, 1956.

Eccles, J. C.: Neurophysiological Basis of Mind: The Principles of Neurophysiology. London, Oxford University Press, 1953.

Eccles, J. C., and Krnjevic, K.: Presynaptic changes associated with post-tetanic potentiation in the spinal cord. *J. Physiol.*, 149:274, 1959.

Emerson, J. D., Bruhn, J. M., and Emerson, G. M.: Simplified nonirritating chronic concentric electrodes for cortical stimulation or recording. *J. Appl. Physiol.*, 7:461, 1955.

Gerard, R. W.: The biological roots of psychiatry. *Am. J. Psychiat.*, 112:81, 1955.

Graham, A. R., and Stavraky, G. W.: Regional physiology of the central nervous system. *Progr. Neur. Psychiat.*, 11:523, 1956.

Greene, M.: The Voice and Its Disorders. New York, The Macmillan Co., 1957.

Heath, R. G.: Studies in Schizophrenia. Cambridge, Harvard University Press, 1954.

Jasper, H., Gloor, P., and Milner, B.: Higher functions of the nervous system. *Ann. Rev. Physiol.*, 18:359, 1956.

Kaada, B. R.: Electrical activity of the brain. *Ann. Rev. Physiol.*, 15:39, 1953.

Krieg, W. J. S.: Connections of the Frontal Cortex of the Monkey. Springfield, Illinois, Charles C. Thomas, 1954.

Lindsley, D. B.: Higher functions of the nervous system. *Ann. Rev. Physiol.*, 17:311, 1955.

Livingstone, R. B.: Central control of receptors and sensory transmission systems. *Handbook of Physiology*, 1:741, 1959.

Marshall, W. H.: Spreading cortical depression of Leao. *Physiol. Rev.*, 39:239, 1959.

Masland, R. L.: Higher cerebral functions. *Ann. Rev. Physiol.*, 20:533, 1958.

Mettler, F. A.: Selective Partial Ablation of the Frontal Cortex. New York, Paul B. Hoeber, 1949.

Meyer, A., and Beck, E.: Prefrontal Leucotomy and Related Operations. Springfield, Illinois, Charles C Thomas, 1955.

Mishkin, M., and Pribram, K. H.: Analysis of the effects of frontal lesions in monkey. II. Variations of delayed response. *J. Comp. Physiol. Psychol.*, 49:36, 1956.

Moore, G. E.: Diagnosis and Localization of Brain Tumors. Springfield, Illinois, Charles C Thomas, 1953.

Morrell, F., Naquet, R., and Gastaut, H.: Evolution of some signs of conditioning. Part I. Normal cat and rabbit. *J. Neurophysiol.*, 20:574, 1957.

Neff, W. D., and Goldberg, J. M.: Higher functions of the central nervous system. *Ann. Rev. Physiol.*, 22:499, 1960.

Olds, J.: Higher functions of the nervous system. *Ann. Rev. Physiol.*, 21:381, 1959.

O'Leary, J. L., and Goldring, S.: Changes associated with forebrain excitation processes: d. c. potentials of the cerebral cortex. *Handbook of Physiology*, 1:315, 1959.

Penfield, W., and Rasmussen, T.: The Cerebral Cortex of Man. New York, The Macmillan Co., 1950.

Poynter, F. N. L.: The History and Philosophy of Knowledge of the Brain and Its Functions. Springfield, Illinois, Charles C Thomas, 1959.

Pribram, K. H.: The intrinsic systems of the forebrain. *Handbook of Physiology*, 1:1323, 1960.

Pribram, K. H., Kruger, L., Robinson, F., and Berman, A. J.: The effects of precentral lesions on the behavior of monkeys. *Yale J. Biol.*, 28:428, 1955–1956.

Pribram, K. H., and Mishkin, M.: Analysis of the effects of frontal lesions in monkey. III. Object alternation. *J. Comp. Physiol. Psychol.*, 49:41, 1956.

Pribram, K. H., and Weiskrantz, L.: A comparison of the effects of medial and lateral cerebral resections on conditioned avoidance behavior of monkeys. *J. Comp. Physiol. Psychol.*, 50:74, 1957.

Rose, J. E., Monnier, M., and Spiegel, E. A.: Interrelationships between cortex and subcortical structures. *Electroencephalography*, Suppl. No. 4: 189, 1955.

Sholl, D. A.: The Organization of the Cerebral Cortex. New York, John Wiley & Sons, 1956.

Von Bonin, G.: Some Papers on the Cerebral Cortex. Springfield, Illinois, Charles C Thomas, 1959.

Zuckermann, E.: Effect of cortical and reticular stimulation on conditioned reflex activity. *J. Neurophysiol.*, 22:633, 1959.

Chapter 60

Wakefulness, Sleep, Attention,

Brain Waves, Epilepsy, and Behavior

In the previous chapters of this section on neurophysiology we have discussed, first, the sensory mechanisms of the nervous system, second, the motor mechanisms of the nervous system, and, third, the functions of the cerebral cortex in relating these two to each other. In the present chapter we will consider (1) the intrinsic mechanisms of the brain that control its overall degree of nervous activity and (2) the neurophysiological basis of behavior.

WAKEFULNESS, SLEEP, AND ATTENTION

Function of the Reticular Activating System in Wakefulness

Until a little over a decade ago it was believed that a "sleep center" existed in the central nervous system and that stimulation of this would cause a person to go to sleep. However, it was then demonstrated that electrical stimulation in the *mesencephalic portion of the reticular formation,* an area discussed in Chapter 58 in relation to the motor functions of the nervous system, or electrical stimulation of the unspecific nuclei of the thalamus will cause immediate and very marked activation of the cerebral cortex and will even cause a sleeping animal to awaken instantaneously. Furthermore, severe damage to the mesencephalic portion of the reticular formation, as occurs (a) when a *brain tumor* develops in this region, (b) when a serious *hemorrhage* occurs, or (c) in diseases such as *encephalitis lethargica,* the person will pass into a state of coma

and be completely nonsusceptible to normal awakening stimuli.

Therefore, it is now apparent that wakefulness results from enhanced activity of the different parts of the brain, while sleep represents lack of adequate brain excitation. The portions of the reticular formation and thalamus that enter into the wakefulness response are called the *ascending reticular activating system.*

Figure 607 A illustrates the extent of this system, showing it to begin in the lower brain stem and then to extend upward through the mesencephalon and thalamus to be distributed throughout the cerebral cortex. Impulses are transmitted from the ascending reticular activating system to the cortex by two different routes. One route passes upward from the mesencephalic portion of the reticular formation to the *subthalamus* and thence directly to the cortex. The other pathway passes upward from the mesencephalon mainly through the intralaminar nuclei of the thalamus and then to the anteroventral nuclei and reticular nuclei of the thalamus and finally through diverse pathways to essentially all parts of the cerebral cortex.

Function of the Mesencephalic Portion of the Reticular Activating System. Electrical stimuli applied to different portions of the reticular activating system have shown that the mesencephalic portion functions quite differently from the thalamic portion. Electrical stimulation of the mesencephalic portion causes generalized activation of the entire brain, including activation of the cerebral cortex, of the thalamic nuclei, of the basal ganglia, of other portions of the brain stem, and even of the spinal cord. Furthermore, once the mesencephalic portion is stimulated, the degree of activation throughout the nervous system remains high for as long as a half minute or more after the stimulation is over. Therefore, *it is believed that the mesencephalic portion of the reticular activating system is basically responsible for normal wakefulness of the brain.*

Function of the Thalamic Portion of the Reticular Activating System. Electrical stimulation in different areas of the thalamic portion of the reticular activating system activates specific regions of the cerebral cortex more than others. This is distinctly different from stimulation in the mesencephalic portion which activates all of the brain at the same time. Therefore, it is believed that the thalamic portion of the reticular activating system has two specific functions:

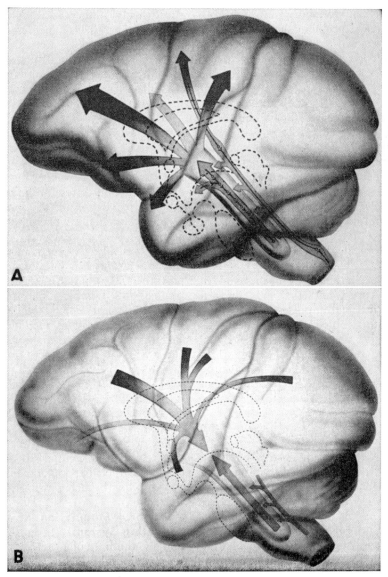

Figure 607.   (A) The ascending reticular activating system schematically projected on a monkey brain. (From Lindsley: Reticular Formation of the Brain. Little, Brown & Co.) (B) Convergence of pathways from the cerebral cortex and from the spinal afferent systems on the reticular activating system. (From French, Hernandez-Peon, and Livingston: *J. Neurophysiol.,* 18:74, 1955.)

first, it relays the diffuse facilitatory signals from the mesencephalic portion to all parts of the cerebral cortex to cause generalized activation of the cerebrum, and, second, stimulation of selected points in the thalamic activating system causes specific activation of certain areas of the cerebral cortex in distinction to the other areas.

Direction of the attention to different cerebral functions. We are all aware of our ability to direct our attention to one type of cerebral activity at a time, such as to some specific visual scene, to a specific motor activity that we may wish to perform, to a mathematical problem that we may be attempting to solve, or even to a certain voice mixed with a hundred other voices. Because local stimulation in different regions of the thalamus excites specific portions of the cerebral cortex, it is believed that the thalamus either controls or helps immensely in directing our attention to the different specific neuronal functions. From the previous chapter we already know that stimulation of specific receptive areas in the cerebral cortex and in lower brain centers can increase or decrease the intensity of signals transmitted from the sensory inputs to the sensory integrative regions of the brain. Therefore, it might be surmised that excitation of a specific region in the thalamus causes, first, excitation of a focal point in the cerebral cortex and that this in turn transmits corticofugal impulses to the sensory pathways to inhibit or in some instances to enhance the degree of sensory transmission to the specific cortical region. This is one of the possible, though yet mainly hypothetical, mechanisms by which we can direct our attention according to our needs.

The Arousal Reaction

The recticular activating system has very little intrinsic activity. Instead, it must be stimulated to action by input signals from other sources. When an animal is asleep, the reticular activating system is in an almost totally dormant state. Yet, almost any type of sensory signal can immediately activate the system. For instance, proprioceptive signals from the muscles, pain impulses from the skin, visual signals from the eyes, or auditory signals from the ears can all cause sudden activation of the reticular activating system and therefore arouse the animal. This is called the *arousal reaction.*

Some types of sensory stimuli are more potent than others in eliciting the arousal reaction, the most potent being pain and proprioceptive somatic impulses. Because of this importance of somatic impulses in maintaining an activated state in the reticular activating system, progressive destruction of the sensory input tracts to this system progressively decreases the degree of wakefulness. When the brain stem is cut at successively higher and higher levels, the animal becomes less and less wakeful until finally he falls asleep permanently when the section is made slightly above the point of entrance of the sensory impulses from the fifth nerve into the pontine region of the reticular formation. At this point all somatic sensory impulses will have been lost. However, even after this procedure, electrical stimulation in the remaining reticular activating system above the transection can still awaken the animal. This experiment illustrates the importance of the arousal reaction and of somatic impulses in maintaining the wakefulness state of the animal.

Anatomically the recticular formation of the brain stem is admirably constructed to perform the arousal functions. It receives tremendous numbers of collateral fibers from the *spinothalamic tract,* the *spinocerebellar tract,* and the *medial lemniscus* so that almost any sensory stimulus in the body can activate it. In addition, many fibers pass directly from the spinal cord to the reticular formation in the *spinoreticular tract.* The reticular formation in turn can transmit signals both upward into the brain and downward into the spinal cord. Indeed, many of the fibers originating from cells in the reticular formation divide, with one branch of the fiber passing directly upward and another branch passing directly downward.

Cerebral Stimulation of the Reticular Activating System. In addition to activation of the reticular activating system by sensory impulses, the cerebral cortex can also stimulate this system and increase its degree of activity. Direct fiber pathways pass into the reticular activating system as shown in Figure 607 B from almost all parts of the cerebral cortex but particularly so from (1) the *sensorimotor cortex* of the pre- and postcentral gyri, (2) the *frontal cortex,* (3) the *cingulate gyrus,* and (4) the *hippocampus* and *entorhinal structures.* Because of the large number of nerve fibers that pass from the motor regions of the cerebral cortex to the reticular formation, motor activity is particularly associated with a high degree of wakefulness, which partially explains the importance of movement to keep a person awake. Also, intense activity of any other part of the cerebrum activates the reticular activating system and consequently can be associated with a high degree of wakefulness.

The Feedback Theory of Wakefulness and Sleep

From the above discussion we can see that activation of the reticular activating system greatly intensifies the degree of activity in the cerebral cortex, and in turn increased activity in the cerebral cortex increases the degree of activity of the reticular activating system.

Likewise, increased activity of this system increases the degree of muscular tone throughout the body, which was discussed in Chapter 58 in relation to the gamma efferent system. Also, stimulation of the reticular activating system increases many autonomic activities throughout the body. In turn, these peripheral effects cause increased somatic impulses to be transmitted into the central nervous system—particularly important are the proprioceptor impulses from the muscles, for these have a very high degree of arousal activity. Thus, here again, we find another feedback. That is, activity in the reticular activating system causes increased peripheral activity and this in turn feeds back to the reticular activating system to promote increased excitation there.

On the basis of these two feedback loops —(1) to the cerebral cortex and back to the reticular formation and (2) to the periphery and back—a feedback theory of wakefulness and sleep can be formulated as follows:

It is assumed that once the reticular activating system becomes activated the feedback impulses from both the cerebral cortex and from the periphery will tend to maintain excitation of the reticular activating system. Thus, after the person has become awakened, he tends to remain awake at least for the time being. After prolonged wakefulness, it can also be assumed that many of the neuronal cells in the feedback loops, particularly the neuronal cells in the reticular activating system itself, will gradually become fatigued or less excitable for other reasons. When this happens, the degree of activation, both cortically and peripherally, begins to decrease. As a result, the intensity of feedback also decreases, which results in further depression of the reticular activating system. Then further depression of the cortex and peripheral functions occurs with still further depression of the reticular activating system. Thus, once the degree of excitability of the neurons has fallen to a critical level, a vicious cycle ensues until all or most components of the two feedback loops fade into inactivity, and this then represents the state of sleep.

The next element of the feedback theory of wakefulness and sleep assumes that, after the reticular activating system has been dormant for a period of time, the neuronal cells involved in the feedback loops gradually regain their normal degree of excitability. Yet, wakefulness still does not occur until some arousal signal initiates activity in the reticular activating system. Once this has occurred, the feedback loops immediately come into play, and the person passes from the state of sleep into the state of wakefulness.

One might immediately ask how it is that a person can also have various degrees of wakefulness and sleep. To answer this, we need only realize that the feedback loops contain literally millions of parallel pathways. If the feedback system is operating only through a few of these, then a person will have a very slight degree of wakefulness, but, if the feedback is operating through tremendous numbers of pathways simultaneously, then the degree of wakefulness will be very great. Furthermore, the numbers of pathways that will be involved at any one time will depend on the various stimulatory influences entering the reticular activating system. That is, the greater the intensity of signals from the sensory systems and the greater the intensity of signals from activated regions of the cerebral cortex, the greater also would be the degree of wakefulness.

One of the most important bits of evidence in favor of the feedback theory of wakefulness and sleep is the fact that complete relaxation of the peripheral musculature throughout the body, even in the absence of muscular or neuronal fatigue, can very frequently cause a person to go to sleep. Obviously, relaxation of the musculature would break one of the major, if not the major, feedback loops for maintenance of wakefulness.

Other Theories of Sleep and Wakefulness. In the past, many theories have assumed that sleep is caused by chemical changes either in the central neurons involved in the wakefulness system or by chemical changes in the peripheral nervous system or even skeletal musculature. For instance, it has been supposed that progressive fatigue of the muscles would decrease the proprioceptive impulses to the reticular activating system and that this in turn would cause the state of sleep. However, critical experiments have demonstrated that the degree of fatigue of the muscles is not a significant factor in causing sleep. Secondly, it was at one time postulated that fatigue of the neuromuscular junction might even cause sleep, but here again it is now known that fatigue at this point in the neuromuscular transmission system of the normal person does not occur coincidentally with sleep. Finally, many different theories have assumed that a metabolic chemical cycle occurs in the cells of the reticular activating system themselves, causing increased neuronal excitability during part of their cycle and decreased excitability during the remainder of the cycle. But, once again, this is based on nothing more than supposition.

Physiological Effects of Sleep

Sleep causes two major types of physiological effects: first, effects on the nervous system and, second, effects on the other structures of the body. The first of these seems to be by far the more important, for any person who has a transected spinal cord in the neck region shows no physiological changes whatsoever in the body beneath the transection that can be attributed to a sleep and wakefulness cycle, and, yet, this lack of sleep and wakefulness causes no significant harm to the body nor even any deranged function. On the other hand, lack of sleep certainly does affect the functions of the central nervous system.

Very prolonged wakefulness is often associated with progressive malfunction of the mind and behavioral activities of the nervous system. We are all familiar with the increased sluggishness of thought that occurs toward the end of a prolonged wakeful period, but, in addition, a person can become irritable or even psychotic following forced wakefulness for prolonged periods of time. Therefore, we can assume that sleep has a very beneficial effect in restoring normal "balance" between the different parts of the central nervous system. This might be likened to the "rezeroing" of electronic computers after prolonged periods of use, for such computers gradually lose their "baseline" of operation; it is reasonable to assume that the same effect might occur in the central nervous system. Therefore, in the absence of any definitely demonstrated functional value of sleep, we might postulate on the basis of known psychological changes that occur with wakefulness and sleep that sleep could perform this zeroing function for the nervous system. Yet, the reader must recognize that this is but a suggestion based purely on psychological data and an analogy with computers.

Even though we pointed out above that wakefulness and sleep have not been shown to be necessary for somatic functions of the body, nevertheless, the cycle of enhanced and depressed nervous excitability that follows along with the cycle of wakefulness and sleep does have moderate effects on the peripheral body. For instance, there is usually enhanced sympathetic activity during wakefulness and also enhanced numbers of impulses to the skeletal musculature to increase muscular tone. Conversely, during sleep sympathetic activity decreases while parasympathetic activity occasionally increases, and the muscular tone becomes almost nil. Therefore, during sleep, the arterial blood pressure falls, the pulse rate decreases, the skin vessels dilate, the activity of the gastrointestinal tract sometimes increases, the muscles fall into a completely relaxed state, and the overall basal metabolic rate of the body falls by some 10 to 20 per cent.

BRAIN WAVES

Electrical recordings from the surface of the brain or even from the outer surface of the head demonstrate continuous electrical activity in the brain. The undulations in the recorded electrical potentials, as shown in Figure 608, are called *brain waves,* and the entire record is called an *electroencephalogram* (EEG).

The intensities of the brain waves on the surface of the scalp range from zero up to about 300 microvolts, and their frequencies range from once every few seconds up to 50 or more per second. The character of the waves is highly dependent upon the degree of activity of the cerebral cortex, and the waves change markedly between the states of wakefulness and sleep.

Much of the time, the brain waves are asynchronous, and no general pattern can then be discerned in the electroencephalogram. However, at other times, distinct patterns do appear. Some of these are characteristic of specific abnormalities of the brain such as epilepsy, which will be discussed later. Others occur even in normal persons and can be classified into four different types of waves: (1) *alpha,* (2) *beta,* (3) *theta,* and (4) *delta,* which are all illustrated in Figure 608.

The *alpha waves* are rhythmical waves occurring at a frequency between 8 and 13 per second and are found in the electroencephalograms of almost all normal persons when they are awake in a quiet, resting state of cerebration. These waves occur most intensely in the occipital region but can also be recorded at times from the parietal and frontal regions of the scalp. Their voltage usually is about 50 microvolts. During sleep the alpha waves disappear entirely, and when the awake person's attention is directed to some specific type of mental activity, the alpha waves are replaced by asynchronous, higher frequency but lower voltage waves. Figure 609 illus-

Eyes open   Eyes closed

Figure 609. Replacement of the alpha rhythm by an asynchronous discharge on opening the eyes.

trates the effect on the alpha waves of simply opening the eyes in bright light and then closing the eyes again. Note that the visual sensations cause immediate cessation of the alpha waves and that these are replaced by low voltage, asynchronous waves.

Beta waves are waves with frequencies of more than 14 cycles per second and sometimes as high as 50 cycles per second. These are most frequently recorded from the parietal and frontal regions of the scalp, and they can be divided into two major types, *beta I* and *beta II.* The beta I waves, which are illustrated in Figure 608, have a frequency about twice that of the alpha waves, and these react to mental activity in very much the same way as the alpha waves—that is, they disappear and in their place appears an asynchronous but low voltage and high frequency recording. The beta II waves, on the contrary, appear during intense activation of the central nervous system or during tension. Thus, one type of beta wave is inhibited by cerebral activity while the other is excited.

Theta waves are those waves of the electroencephalogram with frequencies between 4 and 7 cycles per second. These occur mainly in the parietal and temporal regions in children, but they also occur during emotional stress in some adults, particularly during disappointment and frustration. They can often be brought out in the electroencephalogram of a frustrated person by allowing him to enjoy some very pleasant experience and then suddenly removing this element of pleasure; this causes approximately 20 seconds of theta waves.

The *delta waves* include all the waves of the electroencephalogram below $3\frac{1}{2}$ cycles per second and sometimes as low as 1 cycle every 2 to 3 seconds. These occur in deep sleep, in infancy, and in serious organic brain disease. And they also occur in the cortex of animals that have had subcortical transections separating the cerebral cortex from the reticular activating system. Therefore, delta waves can occur strictly in the cortex independently of activities in lower regions of the brain.

Origin of the Different Types of Brain Waves

The discharge of a single neuron or of a single nerve fiber in the brain cannot be recorded from the scalp. Instead, *synchronous* activity of literally thousands or even millions of neurons must take place simultaneously for a wave to be re-

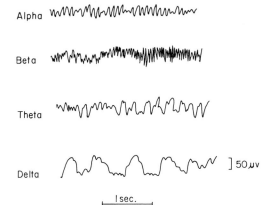

Alpha

Beta

Theta

Delta $]50\,\mu v$

|— 1 sec. —|

Figure 608. Different types of normal electroencephalographic waves.

corded from the scalp, and all brain waves are the result of synchronous electrical potentials in many neurons at the same time. Therefore, for brain waves to occur, some activity must take place in the nervous system that synchronizes the action of thousands or millions of neurons simultaneously. This is particularly brought out by the fact that increased cerebral activity ordinarily *decreases* rather than increases the intensities of the brain waves. This is the result to be expected since intense cerebration is associated with *asynchronous* activity of the brain rather than with synchronous discharge of many neurons at the same time.

Unfortunately, though, the precise causes of the synchronizing mechanisms responsible for the brain waves have never yet been elucidated. Yet, the following few facts are known about the origin of the delta and the alpha waves:

Origin of the Delta Waves. It was pointed out above that separation of the cerebral cortex from the reticular activating system causes delta waves in the cortex. This indicates that some synchronizing mechanism can take place in the cortical neurons entirely independently of lower structures in the brain. Other than this bit of information, the mechanism of synchronization is unknown.

Origin of the Alpha Waves and the "Recruiting Response." The alpha waves result from activity mainly, if not entirely, in the posterior parts of the cortex. These waves begin anteriorly in the parietal occipital regions and sweep posteriorly. Also, they spread from the inner layers of the cortex to the outer surface. The recording of alpha waves from the anterior part of the scalp results mainly from the spread of electrical currents originating in the posterior part of the brain and not in the frontal cortex.

It is known, too, that alpha waves will *not* occur in the cortex without connections with the reticular activating system. It is possible that this system enters into the genesis of the alpha waves in the following manner:

Electrical stimulation of the thalamic portion of the reticular activating system causes slow development of an electrical potential in the cerebral cortex called a *recruiting response*. This is illustrated in Figure 610, which shows comparative excitation of the visual cortex following stimulation of (A) the lateral geniculate body that directly excites the visual cortex and (B) the thalamic reticular activating system that indirectly excites the visual cortex. Note the prolonged delay and slow build-up of the electrical potential following stimulation of the reticular activating system; this is the recruiting response. Another feature of interest regarding the recruiting response is that repetitive stimuli in the thalamus at approximately 10 cycles per second cause

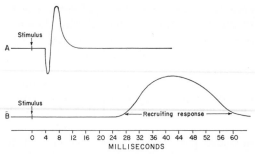

Figure 610.   Response of the visual cortex to stimulation of the lateral geniculate body (which causes direct excitation of the cortex), and the "recruiting response" in the visual cortex following stimulation of the thalamic portion of the reticular activating system. Note the long latent period before appearance of the recruiting response.

the response to become more and more intense with each repetition during the first few repetitive stimuli. And a final point of importance is that strong electrical stimulation of the cortex has been shown to cause reverberation of impulses back and forth between the thalamus and the cortex at frequencies ranging between 8 and 13 per second. On the basis of these facts, then, one might postulate that the recruiting response of the thalamus and perhaps reverberating pathways involving the thalamus could cause both the periodicity of the alpha waves and the synchronous discharge of literally millions of cortical neurons at the same time. But this is about as far as we can go in attempting to delineate the origin of the alpha waves, and even this involves speculation far beyond the available evidence.

The origins of the beta and theta waves are completely unknown, though presumably they also involve reverberating pathways either deep in the reticular activating system or back and forth between the cortex and thalamus.

Effect of Varying Degrees of Cerebral Activity on the Basic Rhythm of the Electroencephalogram. There is a general relationship between the degree of cerebral activity and the frequency of the electroencephalographic rhythm, the frequency increasing progressively with higher and higher degrees of activity. This is illustrated in Figure 611, which shows the existence of delta waves in stupor, surgical anesthesia, and sleep; theta waves occur in psychomotor states and in infants; during relaxed states one finds principally alpha waves; and during

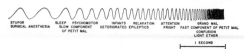

Figure 611.   Effect of varying degrees of cerebral activity on the basic rhythm of the electroencephalogram. (From Gibbs and Gibbs: Atlas of Encephalography. The Authors.)

periods of intense mental activity the frequency rises to the beta state. However, during periods of mental activity the waves usually become asynchronous rather than synchronous so that the voltage falls considerably, as illustrated above in Figure 609.

Clinical Use of the Electroencephalogram

Probably the most important use of the electroencephalogram is to diagnose different types of epilepsy and to find the focus in the brain causing the epilepsy. This will be discussed further below. But, in addition, the electroencephalogram can be used to localize brain tumors or other space-occupying lesions of the brain and to diagnose certain types of psychopathic disturbances.

There are two means by which brain tumors can be localized. Some brain tumors are so large that they block electrical activity from a given portion of the cerebral cortex, and when this occurs the intensity of the brain waves will be considerably reduced in the region of the tumor. However, more frequently a brain tumor, because it compresses the surrounding neuronal tissue, causes abnormal electrical excitation of the surrounding cortical areas, and this in turn leads to synchronous discharges of very high voltage waves in the electroencephalogram as shown in the middle two records of Figure 612. Localization of the origin of these spikes on the surface of the scalp is a very valuable means for locating the brain tumor. The upper part of Figure 612 shows the placement of 16 different electrodes on the scalp, and the lower part of the figure shows the brain waves from four of these electrodes marked in the figure by X's. Note that in two of these very intense brain waves are recorded and, furthermore, that the two recordings are essentially of reverse polarity to each other. This reverse polarity means that the origin of the spikes is somewhere in the area between the two respective electrodes. Thus, the excessively excitable area of the brain has been located, and this is a lead to the location of the brain tumor.

Use of brain waves in diagnosing psychopathic abnormalities is generally not very satisfactory because only a few of these cause distinct brain wave patterns. Yet, by a combination of different types of basic rhythms, reactions of the rhythms to attention, changes of the rhythms with forced breathing to cause alkalosis, the appearance of particular characteristics in the brain waves such as "spindles" of alpha waves, and so forth, an experienced electroencephalographer can detect at least certain ones of the different types of psychopathic disturbances. For instance, it was pointed out above that theta waves are frequently found in persons under severe tension.

EPILEPSY

Epilepsy is characterized by uncontrolled excessive activity of either a part of the central nervous system or of all of it. A person who is predisposed to epilepsy will have his attacks when the basal level of excitability of his nervous system (or of the part that is susceptible to the epileptic state) rises above a certain critical threshold. But, as long as the degree of excitability is held below this threshold, no attack will occur.

Basically, there are two different types of epilepsy: (1) *generalized epilepsy* and (2) *partial epilepsy*. Generalized epilepsy involves essentially all parts of the brain at once while partial epilepsy involves only a portion—sometimes only a minute focal spot and other times a moderate portion of the brain but not the entire brain. Generalized epilepsy can be divided again into two different types: (1) *grand mal epilepsy* and (2) *petit mal epilepsy*.

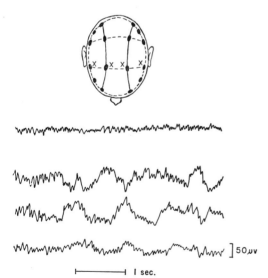

Figure 612. Localization of a brain tumor by means of the electroencephalogram, illustrating above the placement of electrodes and below the records from the four electrodes designated by X's.

Generalized Epilepsy and Its Cause

Grand Mal. Grand mal epilepsy is characterized by extreme neuronal discharges originating in the brain stem portion of the reticular activating system. These then spread throughout the entire central nervous system, to the cortex, to the deeper parts of the brain, and even into the spinal cord to cause generalized *tonic convulsions* of the entire body followed toward the end of the attack by alternating muscular contractions called *clonic convulsions.* The grand mal seizure usually lasts at least three minutes and is characterized by a post-seizure depression of the entire nervous system; usually the person remains in a stupor for one minute to as long as a day or more. The middle recording of Figure 613 illustrates the typical electroencephalogram from almost any region of the cortex during a grand mal attack. This illustrates that high voltage synchronous discharges occur over the entire cortex having almost the same periodicity as the normal alpha waves. Furthermore, the same type of discharge occurs on both sides of the brain at the same time, illustrating that the origin of the abnormality is in the lower centers of the brain that control the activity of the cerebral cortex and not in the cerebral cortex itself.

In experimental animals or even in human beings, grand mal attacks can be initiated by administering neuronal stimulants such as the well-known drug Metrazol, or they can be caused by insulin hypoglycemia or by the passage of alternating electrical current directly through the brain. Electrical recordings from the thalamus and also from the reticular formation of the hind brain during the grand mal attacks show typical high voltage activity in both of these areas similar to that recorded from the cerebral cortex. Furthermore, even after transecting the brain stem of an experimental animal as low as the mesencephalon, a typical grand mal seizure can still be induced in the portion of the brain stem beneath the transection.

Presumably, therefore, a grand mal attack is caused by greatly increased activity in the lower part of the reticular activating system. This perhaps results from intrinsic overexcitability of the neurons that make up the reticular activating structures or from some abnormality of the local neuronal pathways that predisposes to excessive excitability. And the synchronous discharges from this region could result from local reverberating circuits or from a "relaxation" type of oscillation that involves repetitive simultaneous discharge of large numbers of neurons, the synchrony between the different neurons being maintained in the second instance by spread of electrical current from neuron to neuron by the process called "ephaptic" transmission.

One might ask what it is that stops the grand mal attack after a given period of time. This is believed to result from two different effects: (1) *fatigue of the neurons* involved in precipitating the attack and (2) *active inhibition* by certain structures of the brain. Obviously, if the neurons should fatigue, this would decrease the intensity of synchronous discharges or block them entirely, whether these be caused by reverberating circuits or by relaxation oscillation. The change from the tonic type of convulsion to the clonic type during the latter part of the grand mal attack presumably results from partial fatigue of the neuronal system so that some of the excitable neurons fade out for a moment, then return to activity after a brief rest, only to fatigue a second time and then a third time, and so forth, until the entire seizure is over. And the stupor that lasts for a few minutes to many hours after a grand mal seizure is believed to result from the post-depressional stage of the neurons following their intensive activity during the grand mal attack.

The *active inhibition* that helps to stop the grand mal attack is believed to result from feedback circuits through inhibitory areas of the brain. For instance, the grand mal attack undoubtedly excites such areas as the basal ganglia, which in turn emit many inhibitory impulses into other regions of the nervous system. This obviously could depress the extreme excitability and could aid in stopping the attack. But the nature of such active inhibition is very much a matter of speculation.

Petit Mal Epilepsy

Petit mal epilepsy is closely allied to grand mal epilepsy, and it occurs in two different forms, the *myoclonic form* and the *absence form.*

In the *myoclonic form of epilepsy,* a fraction of a second burst of neuronal discharges occurs throughout the nervous system very similar to those at the beginning of a grand mal attack, and the person exhibits a single violent muscular jerk usually involving the arms or head. However, the entire process stops immediately and is usually over before the person loses consciousness

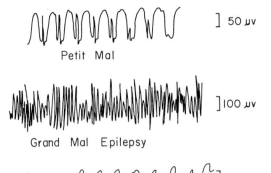

Petit Mal] 50 µv

Grand Mal Epilepsy] 100 µv

Psychomotor] 50 µv

Figure 613. Electroencephalograms in different types of epilepsy.

or even before he stops what he was doing. Yet, this myoclonic type of attack predisposes to grand mal attacks and, therefore, from an etiological point of view can be considered to be essentially the same as a grand mal attack except that some inhibitory influence stops it immediately.

The *absence type of petit mal epilepsy* is characterized by 5 to 20 seconds of unconsciousness during which the person has several twitchlike contractions of the muscles, usually in the head region—especially blinking of the eyes; this is followed by return of consciousness and continuation of previous activities.

This type of epilepsy also is closely allied to grand mal epilepsy, and, in rare instances, it leads to grand mal attacks. Furthermore, persons who have petit mal attacks during early life may later become progressively disposed to grand mal attacks. The first recording of Figure 613 illustrates a typical spike and dome pattern which is recorded during the absence type of petit mal epilepsy. The spike portion of this recording is almost exactly identical to the spikes that occur in grand mal epilepsy, but the dome portion is distinctly different. The spike and dome can be recorded over the entire cerebral cortex, illustrating that the seizure originates in the activating system of the brain.

Since petit mal and grand mal epilepsy both originate in essentially the same locus of the brain stem, it is believed that they probably have the same common cause but that some influence inhibits neuronal activity during the petit mal attack so that it will not progress into the grand mal seizure.

Partial Epilepsy

Partial epilepsy can involve almost any part of the brain, either localized regions of the cerebral cortex or deeper structures of both the cerebrum

and brain stem. And almost always, partial epilepsy results from some localized organic lesion of the brain such as a scar that pulls on the neuronal tissue, a tumor that compresses an area of the brain, a destroyed area of brain tissue, and so forth. Lesions such as these can promote extremely rapid discharges in local neurons, and when the discharge rate rises above approximately 1000 per second, synchronous waves begin to spread over the adjacent cortical regions. These waves presumably result from *localized reverberating circuits* that gradually recruit adjacent areas of the cortex into the discharge zone, and they spread at a rate as slow as a few millimeters a minute to as rapidly as several centimeters per second. When such a wave of excitation spreads over the motor cortex, it causes a progressive "march" of muscular contractions throughout the opposite side of the body, beginning perhaps in the leg region and marching progressively upward to the head region, or at other times marching in the opposite direction. This is called the *Jacksonian type of epilepsy.*

A partial epileptic attack may be confined to a single area of the brain, but in many instances it excites the brain stem portion of the reticular activating system so greatly that it initiates a grand mal epileptic attack.

One type of partial epilepsy is the so-called *psychomotor seizure*, which may cause (1) a short period of amnesia, (2) an attack of abnormal rage, (3) sudden anxiety, discomfort, or fear, (4) a moment of incoherent speech or mumbling of some trite phrase, or (5) a motor act to attack someone, to rub the face with the hand, and so forth. Sometimes the patient cannot remember his activities during the attack, but at other times he will have been conscious of everything that he had been doing but unable to control it.

The lower tracing of Figure 613 illustrates a typical electroencephalogram during a psychomotor attack, showing a low frequency rectangular wave with a frequency between 2 and 4 per second and with superimposed 14 per second waves.

The electroencephalogram can often be used to localize abnormal spiking waves originating in areas of organic brain disease that might predispose to epileptic attacks. Once such a focal point is found, surgical excision of the focus frequently prevents future epileptic attacks.

NEUROPHYSIOLOGY OF BEHAVIOR

In the previous chapter the control of motor responses by the sensory nervous system and by the thought processes was described. This obviously enters very much into the overall behavior pattern of the individual. However, in addition to this, certain specific regions of the brain, particularly of the diencephalon, control a number of specific patterns of behavior.

Pleasure and Displeasure; Reward and Punishment

In the past several years, it has been learned that many of the diencephalic and mesencephalic structures are particularly concerned with the affective nature of sensory sensations—that is, with whether the sensations are *pleasant* or *unpleasant*. These affective qualities have also been called *reward* and *punishment*. Electrical stimulation of certain regions will soothe the animal whereas electrical stimulation of other regions will cause extreme pain, fear, and all the other elements of punishment. Obviously, these two oppositely responding centers greatly affect the behavior of the animal.

Figure 614 illustrates a technique that has been used for localizing the specific reward and punishment areas of the brain. In this figure a lever is placed at the side of the cage and is arranged so that depressing the lever will make electrical contact with a stimulator. Electrodes are placed successively at different areas in the brain so that the animal can stimulate each area by pressing the lever. If stimulating the particular area gives the animal a sense of reward, then he will press the lever again and again, sometimes as much as 4,000 times per hour. Furthermore, when offered the choice of eating some delectable food as opposed to the opportunity to stimulate a reward center of his brain, he often chooses the electrical stimulation. By using this procedure, it has been found that reward centers are located in the *ventromedial, preoptic,* and *anterior nuclei of the hypothalamus,* in the *intralaminar system of the thalamus,* in the *basal tegmentum of the mesencephalon,* in the *septum,* in the *upper fornix,* in the *head of the caudate nucleus,* in the *putamen,* and in certain parts of the *amygdaloid nuclei.*

The apparatus illustrated in Figure 614 can also be connected so that pressing the lever turns off an electrical stimulus rather than turning it on. In this case, the animal will not turn the stimulus off when the electrode is in one of the reward areas, but

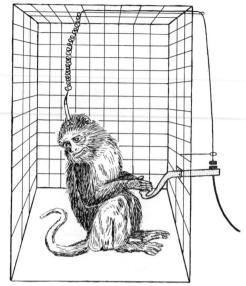

Figure 614. Technique for localizing reward and punishment centers in the brain of a monkey.

when it is in certain other areas he immediately learns to turn it off. Stimulation in these areas causes the animal to show all signs of pain and displeasure. Furthermore, prolonged stimulation for 24 hours or more will cause the animal to become severely sick and will actually lead to his demise. Using this technique, the centers for displeasure or punishment have been found to lie in the *anterior mid-line hypothalamic zone, especially around the end of the fornix,* and then backward into the *periaqueductal gray matter of the mesencephalon.*

Importance of Reward and Punishment in Behavior. Almost everything that we do depends on reward and punishment. If we are doing something that is rewarding, we continue to do it; if it is something punishing, we cease to do it. Therefore, the reward and punishment centers undoubtedly constitute one of the most important of all the controllers of our bodily activities.

Importance of Reward and Punishment in Learning——Habituation and Reinforcement. It has been found in animal experiments that a sensory experience which causes neither reward nor punishment is remembered hardly at all. Also, electrical recordings have shown that new and novel sensory stimuli will always excite the cerebral cortex. But repetition of the stimulus over a period of time leads to almost complete extinction of the cortical response if this stimulus does not excite either reward or punishment centers. Thus, the animal becomes *habituated* to the sensory stimulus. But if the stimulus causes either reward or punishment rather than indifference, then the cortical response becomes progressively more and more intense with repetitive stimulation instead of fading away, and the response is said to be *reinforced*. Therefore, an animal builds up strong memory engrams for sensations which are either rewarding or punishing, but, on the other hand, develops complete habituation to indifferent sensory stimuli. Therefore, it is evident that the reward and punishment centers of the midbrain have much to do with controlling the type of information that we learn.

Emotional Patterns of Behavior

Though little is known about the precise control of different emotional patterns of behavior, it is known that stimulation in the reward regions of the midbrain will normally cause *tameness* and *docility* of animals, while stimulation in the punishment areas will cause behavioral patterns of *fear, rage,* and *escape*. Also, stimulation of the pyriform region of the cerebral cortex will result in *sniffing, salivation, licking,* and *other types of feeding activity*. And stimulation in still other regions of the midbrain will cause *explorative tendencies, cleaning tendencies,* or simply *restlessness*.

The Affective-Defensive Pattern. One particular emotional pattern that has been well characterized by Hess is the *affective-defensive pattern,* which can be described as follows:

Stimulation of the *perifornical areas of the hypothalamus,* which are also the regions that give the most intense sensation of punishment, causes the animal to (1) develop a defense posture, (2) extend his claws, (3) lift his tail, (4) hiss, (5) spit, (6) growl, and (7) develop piloerection, wide-open eyes, and dilated pupils. Furthermore, even the slightest provocation will cause an immediate savage attack. This is approximately the behavior that one would expect from an animal being severely punished, and it is a pattern of behavior that has also been called simply *rage*. It can even occur in decorticated animals, illus-

trating that the basic behavioral pattern for protective activities are present in the lower regions of the brain.

Exactly the opposite emotional behavioral pattern occurs when the reward centers are stimulated, namely, docility and tameness.

Function of the Amygdaloid Nuclei in Behavioral Patterns. Stimulation of different portions of the amygdaloid nuclei can cause almost any type of behavioral pattern. Stimulation of the basal and lateral portions causes *fear* and *escape* or *alert attention* patterns of behavior. Stimulation of the central and medial amygdaloid nuceli gives a pattern of rage similar to the *affective-defensive pattern* described above, and stimulation of other portions of the amygdaloid nuclei can give *feeding activities* or other gastrointestinal activities, such as *vomiting, gastric paralysis, increased stomach acidity, defecation, salivation, sniffing,* and so forth. And stimulation of still other portions of the amygdaloid nuclei can cause sexual activities that include *erection, copulatory movements, ejaculation, ovulation, uterine activity,* and *premature labor*.

In short, stimulation of appropriate portions of the amygdaloid nuclei can give almost any pattern of behavior, and it is believed that the normal function of the amygdaloid nuclei is to help control the overall pattern of behavior demanded for each occasion. A very large portion of the behavioral activities elicited by the amygdaloid nuclei is mediated through impulses that excite different hypothalamic nuclei; these in turn elicit either sympathetic or parasympathetic effects throughout the body.

Psychosomatic Effects

We are all familiar with the fact that abnormal function in the central nervous system can frequently lead to serious dysfunction of the different somatic organs of the body. This is also true in experimental animals, for, as pointed out above, prolonged electrical stimulation in the punishment regions of the brain can actually lead to severe sickness of the animal, culminating in death within 24 to 48 hours. We need, therefore, to understand very briefly the mechanisms by which stimulatory effects in the brain can affect the peripheral organs. Ordinarily, this occurs through three routes:

(1) through the motor nerves to the skeletal muscles throughout the body, (2) through the autonomic nerves to the different internal organs of the body, and (3) through the hormones secreted by the hypophysis in response to nervous activity in the hypothalamus, as will be explained in Chapter 73.

Psychosomatic Disorders Transmitted through the Skeletal Nervous System. Abnormal psychic states can greatly alter the degree of nervous stimulation to the skeletal musculature throughout the body and thereby increase or decrease the skeletal muscular tone. During states of attention the general skeletal muscular tone normally increases, whereas during somnolent states the skeletal muscular tone greatly decreases. In neurotic and psychotic states such as anxiety, tension, and mania, generalized tenseness of the musculature can occur throughout the body. This in turn results in intensive feedback from the muscle proprioceptors to the reticular activating system, which undoubtedly helps to maintain an extreme degree of wakefulness and alertness that characterizes these emotional states. Unfortunately, though, the wakefulness prevents adequate sleep and also leads to progressive bodily fatigue despite the inability to go to sleep.

Transmission of Psychosomatic Effects through the Autonomic Nervous System. Many psychosomatic abnormalities result from either hyperactivity of the sympathetic nervous system or of the parasympathetic system. In general, when hyperactivity of the sympathetic system occurs, it occurs everywhere in the body at the same time rather than in focal areas, and the usual effects are (1) increased heart rate—sometimes with palpitation of the heart, (2) increased arterial pressure, (3) constipation, and (4) increased metabolic rate. On the other hand, parasympathetic stimuli are likely to be much more focal. For instance, stimulation of specific areas in the dorsal motor nuclei of the vagus nerves can cause more or less specifically increased hyperacidity of the stomach with resultant development of peptic ulcer. Stimulation of the sacral regions of the parasympathetic system, on the other hand, is likely to cause extreme degrees of colonic peristalsis with resulting diarrhea. One can readily see, then,

that emotional patterns controlling the sympathetic and parasympathetic centers of the hypothalamus can cause wide varieties of peripheral psychosomatic effects.

Psychosomatic Effects Transmitted through the Adenohypophysis. Electrical stimulation of the posterior hypothalamus has been shown to increase the secretion of both corticotropin and thyrotropin by the adenohypophysis and therefore indirectly to increase the outputs of adrenocortical and thyroid hormones, respectively. One of the effects of increased adrenocortical secretion is a gradual increase in stomach hyperacidity because of the effect of glucocorticoids on stomach secretion. Over a prolonged period of time this obviously could lead to gastric ulcer, which is a well-known effect of hypersecretion of the adrenal cortex. The increased secretion of thyrotropin, on the other hand, increases the output of thyroxine, which then leads to an elevated basal metabolic rate. It is well known that different types of emotional disturbances can in fact lead to thyrotoxicosis, as will be explained in Chapter 75.

Stimulation of the amygdaloid nuclei in lower animals has been shown to increase the output of gonadotropic hormones, and this in turn leads to ovulation. In human beings it is known also that emotional abnormalities can result in (a) anovulatory cycles, (b) abnormal menstrual periods, and (c) irregularity of menstruation.

From these examples, therefore, it is evident that many types of psychosomatic abnormalities of the body can be effected through the control of adenohypophyseal secretion. The precise mechanisms by which stimulation in the central nervous system can cause increased adenohypophyseal secretion will be discussed in Chapter 73. Basically, it results from the formation in the hypothalamus of *neurosecretory substances,* which are then transported through a *hypophyseal portal system* to the adenohypophysis, there exciting the secretion of the adenohypophyseal hormones.

REFERENCES

Adey, W. R., Segundo, J. P., and Livingston, R. B.: Corticofugal influences on intrinsic brain stem conduction in cat and monkey. *J. Neurophysiol., 20:*1, 1957.
Andy, O. J., and Akert, K.: Seizure patterns induced

by electrical stimulation of hippocampal formation in the cat. *J. Neuropath.*, 14:198, 1955.

Bickford, R. G.: New dimensions in electroencephalography. *Neurology*, 7:469, 1957.

Blachly, P. H., and Brookhart, J. M.: Studies on the analeptic action of electrical stimulation in barbiturate poisoning. *Anesthesiology*, 16:151, 1955.

Bremer, F.: Cerebral and cerebellar potentials. *Physiol. Rev.*, 38:357, 1958.

Brodal, A.: The Reticular Formation of the Brain Stem. Springfield, Illinois, Charles C Thomas, 1957.

Brookhart, J. M., Arduini, A., Mancia, M., and Moruzzi, G.: Thalamocortical relations as revealed by induced slow potential changes. *J. Neurophysiol.*, 21:499, 1958.

Cobb, S.: Foundations of Neuropsychiatry. 6th ed. Baltimore, Williams & Wilkins, 1958.

Dean, W. H., and Davis, G. D.: Behavior changes following caudate lesions in rhesus monkey. *J. Neurophysiol.*, 22:524, 1959.

Delafresnaye, J. F.: Brain Mechanisms and Consciousness. Springfield, Illinois, Charles C Thomas, 1955.

Delgado, J. M.: Cerebral structures involved in transmission and elaboration of noxious stimulation. *J. Neurophysiol.*, 18:261, 1955.

DeMolina, A. F., and Hunsperger, R. W.: Central representation of affective reactions in forebrain and brain stem: electrical stimulation of amygdala, stria terminalis, and adjacent structures. *J. Physiol.*, 145:251, 1959.

Eliasson, S. G.: Central control of digestive function. *Handbook of Physiology*, 2:1163, 1960.

Fessard, A.: Brain potentials and rhythms—introduction. *Handbook of Physiology*, 1:255, 1959.

French, J. D., Gernandt, B. E., and Livingston, R. B.: Regional differences in seizure susceptibility in monkey cortex. *A. M. A. Arch. Neur. Psychiat.*, 75:260, 1956.

French, J. D., Hernandez-peon, R., and Livingston, R. B.: Projections from cortex to cephalic brain stem (reticular formation) in monkey. *J. Neurophysiol.*, 18:74, 1955.

Gantt, W. H. (ed.): Physiological Bases of Psychiatry. Springfield, Illinois, Charles C Thomas, 1958.

Gastaut, H.: The Epilepsies. Springfield, Illinois, Charles C Thomas, 1954.

Gastaut, H., and Fischer-Williams, M.: The physiopathology of epileptic seizures. *Handbook of Physiology*, 1:329, 1959.

Gellhorn, E.: Physiological Foundations of Neurology and Psychiatry. Minneapolis, University of Minnesota Press, 1953.

Gloor, P.: Amygdala. *Handbook of Physiology*, 2:1393, 1960.

Green, J. D.: The hippocampus. *Handbook of Physiology*, 2:1373, 1960.

Henry Ford Hospital Symposium: Reticular Formation of the Brain. Boston, Little, Brown & Company, 1958.

Hess, W. R.: Diencephalon, Autonomic and Extrapyramidal Functions. New York, Grune & Stratton, Inc., 1954.

Hill, J. D. N., and Parr, G.: Electroencephalography. New York, The Macmillan Co., 1950.

Hillarp, N.: Peripheral autonomic mechanisms. *Handbook of Physiology*, 2:979, 1960.

Hoffman, B. F., Suckling, E. E., Brooks, C. M., Koenig, E. H., Coleman, K. S., and Treumann, H. J.: Quantitative evaluation of sleep. *J. Appl. Physiol.*, 8:361, 1956.

Hughes, J. R. (ed.) (Translation of W. R. Hess' "Das Zwischenhirn"): Hess: The Functional Organization of the Diencephalon. New York, Grune & Stratton, Inc., 1958.

Ingram, W. R.: Central autonomic mechanisms. *Handbook of Physiology*, 2:951, 1960.

Jasper, H. H.: Unspecific thalamocortical relations. *Handbook of Physiology*, 2:1307, 1960.

Kaada, B. R.: Cingulate, posterior orbital, anterior insular and temporal pole cortex. *Handbook of Physiology*, 2:1345, 1960.

Kandel, E. R., Spencer, W. A., and Brinley, F. J., Jr.: Transient and long-lasting electrical responses to direct hippocampal stimulation. *Am. J. Physiol.*, 198:687, 1960.

Kleitman, N.: Sleep. *Scient. Am.*, 187:34, 1952.

Konrad, L.: Methods of approach to the problems of behavior. *Harvey Lect.*, 54:60, 1959.

Li, C., Cullen, C., and Jasper, H. H.: Laminar microelectrode analysis of cortical unspecific recruiting responses and spontaneous rhythms. *J. Neurophysiol.*, 19:131, 1956.

Lindsley, D. B.: Psychological aspects of consciousness. *Clin. Neurosurg.*, 3:175, 1955.

Livingston, R. B.: Brain mechanisms and behavior. *Psychiat. Res. Rep.*, 6:1, 1956.

Magoun, H. W.: The Waking Brain. Springfield, Illinois, Charles C Thomas, 1958.

Mason, J. W.: Visceral functions of the nervous system. *Ann. Rev. Physiol.*, 21:353, 1959.

Mulder, D. W., Bickford, R. G., and Dodge, H. W., Jr.: Hallucinatory epilepsy: complex hallucinations and focal seizures. *Am. J. Psychiat.*, 113:1100, 1957.

Olds, J.: Higher functions of the nervous system. *Ann. Rev. Physiol.*, 21:381, 1959.

O'Leary, J. L., and Coben, L. A.: The reticular core —1957. *Physiol. Rev.*, 38:243, 1958.

Pampiglione, G., and Falconer, M. A.: Electrical stimulation of the hippocampus in man. *Handbook of Physiology*, 2:1391, 1960.

Pennes, H. H.: Progress in Neurobiology. Vol. 3: Psychopharmacology: Pharmacologic Effects on Behavior. New York, Paul B. Hoeber, 1958.

Schlessinger, B.: Higher Cerebral Functions and Their Disorders. New York, Grune & Stratton, Inc., 1960.

Schmidt, R. P., Thomas, L. B., and Ward, A. A., Jr.: The hyper-excitable neurone. Microelectrode studies of chronic epileptic foci in monkey. *J. Neurophysiol.*, 22:285, 1959.

Strauss, H.: Diagnostic Electroencephalography. New York, Grune & Stratton, Inc., 1952.

Tower, D. B.: Neurochemistry of Epilepsy. Springfield, Illinois, Charles C Thomas, 1960.

Walter, W. G.: Intrinsic rhythms of the brain. *Handbook of Physiology*, 1:279, 1959.

Weiss, E., and English, O. S.: Psychosomatic Medicine. 3rd ed., Philadelphia, W. B. Saunders Co., 1957.

Part Ten

ALIMENTARY TRACT

Chapter 61

Movement of Food

through the Alimentary Tract

The primary function of the alimentary tract is to provide the body with a continual supply of water, electrolytes, and nutrients, but before this can be achieved food must be moved along the alimentary tract at an appropriate rate for the digestive and absorptive functions to take place. Therefore, our discussion of this tract will be presented in three different phases: (1) movement of food through the alimentary tract, (2) secretion of the digestive juices, and (3) absorption of the digested foods, water, and the various electrolytes.

Figure 615 illustrates the entire alimentary tract, showing major anatomical differences between its parts. Each part is adapted for specific functions such as: (1) simple passage of food from one point to another as in the esophagus, (2) storage of food or fecal matter in the body of the stomach and in the descending colon respectively, (3) digestion of food in the stomach, duodenum, jejunum, and ileum, and (4) absorption of the digestive end-products in the entire small intestine and proximal half of the colon. One of the most important features of the gastrointestinal tract that will be discussed in the present chapter is the myriad of autoregulatory processes in the gut that keeps the food moving at an appropriate pace—slow enough for digestion and absorption to take place but fast enough to provide the nutrients needed by the body.

GENERAL PRINCIPLES OF GASTROINTESTINAL MOTILITY

Characteristics of the Intestinal Wall

Figure 616 illustrates a typical section of the gastrointestinal tract, showing the following layers from outside inward: (1) the *serosa*, (2) a *longitudinal muscle layer*, (3) a *circular muscle layer*, (4) the *submucosa*, and (5) the *mucosa*. In addition, a sparse layer of smooth muscle fibers, the *muscularis mucosae*, lies in the deeper layers of the mucosa. The motor functions of the gut are performed by the different layers of smooth muscle.

The smooth muscle of each layer of the gastrointestinal tract forms a functional *syncytium*—that is, the individual muscle fibers lie in such close contact with each

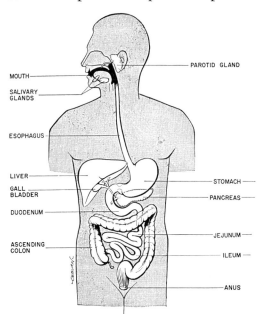

MOUTH

SALIVARY GLANDS

ESOPHAGUS

LIVER

GALL BLADDER

DUODENUM

ASCENDING COLON

PAROTID GLAND

STOMACH

PANCREAS

JEJUNUM

ILEUM

ANUS

Figure 615.   The alimentary tract.

819

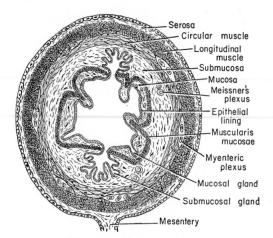

Figure 616.   Typical cross-section of the gut.

other that stimulatory impulses initiated in any part of the muscle tend to spread to adjacent areas. The conduction rate in the muscle itself is approximately 4 mm. per second, or nearly one foot each minute. As this excitatory wave travels through the muscle, a prolonged contraction lasting one to seven seconds occurs, the duration depending on the characteristics of the specific segment of the gut stimulated.

The smooth muscle of the gastrointestinal tract exhibits both *tonus contraction* and *rhythmic contraction,* both of which are characteristic of most types of smooth muscle, as was discussed in Chapter 19.

Tonus contraction is a continuous contraction lasting minute after minute or even hour after hour, sometimes increasing in intensity or decreasing in intensity but nevertheless continuing on and on. The degree of tonic contraction in each segment of the gut determines the amount of steady pressure in the segment, and tonic contraction of the sphincters determines the amount of resistance to movement of food that will be offered by each of the sphincters. In this way the *pyloric sphincter,* the *ileocecal sphincter,* and the *anal sphincter* all help to regulate food movement in the gut.

The *rhythmic contractions* of the gastrointestinal smooth muscle occur at rates as rapid as 15 to 20 times per minute or as slow as 2 to 3 times per minute. These contractions are responsible for the phasic functions of the gastrointestinal tract, such as mixing of the food and peristaltic propulsion of food, as will be discussed below.

Innervation of the Gut—the Intramural Plexus

Beginning in the wall of the esophagus and extending all the way to the anus is an *intramural nerve plexus.* This is composed principally of two layers of neurons and appropriate connecting fibers: the outer layer, called the *myenteric plexus,* or *Auerbach's plexus,* lies between the longitudinal and circular muscular layers, and the inner layer, called *Meissner's plexus,* lies in the submucosa. The myenteric plexus is far more extensive than Meissner's plexus, for which reason many physiologists often refer to the entire intramural plexus as simply the myenteric plexus.

In general, stimulation of the intramural plexus increases the activity of the gut, causing four principal effects: (1) increased tonic contraction, or "tone," of the gut wall, (2) increased intensity of the rhythmical contractions, (3) increased rate of rhythmical contraction, and (4) increased velocity of conduction of excitatory waves along the gut wall.

The intramural plexus is especially responsible for many neurogenic reflexes that occur locally in the gut, such as reflexes from the mucosal epithelium to increase the excitability of the muscle layers or to cause localized secretion of digestive juices by the submucosal glands. This plexus is also intimately involved in the coordination of peristalsis, the major propulsive movements of the gastrointestinal tract, which will be discussed below.

Autonomic Control of the Gastrointestinal Tract. *The parasympathetics.* The entire gastrointestinal tract receives extensive parasympathetic and sympathetic innervation that is capable of altering the overall activity of the entire gut or of specific parts of it. The *parasympathetic supply* to the gut is divided into the *cranial* and *sacral divisions,* which were discussed in Chapter 20. Except for a few parasympathetic fibers to the mouth and pharyngeal regions of the alimentary tract, the cranial parasympathetics are transmitted almost entirely in the *vagus nerves.* These fibers provide extensive innervation to the esophagus, the stomach, and the pancreas, and to a lesser extent to the small intestine, the gallbladder, and the first half of the large intestine. The sacral parasympathetics originate in the second, third, and fourth sacral segments of the spinal cord and pass through the *nervi erigentes* to the distal half of the large intestine. The sigmoidal, rectal, and anal regions of the large intestine are considerably better supplied with parasympathetic fibers than are the other portions. These help in the defecation reflexes, which will be discussed later in the chapter.

The postganglionic neurons of the parasympathetic system lie in the myenteric plexus, and stimulation of the parasympathetic nerves causes a general increase in activity of the gut wall and facilitates most of the intrinsic nervous reflexes of the gastrointestinal tract.

The sympathetics. The sympathetic fibers to the gastrointestinal tract originate in the spinal cord between the segments T 8 and L 3. The preganglionic fibers, after leaving the cord, first enter the sympathetic chains and then pass on through the chains to outlying ganglia such as the *celiac ganglia* and various *mesenteric ganglia*. Here, the postganglionic neurons are located, and postganglionic fibers spread from them to all parts of the gut. The sympathetics, unlike the parasympathetics, innervate essentially all portions of the gastrointestinal tract rather than being more extensively supplied to the most orad and most anal portions, as is true of the parasympathetics.

In general, stimulation of the sympathetic nervous system inhibits activity in the gastrointestinal tract, causing effects essentially opposite to those of the parasympathetic system. However, the sympathetic system elicits excitatory effects in at least three instances: it excites (1) the ileocecal sphincter, (2) the internal anal sphincter, and (3) the smooth muscle fibers of the muscularis mucosae throughout the entire gastrointestinal tract. Thus, strong stimulation of the sympathetic system can totally block movement of food through the gastrointestinal tract, both by inhibition of the gut wall and by excitation of at least two major sphincters of the gastrointestinal tract. By exciting the smooth muscle of the muscularis mucosae at the same time it increases the number of folds in the gastrointestinal tract (and it also increases the activity of the villi, which will be discussed in Chapter 63), in

this way possibly increasing the rate of absorption from the gut.

Effects of parasympathetic and sympathetic denervation. Denervating the sympathetic nervous system normally has no significant effect on the function of the gastrointestinal tract, but, on the other hand, denervation of the parasympathetic system almost always at least temporarily decreases the activity of the denervated portions of the gut. Thus, vagotomy markedly reduces the tone and the degree of peristaltic activity in the terminal esophagus, the stomach, and the upper intestines, while destruction of the sacral parasympathetics decreases the tone of the descending colon, the sigmoid, and the rectum, thereby seriously impairing the process of defecation.

It is evident, then, that the gastrointestinal tract is usually tonically excited by the parasympathetics, and loss of this tone reduces gastrointestinal functions. Fortunately, after several months to a year or more, the intrinsic nervous system of the gut compensates by gradually increasing its intrinsic excitability so that the excitability eventually returns almost to normal.

Regulation of Gastrointestinal Activity by the Central Nervous System. The autonomic centers of the central nervous system, acting through the parasympathetic and sympathetic nerves, can either increase or decrease the activity of the gastrointestinal tract. The parasympathetic centers, in general, increase the activity, and the sympathetic centers, in general, decrease the activity. Usually the sympathetic centers act as a unit to decrease the activity of the entire gastrointestinal tract at once, while, on the other hand, the parasympathetic centers function more discretely, having the capability of controlling specific segments of the alimentary tract separately from others. Some of the specific control functions of the parasympathetic system are (1) parts of the act of swallowing, (2) gastric secretion, (3) intestinal motility, and (4) defecation. Each of these can be controlled separately from the others.

Many of the emotions and other psychic effects that commonly excite the autonomic nervous system can alter the function of the gastrointestinal tract. For instance, continued *excitement, fright,* or *fear* can activate the sympathetic nervous system so greatly that it almost stops gastrointestinal motility entirely. On the other hand, *anxiety*, *resentment*, and *prolonged worry* are said to increase gastrointestinal motility and often to be responsible for the development of diarrhea.

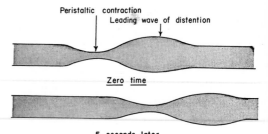

Figure 617. Peristalsis.

FUNCTIONAL TYPES OF MOVEMENTS IN THE GASTROINTESTINAL TRACT

The Mixing Movements

The two basic types of movements in the gastrointestinal tract are the *mixing movements*, which keep the intestinal contents thoroughly mixed at all times, and the *propulsive movements*, which cause the food to move forward along the tract at an appropriate rate for digestion and absorption.

In most parts of the alimentary tract, the mixing movements are caused either by (a) *peristaltic contractions* or by (b) *local rhythmical contractions of small segments of the gut wall.* These movements are modified in different parts of the gastrointestinal tract for proper performance of the respective activities of each part, as will be discussed separately later in the chapter.

The Propulsive Movements—Peristalsis

The basic propulsive movement of the gastrointestinal tract is *peristalsis*, which is illustrated in Figure 617. A contractile ring appears around the gut and then moves forward; this is analogous to putting one's fingers around a thin distended tube, then constricting the fingers and moving them forward along the tube. Obviously, any material in front of the contractile ring will be moved forward.

Peristalsis is an inherent property of any syncytial smooth muscle tube, and stimulation at any point will cause a contractile ring to spread in both directions. Thus, peristalsis occurs (a) in the gastrointestinal tract, (b) in the bile ducts, (c) in other glandular ducts throughout the body, (d) in the ureters, and (e) in any other smooth muscle tube of the body. The usual stimulus for peristalsis is *distention*. That is, if a large amount of food collects at any point in the gut, the distention stimulates the wall at this point, and a contractile ring appears and initiates a peristaltic movement.

Function of the Intramural Nerve Plexus in Peristalsis. Even though peristalsis is a basic characteristic of all tubular smooth muscle structures, it occurs only very weakly or not at all in portions of the gastrointestinal tract which have congenital absence of the intramural nerve plexus. Also, it is greatly depressed or completely blocked in the entire gut when the person is treated with atropine to paralyze the intramural nerve plexus. Finally, the intramural plexus causes the velocity of transmission of peristalsis along the gut to be 1 to 4 centimeters per second, which is some five times as great as the natural conductive velocity of impulses in the smooth muscle itself (4mm./second). Furthermore, since the intramural plexus is principally under the control of the parasympathetic nerves, the intensity of peristalsis and its velocity of conduction can be altered by parasympathetic stimulation.

Therefore, *even though the basic phenomenon of peristalsis is not dependent on the intramural nerve plexus, its degree of activity is usually so slight without the intramural plexus that it is ineffectual.*

Analward Direction of Peristaltic Movements. Peristalsis can occur in either direction from a stimulated point, but most frequently it dies out very rapidly in the orad direction but continues for a considerably longer distance in the analward direction. The cause of this directional transmission of peristalsis has never been ascertained, though several suggestions have been offered as follows:

Receptive relaxation and the "law of the gut." Some physiologists believe the directional movement of peristalsis to be caused by a special organization of the intramural nerve plexus which allows preferential transmission of signals in an analward direction. One reason for believing this is the following effect of electrical stimulation on the gut: An electrical stimulus causes a contractile ring to appear immediately beneath the stimulus, but at the same time it causes relaxation, called "receptive relaxation," several centimeters down the gut toward the anus. It is believed that this relaxation could occur only as a result of myenteric conduction. Obviously, the leading wave of distention caused by receptive relaxation would allow food to be propelled more easily in the analward direction than in the orad direction.

This response to electrical stimulation is also called the "law of the gut" or sometimes simply the "myenteric reflex." It is particularly well demonstrated in the esophagus and in the pyloric region of the stomach. And, even though it has not been demonstrated everywhere in the gut, nevertheless, its occurrence at only a few points would still be sufficient to keep the food traveling in a single direction.

The gradient theory for forward propulsion. Another theory for forward propulsion of intestinal contents is the *gradient theory*. This is based on the fact that the upper part of the gastrointestinal tract usually displays a higher degree of activity than the lower part. For instance, the basic contractile rhythm in the duodenum is approximately 11 contractions per minute, while that in the ileum is in the order of five to seven contractions per minute. Also, in the upper part of the gastrointestinal tract far greater quantities of secretions are formed, and these, because of distending the gut, could initiate far more peristaltic waves than are initiated in the lower gut. Therefore, it is postulated that a greater number of peristaltic impulses originate in the orad portions of the gut than in the more distal regions, thereby causing the peristaltic waves generally to travel down the gut rather than up the gut. This is analogous to the *pacemaker* function of the S-A node in the heart.

Yet, in some circumstances the irritability of the distal gut can increase above that of the proximal gut; this causes waves to travel preferentially in the backward direction, which can explain the reverse peristalsis frequently seen in the duodenum and ileum even under normal circumstances and that seen in almost any part of the gut proximal to a point of obstruction.

THE INGESTION OF FOOD

The amount of food that a person ingests is determined principally by the intrinsic desire for food called *hunger,* and the type of food that he preferentially seeks is determined by his *appetite.* These mechanisms in themselves are extremely important automatic regulatory systems for maintaining an adequate nutritional supply for the body, and they will be discussed in detail in Chapter 69 in relation to the nutrition of the body. But, for the present, we will confine our discussion to the actual mechanical aspects of food ingestion, including especially the processes of *mastication* and *swallowing.*

Mastication

The teeth are admirably designed for chewing, the anterior teeth providing a strong cutting action and the posterior teeth a grinding action. All the jaw muscles working together can close the teeth with a total force of several hundred pounds, and when this is applied to a small object such as a small seed between the jaw teeth, the actual force *per square inch* may be in the order of several thousand pounds.

Most of the muscles of chewing are innervated by the motor branch of the fifth nerve, and the central nervous system is subserved mainly by brain stem centers; therefore, it is principally a subconscious phenomenon. Stimulation of certain areas in the cerebral cortex in close association with the sensory areas of taste and smell or in the facial motor regions can cause continual chewing movements. Furthermore, stimulation of areas in the basal ganglia and brain stem can also result in chewing movements.

Chewing of the food is especially important for digestion of most of the fruits and raw vegetables, because these have undigestible cellulose membranes around their nutrient portions which must be broken before the food can be utilized. However, chewing also aids in the utilization of all other types of food for the following very simple reason: *Since the digestive enzymes act only on the surfaces of food particles*, the rate of digestion is highly dependent on the total surface area exposed to the intestinal secretions. The greater the chewing, the greater also becomes the surface area, thereby increasing the effectiveness of digestion everywhere in the gastrointestinal tract. Finally, very fine particulation of the food prevents excoriation of the gastrointestinal tract and increases the ease with which food is emptied, first, from the stomach into the small intestine and, thence, into all succeeding segments of the gut. Many gastrointestinal problems are caused by either intestinal wall excoriation or by slowness of movement of the food. There is no other part of the gastrointestinal tract that can perform the function of breaking the food into small particles should the teeth fail in this basic operation.

Swallowing (Deglutition)

After food has been chewed, it must be swallowed, and this in itself is a very complicated mechanism, principally because the pharynx most of the time subserves several other functions besides swallowing and is converted for only a few seconds at a time into a tract for propulsion of food. Especially is it important that respiration not be compromised during swallowing.

In general, swallowing can be divided into three major phases: (1) the *voluntary stage,* which initiates the swallowing process, (2) a *pharyngeal stage,* which is involuntary and constitutes the passage of food through the pharynx into the esophagus, and (3) the *esophageal stage,* another involuntary phase which promotes the passage of food from the pharynx to the stomach.

Voluntary Stage of Swallowing. When the food is ready for swallowing, it is "voluntarily" squeezed or rolled posteriorly by pressure of the tongue upward and backward against the palate. Thus, the tongue forces the bolus of food into the pharynx. From here on, the process of swallowing becomes entirely, or almost entirely, automatic and ordinarily cannot be stopped once it has begun.

The Pharyngeal Stage of Swallowing. When the bolus of food is pushed backwards in the mouth, it stimulates *swallowing receptor areas* all around the opening of the pharynx, especially on the tonsillar pillars, and impulses from these pass to the brain stem to initiate a series of automatic pharyngeal muscular contractions as follows:

1. The soft palate is pulled upward to close the posterior nares, in this way preventing reflux of food into the nasal cavities.

2. The palatopharyngeal folds on either side of the pharynx are pulled medialward to approximate each other. In this way these folds form a sagittal slit through which the food must pass into the posterior pharynx, and this slit performs a selective action, allowing food that has been masticated properly to pass with ease while impeding the passage of large objects. Since this stage of swallowing lasts only one second, any large object is usually impeded too much to pass on through the pharynx into the esophagus.

3. The vocal cords of the larynx are strongly approximated, and the epiglottis swings backward over the superior opening of the larynx. Both of these effects prevent passage of food into the trachea. Especially important is the approximation of the vocal cords, but the epiglottis helps to prevent food from ever getting as far as the vocal cords. Destruction of the vocal cords or of the muscles that approximate them can cause strangulation. On the other hand, removal of the epiglottis usually does not cause serious debility in swallowing.

4. The entire larynx is then pulled upward and forward by muscles attached to the hyoid bone; this movement of the larynx actually stretches the opening of the esophagus. At the same time, the *hypopharyngeal sphincter* around the esophageal entrance, which normally prevents air from going into the esophagus during respiration, relaxes, thus allowing the food to move easily and freely from the posterior pharynx into the upper esophagus. The upward movement of the larynx also lifts the glottis out of the main stream of flow of the food so that the food usually passes on either side of the epiglottis rather than over its surface; this adds still another protection against passage of food into the trachea.

5. At the same time that the larynx is raised and that the hypopharyngeal sphincter is relaxed, the superior constrictor muscle of the pharynx contracts, and this is followed by a rapid peristaltic wave passing downward through the pharyngeal constrictors and into the esophagus.

To summarize the mechanics of the pharyngeal stage of swallowing—the trachea is closed, the esophagus is opened, and a fast peristaltic wave then forces the bolus of food into the upper esophagus, the entire process occurring in one to two seconds. The anatomy of the swallowing mechanism is shown in Figure 618.

Nervous control of the pharyngeal stage of swallowing. The most sensitive tactile areas of the pharynx for initiation of the pharyngeal stage of swallowing lie in a ring around the pharyngeal opening, with greatest sensitivity in the tonsillar pillars. Impulses are transmitted from these areas through the sensory portion of the trigeminal and glossopharyngeal nerves into a region of the medulla oblongata closely associated with the *tractus solitarius,* which receives

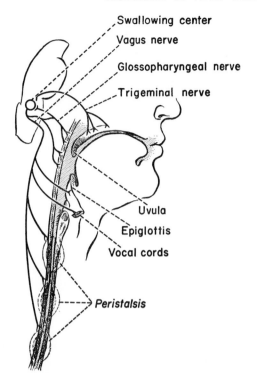

Figure 618.   Anatomy of the swallowing mechanism.

essentially all sensory impulses from the mouth.

The successive stages of the swallowing process are then automatically controlled in orderly sequence by neuronal areas distributed throughout the reticular substance of the medulla and lowest portion of the pons. The sequence of the swallowing reflex remains almost exactly the same from one swallow to the next, and the timing of the entire cycle also remains constant from one swallow to the next. The widely distributed areas in the medulla and lower pons that control swallowing are collectively called the *deglutition, or swallowing, center.*

The motor impulses from the deglutition center to the pharynx and upper esophagus that cause swallowing are transmitted by the 5th through the 12th cranial nerves, and even a few of the superior cervical nerves also enter into the action.

In summary, the pharyngeal stage of swallowing is principally a reflex act. It is almost never initiated by direct stimuli to the deglutition center from higher regions of the central nervous system. Instead, it is almost always initiated by voluntary move-

ment of food into the pharynx, which, in turn, elicits the swallowing reflex.

Effect of the pharyngeal stage of swallowing on respiration. The entire pharyngeal stage of swallowing occurs in less than 1 to 2 seconds, thereby interrupting respiration for only a fraction of a usual respiratory cycle. The swallowing center specifically inhibits the respiratory center of the medulla during this period of time, halting respiration at any point in its cycle to allow swallowing to proceed. Yet, even while a person is talking, the process of swallowing interrupts respiration for such a short period of time that it is hardly noticeable.

Esophageal Stage of Swallowing. The esophagus functions primarily to conduct food from the pharynx to the stomach, and its movements are organized specifically for this function.

Normally the esophagus exhibits two types of peristaltic movements—*primary peristalsis* and *secondary peristalsis.* Primary peristalsis is simply a continuation of the peristaltic wave that begins in the pharynx and spreads into the esophagus during the pharyngeal stage of swallowing. This wave passes all the way from the pharynx to the stomach in approximately 5 to 10 seconds. However, food swallowed by a person who is in the upright position is usually transmitted to the lower end of the esophagus even more rapidly than the peristaltic wave itself, in about 4 to 8 seconds, because of the additional effect of gravity pulling the food downward. If the primary peristaltic wave fails to move all the food that has entered the esophagus on into the stomach, then secondary peristaltic waves result from distention of the esophagus by the retained food. These waves are essentially the same as the primary peristaltic waves, except that they originate in the distended areas rather than in the pharynx. Secondary peristaltic waves continue to be initiated until all the food has emptied into the stomach.

The peristaltic waves of the esophagus are controlled almost entirely by vagal reflexes that are part of the overall swallowing mechanism. These reflexes are transmitted through *vagal afferent fibers* from the esophagus to the medulla and then back again to the esophagus through *vagal efferent fibers.*

The musculature of the pharynx and the

upper one third of the esophagus is skeletal muscle, and, therefore, the peristaltic waves in these regions are always controlled by skeletal nerve impulses. In the lower two thirds of the esophagus, the musculature is smooth, but even here this portion of the esophagus is normally under the control of the vagus nerve. However, when the vagus nerves to the esophagus are sectioned, the intramural nerve plexus of the esophagus becomes excitable enough after several hours to several days to cause weak secondary peristaltic waves, even without support from the medullary swallowing center. Therefore, following paralysis of the swallowing reflex, food forced into the upper esophagus and then pulled by gravity to the lower esophagus will still pass very readily into the stomach.

Receptive relaxation of the stomach. As the esophageal peristaltic waves pass toward the stomach a wave of relaxation precedes the constriction. Furthermore, the entire stomach and to a less extent even the duodenum become relaxed as this wave reaches the lower end of the esophagus. Especially important, also, is relaxation of the *cardiac constrictor* at the juncture between the esophagus and the stomach. In other words, the cardiac constrictor and the stomach are actually prepared ahead of time to receive food being transmitted down the esophagus during the swallowing act.

Function of the Cardiac Constrictor

In lower animals, a ring of sphincteric muscle, called the "cardiac constrictor," lies at the juncture of the esophagus and the stomach. In the human being no such hypertrophied constrictor can be observed anatomically, but physiologically the distal centimeter or more of the esophagus is maintained in a state of tonic contraction so that even in the human being this area is also called the *cardiac constrictor* or simply the *cardia*.

When food is swallowed and reaches the lower end of the esophagus, it normally is slowed in its passage for a second or more before finally entering the stomach, thus illustrating the greater tone of the cardiac area of the esophagus than of other areas. However, "receptive relaxation" of the cardia, as explained above, ordinarily prevents any further delay of esophageal emptying. Rarely, the cardia does not relax satisfactorily, resulting in the condition called cardiospasm, which will be discussed in detail in Chapter 64.

The principal function of the cardiac constrictor is the prevention of reflux of stomach contents into the lower esophagus. The stomach contents are highly acidic and contain many proteolytic enzymes. The esophageal mucosa, on the other hand, is not capable of resisting for long the digestive action of gastric secretions in the esophagus. Fortunately, the tonic constriction of the cardiac constrictor prevents significant reflux of stomach contents into the esophagus except under abnormal conditions.

Tonic contraction of the cardiac constrictor results from continual mild stimulation by the vagus nerves. Therefore, vagotomy frequently relaxes the cardiac constrictor to the point that it has hardly any impeding effect on the passage of material either downward or upward.

MOTOR FUNCTIONS OF THE STOMACH

The motor functions of the stomach are three-fold: (1) storage of large quantities of food immediately after a meal until it can be accommodated in the lower portion of the gastrointestinal tract, (2) mixing of this food with gastric secretions until it forms a semifluid mixture called *chyme*, and (3) slow emptying of the food from the stomach into the small intestine at a rate suitable for proper digestion and absorption by the small intestine.

Figure 619 illustrates the basic anatomy of the stomach. Physiologically, the stomach can be divided into two major parts: (1) the *corpus*, or *body*, and (2) the *antrum*. The *fundus* of the stomach at the upper end of the body is considered by anatomists to be a separate entity from the body, but from a physiological point of view, this can be considered to be part of the body.

The Storage Function of the Stomach. As food enters the stomach, it forms concentric circles in the body of the stomach, the newest food lying closest to the cardia and the food that has been in the stomach the longest lying nearest the wall of the stomach. Normally the body of the stomach has relatively little tone in its muscular wall so

Chapter 62

Secretory Functions

of the Alimentary Tract

Throughout the gastrointestinal tract are secretory glands that subserve two primary functions: First, digestive enzymes are secreted in all areas from the mouth to the distal end of the ileum and to a very slight extent even in the colon. Second, mucous glands, present from the mouth all the way to the anus, provide mucus for lubrication and protection in all parts of the alimentary tract.

Most of the digestive secretions are formed only in response to the presence of food in the alimentary tract, and the quantity secreted in each segment of the tract is almost exactly the amount needed for proper digestion. Furthermore, in some portions of the gastrointestinal tract even the types of enzymes or other constituents of the secretions are varied in relation to the type of food present. The purpose of the present chapter, therefore, is to describe the different types of alimentary secretions, their functions, and regulation of their production.

GENERAL PRINCIPLES OF GASTRO-INTESTINAL SECRETION

Anatomical Types of Glands

To provide the different types of secretions in the gastrointestinal tract, there are several types of glands. First, on the surface of the epithelium in most parts of the gastrointestinal tract are literally billions of *single cell mucous glands* called *goblet cells.* These function entirely by themselves without the necessity of coordination with the other goblet cells of the intestinal tract, and they simply extrude their mucus directly into the lumen of the intestine.

The most abundant type of multicellular gland in the gastrointestinal tract is the *tubular gland,*

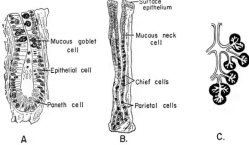

Figure 624. The anatomical types of gastrointestinal glands: (A) A simple tubular gland represented by a crypt of Lieberkühn, (B) a more elongated tubular gland represented by a gastric gland, and (C) a compound acinous gland represented by the pancreas.

two examples of which are illustrated in Figures 624 A and B. Figure 624 A shows a *crypt of Lieberkühn,* which is found throughout the small intestine and in modified form in the large intestine. These are simple pits which are lined with two major types of glandular cells—goblet cells to produce mucus and Paneth cells to produce intestinal enzymes. Figure 624 B illustrates a *gastric gland* in the main body of the stomach. This is a considerably deeper tubular gland, and it is occasionally branched.

Also associated with the gastrointestinal tract are several very complicated glands, the *salivary glands,* the *pancreas,* and the *liver,* which provide secretions for digestion or emulsification of food. The liver has a highly specialized structure that will be discussed in detail in Chapter 72. The salivary glands and the pancreas are compound acinous glands of the type illustrated in Figure 624 C. These glands lie completely outside the walls of the gastrointestinal tract, and in this differ from all the other gastrointestinal glands. The secreting stuctures, called *acini,* are lined with secreting glandular cells; these feed into a system of ducts that finally empty through one or

835

more portals into the intestinal tract itself. The cells of the acini may all be alike, as in the pancreas, or may be of several different types, as in the salivary glands.

Basic Mechanisms of Stimulation of the Gastrointestinal Glands

Effect of Local Stimuli. The mechanical presence of food in a particular segment of the gastrointestinal tract usually causes the glands of that region and often of adjacent regions to secrete moderate to large quantities of digestive juices. Part of this local effect results from direct stimulation of the surface glandular cells themselves by contact with the food. For instance, the goblet cells on the surface of the epithelium seem to be stimulated in this way. However, most of the local effects result from one of the following three methods of stimulation. *First,* tactile stimulation or chemical irritation of the mucosa can elicit reflexes that pass through the intramural nervous system of the intestinal wall to stimulate either the mucous cells on the surface or the deeper glands of the mucosa. *Second,* distention of the gut wall can also elicit nervous reflexes that stimulate secretion. *Third,* either tactile stimuli or distention can result in increased motility of the gut, as was described in the previous chapter, and the motility in turn can then increase the rate of secretion; indeed, this may be a very important mechanism of gastrointestinal secretion, for almost invariably the rate of secretion closely parallels the degree of motility.

Autonomic Stimulation of Secretion. Parasympathetic stimulation. Stimulation of the parasympathetic nerves to different parts of the alimentary tract almost invariably increases the rate of glandular secretion. This is especially true of the secretory glands in the upper portion of the tract, including the salivary glands, the esophageal glands, the gastric glands, the pancreas, and even Brunner's glands, the most proximal glands of the small intestines. Secretion in the remainder of the intestinal tract more frequently occurs in response to local stimuli. However, even the small intestinal glands and the mucous glands of the large intestine can be excited to some extent by parasympathetic impulses.

The parasympathetic stimulation that ex-

cites the alimentary glands can result either from reflexes originating in the alimentary tract itself or from impulses originating in higher centers of the central nervous system.

Sympathetic stimulation of glandular secretion. Stimulation of the sympathetic nerves in most parts of the gastrointestinal tract causes a slight increase in secretion by the respective glands. On the other hand, sympathetic stimulation also results in vasoconstriction of the blood vessels supplying the glands. Therefore, sympathetic stimulation can have a dual effect: First, if only sympathetic stimulation is occurring, there is usually a slight increase in secretion. But, second, if parasympathetic stimulation is causing copious secretion by the glands, superimposed sympathetic stimulation then often reduces the secretion because of reduced blood supply.

A few of the intestinal glands are specifically inhibited, rather than excited, by sympathetic stimulation. Especially important is the inhibition of Brunner's glands, for inhibition of these glands often leaves the initial portion of the duodenum unprotected against the acidic digestive juices from the stomach, thus allowing development of *peptic ulcer.*

Regulation of Glandular Secretion by Hormones. In the stomach and intestine several different *gastrointestinal hormones* help to regulate the volume and character of the secretions. These hormones are liberated from the gastrointestinal mucosa in response to the presence of particular foods in the lumen of the gut. They then are absorbed into the blood and are carried to the respective glands which they stimulate. This type of stimulation is particularly valuable in increasing the output of gastric juice and pancreatic juice when food enters the stomach or duodenum. Also, hormonal stimulation of the gallbladder wall causes it to empty its stored bile into the duodenum, as was discussed in the previous chapter. Still other hormones that are of doubtful value have been postulated to stimulate the secretion by the glands of the small intestine.

Chemically, the gastrointestinal hormones are either proteins or polypeptides, or derivatives of these.

Basic Mechanism of Secretion by Glandular Cells

The basic mechanism by which glandular cells form different secretions and then extrude these to the exterior is yet unknown, though the available experimental evidence points to the following basic mechanism, as illustrated in Figure 625. First, the nutrient material needed for formation of the secretion must diffuse or be actively transported from the capillary into the base of the glandular cell. Second, many *mitochondria* located inside the cell near its base provide oxidative energy for formation of adenosine triphosphate. Third, energy from the adenosine triphosphate (see Chapter 65), along with appropriate nutrients, are then used for synthesis of the organic substances, this synthesis occurring either by or in close association with the *endoplasmic reticulum*. The *ribosomes* adherent to this reticulum seem to be specifically responsible for formation of proteins that are to be secreted. Fourth, the secretory materials aggregate around the Golgi apparatus, which lies near the secretory ends of the cells in close association with the endoplasmic reticulum. Fifth, after the secretory materials have collected, they are then extruded through the secretory surface into the lumen of the gland.

Water and Electrolyte Secretion in Response to Nervous Stimulation. A second necessity for glandular secretion is to provide sufficient water and electrolytes to be secreted along with the organic substances. The following is one postulated method by which nervous stimulation can cause water and salts to pass through the glandular cells in great profusion, which washes the organic substances through the secretory border of the cells at the same time:

(1) Nerve stimulation has a specific effect on the *basal* portion of the cell membrane to cause active transport of chloride ions to the interior. (2) The resulting in-crease in electronegativity inside the cell then causes positive ions also to move to the interior of the cell. (3) The excess of both of these ions inside the cell creates an osmotic force which pulls water to the interior, thereby increasing the hydrostatic pressure inside the cells and causing the cell itself to swell. (4) The pressure in the cell then results in minute ruptures of the secretory border of the cell and causes flushing of water, electrolytes, and organic materials into the lumen of the gland. In support of this theory have been the following findings: First, the nerve endings on glandular cells are principally on the bases of the cells. Second, microelectrode studies show that the electrical potential across this membrane is usually anywhere between 35 and 80 millivolts, with negativity on the interior and positivity on the exterior. Nerve stimulation increases this polarization voltage to values some 10 to 20 millivolts greater than normal, parasympathetic stimulation normally having a considerably greater effect than sympathetic stimulation. This increase in polarization occurs a second or more after the nerve impulse has arrived, indicating that it is caused by movement of ions, principally negative ions, through the membrane.

Though this mechanism for secretion is still more supposition than fact, nevertheless, it does explain how it would be possible for nerve impulses to regulate secretion. Obviously, hormonal effects on the cellular membrane could cause similar results.

The Lubricating and Protective Properties of Mucus and Its Importance in the Gastrointestinal Tract

Mucus is a thick secretion composed of water, electrolytes, and a mucopolysaccharide. Mucus is slightly different in different parts of the gastrointestinal tract, but everywhere it has several very important characteristics which make it both an excellent lubricant and a protectant for the wall of the gut. First, mucus has adherent qualities so that on contact with food or other particles it immediately adheres to and spreads as a thin film over the surfaces. Second, it has sufficient *body* that it coats the wall of the gut and prevents actual contact of mucosa with the food particles. Third, mucus has a

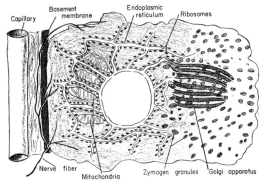

Figure 625. Basic mechanism of secretion by a glandular cell.

low internal resistance to shear or slippage so that the particles can slide along the epithelium with great ease. Fourth, mucus causes particles to adhere to each other to form the fecal masses that are expelled during a bowel movement. Fifth, mucus is strongly resistant to digestion by the gastrointestinal enzymes. And, sixth, the mucopolysaccharide of mucus has amphoteric properties (as is true of all proteins) and is therefore capable of neutralizing small amounts of either acids or alkalies.

With these different properties, then, it is evident that mucus has the ability to allow easy slippage of food along the gastrointestinal tract and also to prevent excoriative or chemical damage to the epithelium. One becomes acutely aware of the lubricating qualities of mucus when his salivary glands fail to secrete, for under these circumstances it is extremely difficult to swallow solid food even when it is taken with large amounts of water.

SECRETION OF SALIVA

The Salivary Glands; Characteristics of Saliva. The principal glands of salivation are the *parotid glands*, the *submaxillary glands*, and the *sublingual glands*, but in addition to these are many small *buccal glands*. The daily secretion of saliva normally ranges between 1,000 and 1500 milliliters, as shown in Table 22.

Saliva contains two different types of secretion: (1) a *serous secretion* containing *ptyalin*, which is an enzyme for digesting starches and (2) *mucous secretion* for lubricating purposes. The parotid glands secrete entirely the serous type, and the sub-

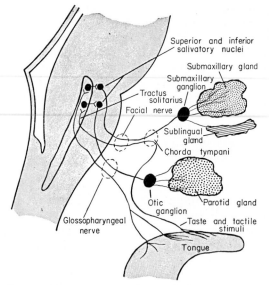

Figure 626. Nervous regulation of salivary secretion.

maxillary glands secrete mainly the serous type but also a large amount of mucus as well. The sublingual glands secrete mainly mucus, and the buccal glands secrete only mucus. Saliva has a pH between 6.0 and 7.0, a range which is very favorable for the digestive action of ptyalin.

Nervous Regulation of Salivary Secretion. Figure 626 illustrates the nervous pathways for regulation of salivation, showing that the submaxillary and sublingual glands are controlled principally by nerve impulses from the *superior salivatory nuclei* and the parotid gland by impulses from the *inferior salivatory* nuclei; these nuclei are located at approximately the juncture of the medulla and pons. The salivatory nuclei in turn are excited by both taste and tactile stimuli from the tongue and other areas of the mouth. Taste stimuli that are agreeable result in copious secretion of saliva, and certain types of tactile stimuli such as the presence of smooth objects in the mouth—a pebble for instance—will cause marked salivation while rough objects will cause less salivation or perhaps will actually inhibit salivation.

Salivation can also be stimulated or inhibited by impulses arriving in the salivatory nuclei from higher centers of the central nervous system. For instance, when a person eats food that he particularly likes, salivation is far greater than when he eats food that he detests. The *appetite area* of

Table 22. Daily Secretion of Intestinal Juices

	Daily volume (ml.)	pH
Saliva	1200	6.0–7.0
Gastric secretion	2000	1.0–3.5
Pancreatic secretion	1200	8.0–8.3
Bile	700	7.8
Succus entericus	3000	78.0–8.0
Brunner's gland secretion	50(?)	8.0–8.9
Large intestinal secretion	60	7.5–8.0
Total	8210	

charides. The enzyme for fat digestion, *pancreatic lipase,* is capable of hydrolyzing neutral fat into glycerol and fatty acids.

The proteolytic enzymes as synthesized in the pancreatic cells are in the forms *trypsinogen, chymotrypsinogen,* and *procarboxypolypeptidase,* which are all enzymatically inactive. These become activated only after they are secreted into the intestinal tract. Trypsinogen is activated by an enzyme called *enterokinase,* which is released from the intestinal mucosa whenever chyme comes in contact with the mucosa. Also, trypsinogen can be activated to a slight extent by trypsin that has already been formed. Chymotrypsinogen is activated by trypsin to form chymotrypsin, and procarboxypolypeptidase is presumably activated in some similar manner.

Regulation of Pancreatic Secretion

Pancreatic secretion, like gastric secretion, is regulated by both nervous and hormonal mechanisms, both of which play important roles as follows:

Nervous Regulation. When the cephalic phase of stomach secretion occurs, impulses are simultaneously transmitted along the vagus nerves to the pancreas, resulting in the secretion of large quantities of enzymes into the pancreatic acini. However, almost none of these flow through the pancreatic ducts to the intestine because very little water and electrolytes are secreted along with the enzymes. Therefore, the enzymes are temporarily stored in the acini.

After food enters the small intestine, distention of the intestine results in local reflexes that cause further nervous stimulation of secretion by the pancreas, but this is probably rather unimportant in comparison with the hormonal control of secretion, which is described below.

Hormonal Control of Pancreatic Secretion. *Secretin stimulation of pancreatic secretion—"hydrelatic" stimulation.* Two different hormones, *secretin* and *pancreozymin,* cause pancreatic secretion in response to food in the upper small intestine. Secretin is a small polypeptide hormone that is present in the mucosa of the upper small intestine in the form of *prosecretin.* When chyme enters the intestine, it causes the release and

activation of secretin, which is subsequently absorbed into the blood. The one constituent of chyme that causes greatest secretin release is hydrochloric acid, though almost any type of food will cause at least some release.

Secretin causes the pancreas to secrete large quantities of fluid containing a very high concentration of sodium bicarbonate but a very low concentration of sodium chloride. This copious flow of fluid is called *hydrelatic secretion* by the pancreas because the fluid is composed principally of a thin watery solution containing almost no enzymes.

The secretin mechanism seems to be especially important for two reasons: First, secretin is released in large quantities from the small intestinal mucosa any time the pH of the duodenal contents falls below approximately 4.0. This immediately causes large quantities of pancreatic juice containing abundant amounts of sodium bicarbonate to be secreted, which results in the following reaction in the duodenum:

$$HCl + NaHCO_3 \rightarrow NaCl + H_2CO_3$$

The carbonic acid immediately dissociates into CO_2 and H_2O, and the CO_2 is absorbed into the body fluids, thus leaving a neutral solution of sodium chloride in the duodenum. In this way, the acid contents emptied into the duodenum from the stomach become neutralized, and the peptic activity of the gastric juices is immediately blocked. Since the mucosa of the small intestine cannot withstand the intense digestive properties of gastric juice, this is a highly important protective mechanism against the development of duodenal ulcers, which will be discussed in further detail in Chapter 64.

A second importance of hydrelatic secretion by the pancreas is to provide an appropriate pH for action of the pancreatic enzymes. All of these function optimally in a slightly alkaline or neutral medium. The pH of pancreatic secretion averages 8.0.

Pancreozymin — "ecbolic" secretion by the pancreas. The presence of food in the upper small intestine also causes a second hormone, *pancreozymin,* to be released from the mucosa. This results especially from the presence of proteoses and peptones, which are products of partial protein digestion.

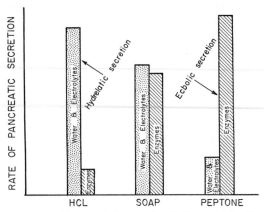

Figure 629. Hydrelatic and ecbolic secretion by the pancreas caused respectively by the presence of acids or peptone solutions in the duodenum.

Pancreozymin, like secretin, passes by way of the blood to the pancreas but, instead of causing hydrelatic secretion, causes secretion of large quantities of digestive enzymes, which is similar to the effect of vagal stimulation. This type of secretion is called *ecbolic secretion* in contradistinction to hydrelatic secretion, which was discussed above. The differences between the effects of secretin and pancreozymin are shown in Figure 629, which illustrates (a) intense hydrelatic secretion in response to acid in the duodenum, (b) a dual effect in response to soap, and (c) intense ecbolic secretion in response to peptones.

How important pancreozymin is in the regulation of pancreatic secretion is not yet known, for ecbolic secretion by the pancreas is also known to occur in response to vagal stimuli and local nervous reflexes, as explained above. Therefore, whether pancreozymin is truly an important intestinal hormone is yet to be determined.

Figure 630 summarizes the overall regu-

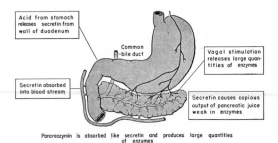

Figure 630. Regulation of pancreatic secretion.

lation of pancreatic secretion. The total amount secreted each day is about 1200 milliliters.

SECRETION OF BILE BY THE LIVER

The secretion of bile by the liver will be discussed in more detail in relation to the overall function of the liver in Chapter 72. Basically, bile contains no digestive enzyme and is important for digestion only because of the presence of bile acids which (1) help to emulsify fat globules so that they can be digested by the intestinal lipases and (2) help render the end-products of fat digestion soluble so that they can be absorbed through the gastrointestinal mucosa into the lymphatics.

Bile is secreted continually by the liver rather than intermittently as in the case of most other gastrointestinal secretions, but the bile is stored in the gallbladder until it is needed in the gut. The gallbladder then empties the bile into the intestine in response to *cholecystokinin*, a hormone extracted from the intestinal mucosa by fats in the intestine. Therefore, bile becomes available to aid in the processes of fat digestion. This mechanism of gallbladder emptying was discussed in the previous chapter.

The rate of bile secretion can be altered slightly in response to three different situations: (1) the greater the blood flow to the liver, the greater is the rate of secretion, (2) secretin has a very mild effect on liver secretion, effecting as much as 10 per cent increase in bile production at the same time that it also causes the hydrelatic response of the pancreas, and (3) the presence of large amounts of bile salts in the blood greatly increases the rate of liver secretion. Most of the bile salts secreted in the bile are reabsorbed by the intestines and then resecreted by the liver over and over again, performing their actions in relation to fat digestion and absorption many times before being lost in the feces. This continual recirculation of bile salts is important for maintaining even the normal daily flow of bile. When the salts are lost to the exterior through a bile fistula rather than being reabsorbed, the rate of bile secretion becomes reduced several fold.

The daily volume of bile production averages 600 to 700 milliliters.

SECRETIONS OF THE SMALL INTESTINE

Secretion of Mucus by Brunner's Glands and by Mucous Cells of the Intestinal Surface

An extensive array of compound mucous glands, called *Brunner's glands,* is located immediately inside the duodenum, mainly between the pylorus and the papilla of Vater, where the pancreatic juices and bile empty into the duodenum. These secrete large quantities of mucus in response to: (a) direct tactile stimuli or irritating stimuli of the overlying mucosa, (b) vagal stimulation, which causes secretion concurrently with the stomach secretion, and (c) intestinal hormones, the exact natures of which have not yet been determined. The function of Brunner's glands is principally to protect the duodenal wall from digestion by the gastric juice, and their rapid and intense response to irritating stimuli is especially geared to this purpose.

Brunner's glands are strongly inhibited by sympathetic stimulation; therefore, such stimulation is likely to leave the duodenal bulb almost totally unprotected and is perhaps one of the factors that cause this area of the gastrointestinal tract to be the site of peptic ulcers in about 50 per cent of the cases.

Mucus is also secreted in large quantities by goblet cells located extensively over the surface of the intestinal mucosa. This secretion results principally from direct tactile or chemical stimulation by the chyme. Additional mucus is also secreted by the goblet cells in the intestinal glands. This secretion is probably controlled mainly by local nervous reflexes.

Secretion of the Intestinal Digestive Juices—the Crypts of Lieberkühn

Located on the entire surface of the small intestine, with the exception of the Brunner's gland area, are small tubular glands called *crypts of Lieberkühn,* one of which is illustrated in Figure 624 A. At the bases of these glands are *Paneth cells,* which secrete the following digestive enzymes: (1) several different *peptidases* for splitting polypeptides into amino acids, (2) four enzymes for splitting disaccharides into monosac-charides—*sucrase, maltase, isomaltase,* and *lactase,* (3) *intestinal lipase* for splitting neutral fats into glycerol and fatty acids, and (4) a very small amount of *intestinal amylase* for splitting carbohydrates to disaccharides.

The secretion from the crypts of Lieberkühn is called *succus entericus,* whose function is to provide final digestion of the food before absorption—that is, to provide amino acids from proteins, monosaccharides from carbohydrates, and fatty acids and glycerol from neutral fats. The succus entericus is mildly alkaline, which aids in the digestive processes since most intestinal enzymes operate optimally in a slightly alkaline medium. The daily rate of succus entericus secretion averages about 3000 milliliters.

Regulation of Succus Entericus Secretion

Local Stimuli. By far the most important means for regulating succus entericus secretion is various local reflexes or direct stimuli, as illustrated in Figure 631. Especially important is distention of the small intestine, which causes copious secretion from the crypts of Lieberkühn. In addition, tactile or irritative stimuli can result in intense secretion. Therefore, for the most part, secretion in the small intestine occurs simply in response to the presence of chyme in the intestine—the greater the amount of chyme, the greater the secretion.

Stimulation by the Hormone "Enterocrinin." In addition to the local reflex effects on intestinal secretion, it has been claimed that food in the small intestine causes a hormone called *enterocrinin* to be

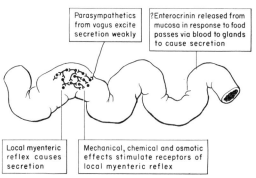

Figure 631. Regulation of secretion in the small intestine.

released from the intestinal mucosa and that this in turn stimulates secretion of succus entericus. However, the secretory effects of enterocrinin preparations have thus far been very weak and usually will not occur in any but denervated intestines. Therefore, it is doubtful that enterocrinin is of significant importance in the regulation of intestinal secretion.

Nervous Regulation. Parasympathetic stimulation can increase small intestinal secretion by two- to three-fold, but this is actually a small increase in comparison with the effects of local reflexes resulting from distention or irritation of the mucosa. Nevertheless, parasympathetic stimulation can aid in the overall process of regulating small intestinal secretion.

SECRETIONS OF THE LARGE INTESTINE

Mucus Secretion by the Large Intestine. The mucosa of the large intestine, like that of the small intestine, is lined with crypts of Lieberkühn, but these only rarely contain Paneth cells. Instead, they are lined almost entirely by goblet cells. Also, on the surface epithelium of the large intestine are very large numbers of goblet cells dispersed among the other epithelial cells.

Therefore, the only significant type of secretion in the large intestine is mucus, and its rate of secretion is regulated principally by direct, tactile stimulation of the surface goblet cells and perhaps local nervous reflexes to the goblet cells in the crypts of Lieberkühn. However, stimulation of the nervi erigentes, which carry the parasympathetic innervation to the distal half of the large intestine, also causes marked increase in the secretion of mucus. This occurs along with an increase in motility, which was discussed in the previous chapter. Therefore, during extreme parasympathetic stimulation, often caused by severe emotional disturbances, so much mucus may be secreted into the large intestine that the person has a bowel movement of ropy mucus as often as every 30 minutes; the mucus contains very little or no fecal material.

Mucus in the large intestine obviously protects the wall against excoriation, but, in addition to this, it provides the adherent qualities for holding fecal matter together.

Furthermore, it protects the intestinal wall from the great amount of bacterial activity that takes place inside the feces, and it also provides a barrier to keep acids formed deep in the feces from attacking the intestinal wall.

Secretion of Water and Electrolytes in Response to Irritation of the Large Intestine. Whenever a segment of the large intestine becomes intensely irritated, such as occurs when bacterial infection becomes rampant during *gastroenteritis*, the mucosa then secretes large quantities of water and electrolytes in addition to mucus. This acts to dilute the irritating factors and to cause rapid movement of the feces toward the anus. The usual result is *diarrhea* with loss of large quantities of water and electrolytes but also earlier recovery from the disease than would otherwise occur.

REFERENCES

Babkin, B. P.: Secretory Mechanism of the Digestive Glands. 2nd ed., New York, Paul B. Hoeber, 1950.

Bachrach, W. H.: Action of insulin hypoglycemia on motor and secretory functions of the digestive tract. *Physiol. Rev.*, 33:566, 1953.

Berger, E. Y., Kanzaki, G., and Steele, M.: Simultaneous flux of potassium into and out of the dog intestine. *Am. J. Physiol.*, 196:1270, 1959.

Bornstein. A. M., Dennis, W. H., and Rehm, W. S.: Movement of water, sodium, chloride and hydrogen ions across the resting stomach. *Am. J. Physiol.*, 197:332, 1959.

Code, C. F., and Watkinson, G.: Importance of vagal innervation in the regulatory effect of acid in the duodenum on gastric secretion of acid. *J. Physiol.*, 130:233, 1955.

Colcher, H., and Hollander, F.: Variability of potassium concentration in gastric secretion. *Am. J. Physiol.*, 197:1070, 1959.

Conly, S. S., Crider, J. O., and Thomas, J. E.: Relation of bicarbonate concentration of pancreatic juice to rate of secretion. *Am. J. Physiol.*, 182:97, 1955.

Conway, E. J.: Biochemistry of Gastric Acid Secretion. Springfield, Illinois, Charles C Thomas, 1952.

Davenport, H. W.: Ion requirements for gastric acid secretion. *Proc. Soc. Exp. Biol. and Med.*, 95:562, 1957.

Davenport, H. W.: Recent advances in the knowledge of the metabolism of the parietal cells. *J. Nat. Cancer Inst.*, 13:985, 1953.

Davenport, H. W.: Some reflections on gastric secretion. *Gastroenterology*, 33:15, 1957.

Davenport, H. W., and Chavre, V. J.: Acid secretion and oxygen consumption by mouse stomachs in vitro. *Am. J. Physiol.*, 174:203, 1953.

Davenport, H. W., Chavre, V. J., and Davenport, V. D.: Sulfhydryl groups and gastric acid secretion. *Am. J. Physiol., 184:1,* 1956.

Denton, R. W., Gershbein, L. L., and Ivy, A. C.: Response of human and canine gallbladder to cholecystokinin. *J. Appl. Physiol., 2:671,* 1950.

Forrest, A. P., and Code, C. F.: Effect of postganglionic sympathectomy on canine gastric secretion. *Am. J. Physiol., 177:425,* 1954.

Fritz, I. B.: A review of the effects of hormones on secretion of pepsin. *Am. J. Gastroenter., 26:458,* 1956.

Graham, A. R., and Stavraky, G. W.: The response of the chronically denervated submaxillary gland to acetylcholine and to adrenaline. *Rev. Canad. Biol., 13:120,* 1954.

Gregory, R. A.: The digestive system. *Ann. Rev. Physiol., 16:155,* 1954.

Grossman, M. I.: Gastrointestinal hormones. *Physiol. Rev., 30:33,* 1950.

Grossman, M. I.: The glands of Brunner. *Physiol. Rev., 38:675,* 1958.

Guth, P. H., Komarov, S. A., Shay, H., and Style, C. Z.: Relationship between protein, nitrogen, proteolytic and lipolytic enzymes in canine pancreatic juice obtained under various conditions of stimulation. *Am. J. Physiol., 187:207,* 1956.

Haslewood, G. A. D.: Recent developments in our knowledge of bile salts. *Physiol. Rev., 35:178,* 1955.

Heinz, E., and Obrink, K. J.: Acid formation and acidity control in the stomach. *Physiol. Rev., 34:* 643, 1954.

Hill, R. W., and Code, C. F.: Changes in concentration of histamine in canine gastric mucosa during secretion. *Am. J. Physiol., 197:5,* 1959.

Hirschowitz, B. I.: Pepsinogen: its origins, secretion and excretion. *Physiol. Rev., 37:475,* 1957.

Hirschowitz, B. I., O'Leary, D. K., and Marks, I. N.: Effects of atropine on synthesis and secretion of pepsinogen in the rat. *Am. J. Physiol., 198:108,* 1960.

Hollander, F.: Current views on the physiology of the gastric secretions. *Am. J. Med., 13:453,* 1952.

Hollander, F.: The two-component mucous barrier; its activity in protecting the gastroduodenal mucosa against peptic ulceration. *Arch. Int. Med., 93:107,* 1954.

Hollander, F., and Colcher, H.: Evidence for the independence of K- and HCl-efflux into gastric secretion. *Am. J. Physiol., 198:729,* 1960.

Ivy, A. C., Lin, T. M., Ivy, E. K., and Karvinen, E.: Effect of histaminase inhibitors on gastric secretion. *Am. J. Physiol., 186:239,* 1956.

Janowitz, H. D., and Hollander, F.: Gastric carbonic anhydrase revived. *Gastroenterology, 30:536,* 1956.

Jenkins, G. N.: The Physiology of the Mouth. Oxford, Blackwell Scientific Publications, 1954.

Jones, F. A.: Modern Trends in Gastroenterology. New York, Paul B. Hoeber, 1952.

Lin, T. M., and Ivy, A. C.: Relation of secretin to the parasympathetic mechanism for pancreatic secretion. *Am. J. Physiol., 189:361,* 1957.

Lundberg, A.: Electrophysiology of salivary glands. *Physiol. Rev., 38:21,* 1958.

Lundberg, A.: Secretory potentials in the sublingual gland of the cat. *Acta Physiol. Scand., 40:21,* 1957.

Lundberg, A.: Secretory potentials in the sublingual and submaxillary glands of the cat. *J. Physiol., 124:* 25P, 1954.

Lundberg, A.: The mechanism of establishment of secretory potentials in sublingual gland cells. *Acta Physiol. Scand., 40:35,* 1957.

Mellinkoff, S.: Digestive system. *Ann. Rev. Physiol., 19:175,* 1957.

Pevsner, L., and Grossman, M. I.: The mechanism of vagal stimulation of gastric acid secretion. *Gastroenterology, 28:493,* 1955.

Schayer, R. W., and Ivy, A. C.: Evidence that histamine is a gastric secretory hormone in the rat. *Am. J. Physiol., 189:369,* 1957.

Tecrell, T.: The acid-base balance of the secreting isolated gastric mucosa. *J. Physiol., 114:267,* 1951.

Thomas, J. E.: The External Secretion of the Pancreas. Springfield, Illinois, Charles C Thomas, 1950.

Thull, N. B., and Rehm, W. S.: Composition and osmolarity of gastric juice as a function of plasma osmolarity. *Am. J. Physiol., 185:317,* 1956.

Villarreal, R., Ganong, W. F., and Gray, S. J.: Effect of adrenocorticotrophic hormone upon the gastric secretion of hydrochloric acid, pepsin, and electrolytes in the dog. *Am. J. Physiol., 183:485,* 1955.

Wakim, K. G.: Physiology of the liver. *Am. J. Med., 16:256,* 1954.

Wolf, A. V.: Thirst. Springfield, Illinois, Charles C Thomas, 1958.

Chapter 63

Digestion and Absorption in the Gastrointestinal Tract

The foods on which the body lives, with the exception of small quantities of vitamins and minerals, can be classified as carbohydrates, fats, and proteins. However, these cannot be absorbed in their natural form through the gastrointestinal mucosa and, for this reason, are useless as nutrients without the preliminary process of digestion. Therefore, the present chapter will discuss, first, the processes by which carbohydrates, fats, and proteins are digested into small enough compounds for absorption and, second, the mechanisms by which the digestive end-products as well as water, electrolytes, and other substances are absorbed.

DIGESTION OF THE VARIOUS FOODS

Hydrolysis as the Basic Process of Digestion. Almost all the carbohydrates are large *polysaccharides*, which are combinations of many *monosaccharides* bound to each other by the process of *condensation*. This means that a hydrogen ion is removed from one of the monosaccharides while a hydroxyl ion is removed from the other; the two monosaccharides then combine with each other at these sites of removal while the hydrogen and hydroxyl ions combine to form water. When the carbohydrates are digested back into monosaccharides, specific enzymes return the hydrogen and hydroxyl ions to the polysaccharides and thereby separate the monosaccharides from each other; this process, called *hydrolysis*, is the following:

$$R_1 - R_2 + H_2O \longrightarrow R_1 OH + R_2 H$$

Almost the entire fat portion of the diet consists of triglycerides (neutral fats), which are combinations of three *fatty acid* molecules condensed with a single *glycerol* molecule. In the process of condensation, three molecules of water

had been removed. Digestion of the triglycerides consists of the reverse process, the fat-digesting enzymes returning the three molecules of water to each molecule of neutral fat and thereby splitting the fatty acid molecules away from the glycerol. Here again, the process is one of hydrolysis.

Finally, proteins are formed from *amino acids* that are bound together by means of *peptide linkages*. In this linkage a hydroxyl ion is removed from one amino acid, while a hydrogen ion is removed from the succeeding one; thus, the amino acids also combine together by a process of condensation while losing a molecule of water. Digestion of proteins, therefore, also involves a process of hydrolysis, the proteolytic enzymes returning the water to the protein molecules to split them into their constituent amino acids.

Therefore, the chemistry of digestion is really quite simple, for in the case of all the three major types of food, the same basic process of *hydrolysis* is involved. The only difference lies in the enzymes required to promote the reactions for each type of food.

All the digestive enzymes are proteins. Their secretion by the different gastrointestinal glands was discussed in the previous chapter.

Digestion of Carbohydrates

The Carbohydrate Foods of the Diet. Only three major sources of carbohydrates exist in the normal human diet. These are sucrose, which is cane sugar, lactose, which is a disaccharide in milk, and, starches, which are present in almost all foods and particularly in the grains. Other types of carbohydrates ingested to a slight extent are glycogen, alcohol, lactic acid, pyruvic acid, pectins, dextrins, and minor quantities of other carbohydrate derivatives in meats. The diet also contains a large amount of cellulose, which is a carbohydrate. However, no enzymes capable of hydrolyzing cellulose are secreted by the human digestive tract. Consequently, cellulose cannot be considered to be a food.

Because starches make up the largest proportion of the carbohydrate intake of the human being, the digestive system is especially geared for their digestion. However, other polysaccharides, such as the pectins, glycogen, the dextrins, etc., are digested in essentially the same manner as the starches.

Digestion of Carbohydrates in the Mouth.

When food is chewed, it is mixed with the saliva, which contains the enzyme ptyalin (a-amylase) secreted mainly by the parotid glands. This enzyme hydrolyzes starch into the disaccharide *maltose*, as shown in Figure 632, but the food remains in the mouth only a very short period of time, and probably not more than 3 to 5 per cent of all the starches that are eaten will have become hydrolyzed into maltose by the time the food is swallowed. One can demonstrate the digestive action of ptyalin in the mouth by chewing a piece of bread for several minutes; after this period of time, the bread tastes very sweet because of the maltose that has been liberated from the starches of the bread.

Most starches in their natural state, unfortunately, are formed into small globules, each of which has a thin protective covering. Therefore, most naturally occurring starches will not be digested by ptyalin unless the food is cooked to destroy the protective membrane.

Digestion of Carbohydrates in the Stomach.

Even though food does not remain in the mouth long enough for ptyalin to complete the breakdown of starches into maltose, the action of this enzyme continues long after the food has entered the stomach. Then, as the contents of the fundus are gradually mixed with the stomach secretions, the activity of salivary amylase is blocked by the acid of the gastric secretions, for it is essentially non-active as an enzyme once the pH of the medium falls below approximately 4.0. Nevertheless, on the average, before the food becomes completely mixed with the gastric secretions, as much as 30 to 40 per cent of the starches will have been changed into maltose.

Hydrolysis of starches and disaccharides by the acid of the stomach.

The acid of the stomach juices can, to a slight extent, hydrolyze starches and disaccharides. However, quantitatively this reaction occurs to such a slight extent that it is usually ignored as an unimportant effect.

Digestion of Carbohydrates in the Small Intestine. *Digestion by pancreatic and intestinal amylase.*

Pancreatic secretion, like saliva, contains a large quantity of a-amylase which is capable of splitting starches into *maltose* and *isomaltose*. Also, a small quantity of amylase is secreted in the intestinal juices. Therefore, immediately after the chyme empties from the stomach into the duodenum and mixes with pancreatic juice, the starches that have not already been split are digested by amylase. In general, all the starches are almost totally converted into maltose and isomaltose before they have passed beyond the upper portion of the small intestine. Indeed, pancreatic amylase seems to be a more powerful enzyme than salivary amylase, for pancreatic amylase can actually digest much of the uncooked starch, which is not true of salivary amylase.

Hydrolysis of Disaccharides into Monosaccharides by the Intestinal Enzymes.

The glands of the small intestine secrete the four enzymes *lactase, sucrase, maltase,* and *isomaltase,* which are capable of splitting lactose, sucrose, maltose, and isomaltose, respectively, into their constituent monosaccharides. Lactose splits into a molecule of *galactose* and a molecule of *glucose.* Sucrose splits into a molecule of *fructose* and a molecule of *glucose.* Maltose and isomaltose split into *two molecules of glucose.* Thus, the final products of carbohydrate digestion are monosaccharides.

In the ordinary diet, which contains far more starches than either sucrose or lactose, glucose represents about 80 per cent of the final products

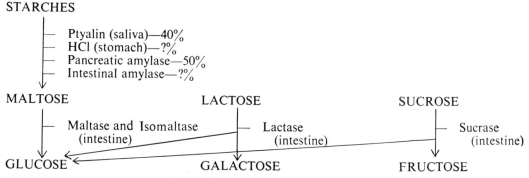

STARCHES
- Ptyalin (saliva)—40%
- HCl (stomach)—?%
- Pancreatic amylase—50%
- Intestinal amylase—?%

MALTOSE   LACTOSE   SUCROSE
- Maltase and Isomaltase (intestine)
- Lactase (intestine)
- Sucrase (intestine)

GLUCOSE   GALACTOSE   FRUCTOSE

Figure 632. Digestion of carbohydrates.

of carbohydrate digestion, and galactose and fructose each represent, on the average, about 10 per cent of the products of carbohydrate digestion.

Digestion of Fats

The Fats of the Diet. By far the most common fats of the diet are the neutral fats, also known as triglycerides, each molecule of which is composed of a glycerol nucleus and three fatty acids, as illustrated in Figure 633. Neutral fat is found in food of both animal origin and plant origin. Many other hydrocarbon compounds, particularly those of the paraffin series, have *physical* characteristics that are very similar to those of the neutral fats. However, the paraffin oils are totally nondigestible.

In the usual diet are also small quantities of phospholipids, cholesterol, and cholesterol esters. The phospholipids and cholesterol esters contain fatty acids and, therefore, can be considered to be fats themselves. Cholesterol, on the other hand, is a sterol compound containing no fatty acid, but it does exhibit some of the physical and chemical characteristics of fats; it is derived from fats, and it is metabolized similarly to fats. Therefore, cholesterol is considered from a dietary point of view to be a fat.

Digestion of Fats in the Intestine. A very small amount of fat is digested in the stomach by gastric lipase and hydrochloric acid. However, the amount of digestion is so slight that it is unimportant. Instead, essentially all fat digestion occurs in the small intestine as follows:

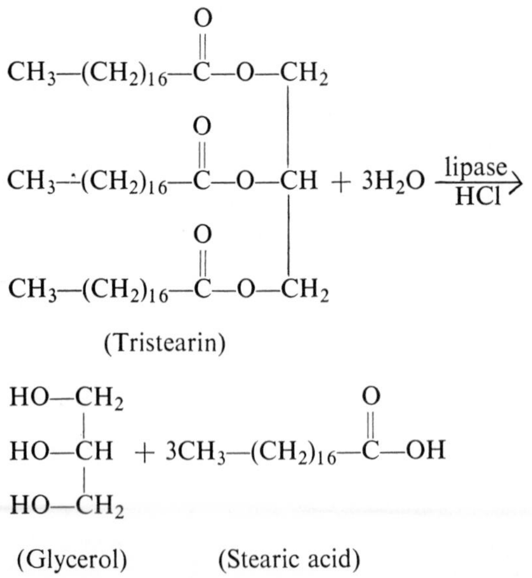

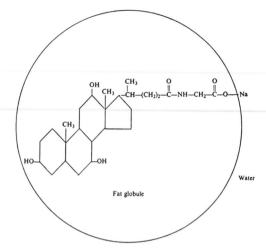

Figure 634. The detergent action of bile salts.

Emulsification of fat by bile acids. Bile, which is secreted by the liver, does not contain any digestive enzymes. However, it does contain a large quantity of bile salts mainly in the form of ionized sodium salts which are extremely important for the digestion of fat. The carboxyl part of the bile salt is highly soluble in water, whereas the sterol portion of the bile salt, as shown in Figure 634, is highly soluble in fat. Therefore, it is believed that bile salts aggregate at the surfaces of the fat globules in the intestinal contents. The carboxyl portion of the bile salt presumably projects outward and is soluble in the surrounding fluids, while the sterol portion is dissolved in the fat itself; this effect greatly decreases the interfacial tension of the fat.

When the interfacial tension of a globule of non-miscible fluid is very low, this non-miscible fluid on agitation can be broken up into many minute particles far more easily than it can when the interfacial tension is great. Consequently, the function of the bile salts is to make the fat globules readily fragmentable by agitation in the small bowel. This action is the same as that of many detergents that are used very widely in most new household cleansers for removing grease.

The fatty acids and monoglycerides which are formed by fat digestion, as discussed below, are also important emulsifying agents in the intestines.

Each time the diameters of the fat globules are decreased by a factor of 2 as a result of agitation in the small intestine, the number of globules is increased 8 times, and the surface area of each globule is decreased 4 times. However, because 8 times as many globules then exist, the total surface area of all of the fat in the intestinal contents increases 2 times. In other

$$CH_3-(CH_2)_{16}-\overset{\overset{O}{\|}}{C}-O-CH_2$$
$$CH_3-(CH_2)_{16}-\overset{\overset{O}{\|}}{C}-O-CH + 3H_2O \xrightarrow{\text{lipase}} {\text{HCl}}$$
$$CH_3-(CH_2)_{16}-\overset{\overset{O}{\|}}{C}-O-CH_2$$

(Tristearin)

$$\begin{array}{l} HO-CH_2 \\ HO-CH \\ HO-CH_2 \end{array} + 3CH_3-(CH_2)_{16}-\overset{\overset{O}{\|}}{C}-OH$$

(Glycerol)   (Stearic acid)

Figure 633. Hydrolysis of neutral fat catalyzed by lipase.

$$\text{Fat} \qquad \underline{(\text{Gastric lipase} + \text{HCl})}\begin{cases}\text{Fat}\\\text{Fatty acids}\\\text{Glycerol}\end{cases}$$

$$\text{Fat} \qquad \underline{(\text{Bile} + \text{Agitation})} \quad \text{Emulsified fat}$$

$$\text{Emulsified fat} \quad \underline{\begin{matrix}(\text{Pancreatic lipase})\\(\text{Enteric lipase})\end{matrix}}\begin{cases}\text{Fatty acids}\\\text{Glycerol}\end{cases}50\% \ (?)\\\text{Glycerides } 50\% \ (?)$$

Figure 635. Digestion of fats.

words, the total surface area of the fat particles in the intestinal contents is inversely proportional to the diameter of the particles.

The lipases are water-soluble compounds and can attack the fat globules only on their surfaces. Consequently, it can be readily understood how important bile salts are for the digestion of fats.

Bile salt circulation. The bile salts are formed by the parenchymal cells of the liver from cholesterol and are then secreted in the bile. After entering the intestine and adsorbing to the globules of fat, they are mostly reabsorbed by the small intestine. Indeed, as they are reabsorbed they exert a "hydrotropic" action on the end-products of fat metabolism, helping to transport these products through the intestinal membrane. Once reabsorbed, they pass again by way of the blood to the liver, where they are resecreted in the bile along with new bile salts which are being formed by the liver. Thus a so-called "bile salt circulation" occurs, as will be discussed in detail in Chapter 72.

When fat digestion is very poor, it can sometimes be benefited by oral administration of bile salts. These enter into the bile salt circulation, increasing the total quantity of bile salts available for performing the detergent and hydrotropic actions on fats.

Digestion of Fats by Pancreatic Lipase and Enteric Lipase. Probably by far the most important enzyme for the digestion of fats is *pancreatic lipase* in the pancreatic juice. However, the glands of the small intestine also secrete a small quantity of lipase known as *enteric lipase*. Both these act simultaneously and alike in the small intestine for hydrolysis of fat; probably as much as 99 per cent of all the digestion of fats in the gastrointestinal tract occurs in the small intestine.

End-Products of Fat Digestion. Some research workers believe that almost all the fat of the diet is finally broken into fatty acids and glycerol, while others believe that large portions are digested only to the mono- and diglyceride stages, as shown in Figure 635. Therefore, it can be seen that the precise process of fat digestion has not been clearly elucidated. Nevertheless,

from a practical point of view, the farther the process of fat hydrolysis proceeds in the intestinal tract, the better is the absorption of the fats. Furthermore, diseases that prevent secretion of pancreatic lipase invariably lead to poor digestion of fats and consequently to poor absorption of fats. In these instances, the stools contain most of the fat that ordinarily would have been absorbed.

Digestion of Proteins

The Proteins of the Diet. The dietary proteins are derived almost entirely from meats and vegetables. These proteins in turn are formed by long chains of amino acids bound together by *peptide linkages*. A typical peptide linkage is the following:

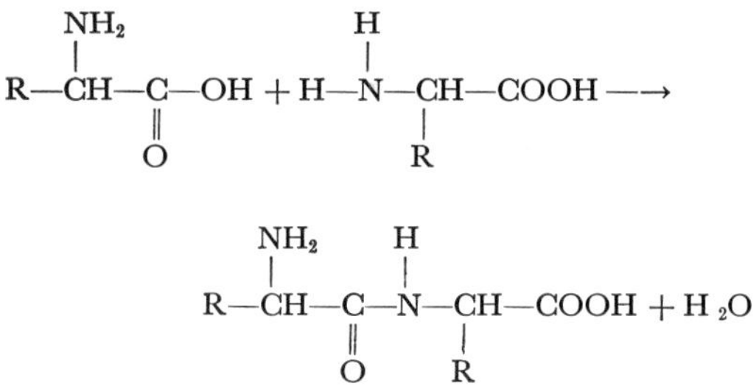

$$R-CH-\underset{\underset{O}{\|}}{C}-OH + H-\underset{\underset{R}{|}}{N}-CH-COOH \longrightarrow$$

with NH_2 on the first carbon and H on the nitrogen

$$R-CH-\underset{\underset{O}{\|}}{C}-\underset{}{N}-CH-COOH + H_2O$$

with NH_2 and H and R groups

The characteristics of each type of protein are determined by the types of amino acids in the protein molecule and by the arrangement of these amino acids. The physical and chemical characteristics of the different proteins will be discussed in Chapter 67.

Digestion of Proteins in the Stomach. Pepsin. Pepsin is most active at a pH of about 2 and is completely inactive at a pH above approximately 5. Consequently, for pepsin to cause any digestive action on protein, the stomach juices must be acidic. It will be recalled from Chapter 62 that the gastric glands secrete a large quantity of hydrochloric acid. This hydrochloric acid is secreted at a pH of less than 1.0, but, by the time it is mixed with the stomach contents,

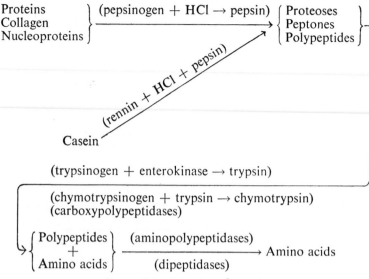

Figure 636. Digestion of proteins.

the pH ranges around 2 to 3, a highly favorable range of acidity for pepsin activity.

Pepsin is capable of digesting essentially all the different types of proteins in the diet. One of the very important features of pepsin digestion is its ability to digest collagen, an albuminoid that is affected very little by other digestive enzymes. Collagen is a major constituent of the intercellular connective tissue of meats, and for the digestive enzymes of the digestive tract to penetrate meats and digest the cellular proteins it is first necessary that the collagen fibers be digested. Consequently, in persons lacking in peptic activity in the stomach the ingested meats are poorly penetrated by the digestive enzymes and, therefore, are poorly digested.

As illustrated in Figure 636, pepsin usually does not complete the process of protein digestion all the way to amino acids but simply splits the proteins into proteoses, peptones, and large polypeptides. This splitting of proteins is a process of "hydrolysis" occurring at the peptide linkages between the amino acids. Hydrolysis is the reverse of "condensation," which was noted above as the means by which amino acids combine. One molecule of water enters the reaction each time two amino acids are split apart, a hydrogen atom from the molecule of water combining with the amino radical of the peptide linkage and the hydroxyl ion re-forming the carboxyl radical.

Hydrochloric acid. Hydrochloric acid without the presence of pepsin can cause hydrolysis of proteins, but this occurs to a major extent only when the pH of the acid is extremely low. Consequently, the amount of protein hydrolysis occurring in the stomach due to the hydrochloric acid alone is probably very slight.

Rennin. Another enzyme secreted by the stomach for protein digestion is *rennin*. This enzyme coagulates the protein casein into a curd, and it is believed that the solid consistency of the curd allows the casein of milk to remain in the stomach long enough for peptic digestion to start. Also, rennin possibly helps to digest casein.

Rennin is found in the gastric juice of babies in large quantities, but it is present only to a very slight extent if at all in the gastric juice of adults. Also, casein seems to be digested by babies much more easily than it is by adults, presumably because of rennin activity in the baby's stomach.

Digestion of Proteins by Pancreatic Secretions. Trypsin. When the proteins leave the stomach, they ordinarily are in the form of proteoses, peptones, and large polypeptides. Immediately upon entering the small intestine, these partial breakdown products of protein are attacked by the pancreatic enzyme *trypsin*. As illustrated in Figure 636, trypsin is capable of hydrolyzing all the partial breakdown products of protein and may actually hydrolyze some of them to the final stage of simple amino acids, but most of the products of trypsin digestion are dipeptides or other rather small polypeptides.

Chymotrypsin and carboxypolypeptidases. Pancreatic secretions also contain *chymotrypsin* and a *carboxypolypeptidase*. Chymotrypsin acts very much like trypsin except that it catalyzes hydrolysis of different types of peptide linkages, that is, linkages involving different amino acids. The carboxypolypeptidase of the pancreatic juice is capable of hydrolyzing some polypeptides to amino acids.

Digestion of Proteins by the Secretions of the Small Intestine. The small intestine secretes several different enzymes for hydrolyzing the final peptide linkages of the different dipeptides and other small polypeptides. Because some of these linkages are slightly different from each other in their quantity of bond energy and other factors, the linkages between specific types of amino acids require separate enzymes for hydrolysis. The enzymes responsible for final hydrolysis of the peptides into amino acids are *amino polypeptidase* and the *dipeptidases*.

When food has been properly masticated and is not eaten in too large a quantity at any one time, probably 95 per cent of all the proteins finally become amino acids. A few molecules of protein are never digested at all, and some of the proteins remain in the stages of proteoses, peptones, and varying sizes of polypeptides.

BASIC PRINCIPLES OF GASTROINTESTINAL ABSORPTION

Anatomical Basis of Absorption

Absorption occurs very readily through the intestinal mucosa of both the small and large intestine; yet, more than nine tenths of all absorption occurs in the small intestine because the chyme is exposed to this organ before passing on into the large intestine.

The total quantity of fluid that must be absorbed each day is equal to the ingested fluid (about 1.5 liters) plus that secreted in the various gastrointestinal secretions (about 8.5 liters). This comes to a total of approximately 10 liters. About 9.5 liters of this are

absorbed in the small intestine, leaving only 0.5 liter to pass through the ileocecal valve each day.

Almost no food, water, or electrolytes are absorbed through the stomach mucosa. However, a few highly lipid soluble substances such as alcohol and some drugs can be absorbed in moderate quantities. From a practical point of view, the stomach can be considered to be a very poor absorptive area of the gastrointestinal tract.

The Absorptive Surface of the Intestinal Mucosa—the Villi. Figure 637 illustrates the absorptive surface of the intestinal mucosa, showing many folds called *valvulae conniventes*, which greatly increase the surface area of the absorptive mucosa. These folds extend circularly all the way around the intestine and are especially well developed in the duodenum and jejunum, where they often protrude as much as 8 millimeters into the lumen of the gut.

Located over almost the entire surface of the small intestine from approximately the point at which the common bile duct empties into the duodenum down to the ileocecal valve are literally millions of small *villi*, which project about 1 millimeter from the surface of the mucosa. These villi lie so close to each other in the upper small intestine that they actually touch in most areas, but their distribution is less profuse in the distal small intestine. Figure 638 illustrates the general organization of a villus, emphasizing especially the advan-

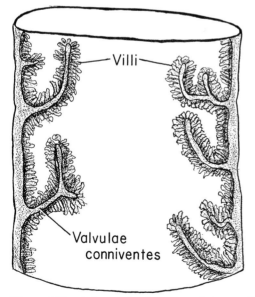

Figure 637. A longitudinal section of the small intestine, showing the valvulae conniventes covered by villi.

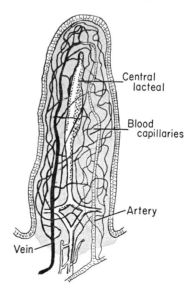

Figure 638. Functional organization of the blood vessels and lymphatics in a villus.

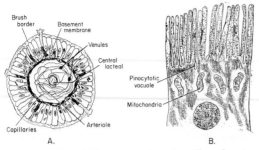

Figure 639. (A) cross-section of a villus, showing the absorptive membrane composed of the epithelial cells and basement membrane; (B) a single epithelial cell, showing the brush border through which most absorption is believed to take place.

tageous arrangement of the vascular system for absorption of fluid and dissolved material into the portal blood and of the *central lacteal* for absorption into the lymphatics.

Figure 639 shows in (A) the cross-section of a villus and in (B) the brush border of a single absorptive epithelial cell. The epithelial cells covering the villus lie on a basement membrane, which is one of the barriers through which absorbed material must pass. This basement membrane is perhaps also responsible for some of the osmotic characteristics of absorption, which will be discussed later.

The *brush border* of the intestinal epithelial cells, illustrated in Figure 639B, is formed by many infoldings of the surface membrane, which greatly increase the surface area exposed to the intestinal materials. Figure 639B also shows many small *pinocytotic* vacuoles, which are pinched off portions of infolded epithelium surrounding extracellular materials that have been entrapped inside the cells. It is possible that some substances are absorbed by this physical process of *pinocytosis*, though, as will be noted later in the chapter, probably most absorption occurs by means of single molecular transfer. Located near the brush border of the epithelial cell are many *mitochondria*, which supply the cell with oxidative energy needed for "active transport" of materials through the intestinal epithelium; this also will be discussed later in the chapter.

Basic Mechanisms of Absorption

Absorption through the gastrointestinal mucosa occurs by *active transport* and by diffusion, as is also true in the renal tubules, as discussed in Chapter 8. The physical principles of these processes can be explained as follows:

Active Transport. Active transport means movement of a substance through a membrane against a concentration gradient or an electrical gradient. That is, if the substance is more concentrated in the interstitial fluids than in the gut, moving the substance out of the gut will require energy merely to concentrate the substance. Secondly, movement of electrically charged substances against an electrical gradient is another example of active transport. For instance, if sodium ions are present in the interstitial fluids in exactly the same concentration as sodium ions in the intestinal lumen, but an electrical potential exists across the intestinal membrane with negativity in the lumen and positivity on the outside, then transfer of sodium against this electrical gradient would be an example of active transport, and a definite quantity of energy would be required to make the transport occur at all.

In short, active transport imparts energy to the substance as it is being transported, either for the purpose of concentrating it on the other side of the membrane or for the purpose of moving it against an electrical potential.

Active transport is believed to occur in the following way: First, the substance to be transported supposedly combines with a *carrier* at the outer surface of the membrane. This combination then diffuses into the cell and to the opposite side of the cell where the substance is enzymatically released from the carrier. Then the carrier returns to the first surface of the cell to pick up still more substance for transfer. When the substance combines initially with the carrier or when it is released from the carrier, energy must be expended to make the chemical reaction occur against the electrochemical gradient. Unfortunately, the precise mechanism of even a single carrier system for active transport has not yet been worked out.

Diffusion of Substances through the Gastrointestinal Membrane. The term *diffusion* means simply transport of substances through the membrane as a result of molecular movement along a diffusion gradient; the principles of diffusion were discussed in Chapter 3.

Water and certain electrolytes diffuse extremely rapidly through the mucosa of the upper small intestine. Therefore, it is believed by many physiologists that large amounts of water and salts diffuse *between* the epithelial cells rather than through the cells. In this case it would probably be the basement membrane that represents the diffusing membrane rather than the cellular membranes. However, this is still in the realm of speculation because studies have not yet demonstrated the actual mode of diffusion through the gastrointestinal mucosa.

In some instances *facilitated diffusion* occurs. This means that an active chemical process makes the substance move through the membrane more rapidly than would be the case otherwise. Though this probably involves a carrier system, it is different from active transport in that it is incapable of moving substances against an electrochemical gradient. On the other hand, it is similar to active transport in that it involves specific selectivity of the material to be passed through the membrane.

Diffusion can also be aided or impeded by electrical potentials across the membrane. For instance, in the colon, sodium is actively transported out of the lumen of the gut, thus creating an electrical potential across the membrane, negative inside and positive in the interstitial fluids. This electrical gradient then enhances the diffusion of chloride and other negative ions from the gut to the interstitial fluids. There is reason to believe that a large proportion of the electrolytes, particularly the negatively charged ions, are absorbed in this way.

ABSORPTION IN THE SMALL INTESTINE

Absorption of Nutrients

Absorption of Carbohydrates. Essentially all the carbohydrates are absorbed in the form of monosaccharides, only a very small fraction of a per cent being absorbed as disaccharides and almost none as larger carbohydrate compounds. Furthermore, almost all carbohydrate absorption results from active transport rather than from diffusion, for the pores of the small intestine are essentially impermeable to water soluble solutes with molecular weights greater than 100.

That the transport of monosaccharides is an active process is demonstrated by several very important experimental observations:

First, their transport can be blocked by metabolic inhibitors such as iodoacetic acid, cyanides, and phlorhizin.

Second, the transport is selective, specifically transporting certain monosaccharides without transporting others. One transport mechanism transports glucose and galactose while another transports fructose and xylose.

Third, there is a maximum rate of transport for each type of monosaccharide. The most rapidly transported monosaccharide is galactose; then comes glucose and finally fructose.

Fourth, there is competition between certain sugars for the carrier system. For instance, if large amounts of galactose are being transported, the amount of glucose that can be transported simultaneously is considerably reduced.

These are identically the same characteristics demonstrated for active transport through the tubular membranes in the kidneys. Therefore, it is reasonable to believe that carbohydrate transport through the tubular epithelium and through the gastrointestinal mucosa involve essentially the same processes.

Maximal rate of glucose absorption. The upper limit for glucose absorption from the gastrointestinal tract in man is approximately 1 gram per kilogram of body weight per hour. This is caused by a limited quantity of enzymes and carrier chemicals in the mucosal cells; when these are already being used to their maximal ability, additional transport of glucose cannot occur. In round figures, *the average 70 kilogram man can absorb a maximum of approximately 70 grams of glucose from the gastrointestinal tract per hour.*

Absorption of Proteins. Essentially all proteins are absorbed in the form of amino acids though small quantities—not in metabolically significant amounts, however—of dipeptides are also absorbed, and extremely minute quantities of whole proteins can be absorbed at times, perhaps by the process of pinocytosis described above, though not by the usual absorptive mechanisms.

The absorption of amino acids also obeys the general principles listed above for active absorption of glucose; that is, certain types of amino acids are absorbed selectively and certain ones of them interfere with each other in the absorptive processes, illustrating that common carrier systems exist. Several different carrier systems are available for transport of different amino acids, and at least certain ones of the amino acids have maximum rates of absorption, the limits being determined by the quantities of enzymes and carriers available. Finally, metabolic poisons block the absorption of amino acids in exactly the same way that they block the absorption of glucose.

Absorption of amino acids through the intestinal mucosa can occur far more rapidly than can protein digestion in the lumen of the intestine. As a result, the normal rate of absorption is determined not by the rate at which they can be absorbed but by the rate at which they can be released from the proteins during digestion. For these reasons, essentially no free amino acids can be found in the intestine during digestion—that is, they are absorbed as rapidly as they are formed.

Absorption of Fats. Fats are believed to be absorbed through the intestinal membrane principally in the form of fatty acids, glycerol, and monoglycerides. Thus far, no active transport process has been proved for the absorption of fatty acids or glycerides. Presumably, these dissolve in the lipid membranes of the epithelial cells, then diffuse to the interior of these cells, and finally diffuse into the interstitial spaces. After passage through the epithelial cells, the fatty acids recombine with glycerol or with mono- or diglycerides to form new molecules of triglycerides. These then conglomerate to form small globules of fat in the interstitial fluid immediately underlying the gastrointestinal mucosa. The glycerol used for synthesis of the new triglycerides is often the same glycerol that had been released from the digested fats, but, if this is not available, the epithelial cells can synthesize new glycerol. Furthermore, the triglycerides formed after absorption often have new combinations of fatty acids in the fat molecule.

The fatty globules that form in the interstitial fluid on the undersides of the epithelial cells pass immediately into the central lacteals of the villi or into other lymphatic channels and are then transported in the form of *chylomicrons* upward through the thoracic duct to empty into the venous system.

Hydrotropic action of bile salts. Even more important than the detergent action of bile salts, which was discussed earlier in the chapter, is their effect on fat absorption, for, in the absence of bile salts, extremely large quantities of fatty acids fail to be absorbed but instead pass on to the distal portions of the intestines where they combine with calcium and other cations to form soaps that are finally lost in the feces. Therefore, it is known that bile salts are very important in the absorption of fatty acids. The fatty acids are believed to combine with the bile salts to form a water soluble compound that can then diffuse through the watery portions of the epithelial cells. After passing through the epithelium, however, the bile salts split away from the fatty acids and pass immediately into the portal blood and thence to the liver for reexcretion while the fat is transported upward through the lymphatics.

Complete digestion of fats can still occur without the emulsifying action of bile salts, though not quite so rapidly as usually, but absorption of fatty acids is very significantly reduced without the hydrotropic action of these salts.

Absorption of Water and Electrolytes in the Small Intestine

Absorption of the Electrolytes. The rate of absorption of electrolytes is greater in the upper small intestine than in the distal portions, which is undoubtedly due partially to greater surface area in the upper regions caused by the valvulae conniventes and the very profuse quantity of villi. But this greater rate of absorption results also from a greater degree of membrane permeability to the ions in the upper intestine than in the lower intestine.

The monovalent electrolytes—sodium, potassium, chloride, nitrate, and bicarbonate—are very easily absorbed through the intestinal membrane while most of the polyvalent electrolytes, such as calcium, magnesium, and sulfate, are very poorly absorbed.

Even though the divalent ions are not

readily absorbed through the gastrointestinal mucosa, these also are usually not required to nearly so great an extent by the body as the monovalent ions. Calcium is the only divalent ion that needs to be absorbed in large quantities, but even this needs to be absorbed in quantities less than a gram a day except under extreme conditions. Though the rate of calcium absorption is usually sufficient to supply the bodily needs, in certain diseases, such as intestinal sprue, absorption does become severely deficient.

Active absorption of sodium, chloride, and other ions in the small intestine. Sodium can be actively absorbed by the mucosa of the small intestine, and it is believed that at least some chloride can also be actively absorbed. However, even if chloride is not actively absorbed, transport of sodium across the epithelial membrane will immediately create large enough electrical potentials to pull chloride ions through the membrane simultaneously.

Far more studies have been performed on the active absorption of electrolytes from the renal tubules than from the small intestine. If we can judge from the results of renal experiments, it is probable that (in addition to sodium and chloride) potassium, calcium, magnesium, phosphate, and bicarbonate can also be actively absorbed in varying amounts through the gastrointestinal mucosa.

Absorption of Water. The exact mode of water absorption from the small intestine is not known, principally because so much water is continually secreted into the intestine along with the gastrointestinal secretions that it is difficult to determine how much is being absorbed at the same time. Some research workers have suggested that large quantities of water are actively absorbed, but most believe that water is absorbed principally by simple diffusion—that is, by osmosis.

Those who believe that water is absorbed principally as a result of osmosis base these conclusions on the following facts: (1) When a hyper- or hypotonic solution is placed in the small intestine, it very soon becomes isotonic, indicating very rapid diffusion across the membrane to establish osmotic equilibrium between the body fluids and the intestinal fluids. (2) When glucose or electrolytes are actively absorbed through the membrane, thereby reducing the os-

molarity of the intestinal fluids and increasing the osmolarity on the opposite side of the membrane, water "follows" through the membrane to maintain isotonicity between the two fluids. This again indicates osmotic absorption of water.

The two major arguments in support of the active transport theory are: (1) large quantities of glucose are consumed when water is transported through the membrane, thus indicating a need for energy to cause the movement of water, and (2) the rate of water transport through the membrane has seemed to some investigators to be considerably greater than could be explained on the basis of osmotic diffusion alone.

For the present, therefore, the available information indicates that there could possibly be an active process for water transport, but mathematical calculations indicate that such transport would require tremendous amounts of energy, probably much more than the intestinal mucosa could reasonably produce. On the other hand, the simple principles of diffusion could quite adequately explain the absorption of water—that is, as the electrolytes and nutrients are absorbed, thus causing the intestinal fluids to become hypotonic, water then is immediately absorbed by osmosis.

ABSORPTION IN THE LARGE INTESTINE; FORMATION OF THE FECES

Approximately 500 ml. of chyme pass through the ileocecal valve into the large intestine each day, and most of the water and electrolytes in this are absorbed in the colon, leaving approximately 100 ml. of fluid to be excreted in the feces.

Essentially all the absorption in the large intestine occurs in the proximal half of the colon, giving this portion the name *absorbing colon*, while the distal colon functions principally for storage and is therefore called the *storage colon*.

Active absorption of sodium, chloride, and water. The mucosa of the large intestine is capable of actively absorbing sodium. Loss of sodium from the lumen of the gut creates a strong electrical potential across the membrane, which results in the movement of chloride and other negative ions also out of the colon into the interstitial fluids.

Because of this mechanism, very little sodium chloride is lost in the feces. The absorption of sodium and chloride then causes osmotic absorption of water as explained above so that little water also is lost in the feces. Left behind as the most abundant salt in the feces is generally a moderate amount of almost insoluble calcium phosphate. Also, the stools tend to have a high bicarbonate concentration because bicarbonate ion, on account of its large size, is absorbed through the membrane very poorly; this is in contrast to chloride, which is absorbed with ease. The unabsorbed bicarbonate results in alkalinity of the outer surfaces of the fecal boluses, while deep in the feces bacterial activity usually creates acidity.

Bacterial action in the colon. Numerous bacteria, especially colon bacilli, are present in the absorbing colon. These are capable of digesting small amounts of cellulose, in this way providing a few calories of nutrition to the body each day. In herbivorous animals this source of energy is sometimes very significant even though it is of negligible importance in the human being. Other substances formed as a result of bacterial activity are vitamin K, vitamin B_{12}, thiamin, riboflavin, and various gases that form much, if not most, of the *flatus* that occurs in the colon. The vitamin K is especially important, for the amount of this vitamin in the ingested foods is normally insufficient to maintain adequate blood coagulation.

Composition of the feces. The feces normally are about three fourths water, and the remaining one fourth is solid matter composed of about 30 per cent dead bacteria, 10 to 20 per cent fat, 10 to 20 per cent inorganic matter, 2 to 3 per cent protein, and about 30 per cent of either undigested roughage of the food or dried constituents of digestive juices such as bile pigment and cellular debris. The large amount of fat is derived either from unabsorbed fatty acids from the diet or from fat formed by the bacteria.

The brown color of feces is caused by *stercobilin* and *urobilin,* which are derivatives of bilirubin. The odor is caused principally by the products of bacterial action; these vary from one person to another, depending on each person's colonic bacterial flora and on the type of food he has eaten. The actual odoriferous products include *indole, skatole, mercaptans, and hydrogen sulfide.*

REFERENCES

Adlersberg, D., and Schein, J.: Clinical and pathological studies in sprue. *J.A.M.A.,* 134:1459, 1947.

Adolph, E. F., and Northrop, J. P.: Absorption of water and chloride. *Am. J. Physiol.,* 168:311, 1952.

Althausen, T. L., Uyeyama, K., and Simpson, G. R.: Digestion and absorption after massive resection of the small intestine. *Gastroenterology,* 12:795, 1949.

Berger, E. Y., Kanzaki, G., Homer, M. A., and Steele, J. M.: Simultaneous flux of sodium into and out of the dog intestine. *Am. J. Physiol.,* 196:74, 1959.

Berger, E. Y., Kanzaki, G., and Steele, J. M.: The effect of deoxycorticosterone on the unidirectional transfers of sodium and potassium into and out of the dog intestine. *J. Physiol.,* 151:352, 1960.

Blickenstaff, D. D., Bachman, D. M., Steinberg, M. E., and Youmans, W. B.: Intestinal absorption of sodium chloride solutions as influenced by intraluminal pressure and concentration. *Am. J. Physiol.,* 168:303, 1952.

Brown, R., and Danielli, J. R. (eds.): Active Transport and Secretion. Society for Experimental Biology, Symposium No. 8, New York, Academic Press, 1954.

Cizek, L. J.: Total water content of laboratory animals with special reference to volume of fluid within the lumen of the gastrointestinal tract. *Am. J. Physiol.,* 179:104, 1954.

Code, C. F., Scholar, J. F., Hightower, N. C., Jr., Dietzler, F. K., and Baldes, E. J.: Absorption of water from the upper part of the human gastrointestinal tract. *Proc. Mayo Clin.,* 29:235, 1954.

Csaky, T. Z., and Thale, M.: Effect of ionic environment on intestinal sugar transport. *J. Physiol.,* 151: 59, 1960.

Grim, E., Lee, J. S., and Visscher, M. B.: Water exchange between intestinal contents, tissues and blood. *Am. J. Physiol.,* 182:359, 1955.

Higgins, J. A., Code, C. F., and Orvis, A. L.: The influence of motility on the rate of absorption of sodium and water from the small intestine of healthy persons. *Gastroenterology,* 31:708, 1956.

Hogben, C. A.: The alimentary tract. *Ann. Rev. Physiol.,* 22:381, 1960.

James, A. H.: The Physiology of Gastric Digestion. Baltimore, Williams & Wilkins Co., 1957.

Jervis, E. L., and Smyth, D. H.: The active transfer of D-methionine by the rat intestine *in vitro. J. Physiol.,* 151:51, 1960.

Knoebel, L. K., and Nasset, E. S.: The digestion and absorption of fat in dog and man. *J. Nutrit.,* 61: 405, 1957.

Lee, P. R., Code, C. F., and Scholer, J. F.: The influence of varying concentrations of sodium chloride on the rate of absorption of water from the stomach and small bowel of human beings. *Gastroenterology,* 29:1008, 1955.

Murphy, Q. R. (ed.): Metabolic Aspects of Transport Across Cell Membranes. Madison, University of Wisconsin Press, 1957.

Newey, H., and Smyth, D. H.: The intestinal absorption of some dipeptides. *J. Physiol. 145:*48, 1959.

Newey, H., Parsons, B. J., and Smyth, D. H.: The site of action of phlorrhizin in inhibiting intestinal absorption of glucose. *J. Physiol., 148:*83, 1959.

Obrink, K. J.: Digestion. *Ann. Rev. Physiol., 20:*377, 1958.

Pogrund, R. S., and Steggerda, F. R.: Influence of gaseous transfer between colon and blood stream on percentage gas compositions of intestinal flatus in man. *Am. J. Physiol., 153:*475, 1948.

Reitmeier, R. J., Code, C. F., and Orvis, A. L.: Barrier offered by gastric mucosa of healthy persons to absorption of sodium. *J. Appl. Physiol., 10:*261, 1957.

Reitemeier, R. J., Code, C. F., and Orvis, A. L.: Comparison of rate of absorption of labeled sodium and water from upper small intestine of healthy human beings. *J. Appl. Physiol., 10:*256, 1957.

Steggerda, F. R.: The digestive system. *Ann. Rev. Physiol., 17:*129, 1955.

Thomas, J. E.: The External Secretion of the Pancreas. Springfield, Illinois, Charles C Thomas, 1950.

Turner, D. A.: Intestinal absorption. Oxford, Blackwell Scientific Publications, 1959.

Uvnas, B.: Digestion. *Ann. Rev. Physiol., 18:*145, 1956.

Visscher, M. B.: Electrolyte and water movement across the intestinal wall. *Ann. N. Y. Acad. Sc., 57:*291, 1953.

Visscher, M. B., Fetcher, E. S., Jr., Carr, C. W., Gregor, H. P., Bushey, M. S., and Barker, D. E.: Isotopic tracer studies on the movement of water and ions between intestinal lumen and blood. *Am. J. Physiol., 142:*550, 1944.

Visscher, M. B., and Roepke, R. R.: Influence of induced changes in blood plasma osmotic activity on intestinal absorption. *Proc. Soc. Exp. Biol. & Med., 60:*1, 1945.

Wilson, T. H., and Landau, B. R.: Specificity of sugar transport by the intestine of the hamster. *Am. J. Physiol., 198:*99, 1960.

Chapter 64

Physiology of Gastrointestinal Disorders

The logical treatment of most gastrointestinal disorders depends on a basic knowledge of gastrointestinal physiology. The purpose of this chapter, therefore, is to point out the types of malfunction that can occur and their physiologic consequences.

DISORDERS OF SWALLOWING AND OF THE ESOPHAGUS

Paralysis of the Swallowing Mechanism. Damage to the fifth, seventh, ninth, or tenth nerves can cause paralysis of significant portions of the swallowing mechanism. Also, a few diseases, most commonly poliomyelitis, damage the swallowing center in the brain stem. Finally, malfunction of the swallowing muscles, as occurs in *muscle dystrophy* or in failure of neuromuscular transmission in *myasthenia gravis* or *botulism,* can also prevent normal swallowing.

When the swallowing mechanism is partially or totally paralyzed, the abnormalities that can occur include: (1) complete abrogation of the swallowing act so that swallowing cannot occur at all, (2) failure of the glottis to close so that food passes into the trachea as well as into the esophagus, (3) failure of the soft palate and uvula to close the posterior nares so that food refluxes into the nose during swallowing, or (4) failure of the cricoesophageal sphincter to remain closed during normal breathing, thus allowing large quantities of air to be sucked into the esophagus.

One of the most serious instances of paralysis of the swallowing mechanism occurs when a person is under deep anesthesia. Often he vomits large quantities of materials from the stomach into the pharynx; then instead of swallowing the materials again he simply sucks them into his trachea because the anesthetic has blocked the reflex mechanism of swallowing. As a result, such patients often choke to death on their own vomitus.

Achalasia (Cardiospasm). Achalasia is a condition in which the lower few centimeters of the esophagus, which constitute the "cardia" of the stomach, fail to relax during the swallowing mechanism. As a result, food transmission from the esophagus into the stomach is impeded or sometimes completely blocked. Pathological studies have shown the cause of this condition to be either a damaged or absent myenteric plexus in the lower portion of the esophagus. The musculature of the lower end of the esophagus is still capable of contracting, and it even exhibits incoordinate movements but has lost the ability to conduct a peristaltic wave and has lost the ability to cause "receptive relaxation" of the cardia as food approaches this area during the swallowing process. Because the cardia fails to relax, this condition is often called *cardiospasm,* even though the cardia is not actually in spastic contraction.

Mega-esophagus. Mega-esophagus means a greatly enlarged esophagus, and it ordinarily results from achalasia. Food is dammed up behind the aperistaltic portion of the esophagus, the middle and upper esophagus dilating progressively until it sometimes becomes as wide as 3 to 4 inches in diameter. In very severe cases of achalasia, food sometimes stays in the esophagus as long as 24 hours before passing into the stomach. Though, normally, very little bacterial action takes place in the esophagus, this prolonged storage of food allows extreme putrefaction of the food and often also allows bacterial penetration of the esophageal mucosa, which results in ulceration of the esophageal wall.

DISORDERS OF THE STOMACH

Gastritis. Gastritis means inflammation of the gastric mucosa. This can result from (a) the action of irritant foods on the gastric mucosa, (b) excessive excoriation of the stomach mucosa by the stomach's own peptic secretions, or (c) occasionally, bacterial inflammation. One of the most frequent causes of gastritis is irritation of the mucosa by alcohol.

The inflamed mucosa in gastritis is often very

painful, causing a diffuse burning pain referred to the lower anterior chest approximately over the heart, which gives it the name *heartburn*. Reflexes initiated in the stomach mucosa cause the salivary glands to salivate intensely, and the frequent swallowing of foamy saliva that results makes air accumulate in the stomach. The person then usually belches the air, a burning sensation occurring in his throat with each belch.

Gastric Atrophy. In about one third of all persons who have gastritis, the mucosa gradually becomes atrophic until very little or no gastric gland activity remains. Loss of the stomach secretions then leads to *anacidity* and, occasionally, to *pernicious anemia*, which may be described as follows:

Anacidity. Anacidity simply means that the stomach fails to secrete hydrochloric acid. Almost invariably when acid is not secreted, pepsin also is not secreted, and, even if it were, the lack of acid would prevent it from functioning because pepsin requires an acid medium for activity. Obviously, then, essentially all digestive function in the stomach is lost when anacidity is present.

The method usually used to determine the degree of anacidity in a patient is to inject 0.5 milligram of histamine and then to aspirate the stomach secretions through a tube for the following hour. Each 10-minute sample of stomach secretion is titrated against sodium hydroxide. The maximum rate of acid secretion during any single 10-minute interval in the normal person rises to almost exactly 1 milliequivalent of hydrochloric acid per minute, and the total hydrochloric acid secreted during the entire hour after the injection averages about 18 milliequivalents. All degrees of hypoacidity occur in different patients, some secreting as much as 5 milliequivalents of hydrochloric acid in an hour, some 2 milliequivalents, and still others absolutely no acid whatsoever.

The acid secretions by the stomach are frequently divided into *free acid* and *combined* acid. The amount of free acid is determined by titrating the gastric secretions to a pH of 3.5, using *dimethylaminoazobenzene* as an indicator. After this titration has been performed, the same secretions are titrated to a pH of 8.5, using *phenolphthalein* as an indicator; this measures the combined acid. Gastric secretions mixed with food in the stomach usually show very little or no free acid but a large amount of combined acid. On the other hand, when the stomach secretes large quantities of gastric juice while it is almost empty of food, the larger portion of the acid may then be free acid while only a small amount is combined acid.

Though anacidity is associated with depressed or even no digestive capability by the stomach, the overall digestion of food in the entire gastrointestinal tract is still almost normal. The reason for this is that trypsin and other enzymes secreted by the pancreas are quite capable of digesting most of the protein in the diet—particularly if the food is well chewed so that no portion of the protein is protected by collagen fibers.

Pernicious anemia in gastric atrophy. Pernicious anemia, which was discussed in Chapter 12, is a very common accompaniment of gastric atrophy. The normal gastric secretions— probably the mucus portion—contain a substance called *intrinsic factor* which must be present in the stomach secretions for adequate absorption of vitamin B_{12} from the small intestine. The exact manner in which intrinsic factor combines with or acts on vitamin B_{12} to make it absorbable is not yet known, but in its absence an adequate amount of vitamin B_{12} is not made available from the foods. As a result, maturation failure occurs in the bone marrow, resulting in pernicious anemia.

Pernicious anemia also occurs frequently when most of the stomach has been removed for treatment of either stomach ulcer or gastric cancer.

Peptic Ulcer

A peptic ulcer is an excoriated area of the mucosa caused by the digestive action of gastric juice. Figure 640 illustrates the points in the gastrointestinal tract at which peptic ulcers frequently occur, showing that by far the most frequent site of peptic ulcers is in the pyloric region of either the stomach or the duodenum. In addition, peptic ulcers also frequently occur anywhere along the lesser curvature of the stomach or, more rarely, in the lower end of the esophagus where stomach juices frequently reflux. A peptic ulcer called a *marginal ulcer* also frequently occurs wherever an abnormal opening such as a gastrojejunostomy is made between the stomach and some portion of the small intestine.

Basic Cause of Peptic Ulceration. The usual cause of peptic ulceration is too much

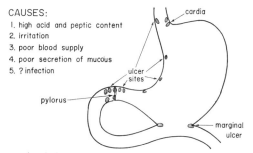

CAUSES:
1. high acid and peptic content
2. irritation
3. poor blood supply
4. poor secretion of mucous
5. ? infection

Figure 640. Peptic ulcer.

secretion of gastric juice in relation to the degree of protection afforded the mucosa by the mucus that is also secreted. It will be recalled that all of the areas normally exposed to gastric juice are well supplied with mucous glands, beginning with the compound mucous glands of the lower esophagus, then including the mucous cell coating of the stomach mucosa, the mucous neck cells of the gastric glands, the deep pyloric glands that secrete nothing but mucus, and, finally, the coiled tubular glands of Brunner of the upper duodenum, which secrete a highly alkaline mucus.

In addition to the mucus protection of the mucosa, the duodenum is also protected by the alkalinity of almost all the small intestinal secretions. Especially important are the pancreatic secretions, which contain large quantities of sodium bicarbonate that react with the hydrochloric acid of the gastric juice to form sodium chloride and carbonic acid. Almost all the carbonic acid immediately dissociates into water and carbon dioxide, and the carbon dioxide is then absorbed into the blood. In this way, the chyme becomes neutral or almost neutral immediately after passing through the pylorus, thus inactivating the pepsin to prevent digestion of the mucosa. Two additional mechanisms insure that this neutralization of gastric juices is complete: (1) When excess acid enters the duodenum, it reflexly inhibits antral peristalsis in the stomach, thereby decreasing the rate of gastric emptying. This allows an increased interval of time for pancreatic secretion to enter the duodenum to neutralize the acid already present. After neutralization has taken place, the reflex subsides and more stomach contents are emptied. (2) The presence of acid in the small intestine liberates secretin from the intestinal mucosa, which then passes by way of the blood to the pancreas to promote rapid secretion of pancreatic juice. Secretin also stimulates the pancreas to secrete a juice containing a high concentration of sodium bicarbonate, thus making more sodium bicarbonate available for neutralization of the acid. These mechanisms were discussed in detail in Chapters 61 and 62 in relation to gastrointestinal motility and gastrointestinal secretion.

Experimental Peptic Ulcer. Experimental peptic ulcers have been created in dogs and other animals in the following ways: (a) *Feeding ground glass* to an animal causes excoriation of the pyloric wall and allows the peptic juices to begin digesting the deeper layers of the mucosa, thus resulting in ulcers. (b) *Transplantation of the pancreatic duct to the ileum* removes the normal neutralizing effect of pancreatic secretion in the duodenum and, therefore, allows the gastric juice to attack the mucosa of the upper duodenum, this, too, resulting in peptic ulceration. (c) *Repeated injection of histamine,* which causes excessive secretion of gastric juice, results in peptic ulcers. (d) *Continual infusion of hydrochloric acid* through a tube into the stomach causes direct irritation of the stomach mucosa and also prevents full neutralization of the gastric juices by the pancreatic and other secretions of the small intestine. Therefore, peptic activity is enhanced, thus resulting in ulcers either in the stomach or duodenum. (e) A peptic ulcer will also develop any time a portion of the *small intestine is anastomosed* directly with the stomach so that gastric juice can pass directly and rapidly into the small intestine. The mucosa of the small intestine, except at the uppermost part of the duodenum, is not sufficiently resistant to gastric juice to prevent peptic digestion. (f) *Obstructing the blood flow* or even reducing the blood flow to an area of the stomach or upper duodenum will cause ulcers to develop because of inability of the local area to produce appropriate protective secretions.

In summary, any factor that increases the rate of production of gastric juice or that blocks the normal protective mechanisms against this juice can result in peptic ulcers. The same general principles apply to the development of peptic ulcers in the human being.

The Cause of Peptic Ulcer in the Human Being. Peptic ulcer occurs much more frequently in the white collar worker than in the laborer, and it seems particularly prone to occur in persons subjected to extreme anxiety over long periods of time. For instance, the number of persons who developed peptic ulcer greatly increased during the air raids of London. Therefore, it is believed that most instances of peptic ulcer in the human being result from excessive stimulation of the dorsal motor nu-

of the voluntary aid to defecation—that is, loss of the increased abdominal pressure, the lifting of the pelvic floor, and the stretching of the anal ring by the pelvic muscles—often makes defecation a very difficult process in a person with spinal cord injuries. Yet, defecation reflexes can still occur, and a small enema given to potentiate the action of these reflexes, usually in the morning shortly after a meal, can usually cause adequate defecation. It is in this way that persons with spinal cord injuries usually control their bowel movements each day.

GENERAL DISORDERS OF THE GASTROINTESTINAL TRACT

Vomiting

Vomiting is the means by which the upper gastrointestinal tract rids itself of its contents when the gut becomes (a) excessively irritated, (b) overly distended, or (c) even overly excitable. The stimuli that cause vomiting can occur in any part of the gastrointestinal tract, though distention or irritation of the upper small intestine—the duodenum especially—provides the strongest stimulus. Impulses are transmitted, as illustrated in Figure 641, by both vagal and sympathetic afferents to the *vomiting center* of the medulla, which lies near the tractus solitarius at approximately the level of the dorsal motor nucleus of the vagus. Appropriate motor reactions are then instituted to cause the vomiting act, and the motor impulses that cause the actual vomiting are transmitted from the vomiting center through the fifth, seventh, ninth, tenth, and twelfth cranial nerves as well as the spinal nerves to the diaphragm and abdominal muscles.

The Vomiting Act. Once the vomiting center has been sufficiently stimulated and the vomiting act instituted, the first effects are (1) a deep breath, (2) then raising of the hyoid bone and the larynx to pull the cricoesophageal sphincter open, (3) closing of the glottis, and (4) lifting of the soft palate to close the posterior nares. Next comes a strong downward contraction of the diaphragm along with simultaneous contraction of all the abdominal muscles. This obviously squeezes the stomach between the two sets of muscles, building the intragastric pressure up to a very high level. At the same time the pyloric region of the stomach becomes tonically constricted, thereby preventing expulsion of the gastric contents downward through the gastrointestinal tract. Finally, the cardia of the stomach relaxes, allowing easy expulsion of the gastric contents upward through the esophagus.

Thus, the vomiting act results from a squeezing action of the muscles on the stomach associated with opening of the esophageal sphincters so that the gastric contents can be expelled.

The Chemoreceptor Trigger Zone of the Medulla for Initiation of Vomiting by Drugs or by Motion Sickness. Aside from the vomiting initiated by irritative stimuli in the gastrointestinal tract itself, vomiting can also be caused by impulses arising in areas of the brain outside the vomiting center. This is particularly true of a small area located bilaterally above the area postrema called the *chemoreceptor trigger zone*. Electrical stimulation of this area can initiate vomiting, but, more importantly, administration of certain drugs, including apomorphine,

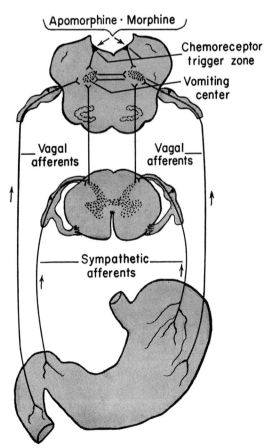

Figure 641. The afferent connections of the vomiting center.

morphine, and some of the digitalis derivatives, can directly stimulate the chemoreceptor trigger zone and initiate vomiting. Destruction of this area blocks this type of vomiting but does not block vomiting resulting from irritative stimuli in the gastrointestinal tract itself.

Also, it is well known that rapidly changing motions of the body will cause certain people to vomit. The mechanism for this is the following: The motion stimulates the receptors of the labyrinth, most frequently the macula of the utricle, and impulses are transmitted either directly or by way of the vestibular nuclei into the cerebellum. After passing through the uvula and nodule of the cerebellum, the signals are believed to be transmitted to the chemoreceptor trigger zone and thence to the vomiting center to cause vomiting.

Cortical Excitation of Vomiting. Various cortical stimuli, including disgusting scenes, noisome odors, and certain psychological factors, can also cause vomiting. Stimulation of certain areas of the hypothalamus can also cause vomiting. The precise neuronal connections for these effects are not known, though it is probable that the impulses pass directly to the vomiting center and do not involve the chemoreceptive trigger zone.

Nausea

Everyone has experienced the sensation of nausea and knows that it is often a prodrome of vomiting. Nausea is the conscious recognition of subconscious excitation in the vomiting center, and it can be caused by irritative impulses coming from the gastrointestinal tract, impulses originating in the brain associated with motion sickness, or impulses from the cortex to initiate vomiting. However, vomiting occasionally occurs without the prodromal sensation of nausea, indicating that only certain portions of the vomiting mechanism are associated with the sensation of nausea.

Another effect associated with activity in the vomiting center and with nausea is intense salivation. Presumably the saliva helps to neutralize any irritative process in the upper gastrointestinal tract should the vomiting act fail to ensue.

Gastrointestinal Obstruction

The gastrointestinal tract can become obstructed at almost any point along its course as illustrated in Figure 642; some common

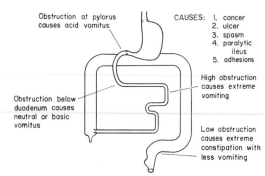

Figure 642. Obstruction in different parts of the gastrointestinal tract.

causes of obstruction are: *cancer, fibrotic constriction resulting from ulceration or from peritoneal adhesions, spasm of a segment of the gut,* or *paralysis of a segment of the gut.*

The abnormal consequences of obstruction depend on the point in the gastrointestinal tract that becomes obstructed. If the obstruction occurs at the pylorus, which results often from fibrotic constriction following peptic ulceration, persistent vomiting of stomach contents occurs. This obviously prevents nutrition, and it also causes excessive loss of hydrogen ions from the body and can result in various degrees of alkalosis.

If the obstruction is beyond the stomach, reverse peristalsis in the small intestine causes the intestinal juices to flow backward into the stomach, and these are vomited along with the stomach secretions. In this instance the person loses large amounts of water and electrolytes so that he becomes severely dehydrated, but the loss of acids and bases may be approximately equal so that little change in acid-base balance occurs. If the obstruction is near the lower end of the small intestine, then it is actually possible to vomit more basic than acid substances; in this case acidosis may result.

Also important in small intestinal obstruction is marked distention of the intestine proximal to the obstructed point. Very large quantities of fluid and electrolytes continue to be secreted into the lumen of the small intestine and even large amounts of proteins are lost from the blood stream, partly into the intestinal lumen and partly into the gut wall, which becomes edematous as a result of the excessive distention. The plasma volume diminishes because of the protein loss, and severe circulatory shock often ensues. One might immediately ask: Why does the small intestine not absorb these fluids and electrolytes? The answer seems to be that distention of the gut greatly stimulates the secretory activity of the gut but does not increase the rate of absorption. Normally this would act to flush the chyme further down the small intestine and therefore relieve the distention. But, if obstruction is present, obviously this normal mechanism backfires and simply causes a vicious cycle of more and more distention.

If the obstruction is near the distal end of the large intestine, feces can accumulate in the colon for several weeks. The patient develops an intense feeling of constipation, but in the first stages of the obstruction vomiting is not severe. After the large intestine has become completely filled and it finally becomes impossible for additional chyme to move from the small intestine into the large intestine, vomiting then begins very severely. Reverse peristalsis can sometimes occur all the way from the ileocecal valve to the stomach, and the character of the vomitus becomes fecal. Prolonged obstruction of the large intestine can finally cause rupture of the intestine itself or dehydration and circulatory shock resulting from the severe vomiting.

Gases in the Gastrointestinal Tract (Flatus)

Gases can enter the gastrointestinal tract from three different sources: (1) swallowed air, (2) gases formed as a result of bacterial action, and (3) gases that diffuse from the blood into the gastrointestinal tract.

Most of the gases in the stomach are nitrogen and oxygen derived from swallowed air, and a large proportion of these are expelled by belching.

Only small amounts of gas are usually present in the small intestine, and these are composed principally of air that passes from the stomach into the intestinal tract. In its transport through the small intestine, only 5 to 15 per cent of the air is absorbed, and a considerable amount of carbon dioxide actually diffuses from the blood into the air to bring it into equilibrium with the carbon dioxide of the tissues fluids.

In the large intestine, the greater proportion of the gases is derived from bacterial action; these gases include especially *carbon dioxide, methane,* and *hydrogen.* When the methane and hydrogen become suitably mixed with oxygen from swallowed air, an actual explosive mixture is occasionally formed. Except for nitrogen, essentially all the gases in the large intestine are highly diffusible through the intestinal mucosa. Therefore, if the gases remain in the large intestine for many hours the final mixture contains approximately 75 per cent or more of nitrogen and very little of the other gases. However, if the gases are passed on through the colon very rapidly, then the composition of the expelled flatus may be as little as 20 per cent nitrogen, with the remaining 80 per cent composed mainly of carbon dioxide, methane, and hydrogen.

Certain foods are known to cause greater quantities of gas in the large intestine than others—beans, cabbage, onions, cauliflower, corn, and certain highly irritant foods such as vinegar. Some of these foods serve as a suitable medium for gas-forming bacteria, but in other instances excess gas results from irritation of the large intestine which prevents adequate absorption of the gases.

The amount of gases entering or forming in the large intestine each day averages some 7 to 10 liters, whereas the average amount expelled is usually only about one-half liter. The remainder is absorbed through the gastrointestinal mucosa. In general, a person expels large quantities of gases not because of excessive bacterial activity but because of excessive motility of the large intestine, the gases being moved on through the large intestine before they can be absorbed.

Oxygen Breathing for Promoting Nitrogen Absorption from the Gut. When it is desirable to remove most of the gases from the gastrointestinal tract, this can be accomplished by having the person breathe pure oxygen for up to 12 hours. This allows the nitrogen of the body fluids to diffuse outward through the lungs, which therefore reduces the nitrogen pressure in the tissue fluids. As a result, nitrogen now becomes rapidly absorable like the other intestinal gases, and the amount of flatus in the gut is rapidly reduced. Instances in which it is desirable to remove the flatus are: (1) during obstruction of the gut, because the excess gas can sometimes so overly distend the gut that it causes physical damage, (2) when x-ray studies of the gut need to be made without interference of excessive gas in the stomach and intestines, and (3) when an aviator must ascend very rapidly to a high altitude, for if he ascends more rapidly than 1000 feet per minute he normally cannot expel the flatus rapidly enough to prevent abdominal cramps.

REFERENCES

Adlersberg, D. (ed.): The Malabsorption Syndrome. New York, Grune & Stratton, Inc., 1957.

Bargen, J. A.: Chronic Ulcerative Colitis (Thrombo-ulcerative Colitis). Springfield, Illinois, Charles C Thomas, 1951.

Bassler, A.: Diseases and Disorders of the Colon. Springfield, Illinois, Charles C Thomas, 1957.

Bedell, G. N., Marshall, R., Dubois, A. B., and Harris, J. H.: Measurement of the volume of gas in the gastrointestinal tract; values in normal subjects and ambulatory patients. *J. Clin. Invest.*, 35:336, 1956.

Block, M. A., Wakim, K. G., and Baggenstoss, A. H.: Experimental studies concerning factors in the pathogenesis of acute pancreatitis. *Surg., Gynec. & Obst.*, 99:83, 1954.

Borison, H. L.: Effect of ablation of medullary emetic chemoreceptor trigger zone on vomiting responses to cerebral intraventricular injection of adrenaline, apomorphine and pilocarpine in the cat. *J. Physiol.*, 147:172, 1959.

Borison, H. L., and Wang, S. C.: Physiology and pharmacology of vomiting. *Pharmacol. Rev.*, 5:193, 1953.

Brocks, F. P.: Experimental methods for the evaluation of therapeutic agents in peptic ulcer. *Am. J. Gastroenter.*, 24:253, 1955.

Cantor, M. O., and Reynolds, R. P.: Gastrointestinal Obstruction. Baltimore, Williams & Wilkins Co., 1957.

Chinn, H. I., and Smith, P. K.: Motion sickness. *Pharmacol. Rev.*, 7:33, 1955

Chinn, H. I., and Wang, S. C.: Locus of emetic action following irradiation. *Proc. Soc. Exp. Biol. & Med.*, 85:472, 1954.

Grace, W. J., Wolf, S., and Wolff, H. G.: The Human Colon: An Experimental Study Based on Direct Observation of Four Fistulous Subjects. New York, Paul B. Hoeber, 1951.

Illingworth, C. F. W.: Peptic Ulcer. Baltimore, Williams & Wilkins Co., 1954.

Jacobs, M. B.: The Chemical Analysis of Foods and Food Products. 2nd ed., New York, D. Van Nostrand Co., 1951.

Necheles, H., and Kirshen, M.: The Physiologic Basis of Gastrointestinal Therapy. New York, Grune & Stratton, Inc., 1957.

Portis, S. A.: Diseases of the Digestive System. Philadelphia, Lea & Febiger, 1953.

Quigley, J. P., and Brody, D. A.: Physiologic and clinical consideration of pressure developed in digestive tract. *Am. J. Med.*, 13:73, 1952.

Sandweiss, D. J. (ed.): Peptic Ulcer. Philadelphia, W. B. Saunders Co., 1951.

Smith, L. A., and Rivers, A. B.: Peptic Ulcer; Pain Patterns, Diagnosis, and Medical Treatment. New York, Appleton-Century-Crofts, 1953.

Swenson, O., Rhinelander, H. F., and Diamond, I.: Hirschsprung's disease: a new concept of the etiology. Operative results in thirty-four patients. *New England J. Med.*, 241:551, 1949.

Wang, S. C., and Chinn, H. I.: Experimental motion sickness in dogs: importance of labyrinth and vestibular cerebellum. *Am. J. Physiol.*, 185:617, 1956.

Wang, S. C., and Tyson, R. L.: Central nervous pathways of experimental motion sickness. *Internat. Rec. Med.*, 167:641, 1954.

Wangensteen, O. H.: Intestinal Obstruction. 3rd ed., Springfield, Illinois, Charles C Thomas, 1955.

Welch, C. E.: Intestinal Obstruction. Chicago, Year Book Publishers, 1958.

Part Eleven

METABOLISM AND TEMPERATURE

REGULATION

Chapter 65

Metabolism of Carbohydrates and the Formation of Adenosine Triphosphate

The next few chapters will deal with the metabolism of the body, which means the chemical processes that make it possible for the cells to continue living. It is not the purpose of this textbook, however, to present the chemical details of all the various cellular reactions, for this lies in the discipline of biochemistry. Instead, these chapters will be devoted to: (1) a review of the principal chemical processes of the cell and (2) an analysis of their physiological implications, especially in relation to the manner in which they fit into the overall concept of homeostasis.

Release of Energy from Foods and the Concept of "Free Energy"

The greater proportion of the chemical reactions in the cells is concerned with making the energy in foods available to the various physiological systems of the cell. For instance, energy is required (a) for muscular activity, (b) for secretion by the glands, (c) for maintenance of membrane potentials by the nerve and muscle fibers, (d) for synthesis of substances in the cells, and (e) for absorption of foods from the gastrointestinal tract.

Coupled Reactions. All the energy foods—carbohydrates, fats, and proteins—can be oxidized with oxygen in the cells, and in this process large amounts of energy are released. These same foods can also be burned with pure oxygen outside the body in an actual fire, again releasing large amounts of energy. However, this time the energy is released suddenly, all in the form of heat. The energy needed by the physiological processes of the cells is not heat but instead energy to cause mechanical movement in the case of muscle function, to concentrate solutes in the case of glandular secretion, and so forth. To provide this energy, the chemical reactions must be "coupled" with the systems responsible for these physiologic functions. This coupling is accomplished by special cellular enzyme and energy transfer systems, some of which will be explained in this and subsequent chapters. Furthermore, the energy must be released in small packets, a little at a time in amounts that can be utilized by the cells, rather than all at once as occurs when food is actually burned in a fire. This, too, is accomplished by the enzymes and energy transfer systems.

"Free energy." The amount of energy liberated by complete oxidation of a food is called the *free energy* of the food, and this is generally represented by the symbol $\triangle F$. Free energy is usually expressed in terms of calories per mol of food substance. For instance, the amount of free energy liberated by oxidation of one mol of glucose (180 grams of glucose) is 686,000 calories.

The Role of Adenosine Triphosphate in Metabolism

Adenosine triphosphate (ATP) is a very labile chemical compound that is present in all cells and has the following chemical structure:

$$NH_2$$

(Structural formula of adenosine triphosphate showing adenine, ribose, and three phosphate radicals:)

$$CH_2-O-\overset{O}{\underset{O^-}{P}}-O\sim\overset{O}{\underset{O^-}{P}}-O\sim\overset{O}{\underset{O^-}{P}}-O^-$$

From this formula it can be seen that adenosine triphosphate is a combination of adenine, ribose, and three phosphate radicals. The last two phosphate radicals are connected with the remainder of the molecule by so-called *high energy bonds,* which are indicated by the symbol $\sim$. The amount of free energy in each of these high energy bonds per mol of ATP is approximately 7,000 calories. Therefore, removal of each of the phosphate radicals liberates 7,000 calories of energy. After loss of one phosphate radical from adenosine triphosphate the compound then becomes *adenosine diphosphate* (ADP), and after further loss of the second phosphate radical the compound becomes *adenosine monophosphate* (AMP). The interconversions between ATP, ADP, and AMP are the following:

$$\text{ATP} \underset{+7000 \text{ cal}}{\overset{-7000 \text{ cal}}{\rightleftharpoons}} \begin{array}{c} \text{ADP} \\ + \\ \text{PO}_4 \end{array} \underset{+7000 \text{ cal}}{\overset{-7000 \text{ cal}}{\rightleftharpoons}} \begin{array}{c} \text{AMP} \\ + \\ \text{PO}_4 \end{array}$$

Adenosine triphosphate is present everywhere in the cytoplasm and nucleoplasm of all cells, and essentially all the physiological mechanisms that require energy for operation obtain this directly from the stored adenosine triphosphate. In turn, the food in the cells is gradually oxidized, and the released energy is used to reform the adenosine triphosphate, thus always maintaining an adequate supply of this substance; all of these energy transfers take place by means of coupled reactions.

Likewise, when adenosine triphosphate is degraded to provide energy for some physiological function, other types of coupled reactions make the energy in the ATP available to cause the function.

In summary, adenosine triphosphate is an intermediary compound that has the peculiar ability of entering into many coupled reactions—reactions with the food to extract energy and reactions in many physiological mechanisms to provide energy for their operation. For this reason adenosine triphosphate has frequently been called a chemical *currency* that can be gained and spent again and again.

The principal purpose of the present chapter is to explain how the energy from carbohydrates can be used to form adenosine triphosphate in the cells. At least 99 per cent of all the carbohydrates utilized by the body is used for this purpose.

TRANSPORT OF MONOSACCHARIDES THROUGH THE CELL MEMBRANE

From Chapter 63 it will be recalled that the final products of carbohydrate digestion in the alimentary tract are almost entirely glucose, fructose, and galactose, glucose representing by far the major share of these. These three monosaccharides are absorbed into the portal blood, and, after passing through the liver, are carried everywhere in the body by the circulatory system. But, before they can be used by the cells, they must be transported through the cell membrane into the cellular cytoplasm.

Monosaccharides cannot diffuse through the pores of the cell membrane, for the maximum molecular weight of particles that can do this is about 100, whereas glucose, fructose, and galactose all have molecular weights of 180. Yet, these monosaccharides do pass to the interior of the cells with a reasonable degree of freedom. Therefore, it is almost certain that they are transported through the membrane by a carrier system. They presumably combine with some carrier substance that makes them soluble in the membrane and then after passing through the membrane become dissociated from this carrier. Yet, thus far, the nature of the carrier mechanism is completely unknown, but it is known that the carrier mechanism works in both directions, both into the cell and out of the cell. Furthermore, the rate of transport is approximately proportional to the diffusion gradient between the two sides of the membrane, and, except in the intestine and renal tubules, the monosaccharides are *not* transported against a concentration gradient. Therefore, the transport mechanism is one of *facilitated diffusion* and not of true active transport.

Facilitation of Glucose Transport by Insulin

The rapidity of glucose transport and also transport of some other monosaccharides is greatly increased by insulin. Insulin is secreted by the *islets of Langerhans* in the *pancreas,* and, after diffusing throughout the body, acts in some yet undetermined way to increase the activity of the carrier system for transport of at least certain monosaccharides, especially glucose. When very large amounts of insulin are secreted by the pancreas, the rate of glucose transport into at least some cells rises to as much as 25 times the rate of transport when no insulin at all is secreted. And, for practical considerations, the amounts of glucose that can diffuse to the insides of most cells of the body in the absence of insulin are far too little to supply anywhere near the amount of glucose normally required for energy metabolism. Therefore, in effect, the rate of carbohydrate utilization by the cells is controlled by the rate of insulin secretion in the pancreas. The functions of insulin and its control of carbohydrate metabolism will be discussed in detail in Chapter 76.

Failure of disaccharides to be transported. Very small amounts of disaccharides are absorbed into the blood from the gastrointestinal tract, but none of these can be transported into the cells. Therefore, no disaccharides or larger polysaccharides are utilized for cellular metabolism but are excreted completely in the urine.

Phosphorylation of the Monosaccharides

Immediately on entry into the cells, the monosaccharides combine with a phosphate radical in accordance with the following reaction:

$$\text{Glucose} \xrightarrow[+\text{ ATP}]{\text{glucokinase}} \text{Glucose 6-phosphate}$$

This phosphorylation is promoted by enzymes called *hexokinases,* which are specific for each particular type of monosaccharide; thus, *glucokinase* promotes glucose phosphorylation, *fructokinase* promotes fructose phosphorylation, and *galactokinase* promotes galactose phosphorylation.

The phosphorylation of monosaccharides is an almost completely irreversible process except in the liver cells, the renal tubular epithelium, and the intestinal epithelial cells in which specific phosphatases are available for reversing the reaction. Therefore, in most tissues of the body phosphorylation serves to *capture* the monosaccharide in the cell— once *in* the cell the monosaccharide will not diffuse back out except in those special cells that have the necessary phosphatases.

Conversion of Fructose and Galactose into Glucose. In liver cells appropriate enzymes are available to promote interconversions between the different monosaccharides, as shown in Figure 643. In essentially all other cells glucose and fructose can be reversibly interconverted, but the enzymes required for conversion of galactose into the other two monosaccharides are missing. Later in the chapter it will be noted that the monosaccharides must all become either *glucose 6-phosphate* or *fructose 6-phosphate* before they can be used for energy by the cells. For this reason, before galactose can be utilized by the tissues, it must first be converted by the liver cells into glucose, which is then transported by the blood to the other cells. Much of the fructose also is converted to glucose by the liver and then transported to the other cells, though this is not a necessary step.

STORAGE OF GLYCOGEN IN LIVER AND MUSCLE

After absorption into the cells, glucose can be used immediately for release of energy to the cells or it can be stored in the

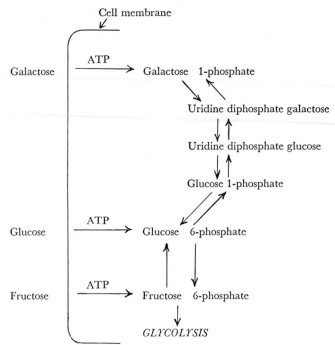

Figure 643.   Interconversions of the three major monosaccharides, glucose, fructose, and galactose, in liver cells.

form of glycogen, which is a large polymer of glucose. Also, after the other monosaccharides are converted into glucose, they, too, can all be polymerized into glycogen.

All cells of the body are capable of storing at least some glycogen, but certain cells can store very large amounts, especially the liver cells, which can store up to 8 per cent of their weight as glycogen, and muscle cells, which can store up to 1 per cent glycogen. The glycogen molecules can be polymerized to almost any molecular weight, the average molecular weight being 5 million or greater, and essentially all the glycogen precipitates in the form of solid granules. This conversion of the monosaccharides into a high molecular weight and precipitated compound makes it possible to store large quantities of carbohydrates without significantly altering the osmotic pressure of the intracellular fluids. Obviously, high concentrations of small molecular weight soluble monosaccharides would play havoc with the osmotic relationships between intracellular and extracellular fluids.

Glycogenesis

Glycogenesis is the process of glycogen formation, the chemical reactions of which

are illustrated in Figure 644. From this figure it can be seen that *glucose 6-phosphate* first becomes *glucose 1-phosphate;* then this is converted to *uridine diphosphate glucose,* which is then converted into glycogen. Several specific enzymes are required to cause these conversions, and any monosaccharides that can be converted into glucose obviously

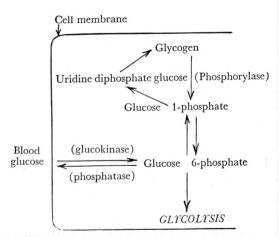

Figure 644.   The chemical reactions of glycogenesis and glycogenolysis, showing also the interconversions between blood glucose and liver glycogen. (The phosphatase required for release of glucose from the cell is absent in muscle cells.)

can enter into the reactions. Certain smaller compounds, including *lactic acid, glycerol, pyruvic acid,* and *some deaminated amino acids,* can also be converted into glucose or closely allied compounds and thence into glycogen.

Glycogenolysis

Glycogenolysis means the breakdown of glycogen to reform glucose in the cells. Glycogenolysis does not occur by reversal of the same chemical reactions that form glycogen; instead, each succeeding glucose molecule in the glycogen polymer is split away by a process of *phosphorylation,* catalyzed by the enzyme *phosphorylase.*

Under resting conditions, the phosphorylase of most cells is in an inactive form so that glycogen can be stored but not reconverted into glucose. When it is necessary to reform glucose from glycogen, therefore, the phosphorylase must first be activated. This is accomplished in the following two ways:

Activation of Phosphorylase by Epinephrine and Glucagon. Two hormones, *epinephrine* and *glucagon,* can specifically activate phosphorylase and thereby cause rapid glycogenolysis. Epinephrine is released by the adrenal medullae when the sympathetic nervous system is stimulated. Therefore, one of the functions of the sympathetic nervous system is to increase the availability of glucose for rapid metabolism. This contributes, along with the other effects of sympathetic stimulation, to the preparation of the body for action, as was discussed in Chapter 20.

Glucagon is a hormone secreted by the *alpha cells* of the pancreas, and it activates phosphorylase in a slightly different way from epinephrine, but the result is the same rapid glycogenolysis. However, the different functional conditions in which the pancreas secretes glucagon have not yet been elucidated. Therefore, it is impossible at present to state the conditions under which glucagon might be of value in glucose metabolism. The possible functions of glucagon will be discussed further in Chapter 76.

Transport of Glucose Out of the Cells. The cells of the liver, of the kidney tubules, and of the intestinal mucosa contain *phosphatases* that can split phosphate away from glucose 6-phosphate and therefore make the glucose available for retransport out of the cell into the interstitial fluids. Therefore, in these cells glucose fails to be captured by the cells but instead can diffuse rather freely in both directions through the cell membrane.

Since glucose can pass out of as well as into liver cells, when it is formed in the liver as a result of glycogenolysis, most of it immediately passes into the blood. Therefore, liver glycogenolysis causes an immediate rise in blood glucose concentration. Glycogenolysis in most other cells of the body, especially in the muscle cells, simply makes increased amounts of glucose 6-phosphate available inside the cells and increases the local rate of glucose utilization but does not release the glucose into the extracellular fluids because the glucose 6-phosphate cannot be dephosphorylated.

RELEASE OF ENERGY FROM THE GLUCOSE MOLECULE BY THE GLYCOLYTIC PATHWAY

Since complete oxidation of one gram mol of glucose releases 686,000 calories of energy, and only 7,000 calories of energy are required to form 1 gram mol of adenosine triphosphate, it obviously would be extremely wasteful of energy if glucose should be decomposed all the way into water and carbon dioxide at once while forming only a single adenosine triphosphate molecule. Fortunately, cells contain an extensive series of different protein enzymes that cause the glucose molecule to split a little at a time in many successive steps with its energy released in small packets to form one molecule of adenosine triphosphate at a time, forming a total of 38 mols of adenosine triphosphate for each mol of glucose utilized by the cells. The purpose of the present section is to describe the basic principles by which the glucose molecule is progressively dissected and its energy released to form adenosine triphosphate.

Glycolysis and the Formation of Pyruvic Acid

By far the most important means by which the glucose molecule is split and its energy released is by the process of *glycolysis,* followed by *oxidation of the end-products of glycolysis.* Glycolysis means the splitting of the glucose molecule to form two molecules

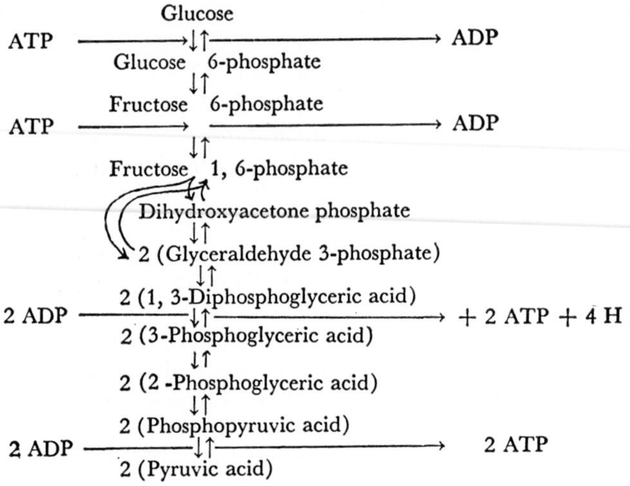

$$\text{Glucose}$$
$$\text{ATP} \longrightarrow \downarrow \uparrow \longrightarrow \text{ADP}$$
$$\text{Glucose 6-phosphate}$$
$$\downarrow \uparrow$$
$$\text{Fructose 6-phosphate}$$
$$\text{ATP} \longrightarrow \downarrow \uparrow \longrightarrow \text{ADP}$$
$$\text{Fructose 1, 6-phosphate}$$
$$\downarrow \uparrow$$
$$\text{Dihydroxyacetone phosphate}$$
$$\downarrow \uparrow$$
$$\text{2 (Glyceraldehyde 3-phosphate)}$$
$$\downarrow \uparrow$$
$$\text{2 (1, 3-Diphosphoglyceric acid)}$$
$$\text{2 ADP} \longrightarrow \downarrow \uparrow \longrightarrow + \text{2 ATP} + \text{4 H}$$
$$\text{2 (3-Phosphoglyceric acid)}$$
$$\downarrow \uparrow$$
$$\text{2 (2 -Phosphoglyceric acid)}$$
$$\downarrow \uparrow$$
$$\text{2 (Phosphopyruvic acid)}$$
$$\text{2 ADP} \longrightarrow \downarrow \uparrow \longrightarrow \text{2 ATP}$$
$$\text{2 (Pyruvic acid)}$$

Net reaction:

$$\text{Glucose} + \text{2 ADP} + \text{2 PO}_4{}^{---} \longrightarrow \text{2 Pyruvic acid} + \text{2 ATP} + \text{4 H}$$

Figure 645. The sequence of chemical reactions responsible for glycolysis.

of pyruvic acid. This occurs by means of the 10 successive steps of chemical reactions illustrated in Figure 645. Each of these steps is catalyzed by means of at least one specific protein enzyme. Note that the glucose is first converted into fructose 1,6-phosphate and then is split into two molecules with three carbon chains. These are then converted through five successive steps into pyruvic acid.

Formation of Adenosine Triphosphate during Glycolysis. Despite the many chemical reactions in the glycolytic series, very little energy is released in most of these reactions, and most of the packets of energy are too small to cause the formation of any adenosine triphosphate molecules. This energy simply becomes heat and is lost to the metabolic systems of the cells. However, between the glyceraldehyde and the glyceric acid stages, and again between the phosphopyruvic acid and the pyruvic acid stages, the packets of energy released are greater than 7,000 calories, the amount required to form ATP, and the reactions are coupled in such a way that ATP is formed. Thus, a total of 4 mols of adenosine triphosphate are formed for each mol of fructose 1,6-phosphate that is split to pyruvic acid.

Yet, it should also be noted that two molecules of adenosine triphosphate had been required to phosphorylate the original glucose before glycolysis could begin. There-fore, the net gain in adenosine triphosphate molecules by the entire glycolytic process is only two mols for each mol of glucose utilized. This amounts to 14,000 calories of energy stored in the form of ATP, but during glycolysis a total of 56,000 calories of energy is lost from the original glucose, giving an overall *efficiency* for ATP formation of 25 per cent. The remaining 75 per cent of the energy is lost in the form of heat.

Release of Hydrogen Atoms during Glycolysis. It should also be noted in Figure 645 that two hydrogen atoms are released from each molecule of glyceraldehyde during its conversion to glyceric acid. And, since two molecules of glyceraldehyde are formed from each glucose molecule, it is evident that a total of four hydrogen atoms are released. Later in the chapter we will see that still many more hydrogen atoms are released when pyruvic acid is split into its component parts and that these hydrogen atoms plus the four released during glycolysis are oxidized to provide most of the energy used in the synthesis of adenosine triphosphate.

Conversion of Pyruvic Acid to Acetyl Co-enzyme A

The next stage in the degradation of glucose is conversion of the two pyruvic acid molecules into two molecules of *acetyl co-*

Chapter 66

Lipid Metabolism

A number of different chemical compounds of the food and body are loosely classified together as *lipids*. These include (1) *neutral fat*, known also as *triglycerides*, (2) the *phospholipids*, (3) *cholesterol*, and (4) a few others of less importance. These substances all have certain similar physical and chemical properties, especially the fact that they are mutually soluble. Chemically, the basic lipid moiety of both the neutral fats and the phospholipids is *fatty acids*, which are simply long chain hydrocarbon organic acids. A typical fatty acid, palmitic acid, is shown in the following formula:

$$CH_3(CH_2)_{14} COOH$$

Though cholesterol does not contain any fatty acids, its sterol nucleus, as will be pointed out later in the chapter, is synthesized from degradation products of fatty acid molecules, thus giving it many of the physical and chemical properties of other lipid substances.

The lipids are used in the body mainly to provide energy for the different metabolic processes; this function they share almost equally with the carbohydrates. However, some lipids, especially cholesterol, the phospholipids or derivatives of these, are used throughout the body to provide structural members for the cells. Therefore, this chapter will present, first, the utilization of lipids, especially the triglycerides, for energy and, second, the other functions of the lipids.

The Basic Chemical Structure of Triglycerides (Neutral Fat). Since most of this chapter deals with the utilization of triglycerides (neutral fat) for energy, it is essential that the student first understand the basic structure of the neutral fat molecule as follows:

$$CH_3—(CH_2)_{16}—COO—CH_2$$
$$CH_3—(CH_2)_{16}—COO—CH$$
$$CH_3—(CH_2)_{16}—COO—CH_2$$
Tri-stearin

In this formula, it will be noted that three long chain fatty acid molecules are bound with one molecule of glycerol. In the human body, the three fatty acids most commonly present in the neutral fat are (1) *stearic acid*, which has an 18-carbon chain and is fully saturated with hydrogen atoms, (2) *oleic acid*, which also has an 18-carbon chain but has one double bond at the middle of the chain, and (3) *palmitic acid*, which has 16-carbon atoms and is fully saturated. These or closely similar fatty acids are also the major constituents of the fats in the food.

TRANSPORT OF LIPIDS IN THE BLOOD

Transport from the Gastrointestinal Tract—the "Chylomicrons"

On referring to Chapter 63, it will be recalled that essentially all the fats of the diet are absorbed into the lymph (with the exception of the very short chain fatty acids which can be absorbed directly into the portal blood but which normally represent only a minute fraction of the fat in the diet). In the digestive tract, most of the triglycerides are split into glycerol and fatty acids or into monoglycerides and fatty acids. Then, on passing through the intestinal mucosa these are resynthesized into new molecules of triglycerides which aggregate together and enter the lymph as minute, disbursed droplets called chylomicrons, having sizes between 0.5 and 1.5 microns. Almost immediately, a small amount of protein in the lymph adsorbs to the outer surfaces of the chylomicrons; this increases their suspension stability in the fluid of the lymph and prevents their adhering to the lymphatic walls.

Essentially all the cholesterol and phospholipids absorbed from the gastrointestinal tract, as well as small amounts of phospholipids that are continually synthesized by the intestinal mucosa, also enter the chylomicrons. Thus, chylomicrons are composed principally of triglycerides, but they also contain small amounts of phospholipids, cholesterol, and protein, as indicated in Table 23. The chylomicrons are then transported up the thoracic duct and emptied into the venous blood at the juncture of the jugular and subclavian veins.

Removal of the Chylomicrons from the Blood. Immediately after a meal that contains large quantities of fat, the chylomicron concentration in the plasma may rise to as high as 1 to 2 per cent, and, because of the large sizes of the chylomicrons, the plasma appears turbid and sometimes yellow. However, the chylomicrons are gradually removed within two to three hours, and the plasma becomes clear once again. The fat of the chylomicrons is removed in two different ways as follows:

Hydrolysis of the chylomicron triglycerides by lipoprotein lipase. The major part of the triglycerides in the chylomicrons is probably hydrolyzed into glycerol and fatty acids under the influence of an enzyme in the blood called *lipoprotein lipase.* The glycerol then diffuses into the blood to be metabolized in much the same way as glucose, as explained in the previous chapter, while the fatty acid molecules are transported in combination with albumin, as will be explained below, to the various cells of the body. The fatty acid molecules can there be directly oxidized for energy, or they can be used to resynthesize triglycerides, which are

then stored in the adipose tissue to be used later for energy.

Only small amounts of lipoprotein lipase are normally present in the blood. However, certain tissues of the body, especially the adipose tissue, heart muscle, and, to a less extent, skeletal muscle, contain large quantities of this enzyme. It is believed that as the chylomicrons pass through these tissues, the enzyme acts in the capillaries of these areas to cause immediate release of fatty acids, and since fatty acids are lipid soluble, they can diffuse extremely rapidly through the capillary and cell membranes to be used by the local cells. Or they can be transported in combination with albumin, as explained below, to any part of the body.

Absorption of whole chylomicrons by the liver cells. The second means by which the chylomicrons are removed from the blood is by transport of whole chylomicrons through the capillary wall directly into cells. This has been shown especially to occur in liver cells, which then either use the lipids of the chylomicrons for energy or convert them into other lipid substances.

Lipoprotein Lipase as a "Clearing Factor"; the Effect of Heparin on Chylomicrons. When heparin is injected into a person who has large quantities of chylomicrons in his plasma, the chylomicrons disappear very rapidly. This effect probably comes about in the following way: Heparin causes large quantities of lipoprotein lipase to be released into the blood from the adipose tissue, muscles, and other tissues. This effect is probably related to the fact that liproprotein lipase itself contains heparin or some heparin-like substance in its molecular complex. The lipoprotein lipase in turn hydrolyzes the triglycerides of the chylomicrons, thereby "clearing" the plasma of its opalescence or turbidity. Therefore, lipoprotein lipase has also been called "clearing factor."

Table 23. The Lipoproteins

	Density	Sf	Neutral fat %	Phospholipids %	Cholesterol %	Protein %
Chylomicrons	0.94	4000–40000	85	7	7	1
Low density lipoprotein						
β_1	0.98	10–400	50	18	23	9
β_2	1.03	2–10	10	22	47	21
High density lipoprotein						
α_1	1.09	−1	8	29	30	33
α_2	1.14	−2	5	21	17	57

Transport of Fatty Acids in Combination with Albumin

A very small and highly variable quantity of fatty acids is always present in the blood combined with the albumin of the plasma proteins. It should be remembered that fatty acids ionize very strongly in water. Therefore, immediately upon release of fatty acids into the blood, either by the action of lipoprotein lipase on chylomicrons or by the action of this same enzyme on triglycerides stored in the adipose tissue, the ionized fatty acid combines almost immediately with the albumin of the plasma proteins. The fatty acids bound with proteins in this manner are called *unesterified fatty acid* because essentially all the remainder of the fatty acid in the plasma is transported in the form of esters of glycerol, cholesterol, or other substances.

The concentration of unesterified fatty acids in the plasma under resting conditions is about 10 mg. per 100 ml. of blood, which is a total of only 0.5 gram of fatty acids in the entire circulatory system. Yet, strangely enough, even this small amount probably accounts for most of the transport of lipids from one part of the body to another for the following reasons: (1) Despite the very minute amount of unesterified fatty acid in the blood, its rate of "turnover" is extremely rapid, *half of the fatty acids being replaced by new fatty acids every two to three minutes.* One can calculate that at this rate about half of all the energy required by the body can be provided in this way. (2) A second reason for believing that the unesterified fatty acids are extremely important in the transport of fats is that all conditions which increase the rates of utilization of fats by the cells also increase the quantity of unesterified fatty acids in the blood; this sometimes increases as much as five-fold. Especially does this occur in starvation and in diabetes when a person is not or cannot be using carbohydrates for energy.

Under normal conditions about three molecules of fatty acid combine with each molecule of albumin, but as many as 30 fatty acid molecules can at times combine with a single molecule of albumin when the need for fatty acid transport is extreme. This shows how variable the rate of lipid transport can be under different physiological needs.

The Lipoproteins

In the post-absorptive state—that is, when there are no chylomicrons in the blood—over 95 per cent of all the lipids in the plasma are in the form of *lipoproteins,* which are mixtures of *triglycerides, phospholipids, cholesterol,* and *proteins.* The protein in the mixture averages about one quarter to one third of the total constituents, and the remainder is lipids. The total concentration of lipoproteins in the plasma averages about 700 mg. per 100 ml., and this can be broken down into the following average concentrations of the individual constituents:

Cholesterol—180 mg. per 100 ml. of plasma

Phospholipids—160 mg. per 100 ml. of plasma

Triglycerides—160 mg. per 100 ml. of plasma

Lipoprotein protein—200 mg. per 100 ml. of plasma

Table 23 illustrates that there are two major groups of lipoprotein: (1) the *low density lipoproteins,* which contain high concentrations of triglycerides and low concentrations of protein, and (2) the *high density lipoproteins,* which contain low concentrations of neutral fat and high concentrations of protein. The lipoproteins can also be classified on the basis of their electrophoretic mobility in an electrophoresis apparatus as (a) *alpha lipoproteins,* which are the high density proteins and which migrate with the alpha globulins in the electrophoresis apparatus, and (b) *beta lipoproteins,* which are low density lipoproteins and which migrate with the beta globulins.

A special classification of the lipoproteins is the Sf classification, which is actually a classification of the rate at which they will either float to the surface during centrifugation of a sample of plasma or the rate at which they will settle to the bottom. The low density lipoproteins have positive Sf values, which means that they float to the surface, and high density lipoproteins have negative Sf values, which mean that they are centrifuged downward.

Function of the Lipoproteins. The function of the lipoproteins in the plasma is very poorly known, though they are believed to represent another means by which lipid substances can be transported from one part of the body to another. For instance, the turnover of triglycerides in the lipoproteins is as much as 1.5 grams per hour, which could account for as much as 10 to 20 per cent of the total lipids utilized by the body for energy. It has especially been suggested that fats synthesized from carbohydrates in the liver are transported to the adipose tissue in the form of lipoproteins because almost no unesterified fatty acids are present in the blood when fat synthesis is occurring, while plenty of lipoproteins are present. Even more important might be the transport of cholesterol and phospholipids by the lipoproteins, because these substances are not known to be transported to any significant extent in any other form.

The lipoproteins are formed either entirely or almost entirely in the liver, which is in keeping with the fact that essentially all plasma phospholipids and cholesterol, as well as a major share of plasma triglycerides, are synthesized in the liver.

THE FAT DEPOSITS

Adipose Tissue

There are two major tissues in the body in which large quantities of fat are frequently stored, the adipose tissue and the liver. The adipose tissue is usually called the *fat deposits* or simply the *fat depots* of the body, though, actually, very large amounts of fats are often "deposited" in the liver as well. The factors that cause storage and removal of fat from adipose tissue are quite different from those that affect the fat in in the liver, as will become evident in the succeeding paragraphs.

The major function of the adipose tissue is storage of triglycerides until these are needed at a later date to provide energy elsewhere in the body. However, a subsidiary function is to provide heat insulation for the body. For this purpose, by far the greater portion of the adipose tissue is in the subcutaneous tissue, and, furthermore, the heat conductivity of adipose tissue is several times less than that of the body fluids. This insulation function of fat is especially important in certain mammals, such as the whale, which exist in extremely cold environments and yet at the same time must maintain a high internal body temperature.

The Fat Cells. The fat cells of adipose tissue are modified fibroblasts which are capable of storing as much as 80 to 95 per cent almost pure triglycerides. The triglycerides are generally in a liquid form, and it is especially interesting that when the tissues of the skin are exposed to prolonged cold, the fatty acids of the triglycerides become either shorter in length or more unsaturated to decrease their melting point, thereby always allowing the fat in the fat cells to remain in a liquid state. This is particularly important because it is only liquid fat that can be hydrolyzed and then transported from the cells.

Fat cells can also synthesize moderate quantities of neutral fat from carbohydrates, this function supplementing the more extensive synthesis of fat in the liver, which will be discussed later in the chapter.

Exchange of Fat between the Adipose Tissue and the Blood—Tissue Lipoprotein Lipase. Very large quantities of lipoprotein lipase are present in adipose tissue. Furthermore, very rapid exchange occurs between the unesterified fatty acids of the plasma and the fatty acids in the triglycerides of the adipose tissue. Therefore, it is believed that a very large proportion, if not the major proportion, of the fat in the adipose tissue, is transported in the blood in the form of unesterified fatty acids and that the exchange between the blood and the adipose tissue occurs by enzymatic action of lipoprotein lipase.

During times of rapid lipid utilization for energy, the rate of fatty acid release from the adipose tissue becomes extremely rapid. It is believed that this rapid release might result from increased secretion of epinephrine by the adrenal medulla, corticotropin by the adenohypophysis, or glucocorticoids by the adrenal cortex, for all of these are capable of mobilizing fatty acids from the adipose tissues; it is also known that stressful conditions increase the rates of secretion of all of these.

The Liver Lipids

The principal functions of the liver in lipid metabolism are: (1) to degrade the triglycerides into small compounds that can be used for energy, (2) to synthesize triglycerides mainly from carbohydrates and to a less extent from proteins, and (3) to synthesize other lipids from triglycerides. To provide these functions triglycerides must first be deposited in the liver cells. As pointed out above, a large share of the triglycerides in the chylomicrons is first deposited directly in the liver and then is either used by the liver for metabolism or later transported from the liver to the adipose tissue for storage.

However, strangely enough, very large quantities of triglycerides appear in the liver (a) during starvation, (b) in diabetes mellitus, or (c) in any other condition in which fat is being utilized rapidly for energy. In these conditions, the triglycerides are mobilized from the adipose tissue and then redeposited in the liver, where the initial stages of fat degradation begin. Thus, under normal physiological conditions the total amount of triglycerides in the liver is controlled to a great extent by the overall rate at which lipids are being utilized for energy.

The liver cells, in addition to containing triglycerides, also contain large quantities of phospholipids and cholesterol, which are continually being synthesized by the liver. Also, the liver cells are especially capable of desaturating the fatty acids so that the liver triglycerides normally have a much higher degree of unsaturation than do the triglycerides of the adipose tissue. This capability of the liver to desaturate fatty acids seems to be functionally important to all the tissues of the body, because many of the structural members of all cells contain reasonable quantities of desaturated fats, and their principal source seems to be the liver. This desaturation is accomplished by a dehydrogenase in the liver cells as discussed below.

USE OF TRIGLYCERIDES FOR ENERGY, AND THE FORMATION OF ADENOSINE TRIPHOSPHATE

Approximately 40 to 45 per cent of the calories in the normal American diet are derived from fats, which is about equal to the calories derived from carbohydrates. Therefore, it is evident that use of fats by the body for energy is equally as important as the use of carbohydrates. In addition, an average of 30 to 50 per cent of the carbohydrates ingested with each meal are converted into triglycerides, then stored, and later utilized as triglycerides for energy. Therefore, as much as two thirds to three quarters of all the energy derived directly by the

cells might be supplied by triglycerides rather than by carbohydrates. For this reason it is equally as important to understand the principles of triglyceride oxidation as to understand carbohydrate oxidation, if not more important.

Hydrolysis of the Triglycerides. The first stage in the utilization of triglycerides for energy is hydrolysis of these into fatty acids and glycerol. This occurs principally in the liver, but it can occur also to a much less extent in other tissues of the body. The glycerol is immediately changed by intracellular enzymes into glyceraldehyde, which enters the phosphogluconate pathway of glucose breakdown and is used for energy as explained in the previous chapter. But before the fatty acids can be used for energy, they must be further degraded in the following way:

Degradation of Fatty Acid to Acetyl Co-enzyme A by the Process of "Beta Oxidation." The fatty acid molecule is degraded by progressive release of two-carbon segments in the form of acetyl Co-A. This process is illustrated in Figure 651, and it is called the *beta oxidation* process for degradation of fatty acids. The successive stages are the following:

1. The fatty acid molecule first combines with co-enzyme A to form a fatty acyl Co-A molecule, as illustrated by the first reaction of Figure 651.

2. The fatty acyl Co-A then loses two hydrogen atoms from the alpha and beta carbons, leaving a double bond at this point. The hydrogen atoms that are removed become attached to a flavoprotein and later are oxidized, as will be discussed below.

3. The unsaturated double bond from the above reaction is then hydrated so that a hydrogen atom attaches to the alpha carbon and a hydroxyl radical to the beta carbon.

4. At this stage still two additional hydrogen atoms are removed, one from the beta carbon and one from the hydroxyl radical. The hydrogen atoms removed in this process combine with DPN and are also oxidized, as will be discussed below.

5. At this point, the compound splits between the alpha and beta atoms, the long portion of the chain combining with a new molecule of co-enzyme A, while the shorter acetyl portion remains combined with the original co-enzyme A to form *acetyl Co-A*.

Thiokinase

(1) $RCH_2CH_2CH_2COOH + Co-A + ATP \rightleftharpoons RCH_2CH_2CH_2COCo-A + AMP + Pyrophosphate$
Fatty acid   *Fatty acyl Co-A*

Dehydrogenase

(2) $RCH_2CH_2CH_2COCo-A + FAD \longrightarrow RCH_2CH{=}CHCOCo-A + FAD\ H_2$
Fatty acyl Co-A

Crotonase

(3) $RCH_2CH{=}CHCOCo-A + H_2O \rightleftharpoons RCH_2CHOHCH_2COCo-A$

Dehydrogenase

(4) $RCH_2CHOHCH_2COCo-A + DPN^+ \rightleftharpoons RCH_2COCH_2COCo-A + DPNH + H^+$

Thiolase

(5) $RCH_2COCH_2COCo-A + Co-A \rightleftharpoons RCH_2COCo-A + CH_3COCo-A$
                                              Fatty acyl Co-A   *Acetyl Co-A*

Figure 651. Beta oxidation of fatty acids to yield acetyl co-enzyme A.

The new fatty acyl Co-A, which now has two carbon atoms less than the original fatty acyl Co-A, reenters reaction number 2 in Figure 651 and proceeds through the four stages of chemical reactions until another acetyl Co-A molecule is released, and still a new fatty acyl Co-A is formed with yet two less carbon atoms. This process is repeated again and again until the entire fatty acid molecule is split into acetyl Co-A. From each molecule of stearic acid, nine molecules of acetyl Co-A are formed.

Oxidation of Acetyl Co-A. The acetyl Co-A molecules formed by beta oxidation of fatty acids enter into the tricarboxylic acid cycle as explained in the previous chapter, combining first with oxaloacetic acid to form succinic acid, which then is degraded into carbon dioxide and hydrogen atoms. The hydrogen is subsequently oxidized by the oxidative enzymes of the cells, which was also explained in the previous chapter. The net reaction for each molecule of acetyl Co-A is the following:

$CH_3CO{-}Co-A + $ Oxaloacetic acid $ + 3\ H_2O$
Tricarboxylic acid cycle
$\longrightarrow$
$2\ CO_2 + 8\ H + Co-A + ATP$

Thus, after the initial degradation of fatty acids to acetyl Co-A, their final breakdown is precisely the same as that of the acetyl Co-A formed from pyruvic acid during the metabolism of glucose.

Adenosine Triphosphate Formed by Oxidation of Fatty Acid. In Figure 651 it is noted that four hydrogen atoms are released from the fatty acid molecule each time a molecule of acetyl Co-A is formed from the initial chain. Therefore, for every stearic acid molecule that is split, a total of 32 hydrogen atoms are removed. In addition to this, for each acetyl Co-A degraded

by the tricarboxylic acid cycle, eight hydrogen atoms are removed, making an additional 72 hydrogens for each molecule of stearic acid metabolized. This added to the above 32 hydrogen atoms makes a total of 104 hydrogen atoms. Of this group 34 are removed from the degrading fatty acid by flavoproteins and 70 are removed by DPN. These two groups of hydrogen atoms are oxidized by the cells, as was discussed in the previous chapter, but they enter the oxidative system at different points, so that one molecule of adenosine triphosphate is synthesized for each of the 34 flavoprotein hydrogens and 1½ molecules of adenosine triphosphate are synthesized for each of the 70 DPN hydrogens. This makes 34 plus 105, or a total of 139 molecules of adenosine triphosphate formed by the oxidation of hydrogen derived from each molecule of stearic acid. And another nine molecules of ATP are formed in the tricarboxylic acid cycle, one for each of the nine acetyl Co-A molecules metabolized. Thus, a total of 148 molecules are formed during the complete oxidation of one molecule of stearic acid.

Formation of Acetoacetic Acid in the Liver and Its Transport in the Blood

Over 60 per cent of the initial degradation of fatty acids occurs in the liver. However, the liver cannot use anything like this amount of fatty acids for its own intrinsic metabolic processes. Instead, when the fatty acid chains have been split into acetyl Co-A, two molecules of acetyl Co-A combine to form one molecule of acetoacetic acid as follows:

Liver cells
$2\ CH_3CO{-}Co-A + H_2O \rightleftharpoons$
(Acetyl Co-A)   Other cells
$CH_3{-}CO{-}CH_2{-}COOH$
(Acetoacetic acid)

The acetoacetic acid is then freely diffusible through the liver cellular membranes and is transported by the blood to the peripheral tissues. Here it again diffuses very freely into the cells where exactly the reverse reactions occur and two acetyl Co-A molecules are formed. These in turn enter the tricarboxylic acid cycle and are oxidized for energy as explained above.

Normally, the acetoacetic acid that enters the blood is transported so rapidly to the tissues that its total plasma concentration rarely rises above 1 milligram per cent. Yet, despite the very small quantities in the blood, tremendous amounts are actually transported; this is analogous to the tremendous rate of fatty acid transport in the unesterified form. The very rapid transport of both these substances probably depends on their high degree of lipid solubility, which allows rapid diffusion through the cellular membranes.

"Ketosis" and Its Occurrence in Starvation, Diabetes, and Other Diseases. Large quantities of acetoacetic acid occasionally collect in the blood and interstitial fluids; this condition is called *ketosis* because acetoacetic acid is a keto acid. It occurs especially in starvation, in diabetes mellitus, or even when a person eats a diet composed almost entirely of fat. In all these states, essentially no carbohydrates are metabolized —in starvation and following a high fat diet because carbohydrates are not available and in diabetes because insulin is not available to cause glucose transport into the cells. There are two different reasons why ketosis often develops in these conditions: First, failure to utilize carbohydrates for metabolism causes the body to mobilize excessive quantities of triglycerides from the adipose tissue, and these are then rapidly degraded in the liver to form far more acetoacetic acid than normally. This increases the acetoacetic acid concentration of the body fluids perhaps as much as two- to three-fold. Second, and probably far more important as a cause of ketosis, is a decrease in the quantity of oxaloacetic acid in all the cells of the body when carbohydrates are not utilized for energy. Oxaloacetic acid is formed from pyruvic acid by a carboxylation process, and when pyruvic acid is not being formed from glucose, the concentration of oxaloacetic acid in the cells cannot be maintained at normal levels. As a result, the acetoacetic acid cannot be utilized readily by the tricarboxylic acid cycle of the cells, and this causes acetoacetic acid to dam up in the extracellular fluids, its concentration sometimes increasing to as much as 30 or more times normal.

The ketone bodies. Acetoacetic acid is readily converted in the body fluids into two other compounds, *beta-hydroxybutyric acid* and *acetone,* in the following manner:

$$CH_3-\overset{\overset{O}{\|}}{C}-CH_2-\overset{\overset{O}{\|}}{C}-OH$$
acetoacetic acid

$$+2H \downarrow \qquad \qquad -CO_2 \searrow$$

$$CH_3-\overset{\overset{OH}{|}}{CH}-CH_2-\overset{\overset{O}{\|}}{C}-OH \qquad CH_3-\overset{\overset{O}{\|}}{C}-CH_3$$
β-hydroxybutyric acid $\qquad\qquad$ acetone

These two substances, along with the acetoacetic acid itself, are called *ketone bodies,* and clinical procedures for analyzing the total concentration of these are often used as a measure of the degree of ketosis in a person. Beta-hydroxybutyric acid has almost the same properties as acetoacetic acid, while acetone is a volatile substance that is blown off in small quantities in the expired air of the lungs, often giving the breath an acetone smell. This smell, too, is frequently used as a diagnostic criterion of ketosis.

Acidosis in ketosis. The acetoacetic acid and beta-hydroxybutyric acid that collect in the body fluids in ketosis frequently cause very severe acidosis for two reasons: First, these acids alone decrease the blood pH a small amount. Second, and even more important, as much as 500 milliequivalents of keto acids are often excreted in the urine each day. These are such strong acids that only about one half of them can be excreted in the free acidic form, as explained in Chapter 10, while the other half must be secreted in combination with some strong cation such as sodium. Often, so much of the keto acids is lost that large proportions of the extracellular sodium ions are lost with the acids into the urine, thereby reducing the availability of sodium to the body fluids. As a result, the body fluids lose a major portion of the alkaline half of their chemical buffer systems, thereby allowing the development of very severe acidosis. This is one of the most serious of the complications that occur in diabetes mellitus or in starvation.

Adaptation to a high fat diet. If a person changes very slowly from a carbohydrate diet to an almost completely fat diet, his body adapts to the utilization of far more acetoacetic acid than usual, and, in this instance, ketosis does not occur. For instance, the Eskimos, who sometimes live almost entirely on a fat diet, do not develop ketosis. Presumably some other process for the formation of oxaloacetic acid develops in the cells, thereby preventing the collection of acetoacetic acid in the body fluids.

SYNTHESIS OF TRIGLYCERIDES FROM CARBOHYDRATES

Whenever a greater quantity of carbohydrates enters the body than can be used immediately for energy or stored in the form of glycogen, the excess is rapidly converted into triglycerides and then stored in this form in the adipose tissue. It has generally been thought that most of this fat synthesis occurs in the liver, though some experiments in lower animals have shown that as much as half of the triglyceride synthesis at times can occur in the adipose tissue itself. And even when the synthesis does occur in the liver, the triglycerides are then transported to the adipose tissue where they are stored until needed for energy.

Polymerization of Acetyl Co-A into Fatty Acids. The basic process for synthesis of triglycerides from carbohydrates is essentially the reverse of the degradation of fatty acids, which was described above. That is, whenever an excess quantity of acetyl Co-A is being formed by the glycolytic breakdown of glucose, then a large portion

of this is automatically converted into fatty acids. However, there is one basic difference between this conversion of acetyl Co-A into fatty acids and the original degradation of the fatty acids. Referring back to Figure 651, it will be noted that the second reaction in the oxidation scheme is irreversible, even though all the remaining reactions are completely reversible. When fatty acids are being synthesized this reaction must be reversed by another enzyme besides the one used in the degradation process, and the hydrogen used in the reversal reaction comes from TPNH rather than from the flavoprotein which takes the hydrogen away in the degradation process. This reverse reaction is the following:

$$RCH_2CH{=}CHCO{-}Co\text{-}A + TPNH + H^+$$
$$\xrightarrow{\text{Reductase}}$$
$$RCH_2CH_2CH_2CO{-}Co\text{-}A + TPN^+$$
$$\text{(Fatty acyl Co-A)}$$

Thus, employing this reaction and the reverse of all the other reactions in Figure 651, one acetyl Co-A can be added to the fatty acid chain at a time until the usual large fatty acids are formed.

Note especially that the hydrogen atoms used in this synthesis of fatty acids are derived from TPNH rather than from flavoprotein hydrogen. Almost all the TPNH in the cells is formed by the phosphogluconate pathway of glucose degradation, which emphasizes the importance of the phosphogluconate system in glucose metabolism—without it fat synthesis could not occur.

Figure 652 illustrates the overall synthesis of fatty acids from glucose, showing formation of acetyl Co-A by the glycolytic pathway, of TPNH by the phosphogluconate

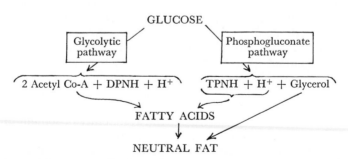

Figure 652. An overall schema for synthesis of neutral fat from glucose.

pathway, and finally utilization of both these to form the fatty acids.

Combination of Fatty Acids with Glycerol to Form Triglycerides. When the fatty acid chains have grown to contain 16 to 18 carbon atoms, these combine with glycerol to form triglycerides. It is especially interesting that the enzymes that cause combination of fatty acids with glycerol are highly specific for fatty acids with chain lengths of 14 carbon atoms or greater. This is what controls the physical qualities of the triglycerides that are stored in the body.

Efficiency of Carbohydrate Conversion into Fat. During triglyceride synthesis, only about 15 per cent of the original energy in the glucose is lost in the form of heat while the remaining 85 per cent is transferred to the stored triglycerides.

Importance of Fat Synthesis. Fat synthesis from carbohydrates is especially important for two reasons: (1) the ability of the different cells of the body to store carbohydrates in the form of glycogen is generally very slight; only a few hundred grams of glycogen are stored in the liver, the skeletal muscles, and all other tissues of the body put together. Therefore, fat synthesis provides a means by which the energy of excess ingested carbohydrates (and proteins, too) can be stored for later use. (2) Another important value of fat synthesis from carbohydrates is that each gram of fat contains approximately 2¼ times as many calories of energy as each gram of glycogen. Therefore, for a given weight gain, a person can store far more energy in the form of fat than in the form of carbohydrate itself, which might well be very important when an animal must be highly motile in order to survive.

Failure To Synthesize Fats from Carbohydrates in the Absence of Insulin. When insulin is not available, as occurs in diabetes mellitus, fats are very poorly, if at all, synthesized by the cells. This seems to result from two different causes, which can be illustrated by referring back to Figure 652. First, when insulin is not available, glucose cannot enter the cells satisfactorily, and very little of the acetyl Co-A needed for fat synthesis can be derived from glucose. Second, lack of glucose in the cells greatly reduces the availability of TPNH, which also makes it difficut for the tissues to form fats.

Synthesis of Triglycerides from Proteins

In the following chapter it will be pointed out that many of the amino acids can be converted into acetyl Co-A. Obviously, this, too, can be synthesized into triglycerides. Therefore, when a person has more proteins in his diet than his tissues can use as proteins, a large share of the excess can be stored as fat.

REGULATION OF ENERGY RELEASE FROM TRIGLYCERIDES

There are several basic methods by which the overall rate of fat metabolism is regulated, some of which can be predicted from the basic principles of the *law of mass action* as follows:

First, the concentration of acetyl Co-A present in the cells undoubtedly has much to do with this regulation. If this concentration is very low, which occurs when acetyl Co-A is being oxidized very rapidly, this would tend to cause degradation of fatty acids to form more acetyl Co-A. On the other hand, the presence of large quantities of acetyl Co-A, which occurs when excessive amounts of glucose are being converted into this substance, would tend to cause its polymerization into fatty acids.

Second, the presence of excess quantities of TPNH, which occurs when large quantities of glucose are being metabolized by the phosphogluconate pathway, undoubtedly predisposes to the storage of fat rather than its breakdown.

Third, increased rate of carbohydrate metabolism automatically decreases the rate of fat mobilization from adipose tissue, while a decrease in carbohydrate utilization increases the rate of fat mobilization. This possibly results from direct changes in carbohydrate utilization in the fat cells themselves.

Hormonal Regulation of Fat Metabolism. At least six of the hormones secreted by the endocrine glands also have very marked effects on fat metabolism as follows:

It has already been pointed out that *insulin lack* causes depressed glucose utilization, which in turn decreases fat synthesis and promotes fat mobilization from the tissues as well as increased rate of fat utilization. In very severe diabetes, a person can become extremely emaciated because of depletion of the fat stores.

Glucocorticoids secreted by the adrenal cortex have a direct effect on the fat cells to increase the rate of fat mobilization. It has been postulated that this results from an effect of glucocorticoids to increase the permeability of fat cells, though this has not been proved. In the absence of glucocorticoids, mobilization of fat is very slight, causing considerable depression in fat utilization. Furthermore, glucocorticoids must be available before sufficient fat can ever be mobilized to cause ketosis. Therefore, glucocorticoids are frequently said to have a *ketogenic effect*.

Corticotropin, especially, and *growth hormone,* to a less extent, from the adenohypophysis both have a fat-mobilizing effect very similar to that of the adrenocortical glucocorticoids, though the precise causes of the mobilization are not known.

Thyroid hormone also causes rapid mobilization of fats, which is believed to result indirectly from an increased rate of energy metabolism in all cells of the body under the influence of this hormone. The resulting reduction in acetyl Co-A in the cells would then be a stimulus to cause fat mobilization.

Finally, *epinephrine* has a direct effect on fat cells to increase their rate of fat mobilization. In times of stress, the release of epinephrine from the adrenal medullae is probably an important means by which fatty acids are made available for metabolism.

The effects of the different hormones on metabolism will be discussed at further length in the chapters dealing with each one of them.

Obesity

Obesity means deposition of excess fat in the body. This subject will be discussed in detail in relation to dietary balances in Chapter 69, but briefly it is caused by ingestion of greater amounts of food than can be utilized by the body for energy. The excess food, whether fats, carbohydrates, or proteins, are then stored as fat in the adipose tissue to be used later for energy. However, strains of rats have been developed in which *hereditary obesity* occurs. In at least one of these strains, the obesity is caused by ineffective mobilization of fat from the adipose tissue while synthesis and storage of fat continues normally.

Obviously, such a one-way process causes progressive enhancement of the fat stores, resulting in severe obesity.

FUNCTIONS OF PHOSPHOLIPIDS AND CHOLESTEROL

Phospholipids

The three major types of body phospholipids, also called phosphatides, include the lecithins, the cephalins, and the sphingomyelins.

In general, phospholipids contain one or more fatty acid molecules, one phosphoric acid radical, and often a nitrogenous base. The chemical structures of phospholipids are

A lecithin

A cephalin

Sphingomyelin

somewhat variant, but the physical properties are similar, for they are all lipid soluble, they are transported together in the form of lipoproteins in the blood stream, and they seem to be utilized similarly throughout the body for various structural purposes.

Formation of Phospholipids. Phospholipids are formed in essentially all cells of the body, though certain cells have a special ability to form them. Probably 90 per cent or more of the phospholipids that enter the blood are formed in the liver cells, though reasonably large quantities can also be formed by the intestinal mucosa, especially following a high fat meal.

The rate of phospholipid formation is to some extent governed by the usual factors that control the rate of fat metabolism, for when neutral fats are deposited in the liver, the rate of phospholipid formation increases. Also, some specific chemical substances are needed for formation of some phospholipids. For instance, *choline*, either in the diet or synthesized in the body, is needed for the formation of lecithin because choline is the nitrogenous base of the lecithin molecule. Also, *inositol* is needed for the formation of some of the cephalins. On the other hand, *biotin* can block the formation of some cephalins, cystine can depress the formation of lecithin, and even vitamin B_1 in large quantities seems to depress the formation of some of the phospholipids.

Fate of Phospholipids in the Body. Very little phospholipid is excreted from the body; therefore, it must be assumed that the phospholipids formed by the liver and by other tissues are later destroyed, perhaps by the tissue cells themselves. Consequently, after phospholipids have performed their functions, presumably they can be split into smaller compounds and metabolized.

Specific Uses of Phospholipids in the Body. Several isolated functions of the phospholipids are the following: (1) Phospholipids possibly help to transport fatty acids through the intestinal mucosa into the lymph, possibly by making the fat particles more miscible with water. (2) Thromboplastin, which is necessary to initiate the clotting process, is probably one of the cephalins. (3) Large quantities of sphingomyelin are present in the nervous system; this substance acts as an insulator around nerve fibers. (4) Phospholipids are donors of phosphate radicals when these are needed for different tissue reactions. (5) Perhaps the most important of all the functions of phospholipids is the formation of structural elements within cells throughout the body, as will be discussed below in connection with cholesterol. (6) And very recent studies indicate that some phospholipids might act as "carriers" in the active transport systems through cellular membranes.

Cholesterol

Cholesterol, the formula of which is illustrated below, is present in the diet of all persons, and it can be absorbed from the gastrointestinal tract into the intestinal lymph without any previous digestion. It is highly fat soluble, but only very slightly soluble in water, and it is capable of forming esters with fatty acids. Indeed, approximately 70 per cent of the cholesterol of the plasma is in the form of cholesterol esters.

Formation of Cholesterol in the Body. Besides the cholesterol absorbed each day from the gastrointestinal tract, which is called *exogenous cholesterol*, an additional large quantity, called *endogenous cholesterol*, is formed in the cells of the body. Essentially all the endogenous cholesterol that circulates in the lipoproteins of the plasma is formed by the liver, but all the other cells of the body probably form at least some cholesterol, which is consistent with the fact that many of the membraneous structures of all cells are partially composed of this substance.

As illustrated by the formula of cholesterol, its basic structure is a sterol nucleus. This is synthesized entirely from acetyl Co-A. In turn, the sterol nucleus can be modified by means of various side chains to form (a) cholesterol, (b) cholic acid, which is the basis of the bile acids formed in the liver, and (c) several very im-

Cholesterol

portant sterol hormones secreted by the adrenal cortex, the ovaries, and the testes (these will be discussd in later chapters).

Factors That Affect the Plasma Cholesterol Concentration. Among the important factors that affect plasma cholesterol concentration are the following:

1. An increase in the amount of cholesterol eaten each day increases the plasma concentration slightly. However, when cholesterol is ingested, the liver normally almost completely compensates for this by synthesizing smaller quantities of endogenous cholesterol. As a result, eating a diet containing very large quantities of cholesterol usually increases the blood cholesterol concentration no more than a few milligrams per cent.

2. Ingestion of a high fat diet can increase the blood cholesterol concentration as much as 40 to 50 milligrams per cent. This presumably results from increased fat deposition in the liver, which then increases the rate of fat metabolism and provides increased quantities of acetyl Co-A in the liver cells for production of cholesterol. Therefore, to decrease the blood cholesterol concentration, it is more important to maintain a diet low in total fat content than to maintain a diet low in cholesterol concentration.

3. Ingestion of fat containing highly unsaturated fatty acids usually depresses the blood cholesterol concentration a slight to moderate amount, but the cause of this is yet unknown.

4. Lack of thyroid hormone increases the blood cholesterol concentration while excess thyroid hormone decreases the concentration. This effect is believed to be related to the increased metabolism of all lipid substances under the influence of thyroxine.

5. The blood cholesterol also rises greatly in diabetes mellitus. This, also, is believed to result from the general increase in lipid metabolism in this condition.

6. In renal retention diseases, the blood cholesterol rises greatly along with similar increases in blood triglycerides and phosphatides. This is believed to result from diminished removal of lipoproteins from the plasma, thus causing their concentration to increase markedly.

Specific Uses of Cholesterol in the Body. By far the most abundant use of cholesterol in the body is to form cholic acid in the liver. As much as 80 per cent of the cholesterol absorbed along with other foods from the gastrointestinal tract eventually is converted into cholic acid. This, in turn, is conjugated with other substances to form bile salts, which have already been discussed in connection with fat digestion.

A very small quantity of cholesterol is used by the adrenal glands to form adrenocortical hormones, by the ovaries to form progesterone and possibly estrogen, and by the testes to form testosterone. However, these glands can also synthesize their own sterols and then form their hormones from these, as will be discussed in the chapters on endocrinology later in the text.

A large amount of cholesterol is precipitated in the corneum of the skin. This, along with other lipids, makes the skin highly resistant to the absorption of water soluble substances and also to the action of many chemical agents, for cholesterol and the other lipids are highly inert to such substances as acids and different solvents that might otherwise easily penetrate into the body. Also, these lipid substances help to prevent water evaporation from the skin; without this protection the amount of evaporation would probably be 15 to 20 liters per day instead of the usual 300 to 400 milliliters.

Structural Functions of Phospholipids and Cholesterol

The specific uses of phospholipids and cholesterol are probably of only minor importance in comparison with their importance for general structural purposes throughout the cells of the body. In Chapter 2 it was pointed out that a reasonably large quantity of phospholipids and cholesterol is present in the membranes of all cells. It has even been claimed that cholesterol and possibly also the phospholipids may have a controlling effect over the permeability of cell membranes. Actually, a number of other membranes exist in cells besides the external cell membrane; these include (1) a membrane around the nucleus, (2) a very fine membrane at the surface of the nucleolus, (3) membrane surfaces at the mitochondria, and (4) presumably, even membrane surfaces between the nuclear sap and the chromatin material of the nucleus. For membranes to develop, substances that are not soluble in water must be available, and, in general, the only substances in the body (besides the inorganic substances of bone) that are not soluble in water are the lipids and some proteins. Thus, the physical integrity of cells throughout the body is probably based mainly on phospholipids, triglycerides, cholesterol, and certain insoluble proteins. Some of the phospholipids are somewhat water soluble as well as lipid soluble, which could give them the important property of helping to decrease the interfacial tension between the membranes and the surrounding fluids.

Another fact that indicates that phospholipids and cholesterol are mainly concerned with the formation of structural elements of the cells is the very slow turn-over rate of these substances. For instance, radioactive phospholipids formed in the brain of mice remain in the brain almost without loss months after they are originally formed. Therefore, these phospholipids are not metabolized, and the fatty acid is not split away from them to any major extent. Consequently, the purpose of their being in the cells of the brain is presumably related to their indestructible physical properties rather than to their chemical properties—in other words, for the formation of actual physical structures within the cells of the brain.

ATHEROSCLEROSIS

Atherosclerosis is principally a disease of the large arteries, in which lipid deposits called *atheromatous plaques* appear in the subintimal layer of the arteries. These plaques contain an especially large amount of cholesterol and often are simply called cholesterol deposits. They usually are also associated with degenerative changes in the arterial wall. In a later stage of the disease, fibroblasts infiltrate the degenerative areas and cause progressive sclerosis of the arteries. In addition, calcium often precipitates with the lipids to develop *calcified plaques*. When these two reactions occur, the arteries become extremely hard, and the disease is then called *arteriosclerosis* or simply "hardening of the arteries."

Obviously, arteriosclerotic arteries lose most of their distensibility, and, because of the degenerative areas, they are easily ruptured. Also, the atheromatous plaques often protrude through the intima into the flowing blood, and the roughness of their surfaces causes blood clots to develop, with resultant thrombus or embolus formation (see Chapter 16). Almost half of all human beings die of arteriosclerosis; approximately two thirds of the deaths are caused by thrombosis of one or more of the coronary arteries and the remaining one third by thrombosis or hemorrhage of vessels in other organs of the body—especially the brain, the kidneys, the liver, the gastrointestinal tract, the limbs, and so forth.

Despite the extreme prevalence of athero-sclerosis, very little is known about its cause. Therefore, it is necessary to outline the general trends of the experimental studies rather than to present a definitive description of the mechanisms which cause atherosclerosis.

Experimental Production of Atherosclerosis in Animals

Very severe atherosclerosis can be produced easily in rabbits by simply feeding them large quantities of cholesterol. Rabbits normally have no cholesterol in their diet, for cholesterol is not present in plants, which constitute their entire dietary intake. Therefore, the metabolic processes of the rabbit are not adapted to utilize the ingested cholesterol. Instead, the cholesterol precipitates in many areas of the body, especially in the liver and in the subintimal layer of the arteries.

In carnivorous animals such as the dog, the production of atherosclerosis is usually much more difficult, but it can be caused in most instances by excessive administration of cholesterol after the thyroid gland has been removed or inhibited by propylthiouracil. Loss of thyroid secretion greatly depresses cholesterol utilization, thus allowing much of the ingested cholesterol to deposit in the arterial walls.

As pointed out above in relation to the metabolism of cholesterol, the plasma cholesterol concentration increases in either a human being or an experimental animal that has a very high fat diet. On the other hand, substitution of unsaturated fats for saturated fats usually decreases the cholesterol level and, in some experimental animals at least, also inhibits the development of atherosclerosis. However, use of unsaturated fats as a substitute for saturated fats in patients with severe atherosclerosis has yet to be proved a valuable therapeutic measure.

Synthesis of Cholesterol by the Arterial Wall. In experimental animals the arterial wall itself can synthesize cholesterol in significant quantities. On the basis of this, it has been suggested that atheromatous deposits of cholesterol might result from local synthesis rather than from deposition of plasma cholesterol. Though the significance of this is yet unknown, it would fit in very well with the fact that many persons develop atherosclerosis even though their plasma cholesterol concentrations are completely normal.

Atherosclerosis in the Human Being

Effect of Age, Sex, and Heredity on Atherosclerosis. Atherosclerosis is mainly a disease of old age, but small atheromatous plaques can often be found even in the arteries of children and almost always in the arteries of young adults. Therefore, the full-blown disease seems to culminate from a lifetime of lipid deposition rather than deposition over a few year's time.

Far more men die of atherosclerotic heart disease than do women. This is especially true of men younger than 50. For this reason, it is believed that the male sex hormone might accelerate the development of atherosclerosis. Another possible explanation of this difference would be that the female sex hormone *protects* a person from atherosclerosis. Indeed, administration of estrogens to men who have already had coronary thromboses seems to decrease the number of secondary coronary attacks. Furthermore, administration of estrogens to chickens with atheromatous plaques in their coronaries has in some instances decreased the degree of the disease.

Atherosclerosis and atherosclerotic heart disease are highly hereditary in some families. In some instances, this is related to an inherited hypercholesterolemia, but in other instances the blood cholesterol level is completely normal, indicating that some other abnormality might also be inherited that can cause the development of atheromatous plaques in the arteries. Inheritance of the tendency to atherosclerosis is often caused by dominant genes, which means that once this trait enters a family a very high incidence of the disease occurs among the offspring.

Other Diseases That Predispose to Atherosclerosis. Human beings with severe *diabetes* or severe *hypothyroidism* frequently develop premature and very severe atherosclerosis. In both of these conditions the blood cholesterol is greatly elevated. Thus, in these two diseases, the general cause of atherosclerosis seems to be the excess quantity of cholesterol in the plasma.

Another disease associated with atherosclerosis, in human beings as well as in experimental animals, is hypertension; the incidence of atherosclerotic coronary heart disease is about twice as great in hypertensives as in normal persons. Though the cause of this is not known, it possibly results from pressure damage to the arterial walls with subsequent deposition of cholesterol plaques.

Relationship of Dietary Fat to Atherosclerosis in the Human Being. There is much experimental evidence that eating a high fat diet, especially saturated fats, will increase one's chances of developing atherosclerosis. It is possible that a high cholesterol diet might predispose at least to some extent to atherosclerosis, though, as discussed earlier in the chapter, a high cholesterol diet is actually not so productive of a high cholesterol level in the blood as is a high total fat diet. In essence, then, there is much reason to believe that decreasing one's dietary fat can help greatly in protecting against atherosclerosis, and some experiments indicate that this can benefit even patients who have already had coronary heart attacks. Also, life insurance statistics show that the rate of mortality — mainly from coronary disease — of normal weight older age persons is about one-half the mortality rate of overweight subjects of the same age.

Relationship of Blood Lipids to Atherosclerosis. Much of the above discussion has already pointed out that atherosclerosis often occurs when the plasma cholesterol is high, but it can also occur in the absence of high cholesterol for reasons not yet understood.

There is also a correlation between atherosclerosis and the concentration low density lipoproteins in the plasma, especially those in the density range between Sf-12 and Sf-20. The significence of this relationship is unknown.

Summary of Factors Causing Atherosclerosis

In summary, atherosclerosis is almost certainly caused by an abnormality of lipid metabolism, but it is also exacerbated by almost any factor that injures the arterial wall. Especially is an elevated blood cholesterol often related to atherosclerosis, but the presence of excess low density lipoproteins may also be an important factor in the genesis of this disease. Finally, perhaps more important than any of these might be some yet undiscovered third factor which is inherited from generation to generation to cause an increased rate of cholesterol production or deposition in the arterial walls themselves, irrespective of the blood cholesterol concentration.

REFERENCES

Bloom, B., Kiyasu, J. Y., Reinhardt, W. O., and Chaikoff, I. L.: Absorption of phospholipids; manner of transport from intestinal lumen to lacteals. *Am. J. Physiol.*, 177:84, 1954.

Campbell, J., and Best, C. H.: Physiologic aspects of ketosis. *Metabolism*, 5:95, 1956.

Cavert, H. M., and Johnson, J. A.: Metabolism of carboxyl-labeled short chain fatty acids by the isolated dog heart. *Am. J. Physiol.*, 184:582, 1956.

Chapman, D. D., Chaikoff, I. L., and Dauben, W. G.: Acetoacetate formation in liver. IV. Studies with pentadecanoin-l-C14, -5-C14, and -14-C14. *J. Biol. Chem.*, 222:363, 1956.

Cook, R. P.: Cholesterol. New York, Academic Press, 1958.

Deuel, H. J., Jr.: The Lipids: Their Chemistry and Biochemistry. New York, Interscience Publishers, Volume I, 1951; Volume II, 1955; Volume III, 1957.

Di Luzio, N. R., Shore, M. L., and Zilversmit, D. B.:

Anerobic Energy during Anoxia. One of the prime examples of anerobic energy utilization occurs in acute anoxia. When a person stops breathing, he already has a small amount of oxygen stored in his lungs and an additional amount stored in the hemoglobin of his blood. However, these are sufficient to keep the metabolic processes functioning for only about two minutes. Any anoxia beyond this period of time requires an additional source of energy. This can be derived for perhaps another minute or so from glycolysis, the glycogen of the cells splitting into pyruvic acid and the pyruvic acid in turn becoming lactic acid and diffusing into the tissue fluids as described in Chapter 65.

Anerobic Energy Usage in Strenuous Bursts of Activity. It is common knowledge that muscles can perform extreme feats of strength for a few seconds but are much less capable during prolonged activity. The energy used during strenuous activity is derived from: (1) adenosine triphosphate already present in the muscle cells, (2) stored creatine phosphate in the cells, (3) anaerobic energy released by glycolytic breakdown of glycogen to lactic acid, and (4) oxidative energy released continuously by oxidative processes in the cells. The oxidative processes cannot operate anywhere nearly rapidly enough to supply all the energy demands during strenuous bursts of activity. Therefore, the other three sources of energy are called upon to their maximum extent.

The amount of adenosine triphosphate in cells is only about 5 millimols per liter of intracellular fluid, and this amount can maintain maximum muscle contraction for less than one-half second. The amount of creatine phosphate in the cells may be as much as 10 times this amount, but even by utilization of all the creatine phosphate, the amount of time that maximum contraction can be maintained is still only a few seconds. Release of energy by glycolysis can occur much more rapidly than can oxidative release of energy. Consequently, most of the extra energy required during very strenuous periods of activity that last for more than 10 seconds but less than 2 minutes is derived from anaerobic glycolysis. As a result, the glycogen content of muscles after strenuous bouts of exercise becomes almost zero, while the lactic acid concentration of the blood rises to a very high level. Then, immediately after the exercise is over, oxidative metabolism is used to reconvert most of the lactic acid into glucose. This reconversion occurs principally in the liver cells, and the glucose is then transported in the blood back to the muscles where it is stored once more in the form of glycogen. On the average, approximately 1 mol of lactic acid is oxidized for each 5 mols of lactic acid reconverted into glucose.

Oxygen Debt. After a period of strenuous exercise is over, the oxidative metabolic processes continue to operate at a high level of activity for many minutes to (1) reconvert the lactic acid into glucose and (2) reconvert the decomposed adenosine triphosphate and creatine phosphate back into their original states. The oxygen that must be used to rebuild these substances is called the *oxygen debt*. This is illustrated in Figure 656 by the shaded area. This figure shows, first, the normal rate of energy expenditure by the body, and, second, the normal rate of oxidative metabolism. At the three-minute mark, the person exercises very strongly for about four minutes. During this period of time the oxidative release of energy provides some of the energy expenditure, but a large share of energy expenditure occurs principally at the expense of glycolysis. At the end of exercise, the oxidative release of energy continues to be high while the rate of energy expenditure returns to normal. The excess oxidative metabolism that must occur even after the period of exercise is over, as represented by the shaded area in the figure, represents the oxygen debt. This is usually expressed in terms of the oxygen that must be utilized to provide this excess metabolism.

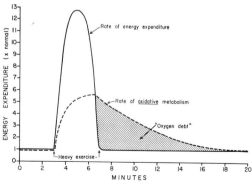

Figure 656.   Oxygen debt occurring after a bout of strenuous exercise.

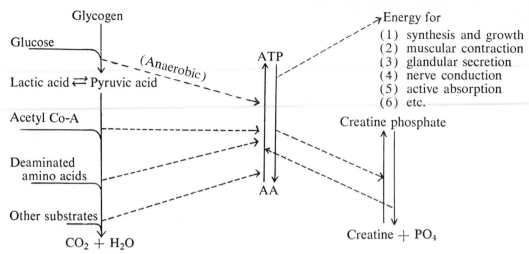

Figure 657. Overall schema of energy transfer from foods to the adenylic acid system and then to the functional elements of the cells. (Modified from Soskin and Levine: Carbohydrate Metabolism. University of Chicago Press.)

Summary of Energy Utilization by the Cells

With the background of the past few chapters and of the above discussion, we can now synthesize a composite picture of overall energy utilization by the cells as illustrated in Figure 657. This figure shows the anerobic utilization of glycogen and glucose to form adenosine triphosphate and also the aerobic utilization of compounds derived from carbohydrates, fats, proteins, and other substances for the formation of still additional adenosine triphosphate. In turn, the adenosine triphosphate is in reversible equilibrium with creatine phosphate in the cells, and, since large quantities of creatine phosphate are present in the cell, much of the stored energy of the cell is in this energy storehouse.

In turn, energy from adenosine triphosphate can be utilized by the different functioning systems of the cells to provide for synthesis and growth, muscular contraction, glandular secretion, impulse conduction, active absorption, and many other cellular activities. If greater amounts of energy are called forth for cellular activities than can be provided by oxidative metabolism, then the creatine phosphate storehouse is first utilized and this is followed rapidly by anerobic breakdown of glycogen. Thus, oxidative metabolism cannot deliver energy to the cells nearly so rapidly as can the anaerobic processes, but in contrast it is quantitatively almost inexhaustible.

Control of Energy Release in the Cell. Almost none of the chemical reactions that cause the breakdown of foods will occur unless *adenosine diphosphate* is available to couple with the reactions and thereby receive the released energy. Therefore, when all the adenosine diphosphate of the cells has been converted to adenosine triphosphate, both glycolysis and oxidative metabolism will come to a halt. However, just as soon as any of the functioning systems of the cells degrade adenosine triphosphate into adenosine diphosphate, immediately the energy acceptor, adenosine diphosphate, becomes available so that all the oxidative and glycolytic reactions are set into force again. *Thus, the rate of energy release in the cell is controlled by the quantity of ADP in the cells.*

METABOLIC RATE

The *metabolism* of the body means simply the total of all the chemical reactions in all the cells of the body, and the *metabolic rate* is normally expressed in terms of the rate of heat liberation during the chemical reactions.

Heat as the Common Denominator of All the Energy Released in the Body. In discussing many of the metabolic reactions of the previous chapters, we have noted that not all the energy in the foods is transferred to adenosine triphosphate, but, instead, large portions of this becomes heat. On the average, about 61 per cent of all the energy in the foods becomes heat during the process of adenosine triphosphate formation. Then still more energy becomes heat as it is transferred from the adenosine triphosphate to the functional systems of the cells, so that finally not more than about 25 per cent of all the energy initially in the food is utilized by the functional systems.

Even though 25 per cent of the energy finally reaches the functional systems of the cells, the major proportion of this also becomes heat for the following reasons: We might first consider the synthesis of protein and other growing elements of the body. When proteins are synthesized, large portions of adenosine triphosphate are used to form the peptide linkages, and this stores energy in these linkages. But we also noted in our discussions of proteins in Chapter 67 that there is continuous turnover of proteins, some being degraded while others are being formed. When the proteins are degraded, the energy stored in the peptide linkages is released in the form of heat into the body.

Now let us consider the energy used for muscle activity. Much of this energy simply overcomes the viscosity of the muscles themselves or of the tissues so that the limbs can move. The viscous movement in turn causes friction within the tissues, which generates heat.

We might also consider the energy expended by the heart in pumping blood. This distends the arterial system, the distention in itself representing a reservoir of potential energy. However, as the blood flows through the peripheral vessels, the friction of the different layers of blood flowing over each other and the friction of the blood against the walls of the vessels turns this energy into heat.

Therefore, we can say that essentially all the energy expended by the body is converted into heat. The only real exception to this occurs when the muscles are used to perform some form of work outside the body. For instance, when the muscles elevate an object to a high height or carry the person's body up steps, a type of potential energy is thus created by raising a mass against gravity. Also, if muscular energy is used to turn a flywheel so that kinetic energy is developed in the flywheel, this, too, would be external expenditure of energy. But, when external expenditure of energy is not taking place, it is safe to consider that all the energy re-leased by the metabolic processes eventually becomes heat.

The Calorie. To discuss the metabolic rate and related subjects intelligently, it is necessary to use some unit for expressing the quantity of energy released from the different foods or expended by the different functional processes of the body. In general, the *Calorie* is the unit used for this purpose. It will be recalled that one *calorie*, spelled with a small "c," is the quantity of heat required to raise the temperature of 1 gram of water 1 degree centigrade. The "calorie" is much too small a unit for ease of expression in speaking of energy in the body. Consequently the large Calorie, spelled with a capital "C," which is equivalent to 1,000 calories, is the unit ordinarily used in discussing energy metabolism.

Measurement of Metabolic Rate

Direct Calorimetry. As pointed out above, it is only when the body performs some external work that energy expended within the body does not become heat. Since a person is ordinarily not performing any external work, his metabolic rate can be very adequately determined by simply measuring the total quantity of heat liberated from the body in a given period of time. This method is called *direct calorimetry*.

In determining the metabolic rate by direct calorimetry the quantity of heat liberated from the body is measured in a large, specially constructed *calorimeter* as follows: The subject is placed in an air chamber so well insulated that no heat can leak through the walls of the chamber. As heat is formed by his body, it warms the air of the chamber. However, the air temperature within the chamber is maintained at a constant value by forcing the air through pipes in a cool water bath. The rate of heat gain by the water bath, therefore, will be equal to the rate at which heat is liberated by the subject's body.

Obviously, the process of direct calorimetry is physically difficult to perform and, therefore, is used only for research purposes.

Indirect Calorimetry. The quantity of energy liberated as a result of metabolizing carbohydrates, fats, and proteins can be expressed in terms of the energy liberated per liter of oxygen metabolized with each type of food, as well as in terms of energy liberated per gram of food burned. For instance, when one liter of oxygen under standard conditions is metabolized with glucose, 5.01 Calories of energy are released; when metabolized with starches, 5.06 Calories of energy are released; with fat, 4.70 Calories; and with protein, 4.60 Calories.

From the above figures it is quite striking how nearly equivalent are the quantities of energy liberated per liter of oxygen when metabolizing any one of the types of food. For the average diet, the *quantity of energy liberated per liter of oxygen utilized in the body averages approximately 4.825 Calories.* Therefore, it is possible to calculate approximately the total quantity of heat liberated in the body from the quantity of oxygen utilized in a given period of time by using this average *energy equivalent* of oxygen.

If a subject should metabolize only carbohydrates during the period of the basal metabolism test, the calculated quantity of energy liberated based on the value for the average energy equivalent of oxygen, 4.825 Calories per liter, would be approximately 4 per cent too little. On the other hand, if the subject were obtaining most of his energy from protein, the calculated value would be approximately 4 per cent too great, and, if he were burning almost entirely fat during the period of the test, the error would be insignificant.

It is obvious, then, that calculating the quantity of energy liberated in the body from the quantity of oxygen utilized by the body in a given period of time cannot be in error by more than approximately 4 per cent. This 4 per cent is far less than many other possible errors and, therefore, is considered to be insignificant. Indeed, it is probable that values for metabolic rate are more accurately determined by the method of indirect calorimetry than by the much more cumbersome and more difficult method of direct calorimetry.

Another real advantage of indirect calorimetry over direct calorimetry is that this method measures the total energy expenditure even when energy is being used to perform work outside the body, while direct calorimetry does not record the energy used for this external work.

The metabolator. Figure 658 illustrates

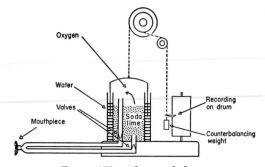

Figure 658. The metabolator.

the metabolator usually used for indirect calorimetry. This apparatus contains a floating drum, under which is an oxygen chamber connected to a mouthpiece through two rubber tubes. A valve in one of these rubber tubes allows air to pass from the oxygen chamber into the mouth through this tube, while air passing from the mouth back to the chamber is directed by means of another valve through the second tube. Before the expired air from the mouth enters the upper portion of the oxygen chamber, it flows through a lower chamber containing pellets of soda lime, which combine chemically with the carbon dioxide in the expired air. Therefore, as oxygen is used by the subject's body and the carbon dioxide is absorbed by the soda lime, the floating oxygen chamber, which is precisely balanced by a weight, gradually sinks in the water owing to the oxygen loss. This chamber is appropriately coupled to a pen that records on a moving drum the rate at which the chamber sinks in the water and thereby records the rate at which the body utilizes oxygen.

Factors That Affect the Metabolic Rate

Any factor that increases the chemical activity in the cells will increase the metabolic rate. Some of these are the following:

Effect of Exercise on Metabolic Rate. The factor that causes by far the most dramatic effect on metabolic rate is strenuous exercise. Short bursts of maximal muscle contraction in any single muscle liberates several hundred times its normal resting amount of heat. In considering the entire body, however, maximal muscle exercise can increase the overall heat production of the body for a few seconds at a time to about 50 times normal or for prolonged periods of time to about 20 times normal, which is an increase in metabolic rate to 2,000 per cent of normal.

Energy requirements for daily activities. When an average man of 70 kilograms lies in bed, he utilizes approximately 1650 Calories of energy. The process of eating increases the total amount of energy utilized each day by an additional 200 or more Calories so that the same man lying in bed and also eating a reasonable diet requires a dietary intake of approximately 1850 Calories per day. If he sits in a chair all day, his total energy requirement reaches 2000 to 2250 Calories. Therefore, in round figures, it can be assumed that the daily energy requirements simply for existing (that is, performing no non-essential functions) is around 2,000 Calories.

Table 24. Energy Expenditure per Hour During Different Types of Activity for a 70 Kilogram Man

Form of Activity	Calories per hour
Sleeping	65
Awake lying still	77
Sitting at rest	100
Standing relaxed	105
Dressing and undressing	118
Tailoring	135
Typewriting rapidly	140
"Light" exercise	170
Walking slowly (2.6 miles per hour)	200
Carpentry, metal working, industrial painting	240
"Active" exercise	290
"Severe" exercise	450
Sawing wood	480
Swimming	500
Running (5.3 miles per hour)	570
"Very severe" exercise	600
Walking very fast (5.3 miles per hour)	650
Walking up stairs	1100

Extracted from data compiled by Professor M. S. Rose.

Effects of different types of work on daily energy requirements. Table 24 illustrates the rates of energy utilization while one performs different types of activities. It is obvious from this table that walking up stairs requires approximately 17 times as much energy as lying in bed asleep. And, in general, a laborer can, over a 24-hour period, average a rate of energy utilization as great as 6,000 to 7,000 Calories, or, in other words, as much as 3½ times the basal rate of metabolism.

Specific Dynamic Action of Food. After a meal is eaten, the metabolic rate in-creases. This is believed to result partly from the different chemical reactions associated with digestion, absorption, and storage of food in the body. However, it is also known that certain ones of the amino acids derived from the proteins of the ingested food have a direct stimulatory effect on cellular chemical processes.

After a meal containing a large quantity of carbohydrates, the metabolic rate usually increases about 4 per cent, but it has been observed to increase to as high as 30 per cent above normal, this increase lasting from 2 to 5 hours. After a meal containing mainly fat, the metabolic rate also normally rises about 4 per cent, but, here again, it has been observed to rise to as high as 10 to 15 per cent above normal, the effect sometimes lasting 7 to 9 hours. After a meal containing large quantities of proteins, the metabolic rate usually begins rising within one to two hours, reaches a maximum usually about 30 per cent above normal but sometimes as high as 50 to 70 per cent above normal, and lasts for as long as 10 to 12 hours. This effect of the different foods on the metabolic rate is called the *specific dynamic action* of food.

The much greater specific dynamic action of proteins than of carbohydrates and fats is probably caused by two factors: First, a greater number of energy-releasing chemical reactions occur during protein digestion, absorption, and metabolism than during digestion of the other two types of food. Second, certain amino acids seem to have a direct stimulatory effect on all chemical reactions of the cell—much the same effect as epinephrine on the metabolic rate, which will be discussed below.

Age. The metabolic rate of the newborn child in relation to his body surface area is almost two times that of a very old person. This is illustrated in Figure 659, which shows the metabolic rates of both males and females from birth until very old age. The very high metabolic rate of young children results from very high rates of cellular reactions, but also partly from very rapid synthesis of cellular materials and growth of the body, which require moderate quantities of energy.

Thyroid Hormone. When the thyroid gland secretes maximal quantities of thyroxine, the metabolic rate sometimes rises to as much as 100 per cent above normal. On the other hand, total loss of thyroid secretion de-

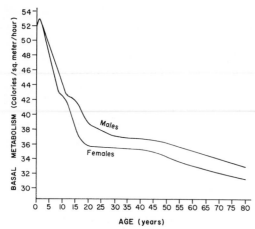

Figure 659. Normal basal metabolic rates at different ages for each sex.

creases the metabolic rate to as low as 50 per cent normal. These effects can readily be explained by the basic function of thyroxine to increase the rates of activity of almost all the chemical reactions in all cells of the body. Obviously, the metabolic rate would be expected to rise when the amount of thyroxine secreted increases. This relationship between thyroxine and metabolic rate will be discussed in much greater detail in Chapter 75 in relation to thyroid function, because one of the most useful methods for diagnosing abnormal rates of thyroid secretion is to determine the basal metabolic rate of the patient. A normal person usually has a basal metabolic rate within 10 to 15 per cent of normal, while the hyperthyroid person often has a basal metabolic rate as high as 40 to 80 per cent above normal, and a hypothyroid person can have a basal metabolic rate as low as 40 to 50 per cent below normal.

Epinephrine and Sympathetic Stimulation. Stimulation of the sympathetic nervous system with liberation of nor-epinephrine and epinephrine greatly increases the metabolic rates of essentially all the tissues of the body. Epinephrine, especially, and nor-epinephrine, to a much less extent, have a direct effect on cells to cause glycogenolysis, and this, probably along with other intracellular effects of these hormones, increases cellular activity.

Maximal stimulation of the sympathetic nervous system increases the metabolic rate about 150 per cent, as will be discussed in the following chapter. This is one of the im-

portant means by which the body is capable of regulating its temperature even when the surroundings become extremely cold.

Male Sex Hormone. The male sex hormone can increase the basal metabolic rate about 10 to 15 per cent, and the female sex hormone can perhaps increase the metabolic rate a few per cent, but usually not enough to be of great significance. The difference in metabolic rates of males and females is illustrated in Fig. 659.

Growth Hormone. Growth hormone can increase the basal metabolic rate as much as 15 to 20 per cent as a result of direct stimulation of cellular metabolism. This is presumably very much the same effect as the effect of growth in childhood on metabolism.

Fever. Fever, regardless of its cause, increases the metabolic rate. The reason for this is that all chemical reactions, either in the body or in the test tube, increase their rates of reaction approximately 130 per cent for every 10° C. rise in temperature. An increase in body temperature to 110° F. increases the metabolic rate almost 100 per cent.

Climate. Studies of metabolic rates of persons living in the different zones of the earth have shown as much as 10 to 20 per cent lower metabolic rates in tropical regions than in cold regions. This difference is caused to a great extent by adaptation of the thyroid gland, with increased secretion in cold climates and decreased secretion in hot climates. Indeed, far more persons develop hyperthyroidism in temperate regions of the earth than in tropical regions.

Sleep. The metabolic rate falls approximately 10 to 15 per cent below normal during sleep. This fall is presumably due to two principal factors: (1) decreased tone of the skeletal musculature during sleep and (2) decreased activity of the sympathetic nervous system.

Malnutrition. Prolonged malnutrition often decreases the metabolic rate as much as 20 to 30 per cent; this decrease is presumably caused by the paucity of necessary food substances in the cells.

In the final stages of many disease conditions, the inanition that accompanies the disease frequently causes marked pre-mortem decrease in metabolic rate, even to the extent that the body temperature may fall a number of degrees shortly before death.

Basal Metabolic Rate

The Basal Metabolic Rate as a Method for Comparing Metabolic Rates between Individuals.

During violent exercise, the metabolic rate of the body can sometimes rise to as high as 20 times the resting rate even for prolonged periods of time, which is a 2,000 per cent change in metabolic rate. Furthermore, many of the other factors listed above can change the metabolic rate as much as 100 to 200 per cent. Therefore, it has been extremely important to establish a procedure that will measure the inherent activity of the tissues independently of exercise and other extraneous factors that would make it impossible to compare one person's metabolic rate with that of another person. To do this, the metabolic rate is measured under so-called *basal conditions*, and the metabolic rate then measured is called the *basal metabolic rate*.

Basal Conditions. The basal metabolic rate means the rate of energy utilization in the body during absolute rest but while the person is awake. The following basal conditions are necessary for measuring the basal metabolic rate:

1. The person must not have eaten any food for at least 12 hours because of the specific dynamic action of foods, as discussed above.

2. The basal metabolic rate is determined after a night of restful sleep, for rest reduces the activity of the sympathetic nervous system and of other metabolic excitants to their minimal level.

3. No strenuous exercise is performed after the night of restful sleep, and the person must remain at complete rest in a reclining position for at least 30 minutes prior to actual determination of the metabolic rate. This is perhaps the most important of all the conditions for attaining the basal state because of the effect of exercise on metabolism, as discussed above.

4. All psychic and physical factors that cause excitement must be eliminated, and the subject must be made as comfortable as possible. These conditions, obviously, help to reduce the degree of sympathetic activity to as little as possible.

5. The temperature of the air must be comfortable and somewhere between the limits of 62° and 87° F. Below 62° F. the sympathetic nervous system becomes progressively more activated to help maintain body heat, and above 87° F. sweating and other factors increase the metabolic rate.

Usual Technique for Determining Basal Metabolic Rate.

The usual method for determining basal metabolic rate is first to establish the subject under basal conditions and then to measure his rate of oxygen utilization with a metabolator of the type illustrated in Figure 658. Then the basal metabolic rate is calculated as follows:

15 liters	— O_2 at standard conditions consumed in 1 hr.
$\times 4.825$	— Calories liberated per liter of O_2 burned
72.4	— Calories liberated per hour
$\div 1.5$	— Body surface area in square meters
48.3	— Calories per square meter per hour
-38.5	— Normal value for 20-year-old man
9.8	— Excess Calories above normal

$$\frac{9.8 \times 100}{38.5} = 25.5 \text{ per cent above normal}$$

$$BMR = +25.5$$

Figure 660. Calculation of basal metabolic rate from the rate of oxygen consumption.

In the upper portion of Figure 660, the quantity of heat liberated in the body of a patient is calculated from the quantity of oxygen utilized. In this figure, it is noted that 15 liters of oxygen (after being corrected to standard conditions) are consumed in one hour. Multiplying this times the energy equivalent for 1 liter of oxygen, 4.825 Calories, the total quantity of energy liberated within the body during this period of 1 hour is 72.4 Calories.

Expression of Basal Metabolic Rate in Terms of Surface Area.

Obviously, if one subject is much larger than another, the total amount of energy utilized by the two subjects will be considerably different simply because of differences in body size. Experimentally, among normal persons the average basal metabolic rate varies approximately *in proportion with the body surface area*. Originally, it was believed that the reason for this proportionality might be that the larger the surface area, the greater is the area through which heat can be lost from the body. However, much experience has shown that this is not the reason why the basal metabolic rates of different persons vary according to the surface area; instead, this relationship is only an empirical one.

Referring once again to Figure 660 it will be noted that the total number of Calories liberated by the patient per hour is divided by his total body surface area of 1.5 square meters. This means that his basal metabolic rate is 48.3 Calories per square meter per hour.

Method for calculating the total surface area. The surface area of the body varies approximately in proportion to weight $^{0.67}$. However, more accurate measurements of the body surface area have shown that it can be determined more accurately by a complicated formula based on weight and height of the subject as follows:

Body surface area =
$$\text{Weight}^{0.425} \times \text{Height}^{0.725} \times 0.007184$$

Figure 661 presents a graph based on this formula. In the formula and in the figure, body surface area is expressed in *square meters*, weight in *kilograms*, and height in *centimeters*.

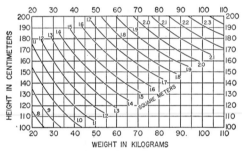

Figure 661. Relationship of height and weight to body surface area. (From DuBois: Metabolism in Health and Disease. Lea & Febiger.)

Expression of Basal Metabolic Rate in Terms of Weight. Measurement of the basal metabolic rates of many different species of animals has shown that the rates do not vary precisely in proportion to the body surface area. Instead, in animals ranging in size from the mouse to the horse, the basal metabolic rate has been found to be proportional to weight $^{0.734}$. Because surface area is approximately proportional to weight $^{0.67}$, it is obvious that correlating basal metabolic rates between animal species on the basis of surface areas would be in extreme error. This fact has considerable implication in human physiology and in clinical medicine, for some physiologists believe that even in comparing basal metabolic rates between human beings the factor weight $^{0.734}$ should be used instead of surface area. *If this is true, overweight subjects would have to have basal metabolic rates considerably above the mean as based on the surface area method in order to be normal, and very thin subjects would have to have basal metabolic rates considerably less than the mean as based on the surface area method in order to be normal.*

Expression of Basal Metabolic Rate in Percentage Above or Below Normal. In Fig. 659 it will be noted that the basal metabolic rate varies tremendously with age; also, males in general have a basal metabolic rate approximately 8 per cent greater per square meter than that of females. Therefore, to compare the basal metabolic rate of any one subject with the normal basal metabolic rate, it is necessary to refer to a chart such as that in Figure 659, which gives the normal basal metabolic rate per square meter at each age and for each sex. Once reference has been made to such a chart, the basal metabolic rate is ordinarily expressed as a percentage above or below normal. For example, in Figure 659 the normal basal metabolic rate for a 20-year-old male is shown to be 38.5 Calories per square meter per hour. Therefore, if the particular patient represented in the calculations of Figure 660 is a 20-year-old male, he liberates 9.8 Calories per square meter per hour above the normal mean value. It is then determined that this is 25.5 per cent above normal. Therefore, the basal metabolic rate is expressed as plus 25.5. Similarly, basal metabolic rates below normal are expressed as minus values.

Constancy of Basal Metabolic Rate in the Same Person. Basal metabolic rates have been measured in many subjects at repeated intervals for as long as 20 or more years. As long as a subject remains healthy, almost invariably his basal metabolic rate as expressed in percentage of normal does not vary more than 5 to 10 per cent.

Constancy of Basal Metabolic Rate from Person to Person. When the basal metabolic rate is measured in a wide variety of different persons and comparisons are made within single age, weight, and sex groups, 85 per cent of normal persons have been found to have basal metabolic rates within 10 per cent of the mean. Thus, it is obvious that measurements of metabolic rates performed under basal conditions offer an excellent means for comparing the rates of metabolism from one person to another.

REFERENCES

Bozler, E.: Plasticity of contractile elements of muscle as studied in extracted muscle fibers. *Am. J. Physiol., 171:*359, 1952.

Bozler, E.: The role of phosphocreatine and adenosinetriphosphate in muscular contraction. *J. Gen. Physiol.*, 37:63, 1953.

Bozler, E., and Prince, J. T.: The control of energy release in extracted muscle fibers. *J. Gen. Physiol.*, 37:53, 1953.

Buchtal, F., Svensmark, O., and Rosenfalck, P.: Mechanical and chemical events in muscle contraction. *Physiol. Rev.*, 36:503, 1956.

Chance, B.: Enzymes in action in living cells: the steady state of reduced pyridine nucleotides. *Harvey Lect.*, 49:145, 1953–1954.

Conway, E. J.: Nature and significance of concentration relations of potassium and sodium ions in skeletal muscle. *Physiol. Rev.*, 37:84, 1957.

Crowell, J. W.: A continuous recording oxygen debt analyzer. *Fed. Proc.*, 19:102, 1960.

Drummond, G. I., and Black, E. C.: Comparative physiology: fuel of muscle metabolism. *Ann. Rev. of Physiol.*, 22:169, 1960.

Greenberg, D. M.: Chemical Pathways of Metabolism. New York, Academic Press, 1954.

Guyton, A. C., and Farish, C. A.: A rapidly responding continuous oxygen consumption recorder. *J. App. Physiol.*, 14:143, 1959.

Hasselbach, W., and Weber, A.: Models for the study of the contraction of muscle and of cell protoplasm. *Pharmacol. Rev.*, 7:97, 1955.

Hsia, D. Y.: Inborn Errors of Metabolism. Chicago, Year Book Publishers, 1959.

Huxley, A. F.: Local activation of striated muscle from the frog and the crab. *J. Physiol.*, 135:171, 1957.

Huxley, A. F.: Muscle structure and theories of contraction. *Prog. Biophys.*, 7:255, 1957.

Huxley, A. F., and Niedergerke, R.: Measurement of muscle striations in stretch and contraction. *J. Physiol.*, 124:461, 1954.

Huxley, A. F., and Niedergerke, R.: Structural changes in muscle during contraction; interference microscopy of living muscle fibers. *Nature, 173:* 971, 1954.

Huxley, A. F., and Taylor, R. E.: Function of Krause's membrane. *Nature, 176:*1068, 1955.

Klotz, I. M.: Some Principles of Energetics in Biochemical Reactions. New York, Academic Press, 1957.

Laidler, K. J.: Introduction to the Chemistry of Enzymes. New York, McGraw-Hill Book Co., Inc., 1954.

Lipmann, F.: Biosynthetic mechanisms. *Harvey Lect., 44:*99, 1948–1949.

Mommaerts, W. F.: Investigation of the presumed breakdown of adenosine-triphosphate and phosphocreatine during a single muscle twitch. *Am. J. Physiol.*, 182:585, 1955.

Mommaerts, W. F.: Is adenosine triphosphate broken down during a single muscle twitch? *Nature, 174:* 1083, 1954.

Mommaerts, W. F.: The effect of adenosine triphosphate upon actomyosin solutions, studied with a recording dual beam light-scattering photometer. *J. Gen. Physiol.*, 39:821, 1956.

Mommaerts, W. F.: The proteins of muscle and their participation in the process of contraction. *Am. J. Phys. Med.*, 34:11,1955.

Mommaerts, W. F., and Hanson, J.: The effect upon actomyosin of stoichiometric amounts of adenosinetriphosphate regenerated in a coupled enzyme system. *J. Gen. Physiol.*, 39:831, 1956.

Neilands, J. B., and Stumpf, P. K.: Outlines of Enzyme Chemistry. New York, John Wiley & Sons, 1955.

Pearl, D. C., Jr., Carlson, L. D., and Sherwood, W. W.: Mechanism of oxygen deficit. *Proc. Soc. Exp. Biol. & Med.*, 92:277, 1956.

Perry, S. V.: Relation between chemical and contractile function and structure of skeletal muscle cell. *Physiol. Rev.*, 36:1, 1956.

Szent-Gyorgyi, A. G.: Bioenergetics. New York, Academic Press, 1957.

Szent-Gyorgyi, A. G.: Structural and functional aspects of myosin. *Adv. Enzymol.*, 16:313, 1955.

Szent-Gyorgyi, A. G., Mazia, D., and Szent-Gyorgyi, A.: On the nature of the cross-striation of body muscle. *Biochim. Biophys. Acta*, 16:339, 1955.

Theorell, H., and Duve, C. Dé: Myohemoglobin. *Arch. Biochem.*, 12:113, 1947.

Umbreit, W. W.: Metabolic Maps. Minneapolis, Burgess Publishing Co., 1952.

Watanabe, S., and Sleator, W., Jr.: EDTA relaxation of glycerol-treated muscle fibers, and the effects of magnesium, calcium and manganese ions. *Arch. Biochem.*, 68:81, 1957.

Weber, H. H.: Adenosine triphosphate and motility of living systems. *Harvey Lect.*, 49:37, 1953–1954.

Chapter 69

Dietary Balances; Regulation of Feeding; Obesity; Starvation

In the nutrition of the human being, or of any animal for that matter, the intake of food must always be sufficient to supply the metabolic needs of the body, but on the other hand, if the intake is too great, obesity will result. And, since different foods contain different proportions of proteins, carbohydrates, or fats, an appropriate balance must be maintained between these different types of food so that all segments of the body's metabolic systems can be supplied with the requisite materials. This chapter therefore will discuss the problems of balance between the three major types of food and also the mechanisms by which the intake of food is regulated in accordance with the metabolic needs of the body.

DIETARY BALANCES

Energy Available in Foods

The amount of free energy in each gram of the three major foodstuffs—carbohydrates, fats, and proteins—is not the same for each one. For instance, the energy liberated from each gram of carbohydrate as it is oxidized to carbon dioxide and water is 4.1 Calories, and that liberated from fat is 9.3 Calories. The energy liberated from metabolism of the average protein of the diet as each gram is oxidized to carbon dioxide, water, and urea is 4.35 Calories. Also, these different substances vary in the average percentages that are absorbed from the gastrointestinal tract. In the average person approximately 98 per cent of the carbohydrate is absorbed, 95 per cent of the fat, and 92 per cent of the protein. Therefore, in round figures the average *physiologically available energy* in each gram of the three different foodstuffs in the diet is as follows:

Carbohydrates, 4.0 Calories
Fat, 9.0 Calories
Protein, 4.0 Calories

Average Composition of the Diet

The average composition of the diet varies tremendously from one person to another, from one locality to another, and from one part of the world to another. For instance, the average American receives approximately 15 per cent of his energy from protein, about 40 per cent from fat, and about 45 per cent from carbohydrates. In most other parts of the world the quantity of energy derived from carbohydrates far exceeds the quantity of energy derived from both proteins and fats. Indeed, in Mongolia the quantity of energy received from fats and proteins combined is said to be no greater than 15 to 20 per cent.

Daily Requirement for Protein. Some of the proteins of the cells are being continually degraded into amino acids, and the liver continually deaminates a proportion of the amino acids in the blood. Therefore, it is necessary for all cells to continue forming new proteins to take the place of those that are being destroyed, and a supply of protein is needed in the diet for this purpose. An average 70 kg. man can maintain his normal stores of protein provided that his *daily intake of protein is approximately 45 grams.* However, this value varies considerably from one person to another because of differences in ability to absorb proteins, differences in ability of the body to utilize carbohydrates and fats instead of protein for energy, and differences in amounts of energy required by different persons' bodies.

Partial proteins. Another factor that must be considered in analyzing the proteins of the diet is whether the dietary proteins are complete proteins or partial proteins. Complete proteins are proteins that have compositions of amino acids in appropriate proportion to each other so that all the amino acids can be properly used by the human body. In general, proteins derived from animal foodstuffs are more nearly complete than are proteins derived from vegetable and grain sources. This subject is more completely discussed in Chapter 67; therefore, for the present, suffice it to say that when partial proteins are in the diet an increased minimal quantity of protein is necessary in the daily rations to maintain protein balance.

Necessity for Fat in the Diet. The human body is capable of desaturating fatty acids to a very slight extent, this process occurring especially in the liver. However, the liver cannot desaturate many fatty acids to such an extent that several double bonds are formed in the fatty chain. For this reason, some of the more desaturated fatty acids, such as *arachidonic, linoleic,* and *linolenic acids,* appear to be essential constituents of the diet for normal operation of the body. In lower animals, scaling and exudative skin lesions appear when these desaturated fatty acids are totally absent from the diet, and the desaturated fatty acids are probably also of special importance for formation of some of the structural elements of all cells throughout the body because lack of these acids causes failure of growth. How much fat is needed in the diet to supply these desaturated fatty acids has not been determined, but, because Mongolians exist on diets with fat contents as low as 10 per cent, it is presumed that only very small quantities of fat are needed in the diet for this purpose. Therefore, fat is probably needed in the diet more for its energy value than for any other reason.

Necessity for Carbohydrates in the Diet. In the discussion of carbohydrate metabolism in Chapter 65 it was pointed out that failure to metabolize carbohydrate in sufficient quantity causes such rapid metabolism of fats that ketosis is likely to develop. Consequently, one of the most important reasons for having carbohydrate in the diet is to prevent the development of ketosis. Also, fats and proteins alone usually cannot supply sufficient energy for all operations of the human body, and, consequently, carbohydrates appear to be essential to prevent weakness. This is especially true when the body undertakes a considerable work load. Finally, as has already been discussed, carbohydrate is a *fat sparer* and a *protein sparer;* that is, carbohydrate is burned in preference to the burning of fat and protein, and this is especially important for preserving the functional proteins in the cells.

Composition of Different Foods. Table 25 presents the composition of a selected group of foods, illustrating especially the high proportions of fats and proteins in meat products and the high proportions of carbohydrates in most vegetable products.

Fat is deceptive in the diet, for it often exists as 100 per cent fat undiluted by any other substances, whereas essentially all the proteins and carbohydrates of foods are mixed in watery media and often represent less than 25 per cent of the weight of the food. Thus, the fat of one pat of butter mixed with an entire helping of potato may contain as much energy as all the potato itself. This is one of the reasons fats are asiduously avoided in the prescription of diets for weight reduction.

Study of Energy Balances

When the quantity of energy in the food assimilated into the body each day is greater than the quantity of energy expanded by the whole body during the same period of time, a net gain of stored energy occurs, and this in general means a net gain in weight of the person. Therefore, it is quite important in many physiologic studies to compute the intake of food and also to compute at the same time the utilization of the different types of foods by the body. Measurement of the intake of the different types of foods can be accomplished by simply weighing the foods before they are eaten and analyzing these foods for their relative contents of carbohydrates, fats, and protein. Then the loss of foods in the fecal and urinary excretions is subtracted from the intake to determine the *net intake*. Though this is a very laborious procedure, nevertheless, it is necessary for the performance of energy balance experiments. On the other hand, special procedures must be performed for determining the *utilization* of the different types of foods for energy, as follows:

Determination of the Rate of Protein Metabolism in the Body. The average protein of the diet contains approximately 16 per cent nitrogen, and the remaining 84 per cent is composed of carbon, hydrogen, oxygen, and sulfur. It has been found by numerous experiments that when protein is metabolized in the body, the average person will excrete approximately 90 per cent of the nitrogen removed from the protein into the urine in the form of urea, uric acid, creatinine, and other less important nitrogen products. The remaining 10 per cent of the nitrogen from the metabolized protein is ordinarily excreted in the feces. It is possible, therefore, to estimate relatively accurately the total quantity of protein metabolized by the body in a given period of time by analyzing the amount of nitrogen excreted in the urine each day. For instance, if 8 grams of nitrogen are excreted into the urine, this means that 50 grams of protein are metabolized in the body in order to release this quantity of nitrogen. It is reasonable also to assume that an additional 10 per cent of protein (5 grams) is

Table 25.   Protein, Fat, and Carbohydrate Content of Different Foods

Food	Protein, %	Fat, %	Carbohydrate, %	Fuel Value per 100 Grams, Calories
Apples	0.3	0.4	14.9	64
Asparagus	2.2	0.2	3.9	26
Bacon, fat	6.2	76.0	0.7	712
broiled	25.0	55.0	1.0	599
Beef, medium	17.5	22.0	1.0	268
Beets, fresh	1.6	0.1	9.6	46
Bread, white, milk	9.0	3.6	49.8	268
Butter	0.6	81.0	0.4	733
Cabbage	1.4	0.2	5.3	29
Carrots	1.2	0.3	9.3	45
Cashew nuts	19.6	47.2	26.4	609
Cheese, Cheddar, American	23.9	32.3	1.7	393
Chicken, total edible	21.6	2.7	1.0	111
Chocolate	(5.5)	52.9	(18.)	570
Corn (maize), entire	10.0	4.3	73.4	372
Haddock	17.2	0.3	0.5	72
Lamb, leg, intermediate	18.0	17.5	1.0	230
Milk, fresh whole	3.5	3.9	4.9	69
Molasses, medium	0.0	0.0	(60.)	240
Oatmeal, dry, uncooked	14.2	7.4	68.2	396
Oranges	0.9	0.2	11.2	50
Peanuts	26.9	44.2	23.6	600
Peas, fresh	6.7	0.4	17.7	101
Pork, ham, medium	15.2	31.0	1.0	340
Potatoes	2.0	0.1	19.1	85
Spinach	2.3	0.3	3.2	25
Strawberries	0.8	0.6	8.1	41
Tomatoes	1.0	0.3	4.0	23
Tuna, canned	24.2	10.8	0.5	194
Walnuts, English	15.0	64.4	15.6	702

Extracted from data compiled by Chatfield and Adams, U.S. Department of Agriculture Circular No. 549, 1940.

metabolized at the same time because of additional nitrogen excretion in the feces.

"Nitrogen balance" in the body. The total quantity of protein in the body in the average man is approximately 12 kg., this quantity being considerably greater in muscular persons and somewhat less in asthenic persons. A number of factors affect the quantity of protein in the body. For instance, testosterone tends to increase the total protein, while the glucocorticoid adrenocortical hormones tend to decrease the total quantity of protein. Also, febrile diseases and undernutrition tend to decrease the total body protein.

Nitrogen balance experiments are frequently performed to determine the rate of protein increase or decrease in the body. These balance studies are performed by simultaneously measuring the rate of protein intake and protein utilization, the total protein utilization being estimated as 6.9 times the quantity of nitrogen in the urine. (To be more accurate in estimating the protein utilization, the total quantity of nitrogen both in the urine and in the feces in a given period of time may be analyzed separately, then added, and the protein calculated as 6.25 times this value.)

Ordinarily, such nitrogen balance studies are not very valid unless they are continued for a week or more because of the difficulty of maintaining steady rates of protein ingestion and of nitrogen excretion. A *negative nitrogen balance* implies greater protein utilization than protein intake, causing loss of protein from the body, and a *positive nitrogen* balance implies a net gain of protein in the body.

Relative Utilization of Fat and Carbohydrates—The Respiratory Quotient. Referring to Figure 662, it will be noted that when one molecule of glucose is oxidized the number of molecules of carbon dioxide liberated is exactly equal to the number of oxygen molecules necessary for the oxidative process. Therefore, the *respiratory quotient*, which is defined as the *ratio of carbon dioxide output to oxygen intake*, is 1.00. On the other hand, oxidation of triolein (the most abundant fat in the body) liberates 57 carbon dioxide molecules while 80 oxygen molecules are being utilized. Consequently, the respiratory quotient in this instance is 0.71. Finally, it is illustrated that oxidation of alanine liberates 5 carbon dioxide molecules for every 6 oxygen molecules entering into the reaction.

Respiratory Quotient:

$$C_6H_{12}O_6 + 6\ O_2 \rightarrow 6\ CO_2 + 6\ H_2O \qquad \frac{6}{6} = 1.00$$
Glucose

$$C_{57}H_{104}O_6 + 80\ O_2 \rightarrow 57\ CO_2 + 52\ H_2O \qquad \frac{57}{80} = 0.71$$
Triolein

$$2\ C_3H_7O_2N + 6\ O_2 \rightarrow (NH_2)_2CO + 5\ CO_2 + 5\ H_2O \quad \frac{5}{6} = 0.83$$
Alanine

Figure 662.   Utilization of oxygen and release of carbon dioxide during the oxidation of carbohydrate, fat, and protein. The respiratory quotient for each of these reactions is calculated.

Thus, the respiratory quotient for oxidation of alanine is 0.83.

The respiratory quotient for utilization of carbohydrates is always 1.00 because the quantity of oxygen in each carbohydrate molecule is always exactly sufficient to oxidize only the hydrogen within the molecule, and oxidation of each atom of carbon in the molecule requires one molecule of respiratory oxygen. On the other hand, the respiratory quotient of the fat of the diet has been found to average approximately 0.707, while the respiratory quotient of the protein of the diet averages 0.801.

Utilization of the respiratory quotient for estimation of relative rates of carbohydrate and fat metabolism. It has already been pointed out that the average person receives only 10 to 15 per cent of his total energy from protein metabolism. Furthermore, referring to the above paragraph, the respiratory quotient of protein is approximately midway between the respiratory quotients of fat and carbohydrate. Consequently, when the respiratory quotient of a subject is measured by determining the total respiratory intake of oxygen and the total output of carbon dioxide from the lungs, one has a reasonable measure of the relative quantities of fat and carbohydrate being metabolized by the body during that particular interval of time. For instance, if the respiratory quotient is calculated to be approximately 0.71, then it is obvious that the body is currently burning almost entirely fat to the exclusion of carbohydrates and proteins. If, on the other hand, the respiratory quotient is found to be 1.00, it is probable that the body is metabolizing almost entirely carbohydrate to the exclusion of fat and protein. Finally a respiratory quotient of 0.85 would indicate approximately equal utilization of carbohydrate and fat.

To be still more accurate in the calculation of relative quantities of fat and carbohydrate metabolized, it is necessary to consider the portion of the respiratory quotient that is due to protein metabolism. To do this the total quantity of protein being utilized by the body is first determined as discussed above; then the quantities of oxygen utilized and carbon dioxide released as a result of the protein metabolism are calculated and subtracted from the intake of oxygen and output of carbon dioxide, respectively, in order to establish the net respiratory quotient as it applies to fat and carbohydrate metabolism.

Variations in the respiratory quotient. Shortly after a meal, almost all the food metabolized is carbohydrates. Consequently, the respiratory quotient approaches 1.00 at this time. Approximately 8 to 10 hours following a meal, the quantity of carbohydrate being metabolized is relatively slight, and the respiratory quotient approaches that for fat metabolism or, in other words, approximately 0.71.

In diabetes very little carbohydrate is utilized by the body, and, consequently, most of the energy is derived from fat. Therefore, most patients with severe diabetes have a respiratory quotient approaching the value for fat metabolism, 0.71.

It is extremely rare in the human being for the respiratory quotient to become greater than 1.00, but such values have been recorded in animals that are actively converting carbohydrate into fat. When carbohydrate is being converted into fat, considerable oxygen is liberated from the carbohydrate molecule, and this oxygen becomes available for oxidation of other foodstuffs; this lessens the quantity of oxygen that must be brought into the body through the lungs. Consequently, if the animal is at the same time metabolizing only carbohydrates, he will be excreting through his lungs amounts of carbon dioxide greater than the intake of oxygen so that the respiratory quotient may rise to values as high as 1.10 or occasionally higher.

REGULATION OF FOOD INTAKE

Regulation of food intake is principally a nervous phenomenon that utilizes specific centers of the brain that cause the sensation of *hunger* when the food stores of the body are in danger of being depleted, but, on the other hand, cause the sensation of *satiety* when the food stores are abundantly filled.

Hunger

The term "hunger" applies to a craving for food, and it is associated with a number of objective sensations. For instance, in Chapter 61 it was pointed out that in a person who has not had food for many hours, the stomach undergoes intense rhythmical contractions called *hunger contractions*. These cause a tight or a gnawing feeling in the pit of the stomach and sometimes actually cause pain called *hunger pangs*. In addition to the hunger pangs, the hungry person also becomes more tense and restless than usual, and he often has a strange feeling throughout his entire body that might be described by the non-physiological term "twitterness."

Some physiologists actually define hunger as the tonic contractions of the stomach. However, even after the stomach is completely removed, the psychic sensations of hunger still occur, and craving for food still makes the person search out an adequate food supply. Therefore, the sensations of hunger certainly should not be limited to the local signs in the gastrointestinal tract.

Appetite. The term *appetite* is often used in the same sense as hunger except that it usually does not imply actual pain as is true in certain instances of hunger. Also, appetite often implies a desire for specific types of food instead of food in general. Therefore, appetite helps a person choose the quality of food he eats.

Satiety. Satiety is the opposite of hunger. It means a feeling of complete fulfillment in the quest for food. Satiety usually results from a filling meal, particularly when the person's nutritional storage depots, the adipose tissue and the glycogen stores, are already filled.

Neural Centers for Regulation of Food Intake

Stimulation of the *lateral hypothalamus* causes an animal to eat voraciously, while stimulation of the *medial nuclei of the hypothalamus* causes complete satiety, and, even in the presence of highly appetizing food, the animal will still refuse to eat. Conversely, a destructive lesion of the medial nuclei causes exactly the same effect as stimulation of the lateral hypothalamic nuclei—that is, voracious and continued eating until the

animal becomes extremely obese. Indeed, the way in which such an animal approaches food demonstrates his extreme desire for food, for he actually *attacks* the food rather than calmly eating. Lesions of the lateral hypothalamic nuclei cause exactly the opposite effects, almost complete lack of desire for food and progressive inanition of the animal. Therefore, we can label the lateral hypothalamus as the *hunger center* or the *feeding center*, while we can label the medial hypothalamus as a *satiety center*.

Other Neural Centers That Enter into Feeding. If the brain is sectioned between the hypothalamus and the mesencephalon, the animal can still perform the basic feeding functions. He salivates, licks his chops, chews food, and swallows. Therefore, the actual processes of feeding are all controlled by centers in the brain stem entirely independently of the hypothalamus or cerebrum. The function of the hypothalamus in feeding, then, is to control the quantity of food intake and not the actual processes by which intake occurs.

The cerebral cortex is also necessary to feeding, for it directs the animal's search for food. Without this, one is incapable of finding food and of selecting it after it is found. The cortical centers also condition the quality of food that is eaten by varying the fondness of the individual for different types of food. For instance, a previous unpleasant experience in eating almost any type of food often kills the person's appetite for that food henceforth. Furthermore, the cortical centers condition one's appetite in relation to the surroundings in which he is eating or in relation to his momentary psychic status.

Factors That Regulate Food Intake

The quantity of food intake is regulated by two different types of physiological stimuli: (1) stimuli associated with the level of nutrient stores in the body and (2) stimuli associated with the immediate effects of feeding on the alimentary tract. And we can divide the regulation of food intake into *long-term regulation*, which results from the first of these stimuli, and *short-term regulation*, which results from the second.

Long-term Regulation. An animal that has been starved for a long period of time and then is presented with unlimited food eats a far greater quantity than will an animal that has been on a regular diet. Conversely, an animal that has been force-fed for several weeks will eat very little when allowed to eat according to his own desires. Thus, the feeding center in the hypothalamus is geared to the nutritional status of the body. One of the means by which this relationship is controlled is through the blood glucose concentration, for a decrease in the blood glucose concentration almost invariably increases the degree of feeding. However, this effect of low glucose concentration is normally very weak in comparison with the effect of prolonged starvation. Therefore, other nutrient factors besides glucose undoubtedly also enter into this long-term regulation of feeding. But, since we do not have precise information on the other factors concerned, we can simply make the following general statement: *When the nutrient stores of the body fall below normal, the feeding center of the hypothalamus becomes highly active, and the person exhibits increased degrees of hunger; on the other hand, when the nutrient stores are abundant, the person loses his hunger and tends toward a state of satiety.*

Short-term Regulation. The degree of hunger or satiety can be temporarily greatly increased or decreased by daily habits. For instance, the normal person has the habit of eating three meals a day, and, if he misses one, he is likely to develop a state of hunger at mealtime despite completely adequate nutritional stores in his tissues. But, in addition to habit, there are several other short-term physiological stimuli that can alter one's desire for food for several hours at a time as follows:

Body temperature. A factor that seems to be specifically related to momentary desire for food is the body temperature—the higher the temperature the less the desire for food. This perhaps is related to the fact that adequate nutrients are required in the tissues for a high temperature to develop. Consequently, it is reasonable to expect that when the body temperature is high, the desire for feeding would be lessened. Furthermore, the temperature-regulating centers are adjacent to the feeding centers of the hypothalamus so that temperature regulation and feeding regulation are closely allied.

Body temperature affects the desire for feeding in at least four important physiological states: (1) When a person has fever, he tends to eat less than normally. (2) When a person is actually eating a meal, and food begins to be absorbed from the gastrointestinal tract, the metabolic and specific dynamic actions of the food cause the body temperature to rise almost 1° C., and this is usually associated with a feeling of complete satiety. Thus, after eating a big meal a person's desire for feeding is usually decreased for the next 2 to 3 hours. (3) During heavy exercise, the body temperature rises and the person does not crave food at all while the exercise is taking place. Yet, as soon as he stops exercising and his body temperature begins to fall, he almost immediately begins to seek food. (4) When a person becomes exposed to high or low temperatures, his appetite changes; high temperatures reduce the appetite and low temperatures whet it.

Gastrointestinal distention. When the gastrointestinal tract becomes distended, inhibitory impulses transmitted through both the vagi and sympathetic nerves inhibit the feeding center, thereby reducing the desire for food. Obviously, this mechanism is of particular importance in bringing one's feeding to a halt during a heavy meal.

Metering of food by "head receptors." If a person with an esophageal fistula is fed large quantities of food, even though this food is immediately lost again to the exterior, his appetite is whetted after a reasonable quantity of food has passed through his mouth. This effect occurs despite the fact that the gastrointestinal tract does not become the least bit filled and even though the body temperature does not rise. Therefore, it is said that various "head factors" relating to feeding, such as chewing, salivation, swallowing, and tasting, "meter" the food as it passes through the mouth, and after a certain amount has passed through, the hypothalamic feeding center becomes inhibited.

Importance of Having Both Long-term and Short-term Regulatory Systems for Feeding. The long-term regulatory system obviously helps the animal to maintain constant stores of nutrients in his tissues, preventing these from becoming too low or too high. However, an animal that forages for food must at times store excess quantities of food for future use even though he has no immediate use for the food. This explains the value of the short-term regulatory stimuli—they make the animal eat in a rhythmical pattern so that the food will pass through his gastrointestinal tract fairly continuously and so that his digestive, absorptive and storage mechanisms can all work at a steady pace rather than just when the animal needs food for energy. Indeed, the digestive, absorptive, and storage mechanisms can increase their rates of activity above normal only four- to five-fold, whereas the rate of usage of stored nutrients for energy sometimes increases to 20 times normal.

It is important, then, that feeding occur rather continuously, which is regulated principally by the short-term regulatory mechanism, but also that the intensity of the daily rhythmical feeding habits be modulated up or down by the long-term regulatory system based principally on the level of the nutrient stores of the body.

OBESITY

Energy Input versus Energy Expenditure. When greater quantities of energy (in the form of food) are put into the body than are expended, the body weight increases. On the other hand, when energy expenditure, including the heat generated by metabolism in the body, the mechanical work output of the muscles, and the foodstuff lost in the feces and urine, is greater than the energy input, then the weight decreases. Therefore, obesity is actually caused by excess energy input over energy output. For each 9.3 Calories excess energy entering the body, one gram of fat is stored.

It should be noted particularly in obesity that excess energy input occurs only during the developing phase of obesity, and once the obesity has developed, the person will remain obese even though energy input then equals energy output. In order to reduce, the output must become *greater* than the input. Indeed, in studies of obese people who have already reached their obese states, the intake of food is statistically identical to that for normal persons.

Effect of Muscular Activity on Energy Output. About half the energy used each day by the normal person goes into muscular activity, and in the laborer as much as three fourths is used in this way. Therefore, it is obvious that muscular activity is by far the most important means by which energy is expended in the body. Therefore, from a practical point of view, it is frequently said that obesity results from *too high a ratio of food intake to the daily rate of exercise.*

Abnormal Feeding Regulation as the Cause of Obesity

In the above discussion of the mechanisms that regulate feeding, it was emphasized that the rate of feeding is normally regulated in proportion to the nutrient stores in the body. When these stores begin to approach an optimal level in a normal person, feeding is automatically reduced to prevent over-storage. However, in the obese person this is not true, for his feeding does not slacken until his body weight is far above normal. Therefore, in effect, obesity is generally caused by an abnormality of the feeding regulatory mechanism. This can result from either psychogenic factors that affect the regulation or actual abnormalities of the hypothalamus itself.

Psychogenic Obesity. Studies of obese patients show that a very large proportion of obesity results from psychogenic factors. Perhaps the most common psychogenic factor contributing to obesity is the prevalent idea that healthy eating habits require three meals a day and that each meal must be filling. Many children are forced into this habit by overly solicitous parents, and they continue to practice it throughout life. In addition, persons are known often to gain very large amounts of weight following stressful situations, such as following the death of a parent, following a severe illness, or even in instances of mental depression. It seems that eating is often used as means of release from tension.

Hypothalamic Abnormalities as a Cause of Obesity. In the above discussion of feeding regulation, it was pointed out that lesions in the medial nuclei of the hypothalamus will cause an animal to eat voraciously, and, therefore, to become obese. Also, many patients with adenohypophyseal tumors that encroach on the hypothalamus develop progressive obesity, illustrating that obesity in the human being, too, can definitely result from damage to the hypothalamus. Though in the normal obese person, hypothalamic damage is almost never found, it is possible nonetheless that the functional organization of the feeding center is different in the obese person from that of the nonobese person. For instance, an obese person who has made himself reduce to a normal weight usually develops a voracious appetite that is demonstrably far greater than that of the normal person. This indicates that the "setting" of his feeding center is at a much higher level of nutrient storage than in the normal person.

Genetic Factors in Obesity. Obesity very definitely runs in families. Furthermore, identical twins will usually maintain weight levels within two pounds of each other throughout life if they live under similar conditions or within five pounds of each other if their conditions of life differ markedly. This might result partly from eating habits engendered during childhood, but it is generally believed that this close similarity between twins is genetically controlled.

The genes can direct the degree of feeding in several different ways, including (1) a genetic abnormality of the feeding center to set the level of nutrient storage high or low and (2) abnormal hereditary psychic factors that either whet the appetite or cause the person to eat as a "release" mechanism.

A genetic abnormality of fat storage is specifically known to cause obesity in a certain strain of rats. In these rats, fat is easily stored in the adipose tissue, but the quantity of lipoprotein lipase formed in the adipose tissue is greatly reduced so that little of the fat can be removed. This obviously results in a one-way path, the fat continually being deposited but never released. This, obviously, is another possible mechanism of human obesity in some human beings, but it has not yet been shown to occur.

Treatment of Obesity

The treatment for obesity depends simply on decreasing the energy input below the energy expenditure. In other words, this means partial starvation. For this purpose, various *reducing diets* have been devised, these depending upon decreased total caloric intake. Most diets are designed to contain large quantities of "bulk" which, in general, are made up of cellulose substances. This bulk fools the subject into believing that he is appeasing his appetite. In lower animals such a procedure simply makes the animal increase his food intake still further, but the hu-

man being can often fool himself because his food intake is sometimes controlled as much by habit as by hunger. As pointed out below in connection with starvation, it is quite important to prevent vitamin deficiencies during the dieting period.

Various *drugs for decreasing the appetite* have been used in the treatment of obesity. In general, these drugs are sympathomimetic agents that inhibit the hunger contractions of the gastrointestinal tract. Also, in addition to inhibiting the hunger contractions, inhibition of the gut by these drugs actually causes almost nauseous antipathy toward food. Therefore, appropriate administration of gastrointestinal inhibitors is a powerful means for overcoming obesity, and such procedures will often work when no others will. However, there is danger in using these drugs because most of them simultaneously overly excite the central nervous system, making the subject nervous, and they also elevate the blood pressure.

Finally, it must be emphasized, though it need not be discussed in detail, that the more muscular activity one performs, the greater will be one's daily energy expenditure and the more rapidly will his obesity disappear. Therefore, forced exercise is often an essential part of the treatment for obesity.

Inanition

Inanition is the exact opposite of obesity, and it can result from either lack of adequate food supply or in some instances from factors precisely the opposite of those that cause obesity. For instance, both psychogenic and hypothalamic abnormalities can cause greatly decreased feeding. One such condition, *anorexia nervosa*, is an abnormal psychic state in which a person loses all desire for food and even becomes nauseated by food; as a result, very severe inanition occurs. Also, destructive lesions of the hypothalamus, particularly vascular thrombosis, frequently cause a condition called *cachexia;* the term simply means very severe inanition.

Starvation

Utilization of Food Stores During Starvation. When a person does not eat sufficient quantities of food, the utilization of energy by the body is greater than the intake of energy. Consequently, the food stores are depleted. It has already been pointed out that the body preferentially uses carbohydrate for metabolism over fat and protein and that fat is preferentially used over protein. Therefore, as illustrated in Figure 633,

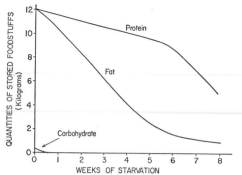

Figure 663. Effect of starvation on the food stores of the body.

the carbohydrate stores are used up almost entirely within 24 to 48 hours. Indeed, the carbohydrate stores, if utilized alone without utilization of either fat or protein, would be sufficient to maintain life for approximately only 13 hours.

Figure 663 also illustrates the rates of fat and protein depletion throughout the weeks of starvation, assuming that this particular subject had approximately 15 per cent body fat at the beginning of the period of starvation. Under these conditions essentially all the fat would be removed within approximately 5 to 6 weeks, and thereafter no fat would remain to act as a protein sparer.

The stages of starvation as shown in Figure 663 are approximately those that would be expected in an originally normal, healthy person. Unfortunately, starvation occurs more frequently in unhealthy than healthy people, such as in cancerous patients, patients with fever, etc. In these, the basal metabolic rate is usually considerably above the mean value, and, therefore, the food stores are depleted at a much more rapid rate than would otherwise occur.

Premortem depletion of proteins. In the early stages of starvation the only utilization of protein each day is the "obligatory" utilization due simply to the degradation of intracellular protein as a result of their participation in the metabolism of the cells. However, after most of the fat is gone—that is, after 5 to 6 weeks—the proteins must also be used for energy. Consequently, the quantity of protein thereafter decreases very rapidly. Obviously, the disappearance of protein from the cells decreases the ability of the cells to perform normal cellular functions, and death soon ensues.

Dehydration during Starvation. Much of the weight loss during starvation is not loss of food stores at all but instead loss of water. First, obligatory loss of electrolytes through the kidneys occurs, as discussed in Chapters 8 and 9. As these electrolytes are lost the kidneys excrete equivalent quantities of water so that osmotic equilibria will be maintained in the body. Also, an additional quantity of water is lost as the cellular stores of foods are depleted because the proteins of the cells have considerable water adsorbed to them.

If starvation is accompanied by cessation of water intake, water depletion due to evaporation, loss in the feces, etc., further exacerbates the dehydration, and under these conditions death will usually occur from dehydration long before starvation causes death.

Vitamin Deficiencies in Starvation. The stores of some of the vitamins, especially the water-soluble vitamins of the vitamin B group and vitamin C, do not last long during starvation. Consequently, after a week or more of starvation mild vitamin deficiencies usually begin to appear, and over a period of several weeks severe vitamin deficiencies may occur. Obviously, these can add to the debility which leads to death.

REFERENCES

Albritton, E. C.: Standard Values in Nutrition and Metabolism. Philadelphia, W. B. Saunders Co., 1954.

Allen, T. H., Peng, M. T., Chen, K. P., Huang, T. F., Chang, C., and Fang, H. S.: Prediction of blood volume and adiposity in man from body weight and cube of height. *Metabolism,* 5:328, 1956.

Bernstein, L. M., and Grossman, M. I.: An experimental test of the glucostatic theory of regulation of food intake. *J. Clin. Invest.,* 35:627, 1956.

Brobeck, J. R.: Mechanism of the development of obesity in animals with hypothalamic lesions. *Physiol. Rev.,* 26:541, 1946.

Brobeck, J. R.: Neural basis of hunger, appetite, and satiety. *Gastroenterology,* 32:169, 1957.

Brobeck, J. R.: Neural control of hunger, appetite, and satiety. *Yale J. Biol.,* 29:565, 1957.

Brobeck, J. R.: Neural regulation of food intake. *Ann. N. Y. Acad. Sc.,* 63:44, 1955.

Brobeck, J. R.: Regulation of feeding and drinking. *Handbook of Physiology,* 2:1197, 1960.

Brobeck, J. R., Larsson, S., and Reyes, E.: A study of the electrical activity of the hypothalamic feeding mechanism. *J. Physiol.,* 132:358, 1956.

DuBois, E. F.: Basal Metabolism in Health and Disease. 3rd ed., Philadelphia, Lea & Febiger, 1936.

DuBois, E. F.: Energy metabolism. *Ann. Rev. Physiol.,* 16:125, 1954.

Edholm, O. C.: Energy expenditure in relation to nutrition. *Proc. Nutrit. Soc.,* 15:80, 1956.

Gelvin, E. P., and McGavack, T. H.: Obesity, Its Cause, Classification, and Care. New York, Paul B. Hoeber, 1957.

Grossman, M. I.: Integration of current views on the regulation of hunger and appetite. *Ann. N.Y. Acad. Sc., 63:*76, 1955.

Grossman, M. I., and Sloane, H. S.: Some relations between body weight, body fat, and calorie intake. *Am. J. Clin. Nutrit., 3:*403, 1955.

Hollander, F., Sober, H. A., and Bandes, J.: A study of hunger and appetite in a young man with esophageal obstruction and jejunostomy. *Ann. N. Y. Acad. Sc., 63:*107, 1955.

Janowitz, H. D., and Hollander, F.: The time factor in the adjustment of food intake to varied caloric requirement in the dog: a study of the precision of appetite regulation. *Ann. N. Y. Acad. Sc., 63:*56, 1955.

Janowitz, H. D., and Ivy, A. C.: Role of blood sugar levels in spontaneous and insulin-induced hunger in man. *J. Appl. Physiol., 1:*643, 1949.

Kaunitz, H., Slanetz, C. A., and Johnson, R. E.: Utilization of food for weight maintenance and growth. *J. Nutrit., 62:*551, 1957.

Keys, A., and Brozek, J.: Body fat in adult man. *Physiol. Rev., 33:*245, 1953.

Kleiber, M.: Body size and metabolic rate. *Physiol. Rev., 27:*511, 1947.

Kleiber, M.: Energy metabolism. *Ann. Rev. Physiol., 18:*35, 1956.

Long, C. N.: Studies on experimental obesity. *J. Endocr., 15:*6, 1957.

Mayer, J.: Genetic, traumatic and environmental factors in the etiology of obesity. *Physiol. Rev., 33:*472, 1953.

Miller, A. T., Jr., and Thomas, B. M.: Pyruvate metabolism in obesity. *Am. J. Clin. Nutrit., 4:*619, 1956.

Morgane, P. J., and Kosman, A. J.: Arhinencephalic feeding center in the cat. *Am. J. Physiol., 197:*158, 1959.

Olson, R. E.: Obesity as a nutritional disorder. *Fed. Proc., 18:*58, 1959.

Pitts, G. C.: Body fat accumulation in the guinea pig. *Am. J. Physiol., 185:*41, 1956.

Quigley, J. P.: The role of the digestive tract in regulating the ingestion of food. *Ann. N. Y. Acad. Sc., 63:*6, 1955.

Silberberg, M., and Silberberg, R.: Diet and life span. *Physiol. Rev., 35:*347, 1955.

Strominger, J. L., and Brobeck, J. R.: A mechanism of regulation of food intake. *Yale J. Biol. & Med., 25:*383, 1953.

Chapter 70

Vitamin and Mineral Metabolism

The study of vitamin and mineral metabolism rightfully falls in the province of biochemistry. Therefore, the present discussion of this subject will be greatly abbreviated, and the student is referred to the available biochemistry texts for detailed information. It is hoped to present in this chapter the major functions of vitamin and mineral metabolism as they relate to the overall physiology of the body.

VITAMINS

A vitamin is an organic compound that is needed in small quantities for operation of normal bodily metabolism and that cannot be manufactured in the cells of the body. Probably hundreds of such substances exist, most of which have not yet been discovered. However, a few of them have been studied to a great extent because they are present in the foods in relatively small quantities, and, as a result, dietary deficiency of one or more of them often occurs. Therefore, from a clinical point of view the agents that are generally considered to be vitamins are those organic compounds that, when lacking in the diet, can cause specific metabolic deficits.

Daily Requirements of Vitamins. Table 26 illustrates the usually recommended daily requirements of the different important vitamins. These requirements vary considerably, depending upon the metabolic condition of each subject. For instance, the greater the person's size, the greater is the vitamin requirement. Second, growing persons usually require greater quantities of vitamins than do others. Third, when the subject performs exercise, the vitamin requirements are increased. Fourth, during disease and fevers, the vitamin requirements are ordinarily increased. Fifth, when greater than normal quantities of carbohydrates are metabolized, the requirements of thiamine and perhaps some of the other vitamins of the B complex are increased. Sixth, during pregnancy and lactation the requirement for vitamin D by the mother is greatly increased, and the requirement for vitamin D is considerable during the period of growth in children. Finally, a number of metabolic deficits may occur pathologically in which the vitamins themselves cannot be utilized properly in the body; in such conditions the requirement for one or more specific vitamins may be extreme.

Storage of Vitamins in the Body. Vitamins are probably stored to a slight extent in all the cells. However, storage of some of the vitamins occurs to a major extent in the liver. For instance, the quantity of vitamin A stored in the liver may be sufficient to maintain a person without any intake of vitamin A for up to two years, and ordinarily the quantity of vitamin D stored in the liver is sufficient to maintain a person for three to five months without any additional intake of vitamin D.

It will be recalled that vitamins A, D, E, and K are fat soluble, whereas the remainder of the vitamins of Table 26 are water soluble. Very little is known about the storage of vitamin E, but the storage of vitamin K and of all the water-soluble vitamins is relatively slight; this applies especially to the vitamin B compounds, for when a person's diet is deficient in vitamin B compounds, clinical

Table 26. Daily Requirements of the Vitamins

Vitamin	Daily Requirement
A	3.1 mg.
Thiamine	1.8 mg.
Riboflavin	1.8 mg.
Niacin	18 mg.
Ascorbic acid	84 mg.
D (children and during pregnancy)	11 μg.
E	unknown
K	none
Folic acid	unknown
B_{12}	unknown
Inositol	unknown
Pyridoxine	1.7 mg.
Pantothenic acid	unknown
Biotin	unknown
Para-aminobenzoic acid	unknown

Table 27. Vitamin Content of Different Foods

Vitamin A mg./100 gm.	Thiamine mg./100 gm.	Riboflavin mg./100 gm.	Niacin mg./100 gm.	Ascorbic acid mg./100 gm.
Apricots 3	Barley 0.450	Dried beans 0.30	Asparagus 1.2	Asparagus 45
Broccoli 2.4	Dried beans 0.540	Almonds 0.50	Barley 4.7	Brussels sprouts 95
Butter 2.1	Buckwheat 0.450	Beef 0.20	Soybeans 4.0	Cabbage 65
Carrots 3.6	Dried cowpeas 0.900	Cheese 0.55	Dried beans 3.0	Butter 70
Collards 4.8	Egg yolk 0.320	Chicken 0.30	Beef 5.4	Cauliflower 82
Chard 5.4	Whole wheat 0.585	Collards 0.25	Chicken 8.5	Lemon juice 53
Endive 9.0	Pork 1.0	Eggs 0.40	Collards 2.3	Mustard greens 115
Kale 12.0	Lamb 0.330	Lamb 0.24	Corn 1.3	Orange juice 45
Liver 42.0	Beef 0.120	Liver 2.60	Lamb 8.0	Fish 20
Mustard greens 6.0	Liver 0.400	Milk 0.18	Liver 17.0	Potatoes 10
Sweet potatoes 1.8	Millet 0.700	Peanuts 0.45	Mackerel 2.1	Lean meats 5
Pumpkin 4.2	Brown rice 0.370	Pork 0.24	Pork 7.0	Liver 25
Spinach 15.0	Wheat germ 2.0	Grains 0.10	Salmon 6.2	
			Wheat 4.3	

	Pantothenic acid mg./100 gm.	Pyridoxine mg./100 gm.	Inositol mg./100 gm.	Biotin mg./100 gm.	Folic acid mg./100 gm.
Meats	0.8	0.1	60	0.007	0.15
Eggs	1.4	0.02	33	0.009	0.90
Milk	0.3	0.13	18	0.005	0.005
Cereals	0.4	0.05	65	0.005	0.10
Fruits	0.2	0.05	95	0.003	0.05
Vegetables	0.5	0.15	70	0.007	0.08

Extracted and modified from data compiled from the literature by Eddy and Dalldorf.

symptoms of the deficiency can sometimes be recognized within a few days. Deficiency of vitamin C, another water-soluble vitamin, sometimes becomes almost lethal in approximately six to eight weeks.

In general, the water-soluble vitamins are threshold substances for secretion by the kidneys so that when excessive quantities are administered in a short interval of time, the excess will pass into the urine almost immediately.

Occurrence of Vitamins in Nature. Table 27 illustrates the quantities of most of the important vitamins in representative foods. Some of the less important vitamins such as vitamin E and vitamin P have not been studied sufficiently to determine their occurrence in different foods. However, vitamin E is present in relatively large quantities in the germ of different grains, and vitamin P in general is present in many of the same foods which contain vitamin C. The content of vitamin D in most foods besides liver is relatively slight, for the usual source of vitamin D is ultraviolet radiation of 7-dehydrocholesterol and other cholesterol compounds in the skin. However, milk contains a small amount of vitamin D, and it has become the practice to irradiate milk with ultraviolet light to increase the quantity of vitamin D. The content of vitamin K in the different foods also is relatively unimportant because vitamin K is synthesized to a major extent by bacteria in the colon; this vitamin K in turn is absorbed into the circulatory system. Therefore, a diet totally deficient in vitamin K usually does not cause vitamin K deficiency in the body. To a certain extent, biotin is also synthesized in the colon, and, therefore, food deficits of biotin are not of especial importance.

Vitamin A

Vitamin A occurs in foods of animal origin in two forms—as vitamin A_1, the formula of which is illustrated below, and as vitamin A_2, which is a closely similar compound. These vitamins do not occur in foods of vegetable origin, but *provitamins* for the formation of vitamin A do occur in

Vitamin A

abundance in many different vegetable foods. These are the yellow and red *carotenoid pigments*, which, since they have chemical structures similar to that of vitamin A, can be changed into vitamin A in the human body, this change occurring mainly in the liver cells.

The basic function of vitamin A in the metabolism of the body is not known except in relation to the retinal pigments. Nevertheless, some of the physiologic effects of vitamin A lack have been well documented. Vitamin A is necessary for normal growth of most of the cells of the body and especially for normal growth and proliferation of the different types of epithelial cells. When vitamin A is lacking, the epithelial structures of the body tend to become stratified and keratinized. Therefore, vitamin A deficiency manifests itself by (1) scaliness of the skin and sometimes acne, (2) failure of growth of young animals, (3) failure of reproduction in many animals, associated especially with atrophy of the germinal epithelium of the testes and sometimes with interruption of the female sexual cycle, and (4) keratinization of the cornea with resultant corneal opacity and blindness.

Also, infection of the damaged epithelial structures often occurs, for example, in the eyes, the kidneys, etc. Therefore, vitamin A has been called an "anti-infection" vitamin. Vitamin A deficiency also frequently causes kidney stones, probably owing to infection in the renal pelvis.

The utilization of vitamin A for formation of retinal pigments has already been discussed in Chapter 53. Formation of these retinal pigments can begin within a matter of minutes after intravenous injection of vitamin A. Therefore, the characteristic night blindness observed in vitamin A deficiency can be reversed within a few minutes to an hour.

Thiamine (Vitamin B₁)

Thiamine operates in the metabolic systems of the body principally as thiamine pyrophosphate, and this compound is believed to be a co-enzyme necessary for function of one or more enzyme systems. For instance, thiamine pyrophosphate has been shown to be either a co-enzyme operating in conjunction with a protein decarboxylase or the responsible prosthetic group of a decarboxylase for decarboxylation of pyruvic acid and other substances, as was discussed in Chapter 65.

Thiamine

It is a well-known fact that thiamine deficiency causes decreased utilization of pyruvic acid by the tissues and increased utilization of fats. Thus, thiamine is specifically needed for final metabolism of carbohydrates. Probably the decreased utilization of carbohydrates by the tissues in thiamine deficiency is the responsible factor for much of the debility associated with this deficiency.

Thiamine Deficiency and the Nervous System. The central nervous system depends almost entirely on the metabolism of carbohydrates for its energy. In thiamine deficiency the utilization of glucose by the central nervous system may be decreased as much as 50 to 60 per cent. Therefore, it is readily understandable how thiamine deficiency could greatly impair function of the central nervous system. The neuronal cells of the central nervous system frequently show chromatolysis and swelling during thiamine deficiency, changes that are characteristic of neuronal cells with poor nutrition. Obviously, such changes as these can disrupt communication in many different portions of the central nervous system.

Also, thiamine deficiency can cause *degeneration of myelin sheaths* of nerve fibers both in the peripheral nerves and in the central nervous system. The lesions in the peripheral nerves frequently cause these nerves to become extremely irritable, resulting in "polyneuritis" with areas of pain radiating along the course of one or more of the peripheral nerves. Also, in very severe thiamine deficiency, degeneration of peripheral nerve fibers and of fiber tracts in the cord can occur to such an extent that *paralysis* may occasionally result.

Thiamine Deficiency and the Cardiovascular System. Thiamine deficiency weakens the muscles, including the heart muscle, so that a patient with severe thiamine deficiency may develop *cardiac failure*. In general, the right side of the heart becomes greatly enlarged in thiamine deficiency. Furthermore, the return of blood to the heart may be increased to as much as three times normal. This indicates that thiamine deficiency causes *peripheral vasodilatation* throughout the circulatory system, possibly as a result of metabolic deficiency in the smooth muscle of the vascular system itself. Therefore, the cardiac effects of thiamine deficiency are due partly to excessive return of blood to the heart and partly to primary weakness of the cardiac muscle. *Peripheral edema* and *ascites* also occur to a major extent in some patients with thiamine deficiency because of the cardiac failure.

Thiamine Deficiency and the Gastrointestinal Tract. Among the symptoms of thiamine deficiency are indigestion, severe constipation, anorexia, gastric atony, hypochlorhydria, etc. All these effects possibly result from failure of the smooth muscle and glands of the gastrointestinal tract to derive sufficient energy from carbohydrate metabolism.

The overall picture of thiamine deficiency, including polyneuritis, cardiovascular systems, and gastrointestinal disorders is frequently referred to as "beriberi"—especially when the cardiovascular symptoms predominate.

Niacin

Niacin, also called *nicotinic acid* and formerly known as vitamin G, functions in the body in the forms of diphosphopyridine nucleotide (DPN) and triphosphopyridine nucleotide (TPN), which are also known as co-enzymes I and II. These co-enzymes are hydrogen acceptors which combine with hydrogen atoms as they are removed from food substrates by many different types of dehydrogenases. The typical operation of both of them is presented in Chapter 65. When a deficiency of niacin exists, the normal rate of dehydrogenation presumably cannot be maintained, and, therefore, oxidative delivery of energy from the foodstuffs to the functioning elements of the cells likewise cannot occur at normal rates.

Niacin

Because co-enzymes I and II apparently operate in essentially all cells of the body, it is readily understood how lack of niacin can cause multiple symptoms. Clinically, niacin deficiency causes mainly (1) gastrointestinal symptoms, (2) neurologic symptoms, and (3) a characteristic dermatitis. However, it is probably much more proper to say that essentially all functions of the body are depressed.

In the early stages of niacin deficiency simple physiologic changes such as muscular weakness of all the different types of muscles, poor glandular secretion, etc., may occur, but in severe niacin deficiency actual death of tissues ensues. Pathologic lesions appear in many parts of the central nervous system, and permanent dementia or any one of many different types of psychoses may result. Also, the skin develops a cracked, pigmented scaliness in areas that are exposed to irritation or sun irradiation; thus, it seems at if the skin were unable to repair the different types of irritative damage.

Niacin deficiency causes intense irritation and inflammation of the mucous membranes of the mouth and other portions of the gastrointestinal tract, thus instituting many digestive abnormalities. It is possible that this results from generalized depression of metabolism of the gastrointestinal tract and failure of appropriate epithelial repair.

The clinical entity called "pellagra" and the canine disease called "black tongue" are probably caused mainly by niacin deficiency.

Riboflavin (Vitamin B₂)

Riboflavin normally combines in the tissues with phosphoric acid and with proteins to form different flavoproteins. These in turn operate as hydrogen carriers in several of the very important oxidative systems of the body. Usually, one of the co-enzymes, DPN or TPN, in association with specific dehydrogenases, accepts hydrogen removed from various food substrates and then passes the hydrogen to a flavoprotein; finally, the hydrogen is released as an ion into the surrounding fluids to become oxidized by nacent oxygen, the system for which is described in Chapter 65.

Riboflavin

Deficiency of riboflavin in lower animals causes severe *dermatitis, vomiting, diarrhea, muscular spasticity* which finally becomes muscular weakness, and then *death* preceded by coma and decline in body temperature. Thus, it is obvious that severe riboflavin deficiency can cause many of the same effects as lack of niacin in the diet, and presumably the debilities that result in each instance are due to generally depressed oxidative processes within the cells.

In the human being riboflavin deficiency has never been known to be severe enough to cause the marked debilities noted in animal experiments, but mild riboflavin deficiency is extremely common. Such deficiency usually causes digestive disturbances, burning sensations of the skin and eyes, cracking at the corners of the mouth, headaches, mental depression, forgetfulness, etc. Perhaps the most common characteristic lesions of riboflavin deficiency is *cheilosis*, which is inflammation and cracking at the angles of the mouth.

In addition, a fine, scaly dermatitis often occurs at the angles of the nares, and keratitis of the cornea may occur with invasion of the cornea by capillaries.

Though the manifestations of riboflavin deficiency are usually relatively mild, this deficiency frequently occurs in association with deficiency of thiamine, or niacin, or both of these substances. Therefore, many of the deficiency syndromes, including pellagra, beriberi, sprue, etc., are probably due to a combined deficiency of a number of the vitamins.

Vitamin B_{12}

Several different *cobalamin* compounds which possess the common prosthetic group illustrated below exhibit so-called "vitamin B_{12}" activity. Almost nothing is known about the manner in which vitamin B_{12} enters into the metabolic organization of cells, though experiments point to the following two functions: (1) Vitamin B_{12} seems to be important for methylation of certain substances such as choline and thymine. Lack of thymine, which is one of the elements required for synthesis of deoxyribose nucleoprotein, limits the formation of genes and therefore reduces the rate at which cells can divide throughout the body. This could easily explain the failure to form normal blood cells in the bone marrow, as will be discussed below. (2) Some experiments have also suggested that vitamin B_{12} helps to form peptide linkages between certain amino acids. If this is true, then it is easy to understand why vitamin B_{12} is such an important growth factor.

The prosthetic group of vitamin B_{12}

In the human being the major functions of vitamin B_{12} are to promote growth and especially to cause red blood cell maturation. When vitamin B_{12} is deficient in the diet, the erythroblastic cells of the bone marrow grow to the stage of normoblasts, but instead of maturing into red blood cells these normoblasts grow in size until they become "megaloblasts." These then remain in an almost static state in the bone marrow, releasing only a few red blood cells into the blood. When vitamin B_{12} is administered, these megaloblasts are very rapidly replaced by normal normoblasts, and normal red blood cells are delivered rapidly into the blood.

When a patient is first treated with vitamin B_{12} following a period of deficiency, the rapid release of new red blood cells into the blood stream causes *reticulocytosis* with sometimes as high as 8 to 10 per cent *reticulocytes* among the circulating red blood cells. The peak of reticulocytosis following treatment usually occurs at approximately the eighth day, and the macrocytic anemia is ordinarily completely or almost completely relieved within approximately one month following treatment.

One of the most interesting aspects of vitamin B_{12} function is the extremely minute amount that is needed for promotion of red blood cell maturation; only a few micrograms of this substance administered to a patient who has a deficiency of vitamin B_{12} can many times restore normal red blood cell maturation for a month.

The cells that are released into the blood during vitamin B_{12} deficiency are mainly macrocytes, and the result is a *macrocytic anemia*, which has already been discussed in Chapter 12. Macrocytic anemias often develop in *pernicious anemia*, in which vitamin B_{12} is poorly absorbed from the intestines because of lack of "intrinsic factor" (see Chapter 62); during pregnancy, when there is a relative vitamin B_{12} deficiency; in sprue, in which various vitamins are not satisfactorily absorbed from the gastrointestinal tract; and occasionally in infancy when the rate of growth of the infant requires excessive quantities of vitamins. Macrocytic anemia can also result from lack of folic acid as well as from lack of vitamin B_{12}. This will be discussed in the following section.

Another effect of vitamin B_{12} deficiency is often demyelination of the large nerve fibers of the spinal cord, especially of the posterior columns and occasionally of the lateral columns. As a result, patients with pernicious anemia frequently have much loss of peripheral sensation and, in very severe cases, can even develop paralysis.

Folic Acid (Pteroylglutamic Acid)

Several different *pteroylglutamic acids*, one of which is illustrated below, exhibit the "folic acid effect." Folic acid enters into the chemical reactions for conversion of glycine into serine and also for formation of purines and thymine. This latter substance, as pointed out above also in relation to vitamin B_{12}, is required for formation of DNA. Therefore, folic acid is required for rapid reproduction of the cellular genes. This perhaps explains one of the most important functions of folic acid—that is, to promote growth.

Folic acid is an even more potent growth promoter than vitamin B_{12}, and, like vitamin B_{12}, is also important for the maturation of red blood cells. In certain instances of macrocytic anemia, such as in pregnancy or in sprue, folic acid is often equally as effective or sometimes even more

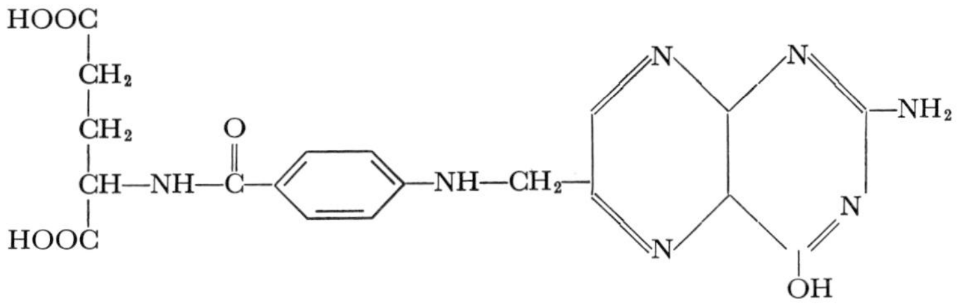

Folic acid (pteroylglutamic acid)

effective than vitamin B_{12} in correcting the anemia. However, in the Addisonian type of pernicious anemia, folic acid administration will not in most instances substitute for vitamin B_{12}. Therefore, it is believed that vitamin B_{12} and folic acid each perform specific but different functions in promoting growth of cells and maturation of red blood cells. Though the two support each other in these actions, they are not interchangeable with each other.

Pyridoxine (Vitamin B₆)

Pyridoxine is in the form of *pyridoxal phosphate* in the cells and functions as a co-enzyme for many different chemical reactions relating to amino acid and protein metabolism. For instance, it is required as a co-enzyme in (a) transamination, (b) decarboxylation, (c) synthesis of at least one amino acid, tryptophane, and (d) conversion of a number of the amino acids into other substances needed by the cells. Thus, among this myriad of chemical functions pyridoxine plays many key roles in metabolism—especially in protein metabolism.

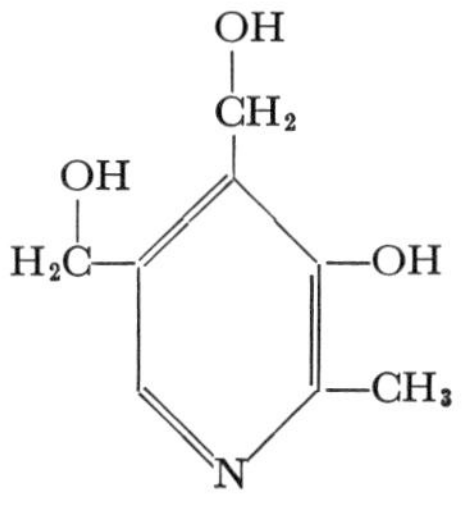

Pyridoxine

Dietary lack of pyridoxine in lower animals can cause dermatitis, decreased rate of growth, development of fatty liver, anemia, and evidence of mental deterioration. However, because pyridoxine deficiency without simultaneous deficiency of other vitamins is very rare in human beings, the human effect of pyridoxine deficiency is not clear.

Pantothenic Acid

Pantothenic acid is incorporated in the body

into co-enzyme A, which has many metabolic roles in the cells. Two of these discussed at length in Chapters 65 and 66 are: (1) decarboxylation of pyruvic acid and formation of acetyl Co-A prior to its entry into the tricarboxylic acid cycle and (2) degradation of fatty acid molecules into multiple molecules of acetyl Co-A. Thus, it is evident that lack of pantothenic acid can lead to depressed metabolism of both carbohydrates and fats.

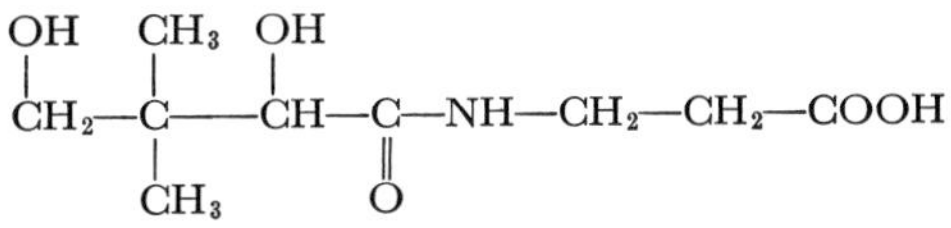

Pantothenic acid

Deficiency of pantothenic acid in lower animals can cause retarded growth, failure of reproduction, graying of the hair, dermatitis, fatty liver, and a number of other different metabolic abnormalities. In the human being, no definite deficiency syndrome has been proved, presumably because of the very wide occurrence of this vitamin in almost all foods. Nevertheless, this does not mean that pantothenic acid is not of value in the metabolic systems of the body; indeed, it is perhaps as necessary as any other single vitamin.

Biotin

Deficiency of biotin has been shown in human experiments to cause a mild dermatitis, lassitude, gastrointestinal symptoms, and hyperesthesias, including muscle pains.

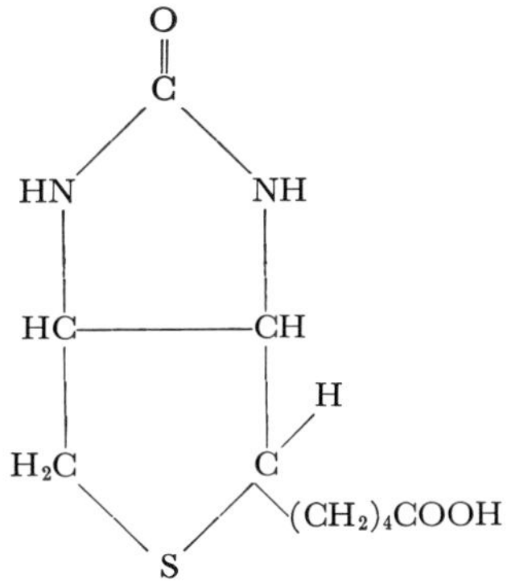

Biotin

Biotin is needed in the body to cause combination of carbon dioxide with pyruvic acid to form oxaloacetic acid which, it will be recalled, is a very important compound for operation of the tricarboxylic acid cycle. Also, it has been claimed that biotin is probably necessary for formation of fatty acids. It is obvious from these possible roles of biotin how biotin deficiency could disorganize the metabolic efficiency of the body, though at present the specific roles of biotin are almost completely unknown.

Inositol

Lack of inositol in lower animals can cause decreased rate of growth, loss of hair, and the development of fatty liver. It is this latter effect of inositol deficiency that has received most attention from clinicians, for it has been supposed that deficiency of inositol might also cause fatty liver in human beings. Inositol is necessary for

Inositol

the liver to form certain types of cephalins, which could explain why inositol might be important for removing neutral fat from the liver, except that the fat that develops in the liver in inositol deficiency ordinarily is cholesterol rather than neutral fat. Therefore, at present the function of inositol in preventing cholesterol fatty liver is completely unknown, and, even though inositol is often used clinically for treatment of fatty liver, it has not been proved to be an effective measure.

Choline. Deficiency of choline also results in the development of a fatty liver, but this time containing large quantities of neutral fat instead of cholesterol. Choline is utilized by the liver for formation of lecithin, and, in so doing, fatty acids are removed from the neutral fat of the liver, thereby decreasing the neutral fat content of the liver. Greater than normal quantities of choline seem to be needed for prevention of a fatty liver when the liver is already damaged, as in cirrhosis

Choline

of the liver, etc. Under normal circumstances it is doubtful that choline deficiency ever exists.

Choline is also needed by the body as a source for methyl radicals, which are used for various synthetic processes and also for detoxification of many toxic compounds. Finally, choline is necessary as a precursor for formation of acetylcholine.

Para-aminobenzoic Acid

Para-aminobenzoic acid is needed to a major extent by many micro-organisms for normal metabolism, but this substance probably is not needed greatly by the cells of the human body. This is fortunate, for sulfonamide drugs have the specific ability to interfere with para-aminobenzoic acid activity in metabolic processes and thereby depress the metabolic activities of many bacteria

Para-aminobenzoic acid

so much that the bacteria die. Yet, at the same time, because para-aminobenzoic acid is not a particularly necessary metabolic substance in animal cells, the human body is not damaged by sulfonamides.

Ascorbic Acid (Vitamin C)

Ascorbic acid is a strong reducing compound, and it probably can be reversibly oxidized and reduced within the body. It is believed that ascorbic acid functions in the body either as a reducing agent in specific metabolic processes or as an oxidation-reduction system, reversibly exchanging electrons with other oxidation-reduction systems. However, the precise function of ascorbic acid is almost totally unknown, though many of the physiologic effects of ascorbic acid deficiency have been well cataloged. For instance, oxidation of tyrosine and phenylalanine requires an adequate supply of ascorbic acid, but it is almost certain from the deficiency symptoms that occur when ascorbic acid is lacking that it performs far more functions than simply these two oxidative processes.

Though the mechanisms are not clear, ascorbic acid enhances the removal of iron from cellular ferritin, thereby increasing the concentration of iron in the body fluids. Also, in some way not yet clarified ascorbic acid potentiates the effects of folic acid in at least some metabolic processes.

Ascorbic acid
(vitamin C)

Rutin (a vitamin P compound)

Physiologically, the major function of ascorbic acid appears to be maintenance of normal intercellular substances throughout the body. This includes the formation of collagen and intercellular cement substance between the cells, formation of bone matrix, and formation of tooth dentin. Deficiency of ascorbic acid results in scurvy, some of the effects of which are the following:

One of the most important effects of scurvy is failure of wounds to heal. This is caused by failure of the cells to deposit collagen fibrils and intercellular cement substance. As a result, healing of a wound may require several months instead of the several days ordinarily necessary.

Lack of ascorbic acid causes cessation of bone growth. The cells of the growing epiphyses continue to proliferate, but no new matrix is laid down between the cells, and the bones fracture easily at the point of growth because of failure to ossify. Also, when an already ossified bone fractures in a patient with ascorbic acid deficiency, the osteoblasts cannot secrete a new matrix for the deposition of new bone. Consequently, the fractured bone does not heal.

The blood vessel walls become extremely fragile in scurvy, presumably because of failure of the endothelial cells to be cemented together properly. Especially are the capillaries likely to rupture, and as a result many small petechial hemorrhages occur throughout the body. The hemorrhages beneath the skin cause purpuric blotches, sometimes over the entire body. To test for ascorbic acid deficiency, such petechial hemorrhages can be caused by inflating a blood pressure cuff over the upper arm; this occludes the venous return of blood, the capillary pressure rises, and red blotches occur in the skin immediately if there is a sufficiently severe ascorbic acid deficiency.

In extreme scurvy the muscle cells may even fragment; lesions of the gums with loosening of the teeth may occur; infections of the mouth may develop; vomiting of blood, bloody stools, and cerebral hemorrhage may all occur; and, finally, high fever may develop.

Vitamin P

Several compounds, one of which is illustrated above, have been classified as vitamin P. These substances appear to operate in conjunction with ascorbic acid to prevent capillary fragility. However, the precise value of vitamin P in human nutrition has not been determined, and it has not yet been proved that vitamin P deficiency ever exists in the human being. Therefore, it is probably best to consider vitamin P as still conjectural, though ascorbic acid and vitamin P possibly operate synergistically with each other to maintain integrity of the capillary membrane.

Vitamin E

Many different compounds, one of which is illustrated below, exhibit so-called "vitamin E activity." The precise functions of vitamin E have not been elucidated, and it is doubtful whether vitamin E deficiency occurs significantly in human beings. In lower animals lack of vitamin E can cause degeneration of the germinal epithelium in the testis and therefore can cause male sterility. Lack of vitamin E can also cause resorption of a fetus after conception in the female, and it is believed that lack of vitamin E may cause malformation of the fetus. Because of these effects of vitamin E dificiency, vitamin E is sometimes called the "anti-sterility vitamin."

Vitamin E deficiency in animals can sometimes cause paralysis of the hindquarters. Pathologic changes occur in the muscles similar to those found in the disease entity "muscular dystrophy" of the human being. However, administration of vitamin E to patients with muscular dystrophy has not proved to be of any benefit.

Because muscle tissue has a low creatine content during vitamin E deficiency, it has been postulated that vitamin E in some way is responsible

Vitamin E (alpha-tocopherol)

for the maintenance of creatine compounds in muscle. Also, it has been suggested that vitamin E might enter enzymatically into some of the oxidation-reduction reactions of cells. For instance, this vitamin is known to inhibit oxidation of unsaturated fats which may be associated with defective fat absorption.

Finally, as is true of almost all the vitamins, deficiency of vitamin E prevents normal growth.

Vitamin D

Vitamin D increases calcium and phosphate absorption from the gastrointestinal tract. Most evidence indicates that vitamin D is concerned especially with the absorption of calcium, and that absorption of calcium in turn causes absorption of proportionate quantities of phosphate by preventing the precipitation of insoluble calcium phosphate in the gut. Because the functions of vitamin D will be specifically presented in Chapter 77, these will not be discussed at the present time.

Several vitamin D compounds exist, one of which is illustrated below. This is the natural

therefore is often used for treatment of patients who have lost their parathyroid glands.

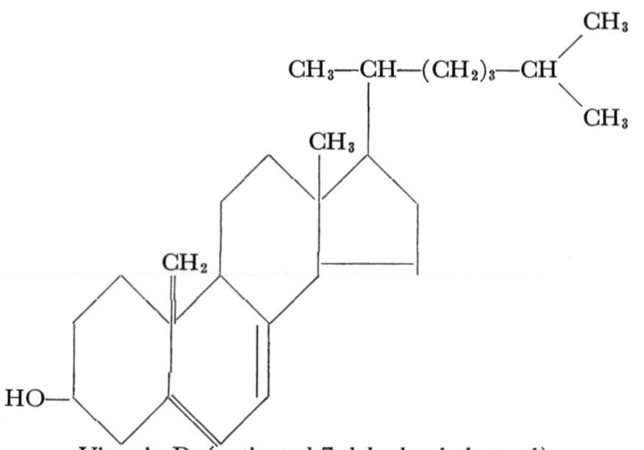

Unfortunately, the chemical manner in which vitamin D operates to increase calcium absorption from the gastrointestinal tract is totally unknown.

Vitamin K

A number of different compounds, both natural and synthetic, exhibit vitamin K activity. The chemical formula for one of the natural vitamin K compounds is illustrated below. Because vitamin K is synthesized by bacteria in the colon, a dietary source for this vitamin is not usually necessary, but, when the bacteria of the colon are destroyed by administration of large quantities of antibiotic drugs, vitamin K deficiency occurs very readily because of the paucity of this compound in the normal diet.

Vitamin K is necessary for the formation by the liver of prothrombin and factor VII, both of which are important in blood coagulation. Therefore, when vitamin K deficiency occurs, blood clotting is thereby retarded. Because this vitamin and its

Vitamin D_3 (activated 7-dehydrocholesterol)

vitamin D, which results from ultraviolet irradiation of 7-dehydrocholesterol in the skin. A synthetic vitamin D compound, calciferol, is formed by irradiation of ergosterol and is used to a major extent in vitamin D therapy. Still another synthetic compound, dehydrotachysterol, has an extremely potent action for increasing the calcium level, as will be discussed in Chapter 77, and

relationships with some of the anticoagulants such as Dicumarol have already been presented, the student is referred to Chapter 16 for further details.

MINERAL METABOLISM

Mineral metabolism is concerned to a great extent with regulation of the ionic concentrations

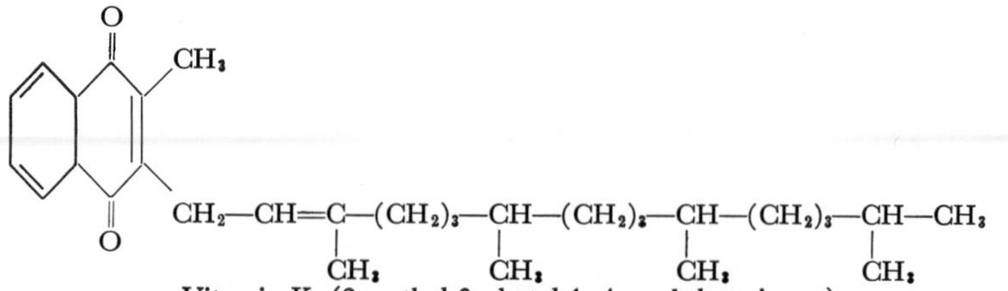

Vitamin K_1 (2-methyl-3-phytyl-1, 4-naphthoquinone)

of extracellular and intracellular fluids; this has already been discussed in Chapters 3 and 9. Also, the functions of many of the various ions have been presented at appropriate points in the text. The body content of the most important minerals is listed in Table 28, and the daily requirements of these are given in Table 29. Therefore, only the

Table 28. Content in Grams of a 70 Kilogram Adult Man

Water	41,400	Mg	21
Fat	12,600	Cl	85
Protein	12,600	P	670
Carbohydrate	300	S	112
Na	63	Fe	3
K	150	I	0.014
Ca	1,160		

Table 29. Daily Requirements of Minerals

Na	3.0 grams
K	1.0 gram
Cl	3.5 grams
Ca	0.8 gram
PO$_4$	1.5 grams
Fe	12.0 mg.
I	250.0 μg.
Mg	unknown
Co	unknown
Cu	unknown
Mn	unknown
Zn	unknown

principal functions of the various minerals are briefly reviewed, as follows:

Sodium. Sodium is a necessary constituent of all extracellular fluids; without a sufficient level of sodium in these fluids the human being will die. Perhaps the most important function of sodium is its importance in the maintenance of membrane potentials. Cellular membranes actively extrude sodium from the interior of cells, and this causes concentration gradients of sodium and potassium to develop across the cell membranes. These concentration gradients in turn cause membrane potentials that are necessary for nerve, muscle, glandular, and other functions of the body, as was disclosed in Chapter 17.

Sodium is the major cation of the extracellular fluids, and, in addition to its membrane potential effect, it exerts as much influence as any other ion on the crystalloidal osmotic pressure and the chemical characteristics of the extracellular fluids.

Potassium. Potassium is the major ion of the intracellular fluid, and it has more or less the same importance in these fluids as does sodium in the extracellular fluid. It combines reversibly with many of the buffers of the cells; it can be ionized and deionized, which is essential

for many of the chemical reactions occurring within cells; and it enters into the development of cellular membrane potentials, which have been discussed in detail in Chapter 17.

The concentration of potassium in the extracellular fluids is not great, but slight variations of this can change many functions in the body. Excess potassium in the extracellular fluids can cause dilatation of the heart, and, when the extracellular concentration of potassium reaches approximately three times normal, the heart stops in diastole. On the other hand, when the level of potassium falls to a low value in the extracellular fluids, transmission of nerve impulses becomes impaired, and muscular paralysis may result.

Magnesium. Magnesium is approximately one sixth as plentiful in cells as potassium, and it undoubtedly performs at least some of the same intracellular functions. But magnesium is also required as a catalyst for many intracellular enzymatic reactions, particularly those relating to carbohydrate metabolism.

The extracellular magnesium concentration is very slight, only 2 to 3 milliequivalents per liter. An increased extracellular concentration of magnesium depresses activity in the nervous system and also depresses skeletal muscle contraction. This latter effect can be blocked by administration of calcium. Low magnesium concentration causes greatly increased irritability of the peripheral nerves and can cause tetany, an effect this time almost identical with that caused by low calcium concentration in the extracellular fluids.

Calcium. Calcium is present in the body mainly in the form of calcium phosphate in the bone. This subject is discussed in detail in Chapter 77, as is also the calcium content of the extracellular fluid.

Excess quantities of calcium ion in the extracellular fluids can cause the heart to stop in systole and can act as a mental depressant. On the other hand, low levels of calcium can cause spontaneous discharge of nerve fibers, resulting in tetany. This, too, will be discussed in Chapter 77.

Chlorine. The chloride ion is the major anion of extracellular fluids and, therefore, in association with sodium, is to a great extent responsible for the control of extracellular fluid crystalloidal osmotic pressure, its electrical properties, and its chemical properties. Chloride ion seems to be needed by the extracellular fluids mainly because of its negative valance and not because of any specific characteristic of chlorine itself, for almost all the chloride ions can be replaced experimentally by sulfate or nitrate ions without greatly upsetting the operation of the body.

The ratio of chloride ion to bicarbonate ion in the extracellular fluids is a major controlling factor of acid-base balance, as has been discussed in Chapter 10.

Phosphorus. Phosphate is the major anion of intracellular fluids. Phosphates have the ability to combine reversibly with a multitude of enzyme systems and also with a multitude of other compounds that are necessary for the operation of metabolic processes. Most of the important reactions of phosphates have been cataloged at other points in this text and need not be discussed in detail at the present time. Suffice it to say that phosphates are perhaps the single most important mineral constituent required for cellular activity. Also, bone contains a tremendous amount of calcium phosphate, which will be discussed in Chapter 77.

Iron. The function of iron in the body, especially in relation to the formation of hemoglobin, was discussed in Chapter 12. The major proportion of iron in the body is in the form of hemoglobin, though smaller quantities are present in other forms, especially in the liver and in the bone marrow. Oxidative enzymes containing iron (especially the cytochromes) are present in all the cells of the body. Therefore, iron is absolutely essential both for transport of oxygen to the tissues and for maintenance of oxidative enzyme systems within the tissue cells, without which life would cease within a few seconds.

Important Trace Elements in the Body. A few elements are present in the body in such small quantities that they are called "trace elements." Usually, the amounts of these in the foods are also minute. Yet, without any one of them a specific deficiency syndrome is likely to develop. Therefore, it must be recognized that a number of trace elements are extremely important for operation of the body.

Iodine. The best known of the trace elements is iodine. This element is discussed in detail in Chapter 75 in connection with thyroid hormone; as illustrated in Table 28, the entire body contains an average of only 14 milligrams. Iodine is essential for the formation of *thyroxin,* which in turn is essential for maintenance of normal metabolic rates in all the cells.

Copper. Copper deficiency has been observed on rare occasions in infants receiving only a milk diet. The effect of the deficiency is a microcytic, normochromic anemia caused by failure of the bone marrow to synthesize an adequate quantity of hemoglobin. Copper is important in iron absorption from the gastrointestinal tract, and it is presumably this effect that causes the deficient hemoglobin formation. Lack of copper also decreases the quantities of certain iron-containing enzymes in the tissue cells.

Zinc. Zinc is an integral part of the enzyme *carbonic anhydrase,* which is present in especially high concentration in the red blood cells. This enzyme is responsible for rapid combination of carbon dioxide from the interstitial fluids with water in the red blood cells of the peripheral capillary blood and for rapid release of carbon dioxide from the pulmonary capillary blood into the alveoli. Carbonic anhydrase is also present to a major extent in the gastrointestinal mucosa, in the tubules of the kidney, and in the epithelium of many of the glands of the body. Consequently, zinc in small quantities is essential for the performance of many reactions relating to carbon dioxide metabolism.

Considerable zinc is present in the pancreas, and zinc combines very readily with insulin. Therefore, even though zinc is not necessary for the function of insulin, it has been suggested that much of the insulin of the pancreas is stored in this organ as a zinc compound.

Zinc is also a component of *lactic dehydrogenase* and, therefore, is important for the interconversions of pyruvic acid and lactic acid. Also, zinc is a component part of some of the *peptidases* and therefore is important for digestion of proteins in the gastrointestinal tract.

Cobalt. Cobalt is an essential part of vitamin B_{12}, and, as discussed earlier in this chapter, vitamin B_{12} is essential for maturation of red blood cells.

Excess cobalt in the diet causes the opposite of anemia, i.e., polycythemia. However, the polycythemic cells formed contain relatively small concentrations of hemoglobin so that the total quantity of hemoglobin in the circulating blood remains relatively normal despite the polycythemia. Thus, it appears that cobalt is concerned principally with the formation of the red blood cell structure and not with the formation of hemoglobin.

Manganese. Lack of manganese in the diet of animals causes testicular atrophy, though the cause of this is not known. Also, manganese is necessary in the body to activate arginase, which is one of the major enzymes necessary for the formation of urea. Consequently, lack of manganese in the diet might prevent the conversion of ammonium ions into urea, and excessive quantities of ammonium compounds developing in the body fluids could cause toxicity. Finally, manganese activates many of the metabolic enzymes, including cholinesterase and at least one of the enzymes required for glycolysis, which was discussed in Chapter 65.

Fluorine. Fluorine does not seem to be a necessary element for metabolism, but the presence of a small quantity of fluorine in the body during the period of life when the teeth are being formed protects against carious teeth. Fluorine does not make the teeth themselves stronger but, instead, seems to block the action of bacterial enzymes that cause caries. It is believed that fluorine in the teeth combines with various trace metals that are necessary for activation of the bacterial enzymes, and, because the enzymes are deprived of these trace metals, they remain inactive and cause no caries.

Excessive intake of fluorine causes *fluorosis*, which is manifest in its mild state by mottled teeth and in a more severe state by enlarged bones. It has been postulated that in this condition fluorine combines with trace metals in some of the metabolic enzymes, including the phosphatases, so that various metabolic systems become partially inactivated. According to this theory, the mottled teeth and enlarged bones are due to abnormal enzyme systems in the odontoblasts and osteoblasts. Even though mottled teeth are highly resistant to the development of caries, the structural strength of these teeth is considerably lessened by the mottling process.

REFERENCES

Aikawa, J. K., Rhoades, E. L., Harms, D. R., and Reardon, J. Z.: Magnesium metabolism in rabbits using Mg^{28} as a tracer. *Am. J. Physiol., 197:*99, 1959.

Albritton, E. D.: Standard Values in Nutrition and Metabolism. Philadelphia, W. B. Saunders Co., 1954.

Anand, B. K., and Brobeck, J. R.: Hypothalamic control of food intake in rats and cats. *Yale J. Biol. & Med., 24:*123, 1951.

Bourne, G. H. (ed.): World Review of Nutrition and Dietetics. Volume 1, Philadelphia, J. B. Lippincott Co., 1960.

Brock, J. F.: Nutrition. *Ann. Rev. Biochem., 24:*523, 1955.

Brown, G. M.: Biosynthesis of water-soluble vitamins and derived coenzymes. *Physiol. Rev., 40:*331, 1960.

Burton, B. T.: The Heinz Handbook of Nutrition. New York, McGraw-Hill Book Co., Inc., 1959.

Cotzias, G. C.: Manganese in health and disease. *Physiol. Rev., 38:*503, 1958.

Greene, I., and Hiatt, E. P.: Behavior of the nitrate ion in the dog. *Am. J. Physiol., 176:*463, 1954.

Grossman, M. I.: Nutrition and nutritional diseases. *Ann. Rev. Med., 8:*177, 1957.

Harris, R. S.: Vitamins and Hormones. Volume XV. New York, Academic Press, 1957.

Hegsted, D. M., Trulson, M. F., and Stare, F. J.: Role of wheat and wheat products in human nutrition. *Physiol. Rev., 34:*221, 1954.

Kidder, B.: Biochemistry and Physiology of Nutrition. New York, Academic Press, 1953.

Lowry, O. H.: Biochemical evidence of nutritional status. *Physiol. Rev., 32:*431, 1952.

Marston, H. R.: Cobalt, copper, and molybdenum in the nutrition of animals and plants. *Physiol. Rev., 32:*66, 1952.

McElroy, W. D., and Bentley, G.: Symposium on Copper Metabolism. Baltimore, Johns Hopkins University Press, 1950.

McLester, J. S., and Darby, W. J.: Nutrition and Diet in Health and Disease. 6th ed., Philadelphia, W. B. Saunders Co., 1952.

Monier-Williams, G. W.: Trace Elements in Food. New York, John Wiley and Sons, 1949.

Novellis, G. D.: Metabolic functions of pantothenic acid. *Physiol. Rev., 33:*525, 1953.

Overman, R. R.: Sodium, potassium and chloride alterations in disease. *Physiol. Rev., 31:*285, 1951.

Petering, H. G.: Folic acid antagonists. *Physiol. Rev., 32:*197, 1952.

Reed, L. J.: Metabolic functions of thiamine and lipoic acid. *Physiol. Rev., 33:*544, 1953.

Snell, E. E.: Summary of known metabolic functions of nicotinic acid, riboflavin, and vitamin B$_6$. *Physiol. Rev., 33:*509, 1953.

Stokstad, E. L. R.: Antibiotics in animal nutrition. *Physiol. Rev., 34:*25, 1954.

Strauss, E. W., and Wilson, T. H.: Factors controlling B$_{12}$ uptake by intestinal sacs in vitro. *Am. J. Physiol., 198:*103, 1960.

Vallee, B. L.: Biochemistry, physiology and pathology of zinc. *Physiol. Rev., 39:*443, 1959.

Vitamins and Hormones. New York, Academic Press, Annually.

Wohl, M. G.: Modern Nutrition in Health and Disease. Philadelphia, Lea & Febiger, 1955.

Wohl, M. G., and Goodhart, R. S.: Modern Nutrition. Philadelphia, Lea & Febiger, 1955.

Chapter 71

Body Temperature,

Temperature Regulation, and Fever

HEAT BALANCE AND BODY TEMPERATURE

Heat is continually being produced in the body as a by-product of the metabolic reactions. On the other hand, heat is also continually being lost to the surroundings. When the rate of heat production is exactly equal to the rate of heat loss, the person is said to be in *heat balance,* but, when the rate of heat production is greater than the rate of heat loss, the total quantity of body heat will be increasing. Conversely, when the rate of heat loss is greater than the rate of heat production, the total quantity of body heat will be decreasing.

Relationship of Body Heat to Body Temperature—Specific Heat of the Tissues. The temperature of an object is a measure of the kinetic activity of its molecules, and this is proportional to the amount of heat stored in the object. Therefore, body temperature is directly proportional to the heat in the body.

On the average, the body temperature increases 1° C. for each 0.83 Calorie of heat stored per kilogram of body weight. In other words, the *specific heat* of the tissues is said to be 0.83 Cal./kg./degree C. For a 70 kg. man, approximately 58 Calories of heat must be added to the body to raise the body temperature 1° C., or 1.8° F.

Normal Body Temperature

"Core" Temperature versus Surface Temperature. When one speaks of the body temperature, he usually means the temperature in the interior, called the *core temperature,* and not the temperature of the skin or tissues immediately underlying the skin. The internal temperature is very accurately regulated, normally varying from the mean by not more than 1° F. On the other hand, the surface temperature rises and falls with the temperature of the surroundings. Therefore, we can express body temperature in three different ways: (1) the internal temperature, or *core temperature,* (2) the *surface temperature,* or (3) the *average body temperature.* In speaking of body temperature regulation we almost always refer to the core temperature; when we refer to the ability of the skin to lose heat to the surroundings, we usually speak of the surface temperature; and when we wish to calculate the total amount of heat stored in the body, we use the average body temperature. The average body temperature can be approximated by the following formula:

Average temperature = 0.7 internal temperature + 0.3 surface temperature

The Normal Body Temperature. No single temperature can be considered to be normal, for measurements on many normal subjects have shown a *range* of normal temperatures, as illustrated in Figure 664, from approximately 97° F. to over 99° F. When measured by rectum, the values are approximately 1° F. greater than the oral temperatures. The average normal temperature is generally considered to be 98.6° F. or 37° C. when measured orally and approximately 1° F. or 0.6° C. higher when measured rectally.

The body temperature varies considerably

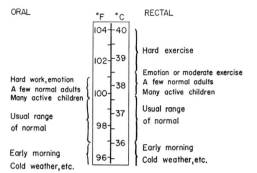

Figure 664. Estimated range of body temperature in normal persons. (From DuBois: Fever. Charles C Thomas.)

with exercise and with the temperature of the surroundings, for the temperature regulatory mechanisms are not 100 per cent effective. When excessive heat is produced in the body by hard exercise, the rectal temperature can rise to as high as 101° to 104° F. On the other hand, when the body is exposed to extremely cold weather, the rectal temperature can often fall to values considerably below 98° F.

FACTORS THAT AFFECT HEAT PRODUCTION AND HEAT LOSS

Heat Production

Figure 665 presents the various factors that affect heat production and also the different means by which heat can be lost from the body. The factors that enter into heat production are the following:

Basal Metabolic Rate. The basal metabolic rate of the body, which was discussed in Chapter 68, causes continual heat production, and the other factors presented at the left in Figure 665 are additional factors over

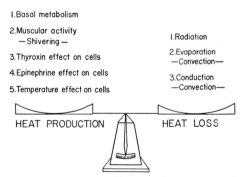

Figure 665. Balance of heat production versus heat loss.

and above the normal basal metabolic rate. Thus, the normal young adult male ordinarily produces at least 40 Calories of heat per hour per square meter of body surface area. This amount of heat production would raise the body temperature about 2° F. in one hour if no heat were lost from the body.

The organ of the body with the highest rate of chemical activity during basal conditions is the liver, for under these conditions the liver generates perhaps 20 to 30 per cent of the heat in the body. As a result of this high metabolic rate, the temperature of the liver is approximately 1 to 2 degrees higher than the temperature in the rectum. Also, the heat produced in the brain is probably about 15 per cent of the total basal heat production.

Effect of Muscular Activity on Rate of Heat Production. Under basal conditions the quantity of heat released to the body from skeletal muscular activity may be as low as 25 per cent of the total heat production, but during exercise the oxygen consumption by muscles may increase sometimes to as great as 60 times normal, thereby increasing the heat of chemical reaction in the muscles a similar amount. When all the muscles of the body are contracted at maximal rate of activity, the metabolic rate of the whole body can rise to 1500 to 2000 per cent above the basal level.

Shivering. When a person begins to shiver, the rhythmic contraction of muscles throughout the body increases the rate of heat production sometimes to as much as two to four times normal. Though this rate of muscular heat production is not nearly so great as that occurring during maximal voluntary exercise, it does nevertheless greatly aid in increasing the body temperature.

Shivering results from excitation of the posterior hypothalamus by cold. Impulses are transmitted through bilateral tracts that pass ventrolateral to the red nuclei, down the brain stem into the lateral columns of the spinal cord, and finally to the anterior motoneurons. These impulses are non-rhythmical and do not cause the actual muscular shaking. Instead, they simply facilitate the anterior motoneurons. This facilitation at first increases the muscle tone throughout the body, which raises the overall metabolic rate as much as 50 to 100 per cent even without any shivering. Then, shivering begins when the degree of facilitation reaches a certain critical level because of oscillation of the muscle spindle feedback mechanism as follows: The highly facilitated motoneurons cause the muscles to contract, which in turn momentarily inhibits the activity of the muscle spindles. Decreased afferent impulses from the spindles reduce the degree of anterior horn cell facilitation so that the muscle contraction stops. After another fraction of a second the muscle spindles begin to transmit impulses again, the anterior horn cells again become facilitated, and the muscles contract once more, thus setting off a new cycle. This oscillation continues as long as the facilitation lasts, causing the shaking which we call shivering, and the rate of heat production in the body then rises to as much as 200 to 300 per cent above normal.

Effect of Thyroxin on the Cells. In Chapter 68 it was pointed out that thyroxin has a direct effect on all cells of the body to increase the local rate of metabolism. This increase in turn causes greater than normal quantities of heat to be released in the body; when thyroxin production rises to maximal levels, the metabolic rate occasionally rises more than 100 per cent above normal.

Effect of Epinephrine and Sympathetic Activity on the Cells. As also pointed out in the previous chapter, epinephrine and sympathetic activity, like thyroxin, directly affect the rate of metabolism in all the cells of the body, and maximal sympathetic activity can increase the rate of metabolism probably as much as 40 to 50 per cent.

Effect of Body Temperature on the Cells. It is well known that increasing the temperature of a solution in which chemical reactions are occurring greatly increases the rate at which these chemical reactions proceed. For every 10° F. increase in body temperature, the rate of heat production by the cells increases approximately 70 per cent; in other words, at a temperature of 108.6° F. the basal metabolic rate of the body will have risen from a normal value in a young male of 40 Calories per hour per square meter up to a value of approximately 68 Calories per hour per square meter. To express this another way, the rate of heat production rises about 7 per cent for each degree Fahrenheit increase in body temperature, or 13 per cent per degree Centigrade.

Once the body temperature begins to rise, progressively greater and greater heat pro-duction occurs because of this temperature effect. Consequently, the higher the body temperature, the more difficult is it for the heat loss mechanisms to dissipate the heat that is produced. Consequently, a high temperature tends to produce a still higher temperature.

Heat Loss

The various methods by which heat is lost from the body are depicted on the right side of the balance in Figure 665. These include *radiation, convection,* and *evaporation.* However, the amount of heat lost by each of these different mechanisms varies with atmospheric conditions.

Radiation. As illustrated in Figure 666, the nude body sometimes loses a tremendous amount of heat by radiation. Indeed, when one is sitting in the nude in a room at so-called normal temperature the average proportion of the body heat lost by radiation is approximately 60 per cent.

Loss of heat by radiation means loss of heat in the form of infrared heat rays, which are electromagnetic waves. Most of the infrared rays radiating from the body have wave lengths of 5 to 20 microns, 10 to 20 times the wavelengths of light rays. All mass in the universe that is not at absolute zero temperature radiates heat rays. Therefore, the body radiates heat rays in all directions, and heat rays are being radiated from the walls and other objects toward the body. If the temperature of the body is greater than the temperature of the surroundings, then a greater quantity of heat will be radiated away from the body than to the body. This is the usual situation. However, at times, especially in the summer, the surroundings become hotter than the human body, under which circumstances more radiant heat is transmitted to the body than from the body.

Heat loss by radiation varies directly with

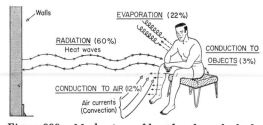

Figure 666.   Mechanisms of heat loss from the body.

the temperature difference between the temperature of the body surface and the average temperature of the surroundings. Therefore, it is impossible to state categorically exactly what percentage of the body heat will be lost by radiation unless all of the conditions surrounding the body are momentarily defined.

The surface of the human body is extremely absorbent for heat rays. When the body is exposed to infrared heat rays from a stove, it absorbs approximately 97 per cent of the rays that hit it. This rate of infrared absorption is approximately equal for human beings with either white or colored skin, for at these wavelengths the different colors of the skin have no effect on absorption. On the other hand, the energy from the sun is transmitted mainly in the form of light rays rather than infrared rays. Approximately 35 per cent of these waves are reflected from the white skin but only a small amount from the dark skin. Consequently, in sunlight a dark skin does absorb more heat than a white skin.

Conduction. Usually, only minute quantities of heat are lost from the body by direct conduction from the surface of the body to other objects such as a chair, a bed, etc. When one first sits on a chair while in the nude state, very rapid conduction of heat from the body to the chair occurs immediately, but within a few minutes the temperature of the chair rises almost to equal the temperature of the body, and thereafter the chair actually becomes an insulator to prevent further loss of heat. Consequently, as illustrated in Figure 666, the loss of heat by *conduction to objects* represents only a small per cent of the total heat loss from the body.

On the other hand, loss of heat by *conduction to air* does represent a sizeable proportion of the body's heat loss even under normal conditions. It will be recalled that heat is actually molecular motion, and the molecules that comprise the skin of the body are continually undergoing vibratory motion. Thus, the vibratory motion of the skin molecules can cause increased motion of the air molecules that come into direct contact with the skin. However, once the temperature of the air immediately adjacent to the skin equals the temperature of the skin, exchange of heat from the body to the air no longer occurs. Therefore, conduction of heat from the body to the air is self-limited unless the

air moves so that new, unheated air is continually brought in contact with the skin.

Convection. Movement of air is known as *convection*, and the removal of heat from the body by convection air currents is commonly called "heat loss by convection." Actually, the heat must first be *conducted* to the air and then carried away by the convection currents. Consequently, to be precise, convective heat loss must be considered to be a type of conductive heat loss.

A small amount of convection almost always occurs around the body because of the tendency for the air adjacent to the skin to rise as it becomes heated. Therefore, a nude person seated in a comfortable room without gross air movement still loses about 15 per cent of his heat to the air by convection.

Cooling effect of wind. When the body is exposed to wind, the layer of air immediately adjacent to the skin is replaced by new air much more rapidly than normally, and heat loss by convection increases accordingly. Figure 667 shows that the cooling effect of wind at low velocities is approximately proportional to the square root of the wind velocity. For instance, a wind of 4 miles per hour is about two times as effective for cooling as a wind of 1 mile per hour. However, when the wind velocity rises beyond a few miles per hour, additional cooling does not occur to a great extent. The reason for this is that once the wind has cooled the skin to the temperature of the air itself, a further increase in rate of heat loss cannot occur regardless of the wind velocity. Instead, the rate at which heat can flow from the core of the body to the skin is then the factor that determines the rapidity with which heat can be lost.

Conduction and convection of heat from a body exposed to water. Water has several thousand times as much specific heat as air so that each unit portion of water adjacent to the skin can absorb far greater quantities of heat than can air. Also, the conductivity of heat through water is very marked in comparison with that in air. Consequently, heating a thin layer of water next to the body does not result in the formation of an "insulator zone" as occurs in air, because the heat in the layer of water adjacent to the skin is very rapidly conducted into the more distant water. For this reason, the rate of heat loss from the body into non-flowing water is

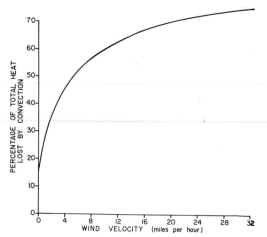

Figure 667. Effect of wind velocity on the percentage of heat loss that occurs by convection.

almost as much as the rate of heat loss into rapidly flowing water.

Because of these differences in heat conduction by air and water, the rate of heat loss to water at moderate temperatures is many times as great as the rate of heat loss to air of the same temperature. However, when the water and air are extremely cold, the rate of heat loss to air then becomes almost as great as to water, for either water or air is then capable of carrying away essentially all the heat that can reach the skin from the body core. Therefore, it is mainly the rate at which heat can be conducted from the interior of the body to the skin that determines the rate of heat loss under these conditions rather than the conductivity of the surrounding medium.

Evaporation. When water evaporates from the body surface, approximately 0.64 Calorie of heat is lost for each gram of water that evaporates, and water evaporates *insensibly* from the skin and lungs at a rate of about 600 ml. per day. This causes continual heat loss at a rate of 15 to 20 Calories per hour. Unfortunately, this insensible evaporation of water directly through the skin and lungs cannot be controlled for purposes of temperature regulation because it results from continual diffusion of water molecules through the skin and alveoli regardless of body temperature. However, evaporative loss of heat can be controlled by regulating the rate of sweating, which will be discussed below.

Evaporation as a necessary refrigeration mechanism at high air temperatures. In the above discussions of radiation and conduction it was noted that as long as the body temperature is greater than that of the surroundings, heat loss by radiation and conduction can occur, but, on the other hand, when the temperature of the surroundings is greater than that of the skin, instead of losing heat the body gains heat by radiation and conduction from the surroundings. Under these conditions, *the only means by which the body can rid itself of heat is evaporation.* Therefore, it is extremely important to remember that any factor that prevents adequate evaporation when the surrounding temperatures are higher than body temperature will permit the body temperature to rise. This occurs occasionally in human beings who are born with congenital absence of sweat glands. These persons can withstand cold temperatures as well as normal subjects, but they are likely to die of heat stroke in tropical zones, for without the evaporative refrigeration system their body temperatures tend to remain continually at values slightly greater than those of the surroundings.

Effect of humid weather on evaporative loss of heat. It is well known that hot, muggy, summer days are extremely uncomfortable, and that sweat pours from the body far more profusely on these days than normally. The reason for this is that the air is already humidified almost to its maximal extent. Consequently, the rate of evaporation may be greatly reduced or totally prevented so that the secreted sweat remains in the fluid state. Consequently, the body temperature approaches the temperature of the surroundings or rises slightly above this temperature even though sweat continues to pour forth. This is the means by which one loses weight in the steam chamber, for the humidity of the steam chamber is 100 per cent, and no evaporation can occur. Unfortunately, weight loss that occurs by this procedure is caused by loss of extracellular fluid, which probably does more harm than good to the body, for this treatment does not cause any significant loss of actual body fat.

Effect of convection air currents on evaporation. As pointed out above, a very thin zone of air adjacent to the skin usually remains relatively stationary and is not exchanged for new air at a rapid rate unless convection currents are present. Lack of air movement prevents effective evaporation in the same manner that effective cooling by conduction of heat to the air is prevented when there is little convection—that is, the local air becomes saturated with water vapor, and further evaporation cannot occur. Therefore, convection currents cause air that has become saturated with moisture to move away from the skin while unsaturated air replaces it. Obviously, this allows greater quantities of evaporation than would occur otherwise. Indeed, convection is probably of even more importance for loss of heat from the body by evaporation than for loss by conduction, for the instances in which one especially needs to lose heat from the body, such as on hot days, are the same times when evaporative loss of heat from the body is far greater than conductive loss. This also explains why fans are in great demand on hot days.

Sweating and Its Regulation by the Autonomic Nervous System

When the body becomes overheated, large quantities of sweat are secreted onto the surface of the skin by the sweat glands to provide very rapid *evaporative cooling* of the body. As pointed out in Chapter 20, stimulation of the anterior hypothalamus excites sweating while stimulation of the posterior hypothalamus decreases sweating by reciprocally inhibiting the anterior hypothalamus. The impulses from the anterior hypothalamus that cause sweating are transmitted in the autonomic pathways to the cord and thence through the sympathetic outflow to the skin everywhere in the body.

It should be recalled from the discussion of the autonomic nervous system in Chapter 20 that the sweat glands are innervated by *cholingeric* nerve fibers. However, the sweat glands can also be stimulated by epinephrine or nor-epinephrine circulating in the blood even though the glands in most parts of the body do not have an adrenergic innervation. It is possible that the sweat glands of the hands and feet do have some degree of adrenergic innervation as well as cholinergic innervation, for many emotional states that excite the adrenergic portions of the sympathetic nervous system are known also to cause local sweating of the hands and feet. Also, during muscular exercise, which normally excites adrenergic activity, localized

sweating on the hands and feet occurs. In this instance, it is believed that the moisture from the sweat helps the surfaces of the hands and feet to gain traction against smooth surfaces and also prevents drying of the thick, cornified layers of skin.

Rate of Sweating. In very cold weather, the rate of sweat production is essentially zero but in very hot weather the maximum rate of sweat production is from 1.5 liters per hour in the unacclimatized person to 3.5 liters per hour in the person maximally acclimatized to heat. Thus, during maximal sweating, a person can lose up to 8 pounds of body weight per hour.

Table 30.   Average Concentrations of Sweat Constituents Relative to Plasma (Modified from Kuno.)

Substance	Sweat	Plasma
Na	80 mEq.	142 mEq.
K	5	5
Ca	1	2.5
Mg	0.5	1.5
Cl	86.5	103
Urea—N	15 mg. %	15 mg. %
Glucose	2	100
Lactic acid	35	15
Protein	0 gm. %	7 gm. %

Composition of Sweat. Table 30 gives the average composition of sweat compared with that of plasma, showing four major differences between these: (1) the concentration of sodium chloride is considerably less in sweat than in plasma, (2) the concentration of glucose is almost zero in sweat in comparison with 100 mg. per cent in plasma, (3) the concentration of lactic acid is considerably greater in sweat than in plasma, and (4) the concentration of proteins in sweat is zero in comparison with 7 gm. per cent in plasma. Therefore, sweat is not merely an ultrafiltrate of plasma but instead is a glandular secretion. The excess lactic acid in the sweat results from metabolic production of lactic acid during the secretion of sweat.

The concentration of sodium chloride in sweat can be as little as one tenth that in the plasma or as great as that in the plasma; this depends on the following mechanism: When the plasma sodium falls below normal, the adrenal cortex begins to secrete large

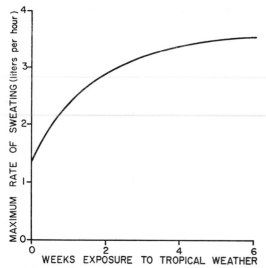

Figure 668. Acclimatization of the sweating mechanism, showing progressive increase in the maximum rate of sweating during the first few weeks of exposure to tropical weather.

amounts of aldosterone, and this hormone conserves sodium principally by its action on the kidneys, as explained in Chapter 9. However, aldosterone has a similar effect on the sweat glands to cause sodium reabsorption by these as well as by the kidneys, and chloride is reabsorbed along with the sodium. Therefore, sodium and chloride concentration in the sweat is principally determined by adrenocortical secretion of aldosterone.

Acclimatization of the Sweating Mechanism. When a person is exposed to very hot weather for several weeks, his sweating becomes progressively more and more profuse, with an average maximum of about 1.5 liters per hour at first, which rises to about double within 10 days and to about 2½ times as much within 6 weeks, as illustrated in Figure 668. This increased effectiveness of the sweating mechanism is caused by a direct increase in sweating capability of the sweat glands themselves. Associated with the increased sweating is usually decreased concentration of sodium chloride in the sweat, which allows progressively better conservation of salt. Most of this adaptation for conserving salt is caused by increased secretion of aldosterone, but it possibly also results in part from local changes in the sweat glands.

Extreme sweating can deplete the extracellular fluids of electrolytes, particularly of sodium and chloride. Consequently, extra sodium chloride usually must be supplied in the diet in tropical climates. A person who sweats profusely may lose as much as 15 to 25 grams of sodium chloride each day until he becomes acclimatized. On the other hand, after 4 to 6 weeks of acclimatization the loss of sodium chloride may be as little as 3 to 5 grams per day.

Long-term Acclimatization of the Sweat Apparatus in the Tropics. In addition to the rapid acclimatization of the sweating mechanism described above, a second type of acclimatization occurs over a period of many years in persons who live in the tropics, especially persons born there. This type of acclimatization accomplishes the following:

First, the person who has lived long in the tropics secretes almost exactly the amount of sweat that can evaporate from the body and does not secrete an excess amount that rolls from the skin in the form of droplets. Droplets cause no evaporative cooling and therefore represent a waste of body fluids and electrolytes. Thus, this additional mechanism of adaptation helps to conserve the person's water and salt supply.

Second, in persons who have lived in the tropics since childhood there are actually greater numbers of active sweat glands in the body. A person is born with a considerable excess of sweat glands, but if he lives in a temperate zone, many of these become permanently inactivated during childhood. However, if he lives in the tropics they remain functional throughout life. Therefore, a person who has spent his childhood in the tropics usually possesses a much more effective sweating mechanism than does a person bred elsewhere.

Panting as a Means of Evaporative Heat Loss. Many lower animals do not have sweat glands, but to offset this they lose large amounts of heat by the panting mechanism. During panting only small quantities of air pass in and out of the lungs with each breath so that mainly dead space air enters the alveoli. Therefore, tremendous amounts of air can be moved over the surfaces of the tongue, mouth, and trachea without greatly over respiring the animal. Evaporation from these respiratory surfaces, especially of saliva on the tongue, provides a very important mechanism for heat control.

A special nervous center in the pons controls panting. This center modifies the normal respiratory pattern to provide the very rapid and shallow breathing required for the panting mechanism.

The Insulator System of the Body

The skin, the subcutaneous tissues, and especially the fat of the subcutaneous tissues are an effective heat insulator for the body. When no blood is flowing from the heated internal organs to the skin, the insulating properties of the male body are approximately equal to three-quarters the insulating properties of a usual suit of clothes. In women this insulation is still better. Obviously, the degree of insulation varies from one person to another, depending to a great extent on the quantity of adipose tissue.

Because most of the body heat is produced in the deeper portions of the body, it is obvious that the insulation beneath the skin is an effective means for maintaining normal internal temperatures, even though it allows the temperature of the skin to approach the temperature of the surroundings.

Flow of Blood to the Skin—The "Radiator" System of the Body

Blood vessels penetrate the subcutaneous insulator tissues and are distributed profusely in the subpapillary portions of the skin. Indeed, immediately beneath the skin is a continuous venous plexus which is supplied in the most exposed areas of the body—the hands, feet, and ears—by direct arteriovenous shunts from the arterioles to the veins. Furthermore, the rate of blood flow into this venous plexus can vary tremendously—from almost zero up to as great as 30 per cent of the total cardiac output. A high rate of blood flow to the venous plexus causes heat to be conducted from the internal portions of the body to the skin with great efficiency, but a reduction in the rate of blood flow decreases the efficiency of heat conduction from the internal portions of the body.

It is obvious, therefore, that the skin is an effective radiator system and that the flow of blood through the skin is the mechanism of heat transfer from the body "core" to the skin. If blood flow from the internal structures to the skin is depressed, then the only means by which heat produced internally can be lost

to the exterior is by diffusion through the heat insulators of the skin and subcutaneous tissue. On the other hand, when it is desirable that heat be lost from the body at a much more rapid rate than can occur by diffusion through the heat insulators, this heat can be conducted to the skin by the blood.

Control of Heat Conduction to the Skin. Heat conduction to the skin by the blood is controlled by the degree of vasoconstriction of the arterioles that supply blood to the venous plexus of the skin, and this vasoconstriction is controlled almost entirely by the sympathetic nervous system. Ordinarily, the sympathetics remain tonically active, causing some degree of continual constriction of the arterioles supplying the skin. When the sympathetic centers of the posterior hypothalamus are stimulated, even greater constriction of the blood vessels occurs, and blood flow to the skin may almost cease, but, when these posterior centers of the hypothalamus are inhibited, decreased numbers of sympathetic impulses are transmitted to the periphery, and the blood vessels dilate.

In addition to the vasoconstrictor system for controlling skin blood flow, sympathetic *vasodilator* fibers also supply all portions of the skin besides that of the hands and feet. Stimulation of these can increase the local blood flow as much as two- to four-fold.

Still another mechanism that possibly aids in the control of skin blood flow operates secondarily to the sympathetic stimulation of the sweat glands. When these glands become active, they supposedly release a substance called *bradykinin* that diffuses to the surrounding tissues and causes vasodilatation. This vasodilatation presumably helps to increase heat flow from the body core to the body surface.

Effect of Clothing on Heat Loss. *Effect on conductive heat loss.* The effect of clothing on conduction of heat from the body is to increase the insulating effect of the zone of air adjacent to the skin. It has already been pointed out that when the air surrounding the body remains very still, a so-called "private zone" of air exists adjacent to the skin, and once this private zone becomes heated essentially no additional heat is lost from the skin by conduction. Clothing entraps additional layers of air next to the skin and in the weave of the cloth, thereby increasing the thickness of the private zone and decreasing the flow of convection currents. Consequently, the rate of heat loss from the body by conduction is greatly depressed as a result of clothing.

A usual suit of clothes decreases the rate of heat loss from the body to about one-half that from a nude body, while arctic-type clothing can decrease this heat loss to as little as one-sixth that of the nude state.

Effect on heat loss by radiation.   The rate of heat loss by radiation is affected by clothing almost in the same manner as the rate of heat loss by conduction. The body must first radiate or conduct its heat to the clothing, and then this heat must be conducted from the inner surface of the clothing to the outer surface of the clothing before radiation to the surroundings can occur. Clothing, by entrapping air, acts as an insulator to suppress the conduction of heat from the body to the outer surface of the clothing. Therefore, even though the skin continues to radiate heat to the clothing and even though the clothing continues to radiate heat from its outer surface, the total radiation is decreased.

About one half of the heat transmitted from the skin to the clothing probably is radiated to the clothing instead of being conducted across the small intervening space, for it has been shown that sputtering the inside of clothing with a thin layer of gold, which reflects radiant heat, makes the insulating properties of clothing far more effective than otherwise. The reason for this is that the heat leaving the skin is reflected back from the clothing to the skin, and, consequently, little heat can then be transmitted to the clothing by the process of radiation. As a result of this new technique, clothing for use in the arctic can be decreased in weight by about one half.

Loss of heat through wet clothing.   The effectiveness of clothing in preventing heat loss is greatly decreased when it becomes wet, for the entrapped air, which normally acts as an insulator, then no longer exists. Instead, the interstices of the clothing are filled with water which, because of its high conductivity for heat, increases the rate of heat transmission some 5- to 20-fold. One of the most important factors for protecting the body against cold in arctic regions is extreme precaution against allowing the clothing to become wet. Indeed, one must be very careful not to overheat oneself temporarily, for

sweating in one's clothes makes them much less effective thereafter as an insulator.

Effect on heat loss by evaporation.   Clothing that is pervious to moisture allows almost normal loss of heat from the body by evaporation, for when sweating occurs the sweat itself can dampen the clothing, and evaporation then occurs from the surface of the clothing. This cools the clothing which in turn cools the skin. Consequently, in tropical regions, the wearing of light clothing that is pervious to sweat but impervious to radiant heat from the sun will prevent the body from gaining radiant heat while at the same time allowing it to lose heat at a rate almost as if one were not wearing clothing at all. It has been found that tightly woven poplin, which is very pervious to sweat, is as effective for the loss of heat by evaporation as is loosely woven twill, for convection currents to the inside of the clothing are not needed to cause the evaporation.

Clothing that is impervious to moisture, on the other hand, may completely block the loss of heat by evaporation. Because plastic fabrics repel droplets of sweat, such fabrics are certain to decrease the rate of evaporation; the only evaporation that can occur under these conditions results from convection air currents that pass through the pores of the clothing. Obviously, if the clothing is solid plastic, loss of heat by evaporation will be totally abrogated.

REGULATION OF BODY TEMPERATURE—FUNCTION OF THE HYPOTHALAMUS

Figure 669 illustrates what happens to the body temperature after a few hours' exposure of the nude body to air at temperatures ranging from 30° to 170° F. Obviously, the precise dimensions of this curve vary depending upon the movement of air, the amount of moisture in the air, and even the nature of the surroundings. However, in general, in the temperature range between approximately 70° and 130° F., the nude body is capable of maintaining indefinitely a normal body temperature somewhere between the limits of 97° to 100° F. The means by which temperature regulation is effected is by controlling the rates of heat production and heat loss as follows:

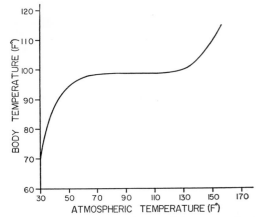

Figure 669. Effect of high and low atmospheric temperatures for several hours duration on the internal body temperature, showing that the internal body temperature remains stable despite wide changes in atmospheric temperature.

Thermostatic Center in the Anterior Hypothalamus for Protection against Overheating

Centers in the hypothalamus are peculiarly responsive to changes in body temperature. The *supraoptic and preoptic areas in the anterior hypothalamus* become excited when the body temperature rises too high, while *centers in the posterior hypothalamus* become excited when the body temperature falls too low. Furthermore, the anterior and posterior centers reciprocally inhibit each other so that when one becomes active the other becomes inactive. It is principally by means of this reciprocal relationship between these two centers that body temperature is regulated.

When the supraoptic and preoptic nuclei of the anterior hypothalamus are locally heated by placing two small electrodes on either side of these nuclei and then passing diathermy current between the electrodes, autonomic changes throughout the body begin to decrease the body temperature within one to two minutes. This occurs in two ways: (1) by increasing the rate of heat loss and (2) by decreasing the rate of heat production.

Increased Heat Loss. Stimulation of the anterior hypothalamus increases the rate of heat loss in three different ways: (1) by stimulating the sweat glands to cause evaporative loss of heat from the body, (2) by directly stimulating vasodilator nerves to the

skin, thereby increasing the transport of heat by the blood to the body surface, and (3) by reciprocally inhibiting the posterior hypothalamus, which removes the vasoconstrictor tone to the skin vessels and thereby allows still more vasodilatation.

Decreased Heat Production. In addition to increasing the rate of heat loss, *stimulation of the anterior hypothalamus decreases the rate of heat production.* This occurs principally by inhibiting the posterior hypothalamus, which in turn reduces the number of adrenergic nerve impulses transmitted throughout the body and therefore reduces the metabolic stimulation of all the cells. In addition, lack of impulses from the posterior hypothalamus also decreases the skeletal muscle tone, this, too, reducing the rate of heat production.

It is obvious, therefore, that stimulating the anterior hypothalamus both decreases the rate of heat production and also increases the rate of heat loss. Therefore, the anterior hypothalamus can be called a *temperature-reducing center.*

Thermostatic Center in the Posterior Hypothalamus for Protection against Overcooling

By chilling the hypothalamus in various ways, it has been found that the posterior hypothalamus is concerned with protection against cold, and that, when the posterior centers are destroyed, the body cannot protect itself against cold. However, the centers for protection against cold are not so discretely localized as is the small area of the anterior hypothalamus for protection against overheating. Nevertheless, when the hypothalamus is cooled, loss of heat from the body is greatly curtailed, and heat production is greatly increased.

Decreased Heat Loss. *Vasoconstriction.* One of the first effects that occur after cooling the hypothalamus is intense vasoconstriction throughout the body. This results from both intense adrenergic vasoconstriction throughout the body and inhibition of the cholinergic vasodilatation.

The vasoconstriction obviously prevents the "radiator system" from transferring heat from the internal portions of the body to the skin. Consequently, with maximal vasoconstriction the only heat that can leave the body is that which can be conducted directly through the insulator layers of the skin. This effect conserves the quantity of heat in the body.

Pilo-erection. A second means by which heat is conserved when the hypothalamus is stimulated by cold is pilo-erection—that is, the hairs "stand on end." Obviously, this effect is not important in the human being because of the paucity of hair, but in lower animals this upright projection of the hairs in cold weather entraps a thick layer of insulator air next to the skin so that the transfer of heat to the surroundings is greatly depressed.

Abolition of sweating. Sweating is completely abolished by sufficient cooling of the posterior hypothalamus, for stimulation of the posterior centers of the hypothalamus reciprocally inhibits the activity of the anterior centers and, therefore, blocks sweating.

Increased Production of Heat. Increased production of heat following stimulation of the posterior hypothalamic regions occurs as a result of two mechanisms: first, adrenergic excitation of heat production, and second, production of heat by the muscles as a result of shivering.

Sympathetic excitation of heat production. It has already been pointed out that epinephrine and nor-epinephrine can cause an immediate increase in the rate of cellular metabolism, this metabolism and rate of heat production probably being increased in all the cells of the body when massive sympathetic discharge occurs as a result of posterior hypothalamic stimulation.

Hypothalamic stimulation of shivering. Occurring simultaneously with sympathetic excitation of heat production, and probably of even more importance, is the process of shivering which is elicited by stimulation of the posterior hypothalamic centers.

As pointed out earlier in the chapter, impulses transmitted from the posterior hypothalamus to the cord facilitate the degree of activity of the anterior motoneurons. This in turn first increases the tone of the muscles and then causes shivering, sometimes increasing the rate of heat production to as much as two to four times normal.

Control of the Hypothalamic Thermostat by the Temperature of the Blood

Heating the carotid blood as it flows to the head through the carotid artery will elicit a

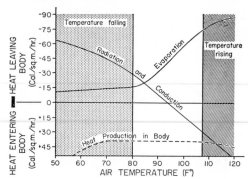

Figure 670. Effect of air temperature on the rate of heat production and on the rates of heat loss or gain by evaporation, radiation, and conduction.

response to cause a falling body temperature, whereas cooling the blood will elicit a response to cause a rising temperature. Therefore, the temperature-regulating mechanisms are definitely responsive to changes in the blood temperature.

When excessive heat is produced in the body and the blood temperature rises, the hypothalamus institutes measures to cause a falling temperature. Likewise, when an excess of heat is being lost from the body and the blood temperature begins to fall, the hypothalamus institutes measures to increase the body temperature.

In summary, the hypothalamus can change both the rate of heat production and the rate of heat loss under varying temperature conditions, thereby maintaining the body temperature at a very exact level. Figure 670 illustrates the general manner in which heat loss and heat production change when the atmospheric temperature changes, showing that evaporative heat loss is particularly important at high temperatures while increased heat production is particularly important at low temperatures.

Peripheral Factors That Help to Regulate Internal Body Temperature

Nerve receptors for both cold and heat are present everywhere in the skin. These help to regulate body temperature in three different ways: (1) First, they simply cause a psychic desire for warmer surroundings and therefore make a person seek appropriate shelter or clothing. (2) They transmit nerve impulses directly to the hypothalamus to increase or decrease its reactivity to heat or cold. (3) They can also elicit local cord reflexes to the skin that help to maintain normal body temperaure.

Effect of Peripheral Temperature Receptors on the Hypothalamus. When the cold temperature receptors of the skin are strongly stimulated, impulses transmitted from these to the hypothalamus enhance the activity of the *temperature-raising center* in the posterior hypothalamus while inhibiting the anterior hypothalamus. These effects obviously increase the rate of heat production while decreasing the rate of heat loss and therefore help to maintain the internal body temperature.

On the other hand, heating the skin causes exactly the opposite effects, this time causing the hypothalamus to increase the rate of heat loss while decreasing the rate of heat production.

Importance of this peripheral control of hypothalamic reactivity. Without the peripheral stimuli, the internal body temperature will vary considerably more than normally when the body is exposed to extremes of cold and heat —from as low as about 97 degrees F. to as high as perhaps 100 degrees F. Nevertheless, if the body temperature does fall low enough or rise high enough, the hypothalamus will eventually become stimulated. Therefore, the real importance of the peripheral control of hypothalamic reactivity is not to substitute for the hypothalamic thermostatic system but instead to increase its degree of effectiveness.

It should be pointed out that it would be impossible for the peripheral receptors alone to regulate internal body temperature. This fact follows from a basic understanding of control principles: Stable operation of a control system requires that the receptors exciting the control system detect the factor that is being controlled. In this instance the factor that is being controlled is the internal body temperature. Therefore, even though skin receptors are a valuable adjunct in controlling internal body temperature, they do not detect this temperature and therefore cannot substitute for the hypothalamic thermostatic control system.

Local Skin Reflexes. When one places a foot under a hot lamp and leaves it there for a short time, he finds that *local vasodilatation* and mild *local sweating* will occur. Conversely, placing a foot in cold water causes vasoconstriction and cessation of sweating. These reactions are caused by local cord reflexes conducted from the skin receptors to the spinal cord and back to the same skin area. Such reflexes can help to prevent excessive heat exchange from locally cooled or heated portions of the body. However, when a local skin area is heated at the same time that the rest of the body is cooled, the hypothalamic system takes precedence over the local mechanism, thus indicating that it is far more important for the body to maintain constant internal body temperature than to provide local regulation of skin temperature.

Adaptation of the Skin Temperature Receptors. The skin receptors for temperature sensations are stimulated not primarily by the absolute temperature of the surroundings but instead mainly by the *rate of change* of temperature. Therefore, when the skin temperature is actively falling, the skin feels much colder than it does when the temperature is equally as cold but not falling. This well-known fact is commonly observed when one enters a tub of very hot water. At first, the person feels as if he were being scalded, but, after he remains in the same water at the same temperature for several minutes, the water may become completely comfortable. The same effect also occurs when one suddenly subjects himself to severe cold. Detailed function of the thermal receptors is presented in Chapter 48.

It should also be pointed out that the skin temperature receptors are stimulated to a greater extent when a person is exposed to alternating temperatures than when he is exposed to a steady temperature. For instance, if the skin temperature is 50° F. and this remains steady, the person will feel much warmer than if the temperature alternates up and down between 45° F. and 55° F., even though the mean temperature remains constant. This again illustrates that temperature receptors are stimulated principally by *changes* in temperature.

Regulation of Internal Body Temperature after Cutting the Spinal Cord. After cutting of the spinal cord in the neck above the sympathetic outflow from the cord, regulation of body temperature becomes extremely poor, for the hypothalamus can then no longer control either skin blood flow nor the degree of sweating anywhere in the body. On the other hand, the local temperature reflexes originating in the skin receptors still exist. Unfortunately, these reflexes are not very powerful, and, since none of the skin receptors are capable of detecting *internal* temperature, automatic regulation of internal body temperature is almost completely lost. In these persons, body temperature must be regulated principally by the patient's psychic response to cold and hot sensations in his head region. That is, if he feels himself becoming too hot or if he develops a headache from the heat, he knows to select cooler surroundings, and, conversely, if he has cold sensations, he selects warmer surroundings.

Function of the Thyroid Gland in Acclimatization to Cold Temperature

Prolonged exposure to cold increases the activity of the thyroid gland, which accounts to a great extent for the ability of persons to become acclimated to different climatic temperatures.

Exposure of animals to extreme cold for several weeks can cause the sizes of their thyroid glands to increase as much as 20 to 40 per cent. Also, military personnel residing for several months in the Arctic have been shown to develop basal metabolic rates of 15 to 20 per cent above normal, while Eskimos naturally have basal metabolic rates even higher than this. Finally, it is well known that the number of toxic thyroid goiters occurring in colder climates is far greater than the number in tropical climates.

Though the exact manner in which cold temperatures increase the activity of the thyroid gland is unknown, exposure to cold in some manner excites the hypothalamus, and this in turn increases *thyrotropin* production in the *adenohypophysis* by mechanisms explained in Chapter 73. The thyrotropin then passes by way of the blood to the thyroid to increase its activity.

ABNORMALITIES OF BODY TEMPERATURE REGULATION—FEVER

Fever, which means a body temperature above the usual range of normal, may be caused by abnormalities in the brain itself or by toxic substances that directly affect the temperature-regulating centers. Some of the

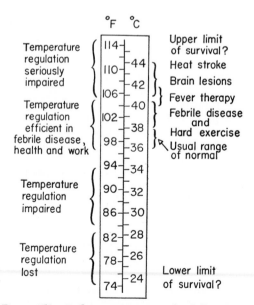

Figure 671. Body temperatures under different conditions. (From DuBois: Fever. Charles C Thomas.)

causes of fever are presented in Figure 671. These include bacterial diseases, brain tumors, and a vicious cycle of heat production which may terminate in heat stroke.

Resetting the Hypothalamic Thermostat in Febrile Diseases—Effect of Proteins

Many proteins or breakdown products of proteins, some of which are formed in the human body and some of which enter the body from the outside, can cause the level at which the body temperature is regulated to rise considerably above normal. This shift in the temperature level at which the regulatory mechanisms regulate body temperature is sometimes termed "resetting the hypothalamic thermostat."

Many of the protein antigens that enter the body fluids during the breakdown of bacteria can cause resetting of the thermostat to very high febrile levels. For instance, 1 mg. of purified type "O" antigen from typhoid bacilli can cause the thermostat to be set at levels as high as 110° F.

The thermostat is also often set at a febrile level when a large amount of tissue is degenerating in the body. The degenerating tissue may result from extensive trauma, from irradiation with x-rays or gamma rays, and from various diseases. A protein product known as *pyrexin* has been isolated from degenerating tissues, which, when injected into an animal, will cause a substantial increase in the body temperature.

Effect of Dehydration on the Hypothalamic Thermostat. Dehydration is another factor that can cause the body temperature to rise considerably. Part of this elevation of temperature probably results from lack of available fluid for sweating, but dehydration can also cause temperature elevation even in a cold atmosphere. Consequently, dehydration almost certainly has a direct effect on the hypothalamic centers to set the hypothalamic thermostat at febrile levels.

Characteristics of Febrile Conditions

Chills. When the setting of the thermostat is suddenly changed from a normal level to a higher-than-normal value as a result of tissue destruction, foreign protein, or dehydration, the body temperature might take several hours to reach the new temperature setting. For instance, the temperature setting of the hypothalamic thermostat, as illustrated in Figure 672, might suddenly rise to 103° F.

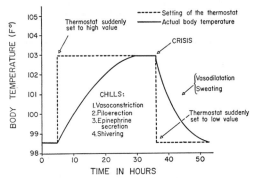

Figure 672. Effects of changing the setting of the "hypothalamic thermostat."

Because the blood temperature is less than the temperature setting of the hypothalamic thermostat, the situation is analogous to excessive cooling of the hypothalamus. Consequently, the usual autonomic responses to cause elevation of body temperature occur. These include intense vasoconstriction, piloerection, epinephrine and nor-epinephrine secretion, and shivering. During this period the patient experiences *chills,* as a result of which he feels extremely cold, even though his body temperature may be already above normal. Also, his skin is cold because of vasoconstriction, and he shakes all over because of shivering. His chills are likely to continue until his body temperature rises to the hypothalamic setting of 103° F. Then, when the temperature of the body reaches this value, the patient no longer experiences chills but instead feels neither cold nor hot. As long as the factor that is causing the hypothalamic thermostat to be set at a high value continues its effect, the body temperature will be regulated more or less in the normal manner but at the higher temperature level.

The Crisis. If the factor that is causing the high temperature is suddenly removed, the hypothalamic thermostat is suddenly set at a lower value—perhaps even back to the normal level, as illustrated in Figure 672. In this instance, the blood temperature is still 103° F., but the hypothalamus is attempting to regulate the body temperature at 98.6° F. This situation is analogous to excessive heating of the anterior hypothalamus. The para-

sympathetics stimulate the sweating mechanism and thereby cause increased evaporative loss of heat. At the same time the posterior hypothalamus becomes inhibited so that intense vasodilatation occurs in the skin, and large quantities of heat leave the skin by conduction or radiation. This sudden change of events in a febrile disease is known as the "crisis." In the old days, the doctor always awaited the crisis, for once this occurred he knew immediately that the patient's temperature would soon be falling.

Specific Characteristics of Some Fevers. Before the days of therapy with antibiotics, diagnosis of different diseases was based to a great extent on the peculiar characteristics of the fever itself in each of the diseases. Even now these characteristics are important, though most febrile diseases are blocked before a definite pattern of fever can be established. For instance, the fever of malaria is a spiking fever that rises very rapidly, is associated with intense chills of short duration, remains elevated for an hour or more, and then within 3 or 4 more hours may fall back to normal. This fever occurs periodically at daily, bi-daily, or tri-daily intervals, depending upon the type of malaria, for it occurs when the gametes are suddenly expelled into the circulating blood.

Spiking fevers also occur in many localized infections, for masses of protein degenerative products seem to be suddenly released into the blood at periodic intervals to cause these spiking fevers.

Prolonged, mild, debilitating diseases such as infectious mononucleosis, salpingitis, etc., are likely to cause almost normal temperature in the morning but a slowly rising temperature by night. The reason for this is probably that the hypothalamic regulatory mechanism can maintain a normal temperature as long as the metabolic rate is very low during sleep, but, when the metabolic rate is elevated by daily activity, the hypothalamus is no longer able to thwart the tendency for the temperature to rise.

In severe febrile diseases such as typhoid fever and pneumonia, the temperature usually rises either rapidly or gradually to a very high level and remains at this level with some ups and downs until the resistance mechanisms of the body have conquered the causative agent. Then the fever may fall by crisis, or it may fall gradually back to normal.

Fever in brain lesions. Brain lesions that excite the posterior hypothalamus or inhibit the anterior hypothalamus often cause elevated body temperature. However, such lesions need not directly damage the hypothalamus in order to cause elevated temperature, for tumors as far distant as the pineal gland very commonly have the same effect. It is possible that these tumors compress the hypothalamus or interrupt various neurogenic tracts that control the functions of the hypothalamus.

Fever resulting from brain lesions often continues for many weeks or even months.

Purpose of Fever. It is well known that artificial inducement of fever can be used for treatment of a number of infectious diseases. For instance, elevating the body temperature for only a few hours to 106° to 107° F. will cause destruction of a very large percentage of active gonococcal or syphilis organisms in the body; indeed, this is one of the most effective means for treatment of central nervous system syphilis. Though the same beneficial effects have not been conclusively demonstrated in other diseases, it is probable that at least some benefit is derived in many other diseases from fever itself.

Also, the increased rate of metabolism in cells possibly allows the cells to increase their production of immune bodies and to increase their ability to phagocytize foreign bodies and thereby prevent bacterial invasion. Therefore, it is perhaps not wise to lower the body temperature artificially in disease conditions unless it rises above 104° to 106° F., above which level the body heat itself may become very harmful.

Heat Stroke

At times the body temperature rises to a very high value as a result of exposure to external heat from the sun, from hot boilers, etc. Once the body temperature rises to such a value, the metabolism in all the cells of the body increases because of the increased cellular temperature, which has already been explained. Consequently, the body now is not only gaining heat from the outside, but it is also producing far greater than normal quantities of heat. At approximately 110° F., the rate of metabolism of the cells has become doubled, and at 114° F. the rate of metabolism has become almost tripled.

Unfortunately, there is a limit to the rate at which the body can lose heat even when the heat loss mechanisms have been activated. Furthermore, when the hypothalamus becomes excessively heated, it also appears to operate very poorly for promoting heat loss. Consequently, the heat-regulating ability of the hypothalamus becomes greatly depressed at high body temperatures, and a vicious cycle results: high temperature causes increased production of heat, which increases the body temperature still higher, which

causes still greater production of heat and a still higher body temperature, etc. Once the body temperature rises above 107° to 110° F., the heat-regulating mechanisms often can no longer dissipate the excessive heat being produced. Therefore, the temperature may then continue to rise until it causes death unless this rise is checked artificially.

Relationship of Dehydration to Heat Stroke. People who work in hot and humid atmospheres can often become excessively dehydrated because of sweating. As pointed out earlier in the chapter, dehydration probably has a direct effect on the hypothalamus to set the thermostat at a high level, and this effect undoubtedly adds to the vicious cycle of hyperpyrexia. Indeed, it is often stated that if one is careful to prevent dehydration, even though he is exposed to the hot sun or hot boilers, heat stroke is not very likely to occur.

One of the factors that are quite important for preventing dehydration is an adequate quantity of sodium chloride in the diet, because sweating causes progressive loss of sodium chloride and this loss causes the extracellular fluid volume to decrease. Consequently, if dehydration is to be prevented, not only must the intake of water be adequate, but at the same time sodium chloride must be provided. This is the reason salt tablets are dispensed in factories where overheating is likely to occur.

Dangers of High Temperature

When the body temperature rises above approximately 106° F., parenchymatous damage of many cells usually begins to occur. The pathologic findings in a person who dies of hyperpyrexia are local hemorrhages and parenchymatous degeneration of cells throughout the entire body. The brain is especially likely to suffer because neuronal cells once destroyed can never be replaced. When the body temperature rises to 110° to 114° F., the patient usually has only a few hours to live unless the temperature is brought back within normal range very rapidly.

In order to prevent death of the patient from high temperatures, the usual cooling method employed is sponging the body with alcohol; rapid evaporation of the alcohol acts as a refrigerant and cools the body. If this does not bring the temperature down rapidly enough, bathing the patient in ice water, though more drastic, is usually effective.

Effects of Chemicals and Drugs on Fever

An extremely large number of foreign substances when injected into the body fluids can cause the body temperature to rise. These substances are called *pyrogens*. Bacteria, pollens, dust, and vaccines are all pyrogenic because of their protein content. Ordinarily, human plasma is not pyrogenic, but it is possible for the plasma proteins and other proteins that normally do not cause pyrogenic reactions to be changed chemically by degradation or denaturization and thereafter to cause pyrogenic reactions. A few nonprotein chemicals are also known to elevate the body temperature; these include especially some of the nitrated phenol compounds.

Antipyretics. Aspirin, antipyrine, aminopyrine, and a number of other substances known as "antipyretics" have an effect on the hypothalamic thermostat opposite to that of the pyrogens. In other words, they cause the setting of the thermostat to be lowered so that the body temperature will fall, though usually not more than a degree or so. Especially are these drugs effective in lowering the hypothalamic setting when pyrogens are attempting to raise the setting. Obviously, these drugs can be used to prevent damage to the body from excessively high body temperature.

Exposure of the Body to Extreme Temperatures

Exposure to Cold. A person exposed to ice water for approximately 20 to 30 minutes ordinarily will die unless treated immediately. By that time, the internal body temperature will have fallen to about 77° F. Yet, if he is warmed rapidly by application of external heat, many times his life can be saved.

Treatment of a patient whose body temperature has fallen into the seventies usually consists of application of wet heat either in the form of tub treatment or hot packs, with the water at a temperature of approximately 110° F. If the temperature of the water is less than this, the rate at which heat is returned to the body is too slow for maximal benefit, and, if it is greater than this, the skin might be severely damaged because it becomes overheated while not receiving a satisfactory blood supply.

Loss of temperature regulation at low temperatures. As noted in Figure 671, once the body temperature has fallen below 85° F., the ability of the hypothalamus to regulate temperature is completely lost, and it is greatly impaired even when the body temperature falls below approximately 94° F. Part of the reason for this loss of temperature regulation is that the rate of heat production in each cell is greatly depressed by the low temperature. Also, sleepiness and even coma are likely to develop, which depress the activity of the central nervous system heat-control mechanisms and prevent shivering.

Frostbite. When blood flow to the surface of the body is extremely slight, surface areas can actually freeze; the freezing is called "frostbite." This occurs especially in the lobes of the ears and in the digits of the hands and feet. If the parts are thawed immediately, especially with water that is not above approximately 110° F., no permanent damage may result. On the other hand, prolonged freezing causes permanent circulatory impairment as well as local tissue damage. Often gangrene follows thawing, and the frost-bitten areas are lost.

Immersion foot. During times of war and after shipwrecks, it frequently is necessary to stand in very cold water for long periods of time. Even though this does not cause freezing of the foot it does cut off circulation, and, because some metabolism usually continues in the foot without circulation, the tissues are likely to become permanently damaged. The usual effect is permanently impaired circulation and excessive sclerosis of the soft tissues. If the feet are not lost as a result of gangrene within six to eight months, ordinarily they will redevelop a relatively satisfactory circulation.

Therapeutic hypothermia. It is possible to decrease the temperature of a patient by giving him a sedative to depress the hypothalamic thermostat and then packing him in ice until his temperature falls. His temperature can then be maintained below 90° F. for several days to a week or more by continual sprinkling of cool water or alcohol on the body. Such artificial cooling is often used during surgery on the heart so that the heart can be stopped for up to ten minutes at a time. The prolonged cooling apparently does not cause any unsatisfactory physiologic results.

Exposure to Extreme Heat. The effects of exposure to extreme heat were discussed earlier in the chapter in connection with heat stroke. The limits of extreme heat that one can stand depend almost entirely on whether the heat is dry or wet. If the air is completely dry and sufficient convection air currents are flowing to promote very rapid evaporation from the body, a person can stand several hours of air temperature at 200° F. with no apparent ill effects. On the other hand, if the air is 100 per cent humidified and evaporation cannot occur or if the body is in water, the body temperature begins to rise whenever the surrounding temperature rises above approximately 94° F.

The method used to elevate the body temperature for therapeutic measures is to place a patient in a tub of water at elevated temperature. Such therapy is used for treatment of central nervous system syphilis and also for treatment of overly excited mental patients, for an elevated body temperature sometimes depresses the "wakefulness" centers of the central nervous system and allows the patient to rest.

REFERENCES

Adolph, E. F., and Richmond, J.: Adaptation to cold in golden hamster and ground squirrel measured chiefly by rates of body cooling. *J. Appl. Physiol.,* 9:53, 1956.

Bass, D. E., Kleeman, C. R., Quinn, M., Henschel, A., and Hegnauer, A. H.: Mechanisms of acclimatization to heat in man. *Medicine, 34:*323, 1955.

Belehradek, J.: Physiological aspects of heat and cold. *Ann. Rev. Physiol., 19:*59, 1957.

Birzis, L., and Hemingway, A.: Descending brain stem connections controlling shivering in cat. *J. Neurophysiol., 19:*37, 1956.

Birzis, L., and Hemingway, A.: Efferent brain discharge during shivering. *J. Neurophysiol., 20:*156, 1957.

Birzis, L., and Hemingway, A.: Shivering as a result of brain stimulation. *J. Neurophysiol., 20:*91, 1957.

Bligh, J.: The receptors concerned in the thermal stimulus to panting in sheep. *J. Physiol., 146:*142, 1959.

Boyarsky, L. L., and Stewart, L.: Neurogenic inhibition of shivering. *Science, 125:*649, 1957.

Burton, A. C.: Man in a Cold Environment. Baltimore, Williams & Wilkins Co., 1955.

Burton, A. C.: Research in applied physiology of the cold. *Rev. Canad. Biol., 16:*293, 1957.

Burton, A. C., Snyder, R. A., and Leach, W. G.: Damp cold versus dry cold; specific effects of humidity on heat exchange of unclothed man. *J. Appl. Physiol., 8:*269, 1955.

Carlson, L. D., and Pearl, D. C., Jr.: Effects of temperature and work on metabolism and heat loss in man. *Proc. Soc. Exp. Biol. & Med., 91:*240, 1956.

Clifford, J., Kerslake, D. McK., and Waddell, J. L.: The effect of wind speed on maximum evaporative capacity in man. *J. Physiol., 147:*253, 1959.

Collins, K. J., and Weiner, J. S.: Excitation and depression of eccrine sweat glands by acetylcholine, acetyl-β-methylcholine and adrenaline. *J. Physiol., 148:*592, 1959.

Cottle, W. H., and Carlson, L. D.: Regulation of heat production in cold-adapted rats. *Proc. Soc. Exp. Biol. & Med., 92:*845, 1956.

DuBois, E. F.: Fever and the Regulation of Body Temperature. Springfield, Illinois, Charles C Thomas, 1948.

Edholm, O. G.: Physiology in the polar regions. *Nature, 178:*954, 1956.

Edholm, O. G., Fox, R. H., and MacPherson, R. K.: The effect of body heating on the circulation in skin and muscle. *J. Physiol., 134:*612, 1956.

Ellis, S.: The metabolic effects of epinephrine and related amines. *Pharmacol. Rev., 8:*486, 1956.

Folkow, B.: Efferent nervous pathways involved in cutaneous vasodilatation induced by activation of hypothalamic heat loss mechanisms. *Acta Physiol. Scand., 17:*327, 1949.

Folkow, B., Strom, G., and Uvnas, B.: Cutaneous vasodilatation elicited by local heating of anterior hypothalamus in cats and dogs. *Acta Physiol. Scand., 17:*317, 1949.

Freeman, W. J., and Davis, D. D.: Effects on cats of conductive hypothalamic cooling. *Am. J. Physiol., 197:*145, 1959.

Froese, G., and Burton, A. C.: Heat losses from the human head. *J. Appl. Physiol., 10:*235, 1957.

Fry, F. E. J.: Temperature compensation. *Ann. Rev. Physiol., 20:*207, 1958.

Hammel, H. T., Hardy, J. D., and Fusco, M. M.: Thermoregulatory responses to hypothalamic cooling in unanesthetized dog. *Am. J. Physiol., 198:*481, 1960.

Hardy, J. D.: Control of heat loss and heat production in physiologic temperature regulation. *Harvey Lect., 49:*242, 1953–1954.

Hardy, J. D., and Stoll, A. M.: Measurement of radiant heat load on man in summer and winter Alaskan climates. *J. Appl. Physiol., 7:*200, 1954.

Hensel, H.: Heat and cold. *Ann. Rev. Physiol., 21:*91, 1959.

Hertzman, A. B.: Heat and cold. *Ann. Rev. Physiol., 17:*79, 1955.

Hertzman, A. B.: Individual differences in regional sweating. *J. Appl. Physiol., 10:*242, 1957.

Horvath, S. M., Spurr, G. B., Hutt, B. K., and Hamilton, L. H.: Metabolic cost of shivering. *J. Appl. Physiol., 8:*595, 1956.

Hsieh, A. C., and Carlson, L. D.: Role of the thyroid in metabolic response to low temperature. *Am. J. Physiol., 188:*40, 1957.

Hurley, H. J., and Shelley, W. B.: The Human Apocrine Sweat Gland in Health and Disease. Springfield, Illinois, Charles C Thomas, 1960.

Jensen, C., and Ederstrom, H. E.: Development of temperature regulation in the dog. *Am. J. Physiol., 183:*340, 1955.

Kanter, G. S.: Effect of heat on regulation of body fluids and electrolytes in dogs. *Am. J. Physiol., 178:*259, 1954.

Kanter, G. S.: Hypoglycemic effect of high environmental temperature on dogs. *Am. J. Physiol., 188:*443, 1957.

Kayser, C.: Physiological aspects of hypothermia. *Ann. Rev. Physiol., 19:*83, 1957.

Kuno, Y.: Human Perspiration. Springfield, Illinois, Charles C Thomas, 1956.

LeBlanc, J.: Morphological and physiological changes in the skin as a result of long exposure to cold. *Am. J. Physiol., 196:*1042, 1959.

Lim, P. K., and Grodins, F. S.: Control of thermal panting. *Am. J. Physiol., 180:*445, 1955.

Lipkin, M., and Hardy, J. D.: Measurement of some thermal properties of human tissues. *J. Appl. Physiol., 7:*212, 1954.

Lyman, C. P. and Chatfield, P. O.: Physiology of hibernation in mammals. *Physiol. Rev., 35:*403, 1955.

Mellinkoff, S. M., and Sonnenschein, R. R.: Identity of sweat glands stimulated by heat, epinephrine, and acetylcholine. *Science, 120:*997, 1954.

Meryman, H. T.: Tissue freezing and local cold injury. *Physiol. Rev., 37:*233, 1957.

Nahas, G. G., and Hemingway, A.: Influences of Nembutal anesthesia on oxygen consumption and temperature regulation in the dog. *J. Physiol., 46:*480, 1954.

Newburgh, L. H.: Physiology of Heat Regulation and the Science of Clothing. Philadelphia, W. B. Saunders Co., 1949.

Pearcy, M., Robinson, S., Miller, D. I., Thomas, J. T., Jr., and Debrota, J.: Effects of dehydration, salt depletion and pitressin on sweat rate and urine flow. *J. Appl. Physiol.*, 8:621, 1956.

Randall, W. C., and Kimura, K. K.: The pharmacology of sweating. *Pharmacol. Rev.*, 7:365, 1955.

Robinson, S.: Physiological effects of heat and cold. *Ann. Rev. Physiol.*, 14:73, 1952.

Robinson, S., Maletich, R. T., Robinson, W. S., Rohrer, B. B., and Kunz, A. L.: Output of NaCl by sweat glands and kidneys in relation to dehydration and to salt depletion. *J. Appl. Physiol.*, 8:615, 1956.

Robinson, S., Nicholas, J. R., Smith, J. H., Daly, W. J., and Pearcy, M.: Time relation of renal and sweat gland adjustments to salt deficiency in men. *J. Appl. Physiol.*, 8:159, 1955.

Robinson, S., and Robinson, A. H.: Chemical composition of sweat. *Physiol. Rev.*, 34:202, 1954.

Selle, W. A.: Body Temperature: Its Changes with Environment, Disease, and Therapy. Springfield, Illinois, Charles C Thomas, 1952.

Spurr, G. B., Hutt, B. K., and Horvath, S. M.: Prolonged hypothermia in the dog. *Am. J. Physiol.*, 178:275, 1954.

Stevens, C. E., D'Angelo, S. A., Paschkis, K. E., Cantarow, A., and Sunderman, F. W.: The response of the pituitary-thyroid system of the guinea pig to low environmental temperature. *Endocrinology*, 56:143, 1955.

Ström, G.: Central nervous regulation of body temperature. *Handbook of Physiology*, 2:1173, 1960.

Sulzberger, M. B., and Herrmann, F.: The Clinical Significance of Disturbances in the Delivery of Sweat. Springfield, Illinois, Charles C Thomas, 1954.

Zotterman, Y.: Special senses: thermal receptors. *Ann. Rev. Physiol.*, 15:387, 1953.

Chapter 72

The Liver and Biliary System

Different functions of the liver have been presented at many points in this text because the liver has so many and such varied functions that it is impossible to separate its actions from those of the other organ systems of the body. Therefore, the present chapter is more a review of hepatic and biliary functions rather than a new presentation. Its purpose is to coordinate the different functions of the liver and to show how the liver operates as an individual organ.

The basic functions of the liver can be divided into: (1) its vascular functions for storage and filtration of blood, (2) its secretory function for secreting bile into the gastrointestinal tract, and (3) its metabolic functions concerned with the majority of the metabolic systems of the body.

The Physiologic Structure of the Liver

The basic functional unit of the liver is the liver lobule, which is a cylindrical structure several mm. in length and 0.8 to 2 mm. in diameter. The human liver contains some 50,000 to 100,000 individual lobules.

The liver lobule is constructed around a *central vein* that empties into the hepatic veins and thence into the vena cava. The lobule itself is composed principally of many *hepatic cellular plates* (two of which are illustrated in Figure 673) that radiate centrifugally from the central vein like spokes in a wheel. Each of the hepatic plates is usually two cells thick, and between the adjacent cells lie small *bile canaliculi* which empty into *terminal bile ducts* lying in the septa between the adjacent liver lobules.

Also in the septa are small *portal venules* which receive their blood from the portal veins. From these venules blood flows into flat, branching *venous sinusoids* that lie between the hepatic plates, and from the venous sinusoids the blood flows into the central vein. Thus, all the hepatic

cells are exposed on one of their sides to portal venous blood flow and on the other side to the bile canaliculi.

In addition to the portal venules, *hepatic arterioles* are also present in the interlobular septa. These arterioles supply arterial blood to the septal tissues, and the capillary blood from these tissues empties into the venous sinusoids.

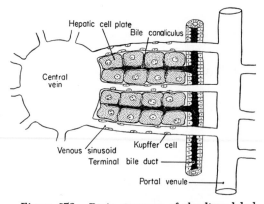

Figure 673. Basic structure of the liver lobule, showing the hepatic cellular plates, the blood vessels, and the bile ducts.

The venous sinusoids are lined with two types of cells: (1) typical *endothelial cells* and (2) large *Kupffer cells,* which are reticuloendothelial cells capable of phagocytizing bacteria and other foreign matter in the blood. The endothelial lining of the venous sinusoids has extremely large pores, some of which are almost 1 micron in diameter. This allows very free exchange of substances in the plasma with the fluids surrounding the hepatic cells. Even the plasma proteins flow freely into these fluids.

In the interlobular septa are also vast numbers of *terminal lymphatics.* Though lymphatics have not been demonstrated to pass into the spaces within the hepatic cellular plates, nevertheless, large quantities of lymph are known to flow from these spaces into the lymphatics.

FUNCTION OF THE HEPATIC VASCULAR SYSTEM

The function of the hepatic vascular system was discussed in Chapter 31 in connection with the portal veins. Briefly, this can be summarized as follows:

Blood Flow through the Liver. About 800 to 1000 ml. of blood flow from the portal vein through the liver sinusoids each minute, and approximately an additional 300 ml. flow into the sinusoids from the hepatic artery, the total averaging about 1200 ml. per minute.

Total hepatic blood flow per minute can be measured by a modified Fick procedure in which the dye *Bromsulphalein* is injected into the circulatory system, and its concentration is measured in the arterial blood and in venous blood collected from the hepatic vein by means of a catheter. From these measurements, the arteriovenous difference of the Bromsulphalein can be calculated. In addition, the rate at which the Bromsulphalein disappears from the blood is determined over a period of 10 minutes or more. Since the only significant route of disappearance is through the hepatic cells into the biliary tract, one can then calculate liver blood flow by the usual Fick formula as follows:

$$\text{Hepatic blood flow} = \frac{\text{Rate of blood clearance of Bromsulphalein}}{\text{A-V difference in Bromsulphalein}}$$

Pressures and Resistance in the Hepatic Vessels. The pressure in the hepatic vein leading from the liver into the vena cava averages almost exactly 0 mm. Hg, while the pressure in the portal vein leading into the liver averages approximately 7 mm. Hg. This shows that the resistance to blood flow from the portal venous system to the systemic veins is normally very small, especially when one considers that about a liter of blood flows by this route each minute. However, various pathological conditions can cause the resistance to rise markedly, sometimes increasing the portal venous pressure to as high as 20 to 30 mm. Hg. The most common cause of increased hepatic vascular resistance is the disease *portal cirrhosis*, in which very dense fibrotic tissue develops in the interlobular septa and encroaches on the liver lobules, progressively replacing the hepatic cells with more and more fibrous tissue.

Effects of high portal pressure. Very high portal pressure increases the capillary pressure throughout the gastrointestinal region. This in turn leads to marked transudation of fluid into the walls of the intestine and into the peritoneal cavity, causing very severe *ascites*. Fortunately, many collateral channels develop from the portal veins to the systemic veins, especially up along the esophageal veins, through the hemorrhoidal veins of the rectum, and through anterior and posterior abdominal wall vessels.

Storage of Blood in the Liver; Hepatic Congestion. An increase in pressure in the hepatic veins dams blood in the liver sinusoids and thereby causes the entire liver to swell markedly. As much as 500 to 1000 ml. of blood can be stored in this way in the liver. For this reason, the liver is frequently said to be one of the *blood reservoirs*. Conversely, if a person hemorrhages so that large amounts of blood are lost from the circulatory system, much of the normal blood in the liver sinusoids drains into the remainder of the circulation to help replace the lost blood.

The most important cause of hepatic congestion is cardiac failure, which often increases the central venous pressure to as high as 10 to 15 mm. Hg. The continual stretching of the liver sinusoids that results and the stasis of blood caused by the hepatic congestion gradually leads to necrosis of many of the hepatic cells in the hepatic cellular plates.

Lymph Flow from the Liver. Even though no lymphatics have ever been demonstrated in the hepatic cellular plates, one can show physiologically that large quantities of fluid from the hepatic sinusoids pass almost directly into the lymphatic system. It is believed that fluids flow in the space between the endothelial linings of the sinusoids and the surfaces of the hepatic cells, these fluids eventually flowing into the interlobular spaces and thence into the lymphatics. Furthermore, the pores in the hepatic sinusoids allow ready passage of proteins; therefore, the lymph draining from the liver has a protein concentration usually about 6 grams per cent, which is only slightly less than the protein concentration of plasma. Also, the extreme permeability of the liver sinusoids allows very large quantities of lymph to form. Indeed, between one third and one half of all the lymph formed in the body under resting conditions arises in the liver.

The Hepatic Reticuloendothelial System. The inner surfaces of all the liver sinusoids are bespeckled with many *Kupffer cells*, which protrude into the flowing blood as illustrated in Figure 673. These cells are very phagocytic, so much so, in fact, that they are capable of removing all bacteria from the portal venous blood before it can pass all the way through the liver. Since the portal blood drains from the intestines, it almost always contains a reasonable number of colon bacilli. Therefore, the importance of the Kupffer cell filtration system is readily apparent. The number of Kupffer cells in the sinusoids increases markedly when increased quantities of particulate matter or other debris is present in the blood.

SECRETION OF BILE AND FUNCTIONS OF THE BILIARY TREE

Physiologic Anatomy of Biliary Secretion

All of the hepatic cells continually form a small amount of secretion called *bile*. This is secreted into the very minute *bile canaliculi,* which lie between the double layer of cells in the hepatic plates, and the bile then flows peripherally toward the interlobular septa, where the canaliculi empty into terminal bile ducts. The bile is then conducted into progressively larger and larger bile ducts, finally reaching the hepatic duct and common bile duct from which it either empties directly into the duodenum or is diverted into the gallbladder.

Storage of Bile in the Gallbladder. In the discussion of bile and its functions in relation to digestion and absorption in Chapter 63, it was pointed out that bile is secreted continually by the liver cells and is normally stored in the gallbladder. The bile is emptied into the duodenum only when food, especially fatty food, is also present in the duodenum. The total secretion of bile by the liver each day is some 600 to 800 ml., and the maximum volume of the gallbladder is only 40 to 70 ml. Nevertheless, at least 12 hours' worth of bile secretion can be stored in the gallbladder, because water and the small electrolytes are continually absorbed by the gallbladder mucosa, thereby concentrating the other bile constituents, including the bile salts. Bile is normally concentrated about five-fold, but it can be concentrated up to a maximum of about 10-fold.

Emptying of the gallbladder. Two basic conditions are necessary for the gallbladder to empty: (1) The sphincter of Oddi must relax to allow bile to flow from the common bile duct into the duodenum and (2) the gallbladder itself must contract to provide the force required to move the bile along the common duct. After a meal, particularly one that contains a high concentration of fat, both these effects take place in the following manner:

First, the fat in the food entering the small intestine extracts a hormone called *cholecystokinin* from the intestinal mucosa, especially from the upper regions of the small intestine. The cholecystokinin in turn is absorbed into the blood and on passing to the gallbladder causes specific contraction of the gallbladder muscle. This provides the pressure that forces bile toward the duodenum.

Second, vagal stimulation causes an additional weak contraction of the gallbladder, which helps to force the bile from the gallbladder into the duodenum.

Third, when the gallbladder contracts, the sphincter of Oddi becomes inhibited, this effect resulting either from a neurogenic or myogenic reflex from the gallbladder to the sphincter of Oddi.

Fourth, the presence of food in the duodenum causes the degree of peristalsis in the duodenal wall to increase. Each time a peristaltic wave travels toward the sphincter of Oddi, this sphincter, along with the adjacent intestinal wall, momentarily relaxes, and, if the bile in the common bile duct is under sufficient pressure, a small quantity of the bile squirts into the duodenum.

In summary, the gallbladder empties its store of concentrated bile into the duodenum mainly in response to the cholecystokinin stimulus. When fat is not in the meal, the gallbladder empties very poorly, but, when adequate quantities of fat are present, the gallbladder normally empties completely in about one hour.

Figure 674 summarizes the secretion of bile, its storage in the gallbladder, and its release from the bladder to the gut.

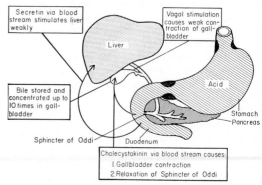

Figure 674.   Mechanisms of liver secretion and gallbladder emptying.

Composition of Bile. Table 31 gives the composition of bile when it is first secreted by the liver and then after it has been concentrated in the gallbladder. This table

Table 31. Composition of Bile

	Liver Bile	Gallbladder Bile
Water	97.5 gm. %	92 gm. %
Bile salts	1.1 gm. %	3 to 10 gm. %
Bilirubin	0.2 gm. %	0.6 to 2.0 gm. %
Cholesterol	0.1 gm. %	0.3 to 0.9 gm. %
Fatty acids	0.12 gm. %	0.3 to 1.2 gm. %
Lecithin	.04 gm. %	0.1 to 0.4 gm. %
Na^+	145 mEq./L.	130 mEq./L.
K^+	5 mEq./L.	9 mEq./L.
Ca^{++}	5 mEq./L.	12 mEq./L.
Cl^-	100 mEq./L.	75 mEq./L
HCO_3^-	28 mEq./L.	10 mEq./L

shows that the most abundant substance secreted in the bile is the *bile salts,* but also secreted or excreted in large concentrations are *bilirubin, cholesterol, fatty acids,* and the usual *electrolytes* of plasma. In the concentrating process in the gallbladder, water and large portions of the electrolytes are reabsorbed by the gallbladder mucosa, but essentially all the other constituents, including especially the bile salts, are not reabsorbed and therefore become highly concentrated in the gallbladder bile.

The Bile Salts and Their Function

The liver cells continually form large quantities of *bile salts.* The precursor of the bile salts is *cholesterol,* which is either supplied in the diet or synthesized in the liver cells during the course of fat metabolism and then is converted to *cholic acid.* This then combines principally with glycine to form *glycocholic acid* and to a lesser extent with taurine to form *taurocholic acid.* The salts of these acids are secreted in the bile.

The bile salts have two important actions in the intestinal tract. First, they have a detergent action on the fatty particles in the food, which decreases their surface tension and allows the agitation in the intestinal tract to break the fat globules into very minute particles. This is called the *emulsifying or detergent function* of bile salts. Second, and even more important than the emulsifying function, bile salts help in the absorption of fatty acids and monoglycerides from the intestinal tract, which is called

their *hydrotropic function.* It is believed that the negatively charged bile salt ions become physically adsorbed to the fatty acids, and the electrical charges of these ions presumably then increase the solubility of the fatty acids, thereby allowing ready passage through the intestinal mucosa. Without the presence of bile salts in the intestinal tract, a large proportion of the fatty acids is lost into the stools in the form of soaps, and the person often develops a metabolic deficit due to this nutrient loss.

Also, when fats are not absorbed adequately, the fat soluble vitamins are not absorbed satisfactorily. Therefore, in the absence of bile salts, vitamins A, D, E, and K are very poorly absorbed. Though adequate quantities of the first three of these vitamins are usually stored in the body, this is not true of vitamin K. Within only a few days after bile secretion ceases, the person usually develops a deficiency of vitamin K. This in turn results in deficient formation by the liver of proconvertin, accelerator globulin, and prothrombin, thus resulting in serious impairment of blood coagulation.

The Enterohepatic Circulation of Bile Salts. Most of the bile salts are reabsorbed by the intestinal mucosa along with the absorption of the fats, but, after passing through the mucosa, the bile salts separate from the fats and pass into the portal blood, while the fats travel in the lymphatics. On reaching the liver the bile salts are absorbed from the venous sinusoids into the hepatic cells and then resecreted into the bile canaliculi. In this way about eight to nine tenths of all the bile salts are recirculated into the bile, so that on the average these salts make the entire circuit some five to ten times before being carried out in the feces. The small quantities of bile salts lost into the feces are replaced by new amounts formed continually by the liver cells. This recirculation of the bile salts is called the *enterohepatic circulation.*

The quantity of bile secreted by the liver each day is highly dependent on the availability of bile salts—the greater the quantity of bile salts in the enterohepatic circulation, the greater is the rate of bile secretion. When a bile fistula forms so that bile is lost directly from the common bile duct to the exterior, the bile salts cannot be reabsorbed. Therefore, the total quantity of bile salts in the enterohepatic circulation becomes greatly depressed, and concurrently the volume of liver secretion is also depressed.

Excretion of Bilirubin in the Bile

In addition to secreting substances synthesized by the liver itself, the liver cells also *excrete* a number of substances formed elsewhere in the body. Among the most important of these is bilirubin, which is one of the major end-products of hemoglobin decomposition, as was discussed in Chapter 12. Briefly, when the red blood cells have lived out their life span, averaging 120 days, and have become too fragile to exist longer in the circulatory system, their cell membranes rupture, and the released hemoglobin is phagocytized by reticuloendothelial cells throughout the body. The hemoglobin undergoes several successive changes eventually to become *bilirubin*. However, bilirubin itself is almost insoluble in the body fluids. Instead, it combines with some of the plasma proteins and is transported in this combination throughout the blood and interstitial fluids. This protein-bound bilirubin eventually is absorbed into the liver cells, and the bilirubin is removed from the protein and conjugated with other substances that make it become highly soluble. About 80 per cent of it conjugates with glucuronic acid to form *bilirubin glucuronide;* an additional 10 per cent conjugates with sulfate to form *bilirubin sulfate,* and the final 10 per cent conjugates with a multitude of other solubilizing substances. It is in these soluble forms that the bilirubin is excreted into the bile.

A small portion of the soluble bilirubin formed by the hepatic cells returns to the plasma. Either this is resecreted by the liver cells directly into the liver sinusoids or it is reabsorbed into the blood from the bile ducts. Regardless of the exact mechanism by which it reenters the blood, this causes a small portion of the bilirubin in the body fluids always to be of the soluble type rather than of the protein-bound type.

Formation and Fate of Urobilinogen. Once in the intestine, bilirubin is converted by bacterial action mainly into the substance *urobilinogen,* which is highly soluble. Most of the urobilinogen is reabsorbed through the intestinal mucosa into the blood and is eventually excreted by the kidneys into the urine. After exposure to air in the urine, the urobilinogen becomes oxidized to *urobilin.* These interrelationships of bilirubin with urobilinogen are illustrated in Figure 675.

Jaundice. The word *jaundice* means a yellowish tint to the body tissues, including yellowness of the skin and also of the deep tissues. The usual cause of jaundice is large quantities of bilirubin in the extracellular fluids, either protein-bound bilirubin or soluble bilirubin in the glucuronide or sulfate form. The normal plasma concentration of bilirubin, including both the protein-bound and the soluble forms, averages 0.5 mg. per 100 ml. of plasma. However, in certain abnormal conditions this can rise to as high as 20 to 30 mg. per 100 ml. The skin usually barely begins to appear jaundiced when the concentration rises to about three times normal—that is, above 1.5 mg. per 100 ml.

There are two common causes of jaundice: (1) increased destruction of red blood cells with very rapid release of bilirubin into the blood and (2) obstruction of the bile ducts or damage to the liver cells themselves so that even the usual amounts of bilirubin cannot be excreted into the gastrointestinal tract. These two types of jaundice are called, respectively, *hemolytic jaundice* and *obstructive jaundice.* They differ from each other in the following ways:

Hemolytic jaundice. In hemolytic jaundice, the excretory function of the liver is not impaired in the least, but red blood cells are hemolyzed very rapidly and the hepatic cells simply cannot excrete the bilirubin as rapidly as it is formed. Therefore, the plasma concentration of *protein-bound bilirubin* rises especially high. Likewise, the rate of formation of urobilinogen in the intestine is greatly increased, and this in turn is absorbed into the blood and later excreted by the kidneys.

Obstructive jaundice. In obstructive jaundice, caused either by obstruction of the bile ducts or by damage to the liver cells, the rate of bilirubin formation is normal, but the bilirubin formed simply cannot pass from the blood into the intestines. However, the protein-bound bilirubin does still enter the liver cells, the bilirubin is split from the proteins and conjugated with glucuronic acid, and this soluble form of bilirubin is finally returned to the blood either by direct resecretion into the blood or secretion into the bile ducts and then reabsorption from these. Thus, most of the bilirubin in the plasma becomes the soluble type rather than the protein-bound type.

Diagnostic differences between hemolytic and obstructive jaundice. A very simple test called the *van den Bergh test* can be used to differentiate between protein-bound and soluble bilirubin in the plasma. If an immediate reaction occurs with the van den Bergh reagent, then it is known that the bilirubin is of the soluble type, and the reaction is called a "direct van den Bergh reaction." However, to demonstrate the presence of protein-bound bilirubin, alcohol must first be added to the plasma. This precipitates the protein and dissolves the bilirubin so that it can then combine with the van den Bergh reagent. Therefore, the test is said to be an "indirect van den Bergh reaction." Thus, *in hemolytic jaundice an indirect van den Bergh reaction occurs (increased protein-bound bilirubin) and in obstructive jaundice a direct van den Bergh reaction occurs (increased soluble bilirubin).*

When there is total obstruction of bile flow, no bilirubin at all can reach the intestines to be converted into urobilinogen by bacteria. Therefore, urobilinogen is not reabsorbed into the blood and is not excreted by the kidneys into the urine. Consequently, in *total* obstructive jaundice, tests for uro-

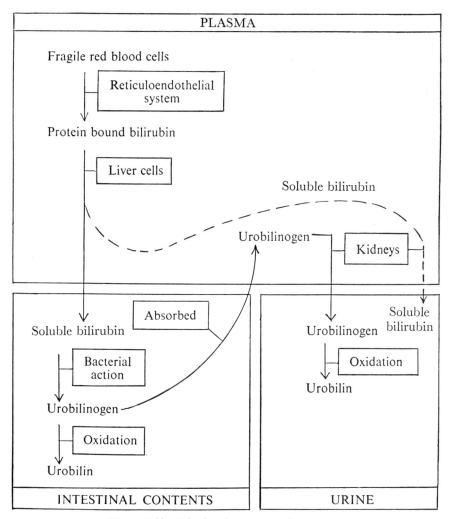

Figure 675. Bilirubin formation and excretion.

bilinogen in the urine are completely negative.

Another major difference between protein-bound bilirubin and soluble bilirubin is that the kidneys will excrete soluble bilirubin but not protein-bound bilirubin. Therefore, in severe obstructive jaundice, large quantities of soluble bilirubin appear in the urine. This can be demonstrated simply by shaking the urine and observing the foam, which is colored an intense yellow.

Thus, by understanding the physiology of bilirubin excretion by the liver and by use of a few simple tests, it is possible to differentiate between obstructive and hemolytic jaundice and also to determine the severity of the disease.

Secretion of Cholesterol; Gallstone Formation

Bile salts are formed in the hepatic cells from cholesterol, and in the process of secreting the bile salts about one tenth as much cholesterol is also secreted into the bile. No specific function is known for the cholesterol in the bile, and it is presumed that it is simply a by-product of bile salt formation and secretion.

Cholesterol is almost insoluble in pure water, but the bile salts, fatty acids, and lecithin in bile exhibit a hydrotropic action on the cholesterol to make it soluble. When the bile becomes concentrated in the gallbladder, all the hydrotropic substances become concentrated along with the cholesterol, which is necessary to keep the cholesterol in solution. Under abnormal conditions, however, the cholesterol may precipitate, resulting in the formation of *gallstones*, as shown in Figure 676. The different conditions that can cause cholesterol precipitation are: (1) too much absorption of water from the bile, (2) too much absorption of bile salts, fatty acids, and lecithin from the bile, (3) too much secretion of cholesterol in the bile, and (4) inflammation of the epithelium of the gallbladder. The latter two of these require special explanation as follows:

The amount of cholesterol in the bile is determined principally by the quantity of fat that the person eats, for the hepatic cells synthesize cholesterol approximately in proportion to the amount of fat metabolized in the body. For this reason, persons on a high fat diet over a period of many years are very prone to the development of gallstones.

Inflammation of the gallbladder epithelium often results from a low grade chronic infection; this changes the absorptive character-

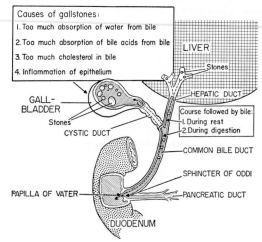

Figure 676. Formation of gallstones.

istics of the gallbladder mucosa, sometimes allowing excessive absorption of water, or bile salts, or other substances that are necessary to keep the cholesterol in solution. As a result, cholesterol begins to precipitate, usually forming many small crystals of cholesterol on the surface of the inflamed mucosa. These, in turn, act as nidi for further precipitation of cholesterol, and the crystals grow larger and larger, usually coalescing to form a few large gallstones, or, sometimes, even a single stone that fills the entire gallbladder.

X-ray Opaque Gallstones. Calcium often precipitates with some of the fatty substances involved in the formation of the gallstones, and in about one fourth of all cases of gallstones, the concentration of calcium in the stones is great enough to make them x-ray opaque. That is, the gallstones will show up on x-ray pictures of the abdomen. In the remaining three fourths of the cases the stones are almost pure cholesterol, which has almost the same x-ray opaqueness as the tissues of the body and therefore cannot be seen on a standard x-ray plate. In these instances, special iodinated drugs can be administered to the patient. These then concentrate in the bile of the bladder, and an x-ray picture shows the outlines of the stones.

In addition to calcium, small quantities of bilirubin precipitate in the gallstones, giving the stones their characteristic greenish-yellow color.

METABOLIC FUNCTIONS OF THE LIVER

The metabolic functions of the liver are so numerous and intricate that they could not possibly be presented completely in this chapter. Therefore, for details, the student will be referred to the preceding chapters on the metabolism of carbohydrates, fats, and proteins. Briefly, the specific roles of the liver in the different metabolic processes are described as follows:

Carbohydrate Metabolism

In carbohydrate metabolism the liver performs the following specific functions: (1) storage of glycogen, (2) conversion of galactose and fructose to glucose, (3) gluconeogenesis, and (4) formation of many important chemical compounds from the intermediate products of carbohydrate metabolism.

Most of these functions of the liver in carbohydrate metabolism are especially important in maintaining a normal blood glucose concentration. For instance, storage of glycogen allows the liver to remove excess glucose from the blood, store it, and then return it to the blood when the blood glucose concentration begins to fall too low. This is called the *glucose buffer function* of the liver. For instance, immediately after a meal containing large amounts of carbohydrates, the blood glucose concentration will rise about three times as much in a person with a non-functional liver as in a person with a normal liver.

Gluconeogenesis in the liver is also concerned with maintaining a normal blood glucose concentration, for gluconeogenesis occurs to a significant extent only when the glucose concentration begins to fall below normal. In such a case, large amounts of amino acids are converted into glucose, thereby helping to maintain a relatively normal blood glucose concentration.

The conversion of galactose and fructose to glucose is also important for maintaining normal blood glucose, because the greater proportion of the glucose formed in this manner is eventually returned by the liver to the blood. This function is particularly important for the metabolism of galactose because almost none of the cells of the body besides those of the liver can convert galactose into glucose. However, fructose can be used by all the cells in much the same manner as glucose.

Fat Metabolism

Though fat metabolism can take place in almost all cells of the body, certain aspects of fat metabolism occur so much more rapidly in the liver than in the other cells that probably 60 per cent or more of the different fat interconversions occur in the liver rather than elsewhere. Some of the specific functions of the liver in fat metabolism are: (1) beta oxidation of fatty acids and formation of acetoacetic acid, (2) formation of the lipoproteins, (3) formation of very large quantities of cholesterol and phospholipids, and (4) conversion of large quantities of carbohydrates and proteins to fat.

To derive energy from neutral fats, the fat is first split into glycerol and fatty acids; then the fatty acids are split by *beta oxidation* into two-carbon acetyl radicals which form *acetyl Co-A*. This in turn can then enter the tricarboxylic acid cycle and be oxidized to liberate tremendous amounts of energy. This process of beta oxidation can probably take place in all cells of the body, but it occurs so rapidly in the hepatic cells in comparison with the others that about 60 per cent of all initial oxidation of fatty acids in the body occurs in the liver. Yet, the liver itself cannot utilize all the acetyl Co-A that is formed; instead, this is converted by condensation of two molecules of acetyl Co-A into *acetoacetic acid*, which is a highly soluble acid that passes from the liver cells into the extracellular fluids and then is transported throughout the body to be absorbed by the other tissues. These tissues in turn reconvert the acetoacetic acid into acetyl Co-A and then oxidize it in the usual manner. In this way, therefore, the liver is responsible for the major part of the metabolism of fats.

Except for the use of cholesterol to form bile salts, the functions of the cholesterol and phospholipids formed in the liver are still in doubt. About 80 per cent of the cholesterol is converted into bile salts, but the remainder enters the blood to be transported principally in the lipoproteins. The phospholipid lecithin likewise is transported principally in the lipoproteins. It is possible that both these substances, along with the proteins and neutral fat fractions of the lipoproteins, are absorbed by cells everywhere in the body to help form the cell membranes and intracellular structures, for it is well known that most of the membranous structures throughout the body are composed of protein, cholesterol, phospholipids, and neutral fats.

The majority of all fat synthesis in the body from carbohydrates and proteins also occurs in the liver. After fat is synthesized in the liver it is then transported to the adipose tissue to be stored. However, it should be noted that moderate quantities of fat are synthesized even in the adipose tissue itself. Here again, therefore, the liver is not unique, but quantitatively it is by far the most important source of fat synthesis in the body.

Protein Metabolism

Even though a very large proportion of the metabolic processes for carbohydrates and fat metabolism occurs in the liver, the body could probably dispense with these functions of the liver and still survive. On the other hand, the body could not dispense with the services of the liver in protein metabolism for more than 24 to 48 hours without death ensuing. The most important functions of the liver in protein metabolism are: (1) deamination of amino acids, (2) formation of urea for removal of ammonia from the body fluids, (3) formation of plasma proteins, and (4) interconversions among the different amino acids and other compounds important to the metabolic processes of the body.

Deamination of the amino acids is required before these can be used for energy or before they can be converted into carbohydrates or fats. A small amount of deamination can occur in the other tissues of the body, especially in the kidneys, but, here again, quantitatively the percentage of deamination occurring extrahepatically is so small that it is almost completely unimportant.

Formation of urea by the liver removes ammonia from the body fluids. Since large amounts of ammonia are formed during deamination, without this function of the liver the plasma ammonia concentration would rise rapidly and would result in *hepatic coma* and death.

Essentially all the plasma proteins, with the exception of part of the gamma globulins, are formed by the hepatic cells. This accounts for more than 95 per cent of all the plasma proteins. The remaining gamma globulins are the immune bodies formed by the reticuloendothelial cells elsewhere in the body. The liver can form plasma proteins at a maximum rate of 50 to 100 grams per day. Therefore, after loss of as much as half of the plasma proteins from the body, these can be replenished in approximately 5 to 8 days.

Among the most important functions of the liver is its ability to synthesize certain amino acids and also to synthesize other very important chemical compounds from the amino acids. For instance, the so-called non-essential amino acids can be synthesized in the liver. To do this, a keto acid having the same chemical composition (ex-cept for the keto radical) as that of the amino acid to be formed is first synthesized. Then an amino radical is transferred through several stages of *transamination* from an available amino acid to the keto acid to take the place of the keto oxygen.

Also, especially important are the formation from amino acids of the purines, the pyrimidines, creatine phosphate, and many other substances. These same interconversions can probably occur in all cells of the body, but their rates are far greater in the liver than anywhere else.

Miscellaneous Metabolic Functions of the Liver

Storage of Vitamins. The liver has a particular propensity for storing vitamins and has long been known as an excellent source of certain vitamins in treating patients. The single vitamin probably stored to the greatest extent in the liver is vitamin A, but also large quantities of vitamin D and vitamin B_{12} are normally stored in the liver. Sufficient quantities of vitamin A can be stored to prevent vitamin A deficiency for as long as one to two years, and sufficient vitamin D and vitamin B_{12} can be stored to prevent deficiency for as long as three to four months.

Relationship of the Liver to Blood Coagulation. The liver forms a large proportion of the blood substances utilized in the coagulation process. These can be listed as follows: (1) fibrinogen, (2) prothrombin, (3) accelerator globulin, (4) proconvertin, and (5) several other less important coagulation factors. Vitamin K is required by the metabolic processes of the liver for the formation especially of proconvertin but also, to a less extent, prothrombin and accelerator globulin. In the absence of vitamin K the concentrations of these substances fall very low and almost prevent blood coagulation.

Storage of Iron. Except for the iron in the hemoglobin of the blood, by far the greater proportion of the iron in the body is usually stored in the liver in the form of *ferritin*. The hepatic cells contain large amounts of a protein called *apoferritin*, which is capable of combining with either small or large quantities of iron. Therefore, when iron is available in the body fluids in extra quantities, it combines with the apoferritin to form ferritin and is stored in this form until needed by the body. When the iron in the circulating body fluids falls low, then the ferritin releases the iron. Thus, the apoferritin-ferritin system of the liver acts as an *iron buffer* for the body fluids and also as an iron storage medium. Other functions of the liver in relation to iron metabolism, especially the formation and storage of hemosiderin, are considered in Chapter 12.

REFERENCES

Banaszak, E. F., Stekiel, W. J., Grace, R. A., and Smith, J. J.: Estimation of hepatic blood flow using a single injection dye clearance method. *Am. J. Physiol., 198:*877, 1960.

Best, C. H., Lucas, C. C., and Ridout, J. H.: Vitamins and the protection of the liver. *Brit. M. Bull., 12:*9, 1956.

Bradley, S. E.: The excretory function of the liver. *Harvey Lect., 54:*131, 1958–1959.

Brauer, R. W.: Liver. *Ann. Rev. Physiol., 18:*253, 1956.

Brauer, R. W., Holloway, R. J., and Leong, G. F.: Changes in liver function and structure due to experimental passive congestion under controlled hepatic vein pressures. *Am. J. Physiol., 197:*681, 1959.

Ciba Foundation: Liver Disease. New York, Blakiston, 1951.

Denton, R. W., Gershbein, L. L., and Ivy, A. C.: Response of human and canine gallbladder to cholecystokinin. *J. Appl. Physiol., 2:*671, 1950.

Dosekun, F. O., Grayson, J., and Mendel, D.: The measurement of metabolic and vascular responses in liver and muscle with observations on their responses to insulin and glucose. *J. Physiol., 150:*581, 1960.

Ducci, H.: Contribution of the laboratory to the differential diagnosis of jaundice. *J.A.M.A., 135:*694, 1947.

Elman, R.: The gallbladder and pancreas; in Sodeman, W. A. (ed.): Pathologic Physiology. 2nd ed., Philadelphia, W. B. Saunders Co., 1956.

Green, H. D., Hall, L. S., Sexton, J., and Deal, C. P.: Autonomic vasomotor responses in the canine hepatic arterial and venous beds. *Am. J. Physiol., 196:*196, 1959.

Haslewood, G. A. D.: Recent developments in our knowledge of bile salts. *Physiol. Rev., 35:*178, 1955.

Hollander, F.: The role of ammonia in hepatic coma. *Gastroenterology, 29:*913, 1955.

Kelly, L. S., Dobson, E. L., Finney, C. R., and Hirsch, J. D.: Proliferation of the reticuloendothelial system in the liver. *Am. J. Physiol., 198:*1134, 1960.

Leevy, C. M.: Liver Disease. New York, Paul B. Hoeber, 1957.

Lichtman, S. S.: Diseases of the Liver, Gall Bladder, and Bile Ducts. Philadelphia, Lea & Febiger, 1953.

Light, H. G., Witmer, C., and Vars, H. M.: Interruption of the enterohepatic circulation and its effect on rat bile. *Am. J. Physiol., 197:*1330, 1959.

Mann, F. C., and Mann, F. D.: Liver. *Ann. Rev. Physiol., 15:*473, 1953.

Morris, C. R., Hohf, R. P., and Ivy, A. C.: Experimental study of role of stasis in etiology of cholecystitis. *Surgery, 32:*673, 1952.

Popper, H.: Liver: Structure and Function. New York, McGraw-Hill Book Co., Inc., 1957.

Schiff, L.: Diseases of the Liver. Philadelphia, J. B. Lippincott Co., 1956.

Sherlock, S.: Diseases of the Liver and Biliary System. 2nd ed., Springfield, Charles C Thomas, 1958.

Sherlock, S.: Pathogenesis and management of hepatic coma. *Am. J. Med., 24:*805, 1958.

Siperstein, M. D., and Chaikoff, I. L.: Conversion of cholesterol to bile acids. *Fed. Proc., 14:*767, 1955.

Sperber, I.: Secretion of organic anions in the formation of urine and bile. *Pharmacol. Rev., 11:*109, 1959.

Sterling, J. A.: The Bilary Tract. Baltimore, Williams & Wilkins Co., 1955.

Twiss, J. T., and Oppenheim, E.: Disorders of the Liver, Pancreas, and Biliary Tract. Philadelphia, Lea & Febiger, 1955.

Wakim, K. G.: Physiology of the liver. *Am. J. Med., 16:*256, 1954.

Wilson, J. W.: Liver. *Ann. Rev. Physiol., 13:*155, 1951.

Part Twelve

ENDOCRINOLOGY AND

REPRODUCTION

Chapter 73

Introduction to Endocrinology;
The Hypophyseal Hormones

The functions of the body are regulated by two major control systems: (1) the nervous system, which has already been discussed, and (2) the hormonal, or endocrine, system. In general, the nervous system controls the rapidly changing activities of the body such as the skeletal motor movements, the smooth muscle contractions of the viscera, and many of the glandular secretions. On the other hand, the hormonal system is concerned principally with the different metabolic functions of the body, controlling the rates of chemical reactions in some or all of the cells. Or it controls the transport of substances through the cellular membranes or other aspects of cellular metabolism such as growth, secretion, and so forth. Some hormonal effects occur in a matter of seconds, while others require several days even to get started and then last for weeks, months, or even years. Thus, the functions of the nervous and hormonal control systems are somewhat different from each other.

On the other hand, many interrelationships exist between the hormonal and nervous systems. For instance, at least two glands secrete their hormones only in response to appropriate nerve stimuli, the *adrenal medullae* and the *neurohypophysis,* and the secretions of essentially all the other glands are controlled at least in part and sometimes to a major extent by either direct or indirect controlling influences from the nervous system. For instance, very few of the adenohypophyseal hormones are secreted to a significant extent except in response to nervous activity in the hypothalamus, as will be detailed later in the chapter.

The Nature of a Hormone

A hormone is a chemical substance secreted into the body fluids by one cell or group of cells that exerts a physiologic effect on other cells of the body. Some hormones cause their effects in the immediate vicinity of their release, and these are called *local hormones.* Other hormones are released into the extracellular fluids of the body and cause effects in distant organs; these are called *general hormones.*

Local Hormones. Throughout this text we have described many local hormones, including *acetylcholine,* released at the parasympathetic and skeletal nerve endings, *norepinephrine,* released at the adrenergic nerve endings, *secretin,* released by the duodenal wall and transported to the pancreas to cause a watery pancreatic secretion, *pancreozymin,* also released by the small intestinal wall and transported to the pancreas to cause secretion of large quantities of enzymes, and so forth.

The General Hormones and the "Endocrine Glands." The general hormones are secreted by specific *endocrine glands* and then are transmitted everywhere in the body fluids to cause physiological actions at distant points in the body. A few of the general hormones affect all, or almost all, cells of the body, such as *growth hormone* from the adenohypophysis and *thyroid hormone* from the thyroid gland. On the other hand, other general hormones affect specific tissues far more than other tissues; for instance, *corticotropin* from the adenohypophysis has a specific stimulatory effect on the adrenal cortex, and the *ovarian hormones* have specific effects on the uterine endometrium. The tissues affected specifically in this way are called *target organs* or *target tissues*. Many examples of target organs will become apparent in the next few chapters on endocrinology.

The different general hormones which have proved to be of major significance and which will be discussed in detail in this and the following chapters are the following:

1. Adenohypophyseal hormones: (a) *growth hormone,* (b) *corticotropin,* (c) *thyrotropin,* (d) *follicle-stimulating hormone,* (e) *luteinizing hormone,* and (f) *luteotropic hormone*

2. Neurohypophyseal hormones: (a) *antidiuretic hormone* and (b) *oxytocin*

3. Adrenocortical hormones: especially (a) *cortisol* and (b) *aldosterone*

4. Thyroid hormones: especially *thyroxine*

5. Pancreatic hormones: (a) *insulin* and (b) *glucagon*

6. Ovarian hormones: (a) *estrogens* and (b) *progesterone*

7. Testicular hormones: especially *testosterone*

8. Parathyroid hormone: *parathormone*

9. Placental hormones: (a) *chorionic gonadotropin,* (b) *estrogens,* and (c) *progesterone*

Negative Feedback in the Control of Hormonal Secretion. At many points both in this chapter and in the succeeding few chapters we will note that, once a hormone begins to accomplish its physiological function, its rate of secretion begins to decrease. This is caused by *negative feedback,* a phenomenon we have already seen to be very important in nervous control systems. In general, each gland has a basic tendency to over-secrete its particular hormone, but, once the normal physiologic effect of the hormone has been achieved, information is transferred in some way back to the producing gland to check further secretion. On the other hand, if the gland under-secretes, the physiological effects of the hormone diminish, and the feedback decreases, thus allowing the gland to begin secreting adequate quantities of the hormone once again. In this way, the rate of secretion of each hormone is controlled in accord with the need of the body for the hormone. The specific mechanisms of negative feedback will be discussed in relation to the different individual hormones.

Chemistry of the Hormones. Chemically, there are two basic types of hormones: (1) proteins or derivatives of proteins or amino acids and (2) steroid hormones. In the case of the pancreas and adenohypophysis, the hormones are either proteins or large polypeptides, while, in the case of the neurohypophysis, thyroid, and adrenal medulla, the hormones are derivatives of proteins or amino acids. The steroids are secreted by tissues derived from the mesenchymal zone of the embryo, including the adrenal cortex, the ovary, and the testis.

The Thymus and Pineal Glands. Two structures, the *thymus* and the *pineal gland,* are frequently called endocrine glands. However, thus far, neither of these two has been proved to secrete a definite and important hormone. Literally thousands of attempts have been made to extract hormones from these two "glands," and many such hormones have been claimed and later disclaimed by different research workers. The two most usual hormonal effects postulated for the two glands have been *growth stimulation* and *sexual stimulation.*

In adults the pineal gland often becomes completely calcified; this does not cause any significant physiologic effect on the body, which makes it doubtful that the pineal gland has any significant function. Also, the thymus usually atrophies to almost nothing after adolescence, which places its endocrine functions also in a very doubtful category. Yet, the following facts are known about these two structures.

The thymus. The thymus gland contains large amounts of lymphoid tissue, which makes one believe that it is related in some way to the lymphogenous system, possibly performing the function of a specialized lymph node. It is also known to hypertrophy in certain infectious diseases, which is a general characteristic of lymphogenous tissue. Occasionally, hypertrophy is so marked that a pathological state called *status thymo-lymphaticus* occurs, which means simply generalized enlargement of the thymus gland and lymph nodes throughout the body.

Glucocorticoid hormones from the adrenal cortex cause the thymus gland to involute, and lack of glucocorticoids causes the gland to become enlarged. These effects presumably result from the general tendency of glucocorticoids to have the same but less marked effect on all lymphogenous tissues.

In one fourth of all patients with myasthenia gravis, a disease discussed in Chapter 18, in which impulse transmission through the neuromuscular junction is blocked, a tumor is present in the thymus, or the thymus itself is enlarged, thus indicating a possible relationship between myasthenia gravis and the thymus. Removal of the enlarged thymus or of the "thymona" benefits about one half of the patients, sometimes very much so. However, other extensive surgical procedures also frequently benefit myasthenia gravis. Therefore, at present it is yet unknown whether thymectomy is of any significance in the treatment of myasthenia gravis. Administration of hydrocortisone, one of the glucocorticoids, occasionally also benefits myasthenia gravis; this effect is perhaps caused by involution of the thymus, which results when this hormone is injected.

The pineal gland. Embryologically, the pineal gland is derived from a third eye that begins to develop early in the embryo and later degenerates. However, the epithelioid cells of this structure persist into adulthood in the pineal body, and it is possible that they could secrete a hormone or hormones of importance to the body. Recently, a substance called *melatonin* that causes melanin, the dark pigment of the skin, to collect in the *melanocytes* of the skin has been extracted from the pineal glands of lower animals. This same substance has also been extracted from other tissues of the body, which makes it doubtful that the pineal gland is of any significance in relation to the skin pigmentation.

Recent experiments have also shown that *glomerulotropin*, a substance which stimulates the secretion of aldosterone by the adrenal cortex, is secreted somewhere in the midportion of the brain—in the region of the mesencephalon or upper pons. Because of the proximity of the pineal gland to the mesencephalon, it has been suggested that this could be the locus of secretion of glomerulotropin, though the fact that this gland calcifies in one third of all adults makes this very unlikely.

THE HYPOPHYSIS AND ITS HORMONES

The hypophysis, which is illustrated in Figure 677, is a very small gland—about 1 centimeter in diameter—that lies in the *sella turcica* at the base of the brain and is connected with the hypothalamus by the hypophyseal stalk. The hypophysis is also known as the *pituitary gland*. Physiologically, it is divisible into two very distinct portions, (a) the *adenohypophysis*, which is also known as the *anterior pituitary gland*, and (b) the *neurohypophysis*, which is also known as the *posterior pituitary gland*. Between these is a small, relatively avascular zone called the *pars intermedia*, which is almost absent in the human being but is much larger and seemingly more functional in some lower animals. The principal hormones of the

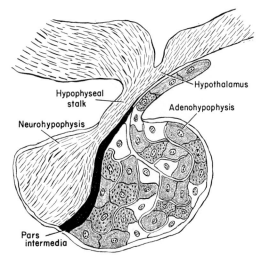

Figure 677.   The hypophysis.

adenohypophysis and neurohypophysis were listed earlier in the chapter and will be discussed in detail later. In lower animals the pars intermedia secretes a *melanocyte-stimulating hormone,* which causes the melanocytes in the skin of certain reptiles to disperse their melanin beneath the skin and thereby turn the animal a gray color. Release of this hormone allows the animal to blend with the surroundings. Though the melanocyte - stimulating hormone perhaps causes slightly increased pigmentation in the human being, this effect is not marked.

Embryologically, the two portions of the hypophysis originate from different sources, the adenohypophysis from *Rathke's pouch,* which is an embryonic invagination of the pharyngeal epithelium, and the neurohypophysis from an outgrowth of the hypothalamus. In the past, it was believed that there was no significance to the contiguity of the two glands. However, it is now known that hormones secreted by the neurohypophysis can stimulate, at least to some degree, the secretion of certain ones of the adenohypophyseal hormones. These interrelations will become apparent later in the chapter. The origin of the adenohypophysis from the pharyngeal epithelium explains the epithelioid nature of its cells, while the origin of the neurohypophysis from neural tissue explains the presence of large numbers of glial type cells in this gland.

The Neurohypophysis and Its Nerve Supply from the Hypothalamus

The neurohypophysis is composed almost entirely of glial-like cells called *pituicytes.* However, there are reasons for believing

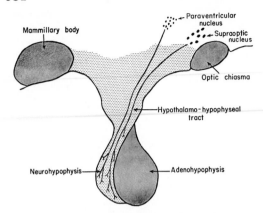

Figure 678. Hypothalamic control of the neurohypophysis.

that the pituicytes do not secrete any hormones but simply store them in accordance
with the following mechanism: Figure 678
illustrates the nervous connections between
the hypothalamus and the neurohypophysis.
If the hypophyseal stalk is cut near the
hypophysis, leaving the entire hypothalamus
intact, the neurohypophyseal hormones continue to be secreted almost to a normal extent. Furthermore, the hormones have been
demonstrated in the nerve fibers as far up as
the supraoptic and paraventricular nuclei
themselves. For these reasons, it is now believed that the neurohypophyseal hormones
are formed either in the supraoptic and paraventricular nuclei themselves or in the nerve
fibers leading from these nuclei and then
are transported along the axons of the nerve
fibers to the neurohypophysis. Here, the hormones seem to be stored in the pituicytes
and are released from these into the blood
when impulses are transmitted from the
supraoptic or paraventricular nuclei.

The Adenohypophysis and Its Cell Types

Basically, the adenohypophysis is composed of three major cell types: (1) the
chromophobes, which account for about 50
per cent of all the cells, (2) the *acidophils*,
also known as *alpha cells*, which account for
approximately 40 per cent of all the cells,
and (3) the *basophils*, also known as *beta
cells*, which account for about 10 per cent of
all the cells.

The *acidophils* are known to produce
growth hormone and *luteotropic hormone*,
while the *basophils* almost certainly produce

*luteinizing hormone, follicle-stimulating hor-
mone,* and *thyrotropin* and probably secrete
corticotropin, though this is not certain.

The chromophobe cells are believed to secrete none of the adenohypophyseal hormones but instead simply to be precursor
cells of either the acidophil or basophil cells.

**The Hypothalamic-Hypophyseal Portal
System.** The adenohypophysis, in contrast
to the neurohypophysis, is a highly vascular
organ with extensive venous sinuses extending among the glandular cells. These sinuses
in turn are supplied mainly with blood that
passes first through the hypothalamus and
then through the *hypothalamic-hypophyseal
portal veins* into the adenohypophysis. Figure 679 illustrates a small hypophyseal artery
supplying the lower portion of the hypothalamus called the *median eminence*. Small
capillary tufts extend into the substance of
the median eminence and then return to its
surface, coalescing to form the small hypothalamic-hypophyseal portal veins. These in
turn spread downward around the hypophyseal stalk to supply the venous sinuses of
the adenohypophysis.

The hypothalamic-hypophyseal portal system seems to be an extremely important
link in hypothalamic control of the adenohypophysis, for many experiments have demonstrated that several *neurosecretory substances* liberated by the nerves in the median
eminence are transported through the hypothalamic-hypophyseal portal system to the
adenohypophysis. Here they stimulate the
secretion of specific adenohypophyseal hor-

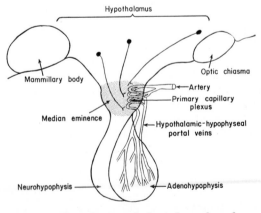

Figure 679. The hypothalamic-hypophyseal portal system, beginning in the primary capillary plexus
of the median eminence and coursing down the
hypophyseal stalk to the adenohypophysis.

mones. This mechanism for the regulation of adenohypophyseal secretion will be discussed in more detail in relation to the specific hormones.

Innervation of the Adenohypophysis. A few very small nerve fibers have been demonstrated to course along the blood vessels that enter the adenohypophysis. These are believed to be sympathetic nerve fibers and not fibers that stimulate secretion by the adenohypophyseal cells, but claims have been made that a few nerve fibers, perhaps of a secretory nature, also pass down the hypophyseal stalk from the hypothalamus to the adenohypophysis. However, if these exist they are (a) extremely small and quite different from the secretory fibers that pass into the posterior hypothalamus and (b) so few in number that it is doubtful that they could innervate all the glandular cells of the adenohypophysis. Therefore, it is believed by most physiologists that secretion by the adenohypophysis is not controlled by nerve impulses from the hypothalamus but instead by neurosecretory products coursing down the hypophyseal portal system.

PHYSIOLOGIC FUNCTIONS OF THE NEUROHYPOPHYSEAL HORMONES

The neurohypophysis secretes two distinct hormones: (1) *antidiuretic hormone,* which is frequently also called *vasopressin,* and (2) *oxytocin.* These two hormones are secreted independently of each other by the neurohypophysis, and their secretion is controlled entirely by nerve impulses from the anterior hypothalamus.

Antidiuretic Hormone

The antidiuretic effect of antidiuretic hormone (ADH) was discussed in detail in Chapter 9. Briefly, this hormone increases the permeability of the collecting tubules in the kidneys to water. Without antidiuretic hormone the collecting tubules are almost completely impermeable to water, and tubular fluid reaching this part of the renal tubular system will pass in very dilute concentration on into the urine, forming a urine with a specific gravity of approximately 1.002. Thus, in the absence of ADH the person loses large amounts of water from his body fluids while retaining the electrolytes. On the other hand, when large quantities of ADH are present, the collecting tubules become highly permeable to water so that most of it is reabsorbed. In this way the

urine is concentrated, and the body conserves most of its water while losing a higher proportion of electrolytes.

In short, antidiuretic hormone dilutes the body fluids, while lack of antidiuretic hormone concentrates the body fluids.

Regulation of ADH Production. Antidiuretic hormone is secreted by the neurohypophysis in response to nerve impulses from the *supraoptic nuclei* and to a less extent from the *paraventricular nuclei* of the anterior hypothalamus. It has been postulated that the neurons of the supraoptic nuclei function as *osmoreceptors,* and histologists have actually observed fluid chambers in these cells which presumably can increase and decrease in size in relation to the degree of concentration of the extracellular fluids. When the extracellular fluids are highly dilute, osmosis of water into the cell supposedly increases the volume of the fluid chamber, while concentrated extracellular fluids supposedly reduce the volume of the fluid chamber. Regardless of whether these effects are true, concentrated body fluids do stimulate the supraoptic nuclei, while dilute body fluids inhibit these nuclei. Therefore, a servoregulatory mechanism is available for regulation of the crystalloidal osmotic pressure of the body fluids, operating as follows:

When the body fluids become highly concentrated, the supraoptic nuclei become excited, impulses are transmitted to the neurohypophysis, and antidiuretic hormone is secreted. This then passes by way of the blood to the kidneys, where it increases the permeability of the collecting tubules to water. As a result, most of the water is reabsorbed from the urine, while electrolytes continue to be lost. This effect dilutes the extracellular fluids, returning them to a reasonably normal osmotic composition. Conversely, dilute extracellular fluid inhibits secretion of ADH, and large quantities of water are then lost into the urine, thereby concentrating the body fluids.

Diabetes Insipidus. Diabetes insipidus is the disease that occurs when the supraopticohypophyseal system for secreting antidiuretic hormone fails. In a person with full-blown diabetes insipidus, lack of antidiuretic hormone keeps his urine from ever being concentrated. The urine specific gravity remains almost constantly between 1.002 and 1.006; the urine output is usually 4 to 6 liters per day but can be as great as 12 to

15 liters per day, depending principally upon how much water the person drinks. Furthermore, the rapid loss of fluid in the urine creates a constant thirst, which keeps the water flushing through his body.

The person with diabetes insipidus has a tendency to become dehydrated and also to "wash out" an excess of electrolytes from his body fluids. However, these tendencies are usually quite well offset by the increased thirst and an increased desire for salt in food. Under conditions of circulatory stress or when water and salt might not be adequately available, the fluid and electrolyte loss can become important.

Diabetes insipidus can be treated easily by simply insufflating a small amount of powdered posterior pituitary gland into the nose several times a day. Though only a very minute amount of antidiuretic hormone is absorbed in this way, it also takes only 0.1 microgram of the hormone to cause a maximal antidiuretic effect.

Diabetes insipidus occurs most frequently as a result of a tumor of the hypothalamus or hypophysis that destroys the neurohypophysis or the portions of the hypothalamus that control antidiuretic hormone secretion. Also, injury to the hypophyseal stalk will temporarily reduce the production of antidiuretic hormone. If the stalk is sectioned near the neurohypophysis, little secretion of antidiuretic hormone will occur for the first few weeks, but gradually secretion will return, sometimes almost to normal, thus illustrating that large amounts of antidiuretic hormone can be secreted by the neural elements above the hypophysis. If the damage extends high up the stalk, and especially if it includes the median eminence, then return of function does not occur.

Pressor Function of ADH. It was pointed out earlier that antidiuretic hormone is also frequently called *vasopressin.* This name is derived from the fact that injection of large quantities of ADH causes the arterial pressure to rise. However, it has never been proved that sufficient vasopressin is secreted under physiological conditions by the neurohypophysis to have significant effects on arterial pressure regulation. Also, removal of the neurohypophysis does not measurably alter arterial pressure regulation. Therefore, it is probable that this pressor effect of antidiuretic hormone is more of a "pharmacological" effect, in which very large doses are given, than a physiological effect.

Other Actions of ADH. Large doses of antidiuretic hormone can also cause contraction of almost any smooth muscle tissue in the body, including contraction of most of the intestinal musculature, the bile ducts, the uterus, and so forth. However, here again the concentration required to cause these effects is far greater than that required to cause antidiuresis, and it is doubtful that these are significant physiological effects for normal functioning of the body.

Oxytocic Hormone—Its Effect on the Uterus

An "oxytocic" substance is one that causes contraction of the pregnant uterus. The hormone *oxytocin,* in accordance with its name, has a very powerful stimulatory effect on the pregnant uterus, especially toward the end of the period of gestation. Therefore, it is believed by many obstetricians that this hormone is at least partially responsible for initiating labor and for effecting birth. Thus far, there is no definite proof that sufficient quantities of oxytocin are secreted to cause this effect. Yet, in a hypophysectomized animal, the duration of labor is considerably prolonged, thus indicating a probable effect of oxytocin during delivery.

Antidiuretic hormone also stimulates the pregnant uterus though not nearly so strongly as oxytocin. Likewise, oxytocin excites contraction of a number of other smooth muscle structures in the body besides the uterus, though usually to a much less extent than ADH. The fact that the functions of the two hormones partially overlap illustrates their physiologic relation to each other; as will be pointed out below, their chemical structures are also very similar.

Effect of Oxytocin on Milk Ejection. Oxytocin has an especially important function in the process of lactation, for this hormone causes milk to be expressed from the alveoli into the ducts so that the baby can obtain it by suckling. This mechanism works as follows: The suckling stimuli on the nipple of the breast cause impulses to be transmitted through the somatic nervous system to the brain, the impulses finally reaching the anterior hypothalamus to cause the release of oxytocin. The oxytocin then is carried by the blood to the breasts where it causes contraction of *myoepithelial cells,* which lie outside of and compress the alveoli. In less than a minute after the beginning of suckling, milk begins to flow. Therefore, this mechanism is frequently called *milk letdown* or *milk ejection.* Antidiuretic hormone also has a moderate effect in promoting milk ejection.

Possible Effect of Oxytocin on Milk Secretion by the Mammary Glands. Oxytocin released by the neurohypophysis also seems to have a direct effect on the adenohypophysis to induce production of luteotropic hormone. It is believed that a small portion of the oxytocin released by the neurohypophysis is transmitted directly from the neurohypophysis to the adenohypophysis through local blood vessels. Then, on reaching the glandular cells of the adenohypophysis, the oxytocin promotes luteotropin production. Luteotropin in turn is one of the hormones principally responsible for milk secretion, which will be discussed in Chapter 80.

Chemical Nature of Antidiuretic Hormone and Oxytocin

Both oxytocin and antidiuretic hormone (vasopressin) have been isolated in pure form from neurohypophyseal glands, and they have also been synthesized from their basic amino acid components. The amino acid compositions of these are the following:

VASOPRESSIN	OXYTOCIN
Tyrosine	Tyrosine
Proline	Proline
Glutamic acid	Glutamic acid
Aspartic acid	Aspartic acid
Glycine	Glycine
Cystine	Cystine
Phenylalanine	Leucine
Arginine	Isoleucine

Note that these two hormones are identical except that in vasopressin phenylalanine and arginine replace leucine and isoleucine of the oxytocin molecule. The similarity of the molecules explains the few functional similarities between these two hormones, while the slight dissimilarities of the molecules illustrate that very slight chemical changes can alter the physiological properties of hormones markedly.

PHYSIOLOGIC FUNCTIONS OF THE ADENOHYPOPHYSEAL HORMONES

The adenohypophysis secretes at least six well-defined hormones that have widespread effects throughout the body, as illustrated in Figure 680, and it is possible that still several other hormones of less importance are secreted, some of which will be mentioned in later chapters of this discussion of endocrinology. *Growth hormone* acts directly on either all or almost all of the tissues of the body, but the other five of the major hormones, *corticotropin, thyrotropin,* and the three *gonadotropins,* exert their effects by stimulating "target glands," the adrenal cortex, the thyroid gland, and the gonads. Therefore, in one sense the adenohypophysis **is a master control center for a major share**

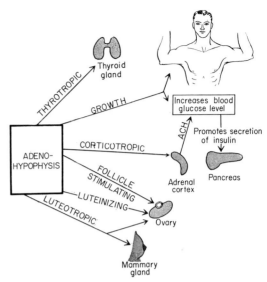

Figure 680. The adenohypophyseal hormones and their functions.

of the endocrine functions of the body. In subsequent chapters the functions of the target glands will be discussed in detail, and certain functions of the adenohypophyseal hormones will be discussed, along with the functions of the stimulated glands.

Corticotropin

Effect on Adrenocortical Secretion of Cortisol. *Corticotropin,* which is also known as *corticotropic hormone* or *adrenocorticotropic hormone (ACTH),* stimulates the adrenal cortex, causing it to secrete greatly increased quantities of *cortisol* (hydrocortisone) and to a less extent *corticosterone* and *adrenal androgenic hormones.* The cortisol in turn acts throughout the body to (1) increase the rate of gluconeogenesis, (2) increase the rate of protein catabolism, and (3) increase the rate of fat catabolism. Therefore, indirectly corticotropin has profound effects on carbohydrate, protein, and fat metabolism. One of the especially important effects of this hormone is an increased blood glucose concentration. Therefore, this hormone is frequently said to be *diabetogenic.*

The enhanced secretion of corticosterone and androgens in response to corticotropin usually is not especially significant. However, when extreme amounts of corticotropin are secreted by the adenohypophysis, these

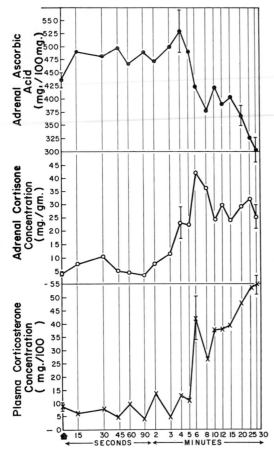

Figure 681. Rapid reaction of the adrenal cortex of a rat to stress caused by fracture of the tibia and fibula. (Courtesy of Drs. Guillemin, Dear, and Lipscomb.)

hormones can then be secreted in sufficient quantities to be of real importance, the first causing considerable retention of electrolytes by the kidneys and the latter masculinizing effects in the body, which will be discussed in the following chapter.

Aside from cortisol, the only very important hormone normally secreted by the adrenal cortex is *aldosterone*, which has a major effect in regulating electrolyte balance in the body fluids. However, corticotropin only very slightly increases the secretion of aldosterone; instead, secretion of aldosterone is regulated by other mechanisms which will be discussed in the following chapter. Therefore, for practical purposes it can usually be considered that corticotropin exerts its principal effect only on adrenocortical secretion of cortisol.

Regulation of Corticotropin Secretion—Corticotropin-Releasing Factor. Normally,

small quantities of corticotropin are secreted continually by the adenohypophysis. This can be enhanced as much as 10-fold in a matter of minutes of physiological stress. This is illustrated in Figure 681, which shows the adrenal response to corticotropin within a few minutes after breaking the tibia and fibula of a rat. It is believed that nervous stimuli caused by the stress are first transmitted to the posterior hypothalamus. This in turn transmits impulses into the median eminence where a neurosecretory product, corticotropin-releasing factor (CRF), is believed to be secreted into the primary capillary plexus of the hypophyseal portal system and then is carried by this portal system to the venus sinuses of the adenohypophysis. The corticotropin-releasing factor then excites the glandular cells to cause corticotropin secretion, which in turn causes adrenocortical secretion of cortisol. This adenohypophyseal-adrenocortical response to stress is especially important in helping the animal survive under adverse conditions. The beneficial effects of cortisol in stress will be discussed in the following chapter.

Inhibitory effect of cortisol on corticotropin secretion. An elevated concentration of cortisol in the blood causes negative feedback to the adenohypophysis to reduce the production of corticotropin. Though the exact means by which this feedback occurs is yet unknown, it is believed by some physiologists that cortisol acts on the hypothalamus to reduce its production of corticotropin-releasing factor, but other physiologists believe that this negative feedback occurs by a direct inhibitory effect of cortisol on the adenohypophyseal cells themselves. Regardless of the precise mechanism, the negative feedback prevents overproduction of corticotropin once sufficient cortisol has been secreted to achieve the desired effects.

Lipolytic Effect of Corticotropin. The actions of corticotropin are not limited entirely to its effect on the adrenal cortex, for even when the adrenal cortices have been removed, corticotropin still causes increased release of fat from the adipose tissue and consequently increased catabolism of fat. This is called the *lipolytic action* of corticotropin. This fact is mentioned to illustrate that almost all hormones of the body affect more than one type of tissue. However, from a quantitative point of view, it is still doubtful that this lipolytic action is important because it usually requires more corticotropin than is normally released by the adenohypophysis.

Thyrotropin

Thyrotropin, or *thyrotropic hormone,* has a tropic action on the thyroid gland, causing the thyroid glandular cells to increase in size, to increase in number, and to produce greatly increased quantities of thyroid hormone. Thyrotropin is known to induce three different metabolic effects in the thyroid glandular cells: (1) It increases the rate at which inorganic iodide is absorbed from the blood into the thyroid cells. (2) It increases the rate of incorporation of iodides into thyroid hormones. (3) It increases the rate at which thyroid hormones already produced are released from the thyroid gland. The thyroid hormones in turn spread throughout the body and increase the rate of metabolism of all the cells of the body. Therefore, indirectly, thyrotropin is a *metabolism-stimulating hormone.*

In the absence of thyrotropin secretion by the adenohypophysis, the thyroid gland secretes less than one tenth its normal amount of thyroid hormone. Therefore, for practical purposes, essentially the entire secretion by the thyroid gland is regulated through the release of thyrotropin from the adenohypophysis.

Regulation of Thyrotropin Secretion. In the normal person, a small amount of thyrotropin is secreted all of the time. However, this can be enhanced by nervous activity in the hypothalamus. For instance, when an animal is exposed to very intense cold, the rate of thyrotropin secretion can be increased at least 50 per cent, and this causes a corresponding increase in thyroxine production as well as an increase in the metabolic rate of the body to about 20 per cent above normal.

The mechanism by which the hypothalamus controls thyrotropin secretion is believed to be very similar to the mechanism for controlling corticotropin secretion—that is, by releasing a neurosecretory hormone, tl yrotropin-releasing factor (TRF), into the primary capillary plexus of the hypophyseal portal system in the median eminence and subsequent transport of the TRF to the adenohypophysis, where it stimulates thyrotropin secretion.

Inhibitory effect of thyroxine on thyrotropin secretion. When the concentration of thyroxine in the body fluids rises to a high level, this automatically decreases the rate of thyrotropin secretion by the adenohypophysis, as is the case with the inhibitory effect of cortisol on corticotropin secretion. Destructive lesions in the hypothalamus prevent this inhibitory effect, which means that thyroxine probably acts directly on the hypothalamus to reduce the secretion of thyrotropin-releasing factor. This negative feedback, like that affecting corticotropin secretion, prevents over-activity of the thyrotropin-thyroid system and provides a means for control of thyrotropin secretion in proportion to the need of the body for thyroxine.

Exophthalmos-Producing Substance. In many patients with toxic goiter of the thyroid gland, the eyes bulge forward, a phenomenon called *exophthalmos.* Since toxic goiter usually results from markedly increased production of thyrotropin, it has long been believed that thyrotropin might cause exophthalmos in addition to its primary effect on the thyroid gland. However, in some patients with hyperthyroidism, exophthalmos fails to occur despite increased thyrotropin secretion. Recently, a new hormonal substance has been extracted from the adenohypophysis, exophthalmos-producing substance (EPS), which can cause typical exophthalmos. This substance seems to be secreted along with thyrotropin in most instances of hyperthyroidism, thus resulting in the exophthalmos. Therefore, it is probable that thyrotropin itself does not have this effect on the eyes. Exophthalmos will be discussed in detail in Chapter 75 in relation to hyperthyroidism.

The Gonadotropins

The adenohypophysis secretes three different hormones that have tropic effects on either the ovaries or testes. These are *follicle-stimulating hormone, luteinizing hormone,* and *luteotropic hormone.* The interrelationships of these hormones with the sexual hormones are complex and will be considered specifically in Chapters 78 and 79, which describe the hormonal aspects of the reproductive systems. The basic functions of the three gonadotropic hormones are the following:

Follicle-stimulating hormone. Follicle-stimulating hormone causes proliferation of the ovarian follicular cells during growth of the follicles. It also stimulates these cells to secrete small amounts of estrogens. However, luteinizing hormone, which will be discussed below, acting synergistically with follicle-stimulating hormone causes the cells to produce very large amounts of estrogens.

Also, follicle-stimulating hormone stimulates spermatogenesis and possibly the production of estrogens by the seminiferous tubules in the male testes.

Luteinizing hormone. Luteinizing hormone acts synergistically with follicle-stimulating hormone to cause the follicles of the ovaries to swell rapidly and also to cause follicular cells to secrete large quantities of estrogens. Luteinizing hormone also causes one follicle each month to rupture, resulting in *ovulation*. And, immediately following ovulation, luteinizing hormone causes the follicular cells of the ruptured follicle to develop fatty characteristics, a process called *luteinization*. Thus, the follicular cells are converted into *lutein cells* with new and different characteristics, and the entire mass of these cells is then called the *corpus luteum*.

Luteinizing hormones also cause the interstitial cells of the testes to secrete testosterone. Because of this effect, luteinizing hormone is frequently also called *interstitial cell–stimulating hormone*. The testosterone in turn causes masculinizing effects in the male.

Luteotropic hormone. Luteotropic hormone causes the cells of the corpus luteum to secrete large quantities of both progesterone and estrogens during the latter half of the ovarian cycle, which will be described in detail in Chapter 79.

Luteotropic hormone also has a stimulatory action on the mammary glands, helping to cause final development of the glandular elements and promoting secretion of milk. Therefore, luteotropic hormone is frequently also called *lactogenic hormone* or *prolactin*. This effect of luteotropic hormone will be discussed in relation to milk formation in Chapter 80.

Regulation of Gonadotropin Secretion. The gonadotropins, like corticotropin and thyrotropin, are often secreted by the adenohypophysis in response to nervous activity in the hypothalamus. For instance, in the female rabbit, coitus with a male rabbit elicits nerve impulses which are transmitted to the hypothalamus; these in turn stimulate the adenohypophysis to secrete follicle-stimulating hormone and luteinizing hormone, which cause rapid ripening of follicles in the rabbit's ovaries followed by ovulation a few hours later. In the human being, it is also known that various psychogenic stimuli feeding into the hypothalamus can cause marked excitatory or inhibitory effects on gonadotropin secretion and in this way sometimes greatly alter the periodicity of the female sexual cycle.

It is believed that the method by which the hypothalamus stimulates the production of gonadotropins is through the hypophyseal portal system. Presumably, neurosecretory products called gonadotropin-releasing factors (GRF) are secreted by nerve fibers in the median eminence. These are then transported through the hypophyseal portal system to the adenohypophysis to cause secretion of the respective gonadotropins.

Puberty. Almost no gonadotropins are secreted by the adenohypophysis in childhood, but at approximately the age of 8 these hormones begin to be secreted in progressively greater and greater quantities, and by the age of 13 the gonads normally attain adult function, which time of life is called *puberty*.

Inverse effect of estrogens and progesterone on gonadotropin secretion. Estrogens inhibit the production of follicle-stimulating hormone by the adenohypophysis, and progesterone inhibits the production especially of luteinizing hormone but also of follicle-stimulating hormone. During the normal sexual cycle of the female, the inhibitory effects of these hormones cause the adenohypophysis to secrete gonadotropins in a monthly rhythmical cycle, as will be described in Chapter 79.

Testosterone also inhibits the production of the gonadotropins—especially luteinizing hormone—thus providing a negative feedback mechanism for regulation of male sex hormone secretion.

Growth Hormone

Growth hormone, which is also called *somatotropin,* causes growth of all tissues of the body that are capable of growing. It promotes both increased sizes of the cells and increased mitosis with development of increased numbers of cells.

Figure 682 illustrates the typical effect of daily injections of growth hormone into a growing rat in comparison with a litter mate which did not receive growth hormone. This figure shows marked exacerbation of growth by growth hormone—both in the early days of life and even after the two rats had reached adulthood. In the early stages of development, all organs of the treated rat increased proportionately in size, but, after adulthood was reached, most of the bones ceased growing while the soft tissues continued to grow. This results from the fact that, once the epiphyses of the long bones have united with the shafts, further growth

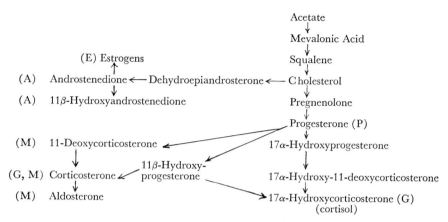

Acetate
↓
Mevalonic Acid
↓
Squalene
↓
(E) Estrogens
↑
(A)   Androstenedione ← Dehydroepiandrosterone ← Cholesterol
↓
(A)   11β-Hydroxyandrostenedione   Pregnenolone
↓
Progesterone (P)
↓
(M)   11-Deoxycorticosterone ←   17α-Hydroxyprogesterone
↓   ↓
(G, M) Corticosterone ← 11β-Hydroxy-progesterone   17α-Hydroxy-11-deoxycorticosterone
↓   ↓
(M)   Aldosterone   → 17α-Hydroxycorticosterone (G)
(cortisol)

Figure 690. Schema showing the stages through which the different corticosteroids are synthesized. The physiologic characteristics of some of these corticosteroids are designated in parentheses as discussed in the text.

which, the mineralocorticoids and glucocorticoids, are extremely important because they are secreted in large quantities and three of which, the adrenal sex hormones, are of only minor importance because they are secreted in very minute quantities. However, a change in even a single enzyme system somewhere in the schema can cause vastly different types of hormones to be formed; occasionally, as will be evident later in the chapter, very large quantities of masculinizing or rarely

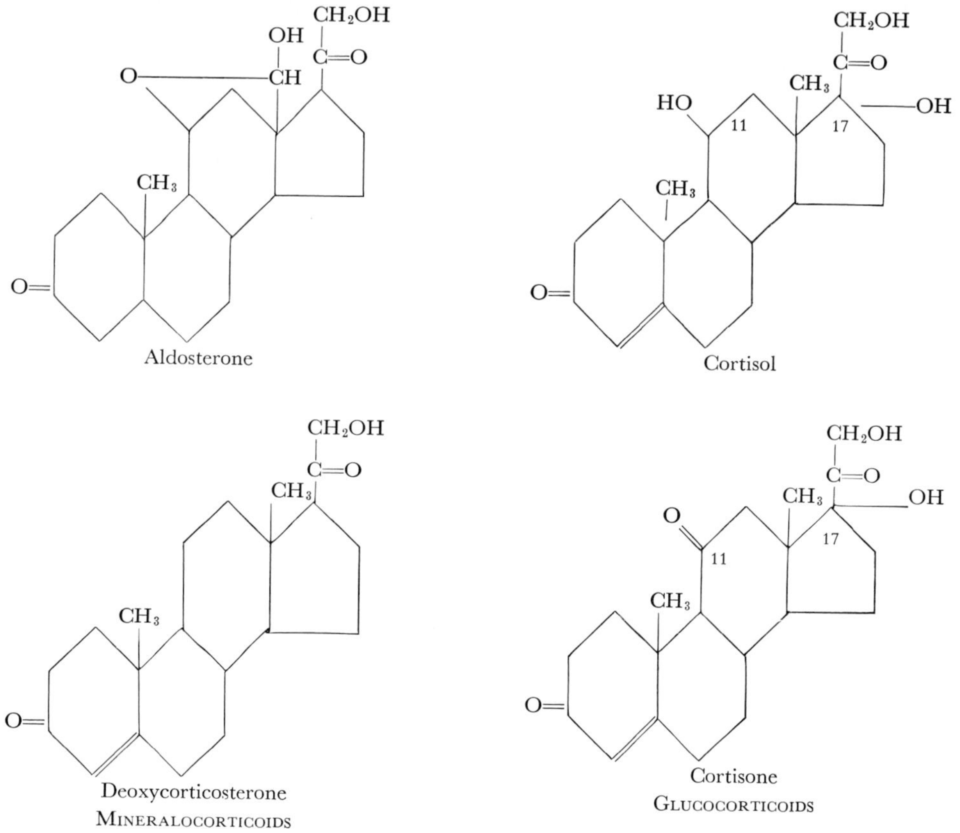

Aldosterone

Cortisol

Deoxycorticosterone
MINERALOCORTICOIDS

Cortisone
GLUCOCORTICOIDS

Figure 691. Four important corticosteroids.

feminizing sex hormones are secreted by adrenal tumors.

Fig. 691 illustrates the chemical formulas of four of the adrenal steroid compounds. Of these, cortisol and aldosterone are secreted in very large quantities by the adrenal cortex. On the other hand, cortisone and deoxycorticosterone are secreted in only minor amounts, but both of these are used to a great extent in therapy because they can be readily synthesized.

The Adrenal Sex Hormones. Several moderately active male sex hormones called *adrenal androgens* (two of which are illustrated in Figure 690) are continually secreted by the adrenal cortex, and progesterone and estrogens have been extracted from the adrenal cortex though these are secreted in only very minute quantities.

In the normal physiology of the human being, even the adrenal androgens have almost insignificant effects. However, it is possible that part of the very early development of the male sex organs might result from childhood secretion of adrenal androgens. The adrenal androgens possibly also exert mild effects in the female, not only before puberty but throughout life. The physiological effects of androgens will be discussed in Chapter 78 in relation to male sexual functions.

The 17-ketosteroids. The adrenal androgens provide a very important clinical test

for assessing the degree of activity of the adrenal cortex, for certain ones of the steroid compounds secreted in the urine, the 17-ketosteroids, are derived in great part from the adrenal androgens. The only other major source of 17-ketosteroids is the testes. Therefore, the quantity of 17-ketosteroids secreted in the urine each day is approximately proportional to the sum of adrenocortical and testicular activity, which is illustrated in Figure 692. In the absence of the adrenal glands in the female, almost no 17-ketosteroids are found in the urine, and, in the adrenalectomized male, the quantity is reduced to about one half normal. On the other hand, in various adrenocortical or testicular diseases, the total quantity of 17-ketosteroids can be increased sometimes to as much as 20 times normal, which is also illustrated in Figure 692.

ABNORMALITIES OF ADRENOCORTICAL SECRETION

Hypoadrenalism—Addison's Disease

Addison's disease results from failure of the adrenal cortices to produce adrenocortical hormones, and this in turn is most frequently caused by *primary atrophy* of the adrenal cortices but also frequently by tuberculous destruction of the adrenal glands or invasion of the adrenal cortices by cancer. Basically, the disturbances in Addison's disease are caused by loss of mineralocorticoids and glucocorticoids, the effects of which can be described as follows:

Mineralocorticoid Deficiency. Lack of aldosterone secretion greatly decreases sodium reabsorption and consequently allows sodium to to be lost into urine in great profusion. Also, chloride ions and water are lost because of secondary failure of the tubules to reabsorb these when sodium is not reabsorbed. The net result is a greatly decreased extracellular fluid volume. Furthermore, the patient develops acidosis because of failure of hydrogen ions to be secreted in exchange for sodium reabsorption.

As the extracellular fluid becomes depleted, the plasma volume falls, the red blood cell concentration rises considerably, the cardiac output decreases, and the patient dies in shock, death usually occurring within 4 to 7 days after complete cessation of mineralocorticoid secretion.

Glucocorticoid Deficiency. Loss of cortisol secretion makes it impossible for the Addisonian patient to maintain normal blood glucose concentration between meals because he cannot synthesize significant quantities of glucose by the

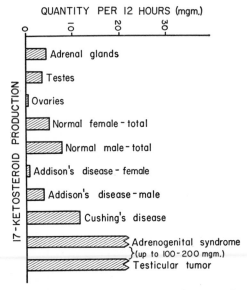

Figure 692. Urinary excretion of 17-ketosteroids in different conditions.

process of gluconeogenesis. Furthermore, lack of cortisol reduces the mobilization of both proteins and fats from the tissues, thereby depressing many other metabolic functions of the body. This sluggishness of energy mobilization when cortisol is not available is perhaps one of the major detrimental effects of glucocorticoid lack. However, even when excess quantities of glucose and other nutrients are available, the person's muscles are still very weak, indicating that glucocorticoids are also needed to maintain other metabolic functions of the tissues besides simply energy metabolism.

Lack of adequate glucocorticoid secretion also makes the Addisonian patient highly susceptible to the deteriorating effects of different types of stress, and even a mild respiratory infection can sometimes cause death of the patient.

Melanin Pigmentation in Addison's Disease. Another characteristic of some Addisonian patients is melanin pigmentation of the skin over most of the body. This melanin is not always deposited evenly but occasionally in blotches and especially in the very thin skin areas such as the mucous membranes of the lips and the thin skin of the nipples.

A suggested cause of the melanin deposition is the following: It is well known that the *pars intermedia* of the adenohypophysis in some lower animals, on appropriate stimulation, secretes large quantities of *melanocyte-stimulating hormone* and that this in turn increases the activity of the melanocytes in the skin. Therefore, it has been assumed that in patients with Addison's disease, lack of glucocorticoid secretion causes the adenohypophysis to secrete excessive amounts of melanocyte-stimulating hormone and that this in turn causes the pigmentation. Unfortunately, it has thus far been impossible to demonstrate the truth of this supposition because of difficulty in demonstrating the secretion of melanocyte-stimulating hormone in the human being.

Diagnosis of Addison's Disease. In addition to the melanin pigmentation in some patients with Addison's disease, the person with this disease also has almost no urinary secretion of 17-ketosteroids except those produced by the testes. Therefore, as illustrated in Fig. 692, Addison's disease can often be diagnosed by the demonstration of diminished, or in the case of women almost absent, secretion of 17-ketosteroids in the urine. In a few laboratories, chemical tests for aldosterone and other corticosteroids in the urine are also now being used to assess the degree of activity of the adrenal cortex.

Treatment of Patients with Addison's Disease. The untreated patient with Addison's disease dies within a few days because of electrolyte disturbances. Yet, he can usually be maintained in a living though weakened condition for years simply by administration of small quantities of mineralocorticoids, usually deoxycorticosterone. Indeed, implantation of small pellets of solid deoxycorticosterone in a fat pad of the back can result in satisfactory electrolyte balance for as long as 6 to 12 months.

Unfortunately, patients treated with mineralocorticoids but without glucocorticoids are still subject to stress reactions that may cause rapid demise. Therefore, full treatment of Addison's disease includes administration of glucocorticoids, usually cortisone or cortisol, as well as mineralocorticoids.

The Addisonian Crisis. Earlier in the chapter, it was noted that tremendous quantities of glucocorticoids are occasionally secreted in response to different types of physical or mental stress. The patient with Addison's disease cannot increase his output of glucocorticoids during stress. Yet, whenever he is specifically subjected to different types of trauma, disease, or other stresses, he is likely to develop an acute need for excessive amounts of glucocorticoids, and, to save his life, he must be given many times normal quantities of glucocorticoids.

This critical need for extra corticosteroids and the associated severe debility of the patient in times of stress is called an *Addisonian crisis*.

Hyperadrenalism—Cushing's Disease

Hypersecretion by the adrenal cortex is called *Cushing's disease*, and this usually results from general hyperplasia of both adrenal cortices. The hyperplasia in turn is most often caused by increased secretion of corticotropin by the adenohypophysis. Most abnormalities of Cushing's disease are ascribable to abnormal amounts of mineralocorticoids and glucocorticoids, but in some patients the secretion of adrenal sex hormones is also of significance.

Effects on Electrolytes, Body Fluids, and the Cardiovascular System. In Cushing's disease sodium retention is moderately enhanced because of the increased mineralocorticoid secretion, and this in turn leads to mildly increased extracellular fluid volume, increased plasma volume, mild degrees of hypokalemia, and mild alkalosis. The increase in extracellular fluid volume is usually not enough to cause frank edema, but it may cause slight puffiness of the skin, especially in the facial region, as illustrated in Fig. 693.

The changes in fluid and electrolyte balance also usually lead to very slightly increased cardiac output, as explained earlier in the chapter, and also to hypertension. Thus, most patients with Cushing's disease have a moderate to severe

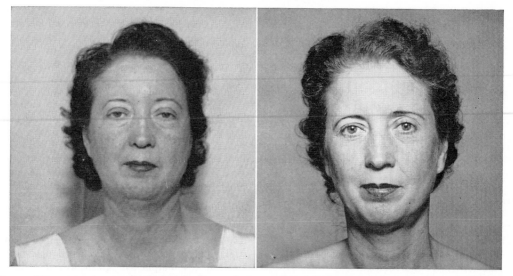

Figure 693.　A patient with Cushing's disease before subtotal adrenalectomy (left) and after subtotal adrenalectomy (right). (Courtesy of Dr. Leonard Posey.)

degree of hypertension, which in most instances is relieved by subtotal removal of the hypersecreting glands.

Effect on Carbohydrate and Protein Metabolism. The abundance of glucocorticoids secreted in Cushing's disease causes increased blood glucose concentration, sometimes to values as high as 140 to 200 milligrams per cent. This effect probably results mainly from enhanced gluconeogenesis. If this "adrenal diabetes" lasts for many months, the beta cells in the islets of Langerhans occasionally "burn out" and cause frank diabetes mellitus, which is then permanent for the remainder of life.

The effects of glucocorticoids on protein catabolism are often profound in Cushing's disease, causing greatly decreased tissue proteins almost everywhere in the body with the exceptions of the liver and the plasma proteins. Even the collagen fibers in the subcutaneous tissue are diminished so that the subcutaneous tissues tear easily, resulting in the development of large *purplish striae;* these are actually scars where the subcutaneous tissues have torn apart. In addition, lack of protein deposition in the bones causes *osteoporosis* with consequent weakness of the bones.

Effects of the Adrenal Sex Hormones. In Cushing's disease the quantities of adrenal sex hormones, the androgens principally, are also increased to significant levels, and these result in typical masculinizing effects in a female (or in a male child), such as growth of a beard, increased deepness of the voice, occasional baldness, growth of the clitoris to resemble a penis or growth of a child's penis to adult proportions. In the male adult with Cushing's disease, the androgenic effects of the adrenal sex hormones will not cause any distinctive changes in the patient because of the much more potent androgenic effects of the normal testicular hormone secretion.

Diagnosis and Treatment of Cushing's Disease. Diagnosis of Cushing's disease is most frequently made on the basis of such typical findings as (a) the buffalo torso, (b) puffiness of the face, (c) masculinizing effects, (d) hypertension, (e) elevated blood glucose concentration that is moderately insulin resistant, and (f) secretion of several times normal quantities of 17-ketosteroids in the urine.

Treatment of Cushing's disease consists of subtotal removal of the adrenal cortices, leaving only the appropriate amount of adrenal tissue to maintain normal function.

Hypersecretion of Individual Hormones

Occasionally, an abnormality of one or more enzyme systems for synthesis of the adrenocortical hormones causes excessive secretion of one or more particular types of adrenocortical hormones. For instance, tumors of the adrenal cortex or congenital absence of one of the enzymes in the adrenal cells can cause excessive secretion of (a) one or more of the adrenal hormones, (b) one of the glucocorticoids, or (c) one of the mineralocorticoids. In these conditions, a person may develop specific ones of the effects noted above in relation to Cushing's disease without having any of the other effects. Three common types of specific hormonal excesses are (1) primary aldosteronism, (2) primary glucocorticoid-hypersecretion, and (3) the adrenogenital syndrome.

Primary Aldosteronism. In primary aldosteronism all the symptoms of Cushing's disease that result from excess mineralocorticoid secretion are seen without the other symptoms. These include particularly *increased extracellular fluid volume, hypertension, hypokalemia, mild alkalosis,* and a *tendency toward hypernatremia.* Ordinarily, the patient has such intense polydipsia that he keeps washing sodium chloride through his kidneys despite a very low concentration of sodium chloride in his urine, and this prevents him from having frank edema in mild cases. However, in severe cases, marked edema does appear. Especially interesting in primary aldosteronism are occasional periods of *muscular paralysis caused by the hypokalemia,* the mechanism of which was explained in Chapter 17.

Primary Excess Glucocorticoid Secretion. Rarely, excess glucocorticoids are secreted without excess secretion of the other adrenocortical hormones. When this occurs, the patient develops (a) adrenal diabetes, (b) signs of protein deficiency, including especially development of purplish striae and osteoporosis, and (c) increased lipogenesis, which results in extreme cases in the buffalo torso.

A high percentage of the patients who secrete excess amounts of glucocorticoids is likely to secrete a reasonable percentage of androgens along with the glucocorticoids. In such an instance, the female patient will develop a beard and other masculinizing effects; the condition is then frequently called *diabetes of bearded women.*

Adrenogenital Syndrome. Tumors of the adrenal cortex that secrete excess adrenal sex hormones, except in rare instances, secrete androgenic hormones that cause intense masculinizing effects throughout the body. For instance, the female will develop extremely virile characteristics, including growth of a beard, development of a much deeper voice, occasionally development of baldness if she also has the genetic inheritance for baldness, development of a masculine distribution of hair on the body and on the pubis, growth of the clitoris to resemble a penis, and deposition of proteins in the skin and especially in the muscles to give typical masculine characteristics.

In the prepubertal male a virilizing adrenal tumor causes the same characteristics as in the female, plus very rapid development of the male sex organs and creation of male sexual desires. Typical development of the male sexual organs in a 4-year-old boy with the adrenogenital syndrome is shown in Fig. 694.

In the adult male, the virilizing characteristics of the adrenogenital syndrome are usually completely obscured by the normal virilizing charac-

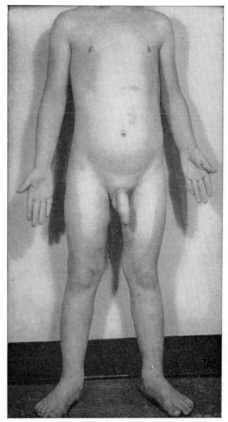

Figure 694. Adrenogenital syndrome in a 4-year-old boy. (Courtesy of Dr. Leonard Posey.)

teristics of the testosterone secreted by the testes. Therefore, it is often difficult to make a diagnosis of adrenogenital syndrome in the male adult. However, an occasional adrenal tumor secretes sufficient quantities of feminizing hormones that the male patient develops *gynecomastia,* which means excessive growth of the male mammary glands. Also, in the adrenogenital syndrome, the secretion of 17-ketosteroids in the urine may be as much as 10 to 15 times normal.

REFERENCES

Bondy, P. K., Ingle, D. J., and Meeks, R. C.: Influence of adrenal cortical hormones upon the level of plasma amino acids in eviscerate rats. *Endocrinology,* 55:354, 1954.

Brodish, A., and Long, C. N.: Changes in blood ACTH under various experimental conditions studied by means of a cross-circulation technique. *Endocrinology,* 59:666, 1956.

Ciba Foundation: Colloquia on Endocrinology. Volume VIII. Human Adrenal Cortex. Boston, Little, Brown and Co., 1955.

Davis, J. O., Bahn, R. C., and Ball, W. C., Jr.: Subacute and chronic effects of hypothalamic lesions on aldosterone and sodium excretion. *Am. J. Physiol.,* 197:387, 1959.

Davis, J. O., Bahn, R. C., Yankopoulos, N. A., Kliman, B., and Peterson, R. E.: Acute effects of hypophysectomy and diencephalic lesions on aldosterone secretion. *Am. J. Physiol.,* 197:380, 1959.

Donovan, B. T., and Harris, G. W.: Pituitary and adrenal glands. *Ann. Rev. Physiol.,* 19:439, 1957.

Engel, F. L., and Fredericks, J.: Contribution to understanding of mechanism of permissive action of corticoids. *Proc. Soc. Exp. Biol. & Med.,* 94:593, 1957.

Farrell, G. L.: Regulation of aldosterone secretion. *Physiol. Rev.,* 38:709, 1958.

Farrell, G. L., Banks, R. C., and Koletsky, S.: The effect of corticosteroid injection on aldosterone secretion. *Endocrinology,* 58:104, 1956.

Farrell, G. L., and Laqueur, G.: Reduction of pituitary output of ACTH by cortisone. *Endocrinology,* 56:471, 1955.

Forsham, P.: Symposium on Adrenal Steroids. New York, Grune & Stratton, Inc., 1958.

Gallagher, T. F.: Steroid hormone metabolism and the control of adrenal secretion. *Harvey Lect.,* 52: 1, 1956–1957.

Ganong, W., and Forsham, P. H.: Adenohypophysis and adrenal cortex. *Ann. Rev. of Physiol.,* 22:579, 1960.

Gardner, L. I.: Adrenal Function in Infants and Children. New York, Grune & Stratton, Inc., 1956.

Germuth, F. G., Jr.: The role of adrenocortical steroids in infection, immunity, and hypersensitivity. *Pharmacol. Rev.,* 8:1, 1956.

Grollman, A. P., and Gambel, J. L., Jr.: Metabolic alkalosis, a specific effect of adrenocortical hormones. *Am. J. Physiol.,* 196:135, 1959.

Guillemin, R.: A reevaluation of acetylcholine, adrenaline, noradrenaline, and histamine as possible mediators of the pituitary adrenocorticotrophic activation by stress. *Endocrinology,* 56: 248, 1955.

Hechter, O., and Pincus, G.: Genesis of adrenocortical secretion. *Physiol. Rev.,* 34:459, 1954.

Hepps, S. A., Hartman, F. A., and Brownell, K. A.: Effect of cortisone and desoxycorticosterone on distribution of radioactive potassium in the adrenalectomized rat. *Am. J. Physiol.,* 196:153, 1959.

Hewlett, J. S., McCullagh, E. P., Farrell, G. L., Dustan, H. P., Poutasse, E. F., and Proudfit, W. L.: Aldosterone-producing tumors of the adrenal gland; report of 3 cases. *J.A.M.A.,* 164:719, 1957.

Ingle, D. J.: Physiological and Therapeutic Effects of Corticotropin and Cortisone. Springfield, Illinois, Charles C Thomas, 1953.

Ingle, D. J.: The role of the adrenal cortex in homeostasis. *Pediatrics,* 17:407, 1956.

International Symposium on Aldosterone (An). Boston, Little, Brown and Co., 1958.

Jailer, J. W.: Hydrocortisone, its newer analogs and alelosterone as therapeutic agents. *Ann. N. Y. Acad. Sc.,* 1955.

Jones, I. C.: The Adrenal Cortex. New York, Cambridge University Press, 1957.

Laborit, H.: Stress and Cellular Function. Philadelphia, J. B. Lippincott Co., 1959.

Liu, T. Y., Brownell, K. A., and Hartman, F. A.: Production of androgenic hormone by the adrenal. *Am. J. Physiol.,* 180:50, 1955.

Long, C. N. H.: Pituitary-adrenal relationships. *Ann. Rev. Physiol.,* 18:409, 1956.

McCann, S. M., and Brobeck, J. R.: Evidence for a role of the supraopticohypophyseal system in regulation of adrenocorticotrophin secretion. *Proc. Soc. Exp. Biol. & Med.,* 87:318, 1954.

Miller, A. T., Jr.: Comparison of some commonly-used indices of adrenal cortical function. *J. Appl. Physiol.,* 7:660, 1955.

Miller, A. T., Jr.: Eosinophil response to graded doses of ACTH and cortisone in man. *J. Appl. Physiol.,* 7:663, 1955.

Mills, J. N., and Thomas, S.: The influence of adrenal corticoids on phosphate and glucose exchange in muscle and liver in man. *J. Physiol.,* 148:227, 1959.

Muller, A. F., and O'Conner, C. M.: Aldosterone. Boston, Little, Brown and Co., 1958.

Overman, R. R., Davis, A. K., and Bass, A. C.: Effects of cortisone and DCA on radiosodium transport in normal and adrenalectomized dogs. *Am. J. Physiol.,* 167:333, 1951.

Rauschkolb, E. W., and Farrell, G. L.: Evidence for diencephalic regulation of aldosterone secretion. *Endocrinology,* 59:526, 1956.

Rauschkolb, E. W., Farrell, G. L., and Koletsky, S.: Aldosterone secretion after hypophysectomy. *Am. J. Physiol.,* 184:55, 1956.

Remington, J. W.: Circulatory factors in adrenal crisis in dog. *Am. J. Physiol.,* 165:306, 1951.

Rochefort, G. J., Rosenberger, J., and Saffran, M.: Depletion of pituitary corticotrophin by various stresses and by neurohypophysial preparations. *J. Physiol.,* 146:105, 1959.

Rolf, D., and White, H. L.: Tissue potassium retention in adrenal insufficiency. *Am. J. Physiol.,* 182: 393, 1955.

Rosnagle, R. S., and Farrell, G. L.: Alterations in electrolyte intake and adrenal steroid secretion. *Am. J. Physiol.,* 187:7, 1956.

Ross, E. J.: Aldosterone in Clinical and Experimental Medicine. Springfield, Illinois, Charles C Thomas, 1959.

Saffran, M., and Saffran, J.: Adenohypophysis and adrenal cortex. *Ann. Rev. Physiol.,* 21:403, 1959.

Santos, R. F.: Extrarenal action of adrenal glands on potassium metabolism. *Am. J. Physiol.,* 197:643, 1959.

Sayers, G., Redgate, E. S., and Royce, P. C.: Hypothalamus, adenohypophysis, and adrenal cortex. *Ann. Rev. Physiol.,* 20:243, 1958.

Simmons, D. H., Harvey, R. B., and Hoshiko, T.: Role of adrenal and hypophysis in regulation of sodium excretion. *Am. J. Physiol.,* 181:379, 1955.

Skelton, F. R.: Adrenal regeneration and adrenal-regeneration hypertension. *Physiol. Rev.,* 39:162, 1959.

Tilton, M. M., Torralba, G., and Ingle, D. J.: Effect of hydrocortisone on the level of plasma amino acids after removal of the intra-abdominal organs in the rat. *Metabolism,* 4:424, 1955.

Tompkins, M. J., Eckman, E., and Share, L.: Extrarenal action of the adrenal cortex on electrolyte metabolism in nephrectomized and nephrectomized-eviscerated rats. *Am. J. Physiol.,* 196:141, 1959.

dides and tryosine. Therefore, it is likely that thyrotropin has some still yet undiscovered primary effect that causes all these generalized increases in thyroid function.

Hypothalamic Regulation of Thyrotropin Secretion by the Adenohypophysis. Electrical stimulation of the anterior hypothalamus, especially in the upper portion of the median eminence or slightly above this region, increases the output of thyrotropin and thereby causes a corresponding increase in activity of the thyroid gland. Conversely, lesions in this same region slightly reduce the normal output of thyrotropin and prevent the adenohypophysis from responding to physical and mental stresses that ordinarily increase thyrotropin secretion. Therefore, the hypothalamus has the ability to control at least partially the adenohypophyseal secretion of thyrotropin. This control is believed to be exerted by hypothalamic secretion of *thyrotropin-releasing factor* (TRF) into the hypophyseal portal blood, and this factor in turn acts on the adenohypophyseal glandular cells to increase the output of thyrotropin. Control of the adenohypophysis by the hypothalamus was discussed in detail in Chapter 73. When the portal system from the hypothalamus to the adenohypophysis is completely blocked, the output of thyrotropin is greatly decreased, though not entirely stopped.

Effect of cold and other neurogenic stimuli in increasing thyrotropin secretion. One of the best known stimuli for increasing the rate of thyrotropin secretion by the adenohypophysis is exposure of an animal to cold. Exposure for several weeks increases the output of thyroxine sometimes more than 100 per cent and can increase the basal metabolic rate of the animal 20 to 30 per cent. Indeed, even human beings moving to arctic regions develop basal metabolic rates 15 to 20 per cent above normal.

In addition to cold, various emotional reactions, especially those that stimulate the sympathetic nervous system, can also increase the output of thyrotropin. This could explain the very high incidence of thyrotoxic goiter in persons who have recently had serious emotional disturbances. Also, it is interesting that thyrotoxic goiter is far more common in cold climates than in warm climates.

The effects of cold and emotions on thy-

rotropin secretion are completely blocked when the hypophyseal portal system is occluded or when lesions are present in the anterior hypothalamus at the upper level of the median eminence.

Inverse Effect of Thyroxine on the Hypophyseal Secretion of Thyrotropin— Feedback Regulation of the Metabolic Rate. Increased quantities of thyroxine in the body fluids decrease the secretion of thyrotropin by the adenohypophysis. Since this effect is lost, or almost lost, when appropriate areas of the hypothalamus are destroyed, it is nearly certain that the inhibitory effect of thyroxine on the adenohypophysis is mediated through the hypothalamus. That is, increased thyroxine increases the rate of metabolism in the hypothalamus; this decreases the hypothalamic stimulation of the adenohypophysis, which decreases the secretion of thyrotropin. Conversely, decreased thyroxine causes the opposite effects, with resultant increase in thyrotropin secretion.

Thus, it is evident that the inverse effect of thyroxine on the adenohypophysis constitutes a feedback mechanism for regulating the metabolic rate of the body, always maintaining this at an appropriate level for most advantageous function of the metabolic systems. These interrelationships of the hypothalamus, adenohypophysis, and thyroid gland are illustrated in Figure 700.

Other Effects of Thyrotropin. Aside from the effect of thyrotropin on the thyroid

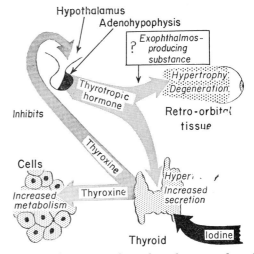

Figure 700. Interrelationships between thyroid secretion of thyroxine and thyrotropin secretion by the adenohypophysis.

gland, administration of very large quantities of this hormone to experimental animals causes fatty infiltration of skeletal muscles, loss of muscle striations, and degeneration of the muscle fibers. For this reason, it is believed by some clinicians that the extreme weakness which often occurs in hyperthyroidism is not necessarily caused by excess thyroxine but instead by excess thyrotropin. Experimentally, the quantity of thyrotropin needed to cause degeneration of muscle fibers is far greater than the quantity of thyrotropin believed to be secreted even in thyrotoxicosis. Therefore, it is still doubtful that thyrotropin is the cause of muscular weakness in human beings.

" Exophthalmos - producing substance " and its relationship to thyrotropin. Often associated with thyrotoxicosis is the disease of the eyes called *exophthalmos.* In the past, this has been ascribed to thyrotropin, but more recently another hormone, *exophthalmos-producing substance,* which seems to be secreted by the adenohypophysis along with thyrotropin in most instances of thyrotoxicosis, has been shown to have this effect, while highly purified thyrotropin has little such effect.

Exophthalmos is characterized by progressive forward protrusion of the eyes, resulting from hypertrophy and swelling of the retro-orbital tissues. In some instances, increased quantities of fat and fibrous tissues are also laid down in the orbit, and the extraocular muscles have at times been noted to swell to sizes as great as eight times normal. The increased mass of tissue behind the eyes causes them to protrude forward.

The Liver in the Regulation of Thyroid Activity. In addition to the adenohypophyseal control of thyroid secretion, the liver can remove excess thyroid hormone from the circulation when a great excess is secreted or injected. Even normally a small quantity of thyroxine is degraded by the liver or conjugated and excreted into the bile, but most of this excreted thyroxine is then reabsorbed and still used by the body. However, in times of excess, the amount of thyroxine degraded and permanently excreted into the feces becomes considerably enhanced. Therefore, it has been suggested that the liver acts as a relief valve to release great excesses of thyroxine.

Antithyroid Substances

Drugs that suppress thyroid secretion are called *antithyroid substances.* The three best known of these are: (1) thiocyanate, (2) propylthiouracil, and (3) high concentrations of inorganic iodides. The mechanism by which each of these blocks thyroid secretion is different from the others, and they can be explained as follows:

Decreased Iodide Trapping Caused by Thiocyanate Ions. Administration of thiocyanates decreases the rate at which iodide is pumped into the thyroid glandular cells, and, therefore, reduces the availability of iodides to the intracellular processes for the formation of thyroxine.

Lack of formation of thyroxine by the gland under the influence of thiocyanates causes the thyroid gland to enlarge—that is, to become a "goiter." The mechanism of this is the following: Lack of thyroxine decreases the metabolic rate, which in turn increases the secretion of thyrotropin by the adenohypophysis. This then stimulates the glandular cells in the thyroid, making them secrete more and more proteinaceous material into the follicles, even though this does not contain significant quantities of conjugated thyroxine. Other goitrogenic agents will be discussed later in the chapter.

Depression of Thyroid Hormone Formation by Propylthiouracil. Propylthiouracil prevents formation of thyroid hormones from intracellular iodides and tyrosine. The precise mechanism by which this occurs is not known, but two different suggestions have been offered: First, it has been suggested that propylthiouracil decreases the quantity of peroxidase available to convert iodides into an oxidized form of iodine. Second, it has been suggested that propylthiouracil competes with tyrosine for the elemental iodine and therefore prevents its availability for formation of the thyroid hormones. In either instance, thyroid hormones are not formed, but, instead, large quantities of globulin continue to be secreted into the follicles without concomitant conjugated thyroxine. Therefore, under the influence of propylthiouracil the thyroid gland also enlarges to form a goiter.

Other substances that have almost identical activity as propylthiouracil are thiouracil, thiourea, and a number of compounds that have aminobenzene groupings. Most of these others have significant toxic side effects, including especially agranulocytosis, which have made propylthiouracil the drug of choice. However, a new drug, *2-methylmercaptoimidazole,* is very effective and seems to have very low toxicity.

Decrease in Thyroid Activity Caused by Iodides. When iodides are present in the blood in very high concentration, all activities of the thyroid gland seem to be decreased. The rate of iodide trapping is reduced, the rate of thyroid hormone formation is decreased, the secretory activity of the thyroid cells is decreased, and the rate of thyroxine release from thyroglobulin is decreased. Since these are almost exactly opposite to the effects of thyrotropin on the thyroid gland, it is believed that high concentrations of iodides in the blood have a direct inhibitory effect on thyrotropin, or it is even possible that iodides inhibit the hypothalamus to reduce the rate of production of thyrotropin, which has been shown to occur in at least certain experimental preparations.

Because iodides decrease all phases of thyroid activity, they decrease the size of the thyroid gland in contradistinction to the increase in size caused by most of the other antithyroid agents. For this reason, iodides are very frequently administered to patients for two to three weeks prior to surgical removal of the thyroid gland to reduce its size and, therefore, to decrease the necessary amount of surgery.

INTERRELATIONSHIPS OF THE THYROID GLAND AND OTHER ENDOCRINE GLANDS

Increased thyroxine secretion increases the rates of secretion of almost all the other endocrine glands of the body, but it also increases the need of the tissues for hormones. For instance, increased thyroxine secretion increases the rate of glucose metabolism everywhere in the body and therefore causes a corresponding need for increased insulin secretion by the pancreas. Also, thyroxine increases many metabolic activities related to bone formation and, as a consequence, increases the need for parathyroid hormone. However, in addition to these general effects, thyroxine has relatively specific effects on the adrenal cortex and on the gonads.

Effect of Thyroxine on the Secretion of Adrenocortical Hormones. Administration of thyroxine increases the rate of glucocorticoid secretion by the adrenal cortex in the following manner: Thyroxine inhibits the production of thyrotropin by the adenohypophysis, but this causes the opposite effect on the secretion of corticotropin, increasing its secretion and thereby also increasing glucocorticoid secretion by the adrenal cortex.

On the other hand, when neurogenic stimuli increase the rate of thyroxine secretion, this is usually accompanied by a decrease in glucocorticoid secretion. The reason for this is that, when the neurogenic stimuli stimulate the adenohypophysis to increase its production of thyrotropin, this decrease is accomplished, along with a corresponding decrease in corticotropin secretion and, consequently, decreased secretion of glucocorticoids by the adrenal cortex.

Basically, then, in most instances the secretion of thyrotropin and of corticotropin by the adenohypophysis are inversely related to each other.

Because of this inverse relationship, it is possible that much of the muscle weakness and other symptoms of thyrotoxicosis might be caused by diminished secretion of adrenocortical hormones.

Effect of Thyroxine on the Gonads. For normal sexual function to occur, thyroid secretion needs to be approximately normal, neither too great nor too little. In the male, for instance, lack of thyroxine is likely to cause complete loss of libido, while, on the other hand, great excesses of thyroxine frequently cause impotence. In the female, lack of thyroxine often causes *menorrhagia* and *polymenorrhea*, which mean, respectively, excessive and frequent bleeding. In other women the lack may cause irregular periods and occasionally, even total *amenorrhea*. A hypothyroid female, like the male, is also likely to have greatly decreased libido. Conversely, in the hyperthyroid female, *oligomenorrhea*, which means greatly reduced bleeding, is usual, and, occasionally, amenorrhea results.

Therefore, it can be seen that the action of thyroxine on the gonads cannot be pinpointed to a specific function but probably results from a combination of direct metabolic effects of thyroxine on the gonads and of excitatory and inhibitory effects operating through the adenohypophysis.

DISEASES OF THE THYROID

Hyperthyroidism

Most of the effects of hyperthyroidism are obvious from the preceding discussion of the various physiologic effects of thyroid hormone. However, some specific effects should be mentioned in connection especially with the development, the diagnosis, and the treatment of hyperthyroidism.

It is believed that essentially all patients with toxic, hyperplastic goiter develop the disease as a result of excessive production of thyrotropic hormone by the adenohypophysis. If this is true, hyperthyroidism is actually an abnormality of the adenohypophysis rather than an intrinsic abnormality of the thyroid gland. Yet, the cause of the excessive secretion of thyrotropic hormone is usually unknown. Hyperthyroidism frequently follows severe physical or emotional disturbances; it occurs several times as frequently in cold climates as in hot climates, and it often occurs in successive generations of the same family.

Characteristics of Hyperthyroidism (Toxic Goiter, Thyrotoxicosis, Graves' Disease). In hyperthyroidism, the thyroid gland is usually increased to two to three times normal size. This slight increase in size is not an indication, however, of the actual increase in rate of thyroid hormone secretion, for thyrotropic hor-

Figure 701. Patient with exophthalmic hyperthyroidism. Note protrusion of the eyes and retraction of the superior eyelids. The BMR was +40. (Courtesy of Dr. Leonard Posey.)

mone causes tremendous infolding of the follicular cells into the follicles so that the number of cells is greatly increased without greatly increasing the size of the gland. Also, thyrotropic hormone probably causes each cell to increase its rate of secretion tremendously. Studies with radioactive iodine indicate that such hyperplastic glands secrete thyroxine at a rate as great as 5 to 15 times normal.

The symptoms of toxic goiter—these are obvious from the preceding discussion of the physiology of the thyroid hormone—are intolerance to heat, increased sweating, mild to extreme weight loss (sometimes as much as 100 pounds), varying degrees of diarrhea, muscular weakness, nervousness or other psychic disorders, and tremor of the hands.

Exophthalmos. In addition to its effect on the thyroid gland, thyrotropic hormone or the closely associated hormone, *exophthalmos-producing substance*, also causes hypertrophy of the tissues behind the eyeballs, an effect that has already been discussed in detail. Most persons with toxic goiter will have at least some degree of *exophthalmos* (protrusion of the eyeballs), as illustrated in Figure 701, though a major degree of exophthalmos occurs in only about one third to one half of the patients. Sometimes the exophthalmos develops so rapidly that the patient actually becomes blind owing to stretching of the optic nerve fibers.

When thyrotoxicosis is treated either by the use of thyroid inhibitors or by removal of the gland, the exophthalmos may increase in severity, for thyroxine secreted by the gland will have been inhibiting to a certain extent the production of thyrotropic hormone and exophthalmos-producing factor by the adenohypophysis, and this inhibition no longer occurs after the formation of thyroxine is depressed. Indeed, when exophthalmos is so severe that it is likely to cause blindness, it is occasionally treated by administering thyroxine to the patient, which obviously makes the thyrotoxicosis worse but depresses the formation of thyrotropic hormone and exophthalmos-producing factor and, consequently, helps prevent further development of the exophthalmos.

One of the effects of exophthalmos is that the superior eyelids have difficulty closing over the protruding eyes. This results from the anatomic arrangement of the orbicularis oculi muscles, for these muscles do not have appropriate mechanical advantage for causing the superior lid to pull down over the eye when the eye is protruding too far forward. The failure of the superior lid to close over the eye frequently leads to corneal ulcerations.

Return to normal production of thyrotropic hormone does not cause the exophthalmic eye to recess back into the orbit. Therefore, once developed, the condition is permanent. If a tendency to blindness persists or if the eye movements are greatly impaired, the superior orbital plates beneath the frontal lobes of the brain can be removed, allowing the contents of the orbits to decompress into the cerebral vault. As a result, the eyes recess.

Diagnostic Tests for Hyperthyroidism. Protein - bound iodine. Essentially all the iodine bound with proteins of the blood is thyroxine iodine, and the normal person has between 4 and 7.5 micrograms of plasma-bound iodine per 100 ml. of plasma. In hyperthyroidism this level increases in proportion to the degree of hyperthyroidism—sometimes to 15 to 20 mg. %. The plasma-bound iodine test is an effective means for making a diagnosis in approximately 85 to 90 per cent of patients with hyperthyroidism, but it occasionally is in error owing to the presence of other iodine compounds in the plasma.

The basal metabolic rate. The basal metabolic rate is usually increased to approximately +40 to +60 in severe hyperthyroidism. A mild increase in basal metabolic rate does not necessarily mean hyperthyroidism. Indeed, an increased basal metabolic rate correctly indicates hyperthyroidism in only 60 per cent of the cases; other factors which were discussed in Chapter 68 can also cause changes in the basal metabolic rate even though thyroid hormone production is normal.

Uptake of radioactive iodine. Another method for measuring the rate of activity of the thyroid gland is to determine its rate of radioactive iodine uptake. A small test dose of radioactive iodine is given intravenously, and the rate of uptake by the thyroid gland is measured by a calibrated radioactive detector placed over the thyroid gland. In the normal person, an average of 4 per cent of the injected radioactive iodine is assimilated by the thyroid gland per hour. In the hyperthyroid patient, as much as 20 to 25 per cent is assimilated per hour.

Physiology of Treatment in Hyperthyroidism. The most direct treatment for hyperthyroidism is surgical removal of the thyroid gland. In general, however, it is desirable to prepare the patient for surgical removal of the gland prior to the operation. This is done by administering propylthiouracil, sometimes for as long as several months, until the basal metabolic rate of the patient has returned to normal and then administration of high concentrations of iodides for two to three weeks immediately prior to operation to cause the gland itself to recede in size. By using these preoperative procedures the operative mortality is less than 1 in 1,000 in the better hospitals, whereas prior to development of these preoperative procedures the operative mortality was as great as 1 in 25.

Treatment of the hyperplastic thyroid with radioactive iodine. As much as 80 to 90 per cent of an injected dose of iodides is absorbed by the hyperplastic, toxic thyroid gland within a day after injection. If this injected iodine is radioactive, it can destroy internally the secretory cells of the thyroid gland. Usually approximately 5 millicuries of radioactive iodine is given to the patient, and then his condition is reassessed several weeks later. If he is still hyperthyroid, an additional dose is given, and this is repeated until he reaches a normal thyroid status. These quantities of radioiodine are about 1000 times as great as those used for diagnosis of hyperthyroidism as discussed above.

Thyroid Storm. Occasionally, patients with extremely severe thyrotoxicosis develop a state called *thyroid storm* or *thyroid crisis* in which all the usual symptoms of thyrotoxicosis are excessively accentuated. The effects may be delirium, high fever, abnormal rhythm of the heart, extreme sweating, shock, vomiting, and dehydration. This condition is particularly likely to occur during the first day following surgical removal of a large hyperplastic thyroid gland, presumably because of excessive release of thyroxine into the circulatory system during the operative procedure. The extreme overactivity of the body's tissues can be so damaging that without treatment almost all persons entering this state die. However, by rapidly cooling the patient with ice or alcohol sponge baths and also administration of large quantities of adrenocortical hormones, it is now possible to save approximately half the patients. The adrenocortical hormones seem to be especially important, for, in some way not yet understood, they allow rapid repair of the damaged metabolic systems of the body.

Thyroid Adenoma. A localized, adenomatous tumor occasionally develops in the thyroid gland and sometimes secretes large quantities of thyroid hormone, causing hyperthyroidism. Also, secretion by the tumor is usually independent of control by thyrotropic hormone from the adenohypophysis. Consequently, administration of iodine to the patient is not effective in treatment of the condition, though other drugs such as the thyroid inhibitors may be partially effective. As long as the adenoma continues to secrete thyroxine, function of the remainder of the thyroid gland may be almost totally inhibited because thyroxine from the adenoma depresses the production of thyrotropic hormone from the pituitary gland. After the adenoma is removed, several weeks to several months are required for return of the remainder of the gland to normal function.

Hypothyroidism

The effects of hypothyroidism in general are opposite to those of hyperthyroidism, but here again, a few physiologic mechanisms peculiar to hypothyroidism alone are involved.

Endemic Colloid Goiter. The term "goiter" means a greatly enlarged thyroid gland. In the discussion of iodine metabolism, it was pointed out that 35 to 50 mg. of iodine are necessary each year for the formation of adequate quantities of thyroxine. In certain areas of the world, notably in the Swiss Alps and in the Great Lakes region of the United States, insufficient iodine is present in the soil for the foodstuffs to contain even this minute quantity of iodine. Therefore, in days prior to fortification of table salt with iodine, many persons living in these areas developed extremely large thyroid glands called *endemic goiters.*

The mechanism for development of the large endemic goiters apparently is the following: lack of iodine prevents production of thyroxine by the thyroid gland, and, as a result, no thyroxine is available to inhibit production of thyrotropic hormone by the anterior pituitary gland; this allows the anterior pituitary gland to secrete excessively large quantities of thyrotropic hormone. The thyroid gland grows larger and larger, but unfortunately, due to lack of iodine, increased thyroxine secretion does not occur, and the production of thyrotropic hormone is never inhibited.

The substance that is secreted into the follicles in endemic goiter is an incomplete form of thyroglobulin having a "colloid" (mucoid) consistency. The follicles become tremendous in size, and the whole thyroid gland may increase to as large as 500 to 700 grams or more.

Idiopathic Non-toxic Colloid Goiter. Enlarged thyroid glands almost identical to those of endemic colloid goiter frequently develop even though the affected persons receive sufficient quantities of iodine in their diets. These goitrous glands may secrete normal quantities of thyroxine but more frequently the secretion of thyroxine is depressed, as in endemic colloid goiter.

The exact cause of idiopathic colloid goiter is not known, though animals fed large quantities of certain foods are known to develop enlarged thyroid glands. These foods contain so-called goitrogenic substances, the actions of which are similar to those of propylthiouacil, which was discussed above. Especially are goitrogenic substances found in some varieties of turnips and cabbages. However, it has not yet been proved that the diet can ever contain enough quantities of goitrogenic substances to cause a large, idiopathic colloid goiter.

Another possible cause of this type of goiter is a neoplastic change of the thyroid cells. That is, the cells become tumor cells that secrete the colloid substance, but because of altered intracellular enzyme systems fail to form the thyroid hormones.

Regardless of the cause of the goiter it is possible that depressed thyroxine production allows the anterior pituitary gland to secrete greater than normal quantities of thyrotropic hormone and that it is actually the thyrotropic hormone that causes the gland to enlarge.

Characteristics of Hypothyroidism. Whether hypothyroidism is due to endemic colloid goiter, idiopathic colloid goiter, destruction of the thyroid gland by irradiation, removal of the thyroid gland by surgery, or destruction of the thyroid gland by various other diseases, the physiologic effects are the same. These include extreme somnolence with sleeping 14 to 16 hours a day, extreme muscular sluggishness, slowed heart rate, decreased cardiac output, decreased blood volume, increased weight, constipation, mental sluggishness, failure of many tropic functions in the body evidenced by depressed growth of hair and scaliness of the skin, development of a frog-like, husky voice, and, in severe cases, development of an edematous appearance throughout the body.

Myxedema. The patient with almost total lack of thyroid function develops an edematous appearance, and the condition is known as "myxedema." Figure 702 shows such a patient, with bogginess under the eyes and swelling of the face. Considerable quantities of proteins collect in the interstitial spaces, either in the form of increased tissue fibers or of a so-called deposit protein; and the total quantity of interstitial fluid also increases throughout the body, the fluid is supposedly adsorbed to the excess tissue proteins. These effects are believed to result from sluggish utilization of proteins by the hypothyroid patient. Because of the protein in the interstitial fluid, the

Figure 702.   Patient with myxedema. (Courtesy of Dr. Herbert Langford.)

excess fluid is relatively immobile, and the edema is non-pitting in type.

Arteriosclerosis in hypothyroidism. It was pointed out in the chapter on fats that lack of thyroid hormone increases the quantity of blood lipids and that an increase in blood lipids is usually associated with atherosclerosis and arteriosclerosis. Therefore, many hypothyroid patients, particularly those with myxedema, develop severe arteriosclerosis, which results in peripheral vascular disease, deafness, and often extreme coronary sclerosis and, consequently, an early demise.

Diagnostic tests in hypothyroidism. The tests already described for diagnosis of hyperthyroidism give the opposite results in hypothyroidism. The BMR in myxedema ranges between −40 and −50, the protein-bound iodine is less than 2 micrograms per 100 ml. of plasma instead of the normal 4 to 7.5, and the rate of radioactive iodine uptake by the thyroid gland ranges less than 1 per cent per hour rather than the normal of approximately 4 per cent per hour. Probably more important for diagnosis, however, than the various diagnostic tests are the characteristic symptoms of hypothyroidism as discussed above.

Treatment of Hypothyroidism. Figure 698 (p. 1017) shows the effect of thyroid hormone on the basal metabolic rate, illustrating that the thyroid hormone normally has a duration of action of more than one month. Consequently, it is easy to maintain a steady level of thyroid hormone activity in the body by daily oral ingestion of a single tablet of desiccated thyroid or thyroid extract, and treatment even once a week is satisfactory provided that a sufficient dose is administered. Furthermore, proper treatment of the hypothyroid patient results in such complete normality that myxedematous patients properly treated have lived into the 90's after treatment for over 50 years.

When a patient with myxedema is first treated, an immediate diuresis ensues, presumably owing to removal of the myxedematous fluid from the interstitial spaces after the protein in this fluid is metabolized. Also, an immediate negative nitrogen balance occurs until the excess protein of the tissue spaces is used up. Obviously, treatment increases the activity in the circulatory system, and, if the patient has already developed severe heart disease, the increased activity of the heart may lead to anginal pain. On the other hand. lack of treatment may lead to increased severity of the heart disease. In this instance the clinician is in a dilemma and must proceed with progressive treatment very slowly if at all.

Unfortunately, no physiologic means have been found for causing greatly enlarged colloid goiters to regress in size except to a minor extent. Consequently, only surgery is adequate for removal of the unsightly enlarged gland.

Cretinism. Cretinism is the condition caused by extreme hypothyroidism during infancy and childhood, and it is characterized especially by failure of growth. Cretinism results either from congenital lack of a thyroid gland (*congenital cretinism*) or from failure of the thyroid gland to produce thyroxine because of iodine lack in the diet (*endemic cretinism*). The severity of endemic cretinism varies tremendously in accordance with the amount of iodine in the diet, and whole populaces of an endemic area have been known to have cretinoid tendencies.

A newborn baby without a thyroid gland may have absolutely normal appearance and function because he has been supplied with thyroxine by the mother while *in utero*, but a few weeks after birth his movements become very sluggish, and both his physical and mental growth are greatly retarded. Treatment of the cretin at any time will usually cause normal return of physical growth, but, unless the cretin is treated within a few months after birth, his mental growth will be permanently retarded. This is probably due to the fact that physical development of the neuronal cells of the central nervous system is very rapid during the first year of life so that any retardation at this point is extremely detrimental.

Skeletal growth in the cretin is characteristically more inhibited than is soft tissue growth, though both are inhibited to a certain extent. However, as a result of this disproportionate rate of growth, the soft tissues are likely to enlarge excessively, giving the cretin the appearance of a very obese and stocky, short child; this obesity is due to enlargement of the soft tissue organs such as the liver, the gastrointestinal tract, etc. Indeed, occasionally the tongue becomes so large

in relation to the skeletal growth that it obstructs swallowing and breathing, inducing a characteristic guttural breathing and sometimes even choking the baby.

REFERENCES

Astwood, E. B.: Symposium on Thyroid Disorders. New York, Grune & Stratton, Inc., 1957.

Barker, S. B.: Thyroid. *Ann. Rev. Physiol.*, 17:417, 1955.

Brunton, C.: Exophthalmos. *Physiol. Rev.*, 29:260, 1949.

Ciba Foundation: Colloquia on Endocrinology. Volume X. Regulation and Mode of Action of Thyroid Hormones. Boston, Little, Brown and Co., 1957.

Cottle, W., and Carlson, L. D.: Turnover of thyroid hormone in cold-exposed rats determined by radioactive iodine studies. *Endocrinology*, 59:1, 1956.

D'Angelo, S. A., Paschkis, K. E., Gordon, A. S., and Cantarow, A.: Thyroid-thyrotropic hormone balance in blood of normal and endocrinopathic individuals. *J. Clin. Endocrinol.*, 11:1137, 1951.

Essex, H. E.: Exophthalmos in hypophysectomized and cortisone-treated albino rats. *Am. J. Physiol.*, 181:375, 1955.

Ficarra, B. J.: Diseases of the Thyroid and Parathyroid Glands. New York, Grune & Stratton, Inc., 1958.

Fredrickson, D. S., Ganong, W. F., and Hume, D. M.: Thyroid uptake of radioactive iodine in the dog; effect of diet, hypophysectomy, and TSH. *Proc. Soc. Exp. Biol. & Med.*, 89:416, 1955.

Ganong, W. F., Fredrickson, D. S., and Hume, D. M.: The effect of hypothalamic lesions on thyroid function in the dog. *Endocrinology*, 57:355, 1955.

Gargill, S. L., and Lesses, M. F.: Diseases of the Thyroid Gland. New York, Oxford University Press, 1955.

Gorbman, A.: Some aspects of the comparative biochemistry of iodine utilization and the evolution of thyroidal function. *Physiol. Rev.*, 35:336, 1955.

Kalant, H., Lee, R., and Sellers, E. A.: Metabolic fate of radioactive thyroid hormones in normal and propylthiouracil-treated rats. *Endocrinology*, 56: 127, 1955.

Levitt, R.: The Thyroid. Edinburgh, Livingstone, 1954.

Levitt, T.: Thyroid. Baltimore, Williams & Wilkins Co., 1954.

McClendon, J. F., Foster, W. C., and Bosshardt, D. K.: Conditions of formation of the thyroid hormone outside the thyroid gland. *Arch. Internat. Pharmacodyn.*, 96:304, 1954.

Michel, R.: Thyroid. *Ann. Rev. Physiol.*, 18:457, 1956.

Pittman, C. S., and Barker, S. B.: Antithyroxine effects of some thyroxine analogues. *Am. J. Physiol.*, 197:1271, 1959.

Pitt-Rivers, R., and Tata, J.: The Chemistry of Thyroid Disease. Springfield, Illinois, Charles C Thomas, 1960.

Roche, J., and Michel, R.: Nature, biosynthesis and metabolism of thyroid hormone. *Physiol. Rev.*, 35: 583, 1955.

Selenkow, H. A., and Asper, S. P., Jr.: Biological activity of compounds structurally related to thyroxine. *Physiol. Rev.*, *35:*426, 1955.

Soderberg, Ulf: Temporal characteristics of thyroid activity. *Physiol. Rev.*, *39:*777, 1959.

Solomon, D. H., and Dowling, J. T.: The thyroid. *Ann. Rev. Physiol.*, *22:*615, 1960.

Vanderlaan, W. P., and Storrie, V. M.: A survey of the factors controlling thyroid function, with especial reference to newer views on antithyroid substances. *Pharmacol. Rev.*, *7:*301, 1955.

Van Middlesworth, L.: Goiter production and prevention in rats. *Science, 121:*871, 1955.

Van Middlesworth, L.: Radioactive iodide uptake of normal newborn infants. *Am. J. Dis. Child., 88:*439, 1954.

Van Middlesworth, L., and Intoccia, A. P.: Metabolism of dietary iodine as revealed by I^{131} balance studies. *Metabolism, 6:*1, 1957.

Weinstein, E. J., and Lein, A.: The response of isolated rat diaphragm to thyroxine in vitro. *Endocrinology, 61:*79, 1957.

Werner, S. C.: The Thyroid. New York, Paul B. Hoeber, 1956.

See also Chapter 73, General bibliography on endocrinology.

Chapter 76

Insulin, Glucagon, and Diabetes Mellitus

The pancreas, in addition to its digestive functions, secretes two hormones, insulin and glucagon, the first of which has proved to be extremely important in regulation of metabolic processes in the body and the second of which has considerable effect on metabolism, though its exact role in the over-all picture of metabolic regulation is yet unknown. The purpose of this chapter is principally to discuss the functions of insulin, regulation of its secretion, and the two diseases, *diabetes mellitus* and *hyperinsulinism,* caused, respectively, by hyposecretion of insulin and excess secretion of insulin.

Physiologic Anatomy of the Pancreas. The pancreas is composed of two major types of tissues, as shown in Figure 703: (1) the *acini,* which secrete digestive juices into the duodenum, and (2) the *islets of Langerhans,* which do not have any means for emptying their secretions externally but instead secrete insulin and glucagon directly into the blood. The digestive secretions of the pancreas have already been discussed in Chapter 62.

The islets of Langerhans of the human being contain two major types of cells, the *alpha* and *beta* cells, which are distinguished from one another by their morphology and staining characteristics; in some animals still other types, known as gamma and delta cells, are also present.

From pathologic studies in animals and patients who have very little or no pancreatic secretion of insulin, it has become almost certain that the beta cells of the islets of Langerhans produce insulin. However, glucagon is not secreted by the beta cells for it can still be extracted from the pancreas even after the beta cells are destroyed by the poison *alloxan.* Furthermore, glucagon can be extracted from the portion of the dog's pancreas that has alpha cells but not from the portion of the same pancreas that does not have alpha cells. Finally, destruction of the alpha cells by cobalt stops the production of glucagon. Therefore, it is believed that glucagon is secreted by the alpha cells.

Beta cells often can still be found in the pancreas of a patient who has very severe diabetes, but these cells then have a hyalinized appearance and contain no secretory granules; also, they do not exhibit staining reactions for insulin in contrast to the normal beta cells, which do give staining reactions for insulin. Consequently, these hyalinized beta cells in diabetic patients are considered to be non-functional.

Chemistry of Insulin. Insulin is a simple protein. It has been isolated in a purified and crystallized form, and its molecular weight is 5,734; however, insulin molecules tend to bind very loosely with each other and to form aggregates having a molecular weight of about 48,000, for which reason this has been reported in the past as the molecular weight of insulin.

Attempts have been made to split the insulin molecule into smaller compounds that might still retain the functional activity

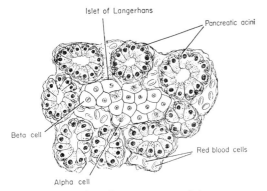

Figure 703. Physiologic anatomy of the pancreas.

1029

of insulin. Thus far all such attempts have been unsuccessful, and, instead, the action of the insulin has either been totally lost or at least partially lost by such procedures. The precise arrangement of amino acids in the insulin molecule has been determined but no specific prosthetic group in the molecule has thus far been found that can account for insulin's functional characteristics.

EFFECT OF INSULIN ON CARBOHYDRATE METABOLISM

The very earliest studies of the effect of insulin on carbohydrate metabolism showed three basic effects: (1) enhanced rate of glucose metabolism, (2) decreased blood glucose concentration, and (3) increased glycogen stores in the tissues. The ability of insulin to increase the rate of glucose metabolism by the tissues is very important to the body, and complete lack of insulin secretion, as occurs in severe diabetes mellitus, is incompatible with life for more than a very short period of time. Therefore, it is important that we understand the basic effects of insulin on carbohydrate metabolism.

Facilitation of Glucose Transport through the Cell Membrane

The one single basic effect of insulin that has now been demonstrated many times is its ability to increase the rate of glucose transport from the extracellular fluids into the intracellular fluids of most of the cells in the body. This effect is illustrated in Figure 704. In the complete absence of insulin the overall rate of glucose transport into the cells of the body becomes only about one fourth the normal value. On the other hand, when great excesses of insulin are secreted, the rate of glucose transport into the cells may be as great as five times normal. This means that, between the limits of no insulin at all and great excesses of insulin, the rate of glucose transport can be altered as much as 20-fold.

Some of the experiments that have been used to prove this accelerating effect of insulin on glucose transport through the cell membranes are the following:

1. Since glucose immediately becomes phosphorylated after entry into the cells and since almost no *free* glucose remains, studies to prove an increase in intracellular glucose under the influence of insulin have been very difficult. However, this has been accomplished in two different types of experiments: first, in experiments in which the concentration of extracellular glucose is so extreme that the glucose entering the cells cannot all be phosphorylated instantaneously, and, second, in experiments in which the temperature of the medium is 4° C., a level at which the glucose-phosphorylating mechanism of the cells is almost blocked.

2. Experiments have also been conducted on the transport of other monosaccharides similar to glucose but which are not metabolized in the cells. For instance, most tissues in the body cannot metabolize galactose; therefore, its intracellular concentration can be measured without difficulty. It has been easy to demonstrate that insulin causes marked increase in galactose transport through the cellular membrane. The same is also true of a number of other monosaccharides, including especially xylose and arabinose.

3. A third group of experiments has been performed to compare the effects of insulin on glucose metabolism in (a) suspensions of whole cells and (b) cellular homogenates. In these, insulin increases the metabolism of glucose by whole cells, but in the cellular homogenates, which have no intact cellular membranes, the rate of glucose metabolism is not altered by the presence of insulin. This indicates that a cell membrane is necessary for the function of insulin.

Mechanism by Which Insulin Accelerates Glucose Transport. In the discussion of the cell membrane in Chapter 3 it was pointed out that glucose cannot pass into the cell through the cellular pores but instead must enter by some transport mechanism through the membrane matrix. Figure 704 depicts the generally believed method by which glucose enters the cell, showing that glucose probably combines with a carrier substance in the cell membrane and then is transported to the inside of the membrane where it is released to the interior of the cell. The carrier then returns to the outer surface of the membrane to transport still additional quantities of glucose. This process can occur to a slight extent even in the absence of insulin, but in the presence of insulin it is greatly accelerated.

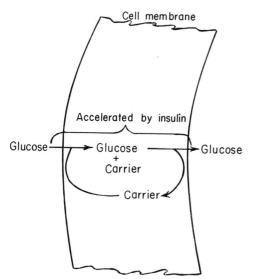

Figure 704. Transport of glucose through the cell membrane, showing the accelerating effect of insulin.

Glucose transport through the cell membrane does not occur against a concentration gradient. That is, once the glucose concentration inside the cell rises to as high as the glucose concentration on the outside, further glucose will not be transported to the interior. Therefore, the glucose transport process is one of *facilitated diffusion,* which means simply that glucose diffuses through the membrane by means of a facilitating carrier mechanism. And the degree of facilitation in most cells of the body can be enhanced as much as 20-fold by insulin.

At this point, it is interesting to note that before insulin causes increased transport of glucose through the membrane, it becomes *fixed to the cell,* and it has been postulated that this fixation is principally in the cell membrane itself.

Tissues in Which Insulin Is Effective. Enhanced transport of glucose through the cell membrane is particularly effective in skeletal muscle and adipose tissue, and these two together make up approximately 65 per cent of the entire body by weight. In addition, insulin enhances glucose transport into the heart and at least into certain ones of the smooth muscle organs such as the uterus.

On the other hand, insulin does not enhance glucose transport into the brain cells and does not enhance its transport through the intestinal mucosa nor through the tubular epithelium of the kidney. However, these tissues together amount to less than 5 per cent of the total body mass. Thus, we know that insulin greatly enhances glucose transport in 65 per cent of the total body mass and fails to enhance glucose transport in less than 5 per cent of the body mass. The effects in the remaining 30 per cent are yet unknown, but there is reason to believe that most of this tissue also responds to insulin.

In summary, insulin is extremely important for glucose transport into the cells of most tissues of the body. The most important exception to this is the brain, transport into which is probably more dependent on transport through the blood-brain barrier (see Chapter 7) than through the cell membrane.

Possible Action of Insulin on Glucokinase Activity. Another theory of the action of insulin in carbohydrate metabolism is that it enhances the activity of glucokinase in the cells to cause rapid phosphorylation of the glucose after it has entered the cell. Such a mechanism obviously could reduce the concentration of *free* glucose in the cellular fluids and thereby increase the glucose gradient across the membrane; this would enhance the rate at which glucose would diffuse through the cell membrane. However, there are three reasons for believing that this theory is not correct: First, insulin does not increase glucose metabolism in cellular homogenates, which indicates that a cell membrane is necessary for the action of insulin and that insulin probably is not an intracellularly functioning hormone. Second, insulin has been observed to increase glucokinase activity only when large quantities of growth hormone are being used specifically to inhibit glucokinase activity, which obviously is a very special condition. Third, studies on the activity of glucokinase show that almost all cells have such extremely rapid glucokinase activity, even in the absence of insulin, that the phosphorylation of glucose is not a "rate-limiting" reaction; this means that the glucokinase activity is always many times as great as that needed to provide complete and rapid glucose phosphorylation, regardless of whether insulin is present. Therefore, there simply is no need for an accelerating effect of insulin on glucokinase activity.

Effect of Insulin on Glucose Utilization and Glycogen Storage in Extrahepatic Tissues

Glucose Utilization. Insulin lack decreases glucose transport into most of the body cells to about one fourth normal. Therefore, without the presence of insulin most of the tissues of the body, with the major exception of the brain and to a less extent the heart, must depend on other metabolic substrates besides glucose for their energy.

Glycogen Storage. Another major effect of insulin is greatly enhanced storage of glycogen in the skeletal muscle cells throughout the body, and moderate enhancement of glycogen storage in other cells such as the skin, glandular tissues, and so forth. Here again this effect is undoubtedly caused by the availability of the greatly increased intracellular glucose.

Action of Insulin on Carbohydrate Metabolism in the Liver

Knowledge of the action of insulin on carbohydrate metabolism in the liver is still somewhat confused because insulin does not cause an immediate increase in glucose transport into the liver cells similar to that which occurs in skeletal muscle and most other tissues of the body. Yet, insulin does have at least three major effects on liver metabolism of carbohydrates.

1. Insulin causes an immediate release of glucose from the liver into the blood, with a corresponding decrease in the liver glycogen stores. This release possibly is a direct effect of insulin on the liver, but it could result secondarily from (a) transport of glucose into the non-hepatic cells, followed by (b) decreased blood glucose concentration, then (c) increased diffusion of glucose out of the hepatic cells.

2. During the next few hours, insulin reverses this transport of glucose, now making glucose go into the liver cells, and, consequently, increasing the stores of liver glycogen.

3. Insulin enhances the rate of glucose metabolism by the liver by as much as 300 to 400 per cent, but this effect occurs very slowly, requiring 12 to 24 hours to take place instead of the rapid effect which occurs in the extrahepatic tissues.

We can summarize the action of insulin on the liver in the following manner: It causes a similar enhancement of glucose metabolism as that which occurs in the extrahepatic tissues, but the effect is very slow to develop, requiring hours instead of minutes. This effect could possibly be a delayed liver cellular membrane effect, but most physiologists believe instead that it is caused secondarily by some effect initiated by insulin on the extrahepatic tissues or that it is caused by some effect of insulin inside the liver cells to enhance the rate of glucose usage.

Transfer of Glycogen from the Liver to the Skeletal Muscles following the Administration of Insulin. Figure 705 illustrates the quantities of glycogen in both the skeletal muscles and the liver, showing that, immediately after an infusion of insulin plus glucose is begun, the effect of insulin is to reduce the glycogen stores in the liver while enhancing the glycogen stores in the skeletal muscle. This can be explained by the very rapid transport of glucose into muscle cells, thus reducing the blood glucose concentration and causing loss of glucose from the liver. Yet, after a period of 8 to 10 hours, the continued injection of insulin and glucose causes the liver to increase its stores of glycogen. Thus, if given enough time, insulin increases the storage of liver glycogen as well as of muscle glycogen.

This difference in action of insulin on the liver and skeletal muscles allows rapid transfer of glycogen from the liver to the muscles when the muscles need the glycogen. If the muscles and the liver utilized glycogen in exactly the same manner, it would be impossible in times of stress for the muscles to call on the glycogen stores of the liver nearly so readily.

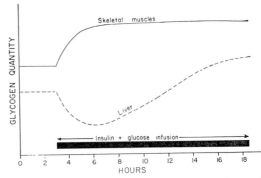

Figure 705. Effect of simultaneous insulin and glucose infusion on liver and skeletal muscle on glycogen stores, showing immediate glycogenolysis in the liver and immediate glycogenesis in skeletal muscles, followed by delayed glycogenesis in the liver as well.

Regulation of Blood Glucose Concentration and Control of Insulin Secretion

Effect of Insulin on Blood Glucose Concentration.

In the absence of insulin, very little of the glucose absorbed from the gastrointestinal tract can be transported into the tissue cells. As a consequence, the blood glucose concentration rises very high—from a normal value of 90 mg. per 100 ml. sometimes to as high as 300 to 1200 mg. per 100 ml.

On the other hand, in the presence of greatly excess insulin, glucose is transported into the cells so rapidly that its concentration in the blood can fall to as low as 20 to 30 mg. per 100 ml. Therefore, it is very important that the rate of insulin secretion by the pancreas be very accurately regulated so that blood glucose concentration also will be accurately regulated at a constant and normal value.

Effect of Glucose on Insulin Secretion by the Pancreas—Feedback Mechanism for Blood Glucose Control.

The glucose concentration of the plasma has a direct effect on the islets of Langerhans to control their rate of insulin secretion. Even the isolated pancreas perfused with a solution containing a high concentration of glucose secretes greatly increased quantities of insulin. On the contrary, it secretes decreased quantities of insulin when the blood glucose concentration falls. Therefore, it is readily evident that the secretion of insulin by the pancreas affords a very important feedback mechanism for continual regulation of blood glucose concentration. This operates as follows:

When the blood glucose concentration becomes elevated, the excess glucose acts directly on the islets of Langerhans to increase their secretion of insulin. Almost immediately, more insulin becomes available to cause glucose transport into most of the cells of the body, and this reduces the blood glucose concentration back toward normal. On the contrary, when the blood glucose concentration falls too low, the pancreas reduces its secretion of insulin, and the rate of glucose transport into the cells also decreases, allowing the blood glucose concentration to rise once again back toward normal. This mechanism of regulation is depicted by the upper half of the diagram in Figure 706.

Hypertrophy of the Pancreatic Islets in Response to Prolonged Elevation of Blood Glucose.

Besides the immediate increase in insulin secretion that results from increased blood glucose concentration, still an additional gradual increase in insulin secretion occurs if the elevated glucose concentration persists for several weeks. Gradually, over a period of 1 to 3 weeks, the islets of Langerhans hypertrophy, and the secretion of insulin increases correspondingly. Therefore, if a person suddenly begins to eat a diet containing excessive amounts of carbohydrates, his normal prancreatic insulin secretion may not be capable of taking care of all the excess glucose, and his blood glucose concentration rises above normal. But after several weeks of pancreatic adaptation, an adequate amount of insulin will then be secreted, and the excess glucose is transported into the cells.

Diabetogenic effect of prolonged elevation of blood glucose concentration.

Prolonged elevation of blood glucose concentration, caused either by excessive indulgence in a high carbohydrate diet or by administration of large amounts of one or more of the diabetogenic hormones mentioned in the previous chapters, *growth hormone, glucocorticoids, luteotropic hormone,* or *thyroxine,* can eventually "burn out" the beta cells of the islets of Langerhans, causing them to take on a hyalinized appearance with loss of their granules and with partial or complete cessation of insulin production. As a result, a typical case of diabetes mellitus ensues.

Regulation of Blood Glucose Concentration by the Sympathetic Nervous System.

Regulation of blood glucose concentration by the sympathetic nervous system was discussed in relation to glucose metabolism in Chapter 65, but it should be reemphasized here in relation to pancreatic regulation of blood glucose concentration. The lower part of Figure 706 shows that decreased blood glucose concentration excites the sympathetic nuclei of the hypothalamus, which then transmits impulses through the sympathetic nervous system to cause epinephrine release by the adrenal medullae and norepinephrine release both by the adrenals and by the sympathetic nerve endings. These hormones, especially the epinephrine, exert a direct effect on the liver cells to increase the rate of glycogenolysis. They do this by

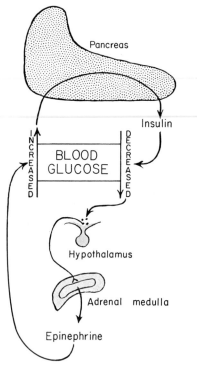

Figure 706. Pancreatic and sympathetic nervous system feedback mechanisms for regulation of blood glucose concentration.

activating the normally inactive phosphorylase in the liver cells, which causes the glycogen to spilt into glucose molecules. The glucose then diffuses into the blood to elevate the blood glucose concentration back toward normal. Thus, this is an additional feedback mechanism for regulation of blood glucose concentration. However, it normally does not become active except in instances of excessively low blood glucose concentration.

Glucose Buffer Function of the Liver.
The liver performs two major functions in blood glucose regulation. First, almost all gluconeogenesis occurs in the liver, as was discussed in Chapter 65. Therefore, between meals, when glucose is not being absorbed from the gastrointestinal tract, the liver then manufactures glucose from amino acids and from glycerol derived from fats. This is one of the principal means by which the blood glucose concentration is maintained at a normal value during the interdigestive period.

The second major function of the liver in blood glucose regulation is to store glucose in the form of glycogen when excess glucose

is available and then to release glucose back to the blood when the blood glucose concentration falls low.

Obviously, the glucose buffer function of the liver keeps the blood glucose from rising very high after a meal and keeps it from falling very low between meals. Figure 707 illustrates the normal hyperglycemic response in the blood following ingestion of 50 gm. of glucose. It also shows the response that occurs in the absence of the liver, illustrating that glucose concentration is then not nearly so well regulated but instead persists at a high level for many hours. The curve illustrated in this figure is called a *glucose tolerance curve,* which will be discussed further in relation to the diagnosis of diabetes mellitus later in the chapter.

Purpose of Blood Glucose Regulation.
One might ask the question: Why is it important to maintain a constant blood glucose concentration, particularly since most of the tissues can shift to utilization of fats and proteins for energy in the absence of glucose? The answer to this question is that glucose is the only nutrient that can be utilized in sufficient quantities by the brain tissues to supply them with their required energy. Therefore, it is important always to maintain a blood glucose concentration at a sufficiently high level to provide necessary brain nutrition.

To emphasize the importance of providing glucose for brain metabolism, it should be pointed out that approximately one-half of all the glucose formed by gluconeogenesis during the interdigestive period is used

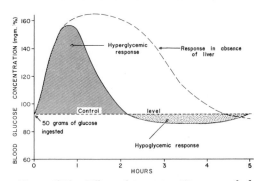

Figure 707. Effect of ingesting 50 grams of glucose on the blood glucose concentration, showing in the normal person an initial hyperglycemic response followed by a secondary hypoglycemic response. The dashed curve illustrates the effect of removing the liver or of liver disease. These curves are known as "glucose tolerance curves."

for metabolism in the brain. Indeed, it is very important that the pancreas not secrete any insulin during this period of time, for otherwise the scant supplies of glucose that are available would all go into the muscles and other peripheral tissues and leave the brain without a nutritive source.

On the other hand, it is also important that the blood glucose concentration not rise too high for three reasons: First, glucose exerts a large amount of osmotic pressure in the extracellular fluid, and, if the glucose concentration rises to excessive values, this can cause considerable cellular dehydration. Second, an excessively high level of blood glucose concentration causes loss of glucose in the urine. And, third, this also causes osmotic diuresis in the kidneys, which can deplete the body of its fluids.

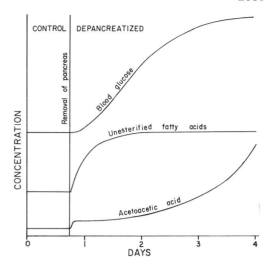

Figure 708. Effect of removing the pancreas on the blood glucose concentration, the plasma unesterified fatty acid concentration, and the acetoacetic acid concentration.

OTHER METABOLIC EFFECTS OF INSULIN

Effects on Fat Metabolism

Insulin is not known to have any direct effect on fat metabolism. However, since fat metabolism and carbohydrate metabolism share the major burden of supplying energy for the body, any factor that affects carbohydrate metabolism indirectly affects fat metabolism in the opposite direction. As long as excess amounts of insulin and glucose are available, glucose will be metabolized fairly rapidly by the cells to supply essentially all the energy required. On the other hand, in the absence of available glucose or in the absence of insulin, the major share of the energy required by the body must then be supplied by fats. Thus, carbohydrates are preferentially used, but when carbohydrates are not available, the required energy is then derived principally from fat.

Fat Mobilization in Insulin Lack. When fat takes over the burden of energy supply to the cells they must first be mobilized from the fat storage areas, but the precise mechanism by which this takes place is not known. At least part of the effect is caused by adrenocortical secretion of glucocorticoids, the glucocorticoids having a direct effect on the fat tissues to increase the rate of fatty acid liberation into the circulating blood.

Figure 708 illustrates the effect of remov-

ing the pancreas on both the blood glucose and the blood fatty acids, showing that the blood glucose begins to rise immediately because of failure of glucose utilization by the cells and also showing a rise in the concentration of plasma unesterified fatty acids which are being transported from the fat storage areas to the liver and other tissues of the body where they can be metabolized.

Effect of Insulin Lack on Blood Lipid Concentration. In addition to the increase in unesterified fatty acids in the circulating blood, essentially all the other lipid components of the plasma also become increased in the absence of insulin. This includes an increase in the overall quantity of lipoproteins and of their constituents, *triglycerides, cholesterol,* and *phospholipids.* At times the blood lipids will increase as much as fivefold, giving a total concentration of plasma lipids of several per cent rather than the normal 0.6 per cent. These very high lipid concentrations, especially the high concentration of cholesterol, have often been suggested as a possible factor in the development of extreme atherosclerosis in patients with serious diabetes.

Ketogenic Effect of Insulin Lack. Associated with increased fat mobilization from the tissues is usually also a ketogenic effect of insulin lack, which was discussed in Chapter 66 in relation to utilization of fats for energy. The reason for this is the following:

The major pathway by which fatty acids are used for energy is (a) conversion of fatty acids into acetoacetic acid in the liver, then (b) transfer of the acetoacetic acid in the blood to the peripheral tissues, where (c) it enters the tricarboxylic acid cycle and is used for energy. There are two reasons for the ketogenic effect of insulin lack: First, mobilization of fats increases the total amount of acetoacetic acid that is being formed and therefore increases the quantity of this acid that has to be transported through the blood. Second, and even more important, lack of insulin prevents the formation of oxaloacetic acid from glucose because glucose cannot get into the cells to be utilized. Oxaloacetic acid, in turn, is the basic chemical substance required in the tricarboxylic acid cycle, and, if it is deficient, acetoacetic acid utilization is correspondingly reduced. As a result, the quantity of acetoacetic acid in the circulating body fluids becomes greatly multipled. Figure 708 illustrates the moderate increase in acetoacetic acid that occurs immediately after insulin lack begins and a progressive increase in acetoacetic acid caused by the depression of oxaloacetic acid.

Obviously, the tremendous increase in acetoacetic acid in the blood can cause acidosis, which will be discussed in detail later in the chapter in relation to diabetes mellitus.

Effect of Insulin on Protein Metabolism and on Growth

Effect of Insulin on Protein Anabolism.
Proteins are continually being formed from amino acids in all cells of the body, and they are also continually being split back into amino acids, which was discussed in Chapter 67 in relation to protein metabolism. The total quantity of protein stored in the tissues of the body is increased by insulin and greatly decreased by insulin lack. Indeed, a person with severe diabetes mellitus can become incapacitated almost as much from protein lack as from failing glucose metabolism.

Most of the effect of insulin on protein metabolism is probably secondary to the action of insulin on carbohydrate metabolism, for utilization of carbohydrates for energy acts as a protein sparer. In the absence of carbohydrate metabolism, both fats and proteins are mobilized in great abundance from the tissues and used for energy. Therefore, it can readily be seen that increased carbohydrate utilization under the influence of insulin

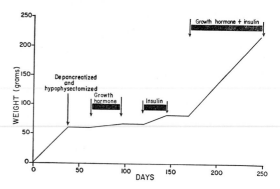

Figure 709. Effect of (a) growth hormone, (b) insulin, and (c) growth hormone plus insulin on growth in a depancreatized and hypophysectomized rat.

would decrease catabolism of the tissue proteins while allowing the anabolic effect to proceed at full speed.

However, studies on isolated tissues in which the carbohydrate metabolism has been strictly controlled have shown that insulin still has a moderate effect in promoting protein anabolism. This is particularly true in the liver. Therefore, it seems that insulin does truly have a slight direct effect on protein synthesis. Part of this effect might result from the fact that insulin increases the transport of amino acids through the cell membranes to a very slight extent in a manner precisely similar to the transport of glucose.

Effect of Insulin on Growth—Potentiation of the Effects of Growth Hormone.
Insulin is essential for growth of an animal, principally because of the protein-sparing effect of increased carbohydrate metabolism, but probably also because of a slight direct effect of insulin on protein anabolism.

In the absence of insulin, growth hormone has almost no effect in promoting growth of an animal. Fig. 709 illustrates this, showing the cessation of growth after removing both the pancreas and the hypophysis of a growing rat. Administration of either growth hormone or insulin without the other causes only slight growth, but administration of both together will cause the original rate of growth. This figure also illustrates that insulin alone without growth hormone is somewhat more effective in promoting growth than is growth hormone alone, though this difference in effect is probably caused principally by the fact that insulin causes an animal to increase its food intake because of the hypoglycemic effect on the feeding center of the hypothalamus, as was discussed in Chapter 69.

Though it is quite certain that growth hormone exerts much or most of its growth effect directly on the tissues of the body, part of this effect might be exerted through the pancreas, for experiments have shown that prolonged administration of growth hormone increases the rate of insulin production by the pancreas, and this insulin in turn can have its usual growth-promoting effect along with the direct action of growth hormone.

Effect of Insulin on Phosphate and Potassium Entry into Cells

At the same time that insulin promotes transport of glucose into the peripheral tissue cells, it also increases the rate of transport of both phosphate and potassium into the cell. The increased rate of phosphate transport is believed to result from an increased quantity of glucose phosphate forming inside the cell; this decreases the phosphate ion concentration in the cell and therefore creates a concentration gradient to move phosphate inward through the membrane. It is also assumed that entry of glucose into cells in some way provides the motive power for movement of potassium into the cells. Thus, both these effects are closely allied to the transport of glucose, but they do not seem to have any specially important functional significance.

RELATION OF OTHER ENDOCRINE GLANDS TO INSULIN SECRETION

Hormones secreted by several other glands have either direct or indirect effects on the blood glucose concentration, which in turn affects the rate of insulin secretion by the pancreas. The following are some of the relationships between the functions of other endocrine glands and insulin secretion:

Relationship of the Adenohypophysis to Insulin Secretion. The adenohypophysis secretes at least four different hormones that have either direct or indirect effects on blood glucose concentration. *Growth hormone* greatly reduces the rate of glucose utilization by the tissues and therefore elevates the blood glucose concentration. *Luteotropic hormone* seems to have essentially the same effect as growth hormone but to much less extent. *Corticotropin* increases the blood glucose concentration indirectly by first increasing adrenocortical secretion of glucorticoids, these in turn promoting increased gluconeogenesis. Likewise, *thyrotropic hormone* increases the blood glucose concentration by increasing thyroid secretion of thyroxine, which also increases the rate of gluconeogenesis but to a much less extent than the glucocorticoids.

The combined effects of a mixture of all the adenohypophyseal hormones, therefore, have a very considerable effect in elevating the blood glucose concentration. If sufficient quantities of these are injected into an animal over a long period of time, prolonged elevation of the blood glucose concentration eventually over-stimulates the beta cells of the islets of Langerhans so much that they burn out and cause frank diabetes mellitus. This is called the *diabetogenic effect* of the adenohypophyseal hormones.

The two hormones most important for the adenohypophyseal effect on blood glucose are corticotropin and growth hormone. Furthermore, growth hormone has an additional effect to stimulate the islets of Langerhans directly, therefore probably exerting more diabetogenic action than any of the other hormones.

The "Houssay dog" created by simultaneous removal of the hypophysis and the pancreas. Removal of the hypophysis reduces the blood glucose concentration because of loss of the diabetogenic hormones, while, on the other hand, removal of the pancreas elevates the blood glucose concentration. When both these procedures are performed simultaneously, the animal is actually in better condition than when only one is performed, principally because the effects tend to nullify each other insofar as carbohydrate metabolism is concerned. A Houssay dog, however, will still develop severe hyperglycemia if he is fed adequate quantities of carbohydrate many times each day. The beneficial effect of pancreatectomy in the hypophysectomized dog is to decrease glucose utilization during the interdigestive period down to a level compatible with the reduced rate of gluconeogenesis.

Relationship of the Adrenal Cortex to Insulin Secretion. Excess secretion of glucocorticoids by the adrenal cortex causes almost the same effects on blood glucose concentration as the administration of a mixture of adenohypophyseal hormones. Indeed, one of the major effects of administering the adenohypophyseal hormones results from the action of corticotropin to increase adrenocortical secretion of glucocorticoids. These hormones promote gluconeogenesis, probably mainly by mobilizing amino acids from the body proteins, thus making these available to the liver to be used in forming glucose.

Removal of the adrenal cortex in a depancreatized dog causes almost the same amelioration of the animal's diabetes as removal of the adenohypophysis. However, when the adrenal cortex is removed rather than the adenohypophysis, the animal's electrolyte balance must be continually controlled by means of adequate mineralocorticoid therapy.

Prolonged secretion or injection of excess quantities of glucocorticoids can have a diabetogenic effect on the pancreatic islets in much the same way as prolonged secretion of the adenohypophyseal hormones. This has been a problem in the treatment of arthritic patients with glucocorticoids, for one of the detrimental side effects has often been development of permanent diabetes mellitus.

Relationship of Thyroxine to Pancreatic Secretion of Insulin. Thyroxine, like the glucocorticoids but to a much less extent, increases the rate of gluconeogenesis and therefore tends to increase the blood glucose concentration. If the person already has a tendency toward diabetes, an increase in thyroid secretion will elevate the blood glucose concentration and may exert a further diabetogenic effect on the pancreatic islets. Indeed, a number of patients who develop hyperthyroidism develop diabetes mellitus as an accompaniment.

DIABETES MELLITUS

In experimental animals diabetes mellitus has been induced many times by many different methods. The method universally effective is *depancreatectomy*, but in order to attain significant diabetes at least 90 to 95 per cent of the pancreas usually must be removed; otherwise, the islets of Langerhans in the remaining pancreatic tissue will often be able to hypertrophy sufficiently to supply enough insulin for normal metabolic needs. This indicates that the islets of Langerhans normally have a tremendous reserve capacity.

A second means for producing diabetes in animals is *administration of a poison known as alloxan.* This substance causes the beta cells of the islets of Langerhans to swell and finally to degenerate. It also causes toxic damage in other parts of the body, including especially the kidneys, and the dosage of alloxan necessary to destroy the beta cells of the islets of Langerhans is only slightly less than the dosage that will cause death of the animal. Therefore, it is difficult to adjust the dosage precisely so that most of the beta cells will be destroyed. Consequently, one is never sure how many remaining functional beta cells are present in the alloxan diabetic animal.

A still less reliable method for inducing diabetes in an experimental animal is *administration of anterior pituitary extract.* Especially when anterior pituitary extract is administered in conjunction with thyroxin, glucocorticoids, or even with some of the sex hormones can it result in extreme swelling and final degeneration of the beta cells of the islets of Langerhans. All of these hormones stimulate the beta cells either directly or by elevating the blood glucose level. As a result of the greatly increased rate of activity the cells tend to "burn out." Though this is not a satisfactory means for producing diabetes in an experimental animal, it does indicate that hormonal abnormalities probably do cause the development of diabetes in some patients.

Most factors that are known to destroy the beta cells are especially likely to destroy these cells when an animal is on a high carbohydrate diet, for such a diet also stimulates the beta cells. Therefore, it is easy to understand why diabetes is believed to result sometimes from excessive ingestion of sweets and other carbohydrates.

Though various factors may cause the beta cells of the islets of Langerhans to "burn out," nevertheless diabetes is, in general, a hereditary disease, for almost all persons who develop diabetes, especially those who develop it in early years, can trace the disease to one or more forebears. Therefore, definite clinical attempts are being made to curtail reproduction by diabetic persons.

Mild diabetes often occurs in older people and especially in older people who are overweight. As long as these people continue to eat excessively, the blood glucose level is elevated, but as soon as they reduce their diet their blood glucose level often reverts to normal. This indicates that the old-age type of diabetes results from incomplete destruction of the beta cells so that as long as dietary indiscretion continues the islets of Langerhans are simply incapable of meeting the demand for insulin.

Pathologic Physiology of Diabetes

Metabolism of Carbohydrate in Diabetes. When insulin production ceases, the metabolism of carbohydrates in most tissues of the body becomes considerably depressed. Fortunately, brain cells do not require insulin for normal utilization of glucose; therefore, diabetes does not depress glucose metabolism in the brain.

Loss of Glucose in the Urine of the Diabetic Patient. Whenever the quantity of glucose entering the kidney tubules in the glomerular filtrate rises above approximately 225 mg. per minute, a significant proportion of the glucose begins to spill into the urine, and when the quantity rises above about

325 mg. per minute, which is the tubular maximum for glucose, as explained in Chapter 8, all the excess above this is lost into the urine. If normal quantities of glomerular filtrate are formed per minute, 225 mg. of glucose will enter the tubules each minute when the blood glucose level rises to 180 mg. per cent. If the level rises progressively above 180 mg. per cent, greater and greater quantities of glucose appear in the urine. Consequently, it is frequently stated that the blood "threshold" for the appearance of glucose in the urine is approximately 180 mg. per cent. When the blood glucose level rises to 200 to 400 mg. per cent—values that are quite common in persons with diabetes—several hundred grams of glucose can be lost into the urine each day. Indeed, this is the means by which the diabetic patient rids himself of the extra carbohydrate that cannot be utilized. The quantity of glucose lost in the urine is almost a direct function of the quantity of carbohydrate ingested if the patient is totally diabetic, and as long as the kidney functions normally this loss of glucose in the urine usually limits the blood glucose level to a value not greater than about 400 to 500 mg. per cent.

The Dehydrating Effect of Elevated Blood Glucose Levels in Diabetes. Tremendously elevated blood glucose levels have occurred under certain conditions in diabetic patients; levels have been recorded as high as 2000 mg. per cent. Also, very high blood glucose levels have been artificially created by rapid infusion of glucose solutions. The only significant effect of the elevated glucose is dehydration of the tissue cells, for glucose does not diffuse easily through the pores of the cell membrane, and the increased crystalloidal osmotic pressure in the extracellular fluids causes osmotic transfer of water out of the cells. A 5 per cent glucose solution is approximately isotonic with the body fluids, which means that elevation of blood glucose from the normal level of approximately 90 mg. per cent up to 200 to 400 mg. per cent increases the crystalloidal osmotic pressure of the extracellular fluid approximately 2 to 6 per cent. This probably does not cause excessive dehydration of the tissues, but elevation to still higher values might cause considerable harm.

In addition to the direct dehydrating effect of excessive glucose, the loss of glucose in the urine causes diuresis because of the crystalloidal osmotic effect of glucose in the tubules, and the diuresis causes obligatory loss of some of the electrolytes from the extracellular fluid. The overall effect, therefore, is dehydration of the extracellular fluid, which then causes compensatory dehydration of the intracellular fluid for reasons discussed in Chapter 4. Thus, one of the very important features of diabetes is a tendency for extracellular and intracellular dehydration to develop.

Acidosis in Diabetes. The shift from carbohydrate to fat metabolism in diabetes has already been sufficiently discussed. It should also be pointed out that when the body depends almost entirely on acetoacetic acid for metabolism, the level of keto acids in the body fluids may rise to as high as 20 milliequivalents per liter. This, obviously, causes a direct increase in the quantity of metabolic acids and is likely to result in acidosis.

A second effect, which is usually even more important in causing acidosis than the direct increase in acid radicals in the body fluids, is a decrease in sodium concentration caused by the following method: Keto acids have a very low threshold for excretion by the kidneys; therefore, when the keto acid level rises in the diabetic, as much as 100 to 200 grams of keto acids can be excreted in the urine each day. About half the acid radicals are excreted in the acidic form, but the other half are excreted combined partly with ammonia synthesized in the kidney and partly with cations, mainly sodium, derived from the extracellular fluid. As a result, the cations of the extracellular fluid usually decrease, and this loss adds to the acidosis that is already caused by the presence of excessive keto acids in the extracellular fluids.

Obviously, all the usual reactions that occur in metabolic acidosis take place in diabetic acidosis. These include *very rapid breathing*, which causes excessive expiration of carbon dioxide and *marked decrease in bicarbonate content of the extracellular fluids*. Likewise, *large quantities of chloride ion are excreted by the kidneys* as an additional compensatory mechanism for correction of the acidosis. These extreme acidotic effects, however, do not occur except in the most severe degrees of untreated diabetes. The overall changes in the electrolytes of

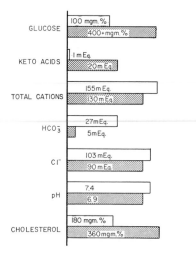

Figure 710. Effect of very severe diabetic acidosis on plasma constituents. Normal values are represented by the clear bars and the coma values are represented by the shaded bars.

the blood as a result of very severe diabetic acidosis are illustrated in Figure 710.

Relationship of Diabetic Symptoms to the Pathologic Physiology of Insulin Lack. The earliest symptoms of diabetes are *polyuria* (excessive elimination of urine), *polydipsia* (excessive drinking of water), *polyphagia* (excessive eating), *loss of weight,* and *asthenia* (lack of energy). As explained above, the polyuria is due to the osmotic diuretic effect of glucose in the kidney tubules. In turn the polydipsia is due to dehydration resulting from polyuria. The failure of glucose utilization by the body causes loss of weight and a tendency to polyphagia. The asthenia apparently also is caused mainly by lack of carbohydrate metabolism, for muscles seem to respond more easily, more rapidly, and with greater energy when they are metabolizing carbohydrates than when they are metabolizing fats. In addition to this cause of asthenia, loss of proteins from the muscles also contributes to the muscular weakness.

Diagnosis of Diabetes

The usual methods for diagnosing diabetes depend upon various chemical tests of the urine and the blood as follows:

Urinary Sugar. Simple office tests or more complicated quantitative laboratory tests may be used for determining the quantity of glucose lost in the urine. In general,

the severity of diabetes can be estimated from the quantity of this glucose loss, but a condition known as *renal glycosuria* sometimes occurs even in persons without diabetes mellitus. This condition results from a low tubular maximum for glucose (as explained in Chapter 8) so that even though the blood glucose level is perfectly normal, a large quantity of glucose may still be lost in the urine.

The Fasting Blood Glucose Level. The fasting blood sugar level in the early morning, at least 8 hours after any previous meal, is normally approximately 80 to 90 mg. per cent, and 120 mg. per cent is generally considered to be the absolute upper limit of normal. If the fasting blood sugar level is above this value, diabetes mellitus is an excellent likelihood.

The Glucose Tolerance Test. As illustrated in Figure 711, when a normal fasting person ingests 50 grams of glucose, his blood glucose level rises from approximately 90 mg. per cent up to approximately 140 mg. per cent and falls back to below normal within 3 hours. The decrease to below normal is caused by continued activity of the insulin secreted during the hyperglycemic phase.

Though an occasional diabetic patient will have a normal fasting blood glucose concentration, his glucose tolerance test is almost always abnormal. On ingestion of 50 grams of glucose, these persons exhibit a progressive, slow rise in their blood glucose level for 2 to 3 hours as illustrated by the upper

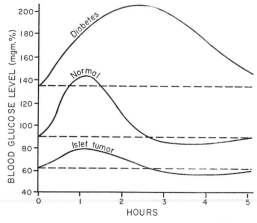

Figure 711. Glucose tolerance curve in the normal person, in a diabetic patient, and in a patient with an islet tumor (hyperinsulinism).

curve in Figure 711, and the glucose level falls back to the control value only after some 5 to 6 hours; yet, it never falls below the control level. This slow fall of the curve and its failure to fall below the control level illustrates that the normal increase in insulin secretion following glucose ingestion does not occur in the diabetic, and a diagnosis of diabetes mellitus can probably be definitely established on the basis of such a curve.

Insulin Sensitivity. To differentiate diabetes mellitus of pancreatic origin from high blood glucose levels resulting from excess secretion of adrenocortical or adenohypophyseal hormones, an *insulin sensitivity test* can be performed. When little insulin is produced by the pancreas, a test dose of insulin causes the blood glucose level to fall markedly, but, when the pancreas is already secreting large quantities of insulin, the test dose will not cause any significant decrease in blood glucose. Therefore, when the blood glucose level is elevated as a result of pancreatic failure, the "insulin sensitivity" is markedly increased, but, when the blood glucose level is high as a result of excessive adrenocortical or pituitary secretion, the "insulin sensitivity" is greatly reduced because the pancreas is already secreting large quantities of insulin.

Acetone Bodies. If diabetes is severe, a reasonable quantity of acetone bodies will accumulate in the blood. In Chapter 66 it was pointed out that small quantities of acetoacetic acid can be converted to acetone, which is volatile and is vaporized into the expired air. Consequently, one frequently can make a diagnosis of diabetes mellitus simply by smelling acetone on the breath of a patient. Also, ketone bodies can be detected by chemical means in the urine, and their quantitation aids in determining the severity of the diabetes.

Treatment of Diabetes

The theory of treatment in diabetes mellitus is to administer enough insulin that the patient will have normal carbohydrate metabolism. If this is done, then most of the consequences of diabetes will also be prevented.

Figure 712 illustrates the action of different preparations of insulin following subcutaneous injection. Regular amorphous insulin and crystalline insulin have an activity lasting from 6 to 8 hours, whereas insulin that has been precipitated very slowly with zinc to form large crystalline particles (lente insulin) or insulin that has been precipitated with various protein derivatives (globin insulin and protamine zinc insulin) are relatively insoluble and are absorbed slowly.

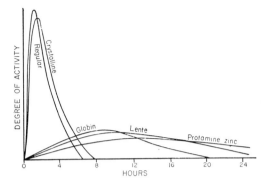

Figure 712. Time-action curves for different types of insulin.

Thus protamine zinc insulin may continue to act for as long as 36 to 48 hours. Ordinarily, the diabetic patient is given one of the long-acting insulins each day, usually lente insulin; this increases his overall carbohydrate metabolism throughout the day. Then additional quantities of regular insulin are given at those times of the day when his blood glucose level tends to rise too high, such as at meal times. Thus each patient is established on his own individualized routine of treatment.

Diet of the Diabetic. The insulin requirements of a diabetic are established with the patient on a standard diet, for any change in the quantity of carbohydrate intake changes the requirements for insulin. In the normal person the pancreas has the ability to adjust the quantity of insulin produced in proportion to the intake of carbohydrate, but in the completely diabetic person this control function is totally lost.

Ordinarily, the carbohydrate intake of the diabetic is established at approximately the average value for a normal person. Likewise, the fats and proteins are regulated in a similar manner though this is probably not so important as the regulation of carbohydrate intake.

Relationship of Treatment to Arteriosclerosis. Diabetic patients develop atherosclerosis, arteriosclerosis, and severe coronary heart disease far more easily than do normal persons. Indeed, a person who has relatively poorly controlled diabetes throughout childhood is likely to die of heart disease in his 20's. It has been claimed by some clinicians that the treatment of the patient does not greatly affect the development of arteriosclerosis, but on the other hand there are indications that the method of treatment does make considerable difference:

In the early days of treating diabetes it was the tendency to reduce the carbohydrates in the diet so that the insulin requirements would be minimized. This procedure kept the blood sugar level down to normal values and prevented the loss of glucose in the urine, but it did not prevent the abnormalities of fat metabolism. Actually, it exacerbated these. Consequently, there is a tendency at present to allow the patient a normal carbohydrate diet and then to give simultaneously large quantities of insulin to metabolize the carbohydrates. This depresses the rate of fat metabolism and also depresses the high level of blood cholesterol which occurs in diabetes as a result of abnormal fat metabolism.

Because the complications of diabetes—such as atherosclerosis, greatly increased susceptibility to infection, diabetic retinopathy, cataracts, hypertension, chronic renal disease, etc.—are more closely associated with the level of the blood lipids than with the level of blood glucose, it is the object of many clinics treating diabetes to administer sufficient glucose and insulin that the quantity of blood lipids becomes normal.

Treatment with Drugs That Stimulate the Release of Insulin. Recently, several drugs which can be taken by mouth and which will cause a hypoglycemic effect have been introduced for treatment of patients with mild diabetes. The drugs that have thus far been tried are either *biguamides* or *sulfonylurea compounds*, the two most important of which are *tolbutamide* (Orinase) and *chlorpropamide* (Diabenese).

These drugs act by stimulating insulin production by the islets of Langerhans. Therefore, they are effective only in patients who still have active islets which for some reason or other are not secreting adequate quantities of insulin. It is possible that in the long run these drugs will prove harmful because of overstimulation of the remaining islet tissues with resultant permanent damage. For obvious reasons, they are of no value whatsoever in the treatment of patients with severe diabetes, for their islets have already lost all potential ability to secrete insulin.

Diabetic Coma

If diabetes is not satisfactorily controlled, then very severe dehydration and acidosis may result, and sometimes even when the patient is receiving treatment sporadic changes in the metabolic rates of the cells can still precipitate dehydration and acidosis. For instance, severe infections can cause fever and thereby greatly increase the rate of cellular metabolism. Also, strenuous muscular exercise can increase the rate of metabolism, thus causing excessive fat metabolism and consequent acidosis.

If the pH of the body fluids falls below approximately 7.0 to 6.9, the diabetic patient may develop coma. Also, in addition to the acidosis, dehydration in the patient is believed to exacerbate the coma. Regardless of the exact cause of this coma, once the diabetic patient reaches this stage, the outcome is almost universally fatal unless he receives immediate treatment.

Treatment of Diabetic Coma. The patient with diabetic coma is extremely refractory to insulin because acidic plasma has an *insulin antagonist,* an alpha globulin, that opposes the action of the insulin. Therefore, instead of the usual 60 to 80 units of insulin per day, which is the dosage usually necessary for control of severe diabetes, as much as 1500 to 2000 units of insulin must often be given the first day of treatment of coma. Administration of insulin alone may be sufficient to reverse the abnormal physiology and to effect a cure. However, it is usually advantageous to correct also the dehydration and acidosis immediately.

The dehydration is ordinarily corrected very rapidly by administering large quantities of sodium chloride solution, and the acidosis is often corrected by administration of sodium bicarbonate or sodium lactate solution; the bicarbonate is expired as carbon dioxide through the lungs, and the lactate is removed from the sodium by the liver, thus increasing the quantity of cations in the extracellular fluids. In general, however, addition of alkalies to the administered fluids has fallen into disrepute because of the tendency to over-use them.

While correcting the dehydration of diabetic coma it is important to maintain the potassium ion of the extracellular fluids at a normal level. During the dehydration process large quantities of potassium will have been removed from the tissue cells along with the removal of water from these cells. Consequently, on administering fluids and insulin to the coma patient, as these fluids and glucose are absorbed into the cells, large quantities of potassium are also absorbed into the cells to reestablish electrolyte balance. This may greatly depress the potassium level in the extracellular fluids and cause skeletal muscular paralysis throughout the body; also, if carried to extremes, excessive systolic contraction of the heart might occur. Patients have been known to die as a result of rapid loss of potassium from the extracellular fluids. Therefore, it is probably advisable to fortify the fluids administered for correction of diabetic dehydration with a small quantity of extra potassium; yet, when this is done caution must be observed against over-use of potassium because a potassium level in the extracellular fluids above approximately three times normal may cause cardiac standstill in diastole.

HYPERINSULINISM

Though much more rare than diabetes, increased insulin production, which is known as *hyperinsulinism*, does occasionally occur. This usually results from an adenoma of an islet of Langerhans. About 10 to 15 per cent of these adenomas are malignant, and occasionally metastases from the islets of Langerhans spread throughout the body causing tremendous production of insulin by both the primary adenoma and by the metastatic cancers. Indeed, in order to prevent hypoglycemia in some of these patients more than 1000 grams of glucose have had to be administered each 24 hours.

Insulin Shock and Hypoglycemia. It has already been sufficiently emphasized that the central nervous system derives essentially all its energy from glucose metabolism and that insulin is not necessary for this metabolism. However, if insulin causes the level of blood glucose to fall to very low values, then indirectly the metabolism of the central nervous system is greatly depressed. Consequently, in patients with hyperinsulinism or in patients who administer too much insulin to themselves, the syndrome called "insulin shock" may occur as follows:

As the blood sugar level falls into the range of 50 to 70 mg. per cent, the central nervous system usually becomes quite excitable, for this degree of hypoglycemia seems to facilitate neuronal activity. Sometimes various forms of hallucinations result but more often the patient simply experiences extreme nervousness, and he may tremble all over. As the blood glucose level falls to 20 to 50 mg. per cent, clonic convulsions and loss of consciousness are likely to occur. As the glucose level is depressed still lower, the convulsions cease, and only a state of coma remains. Indeed, at times it is difficult to distinguish between true diabetic coma as a result of insulin lack and coma due to hypoglycemia caused by excess insulin. However, the acetone breath and the rapid breathing of diabetic coma are not present in hypoglycemic coma.

Obviously, the treatment for a patient who has hypoglycemic shock or coma is immediate intravenous administration of large quantities of glucose. This usually brings the patient out of shock within a minute or more. Also, administration of epinephrine can cause glycogenolysis in the liver and thereby increase the blood glucose level extremely rapidly.

If treatment is not effected immediately, permanent damage to the neuronal cells of the central nervous system will occur, and especially is this likely to occur in prolonged hyperinsulinism due to pancreatic tumors. Hypoglycemic shock induced by insulin administration is frequently used for treatment of psychogenic disorders. This type of shock, like electric shock therapy, frequently benefits especially the melancholic patient.

Decreased Glucose Tolerance and Decreased Insulin Sensitivity in Hyperinsulinism. In addition to the usual signs of hypoglycemia that appear in hyperinsulinism, a definitive diagnosis of the condition can usually be made by performing a glucose tolerance test and an insulin sensitivity test. The glucose tolerance curve is approximately that shown by the lower curve of Figure 711, illustrating that the initial glucose level is low, and the increase after ingestion of glucose is slight. When the insulin sensitivity test is performed, the insulin sensitivity is found to be greatly diminished because the quantity of the injected dose of insulin is so slight in relation to the quantity of insulin already present in the body that almost no effect occurs.

FUNCTIONS OF GLUCAGON

Glucagon, like insulin, is a very small protein having a molecular weight of 3485. Almost nothing is known at present about the quantity of glucagon secreted by the pancreas nor even whether it is secreted in sufficient quantities to cause significant metabolic effects. Removal of the pancreas does not cause any metabolic abnormality that can definitely be ascribed to the lack of glucagon. However, on injecting purified glucagon into an animal a very profound hyperglycemic effect occurs, one microgram per kilogram of glucagon elevating the blood glucose concentration approximately 20 mg. per 100 ml. of blood. For this reason, glucagon is frequently called *hyperglycemic factor*. Furthermore, because of the very minute quantity required to cause this reaction, it is presumed that glucagon does perform some useful function in the body.

Glycogenolysis and Increased Blood Glucose Concentration Caused by Glucagon. The one single primary effect of glucagon that has been proved beyond doubt is its ability to cause glycogenolysis in the liver, which in turn increases the blood glucose concentration. This effect is believed to result from activation of *phosphorylase phosphatase* by glucagon, this in turn acting on the normally inactive phosphorylase in the liver cells and converting this into an active phosphorylase. The active phosphorylase then, as explained in Chapter 65, causes rapid glycogenolysis followed by release of glucose into the blood.

Glucagon does not cause glycogenolysis in the extrahepatic tissues. This is in contrast with the action of epinephrine on glycogenolysis, which causes this effect both in the liver and in the extrahepatic tissues.

Infusion of glucagon for about four hours can cause such intensive liver glycogenolysis that all the liver stores of glycogen will be depleted.

Prolonged hyperglycemic effect of glucagon. Even after all the glycogen in the liver has been exhausted under the influence of glucagon, continued infusion of this hormone causes continued hyperglycemia. This certainly cannot be caused by further glycogenolysis in the liver. Yet, its cause is not known at present. A suggested cause has been that glucagon increases the rate of gluconeogenesis, but this effect could readily result secondarily from depletion of glycogen in the liver cells.

Other Possible Actions of Glucagon. Other actions of glucagon that are known to occur are: (1) reduction of intestinal motility and gastric secretion and (2) enhanced excretion of electrolytes by the kidneys. The first of these is probably secondary to the hyperglycemic effect of glucagon, and the cause of the second is yet unknown and its importance probably doubtful.

Other suggested functions of glucagon which have not yet been proved but which might be of significance in metabolic regulations of the body are: (1) increased glucose uptake by the extrahepatic tissues, (2) increased utilization of glucose by the extrahepatic tissues, (3) mobilization of proteins from the tissues of the body, (4) a ketogenic effect, and (5) a diabetogenic effect. Some of these suggested effects seem to diametrically oppose others, numbers 4 and 5 versus numbers 1 and 2 for instance, thus illustrating the present paucity of information about the overall functions of glucagon.

Possible Metabolic Function of Glucagon. If glucagon does perform a significant metabolic function in the body, it has been assumed to be the following: During times of extreme muscular activity, the glycogen of the liver needs to be transferred rapidly to the muscles to be metabolized for energy. One of the factors that might be important for entry of glucose into the muscle cells during muscular activity is probably the action of insulin, but insulin cannot mobilize glucose from the liver very rapidly. If glucagon were secreted by the pancreas during muscular activity, it could cause the required glucose mobilization from the liver while the insulin would cause entry of the glucose into the muscles. Also, it is known that muscular activity increases glucose entry into the muscle cells by some other mechanism aside from the effect of insulin, though the cause of this has not yet been ascertained.

A second possible function of glucagon would be to prevent the blood glucose concentration from falling too low. For instance, it has been claimed that patients dying of the rare disease called *idiopathic hypoglycemia* have no alpha cells in their islets of Langerhans and, therefore, secrete no glucagon.

REFERENCES

Ashworth, M. A., and Haist, R. E.: Some effects of BZ-55 (carbutamide) on the growth of the islets of Langerhans. *Canad. M. A. J.*, 74:975, 1956.

Ashworth, M. A., Kerbel, N. C., and Haist, R. E.: Effect of chronic caloric insufficiency on growth of the islets of Langerhans. *Am. J. Physiol.*, 171:25, 1952.

Bell, E. T.: A Clinical and Pathological Study of 2519 Cases of Diabetes Mellitus. Springfield, Illinois, Charles C Thomas, 1960.

Best, C. H.: Insulin adjuvants or substitutes. *Canad. M. A. J.*, 74:957, 1956.

Broom, W. A., and Wolff, F. W.: The Mechanism of Action of Insulin. Oxford, Blackwell Scientific Publications Ltd., 1960.

Campbell, J., Munroe, J. S., Hausler, H. R., and Davidson, I. W.: Effects of growth hormone in diabetic dogs. *Endocrinology*, 53:549, 1953.

Ciba Foundation: Colloquia on Endocrinology. Volume IX. Internal Secretions of the Pancreas. Boston, Little, Brown and Co., 1956.

Costa, E., Galansino, G., and Foa, P. P.: Glycogen stores in glucagon-treated rats. I. Time factors. *Proc. Soc. Exp. Biol. & Med.*, 91:308, 1956.

Council for International Organizations of Medical Science: Experimental Diabetes and Its Relation to the Clinical Disease. Springfield, Illinois, Charles C Thomas, 1954.

Danowski, T. S.: Diabetes Mellitus. Baltimore, Williams & Wilkins Co., 1957.

de Bodo, R. C.: The Role of Growth Hormone in Carbohydrate Metabolism. N. Y. Acad. Sc., 1953.

de Bodo, R. C., and Altszuler, N.: Insulin hypersensitivity and physiological insulin antagonists. *Physiol. Rev.*, 38:389, 1958.

Drury, D. R., and Wick, A. N.: Mechanism of insulin action. *Diabetes*, 4:203, 1955.

Duncan, G.: Symposium on Diabetes. New York, Grune & Stratton, Inc., 1957.

Duncan, L. J. P., and Baird, J. D.: Compounds administered orally in the treatment of diabetes mellitus. *Pharmacol. Rev.*, 12:91, 1960.

Field, J. B., and Stetten, D., Jr.: Humoral insulin antagonism associated with diabetic acidosis. *Am. J. Med.*, 21:339, 1956.

Fine, M. B., and Williams, R. H.: Effect of an insulin infusion on hepatic output of glucose. *Am. J. Physiol.*, 198:645, 1960.

Fritz, I. B., Morton, J. V., Weinstein, M., and Levine, R.: Studies on the mechanism of action of the sulfonylureas. *Metabolism*, 5:744, 1956.

Fritz, I. B., Shatton, J., Morton, J. V., and Levine, R.: Effects of epinephrine and insulin on glucose disappearance in eviscerated dogs. *Am. J. Physiol.*, 189:57, 1957.

Fritz, I. B., Weinstein, M., Morton, J. V., and Levine, R.: The effects of carbutamide (BZ-55) on blood sugar levels of depancreatized dogs given insulin. *Endocrinology*, 60:76, 1957.

Haist, R. E.: Factors affecting the islets of Langerhans. *Diabetes*, 2:295, 1953.

Haist, R. E., Hawkins, R. D., and Ashworth, M. A.: Some effects of BZ-55 (carbutamide) in experimental animals. *Diabetes*, 6:21, 1957.

Holton, P., and Jones, M.: Some observations on changes in the blood content of the cat's pancreas during activity. *J. Physiol.*, 150:479, 1960.

Hotta, S., Hill, R., and Chaikoff, I. L.: Mechanism of increased hepatic cholesterogenesis in diabetes; its relation to carbohydrate utilization. *J. Biol. Chem.*, 206:835, 1954.

Houssay, B. A., Anderson, E., Bates, R. W., and Lic, H.: Diabetogenic action in prolactin. *Endocrinology*, 57:55, 1955.

Houssay, B. A., and Penhos, J. C.: Diabetogenic action of pituitary hormones on adrenalectomized hypophysectomized dogs. *Endocrinology*, 59:637, 1956.

Houssay, B. A., Rodriguez, R. R., and Cardeza, A. F.: Diabetogenic action of the pituitary growth hormone. *Soc. Biol. C. Rend.*, 148:910, 1954.

Kauvar, A. J., and Goldmer, M.: Hypoglycemia and the Hypoglycemic Syndrome. Springfield, Illinois, Charles C Thomas, 1954.

Kinash, B., and Haist, R. E.: Continuous intravenous infusion in the rat, and the effect on the islets of Langerhans of the continuous infusion of glucose. *Canad. J. Biochem. & Physiol.*, 32:428, 1954.

Kinash, B., and Haist, R. E.: Effect of ACTH and cortisone on the islets of Langerhans and the pancreas in intact and hypophysectomized rats. *Am. J. Physiol.*, 179:441, 1954.

Kinash, B., and Haist, R. E.: The influence of the thyroid gland on the islets of Langerhans and the pancreas. *Canad. J. Biochem. Physiol.*, 33:380, 1955.

Kinash, B., MacDougall, I., Evans, M. A., Bryans, F. E., and Haist, R. E.: Effects of anterior pituitary extracts and of growth hormone preparations on the islets of Langerhans and the pancreas. *Diabetes*, 2:112, 1953.

Kvam, D. C., and Parks, R. E., Jr.: Hydrocortisone-induced changes in hepatic glucose-6-phosphatase and fructose diphosphatase activities. *Am. J. Physiol.*, 198:21, 1960.

Lawrence, R. T., Salter, J. M., and Best, C. H.: The effect of insulin on nitrogen retention in the hypophysectomized rat. *Brit. M. J.*, 2:437, 1954.

Levine, R., and Fritz, I. B.: The relation of insulin to liver metabolism. *Diabetes*, 5:219, 1956.

Levine, R., and Sobel, G. W.: The mechanism of action of the sulfonylureas in diabetes mellitus. *Diabetes*, 6:263, 1957.

Lukens, F. D. W.: The pancreas: insulin and glucagon. *Ann. Rev. Physiol.*, 21:445, 1959.

Marble, A.: Advances related to diabetes. *Fed. Proc.*, 18:68, 1959.

Park, C. R., Bornstein, J., and Post, R. L.: Effect of insulin on free glucose content of rat diaphragm in vitro. *Am. J. Physiol.*, 182:12, 1955.

Park, C. R., and Johnson, L. H.: Effect of insulin on transport of glucose and galactose into cells of rat muscle and brain. *Am. J. Physiol.*, 182:17, 1955.

Reis, R. A., DeCosta, E. J., and Allweiss, M. D.: Diabetes and Pregnancy. Springfield, Illinois, Charles C Thomas, 1952.

Root, H. F., and White, P.: Diabetes Mellitus. New York, McGraw-Hill Book Co., Inc., 1956.

Salter, J., and Best, C. H.: Insulin as a growth hormone. *Brit. M. J. Suppl.*, 2:353, 1953.

Salter, J. M., Davidson, I. W., and Best, C. H.: The pathologic effects of large amounts of glucagon. *Diabetes*, 6:248, 1957.

Sheppard, L. B.: Current Concepts of Diabetes Mellitus with Special Reference to Ocular Changes. Springfield, Illinois, Charles C Thomas, 1954.

Shoemaker, W. C., Van Itallie, T. B., and Walker, W. F.: Measurement of hepatic glucose output and hepatic blood flow in response to glucagon. *Am. J. Physiol.*, 196:315, 1959.

Sirek, O. V., Sirek, A., and Best, C. H.: Pituitary growth hormone and the question of pancreatic secretion of glucagon. *Am. J. Physiol.*, 188:17, 1957.

Stadie, W. C.: Current concepts of the action of insulin. *Physiol. Rev.*, 34:52, 1954.

Stetten, D., Jr.: The hypoglycemic sulfonylurea drugs; an interim evaluation. *Ann. Int. Med.*, 46:1005, 1957.

Vallance-Owen, J., and Wright, P. H.: Assay of insulin in blood. *Physiol. Review,* 40:219, 1960.

Wick, A. N., and Drury, D. R.: Influence of glucose concentration on the action of insulin. *Am. J. Physiol.,* 174:445, 1953.

Zimmermann, B.: Endocrine Functions of the Pancreas. Springfield, Illinois, Charles C Thomas, 1952.

See Chapter 73, General bibliography on endocrinology.

Chapter 77

Parathyroid Hormone, Calcium and Phosphate Metabolism, Vitamin D, Bone and Teeth

The physiology of parathyroid hormone is closely related to (a) the physiology of calcium and phosphate metabolism, (b) the function of vitamin D, and (c) the formation of bone and teeth. Therefore, these will all be discussed together in the present chapter.

CALCIUM AND PHOSPHATE IN THE EXTRACELLULAR FLUID AND PLASMA

Gastrointestinal Absorption of Calcium and Phosphate

By far the major source of calcium in the diet is milk or milk products, which are also major sources of phosphate, but phosphate is also present in many other dietary foods, including especially the meats.

Calcium is poorly absorbed from the gastrointestinal tract because of the relative insolubility of many of its compounds and also because bivalent cations are poorly absorbed through the gastrointestinal mucosa anyway. On the other hand, phosphate is absorbed exceedingly well most of the time except when excess calcium is in the diet; the calcium tends to form almost insoluble calcium phosphate compounds that fail to be absorbed but instead pass on through the bowels to be excreted in the feces. Therefore, the rate of phosphate loss in the feces is, in general, determined by the rate of calcium loss in the feces. In other words, the major problem in the absorption of calcium and phosphate is actually a problem of calcium absorption alone for, if this is absorbed, both will be absorbed.

Promotion of Calcium Absorption by Vitamin D. The one function of vitamin D which is quite clear is its ability to increase the rate of calcium absorption from the gastrointestinal tract. This apparently is a direct effect of vitamin D on the mucosa to increase its permeability to calcium or to alter the calcium ion in some manner that it can diffuse or be actively transported more readily through the membrane.

Because of vitamin D's effect of increasing calcium absorbability, it also tends to increase *very slightly* the calcium ion concentration in the extracellular fluid.

The vitamin D compounds. Several different sterol compounds belong to the vitamin D family, and all perform more or less the same functions. The two most commonly known D vitamins are vitamins D_2 and D_3 (calciferol and activated 7-dehydrocholesterol, respectively). The second of these is formed in the skin as a result of irradiation by ultraviolet rays from the sun. Consequently, appropriate exposure to the sun prevents vitamin D deficiency.

Effect of vitamin D on phosphate absorption. As pointed out above, phosphate is very readily absorbed except when it combines with calcium to form insoluble calcium phosphate compounds. Consequently, when vitamin D increases the rate of calcium absorption it decreases the loss of calcium phosphate in the feces and thereby increases the rate of phosphate absorption, though this is entirely a secondary effect.

Regulation of Calcium Absorption by the Calcium Ion Concentration in the Extracellular Fluids. Even when plenty of vitamin D is available, all the calcium in the gut still may not be absorbed, for the rate of calcium absorption is then regulated almost entirely by the calcium ion concentration of the extracellular fluids. Even a fraction of a milliequivalent decrease in calcium ion concentration increases the rate of calcium absorption from the gut several fold, whereas a similar slight increase in calcium ion concentration decreases the rate of absorption several fold. The cause of this effect is not yet known, but a similar action occurs in the renal tubules thus illustrating that a feedback control system operates all the time to maintain a normal calcium ion concentration.

It is well known that a feedback mechanism operates to control calcium absorption from the bones, as will be described later in the chapter. This system utilizes parathyroid hormone as the mediating agent to increase calcium absorption. Parathyroid hormone also increases calcium absorption both in the gastrointestinal tract and in the renal tubules; therefore, it is possible that this hormone enters into the regulation of calcium absorption.

Excretion of Calcium and Phosphate

Excretion of Calcium. About seven eighths of the daily intake of calcium is excreted in the feces and the remaining one eighth in the urine. The excretion of calcium in the feces is actually caused by a balance of calcium absorption through the gastrointestinal mucosa and calcium secretion in the intestinal fluids. For instance, an average adult eats about 750 mg. of calcium each day. If we assume that all this is absorbed, and if we assume that 625 mg. of calcium are secreted in the intestinal juices, then we find a net absorption of only 125 mg. per day, which is about the usual amount.

Excretion of calcium into the urine conforms to much the same principles as the excretion of sodium. When the calcium ion concentration of the extracellular fluids is very low, its rate of excretion by the kidneys also becomes very low, while even a very minute increase in calcium ion concentration increases the calcium ion secretion markedly. One of the factors that help to regulate this excretion of calcium ion is parathyroid hormone, for, as pointed out above, increased secretion of parathyroid hormone—which occurs when the extracellular calcium ion concentration falls—increases the rate of calcium reabsorption from the tubules, while decreased parathyroid hormone allows a greater quantity of the calcium to pass on into the urine. The average amount of calcium excreted into the urine each day is approximately 125 mg., which is equal to the net absorption from the gut, except in a person actively depositing bone.

Excretion of Phosphate. Except for that portion of phosphate that is excreted in the feces in combination with calcium, almost all the dietary phosphate is absorbed into the blood from the gut and later excreted in the urine.

Phosphate is a *threshold substance*; that is, when its concentration in the plasma is below the critical value of approximately 1 millimol per liter, no phosphate at all will be lost into the urine; but, above this critical concentration, the rate of phosphate loss is directly proportional to the additional increase. Thus, the kidney regulates the phosphate concentration in the extracellular fluid by altering the rate of phosphate secretion in accordance with the plasma phosphate concentration.

As will be discussed later in the chapter, phosphate excretion by the kidneys is also significantly affected by parathyroid hormone; increased parathyroid hormone causes increased excretion of phosphate and decreased parathyroid hormone causes retention of phosphate in the extracellular fluids. This is opposite to the effects of parathyroid hormone on calcium excretion.

The Calcium in the Plasma and Interstitial Fluid

The quantity of calcium in the plasma is approximately 10 mg. per cent, normally varying between 9 and 11 mg. per cent. This is equivalent to approximate 5 milliequivalents per liter. It is apparent from these narrow limits of normality that the calcium level in the plasma is very exactly regulated. This regulation is effected mainly by parathyroid hormone, as will be discussed later in the chapter.

The calcium in the plasma is present in three different forms, as shown in Figure 713. (1) Approximately 50 per cent of the calcium (2.5 milliequivalents per liter) is combined with the plasma proteins and consequently is non-diffusible through the capillary membrane. (2) Approximately 5 per cent of the calcium (0.2 milliequivalents per

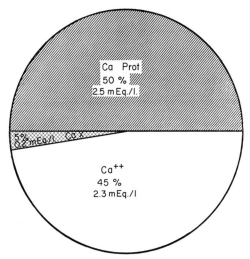

Figure 713. Distribution of ionic calcium (Ca^{++}), diffusible but unionized calcium (CaX), and calcium proteinate (CaProt) in blood plasma.

liter) is diffusible through the capillary membrane but is combined with other substances of the plasma and interstitial fluids in such a manner that it is not ionized. (3) The remaining 45 per cent of the calcium in the plasma is both diffusible through the capillary membrane and also ionized. Thus, the plasma and interstitial fluids have a normal *calcium ion concentration of approximately 2.3 milliequivalents per liter.* It is this ionic calcium that is important for most of the functions of calcium in the body, including the effect of calcium on the heart, on the nervous system, and on the formation of bone.

The Inorganic Phosphate in the Extracellular Fluids

Inorganic phosphate exists in the plasma mainly in two forms: HPO_4^{--} and $H_2PO_4^-$. The concentration of HPO_4^{--} is approximately 2.1 milliequivalents per liter, and the concentration of $H_2PO_4^-$ is approximately 0.26 milliequivalent per liter. When the total quantity of phosphate in the extracellular fluid rises, so does the quantity of each of these individual types of phosphate ions. Furthermore, when the pH of the extracellular fluid becomes more acid, there is a relative increase in the $H_2PO_4^-$ and a decrease in the HPO_4^{--} while the opposite occurs when the extracellular fluid becomes alkaline. These relationships have

already been presented in the discussion of acid-base balance in Chapter 10.

Because it is quite difficult to determine chemically the exact quantities of HPO_4^{--} and $H_2PO_4^-$ in the blood, ordinarily the total quantity of phosphate is expressed in terms of milligrams of *phosphorus* per 100 ml. of blood. The average total quantity of inorganic phosphorus represented by both of the two phosphate ions is about 4 mg. per 100 ml., varying between normal limits of 3.5 to 4 mg. per 100 ml. in adults and 4 to 5 mg. per 100 ml. in children.

Effects of Altered Calcium and Phosphate Concentrations in the Body Fluids

Changing the level of phosphate in the extracellular fluid from far below normal to as high as three to four times normal does not cause significant immediate effects on the body. Similar lack of effects occurs also for variations in most other anions, for even chloride ion can be substituted almost entirely by sulfate ion or nitrate ion in the extracellular fluid without causing marked physiologic effects on the nervous system, which will be discussed below.

Both prolonged hypocalcemia and hypophosphatemia have profound effects in decreasing bone mineralization, as will be explained later in the chapter. On the other hand, elevation or depletion of calcium ion in the extracellular fluid causes extreme immediate effects.

Tetany Resulting from Hypocalcemia. When the extracellular fluid concentration of calcium ion falls below normal, the nervous system becomes progressively more and more excitable, presumably because of increased membrane permeability. This increase in excitability occurs both in the central nervous system and in the peripheral nerves, though most of the symptoms are manifest peripherally. The nerve fibers actually become so excitable that they begin to discharge spontaneously, and these spontaneous nerve discharges initiate nerve impulses that pass to the peripheral skeletal muscles where they elicit tetanic contraction. Consequently, hypocalcemia causes *tetany.* Figure 714 illustrates tetany in the hand, which usually occurs before generalized tetany develops. This is called "carpopedal spasm."

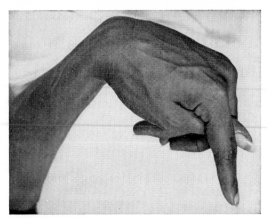

Figure 714. Hypocalcemic tetany in the hand, called "carpopedal spasm." (Courtesy Dr. Herbert Langford.)

Hypocalcemia in the human being ordinarily causes essentially no other acute symptoms besides tetany because tetany kills the patient before other symptoms can develop. Tetany ordinarily occurs when the blood concentration of calcium reaches approximately 7 mg. per cent, which is only 30 per cent below the normal calcium concentration.

When the calcium in the body fluids falls to a level not quite sufficient to cause tetany, "latent tetany" will be present; this can be diagnosed by weakly stimulating the nerves and noting the response. For instance, tapping on the seventh nerve where it passes over the angle of the jaw will cause the facial muscles to twitch if latent tetany exists. Second, placing a tourniquet on the upper arm causes ischemia of the peripheral nerves and also increases the excitability of the nerves, thus causing the muscles of the lower arm and hand to go into spasm if latent tetany exists. Finally, if the person with latent tetany hyperventilates, the resulting alkalinization of his body fluids increases the irritability of the nerves. This effect, combined with the hypocalcemic effect, then causes overt signs of tetany to appear.

In experimental animals, in which the level of calcium can be reduced beyond the normal lethal stage, extreme hypocalcemia can cause marked dilatation of the heart, changes in cellular enzyme activities, and increased cellular membrane permeability in other cells as well as in nerve cells.

Hypercalcemia. When the level of calcium in the body fluids rises above normal, the nervous system is depressed, and reflex activities of the central nervous system become sluggish. The muscles, too, become sluggish and weak, possibly because of calcium effects on the muscle cell membranes. Also, increased calcium ion concentration decreases the QT interval, and it causes constipation and lack of appetite, probably because of depressed contractility of the muscular walls of the gastrointestinal tract.

The depressive effects of increased calcium level begin to appear when the blood level of calcium rises above approximately 12 mg. per cent, and they can become quite marked as the calcium level rises above 15 mg. per cent. When the level of calcium rises above approximately 17 mg. per cent in the body fluids, calcium phosphate is likely to precipitate throughout the body; this condition will be discussed shortly in connection with parathyroid poisoning.

BONE AND ITS RELATIONSHIPS WITH EXTRACELLULAR CALCIUM AND PHOSPHATES

Bone is composed of a tough *organic matrix* which is tremendously strengthened by deposits of *calcium salts.* Average *compact bone* contains approximately 35 per cent matrix and 65 per cent salts. However, *newly formed bone* may have a considerably higher percentage of matrix in relation to salts.

The Organic Matrix of Bone. The organic matrix of bone is approximately 95 per cent *collagen fibers* and the remaining 5 per cent is a homogeneous medium called *ground substance.* The collagen fibers extend in all directions in the bone but to a greater extent along the lines of tensional force. It is these fibers that give bone its very powerful tensile strength.

The ground substance is composed of extracellular fluid plus large quantities of mucopolysaccharides, including especially *chondroitin sulfate* and *hyaluronic acid.* The precise function of these mucopolysaccharides is not known, though perhaps they help to provide a medium for deposition of calcium salts.

The Bone Salts. The crystalline salts deposited in the organic matrix of bone are

reasons why this does not occur. First, so many different ions would have to come into apposition with each other at the same time to form a molecule of this substance that the probability of this happening is almost infinitesimal. Second, even those few molecules that do form develop so slowly that they can almost certainly be destroyed by different phosphatases long before any crystallization could take place. Therefore, hydroxyapatite crystals ordinarily grow only in tissues where CaHPO₄ can be deposited first, crystals of this salt forming nidi for later growth of the hydroxyapatite crystals, as described earlier in the chapter.

Precipitation of Calcium Salts in Non-osseous Tissues under Abnormal Conditions. Under certain abnormal conditions, calcium salts do precipitate in non-osseous tissues. For instance, calcium frequently combines with the fatty substances in atheromatous deposits of arteries, and these in turn become progressively altered into calcium salts that resemble those of bone. Likewise calcium salts can precipitate in cartilage (indeed, they usually do so in old age), and calcium salts frequently deposit in degenerating tissues. Presumably, in these instances, the local conditions become appropriate for deposition of CaHPO₄ or some similar calcium salt. Then these initial salts are progressively changed into salts similar to those in bone.

Occasionally, also, the calcium and phosphate concentrations of the extracellular fluids rise to a supersaturated state, in which case CaHPO₄ then begins to precipitate all through the body. Fortunately, when this occurs the initial precipitation of CaHPO₄ is in a colloidal form only in the extracellular fluids, and the minute crystals are immediately adsorbed to the plasma proteins. Because of this, moderate supersaturation of the calcium and phosphate in the extracellular fluids rarely causes extra-osseous calcification. Yet, extreme supersaturation can cause calcification, sometimes within a matter of hours, as will be discussed later in the chapter in relation to parathyroid hormone poisoning.

Deposition and Absorption of Bone

Deposition of Bone Matrix by the Osteoblasts. Bone is continually being deposited by *osteoblasts,* and it is continually being absorbed where *osteoclasts* are active. Osteoblasts are found on most of the surfaces of the bones and in many of the cavities. The osteoblasts secrete an organic material which, after being secreted, is polymerized mainly into collagen fibers to form the organic matrix of bone.

A small amount of osteoblastic activity occurs continually in all living bones so that at least some new bone matrix is being formed constantly. The matrix in turn possesses the special property to cause CaHPO₄ precipitation. Therefore, after being formed the matrix becomes calcified first with CaHPO₄, which then gradually grows into hydroxyapatite crystals over a period of succeeding weeks and months, as described earlier in the chapter.

Absorption of Bone—Function of the Osteoclasts. Bone is also being continually absorbed in the presence of osteoclasts, which are located in many of the cavities throughout all bones. Osteoclasts can form from osteocytes or osteoblasts, or they can even form from fibroblasts in the bone marrow. Later in the chapter we will see that parathyroid hormone controls the number of osteoclasts in the bones.

Histologically, bone absorption occurs immediately adjacent to the osteoclasts, as illustrated in Figure 715. Recent electron

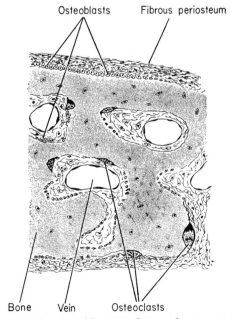

Osteoblasts   Fibrous periosteum

Bone   Vein   Osteoclasts

Figure 715. Osteoblastic and osteoclastic activity in the same bone.

microscopic studies have shown the presence of a few minute bone crystals inside the osteoclasts, which indicates that the osteoclasts in some instances phagocytically devour bony particles, then digest these, and finally release calcium, phosphate, and the digestive end-products of the organic matrix into the extracellular fluids. However, this phagocytic process probably is not the only, and perhaps not even the major, means by which bone is absorbed, for it is believed that most of the bone absorption results from osteoclastic secretion of enzymes or other substances that digest the organic matrix and then cause dissolution of the bone salts.

Equilibrium between Bone Deposition and Bone Absorption. Normally, except in growing bones, the rates of bone deposition and bone absorption are equal to each other so that the total mass of bone remains constant. However, osteoclasts will actually be eating holes in the bone in large areas, while in other areas new bone will be forming. Usually, osteoclasts exist in large masses, and once a mass of osteoclasts begins to develop, it usually eats away at the bone for about three weeks, eating out a hole that may be as great as a millimeter in diameter. At the end of this time the osteoclasts are converted into osteoblasts, and new bone begins to develop. Bone deposition then continues for several months, the new bone being layed down in successive layers on the inner surfaces of the cavity until the entire hole is filled up. Deposition of new bone ceases when the bone begins to encroach on the blood vessels supplying the area. The canal through which these vessels run, called the *Haversian canal,* therefore, is all that remains of the original cavity. Each new area of bone deposited in this way is called an *osteon,* as shown in Figure 716.

Value of continual deposition and absorption of bone. The continual deposition and absorption of bone has a number of physiologically important functions. First, bone ordinarily adjusts its strength in proportion to the degree of bone stress. Consequently, when bones are subjected to heavy loads, they become thickened. Second, even the shape of the bone can be rearranged for proper support of mechanical forces by appropriate deposition and absorption of

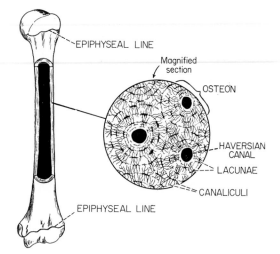

Figure 716. The structure of bone.

bone in accordance with the stress pattens applied to the bone. Third, old bone becomes relatively weak and brittle so that it is desirable to form new organic matrix as the old organic matrix degenerates. In this manner the normal toughness of bone is maintained. Indeed, the bones of children, in whom the rate of deposition and absorption is very rapid, show very little brittleness in comparison with the bones of old age at which time the rates of deposition and absorption are very slow.

Control of the Rate of Bone Deposition by Bone "Stress." It is well known that bone deposition occurs in proportion to the load that the bone must carry. For instance, the bones of athletes become considerably heavier than those of non-athletes. Also, if a person has one leg in a cast but continues to walk on the opposite leg, the bone of the leg in the cast become thin and decalcified, while the opposite bone remains thick and normally calcified. Therefore, it is evident that continual physical stress has a stimulating effect on osteoblastic deposition of new bone.

It is interesting that bone stress also determines the shape of bones under certain circumstances. For instance, if a long bone of the leg breaks in its center and then heals at an angle, the compression stress on the inside of the angle causes increased deposition of bone, while increased absorption occurs on the outer side of the angle where the bone is not compressed. After many years of increased deposition on the inner side of the angulated bone and absorption on the outer side, the bone becomes almost straight. This is especially true in children because of the rapid remodeling of bone that occurs at younger ages.

Repair of a Fracture. A fracture of a bone in some way maximally activates all the periosteal and intraosseous osteoblasts involved in the break. Indeed, even fibroblasts in some of the surrounding tissues become osteoblasts. Therefore, within a short time a large bulge of new organic matrix, followed shortly by the deposition of calcium salts, develops between the two broken ends of the bone. This is called a *callus*.

Many bone surgeons utilize the phenomenon of bone stress to accelerate the rate of fracture healing. This is done by use of special mechanical fixation apparatuses for holding the ends of the broken bone together so that the patient can use his bone immediately. This obviously causes stress on the opposed ends of the broken bones, which accelerates osteoblastic activity at the break and often greatly shortens the period of convalescence.

Blood Alkaline Phosphatase as an Indication of the Rate of Bone Deposition. The osteoblasts secrete large quantities of *alkaline phosphatase* when they are actively depositing bone matrix. This phosphatase is believed to help activate the collagen fibers so that they can aid in the deposition of calcium salts. Some of the alkaline phosphatase diffuses into the blood so that the blood level of alkaline phosphatase is almost always a good indication of the rate of bone formation. When the alkaline phosphatase level falls below normal, one can suspect that the rate of bone formation is depressed, but when it rises above normal, he can then suspect a rapid rate of bone formation at least somewhere in the body.

The alkaline phosphatase level is below normal in only a few diseases; this includes especially hypoparathyroidism. On the other hand, it is greatly elevated in many conditions such as (1) during growth of children, (2) following major bone fractures, and (3) in almost any bone disease which causes bone destruction and must be repaired by osteoblastic activity, such as rickets, osteomalacia, osteitis fibrosa cystica, and many others. Alkaline phosphatase is also secreted by osteoclasts, for which reason it is possible that excessive osteoclastic activity in some of these diseases could be the source of much of the phosphatase.

Another type of phosphatase, *acid phosphatase*, is also found in blood. This substance is called "acid phosphatase" because it is active in an acid medium in contrast to the alkaline medium required to activate alkaline phosphatase. Whenever acid phosphatase is found in the blood, which is rare, it is usually derived from cancer of the prostate that has metastasized very widely to the bones. Presumably, it is the prostatic cancer itself that secretes the acid phosphatase rather than the bone tissues.

PARATHYROID HORMONE

For many years it has been known that increased activity of the parathyroid gland causes rapid absorption of calcium salts from the bones with resultant hypercalcemia in the extracellular fluids and, conversely, that hypofunction of the parathyroid glands causes hypocalcemia often with resultant tetany, as described earlier in the chapter. It will also be obvious in the foregoing discussion that parathyroid hormone is quite important in phosphate metabolism as well as in calcium metabolism.

Physiologic Anatomy of the Parathyroid Glands. Normally there are four parathyroid glands, located immediately behind the thyroid gland—one behind each of the upper and each of the lower poles of the thyroid. Each parathyroid gland is only approximately 6 mm. in length, 3 mm. in width, and 2 mm. in thickness, and they have a macroscopic appearance of dark brown fat; therefore, they are very difficult to locate during thyroid operations. For this reason total or subtotal thyroidectomy frequently resulted in total removal of the parathyroid glands before the importance of these glands was generally recognized. Occasionally, parathyroid glands are located in the anterior mediastinum, or rarely they are even located in the posterior mediastinum. Also, fewer than four glands or as many as five to seven parathyroid glands sometimes exist. The possible location of these glands elsewhere than behind the thyroid gland must always be remembered by the surgeon who is searching for a parathyroid tumor that is causing hyperparathyroidism.

Removal of half the parathyroid glands usually causes very little physiologic abnormality. However, removal of three out of four of the normal glands in an animal will usually cause transient hypoparathyroidism. Thus, it is apparent that even a small quantity of remaining parathyroid tissue is capable of hypertrophying satisfactorily to perform the function of all the glands.

The parathyroid gland of the adult human,

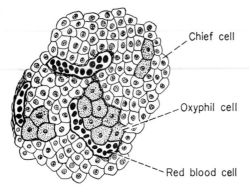

Figure 717.   Histologic structure of a parathyroid
gland.

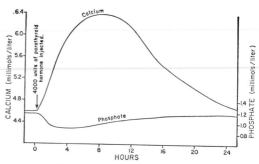

Figure 718.   Effect on plasma calcium and phosphate concentrations of injecting 4000 units of parathyroid hormone into a human being.

illustrated in Figure 717, contains both *chief cells* and *oxyphil cells*, but oxyphil cells are absent in many animals and in young human beings. Consequently, it is almost certain that the chief cells secrete parathyroid hormone; it is not known what the function of the oxyphil cells might be, though these also may be capable of secreting parathyroid hormone.

Chemistry of Parathyroid Hormone. Parathyroid hormone has never been isolated in a crystalline form. Furthermore, parathyroid extracts have at least five separate, distinguishable compounds, all of which exhibit parathyroid activity. It is possible that these are all breakdown products of a single hormone initially formed in the parathyroid glands. They are all either proteins or large polypeptides with molecular weights between 5000 and 10,000.

Effect of Parathyroid Hormone on Calcium and Phosphate Concentrations in the Extracellular Fluid

Figure 718 illustrates the effect of injecting parathyroid hormone into a human being, showing marked elevation in calcium ion concentration of the extracellular fluids and depression of phosphate concentration. The maximum effect of parathyroid hormone on phosphate is reached within 2 to 3 hours, while the maximum effect on calcium ion concentration is reached in about 8 hours and then lasts some 24 to 36 hours. The rise in calcium ion concentration is caused principally by a direct effect of parathyroid hormone to increase the absorption of bone. The decline in phosphate concentration, on the other hand, is caused principally by an effect of parathyroid hormone on the kidneys to increase the rate of phosphate excretion.

Bone Absorption Caused by Parathyroid Hormone. The absorptive effect of

parathyroid hormone in bones is believed to result from the ability of this hormone to increase the number of osteoclasts in bone and also to increase their osteoclastic activity. In turn, the osteoclasts secrete enzymes and other substances that absorb the bone or perhaps directly phagocytize the bony particles, digest these, and finally release calcium and phosphate into the body fluids.

Bone contains such tremendous amounts of calcium in comparison with the total amount in all the extracellular fluids (over 1000 times as much) that even when parathyroid hormone causes enough bone to be absorbed to cause a tremendous rise in calcium concentration of the body fluids, it is impossible to demonstrate any immediate effect at all on the bones. Yet, prolonged administration of parathyroid hormone finally results in discernible absorption in all the bones with development of large cavities filled with osteoclasts.

Increased Urinary Excretion of Phosphate Caused by Parathyroid Hormone. In addition to the primary effect of parathyroid hormone on bone absorption it also has a direct effect on the urinary tubules to decrease phosphate reabsorption, thereby allowing increased quantities of phosphate to be lost in the urine. This obviously decreases the extracellular fluid phosphate concentration.

In the past, it has been taught that parathyroid hormone might not have any direct action on bone itself but that its absorption results secondarily from the increased excretion of phosphate by the kidneys. That is, it was believed that the primary effect of parathyroid hormone was (a) to cause increased excretion of phosphate, which (b) would decrease the extracellular concentration of phosphate so much that bone salts

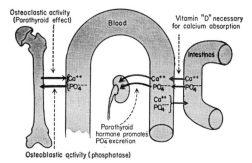

Figure 719. Interrelationships between (1) calcium and phosphate absorption from the intestines, (2) calcium and phosphate deposition and absorption from the bone, and (3) phosphate and calcium excretion via the kidneys and intestine.

would be absorbed, and (c) loss of the bone salts which would then cause the matrix to be absorbed. However, this theory has now been proved to be either completely false or at least to have little significance in the absorption of bone for the following reasons:

1. Implantation of small living sections of parathyroid gland adjacent to a bone causes large numbers of osteoclasts to develop in the immediate area, and this is followed by rapid local absorption of the bone.

2. Injection of parathyroid hormone into animals that have severe rickets will cause reabsorption of the newly formed matrix even though no salts are present in the matrix. Therefore, it is obvious that the matrix is not absorbed secondarily to the absorption of salts and that parathyroid hormone acts on both the matrix and the salts at the same time, indicating once again that the primary effect of parathyroid hormone is to increase the activity of the osteoclasts.

3. In animals with both kidneys removed so that excess excretion of phosphates cannot occur, administration of parathyroid hormone still causes the absorption of bone and also causes hypercalcemia in the extracellular fluids. Indeed, even the phosphate concentration rises under these conditions because the kidneys are not available to excrete the phosphate as the bone is absorbed.

Regulation of Extracellular Calcium Ion Concentration by the Parathyroid Glands

The calcium ion concentration in the extracellular fluids under normal conditions rarely varies more than 5 per cent above or below the normal concentration. Therefore, it is evident that calcium ion regulation is one of the most highly developed homeostatic mechanisms of the entire body. This regulation is effected almost entirely by the parathyroid glands in the following way:

Control of Parathyroid Secretion by Calcium Ion Concentration. Any decrease in calcium ion concentration in the extracellular fluid even to the slightest extent causes the parathyroid glands to increase their rate of secretion and to hypertrophy. For instance, the parathyroid glands become greatly enlarged in *rickets*, in which the level of calcium is usually depressed only a few per cent; also they become greatly enlarged in pregnancy, even though the calcium ion concentration in the mother's extracellular fluid hardly falls a measurable amount; and, finally, they are greatly enlarged during lactation because calcium is used for milk formation.

On the other hand, any condition that increases the calcium ion concentration causes decreased activity of the parathyroid glands and reduced size. Such conditions include (1) excess quantities of calcium in the diet, (2) increased vitamin D in the diet, and (3) bone absorption caused by other factors besides parathyroid hormone (for example, bone absorption caused by disuse of the bones).

Feedback Control of Calcium Ion Concentration. It can now be understood how the parathyroid glands control the calcium ion concentration in the extracellular fluids, for reduced calcium concentration increases the rate of parathyroid secretion, and this in turn increases the bone absorption, thereby raising the calcium ion concentration to normal. Conversely, increased calcium ion concentration inhibits the parathyroid glands, which automatically decreases the calcium ion concentration to normal.

It should be noted particularly that the regulatory properties of parathyroid hormone do not derive only from its effect on bone, for in addition it increases the absorption of calcium from the gut and from the renal tubules, which also helps to raise the calcium ion concentration. This is a particularly valuable effect when the bone salts have been so depleted that parathyroid hormone can no longer cause additional absorption of calcium from the bone.

Buffer Function of the Exchangeable Calcium in the Bones. The parathyroid hormone feedback control system is relatively slow to act, requiring many hours and sometimes days for maximal effect to occur when a new level of parathyroid secretion is required. Yet, at times the amount of calcium absorbed into or lost from the body fluids may be as much as a gram or more within a period of several hours. For instance, in diarrhea, several grams of calcium can be secreted in the intestinal juices into the intestinal tract and lost into the feces each day. Conversely, after a person eats large quantities of calcium in his diet, he may absorb a gram or more in a short period of time. This compares with a total quantity of calcium in all the extracellular fluids of less than a gram. Adding or subtracting one gram from such a small amount of calcium in the extracellular fluids would obviously cause very serious hyper- or hypocalcemia. However, this does not occur for the following reasons:

That portion of the bone salts that has recently been deposited in the bone is still in reversible equilibrium with the calcium and phosphate in the extracellular fluids. That is, an increase in the product of extracellular calcium and phosphate concentrations will cause immediate deposition of more bone salts in the bones. Conversely, a decrease in this product will cause immediate absorption of some of the bone salts. This reaction is so rapid that *a single passage of blood containing a high concentration of calcium through a bone removes almost all the excess calcium.* About 6 per cent of all the blood flows each minute through the bones, and this represents slightly over 1 per cent of all the extracellular fluid each minute going through the bones. Therefore, about one-half of any excess calcium that appears in the extracellular fluids will be removed by this buffer function of the bones in approximately 45 minutes. Or, conversely, the half-time for making up a deficiency in extracellular calcium ion concentration is also about 45 minutes.

The total amount of exchangeable calcium phosphate in the bones is only 5 or 6 grams; yet, before this can all be used up in buffering the calcium and phosphate concentrations in the blood, the parathyroid mechanism can come in to play. Parathyroid ab-

sorption of the bone affects primarily the hydroxyapatite rather than the exchangeable calcium and therefore provides an almost unlimited amount of calcium for maintaining the calcium ion concentration of the body fluids. The ease with which calcium and phosphate ions, as well as other ions in the extracellular fluid, can exchange between the bone and extracellular fluids depends on the fact that the total surface area of all the bone crystals in all the bones is about 30 acres.

Relationship of the Parathyroid Glands to Other Endocrine Glands

There are no known direct relationships between the parathyroid glands and other endocrine glands, though several indirect effects do occur. For instance, hypersecretion of adrenocortical glucocorticoids causes protein mobilization from the organic matrix of bone, thereby decreasing the quantity of matrix. This immediately releases calcium and phosphate into the blood, elevating the calcium ion concentration and reducing the activity of the parathyroid glands. Conversely, hyposecretion of glucocorticoids causes hypertrophy of the parathyroid glands.

Similarly, thyroxine mobilizes proteins, releases calcium, and causes reduced size of the parathyroid glands. On the other hand, the sex hormones and growth hormone increase the deposition of bone matrix, thereby reducing the calcium ion concentration and causing hypertrophy of the parathyroid glands.

PHYSIOLOGY OF PARATHYROID BONE DISEASES

Hypoparathyroidism

When the parathyroid glands do not secrete sufficient parathyroid hormone, the osteoclasts of the bone become extremely inactive. As a result, bone reabsorption is so depressed that the level of calcium in the body fluids decreases. Because calcium and phosphates are not being absorbed from the bone, the bone usually remains strong, and osteoblastic activity is decreased, presumably because there is less bone strain in relation to the strength of the bone. Thus, the bones in hypoparathyroidism are usually normal or almost normal, though new growth of bone may be suppressed.

After all the parathyroid glands are suddenly removed, the calcium level in the blood falls from the normal of 10 mg. per cent down to a value of 7 mg. per cent within 2 to 3 days. When this level is reached, the usual signs of tetany develop. Among the most sensitive muscles of the body to tetanic spasm are the laryngeal muscles. Spasm of these obstructs respiration, which is the usual cause of death in tetany unless appropriate treatment is applied.

Fortunately, improved operative technique for removal of the thyroid glands has greatly reduced the incidence of extreme hypoparathyroidism secondary to thyroidectomy. However, a number of persons do develop mild hypoparathyroidism of unknown cause, and they can exhibit mild to moderate signs of tetany.

If all four parathyroid glands are removed from an animal and the animal is prevented from dying of respiratory spasm by appropriate supportive measures, the total lack of parathyroid hormone secretion will normally cause the blood level of calcium to fall as low as approximately 6 mg. per cent while at the same time the level of phosphorus increases from the normal of about 4 mg. per cent to approximately 12 mg. per cent.

Metastatic Calcification throughout the Body in Hypoparathyroidism. During hypoparathyroidism of long standing the basal ganglia in the brain occasionally become calcified, and calcified cataracts also often develop in the eyes. Therefore, it is considered likely that the calcium and phosphate ions of the body fluids sometimes rise to a supersaturated state during hypoparathyroidism. This could possibly result from the greatly elevated phosphate level in hypoparathyroidism, even though the calcium level falls. It will be noted later that *excess* parathyroid hormone can also cause metastatic calcification of an extremely severe and rapidly developing type.

Aplasia of the Teeth. If hypoparathyroidism occurs in the growing child, the formation of new teeth almost ceases. Though this effect has not been explained, it could possibly result from decreased absorption of calcium in the renal tubules and gut caused by deficient quantities of parathyroid hormone. Patients with hypoparathyroidism are also slow to calcify the organic matrix of new bone. This could possibly be explained by the same mechanism.

Treatment of Hypoparathyroidism. *Parathyroid hormone (parathormone).* Parathyroid hormone is occasionally used for treating hypoparathyroidism. However, because of the expense of this hormone, because its effect lasts only about 24 to 36 hours, and because the tendency of the body to develop immune bodies against it makes it progressively less and less active in the body, treatment of hypoparathyroidism with parathyroid hormone is rare in present-day therapy.

Dihydrotachysterol and vitamin D. In addition to its ability to cause increased absorption of calcium from the gastrointestinal tract, vitamin D also causes a weak effect similar to that of parathyroid hormone in promoting calcium and phosphate absorption from bones. This in turn elevates the calcium concentration in the body fluids. Therefore, a patient with hypoparathyroidism can be treated satisfactorily by administration of large quantities of vitamin D.

One of the vitamin D componds, dihydrotachysterol (A.T. 10), has a more marked ability to cause bone absorption and a less significant tendency to promote calcium absorption from the gastrointestinal tract than most of the other vitamin D compounds have. In other words, dihydrotachysterol has an action very similar to that of parathyroid hormone, and its effect lasts for 3 to 4 days. Therefore, administration of calcium plus dihydrotachysterol three or more times a week can effect almost complete control of calcium level in the extracellular fluid of a hypoparathyroid patient.

Pseudohypoparathyroidism. Recently a condition has been described with symptoms similar to those of true hypoparathyroidism but in which the parathyroid glands seem to be excessively active and to secrete even greater than normal quantities of parathyroid hormone. Pathologically, the parathyroid glands are hyperplastic, even though the patient has hypoparathyroid effects throughout the body, including a low blood calcium level, a high blood phosphate level, and a tendency for depressed rate of bone growth probably because of depressed osteoblastic activity. For instance, the metacarpals of the hand are especially short, the entire stature is very short, and the face has an extremely round appearance.

The cause of pseudohypoparathyroidism is not known, but, because these patients are not responsive to treatment with parathyroid hormone, it is believed that pseudohypoparathyroidism is due to failure of the body to respond to parathyroid hormone. For this reason, the level of calcium in the extracellular fluid is not controlled. Treatment of these patients with dihydrotachysterol and calcium therapy is effective as is true in the usual case of hypoparathyroidism, even though parathormone therapy is ineffective. Thus, it is probable that dihydrotachysterol operates to cause bone absorption by a mechanism different from that of parathyroid hormone.

Hyperparathyroidism

The cause of hyperparathyroidism ordinarily is a tumor of one of the parathyroid glands, and such tumors occur much more frequently in women than in men or children. Consequently, it is believed that pregnancy, lacation, and perhaps other causes of prolonged low calcium levels, all of which stimulate the parathyroid gland, may predispose to the development of such a tumor.

In hyperparathyroidism extreme osteoclastic activity occurs in the bones, and this elevates the calcium ion concentration in the extracellular fluid while usually (but not always) depressing slightly the concentration of phosphate ions.

Bone Disease in Hyperparathyroidism. Though in mild hyperparathyroidism deposition of new bone may occur rapidly enough to compensate for the osteoclastic reabsorption of bone, in severe hyperparathyroidism, the osteoclastic absorption soon far outstrips osteoblastic deposition of new bone, and the bone may be eaten almost entirely away by the osteoclastic activity. Indeed, the reason a patient with hyperparathyroidism comes to the doctor is often a broken bone. X-ray of the bone shows tremendous decalcification and occasionally shows large punched-out cystic areas of the bone that are due to osteoclasts in the form of giant cell "tumors." Obviously, multiple fractures of the weakened bones result from only slight trauma, especially where the cysts develop. The cystic bone disease of hyperparathyroidism is frequently called *osteitis fibrosa cystica* or *von Recklinghausen's* disease.

As a result of the increased osteoblastic activity, the level of alkaline phosphatase in the body fluids rises markedly.

Effects of Hypercalcemia in Hyperparathyroidism. Hyperparathyroidism can at times cause the plasma calcium level to rise to as high as 15 to 20 mg. per cent. The effects of such elevated calcium levels, as detailed earlier in the chapter, are depression of the central and peripheral nervous systems, muscular weakness, constipation, abdominal pain, lack of appetite, and prolonged cardiac systole. Often the most striking of all these is the abdominal pain.

Parathyroid poisoning and metastatic calcification. When extreme quantities of parathyroid hormones are secreted, the level of calcium in the body fluids rises rapidly to very high values, and the extracellular fluid phosphate concentration also often rises markedly, probably because the kidneys cannot excrete rapidly enough all the phosphate being absorbed from the bone. Therefore, the calcium and phosphate in the body fluids become greatly supersaturated, and calcium phosphate crystals begin to deposit in the alveoli of the lungs, in the tubules of the kidneys, in the thyroid gland, in the acid-producing area of the stomach mucosa, and in the walls of the arteries throughout the body. This extensive metastatic deposition of calcium phosphate can develop within a few days, illustrating how rapidly calcium phosphate crystals are deposited whenever a state of supersaturation occurs in the extracellular fluid. This effect further emphasizes the fact that supersaturation in the extracellular fluid probably occurs only under such rare conditions as parathyroid poisoning.

Ordinarily, the level of calcium in the blood must rise above 17 mg. per cent before there is any danger of parathyroid poisoning, but once such elevation develops along with some concurrent elevation of phosphate, death frequently occurs in only a few days.

Formation of kidney stones in hyperparathyroidism. Some patients with mild hyperparathyroidism show few signs of bone disease and few general abnormalities as a result of elevated calcium but, instead, have an extreme tendency to form kidney stones. The reason for this is that almost all the excess calcium and phosphate mobilized from the bones in hyperparathyroidism is excreted by the kidneys, causing proportionate increase in the concentration of these substances in the urine. As a result, crystals of calcium phosphate tend to precipitate in the kidney, forming calcium phosphate stones. Also, calcium oxalate stones develop as a result of the high level of calcium in the urine in association with normal levels of oxalate. Because the solubility of most renal stones is slight in alkaline media, the tendency for formation of renal calculi is considerably greater in alkaline urine than in acid urine. For this reason, acidotic diets and drugs are frequently used for treating renal calculi.

Secondary Hyperparathyroidism. Because a low level of calcium ions in the body fluids directly increases the secretion of parathyroid hormone, any factor that causes a low level of calcium initiates the condition known as *secondary hyperparathyroidism.* This may result from (1) low calcium diet, (2) pregnancy, (3) lactation, (4) rickets, and (5) osteomalacia. The hyperplasia of the parathyroid glands is almost certainly a corrective measure for maintaining the level of calcium in the body fluids at a nearly normal value.

Rickets

Rickets occurs mainly in children as a result of calcium or phosphate deficiency in the body fluids. Ordinarily, rickets is due to a lack of vitamin D rather than to lack of calcium or phosphate in the diet. If the child is properly exposed to sunlight, the 7-dehydrocholesterol in the skin becomes activated by the ultraviolet rays and forms vitamin D_3, which prevents rickets by promoting calcium and phosphate absorption from the intestines as discussed earlier in the chapter.

Children who remain indoors through the winter in general do not receive adequate quantities of vitamin D without some supplementary therapy of vitamin D in the diet. Rickets tends to occur especially in the spring months because vitamin D formed during the preceding summer can be stored for several months in the liver, and, also, calcium and phosphorus absorption from the bones must take place for several months before clinical signs of rickets become apparent.

Calcium and phosphate in the blood of patients with rickets. Ordinarily, the level of calcium in the blood in rickets is only slightly depressed, but the level of phosphate is greatly depressed. The reason for this is that the parathyroid glands prevent the calcium level from falling by promoting bone absorption every time the calcium level begins to fall. On the other hand, there is no good regulatory system for controlling a falling level of phosphate, and the increased parathyroid activity actually increases the excretion of phosphates in the urine.

Effect of rickets on the bone. During prolonged deficiency of calcium and phosphate in the body fluids, increased parathyroid hormone secretion protects the body against hypocalcemia by causing osteoclastic absorption of the bone; this in turn causes the bone to become progressively weaker and weaker and imposes marked physical stress on the bone, resulting in very rapid osteoblastic activity. The osteoblasts lay down large quantities of organic bone matrix, which does not become calcified because even with the "crystal seeding" effect of the matrix the product of the calcium and phosphate ions is still insufficient to cause calcification. Consequently, the newly formed, uncalcified organic matrix gradually takes the place of other bone that is being reabsorbed.

Obviously, hyperplasia of the parathyroid glands is very marked in rickets because of the decreased blood calcium level, and the alkaline phosphatase level in the blood is markedly increased as a result of the rapid osteoblastic activity.

Tetany in rickets. In the early stages of rickets, tetany almost never occurs because the parathyroid glands continually stimulate osteoclastic absorption of bone and therefore maintain an almost normal level of calcium in the body fluids. However, when the bones become exhausted of calcium, the level of calcium then may fall rapidly. As the blood level of calcium falls below 7 mg. per cent, the usual signs of tetany develop, and the child may die of tetanic respiratory spasm unless intravenous calcium is administered, which relieves the tetany immediately.

Treatment of rickets. The treatment of rickets, obviously, depends upon supplying adequate calcium and phosphate in the diet and also upon adequate administration of vitamin D. If vitamin D is not administered along with the calcium, very little calcium will be absorbed, and

this calcium in turn will carry large quantities of phosphate with it into the feces.

Tetany resulting from treatment. Occasionally, tetany occurs when a child is treated for rickets, for the following reason: Administration of calcium and phosphate in the diet without sufficient vitamin D often results in better absorption of phosphate than of calcium. As a result, the phosphate level in the blood is likely to rise rapidly. Then, because the osteoblasts are already extremely active, the increase in the phosphate level apparently causes rapid deposition of bone salts in the newly formed organic matrix, thus removing excessive quantities of calcium from the blood and causing the calcium level to fall so much that tetany supervenes. This difficulty can be prevented by administration of sufficient quantities of vitamin D and larger quantities of calcium than phosphate.

Osteomalacia. Osteomalacia is rickets in adults and is frequently called "adult rickets."

Normal adults very rarely have dietary lack of vitamin D or calcium because large quantities of calcium are not needed for bone growth as in children. However, lack of vitamin D and calcium occasionally occurs as a result of steatorrhea (failure to digest fat), for vitamin D is fat soluble and calcium tends to form insoluble soaps with fat; consequently, in steatorrhea vitamin D and calcium tend to pass into the feces. Under these conditions an adult occasionally has such poor calcium and phosphate absorption that "adult rickets" can occur, though this rarely proceeds to the same stages as it does in childhood.

Osteomalacia and rickets caused by renal disease. "Renal rickets" is a type of osteomalacia resulting from prolonged kidney damage. The kidney disease prevents normal excretion of acids and leads to acidosis. This in turn converts most of the HPO_4^- of the blood into $H_2PO_4^-$, which does not precipitate in bones. Therefore, the essential picture of renal rickets is progressive osteomalacia.

Another type of renal disease that leads to rickets and osteomalacia is *congenital hypophosphatemia* resulting from congenitally reduced reabsorption of phosphates by the renal tubules. This type of rickets must be treated with phosphate compounds instead of calcium and vitamin D, and it is called *vitamin D resistant rickets*.

Osteoporosis

Osteoporosis is a different disease from osteomalacia and rickets, for it results from abnormal organic matrix formation rather than abnormal bone calcification. In general, in osteoporosis the osteoblastic activity in the bone is less than normal, and consequently the rate of bone deposition is depressed. The causes of osteoporosis are (1) lack of use of the bones, (2) malnutrition to the extent that sufficient protein matrix cannot be formed, (3) lack of vitamin C, which apparently is necessary for the secretion of intercellular substances by all cells including the osteoblasts, (4) postmenopausal lack of estrogen secretion, for estrogens have an osteoblastic stimulating activity, (5) old age, in which many of the protein anabolic functions are very poor anyway so that bone matrix cannot be satisfactorily deposited, (6) Cushing's disease, because massive quantities of adrenocortical hormones cause decreased deposition of protein throughout the body and cause increased catabolism of protein, and (7) acromegaly, possibly because of lack of sex hormones, excess of adrenocortical hormones, and often lack of insulin because of the diabetogenic effect of adenohypophyseal hormones.

It is obvious then, that many diseases of protein metabolism can cause osteoporosis. Also, failure to stimulate osteoblastic activity by appropriate stress and strain on the bone, such failure occurring in lack of use of the bone, can result in poor osteoblastic activity.

The bone that is formed in osteoporosis, though thin and porous, is well supplied with bone salts, and there is no abnormality of calcium or phosphate concentrations in the body fluids in this condition.

Paget's Disease

Paget's disease occurs in middle to late life and is characterized by considerably thickened but weakened bones ("marble bones"). Paget's disease apparently is caused by very rapid reabsorption of bone, but the cause of the rapid reabsorption is not known. To offset the rapid reabsorption, rapid osteoblastic activity also occurs, and consequently the level of alkaline phosphatase in the body fluids is considerably increased.

The reabsorption of bone in Paget's disease and the osteoblastic activity occur at such rapid rates that bone deposition does not observe the normal controlling influence of stress and strain. Consequently, the trabeculae of the bones are not properly organized for resisting the usual mechanical forces applied to the bone. Furthermore, malformation of the organic matrix leads to thickened and very highly calcified trabeculae, but, despite this, the bones are weak. The weakness of the bones allows compression of the vertebrae so that one of the signs of the disease is a decrease in the height of the patient.

There is evidence that the deposition of bone salts in Paget's disease may occur in a considerably higher ratio than the normal 3 to 2 ratio for salts to organic matrix. This indicates that Paget's disease results from formation of an abnormal type of bone matrix and not from a primary abnormality in calcium or phosphate metabolism.

PHYSIOLOGY OF THE TEETH

The teeth cut, grind, and mix the food. To perform these functions the jaws have extremely powerful muscles capable of providing an occlusive force between the front teeth of as much as 50 to 100 pounds and as much as 150 to 200 pounds for the jaw teeth. Also, the upper and lower teeth are provided with projections and facets which interdigitate with each other so that each set of teeth fits with the other. This fitting is called *occlusion,* and it allows even small particles of food to be caught and ground between the tooth surfaces.

Function of the Different Parts of the Teeth

Figure 720 illustrates a sagittal section of a tooth, showing its major functional parts, the *enamel,* the *dentine,* the *cementum,* and the *pulp.* The tooth can also be divided into the *crown,* which is the portion that protrudes out of the gum into the mouth, and the *root,* which is the portion that protrudes into the bony socket of the jaw. The collar between the crown and the root where the tooth is surrounded by the gum is called the *neck.*

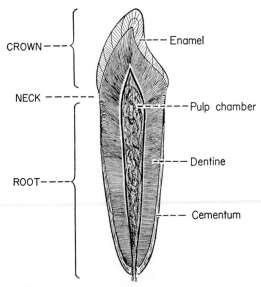

Figure 720. Functional parts of a tooth.

Dentine. The main body of the tooth is composed of *dentine*, which has a very strong, bony structure. Dentine is made up principally of calcium phosphate salts embedded in a strong meshwork of collagen fibers. In other words, the principal constituents of dentine are very much the same as those of bone. The major difference is its histologic organization, for dentine does not contain any osteoblasts, osteoclasts, nor spaces for blood vessels or nerves. Instead, it is deposited and nourished by a layer of cells called *odontoblasts*, which line its inner surface along the wall of the pulp cavity.

The calcium salts in dentine make it extremely resistant to compressional forces, while the collagen fibers make it tough and resistant to tensional forces that might result when the teeth are struck by solid objects.

Enamel. The outer surface of the tooth is covered by a layer of *enamel* that is formed prior to eruption of the tooth by special epithelial cells called *ameloblasts*. Once the tooth has erupted no more enamel is formed. Enamel is composed of very small crystals of calcium phosphate with adsorbed carbonate, magnesium, sodium, potassium and other ions embedded in a fine meshwork of *keratin* fibers. The smallness of the crystalline structure of the salts makes the enamel extremely hard, much harder than the dentine. Also, the keratin meshwork makes enamel very resistant to acids, enzymes, and other corrosive agents because keratin itself is one of the most insoluble and resistant proteins known.

Cementum. *Cementum* is a bony substance secreted by cells in the *periodontal membrane*, that lines the tooth socket. Many collagen fibers pass directly from the bone of the jaw, through the periodontal membrane, and then into the cementum. It is these collagen fibers and the cementum that hold the tooth in place. When the teeth are exposed to excessive strain the layer of cementum increases in thickness and strength. Also, it increases in thickness and strength with age, causing the teeth to become progressively more firmly seated in the jaws as one reaches adulthood and older.

Pulp. The inside of each tooth is filled with *pulp*, which in turn is composed of connective tissue with an abundant supply of nerves, blood vessels, and lymphatics. The cells lining the surface of the pulp cavity are the odontoblasts, which, during the formative years of the tooth, lay down the dentine but at the same time encroach more and more on the pulp cavity, making it smaller. In later life the dentine stops growing and the pulp cavity remains essentially constant in size. However, the odontoblasts are still viable and send projections into small *dentinal tubules* that penetrate all the way through the dentine; these probably are of importance for providing nutrition.

The nerves entering the pulp do not pass into the dentine. Nevertheless, dentine that has had its enamel layer broken away is very pain sensitive, indicating that the projections of the odontoblasts into the dentinal tubules might in some way transmit sensations, particularly pain sensations, from the substance of the dentine into the nerve fibers of the pulp cavity.

Dentition

Each human being and most other mammals develop two sets of teeth during a lifetime. The first teeth are called the *deciduous teeth* or *milk teeth*, and they number 20 in the human being. These erupt between the seventh month and second year of life, and they last until the sixth to the thirteenth year. After each deciduous tooth is lost, a permanent tooth replaces it, and an additional 8 to 12 molars appear posteriorly in the jaw, making the total number of permanent teeth 28 to 32, depending upon whether the four *wisdom teeth* finally appear, which does not occur in everyone.

Formation of the Teeth. Figure 721 illustrates the formation and eruption of teeth. Figure 721 A shows invagination of the oral epithelium into the *dental lamina;* this is followed by the development of a tooth-producing organ. The epi-

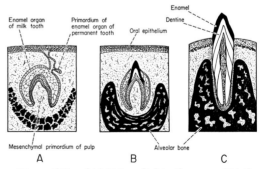

Figure 721. (A) Primordial tooth organ, (B) the developing tooth, (C) the erupting tooth. (Modified from Maximow and Bloom: A Textbook of Histology.)

thelial cells above form ameloblasts, which secrete the enamel on the outside of the tooth. The epithelial cells below invaginate upward to form a pulp cavity and also to form the odontoblasts that secrete dentine. Thus, enamel is secreted on the outside of the tooth, and dentine is secreted on the inside, forming an early tooth, as illustrated in Figure 721 B.

Eruption of teeth. During early childhood, the teeth begin to protrude upward from the jaw bone through the oral epithelium into the mouth. The cause of "eruption" is unknown, though several theories have been offered in an attempt to explain this phenomenon. One of these assumes that an increase of the material inside the pulp cavity of the tooth causes much of it to be extruded downward through the root canal and that this pushes the tooth upward. However, a more likely theory is that the bone surrounding the tooth progressively hypertrophies and in so doing shoves the tooth forward toward the gingival margin.

Development of the permanent teeth. During embryonic life, a tooth-forming organ also develops in the dental lamina for each permanent tooth that will be needed after the deciduous teeth are gone. These tooth-producing organs slowly form the permanent teeth throughout the first 6 to 20 years of life. When each permanent tooth becomes fully formed, it, like the deciduous tooth, pushes upward through the bone of the jaw toward the gingival margin. In so doing it erodes the root of the deciduous tooth and eventually causes it to loosen and fall out. Soon thereafter, the permanent tooth erupts to take the place of the original one.

Metabolic factors in the development of the teeth. The rate of development and the speed of eruption of teeth can be accelerated by both thyroid and growth hormones. Also, the deposition of salts in the early forming teeth is affected considerably by various factors of metabolism, such as the availability of calcium and phosphate in the diet, the amount of vitamin D present, and the rate of parathyroid hormone secretion. When all these factors are normal, the dentine and enamel will be correspondingly healthy, but, when they are deficient, the calcification of the teeth also may be defective so that the teeth will be abnormal throughout life.

Mineral Exchange in Teeth

The salts of teeth, like those of bone, are composed basically of calcium phosphate with adsorbed carbonates and various cations bound together in a very hard crystalline substance. Also, new calcium salts are constantly being deposited while old salts are being reabsorbed from the teeth, as also occurs in bone. However, experiments indicate that deposition and reabsorption occur only in the dentine and cementum, while almost none, if any at all, occurs in the enamel. The rate of absorption and deposition of minerals in the cementum is approximately equal to that in the surrounding bone of the jaw, while the rate of deposition and absorption of minerals in the dentine is only one-third that of bone. The cementum has characteristics, including the presence of osteoblasts and osteoclasts, almost identical with those of usual bone, while dentine does not have these characteristics as was explained above; this difference undoubtedly explains the different rates of mineral exchange.

The mechanism by which minerals are deposited and reabsorbed from the dentine is unknown. It is possible that the small processes of the odontoblasts protruding into the tubules of the dentine are capable of absorbing salts and then providing new salts to take the place of the old. It is also possible, though this too has never been proved, that the odontoblasts provide continuous replacement of the collagen fibers of the dentine. This would be comparable to the rejuvenation of the bone matrix by osteoblasts, which is necessary for adequate maintenance of bone strength.

In summary, mineral exchange is known to occur in the dentine and cementum of teeth, though at present the mechanism of this exchange in dentine is unknown. On the other hand, enamel seems to maintain its original mineral complement throughout life or until some abrasive or eroding action causes its destruction.

Dental Abnormalities

The two most common dental abnormalities are *caries* and *malocclusion*. Caries means erosions of the teeth, while malocclusion means failure of the projections of the upper and lower teeth to interdigitate properly with each other.

Caries. Two major but differing theories have been proposed to explain the cause of caries. One of these postulates that acids formed in crevices of the teeth by acid-producing bacteria cause erosion and absorption of the protein matrix of the enamel and dentine. This theory assumes that the acids are formed by splitting carbohydrates into lactic acid. For this reason it has been taught that eating a diet high in carbohydrate content and, particularly, eating large quantities of sweets between meals can lead to excessive development of caries.

The second theory proposes that proteolytic enzymes secreted by bacteria in the crevices of the teeth or in plaques that develop on the surfaces of unbrushed teeth digest the keratin matrix of the enamel. Then the calcium salts, unprotected by their protein fibers, are slowly dissolved by the saliva.

It is not known which of the above theories correctly describes the primary process for development of caries. Indeed, both of them might be operative simultaneously to cause carious teeth.

Some teeth are more resistant to caries than others. Studies in recent years indicate that teeth formed in children who drink water containing small amounts of fluorine will develop enamel that is more resistant to caries than will the enamel in children who drink water not containing fluorine. Fluorine does not make the enamel harder than usual, but instead it is said to inactivate proteolytic enzymes before they can digest the protein matrix of the enamel. Regardless of the precise means by which fluorine protects the teeth, it is known that small amounts of fluorine deposited in enamel make teeth about twice as resistant to caries as are teeth without fluorine.

Caries during pregnancy. For many years it has been believed that pregnancy causes mineral absorption from teeth and consequently predisposes to caries. Statistical studies, first, have not wholly substantiated the idea that caries occur in pregnant mothers in greater numbers than in other women of the same age. However, if the supposition that the teeth are harmed by pregnancy is true, it is probably not because of mineral absorption but instead because of a change in the bacterial flora in the mouth during pregnancy, for absorption of salts from the enamel does not occur in pregnancy, and the amount of absorption from the dentine is so slight that there is no reason whatsoever to believe that this could result in the development of caries.

Malocclusion. Malocclusion is usually caused by a heredity abnormality that causes the teeth of one of the jaws to grow in an abnormal direction. When malocclusion occurs, the teeth cannot perform their normal grinding or cutting action adequately; occasionally malocclusion results in abnormal displacement of the lower jaw in relation to the upper jaw, causing such undesirable effects as pressure on the anterior portion of the ear or pain in the mandibular joint.

The orthodontist can often correct malocclusion by applying prolonged gentle pressure against the teeth with appropriate braces. The gentle pressure causes absorption of alveolar jaw bone on the compressed side of the tooth and deposition of new bone on the tensional side of the tooth. In this way the tooth gradually moves to a new position as directed by the applied pressure.

REFERENCES

Adams, C. Philip: Design and Construction of Removable Orthodontic Appliances. 2nd ed., Baltimore, Williams & Wilkins Co., 1957.

Albright, F.: The Parathyroid Glands and Metabolic Bone Disease: Selected Studies. Baltimore, Williams & Wilkins Co., 1948.

Bartter, F. C.: The parathyroids. *Ann. Rev. Physiol.*, 16:429, 1954.

Bauer, W., Ropes, M. W., and Waine, H.: The physiology of articular structures. *Physiol. Rev.*, 20:272, 1940.

Black, B. M.: Hyperparathyroidism. Springfield, Illinois, Charles C Thomas, 1953.

Bogdonoff, M. D., Woods, A. H., White, J. E., and Engel, F. L.: Hyperparathyroidism. *Am. J. Med.*, 21:583, 1956.

Buxbaum, J. D., Kohn, H., Proutt, L. M., and Oster, R. H.: The effect of diet on the deposition of glycoprotein in the teeth and its relationship to dental caries in the enamel surface. *J. Dent. Res.*, 36:173, 1957.

Ciba Foundation: Symposia Volumes. Bone Structure and Metabolism. Boston, Little, Brown and Co., 1956.

Copp, D. H.: Calcium and phosphorus metabolism. *Am. J. Med.*, 22:275, 1957.

Daum, K., Tuttle, W. W., Gugedahl, A., Roberts, H., and Salzano, J.: Nitrogen, calcium, and phosphorus utilization by 12- to 14-year-old boys. *J. Am. Diet. Ass.*, 32:36, 1956.

Daum, K., Tuttle, W. W., Weber, A., Schumacher, M. T., and Salzano, J.: Calcium and phosphorus utilization in older men. *J. Am. Diet. Assoc.*, 31:149, 1955.

Ficarra, B. J.: Diseases of the Thyroid and Parathyroid Glands. New York, Grune & Stratton, Inc., 1958.

Foulks, J. G., and Perry, F. A.: Renal excretion of phosphate following parathyroidectomy in the dog. *Am. J. Physiol.*, 196:554, 1959.

Grollman, A.: Effect of cortisone on serum calcium, magnesium and phosphate levels in nephrectomized dogs. *Proc. Soc. Exp. Biol. & Med.*, 85:582, 1954.

Grollman, A.: Parathyroid syndromes and calcium metabolism. *Texas State J. Med.*, 54:476, 1958.

Grollman, A.: The role of the kidney in the parathyroid control of the blood calcium as determined by studies on the nephrectomized dog. *Endocrinology*, 55:166, 1954.

Haldi, J., Wynn, W., Law, M. L., and Bentley, K. D.: Dental caries in the albino rat in relation to the chemical composition of the teeth and of the diet. I. Effect of prenatal and postnatal feeding of high protein, high fat, and high carbohydrate diets. *J. Nutrit.*, 57:215, 1955.

Haldi, J., Wynn, W., Law, M. L., Bentley, K. D., and Ramsey, D. A.: Dental caries in relation to pH on tooth surfaces. I. pH and lactate concentration in relation to the extent of the lesions in rat's teeth. *J. Nutrit.*, *60:*427, 1956.

Howard, P. J., Wilde, W. S., and Malvin, R. L.: Localization of renal calcium transport; effect of calcium loads and of gluconate anion on water, sodium and potassium. *Am. J. Physiol.*, *197:*337, 1959.

Jenkins, G. M.: The Physiology of the Mouth. 2nd ed., Oxford, Blackwell Scientific Publications Ltd., 1960.

Kenny, A. D., Draskoczy, P. R., and Goldhaber, P.: Citric acid production by resorbing bone in tissue culture. *Am. J. Physiol.*, *197:*502, 1959.

Leicester, H. M.: Biochemistry of the Teeth. St. Louis, C. V. Mosby Co., 1949.

McElroy, W. D., and Glass, H. B.: Phosphorus Metabolism. Vols. I and II. Baltimore, Johns Hopkins Press, 1951 and 1952.

McLean, F. C., and Budy, A. M.: Connective and supporting tissues: bone. *Ann. Rev. Physiol.*, *21:* 69, 1959.

McLean, F. C., and Urist, M. R.: Bone. Chicago, University of Chicago Press, 1955.

Nicolaysen, R., Eeg-Larson, N., and Malm, O. J.: Physiology of calcium metabolism. *Physiol. Rev.*, *33:*424, 1953.

Rodahl, K. (ed.), Nicholson, J. T., and Brown, E. M.: Bone as a Tissue. New York, McGraw-Hill Book Co., Inc., 1960.

Ropes, A. W.: Synovial Fluid Changes in Joint Disease. Cambridge, Harvard University Press, 1953.

Schacter, D., Dowdle, E. B., and Schenker, H.: Active transport of calcium by the small intestine of the rat. *Am. J. Physiol.*, *198:*263, 1960.

Shaw, J. H.: Caries-inhibiting agents. *Pharmacol. Rev.*, *11:*705, 1959.

Stetten, D., Jr., Talbott, J. H., Seegiller, J. E., Wyngaarden, J. B., and Laster, L.: The pathogenesis of gout. *Metabolism*, *6:*88, 1957.

Symposium on effects of high calcium intakes. *Fed. Proc.*, *18:*1075, 1959.

Talbott, J. H.: Gout. 2nd ed., New York, Grune & Stratton, Inc., 1957.

Thompson, D. D.: Renal excretion of calcium and phosphorus. *Arch. Int. Med.*, *103:*832, 1959.

Weinmann, J. P.: Bone and Bones. St. Louis, C. V. Mosby Co., 1955.

Wynn, W., and Haldi, J.: Dental caries in the albino rat on fluoridated and distilled water. *J. Nutrit.*, *55:* 235, 1955.

Wynn, W., and Haldi, J.: Dental caries in the albino rat on high sucrose diets containing different amounts of aluminum. *J. Nutrit.*, *54:*285, 1954.

Wynn, W., Haldi, J., Bentley, K. D., and Law, M. L.: Dental caries in the albino rat in relation to the chemical composition of the teeth and of the diet. II. Variations in the Ca/P ratio of the diet induced by changing the phosphorus content. *J. Nutrit.*, *58:* 325, 1956.

See also Chapter 73, General bibliography on endocrinology.

Chapter 78

Reproductive Functions of the Male, and the Male Sex Hormones

The reproductive functions of the male may be divided into three major subdivisions: first, spermatogenesis, which means simply the formation of sperm; second, performance of the male sexual act; and third, regulation of male sexual functions by the various hormones. Associated with these reproductive functions are the effects of the male sex hormones on the accessory sex organs, on cellular metabolism, on growth, and on other functions of the body.

Physiologic Anatomy of the Male Sex Organs. Figure 722 illustrates the various portions of the male reproductive system. It will be

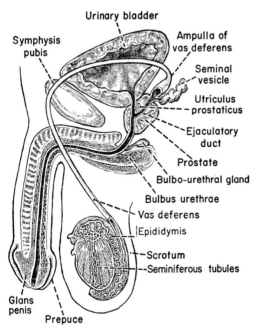

Figure 722. The male reproductive system (Modified from: Maximow and Bloom: Textbook of Histology.)

noted from this figure that the testis is composed of a large number of *seminiferous tubules* where the sperm are formed. The sperm then empty into the *vasa recta* and from there into the *epididymis*. The epididymis leads into the *vas deferens*, which enlarges into the *ampulla of the vas deferens* immediately proximal to the prostate gland. A *seminal vesicle*, one located on each side of the prostate, empties into the prostatic end of the ampulla, and then the contents from both the ampulla and the seminal vesicle pass into an *ejaculatory duct* leading through the body of the prostate gland to empty into the *internal urethra*. Finally, the *urethra* is the last connecting link from the testis to the exterior. The urethra is supplied with mucus derived from a large number of small glands of Littre located along its entire extent and also from large bilateral *bulbo-urethral glands* (Cowper's glands) located near the origin of the urethra.

SPERMATOGENESIS

Spermatogenesis occurs in all of the seminiferous tubules during active sexual life, beginning at the age of approximately 12 as the result of stimulation by adenohypophyseal gonadotropic hormones and continuing throughout the remainder of life.

The Steps of Spermatogenesis

The seminiferous tubules, which are illustrated in Figure 723 A, contain a large number of small to medium-sized cells called *spermatogonia*, which are located in two to three layers along the outer border of the tubular epithelium. These continually proliferate and differentiate through definite stages of development to form sperm, as shown in Figure 723 B.

The first stage in spermatogenesis is

1067

A

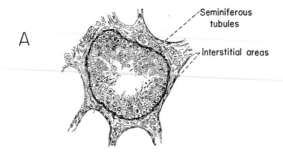

Seminiferous tubules

Interstitial areas

B

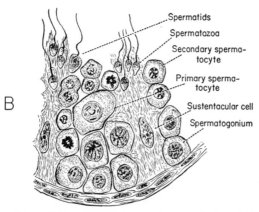

Spermatids

Spermatozoa

Secondary spermatocyte

Primary spermatocyte

Sustentacular cell

Spermatogonium

Figure 723. (A) The seminiferous tubules, (B) spermatogenesis. (Modified from Arey: Developmental Anatomy.)

growth of a portion of the spermatogonia to form considerably enlarged cells called *primary spermatocytes.* Then each of the 46 chromosomes in the primary spermatocyte autocatalytically synthesizes a new chromosome of its own type making a total of 92 chromosomes. Immediately thereafter, the primary spermatocyte goes through two *meiotic divisions* in the following way: First, the cell divides into two *secondary spermatocytes,* each of which contains 46 chromosomes. Soon each of these cells divides again to form two *spermatids,* each of which now contains only 23 chromosomes, none of them paired. Thus, one of each pair of the original 46 chromosomes is now in each spermatid. Later it will be noted that one of each pair of chromosomes is also lost during maturation of the ovum, but, on recombination of a spermatozoon with an ovum, the original complement of 46 chromosomes is again established.

The sex-determining pair of chromosomes in the male is composed of one "X" chromosome, which is called the *female chromo-*

some, and one "Y" chromosome, which is called the *male chromosome.* Furthermore, meiotic division divides the sex-determining chromosomes among the spermatids so that half of the sperm become *male sperm* and the other half *female sperm.* The sex of the offspring is determined by the type of sperm that fertilizes the ovum. This will be discussed further in Chapter 80.

When the spermatids are first formed, they have the usual characteristics of an epithelioid cell, but soon each spermatid begins to grow a flagellum which eventually becomes the tail of the sperm. The cytoplasm of the cell contracts around the cell nucleus and some of the cytoplasmic material apparently is actually cast away from the cell. Simultaneously, the nuclear material is rearranged into a compact mass which forms the major portion of the body of the sperm, as illustrated in Figure 724. Though very little cytoplasm remains around the sperm body, a definite layer of cytoplasm and cellular membrane still surrounds the elongated flagellum which becomes the tail of the sperm. Thus, each spermatid finally becomes a single *spermatozoon,* which is the fully formed sperm.

Function of the Sertoli Cells. The Sertoli cells of the germinal epithelium, known also as the *sustentacular cells,* are illustrated in Figure 723 B. These cells are large, extending from the base of the seminiferous

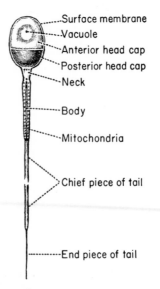

Surface membrane

Vacuole

Anterior head cap

Posterior head cap

Neck

Body

Mitochondria

Chief piece of tail

End piece of tail

Figure 724. Anatomy of the sperm.

epithelium almost all the way to the interior of the tubule. The spermatids attach themselves to the Sertoli cells, and some specific relationship seems to exist between the spermatids and the Sertoli cells that causes the spermatids to change into spermatozoa. For this reason it is believed that the Sertoli cells provide nutrient material, hormones, or enzymes that are necessary for causing appropriate changes in the spermatids. Indeed, there is considerable evidence that the Sertoli cells are capable of forming estrogens which might in turn have some specific effect on the formation of sperm, though no such definite function of estrogens has yet been demonstrated.

The Sperm

Maturation of Sperm in the Epididymis. Following formation in the seminiferous tubules, the sperm pass through the *vasa recta* into the *epididymis*. Sperm removed from the seminiferous tubules are completely nonmotile, and they cannot fertilize an ovum. However, after the sperm have been in the epididymis for some 18 hours or more, they develop the power of motility and also become capable of fertilizing the ovum. It probably is not any special function of the epididymis that changes the sperm from the nonmotile state into the motile and fertile state, but instead this is probably simply an aging process. In other words, the sperm when first released from the seminiferous tubules are still immature and must mature for a number of hours before they become fertile.

Storage of Sperm. A small quantity of sperm can be stored in the epididymis, but probably most of the sperm are stored in the vas deferens and possibly to some extent in the ampulla of the vas deferens. Though the sperm in these areas become motile if they are released to the exterior, they are relatively dormant as long as they are stored, probably for the following reason: The sperm, as a result of their own metabolism, secrete a considerable quantity of carbon dioxide into the surrounding fluid, and the resulting acidotic state of the fluid inhibits the activity of the sperm.

Sperm can be stored, maintaining their fertility, in the genital ducts for as long as 42 days, though it is doubtful that during normal sexual activity such prolonged storage ordinarily occurs. Indeed, with excessive sexual activity storage may not continue longer than a few hours.

Physiology of the Mature Sperm. The usual motile and fertile sperm is capable of flagellated movement through fluid media at a rate of approximately 1 to 4 mm. per minute. Furthermore, sperm tend to travel in a straight line rather than with a circuitous movement. The activity of sperm is greatly enhanced in neutral and slightly alkaline media, but it is greatly depressed in mildly acid media, and strong acid media can cause rapid death of sperm. The activity of sperm increases greatly with increasing temperature, but so does the rate of metabolism, causing the life of the sperm to be considerably shortened. Though sperm can live for many weeks in the genital ducts, the life of sperm in normal ejaculated semen at normal body temperature is only 24 to 72 hours.

The continual metabolism of sperm utilizes glucose from the surrounding fluids, often causing glucose depletion. Some fructose, too, is secreted in prostatic fluid, and this can also be utilized to some extent by sperm in the semen after ejaculation.

Function of the Seminal Vesicles

From early anatomic studies of the seminal vesicles it was erroneously believed that sperm were stored in these vesicles, whence was derived the name "seminal vesicles." However, these structures are only secretory glands instead of sperm storage areas.

The seminal vesicles are lined with a secretory epithelium which secretes a mucoid material containing an abundance of fructose and smaller amounts of ascorbic acid, inositol, ergothioneine, five of the amino acids, and phosphorylcholine. During the process of ejaculation each seminal vesicle empties its contents into the ejaculatory duct at the same time that the vas deferens empties the sperm. This adds greatly to the bulk of the ejaculated semen, and the fructose and other substances in the seminal fluid are of considerable nutrient and protective value for the ejaculated sperm until one of them fertilizes the ovum.

Function of the Prostate Gland

The prostate gland secretes a very thin, milky, alkaline fluid. During ejaculation the capsule of the prostate gland contracts simultaneously with the contractions of the vas deferens and seminal vesicles so that the thin, milky fluid of the prostate gland, containing citric acid, acid phosphatase, and spermine, adds to the bulk of the semen. The alkaline characteristic of the prostate fluid may be quite important for successful fertilization of the ovum, for the fluid of the vas deferens is relatively acid owing to the presence of metabolic end-products of the sperm, and consequently inhibits sperm fertility. Also, it is well known that the vaginal secretions of the female are quite acidic in nature (pH of 3.5 to 4.0). Sperm do not become optimally motile until the pH of the surrounding fluids rises to approximately 6 to 6.5. Consequently, it is probable that prostatic fluid neutralizes the acidity of these other fluids after ejaculation and greatly enhances the motility and fertility of the sperm.

Semen

Semen, which is ejaculated during the male sexual act, is composed of the fluids from the vas deferens, from the seminal vesicles, from the prostate gland, and from the mucous glands, especially the bulbourethral glands. The average pH of the combined semen is approximately 6.5, the alkaline prostatic fluid having neutralized the mild acidity of the other portions of the semen. The prostatic fluid gives the semen a milky appearance, while fluid from the seminal vesicles and from the mucous glands gives the semen a mucoid consistency. Within approximately one-half hour after ejaculation the mucoid consistency of semen disappears because of proteolytic enzymes in the fluid. In the early minutes after ejaculation the sperm remain relatively immobile, possibly because of the viscosity of the mucus. However, after the mucus dissolves, the sperm simultaneously become highly motile. Though sperm can live for many weeks in the male genital ducts, once ejaculated in the semen their maximal life span is only 24 to 72 hours at body temperature. At lowered temperatures, however, semen may be stored for several days, and when frozen at temperatures below —100° C. sperm of some animals have been preserved for over a year.

Male Fertility

The seminiferous tubular epithelium can be destroyed by a number of different diseases. For instance, bilateral orchiditis resulting from mumps usually causes sufficient degeneration of tubular epithelium that sterility results in the majority of males so afflicted. Another disease that frequently localizes in the testes and can cause severe tubular damage is typhus fever. Also, many male infants are born with degenerate tubular epithelium as a result of strictures in the genital ducts or as a result of unknown causes. Finally, a cause of sterility seems to be excessive temperature of the testes, as follows:

Effect of Temperature on Spermatogenesis. In addition to the direct effect of increased temperature in shortening the life of sperm as noted above, increasing the temperature of the testes can inhibit spermatogenesis. Increasing the temperature probably increases the rate of metabolism of the tubular epithelium and thereby causes the regenerative cells to "burn out," for immersion of the testes in a pail of very hot water for prolonged periods of time can cause temporary or even permanent sterility.

It has often been stated that the reason the testicles are located in the dangling scrotum is to maintain the temperature of these glands below the temperature of the body. On cold days scrotal reflexes cause the musculature of the scrotum to contract, pulling the tesicles close to the body, whereas on warm days the musculature of the scrotum becomes almost totally relaxed so that the testicles hang far from the body. Furthermore, the scrotum is well supplied with sweat glands which presumably aid in keeping the testicles cool. Thus the scrotum apparently is designed to act as a cooling mechanism for the testicles, without which spermatogenesis is said to be deficient.

Cryptorchidism. Cryptorchidism means failure of a testis to descend from the abdomen into the scrotum. During development of the male fetus the testes are derived from the genital ridges at the same points as the ovaries in the female. However, during the late stages of gestation, the testes descend through the inguinal canals into the scrotum. Occasionally this descent does not occur at all or occurs incompletely so that one or both testes remain in the abdomen, in the inguinal canal, or elsewhere along the route of descent.

A testicle that remains throughout life in the abdominal cavity is incapable of forming sperm. The tubular epithelium is completely degenerate, leaving only the interstitial structures of the testis. It is believed that even the few degrees higher temperature in the abdomen than in the scrotum is sufficient to cause degeneration of the tubular epithelium and consequently to cause sterility. For this reason operations to relocate the cryptorchid testes from the abdominal cavity into the scrotum prior to the beginning of adult sexual life are frequently performed on boys who have undescended testes. (As will be noted subsequently, testosterone secretion by the male fetus is the stimulus that causes the testes to move into the scrotum from the abdomen. Therefore, it may be that cryptorchidism is caused by abnormally formed testes that are unable to secrete testosterone, rather than cryptorchidism causing the degenerate testes.)

Effect of Sperm Characteristics on Fertility. Sperm from the fertile male are extremely uniform in size, and when such uniformity does not exist, even though the sperm may be motile and appear to be healthy, either total or "relative" sterility usually exists. Also, as illustrated in Figure 725, sperm frequently have grossly abnormal characteristics such as two heads, two tails, abnormally formed heads, bifid tails, etc., and some sperm travel in circuitous routes rather than along straight lines. In general, when more than 25 per cent of the sperm is shown to be definitely abnormal even though the total number of sperm in each ejaculate is completely normal, the man nevertheless is likely to be sterile, for even the 75 per cent of the sperm that appear to be normal still may not be normal enough to fertilize the ovum.

Effect of Sperm Count on Fertility. The usual quantity of semen ejaculated at each coitus averages approximately 3 ml., and in each milliliter of semen is an average of approximately 120,000,000 sperm, though even in "normal" persons this can vary from 35,000,000 to 200,000,000. This means an average total of about 400,000,000 sperm are usually present in each ejaculate. When the number of sperm in each milliliter falls below approximately 35,000,000 sperm, the male becomes less fertile than normal, his fertility decreasing progressively with any further diminishment in sperm count. Thus, even though only a single sperm is necessary to fertilize the ovum, nevertheless, the ejaculate must contain a tremendous number of sperm in order for at least one to reach the ovum.

Function of hyaluronidase secreted by the sperm in fertilization. Hyaluronidase is an enzyme that depolymerizes hyaluronic acid polymers, which are present in large quantity in the intercellular cementing substance, which means that hyaluronidase can cause cells cemented together to separate from each other. When the ovum is expelled from the follicle of the ovary into the abdominal cavity, it carries with it several layers of granulosa cells attached relatively firmly to the surface of the ovum. Before a sperm can reach the ovum to fertilize it, these granulosa cells must be removed; hyaluronidase in the semen is believed to cause the granulosa cells to break away from the ovum, allowing sperm to reach the surface of the ovum.

The quantity of hyaluronidase in the semen is usually proportional to the number of sperm, for which reason it has been postulated that the sperm themselves secrete hyaluronidase, though some experiments have indicated that the quantity of hyaluronidase does not necessarily correlate with the number of sperm and that the hyaluronidase might be secreted into the semen from some other source.

It has been claimed, also, that semen contains a mucolytic enzyme similar to hyaluronidase that is capable of dissolving the mucus plug frequently formed by the female in the cervix of the uterus, and it is believed that lack of this mucolytic enzyme might occasionally be responsible for male sterility.

THE MALE SEXUAL ACT

Neuronal Stimulus for Performance of the Male Sexual Act

The most important source of impulses for initiating the male sexual act is the glans penis, for the glans contains a highly organized sensory end-organ system that transmits into the central nervous system a very special modality of sensation that might be called *sexual sensation.* The massaging action of intercourse on the glans stimulates the sensory end-organs, and the sexual sensations in turn pass through the pudendal nerve, thence through the sacral plexus into the sacral portion of the spinal cord, and finally up the cord to undefined areas of the cerebrum. Impulses may also enter the spinal cord from areas adjacent to the penis to aid in stimulating the sexual act. For instance, stimulation of the anal epithelium, the scrotum, and perineal structures in general may

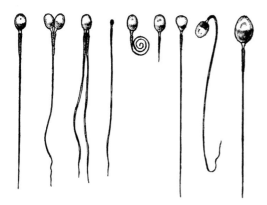

Figure 725. Abnormal sperm.

all send impulses into the cord which add to the sexual sensation. Sexual sensations can even originate in internal structures such as irritated areas of the urethra, the bladder, the prostate, the seminal vesicles, the testes, and the vas deferens. Indeed, one of the causes of "sexual drive" is probably over-filling of the sexual organs with secretions. Infection and inflammation of these sexual organs may sometimes cause almost continual sexual desire, and "aphrodisiac" drugs such as cantharides increase the sexual desire by irritating the bladder and urethral mucosa.

The Psychic Element of Male Sexual Stimulation. Appropriate psychic stimuli can greatly enhance the ability of a person to perform the sexual act. Simply thinking sexual thoughts or even dreaming that the act of intercourse is being performed can cause the male sexual act to occur and to culminate in ejaculation. Indeed, *nocturnal emissions* during dreams occur in many males during some stage of sexual life, especially during the teens.

Integration of the Male Sexual Act in the Spinal Cord. Though psychic factors usually play a very important part in the male sexual act and can actually initiate it, the cerebrum is probably not absolutely necessary for its performance, for appropriate genital stimulation can cause ejaculation in some animals after their spinal cords have been cut above the lumbar region. It may be postulated, then, that the male sexual act probably results from inherent reflex mechanisms integrated in the sacral and lumbar spinal cord, which can be initiated by either psychic stimulation or actual sexual stimulation.

Stages of the Male Sexual Act

Erection. Erection is the first effect of male sexual stimulation, and the degree of erection is proportional to the degree of stimulation, whether this stimulation be psychic or physical.

Erection is caused by parasympathetic impulses that pass through the nervi erigentes from the sacral portion of the spinal cord to the penis. These parasympathetic impulses dilate the arteries and constrict the veins of the penis to a lesser extent, thus allowing arterial blood to flow under high pressure

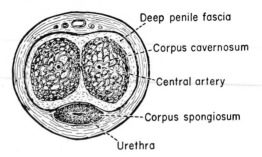

Figure 726.   Erectile tissue of the penis.

into the *erectile tissue* of the penis, which is illustrated in Figure 726. This erectile tissue is nothing more than large, cavernous venous sinusoids, which are normally relatively empty but which can become dilated tremendously when arterial blood flows into them under pressure. Also, the erectile bodies are surrounded by very strong fibrous coats; therefore, high pressure within the sinusoids causes ballooning of the erectile tissue to such an extent that the penis becomes hard and elongated.

Lubrication. During sexual stimulation, parasympathetic impulses, in addition to promoting erection, cause the glands of Littre and the bulbo-urethral glands to secrete mucus. This mucus flows through the urethra during intercourse to aid in the lubrication of coitus. However, most of the lubrication of coitus is probably provided by the female sexual organs rather than by the male sexual organs. Without satisfactory lubrication, the male sexual act is rarely successful because unlubricated intercourse causes excessive pain impulses which inhibit rather than excite sexual sensations.

Ejaculation. Ejaculation is the final culmination of the male sexual act. When the sexual stimulus becomes extremely intense, the reflex centers of the spinal cord begin to emit rhythmical sympathetic impulses which leave the cord at L-1 and L-2 and then pass to the genital organs through the hypogastric plexus to cause ejaculation.

Ejaculation begins with peristaltic contractions in the testis, the epididymis, and the vas deferens to cause expulsion of sperm into the internal urethra. Simultaneously, rhythmic contractions occur in the seminal vesicles and the muscular coat of the prostate gland to expel the seminal fluid and prostatic fluid along with the sperm. Finally, the bulbo-urethral glands discharge still additional quantities of mucus into the urethra at the same time, and all of these different types of fluid combine to form the semen. The process to this point is called *emission*. Then rhythmical nerve impulses are sent from the cord over the pudendal nerves to skeletal muscles that encase the base of the erectile tissue, causing rhythmical increases in pressure in this tissue, which expresses the semen from the urethra to the exterior. This process is called *ejaculation proper*.

TESTOSTERONE AND OTHER MALE SEX HORMONES

Secretion, Metabolism, and Chemistry of the Male Sex Hormone

Production of Testosterone by the Interstitial Cells of the Testes. Two different

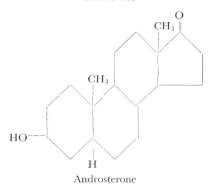

Testosterone

Androsterone

Dehydroepiandrosterone

male sex hormones have been isolated from the venous blood draining from the testes, *testosterone* and △ *4-androstene-3,17-dione*. However, the quantity of testosterone is so very much greater than that of the second hormone that one can consider testosterone to be the single significant hormone responsible for the male hormonal effects caused by the testes.

Both the testicular hormones are believed to be formed by the *interstitial cells of Leydig*, which lie in the interstices between the seminiferous tubules, as illustrated in Figure 727. Interstitial cells are not present in the testes of a child except immediately after birth, but they are present in the testes of a newborn infant and also in the testes of the adult male anytime after puberty; at both these times the testes secrete testosterone. Furthermore, when tumors develop from the interstitial cells of Leydig, tremendous quantities of testosterone are secreted. Finally, when the germinal epithelium of the testes is destroyed by x-ray treatment or by excessive heat, the interstitial cells, which are less easily destroyed, still continue to produce testosterone.

Secretion of "Androgens" Elsewhere in the Body. The term *androgen* is used synonymously with the term male sex hormone, but it also includes male sex hormones produced elsewhere in the body besides the testes. For instance, the adrenal gland secretes at least five different androgens, though the total quantity of all these is normally so slight that they do not cause significant masculine characteristics even in women. But when a tumor of the adrogen-producing cells occurs, the quantity of androgenic hormones may then become great enough to cause all the usual male secondary sexual characteristics, such as growth of the penis or the clitoris, male distribution of hair, bass changes in the voice, changes

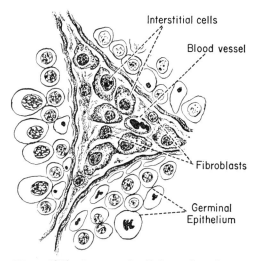

Interstitial cells

Blood vessel

Fibroblasts

Germinal Epithelium

Figure 727. Interstitial cells located in the interstices between the seminiferous tubules. (Modified from Maximow and Bloom: Textbook of Histology.)

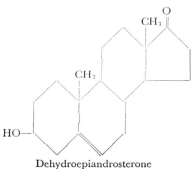

in the skin, and so forth. These effects have already been described in connection with the adrenogenital syndrome in Chapter 74.

Rarely, embryonic rest cells in the ovary can develop into a tumor which produces androgens; one type of such a tumor is the *arrhenoblastoma*. The normal ovary probably also produces very minute quantities of androgens, but these are not enough to measure.

Chemistry of the Androgens. All androgens are steroid compounds, as illustrated by the accompanying formulas for *testosterone, androsterone,* and *dehydroepiandrosterone* (See p. 1073). Both in the testes and in the adrenals the androgens can be synthesized either from cholesterol or directly from acetyl Co-A.

Metabolism of the Androgens. Androgens secreted by the testes or adrenal glands, including testosterone, persist in the free form in the blood for not over 15 to 30 minutes. They are converted very rapidly into *androsterone* and *dehydroepiandrosterone*. These two compounds are conjugated either as glucuronides or sulfates, glucuronides particularly, and are excreted into the urine. The androgenic potency of these is very slight in comparison with that of the original secreted androgens. Therefore, they are considered to be principally end-products of androgen metabolism.

The 17-Ketosteroids in Relation to Testosterone Secretion. From the formulas of androsterone and dehydroepinandrosterone it is evident that both these are 17-ketosteroids, which means simply that they have a keto oxygen in the 17-position of the chemical formulas. Furthermore, essentially none of the other steroid hormones besides androgens are 17-ketosteroids. Therefore, the rate of secretion of 17-ketosteroids in the urine is an excellent index to the rate of androgen production in the body.

In Chapter 74 it was pointed out that approximately 7 mg. of 17-ketosteroids are secreted each 12 hours in the male (4 mg. from the adrenals and 3 mg. from the testes), and approximately 4 mg. are secreted in the urine of women each 12 hours (all from the adrenals). Marked elevation of these 17-ketosteroids indicates excessive production of androgens in either the adrenals or testes—or, rarely, even in an androgen-producing tumor of an ovary.

Production of Estrogen by the Testes. In addition to testosterone, small amounts of estrogens are formed in the male, and a reasonable quantity of these can be recovered from a man's urine even though the functions of estrogens in the male are unknown.

The exact source of the estrogens in the male is still doubtful, but the following facts are known: (a) The quantity of estrogens increases greatly when a tumor of the sustentacular cells

(Sertoli cells) develops in the seminiferous tubules. This indicates that the sustentacular cells synthesize estrogens in men. (b) Small amounts of estrogens are formed from testosterone during its degradation in other parts of the body. (c) Finally, the rate of estrogen secretion from the testes closely parallels the rate of testosterone secretion, for which reason it has also been suspected that the interstitial cells might be the source of the estrogens.

Thus, the problem of estrogen production in the male is yet unsettled except for the known fact that small quantities of estrogens are produced in the testes or are formed from testosterone.

Functions of Testosterone

In general, testosterone is responsible for the distinguishing characteristics of the masculine person. The testes are stimulated by chorionic gonadotropin from the placenta to produce a small quantity of testosterone during fetal development, but essentially no testosterone is produced during childhood until approximately the age of 10. Then testosterone production increases rapidly at the onset of puberty and lasts throughout most of the remainder of life as illustrated in Figure 728, dwindling rapidly beyond the age of 40 to become almost zero by the age of 80.

Functions of Testosterone during Fetal Development. Testosterone probably begins to be elaborated by the male fetus at about the second month of embryonic life. Indeed, some embryologists believe that the

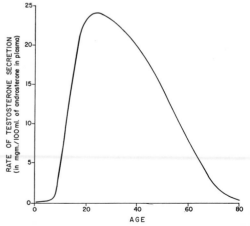

Figure 728. Rate of testosterone secretion at different ages, as judged from the concentrations of androsterone in the plasma.

major functional difference between the female and the male sex chromosomes is that the male chromosome causes the newly developing genital ridge to secrete testosterone while the female chromosome causes this ridge to secrete estrogens. Injection of large quantities of male sex hormone or of female sex hormone into gravid animals will cause the sexual organs of the offspring to develop to a great extent according to the sex of the injected hormone. Therefore, if it is true that the early developing genital ridge is capable of secreting testosterone, this testosterone probably is at least partly, if not wholly, responsible for the development of the male sex characteristics, including the growth of a penis and a scrotum rather than the formation of a clitoris and a vagina. Also, it is possibly this hormone produced during fetal life that causes development of the prostate gland, the seminal vesicles, and the genital ducts.

Effect on the descent of the testes. The testes usually descend into the scrotum during the latter two months of pregnancy, and there are many indications that the testes produce reasonable quantities of testosterone during this period of time. Also, if a male child is born with undescended testes, administration of testosterone will cause the testes to descend in the usual manner if the inguinal canals are large enough to allow the testes to pass. Or, administration of gonadotropic hormones which stimulate the interstitial cells of the testes to produce testosterone will also cause the testes to descend. Thus, the stimulus for descent of the testes is almost certainly testosterone, indicating again that testosterone is probably an important hormone for male sexual development during fetal life.

Effect of Testosterone on Development of Adult Primary and Secondary Sexual Characteristics. Testosterone secretion after puberty causes the penis, the scrotum, and the testes all to enlarge many fold until about the age of 20. In addition to these effects, testosterone causes the "secondary sexual characteristics" of the male to develop at the same time, beginning at puberty and ending at maturity. It is these secondary sexual characteristics that, in addition to the sexual organs themselves, distinguish the male from the female as follows:

Effect on the distribution of body hair. Testosterone causes growth of hair (1) over the pubis, (2) upward along the linea alba sometimes to the umbilicus and above, (3) on the face, (4) usually on the chest, and (5) less often on other regions of the body such as the back. It also causes the hair on most other portions of the body to become more prolific.

Baldness. Testosterone decreases the growth of hair on the top of the head, for a man who does not have functional testes does not become bald. However, many virile men never become bald, for baldness is a result of two factors: first, a *genetic background* must exist for the development of baldness, and, second, superimposed on this genetic background *large quantities of androgenic hormones* must be secreted. A woman who has the appropriate genetic background and who develops a long-sustained androgenic tumor becomes bald in the same manner that a man often becomes bald during adult life.

Effect on the voice. Testosterone secreted by the testes or injected into the body causes hypertrophy of the laryngeal mucosa and enlargement of the larynx. These effects cause at first a relatively hoarse voice, but this gradually changes into the typical masculine bass voice.

Effect on the skin. Testosterone increases the thickness of the skin over the entire body and increases the ruggedness of the subcutaneous tissues. Also, it causes increased quantities of melanin to be deposited in the skin, thereby deepening the hue of the skin.

Testosterone increases the tendency for the body to sweat and it also increases the rate of secretion by some or perhaps all of the sebaceous glands. Especially important is the excessive secretion by the sebaceous glands of the face, for oversecretion of these can result in *acne*. Therefore, acne is one of the most common features of the period of adolescence, when the male body is first becoming introduced to increased secretion of testosterone. After several years of testosterone secretion, however, the skin adapts itself to the testosterone in some way that allows it to overcome the acne.

Effect on nitrogen retention and muscular development. One of the most important male characteristics is the development of increasing musculature following puberty. This is associated with a positive nitrogen balance whch is due to some yet unclarified metabolic effect of testosterone on protein anabolism. Many of the changes in the skin are probably also due to deposition of protein compounds in the skin, and the changes in the voice could even result from this nitrogen retention function of testosterone.

Testosterone has often been considered to be a "youth hormone" because of its effect on the musculature, and it is occasionally used for treatment of persons who have poorly developed muscles.

Effect on bone growth and calcium retention. Following puberty or following prolonged injection of testosterone, the bones grow considerably in thickness and also deposit considerable calcium salts. Thus, testosterone increases the total quantity of bone matrix, and it also causes calcium retention. The increase in bone matrix is believed to result from the general protein anabolic function of testosterone, and the deposition of calcium salts to result from increased bone matrix available to be calcified.

Because of the ability of testosterone to increase the size and strength of bones, testosterone is often used in old age to treat osteoporosis.

When great quantities of testosterone (or any other androgen) are secreted, not only does the rate of bone growth increase, but the epiphyses of the long bones unite at a very early age in life with the shafts of the bones. Therefore, despite the rapidity of growth, this early uniting of the epiphyses prevents the person from growing as tall as he would have grown had testosterone not been secreted at all. Even in normal men the final adult height is slightly less than that which would have been attained had the person been castrated prior to puberty.

Effect on basal metabolism. Injection of very large quantities of testosterone can increase the basal metabolic rate by as much as 15 per cent, and it is believed that even the usual quantity of testosterone secreted by the testes during active sexual life increases the rate of metabolism some 5 to 10 per cent above the value that it would be were the testes not active. This increased rate of metabolism is possibly an indirect result of the effect of testosterone on protein anabolism, the increased quantity of proteins—

the enzymes especially—increasing the activities of all of the cells.

Effect on the red blood cells. When normal quantities of testosterone are injected into a castrated adult, the number of red blood cells per cubic millimeter of blood increases approximately 20 per cent. Also, the average man has 500,000 to 1,000,000 more red blood cells per cubic millimeter than the average woman. However, this difference may be due partly to the increased metabolic rate following testosterone administration rather than to a direct effect of testosterone on red blood cell production.

Effect on electrolyte and water balance. In Chapter 74 it was pointed out that many different steroid hormones can increase the reabsorption of sodium in the distal tubules of the kidneys. Testosterone performs this function to a slight extent but only to a minor degree in comparison with the adrenal mineralocorticoids. Nevertheless, following puberty the blood and extracellular fluid volumes of the male subject in relation to his weight increases to a slight extent; this effect results at least partly from the sodium-retaining ability of testosterone.

Control of Male Sexual Functions by the Gonadotropic Hormones

Puberty. Puberty is the time at which adult masculine features begin to appear; it is initiated by a sudden onset of production of gonadotropic hormones by the adenohypophysis. In the average male child puberty begins at the age of 10, though this age may range from 8 to 14 years. The production of pituitary gonadotropic hormones progressively increases over a period of 5 or more years, causing the testes to enlarge and the rate of spermatogenesis and testosterone production to increase progressively. In turn, testosterone promotes development of the masculine primary and secondary sexual characteristics.

The reason the adenohypophysis suddenly begins to secrete gonadotropic hormones at puberty is not known. At present it is probably wise to accept this increased production of gonadotropic hormones as simply an aging process of the adenohypophysis itself. Associated with this sudden increase in gonadotropic hormones is usually an increased rate of growth of the male child,

progesterone on luteinizing hormone, both these hormones decrease the total quantity of gonadotropic hormone secretion, possibly also including a decrease in the quantity of luteotropic hormone as well as FSH and LH, though less is known about the alterations in LTH.

Feedback Oscillation of the Adeno-hypophyseal-Ovarian System

Though the precise antagonistic relationships between ovarian hormones and the gonadotropic hormones are not known in detail, it can readily be seen from the preceding discussion that the gonadotropic hormones from the adenohypophysis are the basic cause of hormonal secretion by the ovaries, and in turn both the estrogens and the progesterone of the ovaries can then decrease the production of gonadotropic hormones by the adenohypophysis. Thus, conditions are appropriate for feedback oscillation to result. The details of the cyclic changes in hormonal secretion by the adenohypophysis and the ovaries have been postulated to be those shown in Figure 733. These can be explained as follows:

1. The adenohypophysis, when not affected by outside stimuli, secretes mainly follicle stimulating hormone. Therefore, during the first part of the month, follicle stimulating hormone is secreted, and this causes the follicles of the ovaries to begin ripening and to secrete small quantities of estrogens.

2. The estrogens then cause the adenohypophysis to decrease its secretion of follicle stimulating hormone while at the same time increasing its secretion of luteinizing hormone. The luteinizing hormone, acting synergistically with the follicle stimulating hormone, causes the vesicular follicles of the ovaries to grow rapidly and to secrete progressively more and more estrogens. This rapid growth culminates in ovulation by one of the follicles. By this time so many estrogens are being secreted that the output of follicle stimulating hormone from the adenohypophysis becomes greatly reduced.

3. Immediately after ovulation, under the influence of luteinizing hormone the follicular cells of the ruptured follicle take on lutein characteristics and become the corpus luteum. Then, under the influence of luteotropic hormone, which is secreted fairly continuously by the adenohypophysis though perhaps in slightly increased quantity at this period of the cycle, the corpus luteum secretes large quantities of progesterone and also continues to secrete large quantities of estrogens.

4. The progesterone then inhibits adeno-hypophyseal production of luteinizing hormone, and diminishment of this (as well as perhaps of luteotropic hormone) causes the corpus luteum to involute. At this point, lack of production of either estrogens or progesterone automatically allows the adenohypophysis to begin producing follicle stimulating hormone once again in large quantities.

5. The increased follicle stimulating hormone then stimulates development of new primordial follicles, and a new cycle begins.

Oscillation in Anovulatory Cycles— The Sexual Cycle at Puberty. Often ovulation fails to occur, and the cycle is then said to be *anovulatory*. Indeed, in almost all girls immediately after puberty the first few cycles are anovulatory. Lack of ovulation also causes failure of development of a corpus luteum and consequently no secretion of progesterone during that cycle. In such instances the rhythm is often considerably distorted, but an oscillatory cycle of sorts still occurs, usually prolonged and associated with abnormal rates of estrogen secretion as well as abnormal endometrial changes in the uterus. Yet, it is quite evident that adenohypophyseal-ovarian oscillation can still occur even without progesterone secretion by the ovaries. Therefore, the female sexual cycle seems to result principally from reciprocal oscillation between follicle stimulating hormone secretion by the adenohypophysis and estrogen secretion by the ovaries, while the other hormonal changes discussed above are mainly secondary effects precipitated by ovulation.

Puberty

Puberty means the onset of adult sexual life in the female, and, as pointed out earlier in the chapter, it is caused by a gradual increase in gonadotropic hormone secretion by the adenohypophysis beginning approximately the seventh year of life, as illustrated in Figure 734. However, oscillation cannot begin in any oscillating system until the

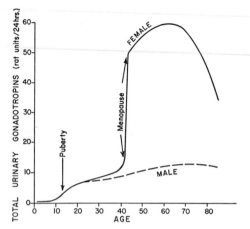

Figure 734. Total rates of secretion of gonadotropic hormones throughout the sexual lives of females and males, showing an especially abrupt increase in gonadotropic hormones at the menopause in the female.

stimulus causing the oscillation becomes potent enough to cause sufficient feedback to keep the rhythm going. It is usually not until about the twelfth year of life that a sufficient amount of estrogens is secreted to cause adequate feedback to the adenohypophysis to initiate an oscillatory cycle. Figure 735 illustrates this onset of oscillation, showing that it occurs with prolonged cycles during the first few anovulatory cycles. Then, as the ovaries become capable of secreting still greater quantities of estrogens and as the quantities of gonadotropins become larger, the feedback becomes strong enough to elicit normal monthly cycles coupled with monthly ovulation.

It should be pointed out that the onset of adult sexual life is not caused entirely by increased

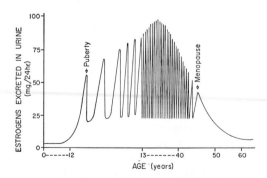

Figure 735. Oscillation of estrogen production throughout female sexual life, showing irregularity both at the beginning and at the end of sexual life when the rates of estrogen secretion are low.

gonadotropic hormones, for the ovary itself also matures during the latter few years of childhood and becomes progressively more capable of secreting ovarian hormones in response to a given level of gonadotropic stimulation.

The Menopause

At an average age of approximately 45 to 50 years the sexual cycles usually become irregular, and ovulation fails to occur during many of these cycles. After a few months to a few years, the cycles cease altogether, as illustrated in Figure 735.

The cause of the menopause (cessation of the sexual cycles) apparently is "burning out" of the ovaries. In other words, throughout a woman's sexual life many of the primordial follicles grow into vesicular follicles with each sexual cycle, and eventually almost all of the ova either degenerate or are ovulated. Therefore, at the age of about 45 only a very few primordial follicles still remain to be stimulated by follicle stimulating hormones. As a result, the production of estrogens by the ovary begins to decrease as the number of primordial follicles approaches zero (which is illustrated in Figure 735), and when estrogen production falls below a critical value, the estrogens can no longer inhibit the production of follicle stimulating hormone sufficiently to cause an oscillatory cycle. Consequently, as illustrated in Figure 734, follicle stimulating hormone is produced in very large quantities continually thereafter. Estrogens are produced in subcritical quantities for a short time after the menopause, but over a period of a few years, as the final remaining primordial follicles become atretic, the production of estrogens by the ovaries falls almost to zero.

The Female Climacteric. The term "female climacteric" means the entire period of time, lasting from several months to several years, during which the sexual cycles become irregular and gradually stop. It is in this period that the woman must adjust her sexual life from one that has been physio logically stimulated by her estrogen production to one that must be motivated primarily by nonendocrine factors. The quantity of estrogens decreases rapidly, and no progesterone at all is secreted after the last ovulatory cycle. The loss of the estrogens, especially, causes several marked physiologic changes in the function of the body, including (1) "hot flashes" due to extreme flushing of the skin, (2) psychic sensations of dyspnea, (3) irritability, (4) fatigue, (5) anxiety, and (6) occasionally various psychotic states. These symptoms are of sufficient magnitude in approximately 15 per cent of women to warrant treatment. If psychotherapy fails, daily administration of an estrogen in small quantities will reverse these symptoms, and by gradually decreasing the dose the menopausal woman is likely to avoid severe symptoms; unfortunately, such treatment prolongs the symptoms, however.

THE ENDOMETRIAL CYCLE AND MENSTRUATION

Associated with the cyclic production of estrogens and progesterone by the ovary is an endometrial cycle operating through the following stages: first, proliferation of the uterine endometrium; second, secretory changes in the endometrium; and third, desquamation of the endometrium, which is known as *menstruation*. The various phases of the endometrial cycle are illustrated in Figure 736.

Proliferative Phase (Estrogen Phase) of the Endometrial Cycle. At the beginning of each menstrual cycle, most of the endometrium is desquamated by the process of menstruation. This includes complete loss of the epithelium and *stratum submucosum* and loss of most of the *stratum vasculare*. Therefore, after menstruation only a thin layer of endometrial stroma remains at the base of the original endometrium, and the only epithelial cells are those located in the remaining deep portions of the glands and crypts of the endometrium. *Under the influence of estrogens,* secreted in increased quantities by the ovary during the first part of the ovarian cycle, the stromal cells and the epithelial cells proliferate rapidly. The endometrial surface is re-epithelized within approximately 4 to 5 days after the beginning of menstruation. For the first two weeks of the sexual cycle—that is, up until the time of ovulation—the endometrium increases greatly in thickness owing to increasing numbers of stromal cells and to progressive growth of the endometrial glands and blood vessels into the endometrium, all of which effects are promoted by the estrogens. At the time of ovulation the endometrium in general has a thickness of approximately 2 to 3 mm.

Secretory Phase (Progestational Phase) of the Endometrial Cycle. During the latter half of the sexual cycle, both estrogens and progesterone are secreted in large quantities by the corpus luteum. The estrogens cause only a little additional cellular proliferation in the endometrium during this phase of the endometrial cycle, but progesterone, probably acting synergistically with the estrogens, causes considerable swelling of the endometrium. The glands increase in tortuosity, secretory substances develop in the glandular epithelial cells, and, finally, the glands secrete small quantities of endometrial fluid. Also, the cytoplasm of the stromal cells increases, lipoid and glycogen deposits appear in some of the stromal cells, and the blood supply to the endometrium increases in proportion to the developing secretory activity, with the blood vessels becoming highly tortuous. The thickness of the endometrium approximately doubles during the secretory phase so that toward the end of the sexual cycle the endometrium has a thickness of some 4 to 6 mm.

The whole purpose of all these endometrial changes is to produce a highly secretory endometrium containing large amounts of stored nutrients that can provide appropriate conditions for implantation of a fertilized ovum should it appear on the scene during the latter half of the monthly cycle. From the time fertilization first takes place until the ovum implants, the fallopian and uterine secretions provide nutrition for the early dividing ovum. Then, once the ovum implants in the endometrium, the trophoblastic cells on the surface of the morula

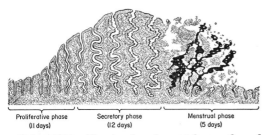

| Proliferative phase (11 days) | Secretory phase (12 days) | Menstrual phase (5 days) |

Figure 736. Phases of endometrial growth and menstruation during each monthly female sexual cycle

can digest the endometrium and absorb the substances digested, thus making still far greater quantities of nutrients available to the early embryo.

Menstruation. Approximately two days before the end of the sexual cycle the gonadotropic hormones and the ovarian hormones decrease sharply to very low levels of secretion, and menstruation follows.

Menstruation is caused by the sudden reduction in both estrogens and progesterone at the end of the monthly ovarian cycle. The first effect is decreased stimulation of the endometrial cells by these two hormones, followed rapidly by involution of the endometrium to about 65 per cent of its previous thickness. During the 24 hours preceding the onset of menstruation, the tortuous blood vessels leading to the mucosal layers of the endometrium become vasospastic, presumably because of some effect of the involution such as the release of a vasoconstrictor material or perhaps because of a direct effect of estrogen withdrawal since estrogens are an endometrial vasodilator. The vasospasm causes beginning necrosis in the endometrium, especially of blood vessels in the stratum vasculare. As a result, blood seeps into the vascular layer of the endometrium, the hemorrhagic areas growing over a period of approximately 24 to 36 hours. Gradually, the necrotic outer layers of the endometrium separate from the uterus at the site of the hemorrhages, until, at approximately 48 hours following the onset of menstruation, all the superficial layers of the endometrium will have desquamated. The desquamated tissue and blood in the uterine vault initiate uterine contractions which expel the uterine contents.

During menstruation, approximately 35 ml. of blood and an additional 35 ml. of serous fluid are lost. This menstrual fluid is normally non-clotting, because a fibrinolysin is released along with the necrotic endometrial material. However, if excessive bleeding occurs from the uterine surface the quantity of fibrinolysin may not be sufficient to prevent clotting. Consequently, the presence of clots during menstruation ordinarily is clinical evidence of uterine pathology.

Within approximately 4 days after menstruation starts, the loss of blood ceases, and by this time the endometrium also has become completely re-epithelized.

Leukorrhea during menstruation. During menstruation a tremendous number of leukocytes are released along with the necrotic material and blood. It is probable that some substance liberated by the endometrial necrosis, perhaps leukotaxine which was discussed in Chapter 13, causes this outflow of leukocytes. As a result of the presence of this large number of leukocytes and maybe still other factors, the uterus is almost totally resistant to infection while the endometrial surfaces are denuded. Obviously, this is of extreme protective value.

INTERRELATIONSHIPS OF THE OVARIES WITH OTHER GLANDS

Relationship of the Ovaries to the Adrenal Glands. The adrenal glands even normally secrete small quantities of both estrogens and progesterone, though these quantities are too small to exert any major effect on the body. However, a very rare tumor of the adrenal gland secretes specifically increased quantities of female hormones and therefore cause feminizing characteristics.

Injection of estrogens causes the adrenal cortices to hypertrophy. This effect probably is mediated through the adenphypophysis, for estrogens, while inhibiting production of follicle stimulating hormone increase the secretion of corticotropin.

Relationship of the Ovaries to the Thyroid Gland. Ovarian function does not have a marked effect on the thyroid gland, but, conversely, thyroid hormone exhibits considerable effect on the activity of the ovaries. For instance, when thyroid hormone production is deficient, the sexual cycles are likely to become anovulatory, often associated with excessive uterine bleeding, which will be discussed below, or the cycles may even disappear entirely. This effect perhaps is due to a decrease in the metabolic rate of the ovarian cells so that sufficient quantity of estrogens cannot be produced. Strangely enough, a marked increase in thyroid secretion is also often associated with ovulatory failure and amenorrhea. This paradoxical effect shows how delicate the monthly oscillation of the female sexual cycle is and that it can be stopped by either excesses or insufficiencies of the same extraneous substance.

Effect of Ovarian Hormones on the Pancreas. Injection of large quantities of estrogens potentiates the effects of growth hormone and adrenocortical hormone in elevating the blood glucose level and in causing a diabetogenic effect on the pancreas. This effect of estrogenic hormones is probably not a direct effect on the islet cells of the pancreas but instead an effect of estrogens to raise blood glucose levels, which secondarily affects the pancreas.

Antagonistic Effects of Estrogens and Testosterone. Estrogens and testosterone exert opposite effects on the sexual glands, the breasts, the prostate gland, and some of the other secondary sexual characteristics. These antagonistic effects are in part mediated through the adenohypophysis because both estrogens and testosterone are capable of decreasing the production of gonadotropic hormones. In general, in order to antagonize the effect of estrogens on the breast, approximately 50 times as much testosterone as β-estradiol must be administered.

ABNORMALITIES OF SECRETION BY THE OVARIES

Hypogonadism. Less than normal secretion by the ovaries can result from poorly formed ovaries or lack of ovaries. When ovaries are absent from birth or when they never become functional, *female eunuchism* occurs. In this condition the usual secondary sexual characteristics do not appear, and the sexual organs remain infantile. Especially characteristic of this condition is excessive growth of the long bones because the epiphyses do not unite with the shafts of these bones at as early an age as in the normal adolescent woman. Consequently, the height of the female eunuch is essentially the same as, or perhaps even slightly greater than, that of her male counterpart of similar genetic background.

When a fully developed woman loses her ovaries, the sexual organs regress to some extent so that the uterus becomes infantile in size, the vagina becomes smaller, and the vaginal epithelium becomes thin and easily damaged. The breasts atrophy and become pendulous, and the pubic hair becomes considerably thinner. These are the same changes that occur in the woman after the menopause.

Irregularity of menses and amenorrhea due to hypogonadism. In the above discussion of the sexual cycle it was pointed out that the quantity of estrogens produced by the ovaries must rise to at least a certain critical value before the estrogens can inhibit the production of follicle stimulating hormone sufficiently to cause an oscillatory sexual cycle. Consequently, when hypogonadism occurs or when the gonads are secreting small quantities of estrogens as a result of other factors such as hypothyroidism, the ovarian cycle likely will not occur normally. Instead, several months may elapse between menstrual periods, or menstruation may cease altogether (amenorrhea). Characteristically, prolonged ovarian cycles are frequently associated with failure of ovulation, presumably due to lack of secretion of sufficient luteinizing hormone or other hormones necessary for ovulation.

Excessive menstrual bleeding. Contrary to what might be expected, excessive menstrual bleeding most commonly occurs in hypogonadism rather than in hypergonadism. Such bleeding is especially likely to result at the end of anovulatory cycles, for these cycles are often prolonged, and estrogens continue to be produced by the ovaries for many weeks at a time, thereby building up a progressively thicker and thicker endometrium that does not slough away easily as occurs in normal menstruation; instead, it denudes slowly and bleeds severely. These patients can usually be very satisfactorily treated by administering large quantities of progesterone for approximately 10 days, beginning 2 weeks after the onset of the previous menstruation and then suddenly withdrawing the progesterone. Normal menstruation usually ensues almost immediately after the progesterone is withdrawn, and the person begins a new cycle. However, repetitive administration of progesterone with each cycle is often required.

Excessive bleeding also frequently results from pathologic conditions in the uterus, such as fibrous scars on the endometrial surface or tumors of the uterus that protrude into the endometrial cavity.

Hypersecretion by the Ovaries. Extreme hypersecretion of ovarian hormones by the ovaries is a very rare clinical entity, for excessive secretion of estrogens automatically decreases the production of follicle stimulating hormone by the anterior pituitary gland, and this in turn limits the production of estrogens. Likewise, excessive production of progesterone by the corpus luteum would result in similar depression of production of pituitary gonadotropic hormones. Consequently, hypersecretion of feminizing hormones is recognized clinically only when a feminizing tumor develops.

A very rare granulosa-theca cell tumor occasionally develops in an ovary, occurring more often after menopause than before. These tumors secrete large quantities of estrogens which exert the usual estrogenic effects, including hypertrophy of the uterine endometrium and irregular bleeding from this endometrium. In fact, bleeding is often the first indication that such a tumor exists.

Ovarian tumors that secrete progesterone are so rare that they are almost non-existent. However, certain tumors of the adrenal gland have been known to secrete large quantities of progesterone. In general, the major effect is excessive retention of body fluids.

Endometriosis. Endometriosis is the development and growth of endometrium in the peritoneal cavity, this growth usually occurring in the pelvis closely associated with the sexual organs. There are two theories for explaining the origin of endometrial tissue that causes endometriosis. Some believe that this tissue results from endometrial "rests" that develop embryologically ir the peritoneal cavity. However, others believe that contraction of the uterus during menstruation occasionally expels viable endometrium backward through the fallopian tubes into the abdominal cavity and that this endometrial tissue then implants on the peritoneum. Indeed, it has been shown that much of the endometrium sloughed during menstruation will grow easily in tissue culture.

During each ovarian cycle the endometrium in the peritoneal cavity proliferates, secretes, and desquamates in the same manner that the intrauterine endometrium menstruates. However, when desquamation occurs within the peritoneal cavity, the tissue and the hemorrhaging blood cannot be expelled to the exterior. Consequently, the quantity of endometrial tissue in the peritoneal cavity progressively increases with each subsequent menstrual cycle.

The presence of necrotic and hemorrhagic material in the abdominal cavity and also the swelling of the endometrial tissue during each ovarian cycle can cause considerable irritation of the peritoneum, sometimes producing severe abdominal pain. Also, fibrosis occurs in the areas of endometriosis, thereby promoting adhesions from one sexual organ to another and from the sexual organs to other intrapelvic and intra-abdominal structures. Endometriosis is one of the most prevalent causes of female infertility, owing especially to fibrotic immobilization of the sexual organs.

THE FEMALE SEXUAL ACT

Stimulation of the Female Sexual Act. As is true in the male sexual act, successful performance of the female sexual act depends upon both psychic stimulation and local sexual stimulation.

The psychic factors that constitute "sex drive" in women are difficult to assess. The sex hormones, and the adrenocortical hormones as well, seem to exert a direct influence on the woman to create such a sex drive, but, on the other hand, the growing female child in modern society is often taught that sex is something to be hidden and that it is immoral. As a result of this training much of the natural sex drive is inhibited, and whether the woman will have little or no sex drive ("frigidity") or will be more highly sexed probably depends upon a balance between natural factors and previous training.

Local sexual stimulation in women occurs in more or less the same manner as in men, for massage, irritation, or other types of stimulation of the perineal region, sex organs, and urinary tract will create sexual sensations. The clitoris is especially sensitive for initiating sexual sensations. As in men, the sexual sensations are mediated to the spinal cord through the pudendal nerve and sacral plexus. Once these sensations have entered the spinal cord, they are transmitted thence to the cerebrum. Also, local reflexes that are at least partly responsible for the female orgasm are integrated in the sacral and lumbar spinal cord.

Female Erection and Lubrication. Located around the introitus and extending into the clitoris is erectile tissue almost identical with the erectile tissue of the penis. This erectile tissue, like that of the penis, is controlled by the parasympathetic nerves that pass through the nervi erigentes from the sacral plexus to the external genitalia. In the early phases of sexual stimulation, the parasympathetics dilate the arteries to the erectile tissues, and this allows rapid inflow of blood into the erectile tissue so that the introitus tightens around the penis; this aids the man greatly in his attainment of sufficient sexual stimulation for ejaculation to occur.

Parasympathetic impulses also pass to the bilateral Bartholin's glands located beneath the labia minora to cause secretion of mucus immediately inside the introitus. This mucus, along with large quantities of mucus secreted by the vaginal mucosa itself, is responsible for appropriate lubrication during sexual intercourse. The lubrication in turn is necessary for establishing during intercourse a satisfactory massaging sensation rather than an irritative sensation, which may be provoked by a dry vagina. A massaging sensation constitutes the optimal type of sensation for evoking the appropriate reflexes that culminate in both the male and the female sexual acts.

The Female Orgasm. When local sexual stimulation reaches maximum intensity, and especially when the local sensations are supported by appropriate conditioning impulses from the cerebrum, reflexes are initiated which cause the *female orgasm,* also often known as the *female climax.* The female orgasm is analogous to the process of ejaculation in the male, and it probably is important for fertilization of the ovum. Indeed, the human female is known to be somewhat more fertile when inseminated by normal sexual intercourse rather than by artificial methods, thus indicating an important function of the female orgasm. Possible effects that could result in this are:

First, during the orgasm the perineal muscles of the female undergo rhythmic contraction, which presumably results from spinal reflexes similar to those that cause ejaculation in the male. It is possible, also, that these same reflexes increase uterine and fallopian tube motility during the orgasm, thus helping to transport the sperm toward the ovum, but the information on this subject is scanty.

Second, in many lower animals copulation causes the neurohypophysis to secrete oxytocin; this effect is probably mediated through the amygdaloid nuclei and then through the hypothalamus to the adenohypophysis. The oxytocin in turn causes increased contractility of the uterus, which also is believed to cause rapid transport of the sperm. Sperm have been shown to traverse the entire length of the fallopian tube in the cow in approximately 5 minutes, a rate at least 10 times as fast as that which the sperm themselves could achieve. Whether this occurs in the human female is yet completely unknown.

In addition to the effects of the orgasm on fertilization, the very intense sexual sensations that develop during the orgasm also pass into the cerebrum and in some manner satisfy the female sex drive.

FEMALE FERTILITY

The Fertile Period of Each Sexual Cycle. The exact duration of time that the ovum remains viable and capable of being fertilized after it is expelled from the ovary is not known. However, this duration is probably not over 24 hours at most. Therefore, sperm must be available soon after ovulation if fertilization is to take place. On the other hand, a few sperm can remain viable in the female reproductive tract for up to 72 hours, though probably most of them not for more than 24 hours on the average. Therefore, for fertilization to take place, intercourse usually

must occur some time between one day prior to ovulation up to one day after ovulation, and even these limits are probably too great. Thus, the period of female fertility during each sexual cycle is very short.

One of the often practiced methods of contraception is to avoid intercourse at or near the time of ovulation. However, the difficulty with this method of contraception is the impossibility of predicting the exact time of ovulation. Yet, the interval of time from ovulation until the next succeeding onset of menstruation is almost always between 13 and 15 days. Therefore, if the woman has a regular menstrual cycle, the time of ovulation averages 14 days prior to the next onset of menstruation. In other words, if the periodicity of her menstrual cycle is 28 days, ovulation will occur within one day of the fourteenth day of the cycle. If, on the other hand, the periodicity of her cycle is 40 days, ovulation will occur within one day of the twenty-sixth day of the cycle. Finally, if the periodicity of her menstrual cycle is 21 days, ovulation will occur within one day of the seventh day of the cycle. Therefore, it is usually stated that avoidance of intercourse within three days on either side of the calculated day of ovulation will prevent conception, and five days on either side of the calculated day of ovulation usually provides absolute safety. Such a method of contraception can be used only when the woman has regular periodicity of her menstrual cycle, for otherwise it is impossible to state when the next onset of menstruation will occur, and, therefore, it is impossible to predict when ovulation will occur.

Abnormal Conditions Causing Female Sterility. Approximately one out of every 6 to 10 marriages is infertile, and in 2 out of 3 of these instances the infertility is due to female sterility rather than male sterility. Thus, it is evident that female infertility is a very common disorder.

Occasionally, no abnormality whatsoever can be discovered in the female genital organs, in which case it must be assumed that the infertility is due either to abnormal physiologic function of the genital system or to abnormal genetic development of the ova themselves.

However, probably by far the most common cause of female sterility is failure to ovulate. This can result from either hyposecretion of gonadotropic hormones, in which case the intensity of the hormonal stimuli simply is not sufficient to cause ovulation, or it can result from abnormal ovaries which will not allow ovulation. For instance, very thick capsules occasionally exist on the outside of the ovaries which prevent ovulation.

Because of the high incidence of anovulation in sterile women, special methods are often utilized to determine whether or not ovulation occurs.

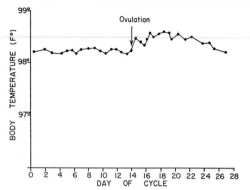

Figure 737. Elevation in body temperature occurring shortly after ovulation.

These are all based on the effects of progesterone on the body, for progesterone is not secreted in anovulatory cycles. In the absence of progesteronic effects, the cycle can be assumed to be anovulatory. One of the tests is simply to analyze the urine for pregnanediol during the latter half of the sexual cycle, the lack of which indicates failure of ovulation. However, another very common test is for the woman to chart her body temperature throughout the cycle. Secretion of progesterone during the latter half of the cycle raises the body temperature about one-half degree, the temperature rise coming abruptly at the time of ovulation. Such a temperature chart, showing the point of ovulation, is illustrated in Figure 737.

A large number of cases of female infertility results from either congenital or acquired deformities of the female genital tract. One of the most common causes of female sterility is endometriosis, for, as described above, *endometriosis* causes fibrosis throughout the pelvis, this fibrosis frequently so enshrouding the ovaries that an ovum cannot be released into the abdominal cavity; often, also, endometriosis occludes the fallopian tubes either at the fimbriated ends or elsewhere along their extent. Another very common cause of female infertility is salpingitis, that is, inflammation of the fallopian tubes, and this in turn causes fibrosis in the tubes, thereby occluding them. In past years, such inflammation was extremely common as a result of gonococcal infection, but with modern therapy this is becoming a less prevalent cause of female infertility.

REFERENCES

Albert, A.: Human urinary gonadotropin. *Recent Progr. Hormone Res.,* 12:227, 1956.

Alvarez, R. R., and Smith, E. K.: Physiological basis for hormone therapy in the female. *J.A.M.A.,* 168:489, 1958.

Bourne, A. W., and Williams, L. H.: Recent Advances in Obstetrics and Gynecology. 9th ed. Boston, Little, Brown and Co., 1958.

Bullough, W. S.: Vertebrates Sexual Cycles. New York, John Wiley and Sons, 1951.

Burrows, H.: Biological Actions of Sex Hormones. 2nd ed., New York, Cambridge University Press, 1949.

Davis, M. E., and Plotz, E. J.: Progesterone, the pregnancy hormone. *Fertility and Sterility,* 8:603, 1957.

Dorfman, R. I., and Ungar, F.: Metabolism of Steroid Hormones. Minneapolis, Burgess Publishing Co., 1953.

Emmens, C. W., and Blackshaw, A. W.: Artificial insemination. *Physiol. Rev.,* 36:277, 1956.

Engle, E. T.: Menstruation and Its Disorders. Springfield, Illinois, Charles C Thomas, 1950.

Farris, E. J.: Human Ovulation and Fertility. Philadelphia, J. B. Lippincott Co., 1959.

Giese, A. C.: Comparative physiology: annual reproductive cycles of marine invertebrates. *Ann. Rev. Physiol.,* 21:547, 1959.

Harrison, R. G.: Studies on Fertility: The Proceedings of the Society for the Study of Fertility: Volume X. Springfield, Illinois, Charles C Thomas, 1959.

Hisaw, F. L.: Development of the graafian follicle and ovulation. *Physiol. Rev.,* 27:95, 1947.

Jones, G. E. S.: Management of Endocrine Disorders of Menstruation and Fertility. Springfield, Illinois, Charles C Thomas, 1954.

Kelly, L. G.: Sex Manual; for Those Married or About to Be. Augusta, Georgia, Southern Medical Supply Co., 1953.

Kinsey, A. C.: Sexual Behavior in the Human Female. Philadelphia, W. B. Saunders Co., 1953.

Levine, L., and Doherty, B.: The Menopause. New York, Random House, 1952.

Merrill, R. C.: Estriol: A review. *Physiol. Rev.,* 38:463, 1958.

Morris, J. McL., and Scully, R. E.: Endocrine Pathology of the Ovary. London, Henry Kimpton, 1958.

Novak, E., and Novak, E. R.: Textbook of Gynecology. 5th ed., Baltimore, Williams & Wilkins Co., 1956.

Papanicolaou, G. N.: The Epithelia of Woman's Reproductive Organs. New York, Commonwealth Fund, 1948.

Pincus, G.: The hormonal control of ovulation and early development. *Postgraduate Medicine,* 24:654, 1958.

Reynolds, S. R. M.: Determinants of uterine growth and activity. *Physiol. Rev.,* 31:244, 1951.

Reynolds, S. R. M.: Physiology of the Uterus. 2nd ed., New York, Paul B. Hoeber, 1949.

Schellen, A. M. C. M.: Artificial Insemination in the Human. Houston, Elsevier Press, 1957.

Simmons, F. A.: The Diagnosis and Treatment of the Infertile Female. Springfield, Illinois, Charles C Thomas, 1954.

Smith, R. A., and Albert, A.: The effect of cortisone on urinary gonadotropin. *Proc. Mayo Clinic,* 32:340, 1957.

Smith, R. A., and Albert, A.: Effects of progesterone on urinary gonadotropin. *Proc. Mayo Clinic,* 31:309, 1956.

Velardo, J. T. (ed.): The Endocrinology of Reproduction. New York, Oxford University Press, 1958.

Whitelock, O. (ed.): The Uterus. *Ann. N. Y. Acad. Sc.,* Vol. 75, January, 1959.

See also Chapter 73, Hypophyseal-ovarian relationships and general bibliography on endocrinology; Chapter 78, Male physiology; Chapter 80, Reproduction.

least three cells thick, and the distance between the maternal blood and the fetal blood is several times the distance across the alveolar membranes of the lung. Nevertheless, nutrients and other substances pass through the placental membrane by the process of diffusion in very much the same manner as through the alveolar membranes and capillary membranes elsewhere in the body.

Permeability of the Placental Membrane. Since the major function of the placenta is to allow diffusion of foodstuffs from the mother's blood into the baby's blood and diffusion of excretory products from the baby back into the mother, it is important to know the degree of permeability of the placental membrane. *Permeability is expressed as the total quantity of a given substance that will cross the entire placental membrane for a given diffusion gradient.* In the early months of development, placental permeability is relatively slight, as illustrated in Figure 741, for two reasons: First, the total surface area of the placental membrane is still small at that time, and, second, the thickness of the membrane is very great. However, as the placenta becomes older, the permeability increases progressively until the last month or so of pregnancy when it begins to decrease again. The increase in permeability is caused by both progressive enlargement of the surface areas of the placental membrane and progressive thinning of the villi. On the other hand, the decrease shortly before birth results from deterioration of the placenta caused by its age and sometimes from destruction of whole segments due to infarction of isolated areas.

Occasionally, "breaks" occur in the placental membrane which allow fetal blood cells to pass into the mother, or more rarely, the mother's cells to pass into the fetus. Indeed, there are instances in which the baby bleeds severely into the mother's circulation because of a ruptured placental membrane.

Diffusion of Oxygen through the Placental Membrane. Almost exactly the same principles are applicable for the diffusion of oxygen through the placental membrane as through the alveolar membranes and cellular membranes, which was discussed in Chapter 40. The dissolved oxygen in the blood of the large placental sinuses simply passes through the villus membrane into the fetal blood because of a pressure

gradient of oxygen from the mother's blood to the baby's blood. The mean Po_2 in the mother's blood in the placental sinuses is approximately 65 mm. Hg toward the end of pregnancy, and the mean Po_2 in the blood leaving the villi and returning to the fetus is about 50 mm. Hg. Thus, a pressure gradient of at least 15 mm. Hg exists for the diffusion of oxygen through the placental membrane.

Even though blood flows through the maternal blood sinuses very rapidly, nevertheless, the rate of diffusion of oxygen through the placental membrane is slow enough that fetal hemoglobin leaving the villi is never completely saturated with oxygen. During approximately the middle of pregnancy, fetal hemoglobin may reach 90 per cent saturation with oxygen. However, during the last month of pregnancy the saturation of fetal hemoglobin falls below 80 per cent, and immediately before parturition the fetal hemoglobin saturation ordinarily is about 65 per cent. This abrupt fall in oxygen saturation of the fetal hemoglobin toward the end of pregnancy is due partly to the decrease in permeability of the membrane and partly to increased use of oxygen by the fetus.

Diffusion of Carbon Dioxide through the Placental Membrane. Because carbon dioxide is an excretory product, the Pco_2 in the fetal blood is greater than the Pco_2 in the maternal blood. However, not nearly so much difference exists between these carbon dioxide pressures as between the oxygen pressures on the two sides of the membrane. The reason for this is that carbon dioxide, because of its water solubility, diffuses through tissues and fluids about 20 times as rapidly as oxygen. Therefore, the concentration of carbon dioxide in the fetal blood ordinarily does not rise to a great extent above that in the maternal blood.

Diffusion of Foodstuffs through the Placental Membrane. Other metabolic substrates needed by the fetus diffuse into the fetal blood in the same manner as oxygen. For instance, the glucose level in the fetal blood ordinarily is approximately 20 to 30 per cent lower than the glucose level in the maternal blood, for glucose is being metabolized very rapidly by the fetus. This in turn causes rapid diffusion of additional glucose from the maternal blood into the fetal blood.

Because of the small molecular size of the

amino acids, these also can diffuse from the maternal blood into the fetal blood. Also, such substances as calcium, phosphorus, and sodium chloride diffuse from the maternal blood into the fetal blood. As these substances are used by the fetal body, their concentrations in the fetal blood fall, and the increased concentration gradients then cause more of the same substrates to diffuse through the placental membrane.

Active Absorption by the Placental Membrane. It was pointed out above that early nutrition of the embryo depends upon phagocytosis of fallopian tube and uterine secretions, and even upon phagocytosis of endometrial tissues. The trophoblastic cells that line the outer surface of the villi can probably also actively absorb certain nutrients from the blood sinus of the placenta at least during the first half of pregnancy and perhaps even throughout the entire period of pregnancy. For instance, the measured amino acid content of fetal blood sometimes is greater than that of maternal blood, and calcium and inorganic phosphate are occasionally in greater concentration in fetal blood than in maternal blood, while ascorbic acid is as much as three times as concentrated in the fetal blood. This indicates that the placental membrane does have the ability to absorb actively at least small amounts of certain substances.

Excretion through the Placental Membrane. In the same manner that carbon dioxide diffuses from the fetal blood into the maternal blood, other excretory products formed within the fetus likewise diffuse into the maternal blood and then are excreted along with the excretory products of the mother. These include especially the nonprotein nitrogens such as urea, uric acid, and creatinine. The level of urea in the fetal blood is only slightly greater than that in the maternal blood because urea diffuses through the placental membrane with considerable ease. On the other hand, creatinine, which does not diffuse as easily, has a considerably higher concentration gradient between the fetal blood and maternal blood. Therefore, insofar as is known, excretion from the fetus occurs entirely as a result of positive diffusion gradients across the placental membrane—that is, higher concentrations of the excretory products in the fetal blood than in the maternal blood.

The Storage Function of the Placenta

During the first few months of pregnancy, the placenta grows tremendously in size while the fetus remains relatively diminutive. During this same period of time considerable quantities of metabolic substrates, including proteins, calcium, and iron, are stored in the placenta itself to be used in the latter months of pregnancy for growth by the fetus. By this means the mother is capable of optimally utilizing her food intake throughout pregnancy for the formation of the fetus.

HORMONAL FACTORS IN PREGNANCY

In pregnancy, the placenta secretes large quantities of *chorionic gonadotropin, estrogens,* and *progesterone,* all of which are essential to the continuance of pregnancy. The functions of these hormones are discussed below.

Chorionic Gonadotropin and Its Effect to Cause Persistence of the Corpus Luteum and to Prevent Menstruation

Menstruation normally occurs approximately 14 days after ovulation, at which time most of the secretory endometrium of the uterus sloughs away from the uterine wall and is expelled to the exterior. If this should happen after an ovum has implanted, obviously, the pregnancy would terminate. However, this is prevented by the secretion of *chorionic gonadotropin* in the following manner:

Coincidentally with the trophoblastic invasion of the endometrium by the developing blastocyst, the cytotrophoblastic cells of the developing placenta secrete the hormone chorionic gonadotropin into the fluids of the mother, and, as illustrated in Figure 743, the rate of secretion rises very rapidly to reach a maximum approximately 7 weeks after ovulation, then decreases to a relatively low value at 16 weeks after ovulation.

Function of Chorionic Gonadotropin. Chorionic gonadotropin has very much the

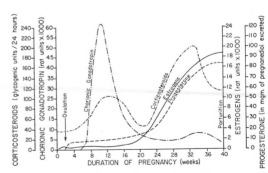

Figure 743. Secretion of chorionic gonadotropin, estrogens, progesterone, and corticosteroids during pregnancy.

same function as a combination of luteinizing and luteotropic hormones secreted by the adenohypophysis. Most important, it prevents the normal involution of the corpus luteum at the end of the sexual month, and it causes the corpus luteum to secrete large quantities of its usual hormones, progesterone and estrogens. These hormones in turn cause the uterine endometrium to continue growing and to store very large amounts of nutrients rather than to be passed in the menstruum. As a result, the *decidua-like cells* that develop in the endometrium during the normal female sexual cycle become actual *decidual cells* by the time the blastocyst begins to implant.

Under the influence of chorionic gonadotropin, the corpus luteum grows to about two times its initial size by a month or so after pregnancy begins, and its continued secretion of estrogens and progesterone maintains the decidual nature of the uterine endometrium, which is necessary to the development of the placenta and other fetal tissues. If the corpus luteum is removed before approximately the eleventh week of pregnancy, spontaneous abortion usually occurs, though after this time the placenta itself secretes sufficient quantities of progesterone and estrogens to maintain pregnancy for the remainder of the gestation period.

Effect of chorionic gonadotropin on the testes. Chorionic gonadotropin also exerts an *interstitial cell–stimulating effect* on the testes, thus resulting in the production of testosterone in male fetuses, and the small secretion of testosterone during gestation helps create the masculine sexual organs. Near the end of pregnancy, the testosterone secreted by the fetal testes causes the testicles to descend into the scrotum.

Clinically, chorionic gonadotropin administered to the cryptorchid child will often cause the testicles to descend into the scrotum by causing testosterone to be secreted, which causes the testicular descent.

Secretion of Estrogens by the Placenta

The placenta, like the corpus luteum, secretes both estrogens and progesterone. Both histochemical and physiological studies indicate that these two hormones are secreted by the *syncytial trophoblasts*, in contradistinction to the secretion of chorionic gonadotropin by the cytotrophoblasts.

Figure 743 shows that the daily production of placental estrogens toward the end of pregnancy may be as great as 50 to 60 times the daily production in the middle of a normal monthly sexual cycle. Thus, estrogens are much more hormones of pregnancy than even of normal female sex life.

In the discussions of estrogens in the preceding chapter it was pointed out that these hormones exert mainly a proliferative function on certain of the reproductive and associated organs. During pregnancy, estrogens cause (1) enlargement of the uterus, (2) enlargement of the breasts and growth of the breast glandular tissue, and (3) enlargement of the female external genitalia.

The estrogens also relax the various pelvic ligaments so that the sacroiliac joints become relatively limber and the symphysis pubis becomes elastic. These changes obviously make for easy passage of the fetus through the delivery canal.

There is much reason to believe that estrogens also affect the development of the fetus during pregnancy, for example, by controlling the rate of cellular reproduction in the early embryo. It is thought that estrogens are partly responsible for the formation of the female sex organs in the fetus.

Secretion of Progesterone by the Placenta

Progesterone is also a hormone essential for pregnancy. In addition to being secreted in moderate quantities by the corpus luteum at the beginning of pregnancy, it is secreted in tremendous quantities, sometimes as much as 1 gram per day, toward the end of pregnancy. Indeed, the rate of progesterone secretion increases by as much as 10-fold during the course of pregnancy, as illustrated in Figure 743.

The special effects of progesterone that are essential for normal progression of pregnancy are the following:

1. As pointed out earlier, progesterone causes decidual cells to develop in the uterine endometrium, and these then play an important role in the nutrition of the early embryo.

2. Progesterone has a special effect to decrease the contractility of the gravid uterus, thus preventing uterine contractions from causing spontaneous abortion.

3. Progesterone also contributes to the

development of the ovum even prior to implantation. It specifically increases the secretions of the fallopian tubes and uterus to provide appropriate nutritive matter for the developing *morula* and *blastocyst*. There is some reason to believe, too, that progesterone might even help to control cellular cleavage in the early developing embryo.

4. The progesterone secreted during pregnancy also helps to prepare the breasts for lactation, which will be discussed in detail later in the chapter.

Other Hormonal Factors in Pregnancy

Almost all the non-sexual endocrine glands of the mother react markedly to pregnancy. This results mainly from the increased metabolic load on the mother but also to some extent from inverse effects of placental hormones on the adenohypophysis and other glands. Some of the most notable effects are the following:

Adenohypophyseal Secretion during Pregnancy. The adenohypophysis enlarges at least 50 per cent during pregnancy and increases its production of corticotropin, thyrotropin, and probably also growth hormone. On the other hand, production of the gonadotropic hormones is greatly suppressed as a result of the inhibitory effects of estrogens and progesterone from the placenta.

Corticosteroid Secretion. Almost immediately after conception the rate of adrenocortical secretion of the glucocorticoids increases to about double normal, and it rises to as much as three to four times normal by the end of pregnancy.

The function of the glucocorticoids in pregnancy is not known, but the pregnant mother usually has a slight degree of hyperglycemia, which presumably results from the glucocorticoids. It is possible also that the glucocorticoids help to mobilize amino acids from the mother's tissues so that these can be used for synthesis of tissues in the fetus.

Some pregnant women also have increased secretion of aldosterone. This, along with the actions of the estrogens and progesterone, causes a tendency for even the normal pregnant women to reabsorb excess sodium from the renal tubules.

Part of the corticosteroids secreted during pregnancy are formed by the placenta rather than by the adrenal cortex, but the quantitative importance of these is yet unknown.

Secretion by the Thyroid Gland. The thyroid gland ordinarily enlarges about 50 per cent during pregnancy and increases its production of thyroxine a corresponding amount. Though most of the increased thyroxine production is caused by increased thyrotropic hormone from the adenohypophysis, minute quantities of thyrotropin are secreted also by the placenta, the significance of which is not yet clear.

Secretion by the Parathyroid Glands during Pregnancy. The parathyroid glands also often enlarge during pregnancy, and this is especially true if the mother is on a calcium deficient diet. Enlargement of these glands causes calcium absorption from the mother's bones, thereby maintaining a normal calcium ion concentration in the mother's extracellular fluids as the fetus removes calcium for ossifying its own bones.

Secretion of "Relaxin" by the Ovaries. A hormone called "relaxin," which is entirely independent of the usual female sex hormones, has been postulated to be secreted by the ovaries during pregnancy, though there is not yet complete agreement among physiologists that such a hormone exists. Relaxin is a water soluble substance, probably a polypeptide, having a molecular weight of 10,000 to 12,000, that is present in the ovaries only during pregnancy—more so toward the end of pregnancy. Claims have been made that it causes the following effects: (1) relaxation of the ligaments of the symphysis pubis in some animals, (2) stimulation of the mammary glands, (3) relaxation of the cervix, and (4) inhibition of uterine motility. The latter two functions of relaxin have made it useful in clinical medicine for three purposes: (1) to treat painful menstruation, called *dysmenorrhea*, (2) to treat threatened abortion or premature labor, and (3) to cause cervical softening prior to delivery.

However, it should be emphasized once again that very little is known about the secretion of relaxin. Also, many of its properties are shared by the estrogens so that many physiologists still doubt the importance of relaxin.

RESPONSE OF THE MOTHER TO PREGNANCY

Obviously, the presence of a growing fetus in the uterus adds an additional physiologic load on the mother, and much of the response of the mother to pregnancy is due to this increased load. The hormones secreted during pregnancy either by the placenta or by the endocrine glands can also cause many reactions in the mother. Among the reactions are increased size of the various sex organs. For instance, the uterus increases from a weight of about 30 grams to about 700 grams, and the breasts approximately double in size. At the same time the vagina enlarges, and the introitus opens more widely. Also, the various hormones can cause marked changes in the appearance of the mother, sometimes resulting in the development of edema, acne, and masculine or acromegalic features.

Changes in the Maternal Circulatory System During Pregnancy

Blood Flow through the Placenta. About 750 ml. of blood flows through the maternal circulation of the placenta each minute during the latter phases of gestation. Obviously, the more rapidly this blood flows, the greater will be the concentration of oxygen and other metabolites in the fetal blood.

Cardiac Output of the Mother. The flow of blood through the placenta decreases the total peripheral resistance of the mother's circulatory system and, consequently, allows increased venous return of blood to the heart, which in turn tends to increase the cardiac output in the same manner that arteriovenous shunts increase the cardiac output. This factor, plus a general increase in metabolism, increases the cardiac output to 30 to 40 per cent above normal by the twenty-seventh week of pregnancy, but then, for reasons yet unexplained, the cardiac output falls near to normal during the last eight weeks of pregnancy, despite the high uterine blood flow.

Blood Volume of the Mother. The maternal blood volume shortly before term is approximately 30 per cent above normal. This increase occurs mainly during the latter half of pregnancy, as is illustrated in the curve of Figure 744. The cause of the increased blood volume is probably mainly hormonal, for adrenocortical hormones, estrogens, and progesterone can all cause increased fluid retention by the kidneys, and all these hormones are secreted into the maternal body in very large quantities during the latter half of pregnancy. It is probable, also, that the shunting effect of blood through the placenta decreases the capillary pressures throughout the mother's body, which may be responsible for some increase in blood volume, for an increased blood volume occurs routinely when any type of arteriovenous shunt is prepared in an animal.

As a result of the increased blood volume in the mother, the hematocrit at first decreases because of dilution of the blood. However, toward the end of pregnancy the bone marrow becomes increasingly active, and the concentration of red blood cells returns to almost normal. Therefore, at the time of birth of the baby, the mother has

approximately 1 to 2 liters of extra blood in her circulatory system. Only about one-fourth of this amount is normally lost during delivery of the baby, thereby allowing a considerable safety factor for the mother.

Weight Gain in the Mother

During the first months of pregnancy, possibly as a result of nausea, the mother ordinarily loses a few pounds of weight, but, during the entire period of pregnancy, the average weight gain is approximately 24 pounds, most of this gain occurring during the last two trimesters. Of this increase in weight, approximately 7 pounds is baby, and approximately 4 pounds is amniotic fluid and fetal membranes. This leaves 13 pounds increase in weight by the mother herself. The uterus increases approximately 2 pounds, and the breasts increase approximately 3 pounds, still leaving an average increase in weight of the mother herself of approximately 8 pounds. On the average, this extra 8 pounds of weight is accounted for by about 3 pounds gain in protein, 3 pounds of fluid (mainly in the blood), and 2 pounds of fat.

Often during pregnancy the mother has a greatly increased desire for food, partly as a result of fetal removal of food substrates from the mother's blood and partly because of hormonal factors. Without appropriate prenatal care some mothers eat tremendous quantities of food, and the weight gain, instead of averaging 24 pounds, may be as great as 75 pounds or more. In these instances, the weight gain is due to actual deposition of fat.

Metabolism in the Mother during Pregnancy

As a consequence of the increased secretion of many different hormones during pregnancy, including thyroxine, adrenocortical hormones, and the sex hormones, the basal metabolic rate of the mother increases about 10 per cent during the latter half of pregnancy, which is not so much as might be expected. However, as the result of this increased basal metabolic rate the mother frequently has sensations of becoming overheated. Also, owing to the extra load that the mother is carrying, greater amounts of energy must be expended than normally for muscular activity. This adds to the heat production and to the mother's discomfort.

Nutrition during Pregnancy. The supplemental food needed by the mother during pregnancy to supply the needs of the fetus and fetal membranes includes especially extra dietary quantities of the various minerals, vitamins, and proteins. The growing fetus assumes priority in regard to many of the nutritional elements in the mother's body fluids, and many portions of

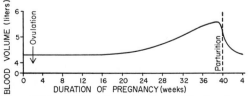

Figure 744. Effect of pregnancy on blood volume.

the fetus will continue to grow even though the mother does not eat a sufficient diet. For instance, lack of adequate nutrition in the mother will hardly change the rate of growth of the fetal nervous system, and the length of the fetus increases almost normally; on the other hand, lack of adequate nutrition can decrease the weight of the baby considerably, can decrease ossification of the bones, and can cause anemia, hypoprothrombinemia, and decreased size of many of the bodily organs of the fetus.

By far the greatest growth of the fetus occurs during the last trimester of pregnancy; the weight of the child almost doubles rapidly during the last two months of pregnancy. Ordinarily, the mother cannot absorb sufficient protein, calcium, phosphorus, and iron from the gastrointestinal tract during the last month of pregnancy to supply the fetus. However, from the beginning of pregnancy the mother's body has been storing these substances to be used during the latter months of pregnancy. Some of this storage is in the placenta, but most of it is in the normal storage depots of the mother.

If appropriate nutritional elements are not present in the mother's diet, a number of maternal deficiencies can occur during pregnancy. Such deficiencies often occur for calcium, phosphates, iron, and the vitamins. For example, approximately 375 mg. of iron are needed by the baby to form its blood and an additional 600 mg. are needed by the mother to form her own extra blood. The normal stores of non-hemoglobin iron in the mother at the outset of pregnancy is often only a hundred or so mg. and almost never over 700 mg. Therefore, without sufficient iron in the food the mother herself usually develops anemia. Therefore, in general, the obstetrician supplements the diet of the mother with the needed substances. It is especially important that the mother receive large quantities of vitamin D, for, even though the total quantity of calcium utilized by the fetus is rather small, calcium even normally is poorly absorbed by the gastrointestinal tract. Finally, shortly before birth of the baby vitamin K is often added to the diet so that the baby will have sufficient prothrombin to prevent postnatal hemorrhage.

Respiration in the Mother during Pregnancy

Because of the increased basal metabolic rate of the mother, and also because of the mother's increase in size, the total amount of oxygen utilized by the mother shortly before birth of the baby is usually approximately 20 per cent above normal. This causes increased elimination of carbon dioxide, and it also causes increased rate and depth of respiration. Simultaneously, the growing uterus presses upward against the abdominal contents, and these in turn press upward against the diaphragm so that the total excursion of the diaphragm is decreased. Consequently, the respiratory rate must be increased to maintain adequate ventilation. Yet, strangely enough, the vital capacity of the mother is usually increased, presumably because of increased development of the respiratory system owing to the increased pulmonary activity.

Function of the Maternal Urinary System During Pregnancy

The rate of urine formation by the pregnant mother is usually slightly increased because of an increased load of excretory products. But, in addition, there are several special alterations of urinary function as follows:

First, it has already been pointed out that there is a greatly increased tendency for reabsorption of sodium, chloride, and water by the renal tubules as a consequence of increased production of steroid hormones by the placenta and adrenal cortex.

Second, the glomerular filtration rate often increases as much as 50 per cent during pregnancy, which tends to increase the rate of water and electrolyte loss in the urine. This factor normally almost balances the first so that the mother ordinarily does not get into trouble from excess water and salt accumulation except when she develops *toxemia of pregnancy*; this disease will be discussed later in the chapter.

Third, the ureters usually dilate during pregnancy because of two different factors: The enlarged uterus compresses the ureters as they pass over the pelvic rim, thereby increasing the intraureteral pressure. But, aside from this compression factor, the hormones secreted during pregnancy have a direct effect in relaxing the ureters. The two hormones that have been particularly implicated are progesterone and relaxin, though there is still much doubt about the ureteral effects of either of these. Ureteral distention and the accompanying renal pelvic distention that also results predisposes to infection in the urinary tract, frequently leading to serious renal debility, one of the very common complications of pregnancy.

The Amniotic Fluid and Its Formation

Normally, the volume of amniotic fluid is between 500 ml. and 1 liter, but, it can be only a few milliliters or as much as several liters. Studies with isotopes of the rate of formation of amniotic fluid shows that on the average the amniotic fluid is completely reformed once every three hours. Yet, strangely enough, the sources of the fluid and the points of reabsorption are yet very much unknown. A small portion of the fluid is derived from renal excretion by the fetus. Likewise, a certain amount of absorption occurs by way of the gastrointestinal tract and lungs of the fetus. However, even after death of the fetus, the rate of turnover of the amniotic fluid is still one-half as great as it is when the fetus is normal, which indicates that much of the fluid is formed and absorbed directly through the amniotic membranes. Regulation of the total volume of amniotic fluid could be accomplished by the amniotic membranes themselves, for as the volume increased the membranes would stretch and presumably would absorb increased quantities of fluid as a result, thus returning the volume to normal.

ABNORMAL RESPONSES OF THE MOTHER TO PREGNANCY

Hyperemesis Gravidarum

In the earlier months of pregnancy, the mother frequently develops *hyperemesis gravidarum,* a condition characterized by nausea and vomiting and commonly known as "morning sickness." Occasionally, the vomiting becomes so severe that the mother becomes greatly dehydrated, and in very rare instances the condition even causes death.

The cause of the nausea and vomiting is unknown, but it occurs to its greatest extent during the same period of time that chorionic gonadotropin is secreted in large quantities by the placenta. Because of this coincidence, it is believed by many clinicians that chorionic gonadotropin is in some way responsible for the nausea and vomiting. For instance, it has been supposed that chorionic gonadotropin might cause a systemic allergic reaction in the mother to elicit the nausea and vomiting. Or perhaps other tissues of the mother besides the corpus luteum are affected by chorionic gonadotropin, thereby predisposing to the development of hyperemesis gravidarum.

On the other hand, during the first few months of pregnancy very rapid trophoblastic invasion of the endometrium also takes place, and, because the trophoblastic cells digest portions of the endometrium as they invade it, it is possible that degenerative products resulting from this invasion, instead of chorionic gonadotropin, are responsible for the nausea and vomiting. Indeed, degenerative processes occurring in other parts of the body, such as following gamma ray irradiation, burns, and so forth, can all cause similar nausea and vomiting.

Toxemia of Pregnancy

Approximately 7 per cent of all pregnant women experience very rapid weight gain, edema, and elevation of arterial pressure. This condition is known as "toxemia of pregnancy," and most obstetricians believe that its major cause is excessive retention of sodium by the distal tubules of the kidneys. Possibly some of the hormones associated with pregnancy may be secreted to a greater extent than normally, or perhaps the kidneys are more responsive than normally to these hormones. It has been shown that aldosterone secretion is considerably increased in many toxemic patients. This hormone is known to cause marked reabsorption of sodium by the tubules and thus to increase the total quantity of extracellular fluid. It is possible that the increase in arterial pressure that occurs in toxemia is attributable to more or less the same causes as the increased arterial pressure in Cushing's disease, in which adrenocortical secretion is greatly increased, as was discussed in Chapter 74.

It is well known among obstetricians that limiting the pregnant mother's intake of salt will usually prevent the development of excessive degrees of toxemia. This supports the view that toxemia is probably a hormonal abnormality affecting retention of sodium chloride by the kidneys. As is true of cardiac edema, it usually is not necessary to limit the mother's intake of water, for limitation of sodium chloride intake alone prevents excessive reabsorption of water by the kidney tubules for reasons discussed in Chapter 9.

Eclampsia of Pregnancy. *Eclampsia* is a very severe degree of toxemia of pregnancy, in contradistinction to *preeclampsia,* which means a milder degree of toxemia. Eclampsia is characterized by extreme vascular spasticity throughout the body, clonic convulsions followed by coma, greatly decreased kidney output, malfunction of the liver, and a generalized toxic condition of the body. Usually it occurs shortly before parturition or sometimes even after birth of the baby.

Exactly how toxemia can change into the severe eclamptic process is difficult to understand, but it is possible that hormones or other factors simply cause extreme vascular spasm throughout the body and that the other effects are degenerative effects resulting from ischemia. For instance, portions of the placenta frequently degenerate, and premature separation of the placenta from the uterus often occurs. Also, unless the vascular spasm is treated immediately, permanent degenerative changes are likely to develop in the kidneys and liver.

Even with the best forms of treatment, some 5 per cent of eclamptic mothers still die. However, injection of vasodilator drugs plus dehydration of the patient can often reverse the vascular spasm and lower the blood pressure, bringing the mother out of the eclamptic state.

PARTURITION

Increased Uterine Irritability Near Term

Parturition means simply the process by which the baby is born. At the termination of pregnancy the uterus becomes progressively more excitable until finally it begins very strong rhythmical contractions with such force that the baby is expelled. The exact cause of the increased activity of the uterus is not known, but at least two major categories of effects lead up to the culminating contractions responsible for parturition; these are, first, progressive hormonal changes that cause increased excitability of the uterine musculature, and, second, progressive mechanical changes that also lead to parturition.

Hormonal Factors That Cause Increased Uterine Contractility. *Ratio of estrogens to progesterone.* Progesterone inhibits uterine contractility during pregnancy, thereby helping to prevent expulsion of the fetus. On the other hand, estrogens have a very mild effect to increase the degree of uterine contractility. Both of these hormones are secreted in progressively greater and greater quantities throughout pregnancy, but from the seventh month onward estrogen secretion increases more than progesterone secretion, and immediately before term relatively large quantities of non-conjugated estrogens ("free estrogens") appear in the extracellular fluids. Therefore, it has been supposed that the *estrogen to progesterone ratio* increases sufficiently toward the end of pregnancy to be at least partly responsible for the increased contractility of the uterus.

Effect of oxytocin on the uterus. Oxytocin is a hormone secreted by the neurohypophysis that specifically causes uterine contraction (see Chapter 73). There are four reasons for believing that oxytocin might be particularly important in increasing the contractility of the uterus near term. (1) The uterus increases its responsiveness to a given dose of oxytocin by about 10-fold during the latter few months of pregnancy. (2) The rate of oxytocin secretion by the neurohypophysis, as judged from thus far rather incomplete studies, seems to be considerably increased at the time of labor. (3) Though hypophysectomized animals and human beings can still deliver their young at term, labor is prolonged. (4) Recent experiments in animals indicate that irritation or stretching of the body or cervix of the uterus can cause a neurogenic reflex to the neurohypophysis to increase the rate of oxytocin secretion.

Mechanical Factors That Increase the Contractility of the Uterus. *Stretch of the uterine musculature.* It is well known that simply stretching smooth muscle organs usually increases their contractility. Furthermore, intermittent stretch, as occurs repetitively in the uterus because of movements of the fetus, can also elicit smooth muscle contraction.

To emphasize the importance of mechanical stretch in eliciting uterine contractions, it should be noted especially that twins are born on the average *nineteen days* earlier than a single child.

Stretch or irritation of the cervix. There is much reason to believe that stretch or irritation of the uterine cervix is particularly important in eliciting uterine contractions. For instance, the obstetrician very frequently induces labor by dilating the cervix or by rupturing the membranes so that the head of the baby will stretch the cervix more forcefully than usual or irritate it in some other way.

The mechanism of this intense stimulating effect of cervical irritation on the body of the uterus is not known. It has been supposed that stretch or irritation of neuronal cells in the cervix might initiate reflexes to the body of the uterus, but the effect could also result simply from myogenic transmission from the cervix to the body of the uterus.

Onset of Labor—a Positive Feedback Theory for Its Initiation

During the last few months of pregnancy the uterus undergoes periodic episodes of very weak and very slow rhythmical contractions called *Braxton-Hicks contractions*. These become progressively stronger toward the end of pregnancy. Then, within a matter of hours, the uterine contractions become strong enough to start stretching the cervix and later to move the baby through the delivery canal, thereby causing parturition. This entire process is called *labor* and the strong contractions that result in final parturition are called *labor contractions*.

Yet, strangely enough, we do not know what suddenly changes the slow and weak rhythmicity of the uterus into the strong labor contractions. Most obstetricians have the feeling that one of the factors discussed above that increase uterine contractility suddenly becomes strong enough to promote these contractions. However, on the basis of experience during the past few years with other types of control systems, the author has proposed a theory for explaining the onset of labor on the basis of "positive feedback." This theory suggests that stretch of the cervix by the baby's head finally becomes great enough to elicit a reflex increase in contractility of the uterine body. This pushes the body forward, which stretches the cervix some more and initiates a new cycle. Thus, the process continues again and again until the body is expelled. This theory is illustrated in Figure 745, and the data supporting it are the following:

First, labor contractions obey all of the principles of positive feedback. That is, once the strength of uterine contraction becomes greater than a critical value, each contraction leads to subsequent contractions that become stronger and stronger until maximum effect is achieved. If we will now refer to the discussion in Chapter 1 of positive feedback in control systems, we will see that this is the precise nature of all positive feedback mechanisms.

Second, the next problem is to explain how positive feedback could develop to set off this crescendo of strength of the uterine contractions. We have two possible types of positive feedback in the uterus at term. First, the propensity for cervical irritation to cause contraction of the body of the uterus could cause positive feedback in the following way: An initial contraction of the uterine body could force the head of the baby or the fluid in the amniotic cavity against the cervix to stretch, tear, or irritate it in several other ways. This stimulus of the cervix could in turn lead to feedback that would cause additional contractility of the uterine body. As a result, the next contraction of the uterus would become stronger, and the process would proceed on and on with progressively stronger contractions until delivery of the baby.

A second positive feedback mechanism might involve the secretion of oxytocin by the neurohypophysis. This could result from the following sequence of events: (a) uterine contraction, (b) cervical stretch or other type of cervical stimulation, (c) a reflex from the cervix to the neurohypophysis, (d) increased secretion of oxytocin, (e) increased contractility of the uterus, which (f) leads to successive contractions that get stronger and stronger.

Third, we now have to explain why all Braxton-Hicks contractions do not lead to labor. Referring once more to the discussion of positive feedback in Chapter 1, we find

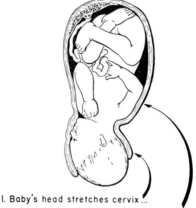

1. Baby's head stretches cervix...
2. Cervical stretch excites fundic contraction...
3. Fundic contraction pushes baby down and stretches cervix some more...
4. Cycle repeats over and over again...

Figure 745.   Theory for the onset of intensely strong contractions during labor.

that positive feedback causes a vicious cycle that goes to completion only when each feedback response is greater than the previous response. Thus, if each *increase* in strength of contraction of the uterus leads to a greater *increase* in strength of contraction the next time, then the process would go to completion, but, if the second *increase* in contraction is not greater than the first increase, the process will fade out. Therefore, the degree of contractility of the uterus and the degree of responsiveness of the positive feedback mechanism must reach a certain stage of development before the positive feedback can become a vicious cycle. Up to that point, the natural contractions can continue to take place without developing into frank labor contractions.

To summarize the theory, we can assume that multiple factors increase the contractility of the uterus toward the end of pregnancy. These are additive in their effects and they cause the Braxton-Hicks contractions to become progressively stronger. Eventually, one of these becomes strong enough that the contraction itself irritates the uterus, increases its contractility because of positive feedback and results in a second contraction stronger than the first, and a third stronger than the second, and so forth. Once these contractions become strong enough to cause this type of feedback with each succeeding *increase* in strength of contraction greater than the preceding *increase,* then the process will proceed to completion —all simply *because positive feedback becomes a vicious cycle when the degree of feedback is greater than unity.*

One might immediately ask about the many instances of false labor in which the contractions become stronger and stronger and then fade away. It should be remembered that for a vicious cycle to continue *each* increase in strength of contraction with each cycle must be stronger than the previous one. If at any time after labor starts some of the cycles fail to reexcite the uterus sufficiently, then the positive feedback would go into a retrograde succession and the labor contractions would fade away.

Abdominal Contraction during Labor. Once the uterine contractions become very strong and painful, neurogenic reflexes from the delivery canal, or perhaps even from the uterus itself, to the spinal cord and thence back to the abdominal muscles cause intense abdominal contraction. This additional contraction of the abdominal muscles and the reflexes causing it add greatly to the positive feedback that eventually causes expulsion of the fetus.

Mechanics of Parturition. In 19 out of 20 births the head is the first part of the baby to be expelled, and in most of the remaining instances the buttocks are presented first. The head acts as a wedge to open the structures of the birth canal as the baby is forced downward from above.

The first major obstruction to expulsion of the fetus is the uterine cervix. Toward the end of pregnancy the cervix becomes soft, which allows it to stretch when labor pains cause the body of the uterus to contract. The so-called *first stage of labor* is the period of progressive cervical dilatation, lasting until the opening is as large as the head of the baby. This stage usually lasts 8 to 24 hours in the first pregnancy but often only a few minutes after many pregnancies.

Once the cervix has dilated fully, the baby's head moves rapidly into the birth canal, and, with additional force from above, continues to wedge its way through the canal until delivery is effected. This is called the *second stage of labor,* and it may last from as little as a minute after many pregnancies up to half an hour or more in the first pregnancy.

The combined contractions of the uterine and abdominal musculature during delivery of the baby cause a downward force on the fetus of approximately 25 pounds during each strong contraction.

It is fortunate that the contractions of labor occur intermittently because very strong contractions impede or even stop blood flow through the placenta and would cause death of the baby were the contractions continuous. Indeed, in clinical use of various uterine stimulants, such as oxytocin, overuse of the drugs can cause uterine spasm rather than rhythmical contractions and can lead to death of the fetus.

Separation and Delivery of the Placenta. Immediately after birth of the baby, the uterus contracts to a very small size, which causes a *shearing* effect between the walls of the uterus and the placenta, thus separating the placenta from its implantation site. Obviously, separation of the placenta opens the placental sinuses and causes bleeding. However, the amount of bleeding is usually limited to an average of about 350 ml. by the following mechanism: The smooth muscle fibers of the uterine musculature are arranged in figures of 8 around the blood vessels as they pass through the uterine wall. Therefore, contraction of the uterus following delivery of the baby constricts the vessels that had previously supplied blood to the placenta.

Labor Pains. With each contraction of the uterus the mother experiences considerable pain. The pain in early labor is probably caused mainly by anoxia of the uterine muscle resulting from compression of the blood vessels to the uterus. This pain is not felt when the *hypogastric nerves,* which carry the sensory fibers leading from the uterus, have been sectioned. However, during the second stage of labor, when the fetus is being expelled through the birth canal, even more severe pain can be caused by cervical stretch, compression of neurons in the cervix, peritoneal stretch, and tearing of structures in the vaginal canal itself. This pain is conducted by somatic nerves instead of by the hypogastric nerves.

Involution of the Uterus

During the first four to five weeks following parturition, the uterus involutes. Its weight becomes less than one-half its immediate postpartum weight within a week after parturition, and in four weeks the uterus may be as small as it had been prior to pregnancy—that is, if the mother lactates. This effect of lactation will be discussed later. During early involution of the uterus the placental site on the endometrial surface autolyzes, causing a vaginal discharge known as "lochia," which is first bloody and then serous in nature, continuing in all for approximately a week and a half. After this time, the endometrial surface will have become re-epithelized and is ready to begin normal, non-gravid sex life again.

LACTATION

Development of the Breasts

The breasts begin to develop during the normal non-gravid sex life of the female,

for the estrogens of the monthly sexual cycles stimulate growth of the stroma and ductile system plus deposition of fat to give mass to the breasts. However, much additional growth occurs during pregnancy, and the glandular tissue only then becomes adequately adapted for actual production of milk.

Growth of the Ductile System—Role of the Estrogens. All through pregnancy, the tremendous quantities of estrogens secreted by the placenta cause the ductile system of the breasts to grow and to branch. Simultaneously, the stroma of the breasts also increases in quantity, and large quantities of fat are laid down in the stroma.

It should be noted, however, that moderate quantities of growth hormone from the adenohypophysis are also required for the estrogens to produce their effect on the breasts.

Development of the Lobule-Alveolar System—Role of Progesterone. The synergistic action of estrogens and growth hormone can cause only a primitive lobule-alveolar system to develop in the breasts at the same time that the ducts are growing, but the simultaneous action of progesterone causes growth of the lobules, budding of alveoli from the lobules, and development of secretory characteristics in the cells of the alveoli. These changes, obviously, are analogous to the secretory effects of progesterone on the endometrium of the uterus.

Initiation of Lactation—Lactogenic Hormone

By the end of pregnancy, the mother's breasts are fully developed for nursing, but only a few ml. of fluid are secreted each day until after the baby is born. This fluid is called *colostrum;* it contains essentially the same amounts of proteins and lactose as milk but almost no fat, and its maximum rate of production is about 100 times less than the subsequent rate of milk production. The absence of lactation during pregnancy is believed to be caused by suppressive actions of estrogens and perhaps also of progesterone on the lactating mechanism.

However, immediately after the baby is born, the sudden loss of both estrogen and progesterone secretion by the placenta removes any inhibitory effects of these two hormones and allows very marked produc-

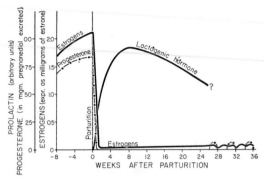

Figure 746. Secretion of hormones shortly before and shortly after parturition, showing especially the sudden increase in lactogenic hormone immediately after parturition.

tion of lactogenic hormone by the adenohypophysis, as illustrated in Figure 746. Within two to three days the breasts begin to secrete copious quantities of milk instead of colostrum.

Lactogenic hormone is frequently called "prolactin" or "lactogen," and it is also the same as "luteotropic hormone," which stimulates secretion by the corpus luteum, as discussed in the preceding chapter. The secretory effect of lactogenic hormone on the breasts is comparable to its secretory function on the corpus luteum.

The Ejection or "Let-down" Process in Milk Secretion—Function of Oxytocin

Milk secretion occurs continuously into the alveoli of the breasts, but milk does not flow easily from the alveoli into the ductile system and therefore does not continually leak from the breast nipples. Instead, the milk must be "ejected" or "let-down" from the alveoli to the ducts before the baby can obtain it. This process is caused by a combined neurogenic and hormonal reflex involving the hormone *oxytocin* as follows.

When the baby suckles the breast, sensory impulses are transmitted through the somatic nerves to the spinal cord and then to the hypothalamus, there causing *oxytocin* and, to a less extent, *vasopressin* secretion, as described in Chapter 73. These two hormones, again principally oxytocin, flow in the blood to the breasts where they cause the *myoepithelial cells* that surround the outer surfaces of the alveoli to contract, thereby expressing the milk from the alveoli into the ducts. Thus, within 30 seconds to a

minute after a baby begins to suckle the breast, milk begins to flow. This process is called *milk ejection* or *milk let-down.*

It is particularly interesting that suckling on one breast causes milk flow not only in that breast but also in the opposite breast.

Inhibition of Milk Ejection. A particular problem in nursing the baby comes from the fact that many psychogenic factors as well as generalized sympathetic stimulation throughout the body can inhibit the oxytocin system and consequently depress milk ejection. For this reason, it is quite important that the mother have an undisturbed puerperium if she is to be successful in nursing her baby.

Continued Secretion of Milk for Many Months following Pregnancy

If milk is not continually removed from the mother's breasts, the ability of the breasts to continue secreting milk is lost within one to two weeks. This is caused by cessation of lactogenic hormone secretion by the adenohypophysis. To state this another way, continued milking of the breasts will cause continued secretion of lactogenic hormone and therefore continued lactation.

The stimulus that causes continued secretion of lactogenic hormone is the suckling of the breasts which, as is true in the milk ejection process, transmits appropriate impulses to the hypothalamus to elicit secretion of lactogenic hormone. However, the mechanism by which the nerve impulses cause lactogenic hormone to be secreted is yet uncertain. There is some reason to believe that some of the oxytocin elaborated during the milk-ejection process might be carried in the hypophyseal portal system to the adenohypophysis to cause lactogenic hormone secretion. If this is true, then the rate of lactation would be controlled by the baby's demand for milk.

Over a period of 7 to 9 months, the rate of lactogenic hormone secretion by the adenohypophysis progressively fails despite continued milking of the breasts, and milk secretion eventually terminates.

Effect of Other Hormones on Lactation

Several other hormones besides lactogenic hormone and oxytocin affect the process of lactation. For instance, adequate secretion of both glucocorticoids and mineralocorticoids is essential to the normal formation of milk, as is also true of thyroxine secretion. And, if the mother is on a diet even slightly deficient in calcium, the parathyroid glands will hypertrophy to remove calcium from the mother's bones, thus maintaining a normal calcium ion concentration in the extracellular fluids despite calcium secretion in the milk.

Effect of Lactation on the Uterus and on the Sexual Cycle

The uterus involutes after parturition far more rapidly in women who lactate than in women who do not lactate. This difference probably results from greatly diminished estrogen secretion by the ovaries during the period of lactation, for estrogens are known to enlarge the uterus and presumably also to prevent rapid uterine involution. The uterus of a lactating mother usually decreases to a size even smaller than that prior to pregnancy, whereas the uterus of a non-lactating mother is likely to remain considerably larger than the pre-gravid size and also to remain soft for many months.

The process of lactation usually prevents the sexual cycle for at least the first few months. Presumably this is caused by preoccupation of the adenohypophysis with the production of lactogenic hormone, which reduces the rate of secretion of the other gonadotropic hormones. However, after several months of lactating, the adenohypophysis usually begins once again to produce sufficient quantities of follicle stimulating hormone to reinitiate the monthly sexual cycle. The rhythmic interplay between the ovarian and adenohypophyseal hormones during the sexual month does not involve lactogenic hormone to a significant extent; therefore, milk production continues.

Milk and the Metabolic Drain on the Mother Caused by Lactation

Table 32 gives the contents of human milk and cow's milk. The concentration of lactose in human milk is approximately 50 per cent greater than that in cow's milk, but on the other hand the concentration of protein in cow's milk is ordinarily two or more times greater than that in human milk. Finally,

Table 32. Percentage Composition of Milk

	Human Milk	Cow's Milk
Water	88.5	87
Fat	3.3	3.5
Sugar	6.8	4.8
Casein	0.9	2.7
Lactalbumin and other protein	0.4	0.7
Ash	0.2	0.7

the ash, which contains the minerals, is several times less in human milk than in cow's milk.

The rate of lactation in a mother subjected to optimal suckling usually increases for the first few months after parturition and thereafter decreases, so that at the end of seven months to a year very little lactation remains. At the height of lactation 1½ liters of milk may be formed each day. With this degree of lactation tremendous quantities of metabolic substrates are drained from the mother. For instance, at this rate of lactation approximately 50 grams of fat enter the milk each day, and approximately 100 grams of lactose, which must be derived from glucose, are lost from the mother each day. Also, some 2 to 3 grams of calcium phosphate may be lost each day, and, unless the mother is drinking very large quantities of milk and has an adequate intake of vitamin D, the output of calcium and phosphate by the lactating mammae will be much greater than the intake of these substances. Indeed, the problem of decalcification of the mother's bones usually is not very great during pregnancy, but it is a very distinct problem during lactation.

REFERENCES

Arey, L. B.: Developmental Anatomy. 6th ed., Philadelphia, W. B. Saunders Co., 1954.

Barron, D. H., and Alexander, G.: Supplementary observations on oxygen pressure gradient between maternal and fetal bloods of sheep. Yale J. Biol. & Med., 25:61, 1952.

Barron, D. H., and Meschia, G.: A comparative study of the exchange of the respiratory gases across the placenta. Sympos. Quant. Biol., 19:93, 1954.

Barron, D. H., and Meschia, G.: The carbon dioxide concentration gradient between the fetal and maternal bloods of sheep and goats. Yale J. Biol., 29:480, 1957.

Bieniarz, J., and Reynolds, S. R. M.: Hemodynamic

changes in the ewe affecting fetal heart rate in utero. *Am. J. Physiol.,* 198:128, 1960.

Black, D. L. and Asdell, S. A.: Mechanism controlling entry of ova into rabbit uterus. *Am. J. Physiol.,* 197:1275, 1959.

Caldeyro-Barcia, R., Pose, S. V., Sica-Blanco, Y., Fielitz, C., and Cibils, L. A.: Reproduction. *Ann. Rev. Physiol.,* 21:499, 1959.

Cole, H. H., and Cupps, P. T.: Reproduction in Domestic Animals. 2 Vols. New York, Academic Press, 1959.

Davies, J., Brown, E. B., Stewart, D., Terry, C. W., and Sisson, J.: Transfer of radioactive iron via the placenta and accessory fetal membranes in the rabbit. *Am. J. Physiol.,* 197:87, 1959.

Eastman, N. J.: Williams Obstetrics. 11th ed., New York, Appleton-Century-Crofts, 1956.

Folley, S. J.: The Physiology and Biochemistry of Lactation. Springfield, Illinois, Charles C Thomas, 1957.

Forbes, T. R.: Reproduction. *Ann. Rev. Physiol.,* 22: 75, 1960.

Hagerman, D. D., and Villee, C. A.: Transport functions of the placenta. *Physiol. Rev.,* 40:313, 1960.

Haley, H. B., and Woodbury, J. W.: Body composition and body water metabolism in normal pregnancy. *Surg. Gyn. Obst.,* 103:227, 1956.

Herbert, C. M., Banner, E. A., and Wakim, K. G.: Circulatory manifestations during pregnancy and nonpregnancy. *Am. J. Obst.,* 68:1553, 1954.

Knobil, E., and Briggs, F. N.: Fetal-maternal endocrine interrelations: the hypophyseal-adrenal system. *Endocrinology,* 57:147, 1955.

Kon, S. K., and Cowie, A. T. (eds.): The Mammary Gland and Its Secretion. New York, Academic Press, 1960.

Lamport, H.: The transport of oxygen in the sheep's placenta; the diffusion constant of the placenta. *Yale J. Biol.,* 27:26, 1954.

Linzell, J. L.: Physiology of the mammary glands. *Physiol. Rev.,* 39:534, 1959.

Lloyd, C. W. (ed.): Recent Progress in the Endocrinology of Reproduction. New York, Academic Press, 1959.

Mann, T., and Lutwak-Mann, C.: Reproduction. *Ann. Rev. Physiol.,* 20:275, 1958.

Marshall, J. M.: Effects of estrogen and progesterone on single uterine muscle fibers in the rat. *Am. J. Physiol.,* 197:935, 1959.

McElroy, W., and Glass, B.: The Chemical Basis of Heredity. Baltimore, Johns Hopkins University Press, 1957.

Meites, J.: Release of lactation at the time of birth. *Ann. Endocr.,* 17:519, 1956.

Meites, J., and Sgouris, J. T.: Effects of altering the balance between prolactin and ovarian hormones on initiation of lactation in rabbits. *Endocrinology,* 55:530, 1954.

Metcalfe, J., Romney, S. L., Swartwout, J. R., Pitcairn, D. M., Lethin, A. N., Jr., and Barron, D. H.: Uterine blood flow and oxygen consumption in pregnant sheep and goats. *Am. J. Physiol.,* 197: 929, 1959.

Needham, J.: Developmental physiology. *Ann. Rev. Physiol.,* 17:37, 1955.

Nelson, W. O.: Reproduction. *Ann. Rev. Physiol.,* 17: 443, 1955.

Page, E. W.: Hypertensive disorders of pregnancy. Springfield, Illinois, Charles C Thomas, 1953.

Parkes, A. S. (ed.): Marshall's Physiology of Reproduction. 3rd ed., New York, Longmans, Green & Co., 1959.

Raven, C. P.: Outline of Developmental Physiology. New York, McGraw-Hill Book Co., Inc., 1954.

Rothschild, L.: Fertilization. New York, John Wiley & Sons, 1956.

Rydberg, E.: The Mechanism of Labour. Springfield, Illinois, Charles C Thomas, 1954.

Sawyer, C. H.: Reproductive behavior. *Handbook of Physiology,* 2:1225, 1960.

Sawyer, C. H., and Critchlow, B. V.: Reproduction. *Ann. Rev. Physiol.,* 19:467, 1957.

Symposium on Nuclear Sex. London, William Heinemann, 1958.

Theobald, G. W.: The Pregnancy Toxaemias or the Encymonic Atelositeses. London, Henry Kimpton, 1958.

Villee, C. A.: Gestation. New York, Josiah Macy Jr. Foundation, 1957.

Visscher, M. B., and Stephens, G. J.: Heart—Circulatory Changes at Parturition and Pathologic Physiology. *Ann. Rev. Physiol.,* 19:381, 1957.

Walker, J. (ed.): Oxygen Supply to the Human Foetus. Oxford, Blackwell Scientific Publications, 1959.

Wishik, S. M.: Nutrition in pregnancy and lactation. *Fed. Proc.,* 18:4, 1959.

See also Chapter 73, General bibliography on endocrinology; Chapters 78 and 79, Male and female sex physiology.

Chapter 81

Special Aspects of Fetal, Neo-Natal, and Childhood Physiology

A complete discussion of fetal development, function of the child immediately after birth, and growth and development through the early years of life lies in the province of a formal course in pediatrics. However, many aspects of this are strictly physiological problems, some of which relate to the physiological principles that we have already discussed for the adult and some of which are peculiar to the infant himself. The present chapter will delineate and discuss the most important of these special problems.

GROWTH AND FUNCTIONAL DEVELOPMENT OF THE FETUS

Early development of the placenta and of the fetal membranes occurs far more rapidly than development of the fetus itself. During the first two to three weeks the fetus remains almost microscopic in size, but thereafter, as illustrated in Figure 747, the dimensions of the fetus increase almost in proportion to age. At 12 weeks the length of the fetus is approximately 10 cm.; at 20 weeks it is approximately 25 cm.; and at term (40 weeks) it is approximately 53 cm. (about 21 inches). Because the weight of the fetus is proportional to the cube of the length, the weight increases approximately in proportion to the cube of the age of the fetus. It will be noted from Figure 747 that the weight of the fetus remains almost nothing during the first few months and reaches 1 pound only at 5½ months of gestation. Then, during the last trimester of pregnancy, the fetus gains tremendously so that two months prior to birth the weight averages 3 pounds, one month prior to birth 4½ pounds, and at birth 7 pounds, this birth weight varying from as low as 4½ pounds to as high as 11 pounds in completely normal infants.

Development of the Organ Systems

Within one month after fertilization of the ovum all the different organs of the fetus have already been "blocked out," and then during the next two to three months the minute details of the different organs are established. Beyond the fourth month, the organs of the fetus are grossly the same as those of the newborn child, even including most of the smaller structures of the organs. However, cellular development of these structures is usually far from complete at this time and requires the full remaining 5 to 6 months of pregnancy for complete development. Even at birth certain structures, particularly the nervous system, the kidneys, and the liver, still lack full development, as will be discussed in more detail later in the chapter.

The Circulatory System of the Fetus. The human heart begins beating during the fourth week following fertilization, contracting at the rate of about 65 beats per minute.

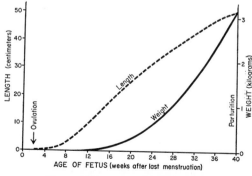

Figure 747. Growth of the fetus.

This increases steadily as the fetus grows and reaches a rate of approximately 140 per minute immediately before birth.

Formation of blood cells. Nucleated red blood cells begin to be formed in the yoke sac and mesothelial layers of the placenta at about the third week of fetal development. This is followed a week later by the formation of non-nucleated red blood cells by the fetal mesenchyme and by the endothelium of the fetal blood vessels. Then at approximately 6 weeks, the liver begins to form blood cells, and in the third month the spleen and other lymphoid tissues of the body also begin forming blood cells. Finally, from approximately the third month on, the bone marrow progressively develops and forms more and more red and white blood cells. During the mid-portion of fetal life, the liver, spleen, and lymph nodes are the major sources of the fetus's blood cells, but, during the latter three months of fetal life, the bone marrow gradually takes over while these other structures lose their ability completely to form blood cells.

An especially interesting characteristic of fetal blood is that it contains an entirely different type of hemoglobin from that of adult blood, called *fetal hemoglobin* in contrast with *adult hemoglobin*. Fetal hemoglobin combines with oxygen at a considerably lower P_{O_2} than does adult hemoglobin. This allows the fetal blood to carry as much as 30 per cent more oxygen in certain P_{O_2} ranges than can adult hemoglobin. This is of special importance in the fetus because its arterial P_{O_2} is always very low.

Respiratory System of the Fetus. Obviously, respiration cannot occur during fetal life. However, respiratory movements do take place beginning at the end of the first trimester of pregnancy. Tactile stimuli or fetal asphyxia especially will cause respiratory movements.

However, during the latter three to four months of pregnancy, the respiratory movements of the fetus are mainly inhibited, for reasons yet unknown. This could possibly result from (1) special chemical conditions in the body fluids of the fetus, (2) the presence of fluid in the fetal lungs, or (3) other possible yet unexplored stimuli.

The inhibition of the respiration during the latter months of fetal life prevents filling of the lungs with debris from the meconium excreted by the gastrointestinal tract into the amniotic fluid. Yet, fluid samples from the lungs immediately after birth show that at least small amounts of amniotic fluid do move continually in and out of the pulmonary passageways.

Function of the Nervous System in the Fetus

Most of the peripheral reflexes of the fetus are well formed by approximately the third to fourth months of pregnancy. However, some of the more important higher functions of the central nervous system are still undeveloped even when the child is born. Indeed, myelinization of some of the major tracts of the infant's central nervous system becomes complete only after approximately a year of postnatal life.

Function of the Gastrointestinal Tract in the Fetus

Even in mid-pregnancy the fetus ingests and absorbs large quantities of amniotic fluid, and during the latter two to three months, gastrointestinal function approaches that of the normal newborn infant. Small quantities of *meconium* are continually formed in the gastrointestinal tract and excreted from the bowels into the amniotic fluid. Excretion occurs particularly when the gastrointestinal tract becomes overly active as a consequence of fetal asphyxia. Meconium is composed partly of unabsorbed residue of amniotic fluid and partly of excretory products from the gastrointestinal mucosa and glands.

Function of the Kidneys during Fetal Life

The fetal kidneys are capable of excreting urine during at least the latter half of pregnancy, and urination occurs normally *in utero*. However, the renal control systems for regulation of extracellular fluid electrolyte balances and acid-base balance are almost non-existent in midfetal life and do not reach full development until about a month after birth.

Metabolism in the Fetus

The fetus utilizes mainly glucose for energy, and it has a high rate of storage of fat and protein, much if not most of the fat being synthesized from glucose rather than being absorbed from the mother's blood. Aside from these generalities there are some special problems of fetal metabolism in relation to calcium, phosphate, iron, and some of the vitamins as follows:

Metabolism of Calcium and Phosphate by the Fetus. Figure 748 illustrates the rate of calcium and phosphate accumulation in the fetus, showing that approximately 22.5 grams of calcium and 13.5 grams of phosphorus are accumulated in the average fetus during gestation. Approximately half of this accumulation occurs during the last 4 weeks of gestation, which is also coincident with the period of rapid ossification of the fetal bones as well as with the period of very rapid weight gain of the fetus.

During the earlier part of fetal life, the bones are relatively unossified and have mainly a cartilaginous matrix. Indeed, x-ray pictures ordinarily will not show any ossification at all until approximately the fourth month of pregnancy.

It should be noted especially that the total amounts of calcium and phosphorous needed by the fetus during gestation represent only about $\frac{1}{50}$ of the quantities of these substances in the mother's bones. Therefore, this is a very minimal drain from the mother. However, a very great drain occurs after birth during the period of lactation.

Accumulation of Iron in the Fetus. Figure 748 shows that iron accumulates in the fetus somewhat more rapidly than calcium and phosphorus. Most of the iron is in the form of hemoglobin, which begins to be formed as early as the third week following fertilization of the ovum.

Small amounts of iron are concentrated in the progestational endometrium even prior to implantation of the ovum; this iron is ingested into the embryo by the trophoblast for early formation of red blood cells.

Approximately one-third of the iron in a fully developed fetus is normally stored in the liver. This iron can then be used for the next several months by the newborn child for formation of additional hemoglobin.

Utilization and Storage of Vitamins by the Fetus. The fetus needs vitamins equally as much as adults and in some instances to a far greater extent. In general, the vitamins function the same in the fetus as in the adult, as discussed in Chapter 70. Special functions of several of the vitamins should be mentioned, however.

1. The B vitamins, especially vitamin B_{12} and folic acid, are necessary for formation of red blood cells and also for overall growth of the fetus.

2. Vitamin C is necessary for appropriate formation of intercellular substances, especially the bone matrix and interstitial fibers of connective tissue.

3. Vitamin D probably is not necessary for fetal growth although the mother needs it for adequate absorption of calcium from her gastrointestinal tract. If the mother has plenty of this vitamin in her body fluids, large quantities will be stored by the fetal liver to be used by the newborn child for several months after birth.

4. Vitamin E, though its precise function is unknown, is necessary for normal development of the early ovum. In its absence in experimental animals, spontaneous abortion usually occurs at an early age.

5. Vitamin K is used by the fetal liver for formation of proconvertin and prothrombin. When vitamin K is insufficient in the mother, proconvertin and prothrombin become deficient in the child as well as in the mother. Since most vitamin K absorbed into the body is formed by bacterial action in the colon, the newborn child has no adequate source of vitamin K for the first week or so of life—that is, until he establishes a normal colonic bacterial flora. Therefore, prenatal storage of at least small amounts of vitamin

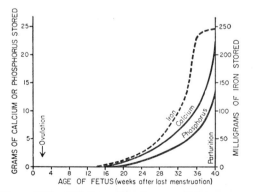

Figure 748. Calcium, phosphorus and iron storage in the fetus at different stages of gestation.

K is helpful in preventing a period of post-natal hemorrhage.

ADJUSTMENTS OF THE INFANT TO EXTRAUTERINE LIFE

Onset of Breathing

The most obvious effect of birth on the baby is loss of the placental connection with the mother, and therefore loss of this means for metabolic support. Especially important is loss of the placental oxygen supply and placental excretion of carbon dioxide. Therefore, by far the most important immediate adjustment of the infant to extrauterine life is the onset of breathing.

Cause of Breathing at Birth. Following completely normal delivery from a mother who has not been depressed by anesthetics, the child ordinarily begins to breathe immediately and has a completely normal respiratory rhythm from the outset. The promptness with which the fetus begins to breathe indicates that breathing is initiated by sudden exposure to the exterior world, probably resulting from sensory impulses originating in the suddenly cooled skin. However, if the infant does not breathe immediately, his respiratory center becomes progressively more and more anoxic and hypercapnic, which provides additional stimulus to the respiratory center and will usually cause breathing within a few seconds to a few minutes after birth.

Delayed and Abnormal Breathing at Birth—Danger of Anoxia. If the mother has been depressed by an anesthetic during delivery, respiration by the child is likely to be delayed for several minutes, thus illustrating the importance of using as little obstetrical analgesia as feasible. Also, many infants who have traumatic deliveries are slow to breathe or sometimes will not breathe at all. This can result from two possible effects: First, in a few infants, intracranial hemorrhage or brain contusion causes a typical concussion syndrome with a greatly depressed respiratory center. Second, and probably much more important, prolonged periods of fetal anoxia during delivery will also cause serious depression of the respiratory center. Anoxia very frequently occurs during delivery because of (a) compression of the umbilical cord, (b) premature separation of the placenta, (c) excessive contraction of the uterus, which cuts off the blood flow to the placenta, or (d) excessive anesthesia of the mother, which depresses the oxygenation of even her blood.

Degree of anoxia that an infant can stand. In the adult, failure to breathe for a period of only two to four minutes is often sufficient to cause death, but a newborn infant often survives as much as 15 minutes of failure to breathe after birth. Unfortunately, though, even when the infant survives, permanent mental impairment often ensues if breathing is delayed more than 7 to 10 minutes.

This ability of the neonatal infant to survive very long periods of anoxia probably results at least partly from special adaptation of its cellular respiratory enzymes to very low Po_2. However, within a week or so after birth, the infant loses this resistance to anoxia.

Expansion of the Lungs at Birth. At birth, the walls of the alveoli are held together by the surface tension of the viscid fluid that fills them. About 25 mm. Hg of negative pressure are required to oppose the effects of this surface tension and therefore to open the alveoli for the first time. But once the alveoli are open, further respiration can then be effected with relatively weak respiratory movements. Fortunately, the first inspirations of the newborn infant are extremely powerful, usually capable of creating as much as 50 mm. Hg negative pressure in the intrapleural space.

The newborn infant that lacks adequate strength in his respiratory muscles or lacks adequate respiratory stimulus will have inadequate initial respiratory movements to expand the lungs. This occurs especially frequently in a condition called *hyaline membrane syndrome*, in which many of the smaller respiratory passageways are filled with an especially viscid "hyaline" substance. Indeed, in this condition even the maximum possible negative pressure in the intrapleural spaces may fail to expand large segments of the lungs.

Circulatory Readjustments at Birth

Equally as important as the onset of breathing at birth are the immediate circulatory readjustments that occur to allow

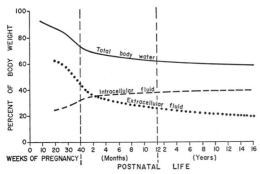

Figure 752. Changes in total body water, intracellular fluid volume, and extracellular fluid volume in the fetus during pregnancy and in the postnatal child. (Modified from Friis-Hansen: *Acta paediat. 46:* suppl. 110, 1957.)

solids until adulthood. At birth the average percentage of water in the infant is 73 per cent; this compares with 58 per cent for the adult. Another interesting aspect of the fetal body fluids is the very high ratio of extracellular fluids to intracellular fluids in contrast to the opposite relationship in the adult. This change presumably results from progressive growth of the cells at the expense of the extracellular spaces. Since extracellular fluids contain mainly sodium chloride in contrast to a preponderance of potassium and magnesium phosphates in the intracellular fluids, the newborn infant has much higher total body sodium and chloride in relation to body weight and much lower total body potassium, magnesium, and phosphate than the adult.

Liver Function in the Newborn Infant. Only small amounts of blood flow through the liver during fetal life, but during the first few days after birth the ductus venosus gradually becomes occluded so that thereafter all portal blood must flow through the liver. During the first few days of life, before all the portal flow goes through the liver, liver function may be quite deficient, as evidenced by the following effects:

1. The liver of the newborn conjugates bilirubin with glucuronic acid very poorly and therefore excretes bilirubin only slightly during the first few days of life.

2. The liver of the newborn is deficient in forming plasma proteins, and the plasma protein concentration averages 1 gram less than that for older children. Occasionally, the protein concentration is so low that the infant actually develops hypoproteinemic edema.

3. The gluconeogenic function of the liver

is particularly deficient. As a result, the blood glucose level of the unfed newborn infant falls to about 30 to 40 mg. per cent, and the infant must depend on its stored fats for energy until feeding can occur.

4. The liver of the newborn usually also forms too little of the factors needed for normal blood coagulation.

Digestion, Absorption, and Metabolism of Energy Foods. In general, the ability of the newborn infant to digest, absorb, and metabolize foods is not different from that of the older child with the following three exceptions:

First, secretion of pancreatic amylase in the newborn infant is deficient so that the infant utilizes starches less adequately than do older children. However, the infant very readily assimilates disaccharides and monosaccharides.

Second, absorption of fats from the gastrointestinal tract is somewhat less than in the older child. Consequently, milk with a very high fat content, such as that of cow's milk, is frequently inadequately utilized.

Third, because the liver functions are imperfect during at least the first week of life, the glucose concentration in the blood is very unstable and also low.

It should be pointed out particularly that the newborn is especially capable of synthesizing proteins and thereby storing nitrogen. Indeed, with a completely adequate diet, as much as 90 per cent of the ingested amino acids are utilized for formation of body proteins. This is a much higher percentage than can occur in adults.

Metabolic Rate and Body Temperature. The normal metabolic rate of the newborn in relation to body weight is about two times that of the adult, which accounts also for the two times as great cardiac output and two times as great minute respiratory volume in the infant.

However, in relation to body surface area, the metabolic rate of the newborn infant is less than that of the adult. This is particularly important in body temperature regulation, for the body temperature of the newborn infant, particularly of premature infants, tends to fall severely. Figure 753 shows that an immediate fall in body temperature normally occurs during the first few hours after birth, but this returns to normal in 7 to 8 hours. Still, the body temperature regula-

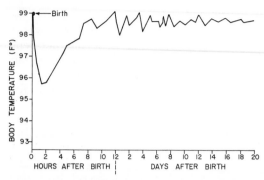

Figure 753. Fall in body temperature of the infant immediately after birth, and instability of body temperature during the first few days of life.

tory mechanisms remain very poor during the early days of life, allowing marked excursions in temperature at first, which is also illustrated in Figure 753.

Nutritional Needs during the Early Weeks of Life. At birth, a newborn infant is usually in complete nutritional balance provided its mother has had an adequate diet. Furthermore, function of the gastrointestinal system is usually more than adequate to digest and assimilate all the nutritional needs of the infant if these are provided in his diet. However, three specific problems do occur in the early nutrition of the infant as follows:

Need for calcium and vitamin D. The newborn infant has only just begun rapid ossification of his bones at birth so that he needs a ready supply of calcium throughout the entire period of infancy. This is ordinarily supplied quite adequately by his usual diet of milk. Yet, absorption of calcium by the gastrointestinal tract is poor in the absence of vitamin D. Therefore, the vitamin D deficient infant can develop a severe case of rickets in only a few weeks time. This is particularly true in premature babies since their gastrointestinal tracts absorb calcium even less effectively than those of normal infants.

Necessity for iron in the diet. If the mother has had adequate amounts of iron in her diet, the liver of the infant usually will store enough iron to keep forming blood cells for 4 to 6 months after birth. But, if the mother has had insufficient iron in her diet, then anemia is likely to supervene in the infant after about 3 months of life. To prevent this possibility, early feeding of egg yolk, which contains reasonably large

quantities of iron, or administration of iron in some other form is desirable by the second or third month of life.

Vitamin C deficiency in infants. Ascorbic acid (vitamin C) is not stored in significant quantities in the fetal tissues; yet, it is required for proper formation of cartilage, bone, and other intercellular structures of the infant. Furthermore, milk has poor supplies of ascorbic acid, especially cow's milk, which has only one-fourth as much as mother's milk. For this reason, orange juice or other sources of ascorbic acid are usually prescribed by the third week of life.

Immunity in the Newborn. Fortunately, the newborn inherits much immunity from its mother because many gamma globulins, which contain the antibodies, diffuse from the mother's blood through the placenta into the baby. Figure 754 shows that the gamma globulin concentration of the newborn baby is relatively high, even though the newborn himself does not form gamma globulins to a significant extent during the first few weeks of life. By the end of the first month, however, the baby's gamma globulins become greatly decreased, with corresponding decrease in immunity. Thereafter, the baby's own immunization processes begin to form immune bodies, and the gamma globulin concentration returns essentially to normal by the age of 5 to 6 months.

Despite the decrease in gamma globulins soon after birth, the immune bodies inherited from the mother still protect the infant for about 6 months against most of the major childhood infectious

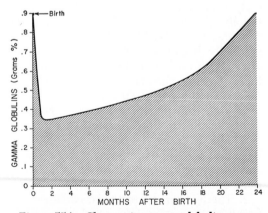

Figure 754. Changes in gamma globulin concentration in the plasma of infants, showing a high concentration immediately after birth resulting from placental infusion of the baby with gamma globulins from the mother; this is followed by a period of depression until the infant can produce its own gamma globulins. (Modified from Orlandi *et al.*: *Pediatrics* 16:575, 1955.)

diseases, including diphtheria, measles, smallpox, and polio. Therefore, immunization against these diseases before 6 months is usually unnecessary. On the other hand, the inherited immune bodies against whooping cough are normally insufficient to protect the newborn; therefore, for full safety he requires immunization against this disease within the first month of life.

Allergy in the infant. Fortunately, the newborn infant is rarely subject to allergy. Yet, several months later when he first begins to form his own immune bodies, extreme allergic states can develop, often resulting in serious eczema, gastrointestinal abnormalities, or even anaphylaxis. As the child grows still older and develops still higher degrees of immunity, these allergic manifestations usually disappear for the remainder of his life. The relationship of mild immunity to allergy was discussed in detail in Chapter 14.

Endocrine Problems in the Newborn Infant. Ordinarily the endocrine system of the newborn infant is already highly developed at birth, and the infant rarely exhibits any immediate endocrine abnormalities. However, there are special instances in which the endocrinology of infancy is important.

1. If a pregnant mother bearing a female child is treated with an androgenic hormone or if she develops an androgenic tumor during pregnancy, the child will be born with a high degree of masculinization of its sexual organs, thus resulting in a type of *hermaphrodism.*

2. The sex hormones secreted by the placenta and by the mother's glands during pregnancy occasionally cause the newborn's breasts to form milk during the first few days of life. Sometimes the breasts then become inflamed or even develop infectious mastitis.

3. An infant born of a diabetic mother will have considerable hypertrophy and hyperfunction of its islets of Langerhans. As a consequence, the infant's blood glucose concentration may fall to as low as 20 mg. per 100 ml. or even lower shortly after birth. Fortunately, the newborn infant, unlike the adult person, does not usually develop insulin shock or coma from this low level of blood glucose concentration.

Because of metabolic deficits resulting from the diabetic state in the mother, fetal and infant growth and tissue maturation are often impaired, and a very high rate of intrauterine mortality results. Of those infants that do come to term, there is still a high instance of mortality. Two thirds of the infants that die succumb to the *hyaline membrane syndrome,* which causes neonatal respiratory distress, as described earlier in the chapter.

4. Occasionally, a child is born with hypofunctional adrenal cortices, perhaps as a result of *agenesis* of the glands or of *exhaustion atrophy* which can occur when the adrenal glands have been overstimulated.

It is interesting that the fetal adrenal glands contain a type of cortical tissue, the so-called *fetal cortex,* which is different from the glandular tissue of the adult adrenal gland. Immediately after birth, the fetal cortex degenerates and is replaced by rapid growth of the adult type of adrenal cortex. Unfortunately, the function of the fetal cortex during gestation is yet unknown.

5. If a mother is treated with thyroid hormone during pregnancy the infant is likely to be born with a temporarily hyposecreting thyroid gland. On the other hand, if a mother has had hyperthyroidism previously but has had her thyroid gland removed, the mother's adenohypophysis usually still secretes tremendous quantities of thyrotropin, and the child will be born with temporary hyperthyroidism.

SPECIAL PROBLEMS OF PREMATURITY

All the problems noted above for neonatal life are especially exacerbated in prematurity. These can be categorized under the following two headings: (1) immaturity of certain organ systems and (2) instability of the different homeostatic control systems. Because of these effects, it is rare that a premature baby lives if it is born more than 2½ to 3 months prior to term.

Immature Development in Prematurity

Almost all the organ systems of the body are immature in the premature infant, but some require particular attention if the life of the premature baby is to be saved.

Respiration in the Premature. The respiratory system is especially likely to be immature in the premature infant. The vital capacity and the functional residual capacity of the lungs are especially small in relation to the size of the infant. As a consequence, respiratory distress is a common cause of death.

As pointed out earlier in the chapter, the very low functional residual capacity in the premature infant is very often associated with periodic breathing of the Cheyne-Stokes type.

Gastrointestinal Function. Another major problem of the premature infant is to provide it with adequate food. If the infant is more than two months premature, the digestive and absorptive systems are almost always inadequate. The absorption of fat is so poor that it is important to feed the premature infant a very low fat diet. Furthermore, the premature infant has unusual difficulty in absorbing calcium and therefore can develop very severe rickets before one recognizes the difficulty. For this reason, special attention must be paid to adequate calcium and vitamin D intake.

Function of Other Organs in Prematurity. Immaturity of other organ systems which frequently causes serious difficulties in the premature infant include: (a) immaturity of the liver, which results in poor intermediary metabolism and often also a bleeding tendency as a result of poor formation of coagulation factors, (b) immaturity of the kidneys, which are particularly deficient in their ability to rid the body of acids, thereby predisposing to acidosis as well as to many other serious fluid balance abnormalities, (c) immaturity of the blood-forming mechanism of the bone marrow, which allows rapid development of anemia in the premature infant, and (d) depressed formation of gamma globulin by the reticuloendothelial system, which is often associated with serious infection.

Instability of the Control Systems in the Premature Infant

Immaturity of the different organ systems in the premature infant creates a high degree of instability in the homeostasis of the body. For instance, the acid-base balance can vary tremendously, particularly when the food intake varies from time to time. Likewise, the blood protein concentration is usually somewhat low because of immaturity of liver development, thus often leading to *hypoproteinemic edema*. And inability of the infant to regulate its calcium ion concentra-

tion frequently precipitates hypocalcemic tetany. Also, the blood glucose concentration can vary between the extremely wide limits of 20 mg. per 100 ml. up to over 100 mg. per 100 ml., depending principally upon the regularity of feeding. It is no wonder, then, with these extreme variations in the internal environment of the premature infant, that mortality is very high.

Instability of Body Temperature. One of the particular problems of the premature infant is its inability to maintain normal body temperature. Its temperature tends to approach that of its surroundings. At normal room temperature the temperature may stabilize in the low 90's or even in the 80's. Statistical studies show that a body temperature maintained below 96° F. is associated with a particularly high incidence of death, which explains the common use of the incubator in the treatment of prematurity.

Danger of Oxygen Therapy in the Premature Infant

Because the premature infant frequently develops respiratory distress, and because its propensity for developing periodic breathing makes the physician feel that it is in respiratory distress even when it is not, oxygen therapy has frequently been used in treating prematurity. However, in the last few years it has been discovered that use of high oxygen concentrations in treating premature infants, especially in early prematurity, causes vascular ingrowth into the vitreous humor of the eyes, followed later by fibrosis. This condition, known as *retrolental fibroplasia*, causes permanent blindness. For this reason, it is particularly important to avoid treatment of premature infants with high concentrations of respiratory oxygen. Physiological studies indicate that the premature infant might be safe in up to 40 per cent oxygen, but some child physiologists believe that complete safety can be achieved only by normal or even low oxygen concentrations because this more nearly approaches intrauterine conditions.

GROWTH AND DEVELOPMENT OF THE CHILD

The major physiological problems of the child beyond the neonatal period are related to special

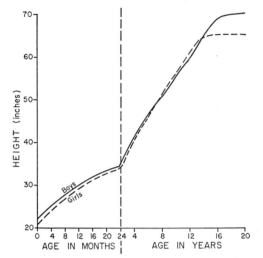

Figure 755. Height of boys and girls from infancy to 20 years of age.

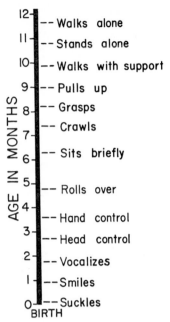

Figure 756. Behavioral development of the infant during the first year of life.

metabolic needs for growth. These do not need reemphasis for they have been fully covered in the sections on metabolism and edocrinology.

Figure 755 illustrates the changes in heights of boys and girls from the time of birth until the age of 20 years. Note especially that these parallel each other almost exactly until the latter part of the first decade. At this time, the female estrogens cause rapid growth but early uniting of the epiphyses at about the fourteenth year of life, so that growth in height ceases. This contrasts with the effect of testosterone in the male which causes growth at a later age but much more prolonged growth so that the final height is considerably greater than that of the female.

Behavioral Growth

Behavioral growth is principally a problem of maturity of the nervous system. Here, it is extremely difficult to dissociate maturity of the anatomical structures of the nervous system from maturity cause by training. Anatomical studies show that complete myelinization of certain major tracts in the central nervous system does not occur until the end of the first year of life. For this reason we frequently state that the nervous system is not fully functional at birth. On the other hand, we know perfectly well that most of the reflexes of even the fetus are fully developed by approximately the third to fourth month of intrauterine life, and we know also that unmyelinated nerve fibers can be equally as functional as myelinated nerve fibers. Therefore, much of the functional immaturity of the nervous system at birth might well be caused by lack of training rather than actual immaturity of the anatomical structures.

Nevertheless, the brain weight of the child increases rapidly during the first year and less rapidly during the second year, reaching almost adult proportions by the end of the second year of life. This is also associated with closure of the fontanels and sutures of the skull, which prevents much additional growth of the cranium after the first 2 years of life.

Figure 756 illustrates a normal progress chart for the infant during the first year of life. Comparison of a baby's actual development in relation to such a chart is frequently used for clinical assessment of a child's mental and behavioral growth.

REFERENCES

Amoroso, E. C., Dawes, G. S., Mott, J. C., and Rennick, B. R.: Occlusion of the ductus venosus in the mature foetal lamb. *J. Physiol.*, 129:64, 1955.

Baker, J. B. E.: The effects of drugs on the foetus. *Pharmacol. Rev.*, 12:37, 1960.

Barth, L. G.: Developmental physiology. *Ann. Rev. Physiol.*, 19:41, 1957.

Born, G. V., Dawes, G. S., Mott, J. C., and Rennick, B. R.: The constriction of the ductus arteriosus caused by oxygen and by asphyxia in newborn lambs. *J. Physiol.*, 138:304, 1956.

Conel, J. L.: The postnatal development of the human cerebral cortex. Cambridge, Harvard University Press, 1939.

Cook, C. D., Sutherland, J. M., Segal, S., Cherry, R. B., Mead, J., McIlroy, M. B., and Smith, C. A.: Studies of respiratory physiology in the newborn infant. III. Measurements of mechanics of respiration. *J. Clin. Invest.*, 36:440, 1957.

Cross, K. W., Dawes, G. S., and Mott, J. C.: Anoxia, oxygen consumption, and cardiac output in newborn lambs and adult sheep. *J. Physiol.*, 146:316, 1959.

Dawes, G. S.: Some respiratory and cardiovascular problems after birth. *Arch. Dis. Childhood.*, 34:281, 1959.

Dawes, G. S., and Mott, J. C.: The increase in oxygen consumption in the lamb after birth. *J. Physiol.*, 146:295, 1959.

Delafresnaye, J. F. (ed.): Anoxia of the new-born infant. Springfield, Illinois, Charles C Thomas, 1953.

Gyorgy, P.: Nutrition in infancy. *Fed. Proc.*, 18:9, 1959.

Infant Metabolism. Proceedings of the World Health Organizations. New York, The Macmillan Co., 1956.

Josiah Macy, Jr. Foundation: Physiology of Prematurity. Transactions of the Fourth (1959) Conference. New York, Josiah Macy, Jr., Foundation, 1960.

Lemman, J. T.: Physiology of Prematurity. New York, Josiah Macy, Jr., Foundation, 1957.

Nicholas, J. S.: Developmental physiology. *Ann. Rev. Physiol.*, 22:95, 1960.

Parmelee, A. H.: Management of the Newborn. 2nd ed., Chicago, Year Book Publishers, 1959.

Roberts, G. F.: Comparative Aspects of Haemolytic Disease of the Newborn. New York, Grune & Stratton, Inc., 1957.

Smith, C. A.: The Physiology of the Newborn Infant. 3rd ed., Springfield, Illinois, Charles C. Thomas, 1959.

Watson, E. H., and Lowrey, G. H.: Growth and Development of Children. 3rd ed., Chicago, Year Book Publishers, 1958.

Willier, B. H., et al.: Analysis of Development. Philadelphia, W. B. Saunders Co., 1955.

See also Chapter 80, Reproduction.

Part Thirteen

RADIATION

Chapter 82

Nuclear Physics, X-Rays, and Their Relationships to the Human Body

During the past few years nuclear physics has become of extreme importance to medicine for several reasons: First, radiations from radioactive materials can affect the body greatly, even to the extent of destroying cells and killing the human being. Second, this destructive effect of radioactive emissions can be used for treatment of various cancerous conditions. Third, with the coming of the atomic bomb, new destructive forces have added additional hazards to the function of the body. And fourth, radioactive substances are used to a great extent in experimental medicine for tracing different chemical substances through the body; in this manner the chemistry of the cells and of different organs is being rapidly elucidated.

X-rays are also considered in the present chapter, for these radiations have very much the same effect on the body as certain of the radioactive emissions. Also, the daily use of x-rays in clinical diagnostic procedures justifies a detailed discussion of their effects on the body.

The body is also exposed to many radiations from its surroundings, such as from naturally radioactive substances in the body—potassium, for example—and especially from cosmic radiation. The exposure of the normal person to radiation can be divided into the following categories:

1. Medical (x-rays in particular)—40%
2. Background (cosmic rays and natural radioactive substances)—59%
3. Fallout from nuclear explosions—1%

NUCLEAR STRUCTURE, NUCLEAR REACTIONS, AND RADIOACTIVE EMISSIONS

The Basic Particles of Atoms

The science of chemistry until this century was based on the belief that no particles exist in nature smaller than the atom. However, during the past 50 years it has become increasingly evident that the atom is a very large particle and is made up mainly of three basic smaller particles known as *neutrons*, *protons*, and *electrons*. Other small particles such as *positrons* and *mesons* exist in nature, but these are relatively unimportant from the point of view of the present discussion.

The Electron. The electron is a minute particle having a single negative electrical charge. It can often move from one atom to another with ease, and it is this movement which is known as electric current.

Electrons are arranged in orbits around the nucleus of each atom and are never present as such in the nucleus. However, it is possible for electrons to enter the nucleus and combine therein with a proton to form a neutron. Also, neutrons can discharge electrons and thereby form protons.

The Proton. Protons are found only in the nuclei, and they have a weight approximately 1800 times the weight of the electron. Each proton has a single positive charge which is equal and opposite to the charge of the electron. As noted above, should an electron enter the nucleus and combine with a proton, this proton would become a neutron.

The Neutron. The neutron has essentially the same weight as the proton, but it has no electrical charge. The neutron probably is made up of many smaller particles which do have electrical charges, both positive and negative. However, these positive and negative charges are equal in number in the neutron, and, consequently, the overall aggregate has no outward electrical charge.

It is possible for a neutron to discharge an electron and thereby become a proton. Also, it is possible for a neutron to capture a positron and thereby become a proton, though this reaction is very unlikely to occur.

The Positron. A proton can on occasion release a positron and become a neutron. Positrons are sometimes called positive electrons because they have exactly the same weight as electrons but have positive electrical charges rather than negative charges. The positron does not exist in nature more than approximately a millionth of a second at most. The reason for this is that electrons and positrons are mutually attracted, and, when they approach each other, both are annihilated. This means that both the electron and the positron lose completely all of their mass, but in doing so they liberate two quanta of energy in the form of gamma rays. This fact supports Einstein's original theory of relativity that mass can be changed into energy and, also, that energy can be changed into mass.

The Meson. Mesons are nuclear particles having sizes between those of electrons and protons. The only real significance of mesons at present appears to be their relationship to cosmic rays and the fact that they probably play a role in nuclear binding. Cosmic rays originate from some unknown source far off in space, and they are mainly very high speed protons or nuclei up to atomic number 26. When these rays strike the upper atmosphere they interact with the air to form mesons, protons, and nuclei of lower atomic number. These products then spread earthward. The mesons in particular have the ability to penetrate extremely deeply through all substances. Indeed, mesons have been detected many hundreds of feet deep in caves in the earth after having passed through solid rock above.

Stable versus Radioactive Atoms

Figure 757 illustrates the makeup of the nuclei of a number of different atoms. Hydrogen is illustrated with a single proton in the nucleus. However, all other elements contain both protons and neutrons in their nuclei. The *mass number* of an atom is the total number of both protons and neutrons in the nucleus, and is indicated thus: C^{12}, C^{13}, and C^{14}, which are three forms of carbon having mass numbers of 12, 13, and 14, respectively. The *atomic number* is the number of protons in the nucleus, and this is also equal to the number of electrons in all the orbits around the nucleus. The *atomic weight* of an element is the weight of one of its atoms as compared to a standard in which the weight of an oxygen atom is taken as 16. The atomic weights of most elements are very close to or identical with their mass numbers.

Whether a given nucleus will be stable depends upon the relative number of protons and neutrons in the nucleus. Not much is known about the forces within the nuclei that bind neutrons

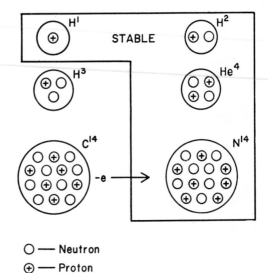

O — Neutron

⊕ — Proton

Figure 757. Stable and unstable (radioactive) atoms.

and protons together, but it is known empirically that for every proton in a nucleus approximately one or slightly more than one neutron can also be present in the nucleus, and, yet, the nucleus will remain stable. Indeed, as the nuclei get larger and larger, an average of slightly more than one neutron per proton is *necessary* for the nucleus to remain stable. Thus H^2, known also as deuterium or heavy hydrogen, has a stable nucleus. This H^2 has exactly the same chemical properties as H^1 because only one electron exists in the orbit around the nucleus, and it is the number of electrons in the orbits that determines the chemical properties of an element.

H^3, or tritium, has two neutrons and one proton in the nucleus. In this instance, too many neutrons are present for the nucleus to be completely stable. Consequently, once in a long while one of the neutrons in the nucleus of H^3 suddenly discharges an electron, the neutron becoming a proton. The nucleus then becomes a helium nucleus because after emitting the electron from the nucleus two protons are present in the nucleus, and the new proton immediately captures a new orbital electron so that the element thereafter, instead of being hydrogen, is helium.

It will be seen from Figure 757 that He^4, having two protons and two neutrons, is also a stable element, and that N^{14}, having seven protons and seven neutrons, is a stable element. On the other hand, carbon[14], having six protons and eight neutrons, has one too many neutrons to be stable. Carbon is found in two very stable forms, C^{12} with six protons and six neutrons, which comprises about 99 per cent of all the carbon on earth, and C^{13} with six protons and seven neutrons, comprising about 1 per cent of the carbon on earth. However, C^{14}, having one too many neutrons, is a radioactive substance, and every now and then one of the C^{14} atoms suddenly emits an electron, and the neutron from which the electron is derived becomes a prcton. Thus, the carbon nucleus becomes a stable nitrogen nucleus with seven protons.

In general, then, it can be said that if a nucleus has either too few or too many neutrons in relation to its number of protons it will be unstable and will show signs of "radioactivity." The term "radioactivity" refers to aspects of the behavior of a nucleus that cannot continue to exist in its present form. When an unstable atom suddenly changes to another type of atom, it always gives off some sort of radiation. This may be the emission of an electron; it may be the emission of a positron, which is suddenly annihilated and becomes gamma rays; it may be gamma ray radiation due to loss of mass in the nucleus; it may be the emission of some large particle such as a helium nucleus, which is also known as an *alpha ray*; or under certain conditions it might be the emission of a neutron or a proton, though these latter two types of emission are very rare.

The Radioactive Half-life. Disintegration of radioactive atoms is a probability phenomenon. For instance, if a chamber contains 100,000 atoms of tritium, it is probable that 50,000 of these atoms will disintegrate within 12.1 years from the present moment. It is then probable that 25,000 more of these atoms will disintegrate during the following 12.1 years and that 12,500 more will disintegrate during the next 12.1 years. In other words, those atoms that survive the first year are just as likely to survive the second year as they were to survive the first one, and the age of each atom does not make any difference. Yet, each year a certain proportion of the remaining radioactive atoms disintegrates.

This "half-life" phenomenon holds for all radioactive atoms. Therefore, the length of time that radioactive elements can exist is mathematically expressed in terms of the half-life. For instance, the half-life of tritium is 12.1 years; the half-life of C^{14} is 5100 years; the half-life of radium is 1622 years, that of I^{131} is 8 days, and that of Na^{24} is only 14.8 hours. A little more than 1000 different radioactive substances exist, many of which have half-lives as short as only a few millionths of a second.

Measurement of Intensity of Radioactivity. The intensity of radioactivity of a given sample of radioactive material is measured in *curies*, *millicuries*, or *microcuries*, which are units indicating the number of atoms disintegrating each second in the sample. One curie is 3.7×10^{10} disintegrations per second.

The Principal Types of Nuclear Radiation

Beta Rays. Electrons emitted as a result of radioactive disintegrations are known as beta rays. These are emitted from the disintegrating nuclei with varying degrees of force; some disintegrating nuclei eject the electrons with tremendous force while others only barely eject the electrons.

Measurement of beta ray energy. The force with which the electrons are emitted from the disintegrating nucleus is designated in terms of *electron volts*. If an electron in a vacuum leaves a metal plate charged to zero volts, and another plate charged to 1 million volts is placed a few feet away, the electron will suddenly accelerate toward the million volt plate, and, by the time it strikes that plate, it will have achieved considerable energy, in this instance 1 million electron volts of energy. If the metal plate has been charged at 2 million volts, then the electron will have been attracted with even greater force and it will have achieved 2 million electron volts of energy before striking the plate.

Some radioactive elements emit electrons with energies as low as a few electron volts, whereas other radioactive elements emit electrons with energies of 1 million to 5 million electron volts.

Each radioactive element does not emit all its electrons at exactly the same energy level. For instance, radioactive phosphorus, which is capable of emitting electrons at an energy level as high as 1.7 million electron volts, also emits some with energies as low as a few electron volts. Usually, the average energy of the electrons emitted from a radioactive element will be approximately halfway between zero and the highest energy at which the electrons can be emitted from that type of radioactive element. Consequently, the average energy of electron emission for phosphorus is approximately 850,000 electron volts.

Penetration of tissues by beta rays. When beta rays pass through an absorbing medium such as the tissues of the body, they repel electrons from the orbits of the elements in their pathway. In other words, the passage of beta rays at very high speed through tissues causes *ionization* to take place in the absorbing medium, as is illustrated in Figure 758. Every time the moving electron displaces an electron from the orbit of an element, a certain amount of the energy is also removed from the moving beta ray. Consequently, after a beta ray passes so far through tissues, it stops completely.

The *distance that the beta ray will travel through tissues is dependent upon its original energy* and also upon the density of the tissues through which it passes. In tissues that have a

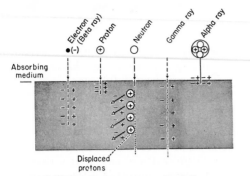

Figure 758. Penetration of tissues by different types of radioactive emissions.

density of approximately 1, and this includes most of the tissues of the body except the bones, beta rays travel approximately 5 mm. for every 1 million electron volts of energy that the original ray possessed. Therefore, low-energy beta rays can penetrate tissues only to a slight extent, but high energy beta rays can penetrate a centimeter or more.

Gamma Rays. When a proton of a radioactive substance releases a positron, the positron eventually approaches an electron, and the two annihilate each other. This releases two "quanta" of energy in the form of gamma rays. Also, other reactions taking place within the nucleus itself release gamma rays. For instance, mass may be annihilated within the nucleus, this mass being converted into gamma rays in accordance with Einstein's law of relativity. Or different atomic bonding energies may be converted into gamma rays.

Units of measurement for gamma ray energy. Short wavelength gamma rays contain much more energy in each quantum of electromagnetic radiation than do long wavelength gamma rays, and, conversely, the higher the energy the shorter is the wavelength. Gamma ray energy is generally expressed in terms of *electron volts*, as is beta ray energy. This is based on the electron volts of energy that must be applied to accelerated electrons in an x-ray tube to produce x-rays having wavelengths equal to those of the measured gamma rays. In other words, an x-ray tube with 1 million volts applied between the cathode and the target of the tube can emit x-rays with energies of only 50,000 electron volts and gamma rays having the same wavelength as these x-rays are also said to have an energy of 1 million electron volts. Similarly, still shorter wavelength gamma rays may have energies of 2 million, 3 million, or more electron volts.

Relationship of gamma rays to x-rays. Gamma rays and x-rays are in reality the same. In the early days of studying gamma and x-rays, radium was the usual source of gamma rays. Radium emits a very short wavelength electromagnetic wave having an energy of approximately 1.8 million electron volts. On the other hand, the old x-ray machines were capable of generating x-rays with energies of only 50,000 electron volts or thereabouts. Consequently, in the early designation of these electromagnetic radiations, long wavelength rays were considered to be x-rays, and short wavelength rays were considered to be gamma rays. Today x-ray machines can deliver x-rays at energies as high as several million electron volts, and many radioactive substances are known to deliver rays at energies as low as a few thousand electron volts. Consequently, gamma and x-rays are the same, except that the term "gamma rays" is still used usually to designate the electromagnetic rays emitted as a result of radioactivity.

Penetration of tissues by gamma rays. Gamma rays are quite different from electrons, protons, and alpha rays in their ability to penetrate tissues. It was pointed out above that beta rays travel only so far in tissues and then are totally stopped. This is not true of gamma rays. As gamma rays pass through tissues, a certain percentage of these is stopped completely in the first centimeter, and then the same percentage of the remaining gamma rays is stopped in the next centimeter. In the third centimeter the same percentage of the gamma rays remaining after passing through the first two centimeters again is stopped. Theoretically, then, gamma rays, in passing through tissues, are never totally absorbed. For instance, if one-half of the gamma rays are absorbed in the first centimeter, after 2 cm. the total quantity of gamma rays is still one-quarter of the original incident beam. After 3 cm. the total quantity is one-eighth; after 4 cm. the total quantity is one-sixteenth, etc., but, as indicated in Figure 758, the beam is never entirely blocked.

Alpha Rays. Some of the very large radioactive atoms, on disintegrating, discharge *alpha particles* which are helium nuclei containing two protons and two neutrons. These particles carry two positive charges because of the two protons. This is in contradistinction to the single negative charge carried by electrons.

Penetration of tissues by alpha rays. On striking tissues alpha particles cause tremendous ionization. However, their mass is approximately 7000 times that of electrons, which prohibits satisfactory penetration, and their two positive charges slow up their movement twice as rapidly as would one charge. For these reasons, even high-energy alpha particles penetrate tissues only a few microns before they are totally stopped. Alpha ray irradiation on the surface of the body is not harmful at all because these rays do not penetrate even deep enough to strike the germinative layers of the skin. On the other hand, if an alpha ray emmitter is ingested, it will destroy

posure. Also, radon, which is a gas formed by disintegration of radium, can be used for the same purpose. Radon has a short half-life and, therefore, once implanted, need never be removed. This gas is collected in silver tubes which are pinched off at intervals of approximately every 2 mm. This forms a small cylinder which contains the radon gas. These silver cylinders then are implanted directly into areas of cancer and left there. Over a period of several days the radon causes destruction of the cancerous tissues, but after several weeks the degree of radiation from the radon "seed" is so slight that it cannot cause any more harm either to the cancer or to the surrounding tissues.

Several artificial radioactive isotopes are also beginning to be used for implantation therapy. The one that has proved most feasible has been radioactive cobalt. This substance has a half-life of approximately 5 years. Therefore, radioactive cobalt needles, like radium, can be used over and over again for many years. Furthermore, radioactive cobalt is much less expensive than radium. Therefore, even though cobalt has no especial advantage over radium from a medical point of view, it is, nevertheless, more economically feasible.

External Treatment with Radioactive Isotopes. If large quantities of gamma-emitting isotopes are collected in one mass, then the amount of radiation emanating from the mass can be made comparable to the radiation delivered by a high-milliamperage x-ray machine. Several cobalt and cesium therapy machines have been made for this purpose.

Obviously, the use of radioactive isotopes in such extreme concentration is a very dangerous hazard to the operator of the machine. Therefore these sources are usually contained in large lead shields, which weigh approximately 1000 pounds. The radioactive source is embedded in a small hole about 1 to 2 cm. in size in the very middle of the lead mass. An electric motor is then coupled to a large, lead shutter device which, when opened by remote control, allows the gamma rays to pass out of the lead mass through an open port. The portion of the patient to be treated is placed in front of this open port.

The Atom and Hydrogen Bomb in Relation to Medicine

In recent years atom and hydrogen bombs have assumed much medical importance because of the effects of radiations and mechanical forces on the bodies of subjects exposed to the blast.

The atom bomb is, in reality, an instantaneous atomic pile that utilizes the chain reaction in a slightly different manner from the usual atomic pile. The difference between the atom bomb and the atomic pile is that all methods possible are used in the atom bomb to speed up the chain reaction, whereas special precautions are taken to keep the chain reaction in the atomic pile at a slow and controllable speed. Only a few substances are known that can react at speeds rapid enough to make a bomb. These substances are $uranium^{235}$, $uranium^{233}$, and $plutonium^{239}$.

The atom bomb reaction is a reaction of nuclear fission. In other words, the nuclei of uranium or plutonium split approximately in half. Each nucleus of uranium that splits liberates an average of 2.3 neutrons. Each one of these neutrons in turn can cause another uranium atom to split. Consequently, if none of the neutrons is lost from the mass of material, then each uranium atom that splits will cause an average of 2.3 more uranium atoms to split, until, finally, the whole mass has disintegrated. Consequently, all one needs to do to build an atom bomb is to collect a sufficient quantity of $uranium^{235}$ or one of the other rapidly fissionable substances into one single mass, and an explosion will take place.

For a chain reaction to be set off, a neutron must be derived from some source. A small amount of natural fission takes place all the time, and this can be the source of the original neutron. Also, cosmic rays can occasionally release neutrons from various substances and can thereby set off the reaction. Therefore, once a sufficient mass of fissionable material is gathered in one collection, within a millionth of a second or less a stray neutron sets off the chain reaction, and the explosion occurs.

One of the main problems in building the atom bomb is to hold a mass of uranium together in large enough quantity to cause an explosion. The method that is used is "a cannon within the bomb." The bomb is an elongated structure at each end of which is a hemisphere of uranium or plutonium. One of these hemispheres of uranium or plutonium is then shot toward the other hemisphere by a charge of chemical explosive. This slams the two hemispheres of uranium together and the atomic bomb reaction takes place.

It should be noted particularly that the size of the hemispheres of uranium (or plutonium) is very critical. The reason for this is that small masses of uranium have a much larger surface area in proportion to the mass of uranium than do large masses. Consequently, a greater proportion of the neutrons will be lost from the surfaces of the small masses than from large masses. When a large proportion of the neutrons is being lost from the surface of the uranium, a chain reaction cannot occur, but, when the two hemispheric masses in the atom bomb come together, the proportion of neutrons retained within the mass becomes great enough to allow such a reaction. The size of each hemisphere is calculated to be slightly

Table 33. Summary of Effects of the Assumed Nuclear Weapons 1 to 10 Megatons.

(From: Hearings on radiation before Joint Committee on Atomic Energy, Congress of the United States, June 22, 1959.)

	1 megaton	10 megatons
A. Inanimate objects		
1. Crater (dry soil)	Radius, 650 feet Depth, 140 feet	Radius, 1,250 feet. Depth, 240 feet.
2. Brick apartment houses collapse	Radius, 3 miles	Radius, 7 miles.
3. Ignition of light kindling materials	Radius, 9 miles	Radius, 25 miles.
B. Man:		
1. Blast injury (flying debris)	Radius, 3 miles Area, 28 square miles	Radius, 7 miles. Area, 150 square miles.
2. 2d degree burns on bare skin	Radius, 9 miles Area, 250 square miles	Radius, 25 miles. Area, 2,000 square miles.
3. Initial nuclear radiation (700 r.e.m.).	Radius, 1.5 miles Area, 7 square miles	Radius, 2 miles. Area, 12.5 square miles.
4. Fallout, 15-knot winds (450 r.e.m. in 48 hours, no shielding).	40 miles downwind, 5 miles crosswind. Area, 200 square miles	150 miles downwind, 25 miles crosswind. Area, 2,500 square miles.

less than that which would sustain a chain reaction, whereas, when the two hemispheres are slammed together, the size is calculated to be as much as possible above the "critical" mass for the attainment of a chain reaction.

A hydrogen bomb is merely a collection of hydrogen heavily fortified with hydrogen[3] (trituim) in a shell around an atom bomb. The very high temperatures and pressures set off by the atom bomb cause *fusion* of the hydrogen to form larger atoms, particularly helium.

Effects of the Nuclear Bomb Blast on the Body.

When the nuclear bomb bursts, several different types of energy are released as the result of the blast. First, during the actual nuclear reaction of the bomb, a tremendous quantity of gamma rays is emitted in all directions. Second, immediately after the nuclear reaction, the entire bomb is disintegrated into a gaseous mass having a temperature of 50,000° to 1,000,000° C. At this very high temperature the gaseous mass forms a very bright fireball, which emits electromagnetic radiation as a direct result of the heat. These electromagnetic radiations are mainly light rays and heat rays. Third, the extreme heat caused by the atom bomb burst causes rapid expansion of the surrounding atmosphere. This creates a "blast wave" that travels through the atmosphere at the speed of sound, i.e., it travels a mile in approximately 5 seconds and reaches 10 miles in approximately 50 seconds.

The radius of damage varies with size of the bomb. Table 33 gives the radii of different effects for the 1- and 10-megaton hydrogen bombs. Note particularly that disintegration of a hydrogen bomb releases tremendous quantities of radioactive substances into the air, which later fall to the earth; if they are eaten or breathed they cause gradual internal radioactive irradiation for years.

Thus, a person exposed to a nuclear bomb may be killed outright as a result of the blast, or he may die as the result of burns within a few days, or, finally, he may die from 12 hours to many years later as the result of irradiation. The cause of death in the first two instances is obvious. In the instance of irradiation, the cause of death is the destruction of one or more of the different types of cells in the body, as follows:

Effects on the body of irradiation from the nuclear bomb.

Gamma rays and other ionizing radiations completely or almost completely block mitosis for varying intervals after exposure. Certain cells of the body must be formed anew every few hours to few days because these cells are needed by the body for specific purposes. The cell that must be formed about as rapidly as any other is the *lymphocyte*, which appears to be necessary for protecting the body by formation of tissue-wandering macrophages and cells that form antibodies. A second type of cell that must be formed very rapidly is the *granulocyte*. Consequently, one of the earliest effects following excessive irradiation is *leukopenia*, which allows the body to be invaded by different organisms; therefore, the patient often dies from septicemia. The usual points of invasion are the mouth and the gastrointestinal tract. Also, *thrombocytopenia* is frequently so severe that the person bleeds to death.

A second major effect of irradiation on the body occurs *in the gastrointestinal tract*. The glandular and epithelial cells of the gastrointestinal tract must undergo mitosis at a very rapid rate to keep forming intestinal secretions and to protect the intestinal wall from destruction. After sufficient gamma ray irradiation, the epithelium of the gastrointestinal tract is no longer capable of performing these functions. Gastrointestinal symptoms, including nausea, vomiting, diarrhea, bleeding, ulceration, etc., begin a few hours after intense gamma ray irradiation.

The *germinative layer of the skin* is another area affected to a great extent by the gamma rays. Because of failure of mitosis in the skin, the skin may become quite atrophic, and, after a period of several days to several weeks, the skin may even become extensively ulcerated.

Finally, some paients who have received intense gamma ray irradiation die of *anemia*. Ordinarily, red blood cells, once formed, last approximately 120 days in the blood stream. Therefore, failure of the bone marrow to form red blood cells will not cause any immediate harm, but a month or more later the patient may become extremely anemic.

It is fortunate that many of the vital areas of the body, including muscles and the nervous system, do not depend upon rapid mitosis. Consequently, very little or no damage occurs in the nervous system or in the muscular system of the body.

Though mitosis is greatly depressed for a few hours to several months after intensive gamma ray or x-ray irradiation, when mitosis does return it usually returns almost to a normal rate. If a patient can be preserved through the period of depressed mitosis, he may return to a normal state of physiologic activity several months later. Therefore, the medical treatment of patients exposed to gamma ray irradiation is simply supportive measures designed to tide the patient over until his natural recovery of mitosis takes place.

A few very unfortunate late effects of irradiation may occur. One of these is the development of *cataracts in the eyes*, especially if neutrons are in the radiations. This results from destruction or inhibition of the cellular layer of the anterior surface of the lens capsule. A second very important late effect is the *predisposition of irradiated persons to cancer*, which will be discussed later in connection with x-rays. The persons exposed to the atom bomb blasts in Japan show a significantly higher than normal cancer rate.

A third late effect of gamma ray irradiation, about which very little is known in relation to the human being, is the genetic effects of such irradiation. Obviously, gamma rays passing through the body affect the germinal cells of the ovaries and of the testes. Consequently, some of the genes of the ova and of the sperm mutate, and it is to be expected that persons exposed to gamma rays might produce mutant offspring. Thus far, the studies in Japan show only a slight number of mutant offspring. However, it is impossible to tell the damage from mutation of genes in the first generation. The reason for this is that almost all of the mutated genes are re-

cessive, and the recessive characteristics will not appear in an overt form until two of the same recessive genes appear in the same person; this will occur, however, in later generations. Therefore, it is necessary that all precautions be observed against irradiation as a protective measure for the future generations.

X-RAYS AND THEIR USE IN MEDICINE

X-rays are identical with gamma rays, which have been discussed in the preceding portions of this chapter. The wavelengths of x-rays and gamma rays normally encountered in medicine range between approximately 0.01 angstrom and 1.0 angstrom. These wavelengths are in the order of molecular diameters, so that many of the x-rays and gamma rays can pass directly through solid structures. It is this quality of x-rays that makes them extremely valuable in medicine, for they can be used to penetrate deeply into the body. Therefore, x-rays are used for taking "shadowgraph" pictures of various internal structures, and they are also used to destroy certain cells deep within the body by causing ionization within these cells.

Generation of X-rays

The X-ray Machine. Figure 768 illustrates the basic essentials of the x-ray machine, which includes an x-ray tube, a filament transformer, a plate transformer, and a timer. The x-ray tube is nothing more than an evacuated chamber having an angulated "target" anode and a hot wire for

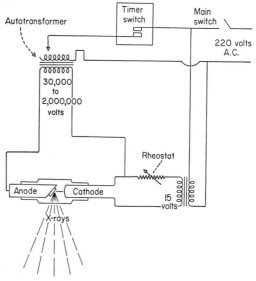

Figure 768. The x-ray machine.

a cathode. A low-voltage transformer supplies up to 15 volts to the heater wire of the cathode, and this voltage is regulated by means of a rheostat. The greater the current flowing through the heater wire, the greater is the temperature of the cathode. A hot wire—the cathode in this instance—in a vacuum liberates electrons from its surface. Ordinarily, these electrons fall back into the wire after bouncing away from it. However, if a second electrode is placed in the evacuated chamber and the second electrode is strongly positive with respect to the wire emitting the electrons, some of these electrons will move toward the positive electrode rather than falling back into the heated wire. Thus, electrons in the x-ray tube move from the cathode toward the positively charged target anode.

The transformer supplying voltage between the cathode and the anode of the x-ray tube is usually of the autotransformer type having a maximum voltage output between 30,000 and several million volts. This transformer supplies an alternating current between the cathode and the anode. Consequently, the anode is positive with respect to the cathode during only half of the electrical cycle, whereas during the other half of the cycle the anode is negative with respect to the cathode. Because the anode is not hot, electrons cannot flow backward from the anode to the cathode. Consequently, electrons flow through the x-ray tube in the usual x-ray machine during only half of the cycle—that is, during the half of the cycle when the anode is positive with respect to the cathode. Consequently, x-rays are emitted in short bursts occurring 60 times per second when the power source is 60 cycle alternating current.

The higher the voltage between the cathode and the anode, the greater will be the velocity with which the electrons strike the anode, and the greater will be the force with which these electrons attack the atoms in the anode to cause emission of x-rays.

Emission of X-rays by the X-ray Tube Anode.

When high-velocity electrons strike atoms, x-rays are emitted from these atoms by two principal means: First, if the electron succeeds in reaching a nucleus, much of the kinetic energy of the moving electron is immediately converted into x-rays. Second, the high-velocity electrons from the cathode can knock other electrons out of the orbits of the atoms in the target. Immediately thereafter, electrons from other sources move back into the orbits of the target atoms in order to re-establish electrical neutrality. These electrons moving into the orbits travel with considerable kinetic energy, and, upon reaching the orbit, this kinetic energy is dispelled in the form of x-ray energy which adds to the x-ray energy liberated by head-on collisions of electrons with the nuclei.

Effect of Voltage Applied to the X-ray Tube on the Wavelength of the Emitted X-rays.

The greater the voltage applied between the cathode and the anode of the x-ray tube, the greater is the kinetic energy with which electrons strike the anode. This energy is generally rated in terms of *electron volts*. In other words, 1 million volts between the electrodes imparts 1 million electron volts of energy to the electrons striking the anode. Thus, the kinetic energy with which the electrons strike the anode is directly proportional to the voltage between the electrodes. This kinetic energy is suddenly lost when the electrons strike the target, and some of it is immediately converted into x-ray energy. The greater the energy available in the moving electrons of the x-ray tube, the greater will be the frequency of these x-rays, and the shorter will be the wavelength. For this reason, the minimum wavelength of the rays is dependent upon the voltage between the electrodes of the x-ray tube in accordance with the following formula:

$$\text{Wavelength (minimum)} = \frac{12{,}395}{\text{Voltage}} \text{A}$$

Not all the x-rays emitted by the target have this minimum wavelength, for many of the electrons are slowed up by orbital electrons before they can strike the nuclei. Therefore, the target emits some of all x-ray wavelengths greater than the minimum value. That is, it emits a *spectrum* of wavelengths, which is illustrated in Figure 769.

Figure 769 also illustrates several peaks of x-ray emission. These peaks are due to the second type of x-ray emission discussed above. That is, when electrons from the cathode knock electrons out of their atomic orbits, the electrons that return to these orbits emit x-rays of characteristic wavelengths. However, unless the electrons from the cathode of the x-ray tube have enough energy to knock orbital electrons out of position, the characteristic spectral peaks cannot appear. The electrons in the inner orbits possess considerably greater energy than do the electrons in the outer orbits. For this reason, greater energies are

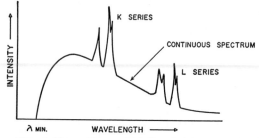

Figure 769. The general form of the x-ray spectrum. The exact values for wavelength depend on the anodal voltage in the x-ray tube. (From Weyl: Radiologic Physics. Charles C Thomas.)

necessary to knock these inner orbital electrons out of position, but, also shorter wavelength x-rays are emitted when electrons return to these orbits than when they return to the outer orbits.

The Target Material for an X-ray Tube. The efficiency of the x-ray tube for converting electron energy into x-ray energy is less than 0.1 per cent. The remainder of the energy becomes heat at the surface of the target. However, the efficiency for converting electron energy into x-ray energy is greater the higher the atomic number of the target material. Thus, the requirements for a good target material in an x-ray tube are: first, it must be able to withstand tremendous quantities of heat; second, it must conduct heat away from the surface of the target with ease; and third, it must have a high atomic number. Tungsten is the material that best fits all these requirements, for its melting point is extremely high, and its atomic number is also near the maximum. To increase the conductivity of heat away from the target, a small button of tungsten approximately 2 mm. in thickness is usually welded onto the tip of a copper rod, which then conducts the heat away. Also, when tremendous quantities of x-ray energy must be generated by the x-ray tube, the anode is made to rotate by means of an electric rotor inside the tube. In this manner, the focal spot of the x-ray tube remains at any one point on the target for such a short period of time that very high intensities of electron current from the cathode can be tolerated by the target.

Control of Intensity of X-ray Radiation from the X-ray Tube. It was noted above that every x-ray machine has a means of controlling the temperature of the cathode. The hotter this cathode, the greater is the number of electrons emitted from its surface into the evacuated tube. If only a few such electrons are emitted, then the total number striking the target will be few, and the quantity of x-rays will also be slight. On the other hand, if the number of electrons emitted from the surface of the cathode is great, then the number of electrons striking the anode will be great, and the quantity of x-ray radiation from the target will also be great. Thus, the intensity of x-ray radiation from the x-ray tube can be controlled by controlling the rheostat in the cathode circuit.

Transmission of X-rays through the Body, and X-ray Shadows

The X-ray Shadowgraph. An x-ray picture is, in reality, nothing more than a "shadowgraph" of various internal structures of the body or whatever other object is being x-rayed. Certain types of matter, as will be discussed subsequently, are more opaque to the passage of

x-rays than are other types. For example, structures such as bone absorb much larger quantities of x-rays than do the soft tissues. By the time x-rays pass through the body and impinge on the x-ray plate, the intensity of x-rays passing through only the soft tissues will still be very great, whereas the intensity of x-rays passing through the bones will be correspondingly decreased. This difference in intensity gives a shadow of the bones.

Relationship of Target Area to the Detail of the X-ray Shadowgraph. When the cathode of the x-ray tube sprays electrons over a large target area, x-rays will be emitted from the tube also over a large area. As illustrated in Figure 770, when x-rays come from a large target area, the edges of the shadows will be extremely hazy. This is a well-known effect when certain types of lighting fixtures are used, for a long fluorescent tube gives only hazy edges to the shadows that are formed, whereas a small pin-point of light causes very sharp edges to the shadows. Consequently, in taking x-ray pictures it is desirable to use a very small target area on the anode of the x-ray tube.

Relationship of Distance of the Tube to the Sharpness of the Shadow. If the sun were a few thousand miles away from the earth, then shadows on earth would be almost non-existent because light rays would be coming from all directions toward the objects. Yet, with the sun 93 million miles away the shadows on earth as the result of sunlight are quite distinct. In other words, even though the target area in an x-ray tube might be extremely large, if this target is moved farther and farther away from the object and from the x-ray plate, the distinctness of the edges of the x-ray shadows becomes greater and greater.

Relationship of Shadow Size to the Size of the Object, and the Effect of Tube Distance on This Relationship. If the x-ray target is located only a few inches above the body and yet the x-ray plate is located several

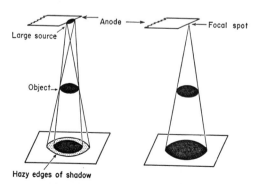

Figure 770. Effect of anodal focal spot size on the sharpness of the x-ray picture image.

inches on the other side of the body, obviously, the shadows on the x-ray plate will be far greater in size than the sizes of the internal body structures. Consequently, it is desirable to move the x-ray tube as far as possible away from the body before taking x-ray pictures. When the x-ray tube is an infinite distance away from the body, the size of the shadow becomes exactly the size of the internal organs. For practical purposes, an x-ray tube placed 6 to 8 feet away from the body will give shadows so nearly the same size as the actual internal structures that the disparity is almost negligible. Consequently, most x-ray pictures taken of the chest are now made in this manner, and occasionally x-ray pictures even of the more dense areas of the body such as the abdomen are also made with the x-ray tube placed far away from the body.

Relationship of X-ray Intensity to the Tube Distance. The propagation of x-rays obeys the same inverse square law as the propagation of light waves. Thus, the intensity of x-rays varies inversely with the square of the distance away from the x-ray tube. This means that the intensity of radiation 1 foot from an x-ray tube is four times the intensity of radiation 2 feet from the x-ray tube and 16 times the intensity of radiation 4 feet from the x-ray tube. Consequently, in taking x-ray pictures, the farther the distance of the x-ray tube from the x-ray plate, the greater must be the quantity of x-rays emitted from the tube in order for a sufficient intensity of radiation to reach the x-ray plate.

Absorption of X-rays—the Absorption Coefficient. The x-ray absorption coefficient of an element is the proportion of the x-rays absorbed during passage through a sheet of the element having a weight of 1 gram per square centimeter. The absorption coefficient of different elements of different atomic numbers is expressed by the following formula.

$$\mu = K\lambda^3 Z^4 + 0.2$$

In this formula μ is the absorption coefficient, K is a constant, λ is the wavelength of the x-rays, Z is the atomic number of the absorbing element, and the second factor in the formula, 0.2, is the "coefficient of scatter."

It will be observed from the above formula that the absorption coefficient is a sum of two factors. One of these factors is highly dependent upon the wavelength and the atomic number of the substance, whereas the second factor is a constant. The analysis of this formula is extremely important in the use of x-rays in medicine, as follows:

If the wavelength of the incident x-rays is very long, then the first factor of the formula $(K\lambda^3 Z^4)$ becomes extremely important because this factor is directly proportional to the third power of the wavelength; and the second factor of the formula, which remains constant, then becomes quantitatively insignificant in comparison with the first factor. Furthermore, when the wavelength is long, the atomic number becomes extremely important in the absorption of x-rays because the degree of absorption is proportional to the fourth power of the atomic number. This means that one atom of uranium absorbs several million times as much long wavelength x-rays as does one atom of hydrogen.

On the other hand, when the x-ray wavelength is extremely short or the atomic number of the absorbing material is extremely small, then the first factor of the formula becomes relatively insignificant in comparison with the second factor. Consequently, when using extremely short x-rays the degree of absorption is almost directly proportional to the weight of the absorbing medium rather than to the atomic number.

Contrast in the X-ray Picture. Applying the above principles of x-ray absorption to the body, when very short wavelength x-rays are used, the proportion of x-rays absorbed by the bones is approximately three times the proportion absorbed by the muscles because the bones are approximately three times as dense as the muscles. On the other hand, when long wavelength x-rays are used, the absorption contrast between different elements in the body may be many thousand to one.

It is obvious, therefore, that the degree of contrast in the x-ray picture can be determined to a great extent by changing the wavelength of the x-rays used in making the picture. The wavelength, in turn, can be increased or decreased by increasing or decreasing the voltage on the x-ray tube. High-voltage, short wavelength x-rays are known as "hard" x-rays in clinical terminology, for these x-rays penetrate with greater ease than do the long wavelength x-rays. On the other hand, x-rays delivered by the low-voltage x-ray machine, which have a very long wavelength and penetrate poorly, are said to be "soft" x-rays.

When extreme contrast is desired, as is necessary in the differentiation of fatty tissue from muscle tissue, one uses "soft" x-rays. In this manner it is possible to take x-ray pictures of many of the soft structures of the body and delineate these from other soft structures. A factor that helps in the delineation of organs such as the kidneys and the liver is that these organs are surrounded by interfascial fat. Fat has a very high proportion of carbon and hydrogen atoms, whereas muscle and other tissues of the body have a larger proportion of oxygen atoms. Therefore, the opacity of fat to soft x-rays is approximately 0.8 the opacity of water to these x-rays, and the opacity of muscle to soft x-rays is a little greater than that of water. Consequently, on the so-called "soft plate" x-ray picture, one can distinguish the boundaries of the kidneys, the liver, etc., quite easily. However, on the "hard plate" x-ray picture, these structures cannot be demonstrated.

In order to study fracture lines in bones, it is usually necessary to use relatively hard x-rays. The reason for this is that, for practical purposes, soft x-rays will not penetrate bone at all. Therefore, a soft plate of a bone shows only total shadows of the different fragments, and the fracture lines as they travel through the body of the bone cannot be seen. On the other hand, when hard x-rays are used, the degree of contrast is greatly reduced, and structure within the bone can also be observed.

In making x-ray pictures of structures such as the chest, which contain large quantities of air, x-rays of approximately medium wavelength are usually used. The reason for this is that air within the chest does not absorb x-rays to any appreciable extent though the solid structures do. Consequently, plenty of contrast is already available. On the other hand, there is no need for very short wavelength x-rays because in this instance one is not attempting to penetrate dense structures such as bones.

Recording X-ray Pictures

Effect of X-rays on the X-ray Film. As x-rays pass through a photographic film a small proportion of these rays is absorbed by the emulsion of the film. These absorbed x-rays ionize the sensitive substance of the emulsion and create a so-called "latent image." This latent image is a small amount of reduced silver which has been produced from the AgI or AgBr in the emulsion by the action of the radiation. When the film is then placed in a developing solution, the small amount of reduced silver in the areas exposed to x-rays acts as a catalyst to cause reduction of increased quantities of silver iodide and silver bromide. Because the elemental silver granules are opaque to light, the areas of the plate that have been exposed to x-rays become dark upon development. Therefore, the developed x-ray film is a "negative," the darker areas being the areas that have received the greater quantities of x-rays and the lighter areas being the portions of the film that have received smaller quantities of x-rays and, therefore, represent the shadows.

Use of intensifier screens with x-ray film. By far the greater percentage of the x-rays impinging on the x-ray plate pass on through the film without affecting the emulsion. This great loss of x-ray energy makes it necessary to expose the patient to far greater quantities of x-ray irradiation than would be necessary if this energy could be conserved. A means for conserving some of the x-ray energy is to place thin fluorescent "intensifier screens" on each side of the x-ray film. These screens usually contain millions of small *calcium tungstate crystals*, which fluoresce brilliantly when x-rays strike them. Therefore, as x-rays pass through the intensifier screens they cause fluorescence in the screens, and the light energy then adds to the x-ray energy in exposing the film.

Intensifier screens are made in several thicknesses. The thicker the screen, the greater is the amount of x-rays absorbed, and the greater is the fluorescence exposing the emulsion of the film. However, the thicker the screen, the less sharp is the x-ray picture. The reason for this is that the outer surface of the screen allows its fluorescent light to spread at wide angles away from the spot on the screen directly affected by the x-rays, thus exposing wide areas of the film rather than discrete points. Very thin intensifier screens intensify the film image approximately 20 times and at the same time do not destroy the sharpness of the picture to a major degree. On the other hand, intensifier screens are available that intensify the image as much as 60 times, but these greatly curtail the image sharpness. Obviously, if fine detail of an x-ray is necessary, intensifier screens are not used at all. On the other hand, if it is desirable to expose the patient to the least amount of x-rays and extreme detail is not necessary, then it is desirable to use the intensifier screens.

Fluoroscopic Screens. Instead of taking x-ray pictures, it is sometimes desirable simply to examine the patient by fluoroscopy. In this instance the x-rays after passing through the body are impinged on a fluorescent screen, and the observer can immediately discern the internal structure of the body. There is no real difference between the intensifier screens used with x-ray film and the fluorescent screens used for fluoroscopy. The difference is merely mechanical. The intensifier screens are arranged so that fluorescent materials are embedded in the surface of a smooth plastic, and this plastic is clamped tightly against the film. In the fluorescent screen the fluorescent material is deposited on the surface of glass so that when it fluoresces the light can pass through the glass to the observer.

Calcium tungstate, which is the usual fluorescent material used in intensifying screens, can also be used in fluoroscopic screens, but substances with better spectral characteristics for vision are *cadmium tungstate* and *zinc cadmium sulfide*. Cadmium tungstate gives a greenish image, and zinc cadmium sulfide give a yellowish image on the fluorescent screen.

In extreme darkness, when only the rods can be used for vision, the eyes cannot see minute detail. Consequently, attempts to make the so-called "grain" of the fluorescent screen extremely fine are not necessary. Instead, large granules are used to increase the brilliance of the image. Because of the limitation of the detail that can be seen by the rods and because the fluorescent image cannot usually be made bright enough to excite the cones, any x-ray study requiring extremely fine detail must be accomplished by use of x-ray films and not by the fluoroscopic method.

The electronic image intensifier. Recently electronic systems have been devised to increase the intensity of the fluoroscopic image a hundredfold or more. These systems employ a modified television apparatus using a pickup tube that can respond to extremely weak x-ray energy. The signals are then amplified and deployed on a typical television tube type of screen. The real advantages of such a system are: (1) only very little x-ray exposure of the subject is required, and (2) the intensity of the image on the screen can be made bright enough for observation in the non-darkened rooms.

X-ray Scatter. One of the problems in making x-ray pictures is x-ray "scatter," which may be explained as follows: Referring once again to the formula presented above for the absorption coefficient, it can be seen that one of the factors causing x-ray absorption is the scatter factor. The scatter effect is very minor in proportion to the total absorption when long wavelength x-rays are used. On the other hand, when short wavelength x-rays are used, this scatter factor is the major means by which x-rays are absorbed. When x-rays are generated by x-ray tubes at voltages higher than 60,000 to 80,000 volts, the scatter effect becomes important enough that it must be considered in taking almost all x-ray pictures.

Figure 771 illustrates the most important mechanism by which the scatter effect occurs

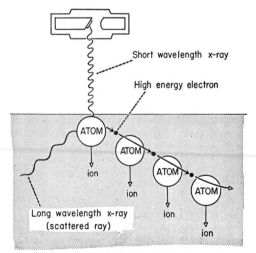

Figure 771. Scatter and ionizing effect of x-ray radiation.

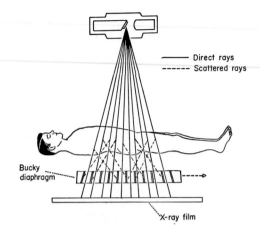

Figure 772. Filtration of scattered x-rays by the Bucky diaphragm.

when short wavelength x-rays are absorbed. First, the short wavelength x-ray strikes an atom in the absorbing substance. This causes extreme excitation in the atom by knocking an electron out of one of the orbits. The x-ray energy that is left over after knocking the electron out of the orbit is then emitted from the excited atom, but, because this energy is less than before the impact, the wavelength of the secondarily emitted x-ray is always longer than the wavelength of the original x-ray. This is known as the *Compton effect.*

The secondarily emitted x-ray may travel in any direction from the excited atom. This is the reason this secondary emission is known as "scatter." In other words, an original short wavelength x-ray strikes an atom, and then from that atom a secondary radiation may travel in any direction instead of continuing in the same direction of travel as the original beam.

Prevention of loss of picture detail as a result of scatter. Remembering once again that an x-ray picture is nothing more than a shadowgraph and, secondly, that good detail of a shadowgraph requires that the x-ray beam emanate from a single point source at the anode of the x-ray tube, it becomes obvious that secondary radiation traveling in any other direction besides directly from the x-ray anode will destroy the distinctness of the shadows. Consequently, several methods are used to prevent loss of clarity in an x-ray picture as a result of scatter. One of these methods is the "Bucky diaphragm," which is illustrated in Figure 772. After the x-rays from the anode of the tube penetrate the body, they then must pass through the Bucky diaphragm before reaching the x-ray film. This Bucky diaphragm is made up of many small lead vanes arranged parallel to the x-rays from the target of the tube, thus allowing these rays to pass between the vanes and impinge upon the film. However, because the vanes are directed toward the target of the tube, most of the scattered x-rays emanating from other directions will not be traveling parallel to the vanes. Consequently, as they attempt to pass through the diaphragm they strike one of the lead vanes and are stopped. Thus, the clarity of the shadows in the x-ray image will not be clouded by a great number of scattered rays.

If the Bucky diaphragm should remain stationary while x-ray pictures are being exposed, it would cause "grid lines" in the x-ray pictures. To prevent this, the Bucky diaphragm is always moving in the direction of the arrow while the x-ray picture is being made. Therefore, no one portion of x-ray film is exposed to the shadows of the vanes in the Bucky diaphragm for a continuous period of time.

Stereoscopic X-ray. Depth perception for objects that are near to the eyes depends mainly upon binocular parallax. In other words, each eye sees each object from a slightly different angle from that of the other eye. In order to get depth perception by means of x-ray pictures, it is necessary for the two eyes to see slightly different views of the internal structures. This can be accomplished as shown in Figure 773. In this instance two separate x-ray pictures are taken of the same object but the x-ray tube is moved slightly between exposures. Therefore, the two x-ray pictures are views of the same object taken at slightly different angles. Then, to provide appropriate parallax in the eyes, these two pictures are placed

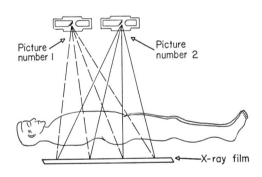

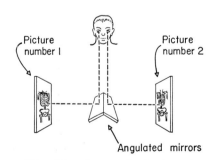

Figure 773. Recording and viewing stereoscopic x-rays.

on two separate viewing boxes, and one eye sees one of the pictures through an angulated mirror while the other eye sees the second picture through another angulated mirror. The pictures and mirrors are adjusted so that the two images in the two eyes fuse with each other, and because the two images are pictures taken at slightly different angles to each other, the eyes achieve the phenomenon of parallax. Thus, depth perception occurs. Using this method, one can assess the depth relationships of different internal structures of the body.

X-ray Therapy

Destruction of Tissues by X-rays. X-rays can be used for destroying unwanted tissues in the body, particularly tissues deep within the body. X-rays destroy tissues by causing ionization, for x-rays impinging on atoms knock electrons out of the orbits, thereby ionizing these atoms. Also, secondary electron emission within the absorbing cells causes even more ionization. It is probable that ionization frequently destroys cells by ionizing portions of the genes within the chromosomes. For instance, if an x-ray strikes one of the carbon atoms of a purine ring in a gene, a bond of the ring might be broken or new polymers might be formed, thus altering the gene. As a result, the developmental characteristics of the cell would be changed. In most instances when developmental characteristics of cells are changed, reproduction of the cells is thereafter greatly suppressed. After considerable exposure of cells to x-rays, mitosis of these cells is almost completely blocked for the next several days and sometimes for much longer periods than this. However, after the period of depressed mitosis, the rate of mitosis returns to normal and sometimes even slightly above normal for a few days, but thereafter the rate of mitosis becomes subnormal and remains thus. The idea that x-rays can stimulate cellular reproduction, as has been claimed by a number of x-ray technicians, appears to be entirely false. Therefore, from a therapeutic point of view, x-rays are used almost entirely for the destruction of unwanted tissues in the body. This means mainly for treating cancerous tissues.

Superficial Therapy versus Deep Therapy. It has already been pointed out that extremely long wavelength x-rays are absorbed before they can penetrate almost any thickness of a solid object. Consequently, x-rays generated by a machine having a low voltage on the anode will be almost entirely absorbed before they can penetrate more than a few millimeters of a patient's skin. Thus, surface growths are frequently destroyed by means of "superficial therapy," in which case very long wavelengths are used.

On the other hand, when lesions are deep within the body, the major problem in treating these lesions is to prevent skin damage which shows up as "radiation burns," a thinning of the dermis, in severe exposure. If long wavelength x-rays were used for treating a deep lesion, these x-rays would never reach the lesion but instead would destroy the skin and overlying superficial structures. On the other hand, if very short wavelength x-rays are used, a major proportion of these x-rays will reach the lesion, and the quantity of x-rays impinging on the skin overlying the lesion will be only slightly greater than the quantity finally arriving at the lesion.

A means by which a deep lesion can be irradiated with greater quantities of x-rays than the overlying skin is to irradiate the lesion through several different *portals*. This means that the x-ray beam is directed first from the front toward the lesion, then from the back toward the lesion, then from a 45 degree angle anteriorly, then from a 45 degree angle posteriorly, and from many other different angles toward the lesion. In this manner, every time an x-ray treatment is given, the lesion is irradiated but a different portion of the skin is irradiated.

A new method for irradiating a deep lesion with greater quantities of x-ray than the skin is the *rotational method*. In using this method, the patient is placed on a rotating table so that the lesion is in the center of rotation, or, conversely, the patient remains stationary and the therapy tube rotates about him. The x-rays pass through many different portions of the skin but always pass through the lesion, which is placed at the center of rotation. Consequently, the skin is irradiated only during part of the treatment, whereas the lesion is irradiated during all of the treatment.

Because shorter wavelength x-rays penetrate the body with less absorption in the superficial layers of the body than do longer wavelength x-rays, it is the object of all deep therapy units to attain the shortest x-rays possible. Consequently, many x-ray machines for deep therapy operate with an anode voltage of several million volts. However, the usual machines in use have an anode voltage of 250,000 to 400,000 volts.

X-ray Filtration in Relation to X-ray Therapy. Figure 774 illustrates the spectrum of x-rays generated by an x-ray tube operating at an anode voltage of approximately 250,000 volts. This tube delivers a considerable quantity of both short and long wavelength x-rays. Returning once again to the formula for the absorption coefficient of x-rays, it will be noted that long wavelength x-rays are absorbed to a tremendous extent by materials that have a very high atomic number, whereas very short wavelength x-rays are not affected to anything like the same extent by these materials. Placing a sheet of copper 0.25 mm. in thickness in front of the

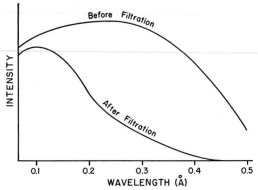

Figure 774. X-ray spectrum before and after filtration.

x-ray tube removes almost all of the x-rays that have a wavelength of 0.5 angstrom. At 0.2 angstrom the same copper filter removes approximately 50 per cent of the x-rays, whereas at 0.1 angstrom only 10 per cent of the x-rays are removed from the beam. Consequently, a thin layer of copper removes essentially all of the very long wavelength x-rays and allows essentially all of the very short wavelength x-rays to pass. By use of such a filter, burning of the skin can be considerably reduced, particularly when low-voltage x-ray machines are used for deep therapy purposes.

Measurement of Quantity of X-ray Irradiation—the Roentgen Unit. It has been impossible to formulate an exact biologic measurement of the quantity of x-rays impinging on the human body. Consequently, a physical measurement known as the *roentgen unit* is used as the standard measure of the amount of x-rays impinging on the treatment area. This roentgen unit (r) is equal to the *quantity of x-rays required to produce 1 electrostatic unit of ions in each 1 ml. of air under standard conditions.* It should be pointed out particularly that when one speaks in terms of the number of roentgen units of irradiation, this does not mean the total quantity of x-rays striking the body, but it refers simply to the quantity of x-rays striking the body *in each unit area* being irradiated. Also, it is not the rate at which x-rays are striking, but it is the total cumulative quantity delivered per unit area during the period of treatment.

Sensitivity of Cells in the Body to Destruction. Different animals have different degrees of sensitivity to x-rays, and different cells within the body of each animal respond to different degrees. For instance, lymphoid cells are destroyed readily. Also, many of the glandular cells are destroyed easily. On the other hand, connective tissue cells and muscle cells are not very sensitive to x-rays. It appears, then, that the cells that are most sensitive to x-ray destruction are those cells that normally are very active mitotically. Indeed, cancer cells, which are usually very active mitotically, usually also are highly responsive to x-rays. Consequently, it is frequently very easy to cause remission of a cancer by x-ray treatment while at the same time not destroying the surrounding tissues of the body. Fortunately, also, those cancers that grow very rapidly are often the most responsive to x-ray treatment.

It is impossible to say exactly how much x-ray exposure is usually required to kill cells. In the human being it is believed that the average cell of the body is destroyed by exposure to approximately 600 roentgens of irradiation. This value is as low as 200 roentgens in some rodents and as high as 15,000 roentgens for destruction of the average cell in the bat.

Development of Cancer Secondary to X-ray Irradiation

Even though x-rays destroy or suppress most of the cells irradiated, it is possible for x-rays to change the genes of one cell out of a great many so that it becomes capable of proliferating to a greater extent than normally. If a single cell is thus changed so that it is not influenced by the usual limits on growth, then this cell can eventually develop into a cancer. In other words, cancer can actually be induced by x-ray irradiation because of changes in one or more genes, these changes allowing the cell not to be influenced by any natural checks on cell growth. Fortunately, this effect occurs probably not any more frequently than in one out of every billion or more cells affected by x-rays. The remaining cells are either destroyed or are changed in some other manner.

REFERENCES

Bacq, Z. M.: Fundamentals of Radiobiology. New York, Academic Press, 1955.

Bacq, Z. M., and Alexander, P.: Fundamentals of Radiobiology. New York, Academic Press, 1955.

Blair, H. A.: Biological Effects of External Radiation. New York, McGraw-Hill Book Co., Inc., 1954.

Bond, V. P., and Cronkite, E. P.: Effects of radiation on mammals. *Ann. Rev. Physiol., 19:*299, 1957.

Buchanan, J. M., and Hastings, A. B.: The use of isotopically marked carbon in the study of intermediary metabolism. *Physiol. Rev., 25:*121, 1946.

Canzanelli, A., Sossen, R., and Rapport, D.: Succinin and cytochrome oxidase activity of rat liver mitochondria after in vitro irradiation with ultraviolet light. *Am. J. Physiol., 188:*547, 1957.

Ciba Foundation: Symposia Volumes. Ionizing Radiations and Cell Metabolism. Boston, Little, Brown and Co., 1957.

Clark, C. L.: Applied X-Rays. New York, McGraw-Hill Book Co., Inc., 1955.

Cronkite, E. P., and Bond, V. P.: Effects of radiation on mammals. *Ann. Rev. Physiol., 18:*483, 1956.

Cronkite, E. and Bond, V. P.: Radiation Injury in Man. Springfield, Illinois, Charles C. Thomas, 1960.

Crouch, B. G., and Overman, R. R.: Chemical protection against x-radiation death in primates; a preliminary report. *Science, 125:*1092, 1957.

Davidson, H. O.: Biological Effects of Whole-Body Gamma Radiation on Human Beings. Baltimore, Johns Hopkins University Press, 1957.

Giese, A. C.: Action of ultraviolet radiation on protoplasm. *Physiol. Rev., 30:*431, 1950.

Glasser, O.: Physical Foundations of Radiology. New York, Paul B. Hoeber, 1944.

Hine, G. J., and Brownell, G. L.: Radiation Dosimetry. New York, Academic Press, 1956.

Hollaender, A.: Radiation Biology. Volume 1. New York, McGraw-Hill Book Co., Inc., 1954.

Hollaender, A.: Radiation Biology: Visible and Near-visible Light. Volume III. New York, McGraw-Hill Book Co., Inc., 1956.

James, R. W.: The Optical Principles of the Diffraction of X-rays. New York, The Macmillan Co., 1949.

Kamen, M. D.: Isotopic Tracers in Biology. 3rd ed., New York, Academic Press, 1957.

Lapp, R. E., and Andrews, H. L.: Nuclear Radiation Physics. New York, Prentice-Hall, 1948.

Laughlin, J. S.: Physical Aspects of Betatron Therapy. Springfield, Illinois, Charles C Thomas, 1954.

Mitchell, J. S.: Studies in Radiotherapeutics. Oxford, Blackwell Scientific Publications, 1960.

Neary, G. J., Munson, R. J., and Mole, R. H.: Chronic Radiation Hazards. New York, Pergamon Press, 1957.

Ord, M. G., and Stocken, L. A.: Biochemical aspects of the radiation syndrome. *Physiol. Rev., 33:*356, 1953.

Osborn, G. K., and Kimeldorf, D. J.: Some radiation responses of two species of bats exposed to warm and cold temperatures. *J. Exp. Zool., 134:*159, 1957.

Oughterson, A. W., and Warren, S.: Medical Effects of the Atomic Bomb in Japan. New York, McGraw-Hill Book Co., Inc., 1956.

Owen, C. A., Jr.: Diagnostic Radioisotopes. Springfield, Illinois, Charles C Thomas, 1959.

Patt, H. M.: Protective mechanisms in ionizing radiation injury. *Physiol. Rev., 33:*35, 1953.

Patt, H. M.: Radiation effects on mammalian systems. *Ann. Rev. Physiol., 16:*51, 1945.

Quimby, E. H., Feitelberg, S. and Silver, S.: Radioactive Isotopes in Clinical Practice. Philadelphia, Lea & Febiger, 1958.

Ramsey, G. H. S., Watson, J. S., Jr., Tristan, T. A., Weinberg, S., and Cornwell, W. S.: Cinefluorography: Proceedings of the First Annual Symposium on Cinefluorography, Sponsored by the Department of Radiology, University of Rochester, School of Medicine and Dentistry, Rochester, New York. Springfield, Illinois, Charles C Thomas, 1959.

Richardson, A. W.: The effectiveness of microwave diathermy therapy as a hyperthermic agent upon vascularized and avascular tissue. *Brit. J. Phys. Med. 18:*143, 1955.

Selman, J.: The Fundamentals of X-Ray and Radium

Physics. Springfield, Illinois, Charles C Thomas, 1959.

Sheppard, C. W., Slater, M., Darden, E. B., Jr., Kimball, A. W., Atta, G. J., Edington, C. W., and Baker, W. K.: Biological effects of fast neutrons from an internal target cyclotron: physical methods and dominant lethals in Drosophila. *Radiation Res.*, 6:173, 1957.

Stacy, R. W., Williams, D. T., Worden, R. E., and McMorris, R. O.: Essentials of Biological and Medical Physics. New York, McGraw-Hill Book Co., Inc., 1955.

Van Went, J. M.: Ultrasonic and Ultrashort Waves in Medicine. Houston, Elsevier Press, 1954.

Weyl, C., and Warren, S. R., Jr.: Radiologic Physics. Springfield, Illinois, Charles C Thomas, 1951.

INDEX